Contemporary
Theory and Research
in Visual
Perception

Contemporary
Theory and Research
in Visual
Perception

Edited by RALPH NORMAN HABER

UNIVERSITY OF ROCHESTER

Holt, Rinehart and Winston, Inc.

NEW YORK   CHICAGO   SAN FRANCISCO   ATLANTA   DALLAS
MONTREAL   TORONTO   LONDON

To My Students,
Who Convinced Me of
   the Need for this Book and Provided
the Incentive to Complete It

Preface

With its century-long research history, much (though by no means all) of the basic empirical information about visual perception has been demonstrated and even replicated. The search for theoretical explanations and models of perceptual behavior has been fruitful, although there is no guarantee that current theories and models are the correct ones. They are securely anchored in data, however, and, more importantly, many are quite sophisticated—in taking account of the behavioral data, in drawing upon potential neurophysiological underpinnings, and in considering theoretical developments in other areas of psychology.

While these comments suggest a healthy scientific enterprise, they make the task of compiling a book of readings that much more difficult. In preparing the present volume I examined four thousand experimental studies, theoretical and review articles, and books on visual perception. The search covered thirty-five years of publication, though I concentrated most heavily on the past ten years. I seriously considered for inclusion some four hundred of these articles; most of the hard editorial work was to reduce the four hundred to the eighty that actually appear in this book.

I have a strong feeling for timeliness, so whenever there were two papers of comparable quality on other dimensions, I chose the more recent one. Nearly all the papers appeared after 1959; many in the mid-1960s. This reflects, of course, the rapid growth of the field, as well as my own bias against history for history's sake. As a consequence, a number of classic experiments have been omitted, many of which I regret. I have selected research concerned not only with hard scientific theorizing, but with thinking about the perceiver as a human being in his natural environment. This is frequently hard to reconcile with laboratory research, but our ultimate aim is to explain the human being in his natural environment and not in a highly artificial laboratory. For this reason I searched for papers having some relevance to the real world. I also was sensitive to studies which applied converging operations and were concerned with information processing approaches.

Included in the Introduction are some of the criteria I used to select the topics, but a word is needed regarding those topics not represented. The word *perception* is used to specify several rich research areas in psychology, such as the perception of causality, of time, or of person. While these are important and substantial subdivisions, the operation usually implied should be one of judgment, not perception. With rare exceptions, little of this research is concerned with reception of stimulaiton at a sensory receptor, or with the maintenance of that registration in memory.

v

While it will be clear throughout this book that memory and what is traditionally known as perception cannot be distinguished by any but the most arbitrary of rules, such topics as the perception of time primarily involve data outside the realm of the areas covered in these readings. Thus, even if there had been no space limitation, I would not have considered papers on these topics. I have also chosen (even somewhat more arbitrarily) to exclude extensive material on what is called either visual science or physiological optics.

An author or editor always has the problem of subdividing his book into sections and chapters. Since my intention is to cover the traditional topics of a course in visual perception, I have attempted to follow such an outline. But since every instructor teaches a slightly different course, rather than to attempt to adapt this book to all teachers—and thereby probably to satisfy none—I decided to organize it as I teach my own course. Its subdivision into seven chapters is fairly arbitrary, and many of the chapters are not at all homogeneous. The instructor can split the chapters into a traditional fourteen- or fifteen-week semester, or spread them over a full year. Further, there is no need that the chapters be taught in the order in which they are presented. This order represents my own way of covering the material, but there is relatively little of a cumulative nature in this approach. In fact, the last chapter could be taught first, since it presents most of the problems to which the rest of the course could then be addressed.

Many persons have helped in the compilation of these readings. I have received advice and suggestions from a number of colleagues in the area of perception, including Joseph McFarland, Howard Gruber, Jacob Nachmias, Tom Natsoulas, Michael Posner, and Maurice Hershenson. Where I have not followed their advice, it is almost always because space did not permit the inclusion of all their excellent suggestions.

I am grateful also to those who helped with the actual production of the manuscript, particularly Elsie Hayes, Betsy Whitehead, and Barbara Herr, and especially my wife, Ruth, who not only helped with the work but accepted the time I devoted to it.

Finally, I extend deep appreciation to the authors and publishers of each of the papers for granting me permission to reprint them here.

R.N.H.
Rochester, New York
February 1968

Contents

Contemporary
Theory and Research
in Visual
Perception

Introduction

The study of perception is the oldest area in psychology, and at one time it encompassed all other branches, including learning, motivation, clinical and abnormal, and physiological. With the development of psychology as a science, each of these areas has become more distinct and perception is now considered a separate, quite independent branch. It is, however, still possible to teach a first course in psychology organizing all of the topics around principles of perception. This is far less common than using learning as a unifying principle, but it still can be done. Nevertheless, compartmentalization in psychology has been much more the rule of the day in the last several decades, and perception, as well as most of the other areas, has paid for this dearly. One of the morals repeated throughout this book is the importance of the interrelations between perception and other areas, particularly those of learning and memory.

As it is with the other areas in psychology, the most difficult task is to define the topic under consideration. The only definition offered by the editor is a general one, highlighting the issues rather than defining the field. Thus, perception is defined as the study of the interaction of the perceiver with his environment. This makes clear that careful specification is needed of the environment (the stimulus conditions) and of the behavior of the perceiver. This interaction may result in a change in the perceiver's experience or awareness without any change in his overt behavior, suggesting that the perceiver's verbal report of his experience is a critical part of the study of perception. This definition implies clearly that perception is a process and not a thing, and it also implies that perception is inferred and cannot be directly observed.

There have been many different theories regarding the locus of this process and how inferences about it can be drawn. In fact, much of the theoretical discussion in this book is concerned with such differences in theory. The simplest version is to treat the study of perception very much as an optical problem, that is, the determination of how stimulation falls onto the retina, and then observing the transformations and correlations between the stimulus and the pattern of receptor excitation. It will be apparent in many places that such a model is grossly inadequate to handle the full range of behaviors covered under this definition. This kind of model really treats the act of perception like the act of taking a camera picture in that a knowledge of lenses, optics, and light-sensitive chemicals is all that is needed to understand how perception works. A moment's reflection will show, however, that while the retina may reproduce patterns of activity in much the same way as the film in a camera, this is true only for very short, separate exposures. Further, this is not in general what we mean by perception. The film will

1

be a record of what momentarily passed through the lens, but there is no provision within the camera for reading the film. Most of the interesting questions in the study of perception concern how the information that fell on the retina is translated into perceptual experience, perceptual memory, and perceptual responses.

Some theorists have attempted to handle this problem on a strictly neural level. Something must happen in the neural transmission between the retina and the central nervous system to add and organize all of the characteristics that were not present in the retinal pattern. In general, this is placing the issue and the problem just one step higher than the retina itself. Other theorists have ignored this problem by definition and have taken a purely behavioristic point of view. Thus, perception is contained in the response and nothing need be inferred about any intervening process. The clearest example would be in an analysis of discrimination learning. If the perceiver makes the same response to two stimuli initially, but after differential reinforcement makes two differential responses, then we can say that his ability to discriminate the two stimuli is equivalent to his ability to perceive their differences. The difficulty with this position is that it is quite possible that the perceiver could perceive the differences before but did not care. In this sense the training changed his motivation, not his perception. Alternatively, the training may have taught him to differentiate the two responses without changing what he perceived.

At the opposite extreme, there are those who say that perception is concerned entirely with the experience of the perceiver—private and internal—which normally occurs without the necessity of any response being made. While this particular position may conceivably be true, it has no, or little, scientific value, since it is not open to testing or verification.

One compromise between these two extremes is to consider awareness and experience completely separate from perception altogether, and treat them as epiphenomena. Thus, they do exist and can be studied, but they do not have any important function in perception, whether they are or are not correlated with perception. In this sense, then, we can be aware of seeing something, depending upon a large number of variables, but that awareness does not influence our ability to report, to respond, or to remember the stimulus. There will be occasions on which we could give a direct verbal report of it; other times on which we cannot. Our ability to make other kinds of responses, however, would be uncorrelated.

This particular point of view does not provide an entirely satisfactory answer. For one thing, it destroys our humanness, because it says that conscious experience is not a very important part of perceptual (and by implication any) behavior. It does recognize that it might be of interest to study occasions when conscious experience and overt responses agree and when they do not, but since it says that consciousness has little to do with perceptual behavior, it minimizes this role. It seems reasonable, however, that there should be a large number of occasions in which the nature of awareness or perceptual experience may in fact determine the course of subsequent perceptual behavior, particularly perceptual memory.

Within the context of problems concerning a basic definition of perception, three different kinds of philosophical issues have been raised. This will be the first and last time in this book that these will be discussed, but perhaps it is appropriate to have them brought to the fore at least once. These concern the mind-body problem, the nature of objective reality, and the uses of introspective reports.

The mind-body problem is usually expressed in psychology as psychoneural isomorphism, which dates back to the concept of parallelism of Leibnitz. Psychoneural isomorphism maintains that for every dimension of consciousness (mind), there must be a correlated dimension in the brain (body). While these physiological or neurological correlates may be complex, this theory says they must exist. Further, it implies that with the development of more sophisticated techniques, we could read thoughts on dials of instruments which record neural activity. It should be noted that psychologists do not seriously question this belief today, though generally they do not think very much about it. Obviously, its ultimate test will be far in the future. No statement is made or implied about the mutual interaction between consciousness and neural activity, nor, obviously, anything about what is causing what. The theory merely asserts that states of consciousness or awareness are represented neurologically.

Concern about a belief in objective reality is a much more complex problem because the issues are not at all clear. Not all scientists make good philosophers, and even when they *are* good philosophers, they do not always agree with each other. Early psychologists did not assume any kind of objective reality, but rather believed that reality was what the senses told us. In general, psychologists now believe that the world exists outside of ourselves as perceivers. While our senses may not be perfect, they give evidence of objective reality, but reality exists whether or not our senses are accurate. Anyone who does not hold this belief is left with a basic introspectionism—that reality is based only upon what his senses tell him. From many different points of view, this does not make a good cornerstone for a science. However, even with a belief in objective reality, the proposition does not specify clearly what one should do about experience. While we may believe the world exists outside of ourselves, our experience is internal and private and immediate, not out there. Hence, reality has to be an inference based upon each of our experiences. Then how do we know what reality is like? How, for example, can we attempt to correlate stimulus magnitude with response magnitudes? Should it be considered a measure of the degree of correlation between experience and reality? But, if the stimulus is too dim, then the response will be "No, I did not see anything." Does that mean there is no reality, or no experience? Obviously, at least the latter, but what about the former?

The two philosophical issues just outlined have not generated much argument among perception psychologists; in fact, they have not even been raised very frequently. But the third issue, which concerns the place of introspection as data in perception, has been argued vociferously. This issue has become the basis of several schools, both supporting and rejecting introspectionism.

There are two separate aspects to be considered. One concerns the use of an introspective report as a response indicator in perception, and the second concerns the use of introspection as a technique for analyzing perception. The latter is based strongly on a belief in nonobjective reality, that reality is only what the perceiver knows. According to this view, to study perception all one needs to do is investigate the reports of the perceiver, not to vary the stimulus. It was this characteristic of those using introspective reports that raised the greatest problem and accounted for the bad publicity given introspection as a technique. The introspectionists had no independent check, no antecedent variation to correlate with a perceiver's responses. All they ended up with was private experience; they had no way of telling whether it was a useful dimension to analyze, let alone if it correlated with a stimulus.

In the field of perception we still depend almost exclusively on verbal reports—on what the perceiver saw and experienced. While the report is private, in the sense that the perceiver can lie or distort without our knowing it, it is still permissible to accept these reports in science. The crucial requirement is to have several independent parameters under measurement. The introspectionists only recorded the perceiver's responses to a stimulus, with no concomitant variation in the stimulus.

We now use what we call psychophysics, in which the psychological responses are correlated with the physical dimensions of the stimulus. In this way verbal reports are like any other response measure—they can be tested for usefulness, fertility, and so on. Whenever the perceiver can provide responses that represent realistic correlations with the physical dimensions of the stimulus, then it is useful, both with regard to the correlation and as a way of understanding what the perceiver is experiencing. When several different measures are used—especially at different levels—then science progresses, so that when the verbal response is correlated with the stimulus, with the conditions of measurement, and even with the measurement of some other characteristic such as a neural response, we can be confident in our description of the process. In this sense verbal report is not introspective at all, but is a perfectly legitimate response measure. Introspective responses should be objected to only when they are elicited under free conditions and not tied down to specific stimulus and response conditions. In other words, there needs to be a prior structuring of the form or the content of the report and a specification for encoding that report into categories. Free introspections may be appropriate to gain hunches or ideas, but they are not raw data. It should be noted that perception is one of the few fields in psychology where the multiple angles of measurement or converging operations have been worked out well and have been used with great fertility.

Returning for a moment to the comments about compartmentalization of the different areas of psychology, I would like to argue vigorously that perception cannot be isolated from the study of sensation, or from the study of memory; that, in fact, it represents a continuum along which the classical problems of sensation, and perception, and memory can be placed. More importantly, to understand any particular problem, be it form recognition, temporal summation, or the effect of motivation on perception, one has to take into account the entire continuum. It is obvious that as perceivers we can remember what we have seen, but as psychologists we tend theoretically to isolate the study of processes that give rise to perception from those that give rise to memory. Although it is likely that some of these processes differ, they share a common antecedent (stimulation), and except in some unusual situations both always occur as a result of stimulation. Thus, not only do we have a percept of stimulation while that stimulation lasts, but we also have a memory of the stimulus and its percept lasting for minutes to decades after the stimulation itself is terminated. Since at least in many natural and most research settings the stimulus is either changed, or is no longer present when the response is given, we must worry about the content and organization that stimulation has taken in memory.

The notion of a continuum is paramount to the concepts of information processing as an approach to the study of visual perception. Information processing notions imply two major changes in the general trend of perceptual thinking in research. One of these is the application of a process model, which means looking at perception as a multistage or multiprocess set of operations, rather than something which occurs immediately, instantaneously, and indivisibly. Recent research has been greatly concerned with delineating the various stages and devising operations for separate measurement of each stage. Secondly, this approach is distinguished by its emphasis on information as what is being processed. The focus has been to treat stimulation as it falls on receptors as a pattern of information, and then to examine the content of this information as it passes through the various stages. Defined in this way, it is possible to analyze correlations on the amounts of information from stage to stage so that the transformations of information can be examined explicitly. In this way, it is much easier to see exactly how the processing occurs. Using a common set of units at each level also avoids serious problems in communication so that we can talk about spectral energies on the one hand being related, for example, to particular perceptual experiences of color on the other.

In this area I consider the application of information processing analyses to visual perception a critical development in current theorizing and research. I think it holds the promise of major discoveries and major advances, because it provides researchers with a way of thinking and a set of operations that are much more geared to handling the complexities of data in visual perception. An entire chapter in the present volume is devoted to analyzing these approaches and presenting some of the data obtained therefrom.

Information processing analyses also illustrate another major concern in the research on visual perception. This has to do with the application of converging operations for theory testing. While theory testing applies equally to all areas of psychology, it is far better realized in this area than in any other. Because there is so much more data in visual perception, and because the theorizing is more complex and sophisticated, the typical experiment generally cannot be a crucial one, in that it rarely is able to make a critical choice between two theories or two predictions stemming from two theories. Because of this, the concept of a converging operation has been increasingly applied in research in visual perception. The concern is that there should be a separate and distinct operation applied for each possible alternative hypothesis or prediction. The multiple operations should be chosen in such a way that each one represents a choice between alternatives. This means that to draw any kind of conclusions from an experiment, it must be a complex experiment with many controls, and with many different levels of measurement.

The selection of papers in this volume has not followed historical trends in any way. I have not been concerned as much with representing the sources of ideas and data and theory as I have been with portraying them in their contemporary perspectives and directions. A reader who is primarily interested in the history of research in visual perception can therefore gain relatively little from this volume unless he reads very carefully between the lines. In fact, many of the research areas that are contemporary in the book did not exist twenty years ago, even though each of them had its antecedents further back. There are several reasons for the modern discontinuity. One, of course, is the application of information processing analysis already discussed. The second is the increasing usefulness of electrophysiological data, both the study of cortical evoked potentials (several examples of which are included in this collection), and the work on receptive fields located by electrophysiological probes at different levels of the visual pathways. Nearly all of this has been accomplished within the last decade. My own belief is that the history of a science is not directly relevant to the understanding of the contemporary nature of that science, except insofar as there are clear antecedents in history to the contemporary problems and that that knowledge of these antecedents would shed some light on the points of view and biases of current researchers. While there are undoubtedly a number of instances in visual perception where this is relevant, I think much of the material here included can be read as current slices of thought without relevance to the early history. Each paper, of course, makes reference to immediate ancestors in terms of earlier research that it is replicating, extending, or criticizing.

CHAPTER *1*

Concepts and Methods in Visual Perception

The Psychophysics of Vision[*]

ROBERT M. BOYNTON
University of Rochester

Introduction

Visual psychophysics is an interdisciplinary area of scientific investigation relating the reactions of human observers to physically measurable aspects of the visual environment in which they live. One can perhaps readily understand that a physicist would learn rather little about the principles of gravitation from poetic descriptions of the way that leaves fall from trees. It is equally true that the psychophysicist would learn little about the nature of the visual process merely by introspecting about his visual experiences in an uncontrolled situation. In either case it is necessary to simplify and control conditions in order to gain quantitative understanding. In visual psychophysics, the stimulus (light) must be delimited and simplified until its precise physical specification is possible. Further, the nature and number of responses allowed to the observing subject must also be severely restricted. Assuming that other conditions of the experiment are properly controlled, these simplifications will lead the experimenter who asks intelligent questions to a progressively better understanding of the nature of the visual process.

Psychophysical investigation is capable of providing a specification of the performance characteristics of the visual system as a whole. It is analogous, for example, to the specification of the operating characteristics of a complex machine in terms of input-output variables alone. For example, a good deal could be learned about how an automobile works by measuring such things as time required to accelerate to 60 mph, rate of fuel consumption at various constant velocities, braking distance, steering ratio, etc., all of which can be measured without pulling the wheels or taking the engine apart. But one would not rest content with such external measures; there would be a strong temptation to look inside the body of the car to see what was going on there. One also likes to look inside the living organism for explanations of psychophysical performance data. This is often difficult to do with human subjects, but there is a vast body of relevant anatomical and physiological literature based primarily upon animal subjects. The methods and results of many such investigations will be reported elsewhere in this symposium. Nevertheless, reference to concepts derived from such data will necessarily be made in this discussion of psychophysics.

Measurement and Methodology

PHYSICAL MEASUREMENT

Strange as it may seem, the results of many psychophysical experiments are ex-

[*] *Proceedings of the International Congress on Technology and Blindness,* 1964, vol. 2, pp. 5–30.

pressed entirely in physical units. (Just how this happens will be explained later.) This being the case, it is obvious that the results of such experiments can be no more precise than the physical calibration of the experimental apparatus used in obtaining them.

Physicists talk about light by using either wave or quantum concepts. In terms of quantum concepts—and these are the ones that now seem most related to problems in vision—the critical variables are (1) *intensive*: the numbers of quanta reaching the eye in a short burst, or the number per unit time in a prolonged stimulus; (2) *spectral*: the energy that each quantum possesses, and the distribution of such energies in a complex stimulus; (3) *geometrical*: the relation of the stimulus, especially its shape, area, the directionality of the quanta emitted or reflected, and the position of the eye with respect to these; (4) various *temporal* aspects of the stimulus.

Quanta, Energy, and Wavelength. It is conventional, in visual research, to measure the intensive aspects of the stimulus in terms of energy (rather than numbers of quanta) and wavelength (rather than energy per quantum). Although this convention will be followed in this report, it will be well to spell out exactly what the relations are between the two sets of concepts. Wavelength (λ) is directly related to the energy per quantum (ϵ) by the relation

$$\epsilon = hc/\lambda \qquad (1)$$

where c is the velocity of light (2.998×10^{17} mμ/sec) and h is Planck's constant (6.62377×10^{-27} erg-sec). In this equation, wavelength is specified in millimicrons (mμ), this being the convention in vision research, and the velocity of light is given in the same units. Thus it will be seen that a simple inverse relation exists between energy per quantum and wave-

length. If either of these variables were plotted on a log scale, any function of one of them could be represented by the mirror image of the other (unfortunately this is seldom done).

Radiance. The radiant *intensity* of a point source of light can be specified as the number of ergs per second irradiated by that source per unit solid angle in a given direction. Most sources have an intensity which is different in different directions. For visual purposes, one is more often concerned with surfaces than with points. A surface can be considered to be made up from a very large number of points. The *radiance* of a surface is the *intensity* per unit projected area in a particular direction ("projected" meaning that a cosine correction is introduced to account for the apparent reduction in area as the surface is viewed obliquely). In general, any given small region of a surface will, like the point source, have an intensity that depends upon direction; furthermore, the intensity in any given direction will vary depending upon the region of the surface considered. A *perfectly diffuse* surface is one whose intensity per unit area is independent both of direction and the region selected. In most of what follows, we will pretend that we are dealing with perfectly diffuse surfaces and/or that we are concerned only with the uniform radiance of the surface in one direction. The latter is very often the case in visual experiments where the position of the eye is fixed relative to the source.

In the discussion to follow, we will deal mainly with radiance as the intensive variable and wavelength as the spectral variable. It should however be noted in passing that this choice, while it follows the current (and long-standing) convention, is not necessarily the best one, and that the graphical appearance of experimental data depends upon one's arbitrary choice of units for plotting. For example, one often hears of an *equal-energy spec-*

trum, by which is meant a stimulus containing the same number of ergs per unit wavelength throughout the spectrum. It would be represented as a horizontal straight line on a plot of energy vs. wavelength. However, if plotted as energy vs. energy-per-quantum, or as numbers-of-quanta vs. energy-per-quantum, or as numbers-of-quanta vs. wavelength, the same information would be represented in each case other than as a horizontal straight line.

REPLICATION

Physicists and psychologists alike are very alert to problems of measurement error: no single measurement can be perfectly precise and therefore a number of replications (repeats) of any measurement must be made in order to establish a reliable mean value and the standard error of the mean. In visual psychophysics, there is sufficient variability that little is to be learned from the single response to a single stimulus, many repetitions of each stimulus condition being necessary to establish reliable mean values. This tends to make experiments long and tedious, a condition for which there is no obvious remedy short of patience and determination.

Some psychophysicists have been interested primarily in the nature of the variability found in the experiment. For example, some have felt (19) that great insight could be gained through a study of the shape of the *frequency-of-seeing curve,* which relates the number of "yes, I see it" responses given by the subject to the radiance of the stimulus. (A typical frequency-of-seeing curve is shown in Figure 1, where the procedure used for calculating the *threshold* radiance—that required for 50 percent "yes" responses—is shown.) Others have noted that the ordering of "yes" and "no" responses in a long series of stimulus presentations, all of the same radiance, is not random. They have felt that important conclusions about the visual process could be drawn from the study of

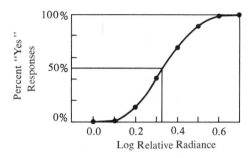

FIGURE 1   Hypothetical data to illustrate the method for computing the visual threshold. A smooth curve is drawn through the experimental points (although much more elaborate curve-fitting procedures can be used). The value of log relative radiance corresponding to 50 percent "yes, I can see it" responses is then determined as shown. In this example, the threshold is apparently 0.32 log relative radiance units.

such sequences. The writer is skeptical that it is fruitful to emphasize the nature of the variability found in vision experiments. In the past such emphasis has produced mainly a great deal of argument without much subsequent illumination, probably because there are a number of unrelated sources of variability in psychophysical experiments. When efforts are made to study only one of these sources of variability, the results are unavoidably contaminated by the influence of the others. All sources of variability are a problem from the standpoint of measurement. Some are listed and discussed below. In the description of experiments to follow, the emphasis will be upon average values, and the significance of these with respect to the structure and function of the visual system.

SOURCES OF VARIABILITY

Physical. The number of light quanta emitted from an optical system will never be exactly the same twice, regardless of the degree of precision attempted in the control of source intensity, flash duration, etc. For example, if the transmittance of a train of optical elements is, say, 90 percent, this means that nine quanta in ten, *on the average,* will pass through without being scattered out or absorbed. This does not mean, however, that for every ten quanta entering the system, exactly nine will emerge. Occasionally, all ten might get through, while at many other times less than nine will make it (in accordance with the so-called *Poisson distribution*). Exactly the same kind of considerations obtain with regard to the numbers of quanta that will pass through a shutter, even if the shutter's characteristics were perfectly reproducible (which they are not), or with respect to the passage of quanta through the optical media of the eye (where an average of more than one in two may be absorbed), or with respect to the probability of a quantum being absorbed by a given molecule of visual photopigment (this probability is in general very low). The number of quanta that must be absorbed in the retina in order to produce a visual sensation is believed to be very small (perhaps five or six) under ideal conditions (14). For all of the above reasons, the number that actually will be absorbed from a given stimulus flash, despite meticulous physical control, will vary from a logical minimum of zero, to a possible but very unlikely maximum which is the entire number incident upon the cornea of the eye (this may be some thousands). Efforts based upon the shape of the frequency-of-seeing curve have been made to infer how many quanta n must be absorbed by the photoreceptors in order for a visual sensation to occur. These efforts have not been very successful because any nonphysical source of variability tends to flatten the frequency-of-seeing curve. If one assumes the variability to be restricted to the stimulus, this leads to an underestimation of the actual numbers of quanta involved. Furthermore, the variability in even the best controlled experiments is such that it is generally not possible to discriminate statistically between a Poisson integral that implies an n of five or six, and that for an n of infinity (the

integral of the normal distribution curve) (6).

Physiological. The sensitivity of the visual system has been shown to possess seasonal and diurnal variations, and can be influenced by the use of drugs. A spectacular effect is the considerable loss of sensitivity that occurs in subjects who, for one reason or another, are deficient in Vitamin A, a substance which is required for the reconstitution of the visual rod photopigment, *rhodopsin* (13). Sensitivity can also be altered by injury or pathology anywhere in the visual system from retina to visual cortex. It is moreover the common experience of workers in visual psychophysics that the sensitivity level of the normal subject often shifts up and down from day to day by as much as a factor of two even with the best physical control. Variability due to physiological factors is probably the major culprit.

Psychological. Anyone who has ever observed dim light flashes will realize that merely to judge whether a flash is seen (or not seen) involves a process of decision which goes beyond the immediate sensation. The subject must therefore adopt some criterion according to which he will say "yes" or "no" in response to a given sensation. Different subjects adopt different criteria, and a given subject's criterion varies from one time to another. This has been shown in experiments where some of the "flashes" randomly presented are "blanks"; that is, no light is delivered to the eye. Some subjects report as many as 30 or 40 percent "false positives" under these conditions; others virtually none. Methods have been developed to circumvent the criterion problem. These methods allow the experimenter to record whether a response is "correct" or "incorrect," rather than merely whether the subject reports "yes" or "no." For example, a light may be flashed in one of four possible spatial positions or time intervals, with the subject being required to specify which one contained the flash. This "forced choice" method cannot however always be used (5). For example, if a subject is asked to judge which of two different colored lights appears brighter, he is himself the court of last resort since no independent physical specification is possible and therefore his responses cannot be classified right or wrong.

There has been a suggestion made recently that because of the criterion problem, the concept of "threshold" is not valid and should perhaps be thrown out (27). Detection, it is said, properly concerns whether the appearance of signal-plus-noise is sufficiently different from that of noise alone for a subject to report the presence of the signal. From this writer's viewpoint, there is a serious question of whether the signal-to-noise conception—which began in electronics and has had its main sensory application in the domain of hearing—has much validity in the visual case. The threshold concept has in any event been extremely useful, and it is not likely that those who have utilized it in experiments whose aim is to understand the nature of the visual process will soon abandon it.

Another source of psychological variability has been studied under the heading of *vigilance*. It has been shown that in an impoverished environment (where stimuli are few and far between) one cannot pay attention indefinitely to a place where a stimulus *might* appear (1). Many light flashes, which would ordinarily be seen very clearly, will pass unnoticed. In the type of psychophysical experiment to be reported here, the vigilance problem is met through proper training of the subject, the use of auditory indicator signals just before the light is presented, the use of rest periods within sessions, and the use of sessions of reasonably short length.

Still another source of variability is found in experiments where the subject must search for the target to be detected.

Because the contrast threshold (*contrast* is the ratio of an increment spot to the background, each independently measured in radiance units) is lowest at the point of fixation in the visual field, a test spot of very low contrast can be seen only when directly fixated. It may take some minutes to find such a test spot, even when it is quite obviously visible when finally discovered (16).

It should be noted that although thresholds have been used illustratively in this section, most of the points made apply equally well to other kinds of discrimination experiments, for example those involving brightness matching, which will be discussed in a later section.

PSYCHOPHYSICAL METHODS

Sensory Scaling Methods. The strength of visual sensation is of variable magnitude, ranging from something just barely visible to the brightest light that one can imagine. However, the investigation of the subjective visual response is rendered difficult by the inaccessibility of subjective response magnitude. This magnitude, incidentally, is only partly under the control of the radiance of the physical test stimulus, being influenced also by the state of adaptation of the eye and also the influence of background and surround fields (18). The magnitude of visual sensations is not directly measurable in the same sense that physical quantities are, because sensation is private, unshared experience. Estimates of the magnitude of visual sensations have nevertheless very often been attempted in recent years, in what have been called "sensory scaling" experiments (18, 24). In one variation of the method (*magnitude estimation*), the subject is asked to estimate brightness in terms of a numerical scale, usually with reference to some arbitrary standard (which might, for example, be called "100"). In another variation (*fractionation*) the subject may be asked to tell whether one stimulus looks "more or less than half as bright" as another. The variability in the results of these methods, as might be expected, is rather great, and has sometimes been disguised by combining the divergent results of many subjects and by a failure explicitly to state the size of the measurement error. Moreover, the matter of what a statement like "twice as bright" really means (in a philosophical sense) is unsettled and controversial.

Classical Methods. Rather than to attempt direct estimates of sensory magnitude, the classical approach to the problem, involves methods which are less direct, but yields results which are much more accurate. These methods may be introduced with an analogy. Imagine that you are given a photocell and a microammeter, with no information provided about the linearity of response of either instrument. To make matters worse, suppose that the face of the meter is blank and that in the absence of any illumination of the photocell, there is a steady quivering of the meter needle at some low but finite value. It may be assumed—and this is indeed fortunate—that there is a monotonic relation between the intensity of a light delivered to the photocell and the magnitude of the mean needle deflection of the meter, so that the one value increases with the other.

As an example, let us consider the task of finding the spectral sensitivity of the system. One could start by delivering equal-energy amounts of light to the photocell at various wavelengths over which the system displays a measurable response. The wavelength of peak response could be identified this way, but the meaning of all other values would be ambiguous, due to the lack of a scale on the meter (inaccessibility of response magnitude) and the probable nonlinearity of the system.

A preferred solution requires first that some arbitrary point on the scale of the meter be identified and marked. One then takes a calibrated monochromator and irradiates the photocell at some wavelength until the needle is driven to the arbitrary point. Because of the quiver, it will be necessary to make several such estimates. The system may also show adaptation or fatigue. In such a case it would be better to irradiate the cell with short pulses of light and judge whether the needle did or did not reach the criterion point. One could then determine the energy required, at each wavelength tested, to produce a .50 probability of producing the criterion deflection.

This analogy is very close to what can be done to measure the spectral sensitivity of the human observer. Substitute the eye for the photocell, the remainder of the organism for the microammeter, and subjective magnitude for the deflection of the needle, and the analogy is complete. This is a perfectly respectable way to measure the spectral sensitivity of the eye, and the results will be much more reliable than those derived from sensory scaling.

It was mentioned earlier that the results of psychophysical experiments are very often expressed entirely in physical units. We now have an example of this, since what has been done is to find a combination of two physical variables which interact to produce some criterion response. In the case just cited, the two variables were stimulus radiance and wavelength. Many other combinations are possible, since at least the following physical variables are known to exert an influence on the probability of occurrence of a criterion response to a visual stimulus: size of target, duration of stimulus flash, position of flash with respect to a fixation point, size of background upon which flash is superposed, radiance of background, spectral composition of flash and background, shape of target, presence and characteristics of surround fields, time of exposure of background and/or surround fields, and the history of exposure of the eye to light (which helps to determine its state of adaptation). These variables, in turn, interact with one another in complex ways. Not all possible combinations of these variables have been, or probably ever can be, investigated.

One of the more common types of stimulus configurations used in visual psychophysics is the split, or "bipartite," field which can be used to make brightness matches. With one half the field set at a particular radiance level, experimental operations are carried out to determine that radiance of the other half of the field which will cause it to match the fixed half for brightness. There are two fundamental ways that this may be done. In the first, *the method of adjustment,* the subject is given a control knob by means of which he can himself adjust the luminance of the variable half of the field. The second way to determine the matching luminance allows no adjustment by the subject. Rather, the experimenter sets the luminance of the variable half and then asks the subject to report (for an exposure of finite duration) whether it is brighter or dimmer than the fixed half. That luminance at which "brighter" and "dimmer" judgments occur with equal probability is taken as the matching luminance. There are a number of variations of this basic method. In the *method of constant stimuli,* several fixed luminances of the variable field are decided upon before the experiment begins; these are then presented to the subject in random order, each many times, until the matching luminance can be calculated. In another, the *method of limits,* the luminance of the variable field is systematically adjusted, by the experimenter. In one half the trials, the variable field will at first be obviously too bright and then will be gradually reduced until the subject reports a match. In the other trials, the variable field is brought up from an initial dim state. In still another method, the *up-and-down method* (staircase method) the luminance of the variable field is determined in part by the subject. The experimenter predetermines

the size of the increments and decrements of luminance of the variable field that he will use. When the subject says "brighter," the luminance of the variable field will be decreased by one step and this continued until a "dimmer" judgment is elicited. In that case, the luminance of the variable field will be increased, and so on. There is a considerable literature pertaining to these various psychophysical methods (and others), including detailed instructions for the proper calculation of the matching luminance (12).

When both halves of the field are of the same color, the matching luminance of the variable field will turn out to be very close to a physical match, and such an experiment is of very limited interest. When however the spectral composition of the two halves of the field is different, the subject himself (as previously noted) must be the final judge concerning the appearance of fields of equal brightness in the face of obvious color differences. The basic experiment underlying the science of *photometry* (measurement of light) is of just this sort. For example, if a green light at 555 mμ is placed on the fixed half of the field, while light of 630 mμ (red) is placed on the other, it might be determined that for a particular observer four times the radiance is required on the red half in order for it to look equally bright as the green. By definition, the *sensitivity* of this observer for 630 mμ is stated to be one-fourth that for 555 mμ. By repeating this experiment many times at many wavelengths, a *spectral sensitivity* function may be determined. Because the color differences are bothersome in making such brightness matches, other techniques have been attempted to render them less noticeable, in particular the "step-by-step method" where one works through the spectrum in small steps in order to minimize color differences. By this, and a less direct technique called *flicker photometry,* the International Commission on Illumination (CIE) in 1924 adopted the so-called *relative photopic luminous efficiency curve* (22), which is shown in Figure 2 as the righthand curve.

Facts and Concepts about Vision Derived from Psychophysical Experiments

ABSOLUTE SENSITIVITY

Something on the order of 100 quanta incident upon the eye can produce a visual sensation (14). In order for this small number of quanta to be effective, it is necessary that they arise from a small spot in the visual field (so as to be focused by the optics of the eye into a small spot on the retina of the eye) and that they be delivered in a short burst. This is because of the limited capacity of the eye to integrate light input over space and time (17). Furthermore, the light quanta must be of an energy per quantum corresponding to about 505 mμ wavelength, to which the eye is most sensitive when dark-adapted and stimulated at low levels. Finally, the stimulus must be imaged in a part of the retina containing a high density of rod photoreceptors. Under these ideal conditions, it can be shown that only about a half-dozen or so quanta are actually *absorbed* by the photoreceptors. Since the number of rod receptors involved in even the smallest flash image is a few hundred, the conclusion may be reached that the absorption of a single quantum of light by a single rod can produce some kind of a signal, although perhaps a half-dozen such signals must occur within a restricted region of the retina in order for a sensation to be produced. These results agree with the modern photochemical view that the action of light upon photoreceptors involves the absorption of individual light quanta by individual molecules of photopigment, and that all vision (even at high intensities) is based upon this kind of elemental activity.

SPECTRAL SENSITIVITY

The spectral sensitivity of the eye can be obtained, as previously indicated, by finding the radiance required at other wavelengths to produce a criterion response (e.g., brightness match or threshold). A *scotopic spectral sensitivity curve*, appropriate to the threshold of the dark-adapted eye outside the foveal region, is shown in Figure 2. (It is the left-hand curve of the two that are shown in the figure.) In this figure, the ordinate is labelled on one side to indicate the number of quanta that must be delivered to the eye in order for a threshold response to take place, assuming that number to be 125 at the wavelength of peak sensitivity. It is generally agreed that the larger number required at other wavelengths reflects the decreasing probability of absorption by photopigment molecules of quanta having other energy values than the optimal one. The response of a given molecule is believed to be nonspecific, carrying with it no information about what wavelength of light activated it. Thus, 10,000 quanta at wavelength $\mu = 610$ mμ (see Figure 3) each stand only 1/100th as much chance of being absorbed as do those at $\lambda = 505$ mμ. But if 100 times as many are delivered, the resulting sensation will be indistinguishable in every way from the much smaller number delivered at the wavelength of peak sensitivity. Thus the total effectiveness of a stimulus of complex spectral distribution may be estimated by integrating it with the scotopic spectral sensitivity curve. Therefore, if V' represents the scotopic relative spectral sensitivity curve (see Figure 3), and if $E\lambda_1$ and $E\lambda_2$ represent the spectral energy distributions of two stimuli, these stimuli will match for brightness if

$$\int E_{\lambda_1} V_\lambda' \, d\lambda = \int E_{\lambda_2} V_\lambda' \, d\lambda \quad (2)$$

where in this and other cases to follow,

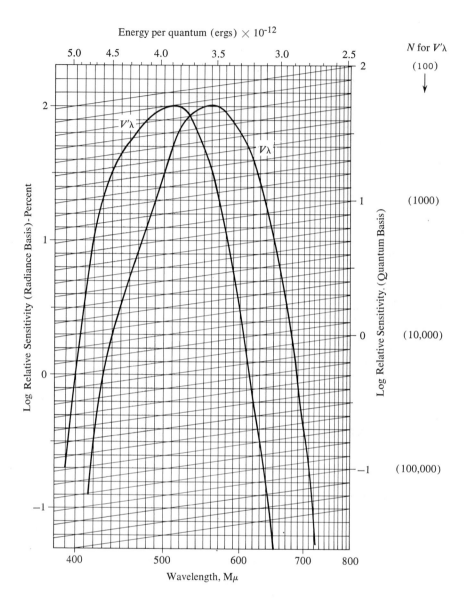

FIGURE 2   Scotopic (left) and photopic (right) luminous efficiency (spectral sensitivity) functions ($V'\lambda$ and $V\lambda$, respectively). The horizontal coordinates give the log relative spectral sensitivity (in terms of 100 percent at peak) based on energy units. For example, 10 percent sensitivity (1.0 log unit) for scotopic vision will be found at wavelength values of about 416 and 588 mμ, by following a horizontal straight line across from the value labeled "10." The oblique coordinates give the log relative spectral sensitivity on a quantum basis. The number of quanta required for threshold visibility for scotopic vision is indicated at the extreme right (N), assuming this value to be 100 at the wavelength of peak sensitivity. In this case, 10 percent sensitivity would be determined by following the oblique coordinate labeled "1000" (which is ten times the number of quanta required at the peak of the curve) to the points of intersection (approximately 417 and 570 mμ). This plot is made possible because all values are given on logarithmic scales.

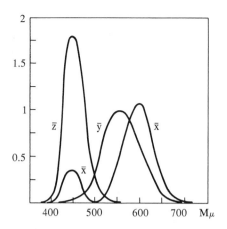

FIGURE 3   Tristimulus values for an equal-energy spectrum in the CIE system. These are used to compute metameric color matches. (Reference 17)

the limits of integration will be taken from $\lambda = 380$ mμ to $\lambda = 750$ mμ.

COLOR MIXTURE

When two fields containing different spectral distributions of energy are directly compared under scotopic conditions, they will match exactly if the radiance of one is suitably adjusted with respect to the other. This is not however true at higher radiances. Under conditions of daylight vision (*photopic vision*) no exact match can in general be made, since a color difference will remain as previously mentioned in connection with the brightness matches underlying photometry. It has however been established that many exact matches are possible under these conditions, in accordance with certain rules discovered experimentally to be at least approximately true. (An exact match between two stimuli which physically differ is known as a *metameric match*.)

Consider a split field, divided into left- and right-hand parts, to which energy may be delivered independently to the two halves. Suppose that a given stimulus, which we will call C, is delivered to, say, the left half of the field, and that three other stimuli, to be called R, G, and B, are available to the experimenter and can be added to either side of the field. The results of "color mixing" experiments, in which R. G, and B are called "primary" stimuli, indicate that

$$c(C) = r(R) + g(G) + b(B) \quad (3)$$

where r, g, and b are the amounts of the three primaries required to equal c units of the color to be matched, C. In order to translate this mathematical statement into experimental terms, it is necessary to be explicit about the empirical meaning of the operations of "=" and "+". Equality in the mathematical realm translates to "matches with" in the laboratory; the operation of addition implies optical superposition, meaning that the quantities indicated are added together by combining the lights, in one way or another, so that they superpose in the visual field. Finally, if one of the quantities should happen to be negative (for example, "b") this must imply (since negative amounts of light are physically unrealizable) that this quantity must be *added* to the opposite side of the equation. For example,

$$c(C) = r(R) + g(G) - b(B) \quad (4)$$

is experimentally realized only as

$$c(C) + b(B) = r(R) + g(G). \quad (5)$$

An important outcome of experiments in this domain has been to establish that for a given amount, c, of the color to be matched, exactly three primaries are required (for the normal subject) to establish a unique match. No match will in general be possible if only two primaries are allowed to vary, and with four or more primaries the values required for a match are not unique. Photopic vision is therefore said to be "trivariant." Furthermore, an important constellation of rules known as "Grassman's Laws" may be summarized by stating that an isomorphism exists between the formal mathematical statement of equation (1) and the experimental domain of color matching to which it relates. Therefor, the additive, multiplicative, associative, and transitive operations of algebra can be applied to the quantitative description of color matches. This makes it possible to relate color-matching data obtained with one set of primaries to those obtained with any other set under otherwise similar experimental conditions. One such set, the standard so-called "distribution coefficients" of the CIE system is shown in Figure 3. These show the amounts of "red," "green," and "blue" primaries ($\bar{x}$, $\bar{y}$, and $\bar{z}$) required to match one energy unit of the monochromatic test stimulus of the wavelength shown on the abscissa. Depending on choice of primaries, many other such sets of curves are possible; each accurately predicts which physically different stimuli will match. In order to find out, one carries through the following calculations, each analogous to the one previously discussed for scotopic vision:

$$X = \int E_\lambda \bar{x} \, d\lambda$$

$$Y = \int E_\lambda \bar{y} \, d\lambda \qquad (6)$$

$$Z = \int E_\lambda \bar{z} \, d\lambda$$

where $E\lambda$ is again the spectral energy distribution of the stimulus reaching the eye. For any two stimuli where $X_1 = X_2$, $Y_1 = Y_2$, and $Z_1 = Z_2$, a metameric match is predicted.

Why does the eye behave this way? The most common interpretation, stripped of all superfluous assumptions and details, is simply this:

(1) There are three kinds of visual photopigments in the photopic receptors (cones) of the eye. These differ in their spectral sensitivities,

which are either proportional to $\bar{x}$, $\bar{y}$, and $\bar{z}$, or to some other set related to these through a change of primaries.

(2) The relative probability of light absorption in a given visual cone pigment is given by these functions, which are unchanged in shape regardless of the actual rate of light absorption.

(3) The three types of pigments are unequally distributed in different kinds of photopic receptors (*cones*), so that the relative responses of these cones differ depending upon wavelength. This information is kept separated in the visual pathways, although it may be recoded.

Although the three hypothetical types of photopigments have not yet been directly identified by chemical techniques, experiments called *reflection densitometry* have been carried out which have involved the measurement of light reflected from the fundus of the eye, after having twice passed through the photopigment-bearing receptors. These measurements have limited accuracy, but strongly lend support to the three-pigment idea (20). This is a good example of a photochemical concept which although very probably true still has its experimental basis almost entirely within the domain of visual psychophysics, bolstered by the purely physical measurements of reflection densitometry.

SENSITIVITY CHANGES
IN VISION

One of the most remarkable properties of the eye is its ability to respond effectively over an enormous range of stimulus radiances. From the absolute threshold of vision to the brightest light that one can stand there is a range of radiances of about 10 billion to one. An explanation of how this happens will bring into play a good deal of evidence that has been obtained by psychophysical methods, much of which ties in well with what is known of the underlying anatomy and physiology.

Pupillary Responses. When the photographer wishes to reduce the exposure of his film, he will either decrease the exposure duration or reduce the size of the diaphragm. The eye operates with a continuous exposure, but the pupil size is variable. Pupillary responses are both static and dynamic: a change in illumination produces a transient response, usually with overshoot, with an ultimate settling down at a fairly stable level. So far as light control is concerned, however, the capability of the pupillary response is limited: the range of pupillary openings is from about 2 mm diameter to about 8 mm diameter, corresponding to a ratio of areas of only about 16 to one. This is a very small part indeed of the total range of 10 billion to one. Actually, the pupillary response has other functions that may be more important. Under low conditions of illumination, where the eye needs all the quanta it can gather, a large pupil is very helpful. But to have such a large pupil under high intensity conditions would produce a significant loss of visual resolution due to spherical and chromatic aberrations introduced by the wide-open optical system of the eye. Since one problem at high levels is to reduce the effectiveness of the incident light, a large pupil would be disadvantageous on both counts. But the decrease in sensitivity that comes with the smaller pupil may be no more important than the improvement in the quality of the retinal image that accompanies it and may be merely a by-product.

Shift from Rod to Cone Vision. Dark adaptation is measured by exposing the subject to an intense field of light, which is then extinguished to be followed by small "test flashes" of light which are delivered at various times after the extinction of the adapting light. The experiment then consists of finding the radiance of the test light which is required for a criterion response to occur. The most common criterion is the threshold response to a simple disk of light. When a disk of small area is used, but delivered to one side of the fixation point, a "dark adaptation curve" like the one shown in Figure 4 (Curve A) can be obtained. The point to be noted here is the duplex shape of the curve, which is accounted for by postulating that a shift occurs from vision mediated by one class of receptor to that mediated by another. On the basis of histological evidence, it is known that the receptors of the human eye fall into two broad categories, the rods and the cones. Although these share, to some extent, common pathways to the brain, there is sufficient separateness for one to conceive that the visual system is in reality two visual systems; these have been called scotopic and photopic, respectively. The duplex nature of the dark adaptation curve is held to represent the fact that, during the first few minutes of dark adaptation, the cones are more sensitive than the rods, with the rods taking over later to provide the basis for the second branch of the curve. The full story is more complicated than this, since it involves also changes in the integrative capacity of the eye during the course of adaptation (29). From an earlier discussion, it will be recalled that only about six quanta of light need be absorbed, under ideal conditions, for a visual sensation to occur, and that these quanta are absorbed in separate receptors. This implies that the activity set up in separate receptors somehow combines at a common junction, where some kind of summation occurs. All evidence indicates that the degree of such summation is greater for the scotopic than for the photopic system, and moreover that it increases considerably during the course of dark adaptation (2). Thus, part of the reason for the threshold drop

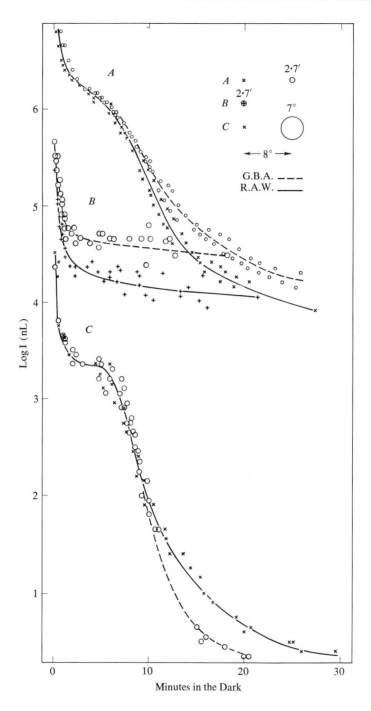

FIGURE 4   Dark-adaptation curves. Ordinate: log luminance (in nanolamberts) required for threshold visibility. Abscissa: time in the dark following extinction of pre-adapting field. Inset shows that curve A is for a small field to one side of the fixation point, and curve C is for a large field to one side of the fixation point. The dramatic differences among the shapes of the curves reveal the importance of changes in the summative properties of the eye during the adaptational process. (Reference 2)

is related to the increase in sensitivity of each relevant receptor, but part of it is also related to the increase in the size of the summation area.

If a grating test object, consisting of alternate dark and light bars, is substituted for the simple disk, it is found that the finer the disk, the smaller is the drop in the dark adaptation curve, assuming that resolution of the stripes of the disk is required of the subject. This is consistent with the above interpretation. If the test disk is made small and is directly fixated, the rod branch of the dark adaptation curve fails to appear. This is consistent with the anatomical finding that there are no rods in the *fovea* of the retina, which corresponds to that area receiving the image of objects located at or near the point of fixation (10).

Spectral sensitivity is measured either by the comparison of fields for brightness, or by the threshold technique, by utilizing small foveal stimuli in the latter case in order to restrict stimulation to the photopic (cone) system. The results of the threshold type of experiment would lead to relative sensitivity values similar (though not exactly the same) to those shown in Figure 3. The curve on the left is appropriate for a stimulus imaged upon a retinal area containing a mixed rod-cone population, and where the rods should be most sensitive. That on the right is for the foveal condition. It should be noted that the wavelength of peak sensitivity shifts from about 505 mμ to 550 mμ as one goes from rod to cone vision. For a comparison of absolute sensitivity values, the photopic curve would have to be lowered nearly two log units, which would bring the two curves into close correspondence at a wavelength of 650 mμ. The spectral sensitivity curve for the scotopic (rod) condition is very close to that of the visual photopigment, rhodopsin, measured spectrophotometrically in solution, after certain complicating factors have been taken into account (14, 28). The shape of the curve is therefore

believed to be attributable mainly to the probability of quantum absorption by rhodopsin, which is known to be the photopigment contained by rods. As previously noted, the photopigments of the cones have not yet been experimentally isolated.

Color vision is entirely a property of photopic vision. It is lacking when intensity levels are too low to permit the cones to be effective.

The increment threshold is measured by adapting the eye to a large, steady field of light, and then determining the threshold to a superposed increment flash in the center of the adapting field (26). Typical results of such an experiment are shown in Figure 5, where the threshold radiance of the increment flash is shown as a function of the radiance of the background, each on a logarithmic scale. Again a rod-cone "break" is evident in the rather abrupt change in the slope of the ascending curve corresponding to a background radiance of about —6. The rate at which

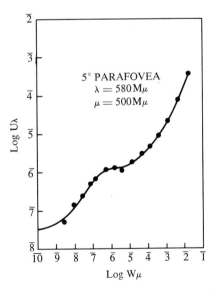

FIGURE 5 Increment threshold curve. Ordinate: log radiance required for threshold of increment test flash. Abscissa: log radiance of background field upon which flash is superposed. The two branches of the curve reveal that cone function replaces rod function starting at a field value of about —6. (Reference 25, 26)

a given branch of this kind of curve rises from a slope of zero toward a slope of one depends upon the area of the test stimulus: the larger the test stimulus, the more abrupt the rise. It is also true that very brief test flashes produce a more gradual rise than do relatively long ones (4). This is consistent with the idea of threshold changes being due to changes in spatial summation as well as in the sensitivity of individual receptors.

The unit-slope portion of this curve (upper right) is the range over which *Weber's Law* holds. In this region, a given ratio increase in the radiance of the background produces the same ratio of increase in the threshold of the test flash. This type of behavior is very important in everyday vision, since the ratios of light to dark in the visual field are independent of the intensity of an illuminating source (assuming unchanged geometry of the lighting), being based on an important property of objects which is independent of the absolute amount of incident radiant energy: their *reflectance*. This is simply a measure of the ratio of the amount of light reflected to that incident. A full specification requires a separate reflectance value for each wavelength of the incident light; such a *spectral reflectance curve* is the principal determinant of the perceived color of an object under ordinary conditions of illumination.

Rather little is yet known about the mechanisms underlying the phenomenon of adaptation. A previous view, based entirely upon psychophysical observation, has proven to be incorrect. This was the notion that visual sensitivity decreased with increasing levels of adaptation because of the severe bleaching of molecules of photosensitive pigment, which then became unavailable for further stimulation. Direct measurements of the amount of bleaching have subsequently been made by the reflection densitometry technique, and these reveal only trivial amounts of bleaching in comparison to the sensitivity

changes noted psychophysically. Readers are referred to recent reviews of the subject for some current theoretical speculations about this problem (9, 21).

The concepts and experiments discussed in this section are only a sample of those data concerned with the static eye, monocular case. Many more experiments and concepts emerge when one deals with the mobile eye and binocular vision, but these go beyond the scope intended for this review. It should be noted in passing, however, that eye movements add a very active component to what otherwise would be a merely passive process—the reception of light. The full appreciation of the visual environment is built up from a series of "snapshots," each occuring during a fixational pause between eye movements which occur many times each minute.

Processing of Information

Psychophysical techniques are being applied these days to the investigation of a wide variety of problems having to do with the manner in which the visual system processes information. Without going into details regarding specific experimental techniques, an effort will be made in this concluding section to portray the writer's current view of what is going on, a view which results largely from inferences based upon the results of psychophysical experiments.

In photopic vision, information about color, although based initially upon the relative spectral absorptances of three types of visual photopigment, is coded almost immediately into three different kinds of signals: red-green, yellow-blue, and white-black. Since signals carrying information about the the red and green parts of the visual field must be carried over the same pathways, no single region of the field should look reddish and greenish at the same time, which is in accord with the failure of such sensations to appear. Moreover, the meaning of a given message in a given nerve pathway is dependent not only on the spectral character of the light illuminating receptors to which that pathway is directly connected, but also upon the illumination of surrounding receptors. Indeed, messages meaning "black" cannot be induced except by the action of surround fields upon a darker test area. Thus, considerable recoding of the initial trivariant information takes place before messages are sent to the brain (15).

Spatial vision depends upon interaction effects in whole regions of the eye, and not simply upon point-to-point projection from external object to retina to brain. Thus there are changes in the ability of the eye to resolve fine detail depending upon the state of adaptation of the eye, the nature and orientation of the test object, the orientation of the head, and many other factors. For example, the detectability of a very fine black line in an otherwise bright field depends upon its length, and such a line will disappear if its image is frozen on the retina (8).

The temporal resolving power of the eye has a number of fascinating aspects. From one point of view, it seems to be very poor: the observer can be fooled into thinking he sees continuous motion when actually he is seeing a "motion" picture consisting of successive still frames, alternated with periods of darkness, at a rate of only about 15 frames per second. One cannot tell the difference, under some conditions, between a flash lasting a microsecond and another lasting a tenth second, so long as their energy contents are equated. On the other hand, experiments involving how the visibility of one flash is affected by another indicate that information about time differences of only a few milliseconds is retained in the peripheral parts of the visual system, indicating that such information must be lost at a subsequent stage (7).

A number of experiments have shown that the informational content of a flash of light can be wiped out by the presentation of a subsequent flash (about 50 msec later). This has consequences with regard to the temporary memory storage of visual input and the way that this memory can be obliterated by a subsequent signal (3).

As one goes from a relatively dark-adapted to a relatively light-adapted state, improvements take place in both temporal and spatial resolving power. The failure of the full potential of temporal resolving power to be retained all the way to the brain suggests that it is sacrificed in order to provide better spatial resolving power than would otherwise be possible through the communications pathways that are available: such trades between spatial and temporal resolution are well known in communications devices.

There is an important lesson to be learned from the experiments which have led to these and other ideas about information processing in the visual system, namely that the system works in several stages, with complex recoding of the information at each stage. Most of this data processing occurs in the retina, in a system containing many millions of interconnected neural elements in addition to the photoreceptors. Little is yet known, on a neurophysiological level, about the specific details of many of these events. Even when a great deal is known, the difficulties of providing a man-made device to stimulate this retinal activity are formidable almost beyond imagination.

Summary

In a section on *Measurement and Methodology*, the classical "trick" of psychophysical measurement was revealed as the determination of combinations of physical variables which interact to produce a criterion response from a human observer. Threshold measurements and brightness matches were used as examples. The emphasis in the discussion was upon psychophysical methods as a tool for finding out how the visual system works, rather than upon psychophysical methods as an area of research for their own sake.

In the section entitled *Facts and Concepts About Vision Derived from Psychophysical Experiments,* concepts about absolute sensitivity, spectral sensitivity, color mixture, visual adaptation, visual resolution, and the classical dichotomy between photopic (cone) and scotopic (rod) vision were used to illustrate the kinds of ideas that emerge from classical psychophysical experiments in vision.

In the final section on *Processing of Information,* certain ideas about visual performance, looked at from the standpoint of communications concepts, were very briefly discussed. These included the recoding of information related to color, the probable sacrifice of temporal resolving power in the visual system in favor of spatial resolving power, and the temporary storage of information in the visual system. It was concluded that it would be a most formidable task to build a man-made device capable of preprocessing visual information, before delivering it to the visual brain, in the complex manner of the retina of the eye.

References

1. ADAMS, J. A., "Vigilance in the Detection of Low-Intensity Visual Stimuli," *J. Exp. Psychol.,* vol. 52 (1956), pp. 204–208.
2. ARDEN, G. P., and R. A. WEALE, "Nervous Mechanisms and Dark Adaptation," *J. Physiol.,* vol. 125 (1954), pp. 417–426.
3. AVERBACH, E., and A. S. CORIELL, "Short-Term Memory in Vision," *Bell System Tech. J.,* vol. 40 (1961), pp. 309–328.
4. BARLOW, H. B., "Intrinsic Noise of Cones," in *Visual Problems of Colour,* Paper No. 28. London: Her Majesty's Stationery Office, 1958.
5. BLACKWELL, H. R., "Studies of Psychological Methods of Measuring Visual Thresholds," *J. Opt. Soc. Amer.,* vol. 42 (1952), pp. 606–616.
6. BLACKWELL, H. R., "Studies in the Form

of Visual Threshold Data," *J. Opt. Soc. Amer.,* vol. 43 (1953), pp. 456–463.
7. BOYNTON, R. M., "Some Temporal Factors in Vision," in W. A. Rosenblith, (ed.) *Sensory Communication.* New York: J. Wiley and MIT Press, 1961.
8. BOYNTON, R. M., "Spatial Vision," *Ann. Rev. Psychol.,* vol. 13 (1962), pp. 171–200.
9. BOYNTON, R. M., "Contributions of Threshold Measurements to Color Discrimination Theory," *J. Opt. Soc. Amer.,* (in press).
10. BROWN, J. L., L. PHARES, and D. E. FLETCHER, "Spectral Energy Thresholds for the Resolution of Acuity Targets," *J. Opt. Soc. Amer.,* vol. 50 (1960), pp. 950–960.
11. GRASSMAN, H., "On the Theory of Compound Colours," *Phil. Mag.,* vol. 7 (1854), pp. 254–265.
12. GUILFORD, J. P. *Psychometric Methods.* New York: McGraw-Hill, 1954.
13. HECHT, S., and J. MANDELBAUM, "Rod-Cone Dark Adaptation and Vitamin A," *Science,* vol. 88 (1938), pp. 219–221.
14. HECHT, S., S. SCHLAER, and M. H. PIRENNE, "Energy, Quanta, and Vision," *J. Gen. Physiol.,* vol. 25 (1942), pp. 819–840.
15. JAMESON, D., and L. M. HURVICH, "Perceived Color and Its Dependence on Focal, Surrounding, and Preceding Stimulus Variables," *J. Opt. Soc. Amer.,* vol. 49 (1959), pp. 890–898.
16. KRENDEL, E., and J. WODINSKY, "Search in an Unstructured Visual Field," *J. Opt. Soc. Amer.,* vol. 50 (1960), pp. 562–568.
17. LE GRAND, Y. *Light, Colour, and Vision.* New York: J. Wiley, 1957, ch. 13.
18. ONLEY, J. W., "Light Adaptation and the Brightness of Brief Foveal Stimuli," *J. Opt. Soc. Amer.,* vol. 51 (1961), pp. 667–673.
19. PIRENNE, M. H., and F. H. C. MARRIOTT, "The Quantum Theory of Light and the Psycho-physiology of Vision," in Koch, S. (ed.) *Psychology: A Study of a Science,* vol. 1. New York: McGraw-Hill, 1959, pp. 288–361.
20. RUSHTON, W. A. H., "Visual Pigments in Man," *Sci. Amer.,* vol. 207 (1962), pp. 120–132.
21. RUSHTON, W. A. H., "Increment Threshold and Dark Adaptation," *J. Opt. Soc. Amer.,* (in press).
22. *The Science of Color.* (Committee on

Colorimetry, Optical Society of America.) New York: Crowell, 1953.

23. SPERLING, G., "The Information Available in Brief Visual Presentations," *Psychol. Monogr.*, vol. 74 (1960).

24. STEVENS, S. S., "The Psychophysics of Sensory Function," *Amer. Sci.*, vol. 48 (1960), pp. 226–253.

25. STILES, W. S., "Investigations of the Scotopic and Trichromatic Mechanisms of Vision by the Two-Colour Threshold Technique," *Rev. Optique*, vol. 28 (1949), pp. 215–237.

26. STILES, W. S., "Color Vision: The Approach Through Increment-Threshold Sensitivity," *Proc. Natl. Acad. Sci. U.S.*, vol. 45 (1959), pp. 100–114.

27. SWETS, J. A., "Is There a Sensory Threshold?," *Science*, vol. 134 (1961), pp. 168–177.

28. Wald, G., "Human Vision and the Spectrum," *Science*, vol. 101 (1945), pp. 653–658.

29. WEALE, R. A., "The Duplicity Theory of Vision," *Ann. Roy. Coll. Surg. Eng.*, vol. 28 (1961), pp. 16–35.

What Are Perceptual Reports About?[*]

THOMAS NATSOULAS
University of California, Davis

A discussion is presented of some methodological and substantive issues associated with the use of reports in perceptual experiments. The distinction between "report" and "response" is 1st clarified and a definition of report behavior is proposed. The relation of reference (aboutness) is next considered in the context of phenomenal vs. cognitive reports. At a less abstract level, 2 pairs of contrasting proposals on the referents of perceptual reports are used to bring earlier questions to focus. 1 pair stems from philosophical approaches to the question of this article. The other arises in a current controversy concerning what psychophysical scales measure. A brief discussion of the role of E's own perceptual experience is followed by a review of methods for establishing report validity.

"The question of the relation between report and experience is 'one of the most complex questions that mankind could well raise.' It has been 'bypassed' by psychology in recent times. Some little can be said about the relationship now, but not much. It is not, however, a question that is 'closed in principle, to progress [Wann, 1964, p. 162],'" commented Sigmund Koch (as paraphrased by Wann) at a recent symposium. And in his own presentation, Koch (1964) insisted that "the fate of psychology must be very much bound up with progress" in the understanding of the relation of report to experience. Koch's claims, although not evaluated here, do serve as motivation for an attempt to say some of what can be said now about how perceptual experiences and reports are related. The purpose of this article is to set the stage for a fuller discussion of the problems which arise in the attempt.

[*] *Psychological Bulletin*, 1967, vol. 67, pp. 249–272. Some of the work on this article was done while the author held a Summer Faculty Fellowship from the University of California.

Defining Report Behavior

A DEFINITION

The difference in meaning between "report" and "response" is recognized implicitly in the frequent use of "report" to designate what the subject does in many perceptual experiments. The psychologist's focus of interest is not the properties of the subject's responses; the perceptual report is of *mediate* interest, yielding, at its best, information about another event hidden from the experimenter's observation. Prentice (1959) made it clear that in an important sense, experiences are the dependent variables of the gestalt approach, while behavior has a subsidiary role as a means of knowing about perceptual experience. To make a similar point, Perkins (1953) drew a careful analogy between the reports of a subject in a perceptual experiment and reports by a physicist concerning his experimental observations. If the properties of the reporting responses (rather than their referents) were themselves of focal interest, the positivist view of perception as a subarea of the science of behavior would be correct. This would force, however, the absurd (for most) conclusion that physics is the science of the physicist's behavior. (*See also* Burt, 1962, p. 231.)

In addition to playing this mediational role, reports have a statistical association with the use of instructions. In fact, it would seem the path of least effort to make control by instructions a defining attribute of "report." Many psychologists (most recently, Schoenfeld and Cumming, 1963) point out, however, that instructions are not a necessary concomitant of report behavior; they are an efficient means of affecting the subject's response system *in a way that could be achieved by other procedures*. This view of instructions suggests that given the appropriate training procedures, reports of events in their perceptual systems can be secured from lower animals. Some attention to such procedures will help clarify the meaning of "report."

A psychophysical method has been applied by Blough (1958) to the study of the pigeon's absolute visual threshold. During both training and randomly spaced intervals during testing, eating is made contingent on pecking Key B when the light is off, and the light's going off depends on pecking Key A. Blough described this procedure as establishing stimulus control of the two classes of pecks. Once this is accomplished, the pecks can be used as reports of seeing or not seeing, because the pigeon is unable to discriminate two kinds of darkness, that produced by turning the light off, and that produced by dimming the light to below-threshold intensities.

The continuous character of the record collected during test sessions is due to the fact that pecks on Key A reduce the intensity of the light, while pecks on Key B increase it. Given the conditions of training, the pecks drive the intensity down and up, around a threshold value. Obstructing a direct inference from response to perceptual state is the possibility that the pigeon learns merely to alternate keys. Variable ratio reinforcement is used which reduces the chances of this occurring by making it impossible for the pigeon to base his switching from one key to the other on how long or often he has pecked the one. To reduce the likelihood that what is learned is to switch keys after *long* bursts of responding, a "punishment" for "false" responses is included: If the subject pecks A (B) when the light is off (on), this subtracts from his accumulation of responses toward secondary (primary) reinforcement. In addition, the pigeon is required to pause briefly in switching keys to insure that he looks at the light. Also to avoid automatic switching to A, pecking B after primary reinforcement is sometimes reinforced again. Once the training procedure has eliminated the relevance of alternative interpretations of the pigeon's systematically variable behavior, the inference becomes very direct: Pecking A means the light is visible, pecking B that it is not. With this, the two behaviors qualify as reporting responses.

The defining attribute of "report," as distinct from the more general "response," is *a presumed or confirmed relationship between some preceding or synchronous event* (e_i) *and the response. This relationship must be such as to make possible direct inferences from knowledge of the response to* e_i. In the case of a *presumed* relationship, the lack of evidence to the contrary *as well as* the absence of reasonable negative arguments (for the particular case) would permit continued use of a set of responses as reports. Any ambiguity, with respect to which *e* to infer, reduces the report character of the response. When a number of alternative inferences are possible, it becomes necessary to use other indicators to narrow down the possibilities. The inference from response to e_i becomes indirect, consequently, in that the response alone cannot be relied on as the source of information concerning e_i. The mere use of a subject's responses, for example, his verbal utterances, in the process of securing evidence on e_i does not suffice for purposes of classifying these responses as reports. It is how they are used, in a simple, direct way, that makes the difference.

This distinction between reports and responses in general is closely related to Heider's (1960) differentiation between object and mediation based on Lenzen's (1938) analysis of the object-observer partition. Heider (1960) stated that Lewin neglected output characteristics except insofar as they served as indicators of the processes in the life space. He described behavior as a surface phenomenon, an offshoot, a manifestation, a phenotype, a tool used by Lewin to acquire information about the laws of the life space. He quoted Lenzen's (1938) paraphrase of Niels Bohr:

the observer and his instruments must be presupposed in any investigation, so that the instruments are not part of the phenomenon described but are used. The problem accordingly arises of defining the partition between object and the observer and his apparatus [p. 28].

A related view of the subject's reports, as extensions of the observer-experimenter, has been adumbrated recently. According to Attneave (1962), the subject's response system can be considered a set of instruments through which observations of "subjective variables" are made. As in physical measurement, the instrument may be unreliable, may require calibration, or may interfere with the phenomena of interest. In both cases, measures are taken to increase precision and to remove interference by the instrument from the data. The object-observer partition is drawn here, with Lewin, Heider, and Attneave, between perception and report; even for perceptual experiments it is often drawn, by positivistic psychologists, between the responses and the instrument or observer measuring, counting, or identifying the response.

METHODOLOGICAL OBJECTIONS

Among those who draw the partition between behavior and experimenter and, therefore, consider the subject's reports as responses whose characteristics are to be studied are Bergmann and Spence (1944) and Graham and Ratoosh (1962). That this is more than a mere preference in the mode of describing the scientist's activities can be seen from the concrete implications it has for the use of numerals contained in psychophysical reports. In the method of magnitude estimation, the subject assigns numerals to stimuli as an indication of their experienced intensity, loudness, brightness, sweetness, etc. According to Graham and Ratoosh (1962), "there seems to be nothing more intrinsically quantitative in the response involved in brightness estimates than there is in the responses of color naming [p. 490]." Thus reports are not to be treated as measures; the numerals recorded are only representations of the responses made. Each different numeral used by the subject, even when responding to the same stimulus, must be considered a different response and not averaged. These responses take the particular numerical form that they do because of the restrictions on response which the instructions somehow achieve and because of prior conditioning to aspects of stimulus objects.

Bergmann and Spence (1944) were fairly explicit in stating their grounds for drawing the partition between object and observer as they did.

(a) Partly, it follows from an explicit, emphatic distinction between scientist and subject. Bergmann and Spence (1944) said that "the empiricist scientist should realize that his behavior, symbolic or otherwise, does not lie on the same methodological level as the responses of his subjects [p. 4]." What the subject says belongs necessarily to the "object language" and not to the "pragmatic metalanguage" of the experimenter. In a sense, the present article can be viewed as an attempt to qualify the experimenter-subject distinction, and a number of the particular discussions pertain to the conditions that must be satisfied if the subject is to be treated as a kind of "fellow experimenter." Let it merely be noted at this point that the rigid distinction between scientist and subject drawn by Bergmann and Spence (1944) has been questioned by Perkins (1953) as follows: The psychologist can, and in perception experiments often does, make observations of the kind his subjects do: At times all of the subjects may be psychologists. On the other hand, sophistication is not necessary for someone to serve as experimenter; he need not be cognizant of the hypothesis or of the theory being tested.

(b) An additional basis for drawing the partition as Bergmann and Spence (1944) did between the experimenter and the sub-

ject's behavior is the requirement that all psychological terms, including mentalistic ones, be introduced by "operational definition from a physicalistic meaning base." All concepts must be "behavioristically defined" unless defined in terms of stimuli or other physical conditions.

Logical behaviorists (e.g., Bergmann, 1957) insist that the subject matter of psychology be limited to aspects of behavior, with which we are *directly acquainted*. In this sense we are directly acquainted only with particular objects and their properties. The notion of "directly acquainted" was used by Bergmann (1957) in a commonsensical way; the intention was to limit "directly acquainted" to something everyone understands and about which there can be, therefore, a minimum of disagreement. Nevertheless, Zener (Zener and Gaffron, 1962) claimed that the reference of the term is constantly shifting; therefore, a decision to limit what the psychologist is to study on its basis would be "strange." A similar criticism of the notion of "direct acquaintance" was given by Perkins (1953), and the later discussion of "observation through causality" in the present article is directly relevant. In addition, Carnap (1956) has argued:

> Although many of the alleged results of introspection were indeed questionable, a person's awareness of his own state of imagining, feeling, etc., must be recognized as a kind of observation, in principle not different from external observation, and therefore a legitimate source of knowledge though limited by its subjective character [pp. 90–91].

(c) The insistence that all terms be defined physicalistically has in turn its probable source in a *certain* understanding of the need for intersubjectivity. A typical argument based on the intersubjectivity requirement was made by Treisman (1962). The claim that a subject can report in a scientifically useful way about variables not observed by the experimenter, he contended, is unjustified. Treisman appealed to a definition of observational reports in science, the key aspect of which is the criterion of intersubjective confirmability. Accordingly, reports concerning "private data," because they can not be checked for accuracy by others, must not be included in science *as reports*. Perkins (1953) contended, however, that the properties predicated by a statement referring to perception can be observed by many people. His discussion has stimulated the following analysis.

A distinction between statements of law and of fact needs to be drawn. The non-logical terms contained in statements of law refer to classes of things and properties of such classes, while statements of fact are about particular things and their properties. The intersubjectivity criterion pertains to the confirmation of laws. In the case of perceptual reports, it may be true that the same exemplar of a class cannot be observed by another subject, but *an* exemplar *can* be observed which is sufficient to add confirmation to a law. Since a specific event takes place only once, one seldom intersubjectively confirms *a fact* in science; it requires simultaneous observation. Zener's "reformulated criterion of objectivity" is consonant with this analysis. One statement of his criterion is "the requirement of consistency among the observations by different observers of events independently produced by repeated realizations of specified conditions by different experimenters [Zener and Gaffron, 1962, p. 555]." (See also Bakan, 1954.)

According to Treisman (1962), in contrast to the observational report in science, "no procedure can be meaningfully prescribed for the subject to follow in making a 'report' on private data [p. 137]." But how do we prescribe procedures for observation in science? We describe to the observer how he can produce the appropriate environmental stimuli or where he should go to be exposed to them. Next to nothing about the observing itself is said, although an exception occurs when the observations appear to be subject to systematic biases. Usually we assume that given the identified circumstances, the necessary observations can be made without further instructions or guidance. There are, of course, instances of naïve observers who must be trained to observe. This is accomplished through practice in observation and the giving of reports which are checked against those of others and corrected. Similarly, the reports of perceptual subjects can be checked against those of other subjects and especially against known laws in those situations which have received sufficient previous study. A more detailed discussion of report validity is given in a later section.

Cognitive and Phenomenal Reports: A Concept of Reference

When one speaks of a report being about a certain object or event, what is meant seems intuitively obvious. However, from a psychological or functional point of view, "aboutness" is far from clear. An attempt is made next to clarify this relationship through an analysis of the distinction between what are commonly believed to be two different kinds of reports. Beginning from very different theoretical orientations, Graham and Ratoosh (1962) and Zener (Zener and Gaffron, 1962) have advocated the comparative study of cognitive and phenomenal reports in perception experiments. Graham and Ratoosh (1962) wrote:

> It would be of considerable interest to compare a subject's behavior under instructions to introspect or give a phenomenal description with instructions to describe objects . . . While the problem should not deter us, it may have implications for a behavioristic account of perception [486].

Zener has paid particular attention to the

area of size constancy, arguing for the necessity of careful differentiation between cognitive and phenomenal reports if consistency and lawfulness are to be discovered. Thus the usual instructions in such experiments are considered ambiguous with respect to eliciting one or the other of the two kinds of reports.

In this section, four means of differentiating cognitive and phenomenal reports will be discussed. The final means is a proposal that the distinction be based on a certain interpretation of "reference."

1. A behavioristic orientation would differentiate phenomenal and cognitive reports by means of their instructional conditions. It is a characteristic differentiation, based on a simple reliably applied criterion. Phenomenal reports are ones produced in response to instructions to give a phenomenal description or to introspect; cognitive reports are those given under instructions to describe the stimulus object. This way of defining the difference will not satisfy those who recognize that factors other than instructions will affect the kind of report given. An important implicit difference between the two report types is not embodied in the behavioristic definitions.

That instructions stating precisely what the experimenter wants the subject to report can be a poor way to secure phenomenal or cognitive reports was argued by Joynson and Newson (1962). They pointed out that the subject may be unable to give the kind of report required in the particular experimental case, and that the instructions can impose on the reports an artificial, nonspontaneous character including support for the preconceptions implicit in the instructions. There is also the matter of how the subject interprets the instructions. Leibowitz, Waskow, Loeffler, and Glaser (1959) used "non-directing" instructions ("looks the most like the shape of the disc") in a study relating intelligence to shape constancy under conditions of inclination of the

object from the frontal plane. As had Thouless (1932), they found that with lower intelligence there occurred greater shape constancy. This finding was interpreted as due to the instructions themselves, which the authors claimed required an analytic attitude, together with the greater ability of the more intelligent subjects to follow them. An alternative interpretation is that the more intelligent subjects understood "looks the most like" in a different way, in a sense giving themselves analytic (projective) instructions. In either case, the point is that instructions can interact with individual characteristics, resulting in different kinds of reports.

2. Zener (Zener and Gaffron, 1962) included *intent* as an essential aspect of the distinction between phenomenal and cognitive reports: "The physicist is not *by intent* reporting on his experience; therefore, in a real sense, he is not reporting on it [p. 552]." It would seem meaningful and probably scientifically useful to say, however, that the subject intends to give phenomenal reports throughout an experimental session, but that he frequently slips into another attitude "unintentionally" and gives judgments of the stimulus objects instead. Gibson (1963) suggested that this happens under "impoverished, ambiguous, or conflicting" stimulus conditions; the subject is more likely to guess concerning the character of the objects presented to him than to report on his perceptual experience. Uncertainty concerning the environmental source may lead the subject into a guessing strategy not relevant to the task as instructed or understood.[1] Zener (Zener and Gaffron, 1962) recalled a subject in a tachistoscopic experiment who

[1] If, in the face of difficulty in making phenomenal reports, one resorts to guessing about the objective source of stimulation, there will be instances in which phenomenal and cognitive reports (as instructed), although different under easier conditions, become very similar. Carlson (1960) provided evidence for this statement in the case of apparent-size matches. This evidence is discussed later in the present article.

"could not tell what he experienced because he was uncertain of the cues to which he was responding [p. 558]."

The difficulties which attend an attempt to carry out one's intention to describe his own perceptual experience have been stressed by Quinton (1955). It was claimed that the description of perceptual experience requires a special, sophisticated frame of mind or attitude, rather than a naïve one as some psychologists would have it. The suspension of beliefs concerning the world is included. One should add that preconceptions concerning oneself and one's perceptual processes may also need to be suspended.

3. Alternatively, it may be argued that a differentiation of the two kinds of reports should be made on the basis of analyses of the collected reports themselves. Such a view would need, as a basis, the assumption that phenomenal reports involve the use of a language distinct from that used to describe external objects and events (or have unique behavioral characteristics). The existence of such a language is itself a controversial issue. MacCorquodale and Meehl (1954) "express serious doubt as to whether there exists a phenomenal language which is not really a physical stimulus language with the subject reporting under special instructions [p. 236]." And, less extremely, Zener (Zener and Gaffron, 1962) recognized that "the most available descriptive terms for phenomenal characterization are often words whose current meanings tend to be determined by reference to objective properties of physical objects [p. 545]." A statement by Feigl (1963) clearly illustrates the problem:

Directly verifiable introspective reports about immediately experienced states utilize phenomenal predicates such as "hot", "cold", "loud", "soft", "red", "green", etc., i.e., without any attempt at interpretation as in the physical mode (did I hear a telephone bell?) or in the psychological mode (did I feel cold because I was "chilled" by fear or anxieties?) [p. 234].

The six predicates are ones commonly used to describe objects. In fact it is how they are used, without interpretation, that makes them phenomenal predicates according to Feigl.

4. It is proposed here that phenomenal and cognitive reports be distinguished in terms of their hypothesized determinants. Truly phenomenal reports are presumed to provide the experimenter with information about his subject's perceptual experience; cognitive reports are supposed to provide information about the subject's modes of identifying and describing objects. Ideally, certain systematic variations in the characteristics of phenomenal reports would depend exclusively on the corresponding phenomenal aspects of the subject's immediate perceptions. The role of instructions, when they are successful, is the restriction of reports so that systematic variation in them corresponds to variation on the dimensions of perceptual experience in which the experimenter has an interest. Any direct effects that cognitive processes have on phenomenal reports should be of the kind that does not distort the relation between report and experience. However, indirect influences through the changes in perceptual experience resulting from its interaction with classificatory, reasoning, and inferential processes would not disqualify a report as phenomenal.

On the other hand, a purely cognitive report would be one which depends exclusively on the operations involved in the identification and description of the object. The effect of the present percept on the cognitive report would have to be through its effects on the cognitive operations whose achievements are reported. For example, in their study of size estimates of familiar objects with and without (visual) perception of the objects, Bolles and Bailey (1956) argued and gave evidence that the very slight but significant improvement given the visual stimulus was due to the better identification of the objects which seeing allowed (as compared with receiving verbal information only on the identity of the objects).

The present psychological interpretation of the "aboutness" relation between reports and the antecedent or attendant perceptual processes is similar to that of Schoenfeld and Cumming (1963). These writers identified the reporting response in perceptual experiments as a tact whose discriminative stimulus or "referent" is the normally unobserved perceptual response. In turn, a tact was defined as a verbal response "under the discriminative control of an S^D," and the class of tacts was said "to encompass that part of the language which is engaged in identification and naming." They equated a tact's referring to a perceptual response with its being under the discriminative control of the occurrence of that response. By virtue of its reinforcement history, a tact is descriptive of its S^D. The verbal community has provided a variety of reinforcers "to ensure the correlation of a tact with its proper S^D."

As already expressed, the present view claims the relation of reference between phenomenal reports and perceptual experience to be such that systematic variations on experiential dimensions are mirrored in variations in the report. This implies the absence of systematic, *direct* effects of other variables which confound the relationship of the reports to those aspects of perceptual experience of interest. The present view differs from that of Schoenfeld and Cumming (1963) in that it distinguishes two kinds of central control of reports, cognitive and phenomenal.

Referents of Specific Perceptual Reports

Although the above discussion possibly helps to clarify the question of this article, it does little to settle controversies as to what particular reports are about in spe-

cific perceptual experiments, for example, when someone reports seeing a blue-green afterimage or that one tone is twice as loud as another. Consider the subject of an experiment who, so far as the experimenter is concerned, is following instructions to describe how he experiences what is presented to him. To what do the terms which he uses, such as "above," "red," "sharp boundary," "near," etc., refer?

EXPERIENTIAL PROPERTIES VERSUS OBJECTIVE REFERENCE SITUATIONS

Zener (Zener and Gaffron, 1962) insisted that such terms can have, often do have, and must have if they are to adequately characterize a perceptual experience, "a direct experiential reference,"—in fact that it is impossible "technically" to describe any perception qua mental event in "radically nonphenomenal terms." He argued that the central process of perception has experiential properties which are "real, specifiable and can, within limits, be reliably reported by the experiencing person [p. 556]." Zener's position contains a dualistic premise of experiential properties belonging to certain brain processes. One of the psychologist's strategies vis-à-vis perception as experience takes a neurological detour: Perceptions are described first as neural processes; then some of their properties are hypothesized on a combination of behavioral and neurophysiological evidence; finally, experience is introduced in some relation to this physiological base. Zener (Zener and Gaffron, 1962) followed a version of this procedure, positing a relation of property to object between experience and brain process; he wrote of a set of "experiential properties" which belong to the perceptual process. Although he also wrote of experiential events, experiential processes, and direct experience, these usages appear to be consistent with the notion of experiential properties: Experience itself was said to be a property of the perceptual process, and experiential events are events in the brain which have experiential properties. An interpretation of Zener consistent with all this is that whenever he writes of reporting one's experiences, a specification of experiential properties is meant, these properties being among those of a neural process. Thus perceptual reports (when properly made—see p. 545 in Zener and Gaffron, 1963) refer to experiential properties of certain processes in the brain.

Place (1956), Smart (1959, 1960, 1961, 1963, 1965), and Attneave (1962) have proposed a distinctly opposed view. Attneave (1962) claimed that all perceptual reports are a kind of cognitive report:

> Phenomenological terms necessarily refer to objective reference situations, however obscure; otherwise they could never have been acquired by the person using them, and in any case could not be used for communication with another person. Sometimes the physical reference is obvious; thus, when an observer reports a red afterimage, he is merely asserting that his experience is like the one he gets from light of a certain wavelength, and when he reports phi movement he is clearly saying that his experience is like that obtained from objective movement [p. 628].

To link subjects' perceptual reports to *his own* interpretation of them, Attneave used such phrases as the subject is "in effect saying," "merely asserting," and "clearly saying"; Smart (1959) used "he is saying something like" in his own statement of this position:

> When a person says, "I see a yellowish-orange afterimage," he is saying something like this: *"There is something going on which is like what is going on when* I have my eyes open, am awake, and there is an orange illuminated in good light in front of me, that is when I really see an orange [p. 149]."

Attneave's (1962) most detailed example has his subject "in effect saying," when he says that one line looks longer than another,

> "My experience in looking at these lines is similar to previous experiences in which I found, by manipulation or measurement, that a line corresponding to A was physically longer than a line corresponding to B . . . [p. 620]."

Place (1956) has expressed the same view somewhat differently: The phenomenological fallacy is the assumption that when we describe the objects of our environment, we are in fact describing our own conscious experience, that objects and events of the geographical environment are "secondarily, indirectly and inferentially" described. According to Place, we learn to recognize and describe objects in the physical world by how they look, sound, smell, taste, and feel and *only then can we describe our experiences.* This we do in terms of physical objects which ordinarily produce the experience we are trying to describe.

The distinction between cognitive and phenomenal reports expressed earlier would correspond, from the point of view under discussion, to the difference between descriptions of the present situation (cognitive) and identification of the present experience in terms of a past reference situation (phenomenal). For example, identifying the visual experience of movement in terms of the present conditions for producing apparent movement would be a cognitive report, a report determined by knowledge of the present situation. On the other hand, identifying the present experience by describing certain objective conditions ordinarily the case when real movement is experienced would correspond to a phenomenal report within the Place-Smart-Attneave scheme as here extended.

Certain pairs of statements are treated as somehow equivalent by these authors. For example, "I see a yellowish-orange afterimage" is somehow equivalent to the statement which begins "There is something going on in me which is like. . . ." What is the relationship between the members of each pair of such statements? This is an important question to raise because the arguments made by these writers concerning the referents of perceptual reports rest on this kind of translation of the reports. It seems that the relation between the statements is one between a statement and a description of the situation in which its use was learned or in which it is ordinarily used. Smart (1963, 1965) has clarified his view by stating that the two statements are not translations of each other. What is intended by the peculiar construal of perceptual reports is that making reports on perceptual experiences is not a matter of describing them; it is a matter of making reports of similarities and dissimilarities between them. "Normally in reporting these likenesses and unlikenesses we are unaware of what they consist; they in fact consist in likenesses and unlikenesses of patterns of brain processes [Smart, 1965, p. 82]." Smart (1960) described the nervous system as being capable of responding to similarities between its own processes while "being unable [always or through lack of training?] to issue descriptions of these likenesses."

To summarize this point of view: Perceptual reports do not describe perceptions except in terms of similarity to each other and in terms of the circumstances which ordinarily accompany or give rise to them. Perceptual reports do identify, classify, or name particular perceptions but not in terms of their intrinsic properties. "To see blue" does not mean that one's perception has itself the property of blue (the phenomenological fallacy), or that blue is an "experiential property" (Zener and Gaffron, 1962), or that something going on within me has that property. To say that I am perceiving blue is to include the

present experience in a certain class, to identify it in terms of conditions for its occurrence. These conditions may include the presentation of a blue object or may be conditions which give rise to images or hallucinations of blue objects. To be called blue, a perception would have to behave in the same way as blue objects, namely, be capable of producing in someone perceptions similar to those produced by blue objects.

SENSORY MAGNITUDES VERSUS PHYSICAL CORRELATES

A controversy is in progress in the psychological literature between S. S. Stevens and Richard M. Warren on the referents of psychophysical scales. It will be seen that the issue raised is more basically which class of central processes controls the reports of subjects in psychophysical experiments.

Stevens. The methods of psychophysics were repeatedly described by Stevens as means of measuring *perception*:

> The methods of psychophysics are ordinarily designed to solve problems related to the nature of organisms. The focus of interest is typically the normal observer, his thresholds, his resolving powers, and the magnitudes of his perceptions [Stevens, 1958, p. 194].

Two possible psychophysical foci of interest were explicitly discriminated (Stevens, 1958): (*a*) the observer-subject as a judge, a complex instrument used to "measure" objective (stimulus) values; (*b*) the "instrument" itself, in getting estimates of *perceptual* attributes, for example, the *apparent* loudness heard (rather than an estimate of the decibels produced by a sound source). By setting the subject for the proper task, the psychophysical methods can be used for the study of either focus. As evidence for people's ability to do either task, Stevens (1957) cited an informal study of "at least six" acoustical engineers whose subjective scales of loudness

> are not systematically different from those of other listeners. They can tell me, for example, both that one sound seems about half as loud as another, and also that one is about 90db and the other about 100db [p. 169].

Nevertheless, in an article in which psychophysical methods were treated as means of learning about perception, Stevens (1958) said, "Psychophysics concerns the functional relation between stimulus and response: $R = f(S)$ [p. 178]"; and in a discussion of "sensation," Stevens (1959) insisted that the admitted privacy of sensation constitutes no scientific problem "because the sensation that science deals with is the type of human reaction that lends itself to public scrutiny [p. 612]." A strictly positivistic view of sensation was championed: "The term 'sensation' derives its meaning from the reactions, verbal or otherwise, made by organisms in response to stimuli [p. 612]." One might try to interpret Stevens' approach as an S-R psychology: The relationships between inputs and outputs are studied and various physicalistic mechanisms are hypothesized to explain and integrate them. The lapses into mentalism would be understandable, as descriptions of the psychological situation from the subject's perspective: To speak of the subject as making estimates of the magnitudes of certain aspects of his perceptions is to describe the instructions given to him or what he would say if asked what he was doing.

However, the responses of his observers have not, in fact, been treated by Stevens as mere responses; rather, they have been reports, estimates, or judgments of something usually called sensation, perception, subjective value, or sensory magnitude. To illustrate, consider subjects asked to indicate apparent loudness by squeezing a hand dynamometer. A relationship is found between the stimulus intensity of the sound (Φ_1) and the stimulus (or response) intensity of the squeeze (Φ_2). It turns out to be a straight line in a log-log plot. To predict the exponent of this power function, Stevens, Mack, and Stevens (1960) assumed that two sensory magnitudes, apparent loudness (Ψ_1) and apparent force of handgrip (Ψ_2), were being matched. In previous studies, these sensory magnitudes had been found by the methods of magnitude estimation and production to relate to their respective stimulus dimensions according to the power law. Thus $\Psi_1 = \Phi_1{}^m$ and $\Psi_2 = \Phi_2{}^n$. On the assumption that what the subject does is set $\Psi_1 = \Psi_2$: $\Phi_1{}^m = \Phi_2{}^n$ and $\Phi_2 = \Phi_1{}^{m/n}$. The new exponent can be easily calculated from those previously discovered. To predict the exponents of power functions derived from cross-modality matches, Stevens (1961; Stevens, Mack, and Stevens, 1960) found it necessary to assume that the subject matches two subjective values not given directly to the experimenter (as is presumed to be the case for magnitude estimates). Since the *unobserved* matching of Ψ_1 and Ψ_2 *results* in a certain observed relationship between Φ_1 and Φ_2 *this matching cannot be equated definitionally with the operations of the experiment.*

Still open, then, is the question of to what "sensation," "perception," "subjective value," and "sensory magnitude" refer as Stevens uses them. In other words, what are Ψ_1 and Ψ_2 which are assumed to be matched, if they are not behaviors? One must conclude that they refer to processes, events, or their properties *which can be described in both physicalistic and mentalistic terms.* Stevens' use implies an identity theory (Smart, 1959) of the physical and the mental. There are many instances in which Stevens alternates between the languages of consciousness and sensory physiology. For example, an explanation for a subject's numerical estimates differing consistently from the median is asked for in two ways. One article (Stevens, Mack, and Stevens, 1960) asked "whether his hearing is different or whether he simply estimates differently"; another (Stevens, 1961) asked whether "the action of one man's sensory transducers is different from another's." In both places, the same solution is proposed: several cross-modality experiments, through which errors in reporting behavior can be eliminated from consideration.

The use of the latter procedure is an example of the application of converging operations as described by Garner, Hake, and Eriksen (1956). No specific test could answer the question posed; any one cross-modality experiment would leave the question of differential hearing versus differential overt matching open. Combining several tests using different means of reporting is assumed to eliminate alternatives to the hypothesis of differential hearing. Another assumption is that matching and magnitude estimates are not transforms of each other. They would be if in the matching experiment numbers were assigned privately to sensory magnitudes and responses were made to these numbers. In any case, it seems certain that Stevens, through his language, his means of deriving predictions, and his method of establishing report validity, is differentiating subjective variables from S-R relationships and identifying these variables with the functioning of the nervous system.

The controversy. In the psychophysical literature Warren (1958) may be said to represent the position of Place (1956) and Smart (1959) vis-à-vis allegedly phenomenal reports. According to Warren's physical-correlate theory of judgments of sensory intensity, psychophysical reports are based not on intensity of sensation but on *learned associations to sensation,* "experience with the manner in which sensory excitation is correlated with the amount of some physical attribute associated with the stimulus [Warren, 1958, p. 676]."

Warren and Warren (1958) found that one subject who had much experience with light meters gave a median value of 48% intensity for half-brightness judgments of large fields of various reflectances while an additional 40 subjects provided median judgments that clustered around 25% intensity. Whereas in the case of the one man the physical correlate was proposed to be readings from a light meter, for the majority it was the distance from light source to illuminated field:

> Since doubling the distance of an object from its light source reduces intensity to approximately one-quarter, the physical correlate theory predicts that close to 25 percent of the standard luminance would be judged half as bright for all intensities of the standard [Warren, 1958, p. 679].

Using the fact that the condition of the receptor, such as after light adaptation, affects the exponent of the respective power function as an argument against the physical-correlate theory, Stevens (1963) misinterpreted Warren's proposal. What the theory says is that the sensory excitation it produces—not the stimulus—is being assigned a value. Warren's important point is that this value is not a measure of the level of excitation, as Stevens believes, but of the physical correlate. Light adaptation changes the level of sensory excitation that results from a particular stimulus; thus a different value of the correlated distance variable would be applied.

In support of the physical-correlate theory, Warren (1958) reviewed results involving half-judgments of sweetness, sourness, saltiness, bitterness, heaviness, loudness, and pitch. For dimensions of taste and for heaviness, 50% was the half-magnitude value expected (and found) on the grounds that the physical correlate in these instances is proportional to the stimulus intensity. For taste it is the known concentration of soluble material which is the physical correlate, and for heaviness it is "the experience of lifting two similar objects together and separately [Warren, 1958, pp. 676–677]." The physical correlate for pitch was claimed to be experience with the musical scale, the basic unit of which is the octave. Within the range of experience with musical instruments, half-pitches had a value of 57%, while a value of 50% was expected on the grounds of familiarity with the octave relationships of doubling and halving.

Half-loudness judgments (a kind of report which Stevens, 1959, 1963, rejected because of its sensitivity to context effects) and the change in judgments of loudness with doubling the distance both approximated 25% for tones (Warren, Sersen, and Porres, 1958). The physical correlate for loudness judgments was claimed to be the distance of the sound source from the subject. Previous experiments had not yielded the 25% value, a matter which was attributed by Warren, Sersen, and Porres (1958) to the greater approximation of their experiment to the conditions in which subjects acquired the physical correlates, that is, familiar, reverberating surroundings, the source across the room rather than in earphones. Stevens and Guirao (1962) cited evidence from earlier experiments that even under natural listening conditions, the exponent of the power function for loudness is smaller than .5 (for sound pressure), which the physical-correlate theory predicts. Warren (1963a, 1963b) rejected these experiments on the grounds that subjects were not prevented from seeing the source at a constant distance (Warren, Sersen, and Porres blindfolded their subjects); the fixed source would have localized all the sounds at the same distance, presumably operating against their being given different values, thus reducing the slope of the power function.

It follows from the physical-correlate theory that loudness judgments (being cognitive rather than phenomenal reports) will be affected by whatever affects the subject's estimate of the relative distance from the person to the source. The finding of Warren, Sersen, and Porres (1958), among others, that half-loudness judgments of speech are of smaller magnitude than those for pure tones supports the theory. The explanation offered involved the compensatory attenuation by the subject of the variable, because under these experimental conditions speech intensity was reduced without changing the qualitative indicators of distance. The absence of these qualitative changes fixes the distance of the source, requiring a smaller fraction to indicate half-loudness. The theory is also consistent with the results of Stevens and Guirao (1962) who found that loudness, softness, and apparent distance of heard stimuli are all related to a measure of acoustical stimulus intensity by power functions with exponents of equal absolute size. Loudness judgments were expected by Warren to be based on the correlate of distance from source to subject. This correspondence of exponents was interpreted by Stevens and Guirao (1962) in a reversed way: The subjects, having no distances to judge, judge loudness even when distance is required; distance judgments are based on loudness sensations. No independent evidence was cited.

Stevens (1963) argued that power functions have been found for "continua with which the observers claimed to have had no prior experience in the form of a graded series of stimuli [p. 612]." He asked as well that the physical-correlate theory explain the fact that binaural hearing yields a larger exponent than monaural hearing, while exponents for monocular and binocular brightness estimates do not differ. This sort of challenge illustrates the problems that can be made for any perceptual learning theory, the demand for treatment of a still larger variety of effects in terms of the theory. Warren and Warren (1963) admitted that the physical-correlate theory cannot predict or explain all of the exponents found in psychophysical studies. They also pointed out that the exponent is highly sensitive to the experimental conditions employed, so that an explanation in terms merely of the functioning of the sensory transducers is unlikely.

A possible resolution. It may be true that reports collected in perceptual experiments ordinarily refer (in the functional sense explicated earlier) to a central representation of the physical correlates of the class to which the perceptual experience reported belongs. There is a question, however, as to whether this is a *necessary* state of affairs, as, for example, Attneave (1962) would have it ("Phenomenological terms necessarily refer to objective reference situations, however obscure; . . ."). His belief is based on the assumption that it is impossible to acquire a purely phenomenal language. Similarly, Treisman (1962) insisted that psychophysical scales are cognitive, that is, represent the subject's judgments of *stimulus* magnitudes. The basis for Treisman's belief is that only in connection with stimulus magnitudes can a subject have learned to assign numbers: "But how could rules be taught that would refer essentially to the private subject matter alone?"

Consider as a response to Treisman's rhetorical query the following hypothetical training procedure. The subject is also hypothetical, someone naïve of past experiences with hues. The procedure provides for this subject a series of brand-new perceptions and a set of terms that correspond to values on a dimension along which these perceptual experiences vary. It does not provide any physical correlates in Warren's sense. This example is constructed to distinguish between what is learned (to name properties of perceptual experience) and the unquestionably objective circumstances in which such learning takes place.

Undifferentiated physical arrangements give rise from trial to trial to different experiences of hue. The experimenter is heard to label these experiences "l", "m", "n", etc. The perceptual experiences in this series of trials are identical except with respect to certain characteristics which are correlated with the experimenter's identifications. When the subject subsequently reports with these terms, the referents (in the sense defined earlier) of the terms must be certain properties of his perceptual experiences. That the referents are values along the physical dimension of wavelength can be disposed of by noting that the subject in this experiment has no measure of wavelength other than experience of hue.

In a further experimental session when the subject sees a yellowish-orange afterimage, he would have available a term, say, "l", which would designate one of its nonrelational properties. Although the term might be said to refer in a vague sense to the general conditions of training, as a term in a report which is communicating and differentiating, its referent would have to be considered a property of the earlier perception which the experimenter called "l." This property is one of those of the experience of having a yellowish-orange afterimage. The basis of generalization of the report to the present experience is the recurrence of an experience with the property called "l." One might have been tempted prior to the afterimage demonstration to wield a parsimonious razor by saying: "Although the various wavelengths were indeed unknown to the subject, they controlled the differentiated reporting and were, consequently by definition, the referents of the various reports. The afterimage demonstration necessitates a view of the reports as referring to (being controlled by) a certain dimension of perceptual experience."

A possible resolution of the controversy may have its basis in an analysis by Treisman (1962) of the events between stimulus and response. As will be evident, an important distinction which he made parallels the present one between phenomenal and cognitive reports. The direct psychophysical methods, such as magnitude estimation, yield a relation between the intensity of the stimuli (Φ) and the subjects' estimates which is a power function. Treisman (1962) suggested that two successive stages may underlie this input-output relation. The first stage terminates in what might ordinarily be labeled perception. The second stage involves the relation between "the measure [of the stimulus] initially taken by the subject" and the response. Two possibilities were considered for the second stage: (*a*) a linear relation of the response to the measure—which would require that in the first stage the measure be a power function of Φ, or (*b*) an exponential transformation of the measure permitting Φ and the measure to be log-related. Both possibilities would yield a power function between output and input.

If one believes that a subject's psychophysical reports of magnitudes do refer to his perceptual experiences, then the second alternative for what occurs in Treisman's second stage would seem strange. The subject, rather than simply reporting the magnitudes of his sensations, transforms them exponentially. However, the additional transformation is comprehensible if the subject is giving (or can do nothing other than give) cognitive reports, that is, describing his sensations in terms of a physical correlate. For the subject to make a cognitive report, the measure must be transformed to yield values reinforced in accordance with their correspondence to the nature of the stimulus object and its correlates. This interpretation is favored by the fact that with respect to some dimensions, power functions are found when direct estimation methods are used, while logarithmic functions emerge when indirect methods are the basis for relating physical to sensory magnitudes. That the direct methods involve an additional trans-

formation is supported, according to Treisman (1962), by "the fact that subjects often find magnitude estimation surprisingly difficult—some can not do it at all."

Treisman (1962), although very critical of the use of responses in psychophysical experiments as reports of perceptual experience, opened the door to such a use. He argued, first, that for adaptational purposes it may be necessary to transform the "measure" the subject takes of the stimulus, to transform it in such a way as to produce a nonlogarithmic relationship between the intensity of the stimulus and the numerical judgment. Adaptational purposes would exist if, for example, the subject had to add stimulus quantities, that is, to make judgments of them in terms of how they would total when placed together, say, end to end. On the other hand, phenomenal reports would be reports of the nontransformed logarithmic measure:

> If for a particular stimulus dimension there were no environmental pressures tending to bring about some transformation of the initial measure, then none would occur, and we might expect subjects operating on such a dimension to fractionate and make other judgments in terms of the untransformed logarithmic measure [Treisman, 1962, p. 140].

Remaining issue: The quantity objection. Of broader significance than Warren's (1958) conclusion that judgments of sensory intensity are really judgments of a physical correlate of the particular sensory experience is his statement (1958) that "sensory intensity cannot be measured as it does not exist [p. 687]." Later (Warren and Warren, 1963), the same idea was stated again: "Sensation by its very nature can not be quantified—one sensation can not be considered double another [p. 798]." This amounts to the "quantity objection," put forward against psychophysics in the 1880s and 1890s and phrased by Boring (1921) thus: "Sensational magnitude is certainly not multitude, and intense sensations are not integrated of more sensory stuff than are weak [p. 453]." One might say that my experience now is twice as intense as the one I had just before in the sense that some physical correlate of their occurrence has corresponding values in that ratio. The intrinsic properties of experience are not described by such a report. But Warren was going further saying, in effect, not only that "experience is described in material object language, not in phenomenal language, for there is no such thing [Smart, 1959, p. 151]," but also that *sensory experience does not vary in intensity.*

One's answer to the quantity objection depends on the relation assumed between perceptual experience and the degree of excitation of the respective perceptual system. On the identity *assumption* of the relation of mind to brain (see Smart, 1959), sensations must be said to vary in magnitude since excitation of the perceptual system certainly varies. (It is a further question as to whether a subject assigns or can learn to assign meaningful values to the excitation value of his perceptual system independently of how he assigns numbers to physical correlates of the excitation.) Smart (1963) has argued that one can report concerning one's experience in two ways which go beyond mere similarity and difference; one of these involves describing a sensation, such as pain, as waxing and waning. Smart was willing to admit intensity as an attribute of sensation which can be reported, because of its topic-neutrality, that is, because it does not introduce a phenomenal property distinct from the physical properties of the relevant central process. A subject may be said to be reporting about his brain process when he says that a pain is waxing or waning, thus maintaining the identity theory.

Role of the Experimenter's Experience

Reports are basically communicative acts. A common observation of the reporting subject finds him in a highly motivated state which is reduced when he observes the experimenter showing some sign of understanding. Phenomenal reports may well be viewed as means of producing in the listener or observer a similar, though *non*perceptual experience. Through his own previous perceptual experience, the experimenter knows what the subject is talking about. Even when the perceptual experience is not described, but merely classified in terms of objective conditions for its usual occurrence, as, for example, when the subject says that his auditory experience is like ones he has near waterfalls, the experimenter knows something of the experience's intrinsic character. The experimenter taking the subject's place, however, might have a very different experience. The experimenter's previous perceptual experiences serve as a basis for having some idea of what the *subject* is experiencing here and now and not what the experimenter would experience were he in the subject's place. The degree to which the subject's communication succeeds depends on how close the correspondence is between the subject's reported experience and the experiences of the experimenter that are redintegrated.

Several writers have concerned themselves with the relationship between the experimenter's and the subject's perceptual experience as it pertains to the problem of giving meaning to the terms that the subject uses in his perceptual reports. Bridgman (1959) suggested that there exists a special class of words, which he called "introspectional," whose operational meaning depends on who it is that performs the operations. These words are used ordinarily "in their private mode"; the operations by which these words are given meaning are unique to the individual in that only he can perform them. Bridgman (1959) claimed further that this restriction does not hinder communication; one talks in this private mode of his experiences and others do understand. Adequate communication is possible as a consequence of the use of an additional operation:

I shall call it the operation of "projection." I "project" myself into your position, that is, I imagine myself in your position, and I ask myself what I would be saying or doing in such a position. If I can imagine that I myself would be using the same word in that position, then I understand the meaning of your word and you have been successful in your communication. For present purposes it is not necessary to attempt to analyze the operation of projection further [Bridgman, 1959, p. 220].

An underlying assumption in the use of this "operation" is that we are similar to each other to a degree that justifies its use.

Statements which contain terms that make reference to subjects' perceptual experiences were accepted by Rosner (1962) as part of the science of psychophysics on the grounds mainly of the experimenter's ability to serve as subject and "see (or hear) for himself":[2]

Statements of first-order invariances which contain experiential terms rest on a complex correlation between the psychophysicist's experiences as a subject, including observations of his own overt behavior as a formal subject, and his observations of the overt responses of other subjects to experiential stimuli. . . . As a subject, the psychophysicist notices a chain of experiences alternately ascribable to environmental stimuli and to his own overt responses. This strongly suggests a representation of another subject in a psychophysical experiment which runs $S_{i}\epsilon^{l}R_{k}S_{j}\epsilon_{e}R_{i}S\epsilon_{r}R_{m}$ . . . where S and R represent stimulus and response respectively and ϵ represents aspects of the subject's experience [Rosner, 1962, pp. 310–311].

Confirmation of a subject's statements about experience includes the experi-

---

[2] A similar process appears in attempts to *demonstrate* perceptual laws. At times one communicates such evidence by asking one's fellow scientist to serve as "subject," presenting the stimulus conditions, and calling attention to the relevant aspects of the accompanying experience. This is the only *direct* evidence that *psychologists* can have about laws of perception. All other evidence is indirect or inferential.

menter's serving as subject himself and making the same observations as well as observations of the subject's behavior, the experimenter's own behavior, and that of others under the given conditions.

Both Bridgman (1959) and Rosner (1962) were discussing inference by analogy. For clarification of the procedure of analogical inference, we may use as a guide Pap's (1962) textbook on the philosophy of science. In it he argued, as Rosner (1962) implied, that an argument from analogy can serve as confirmation of statements concerning mental events. An argument of this type is a form of *probable* reasoning, which means that the premises may be true and the conclusions false. We begin with a sample (S) of observed individuals "where S may have just one, or more than one, member"; in the present instance the sample is restricted to just one, the experimenter himself having access to his own perceptual experiences and characterizing them.

The members of S have the properties in common that define the class K, they further have P in common, x resembles the members of S in being a member of K (i.e., having properties that define K), therefore, x also resembles the members of S in having P [Pap, 1962, p. 146].

The class (K) to which the psychophysicist (S) and the subject (x) belong is that of live, intact adult *Homo sapiens*. P may be taken to refer to having, under certain conditions, a certain perceptual experience. The probability of the analogical inference that x as well has P (i.e., the soundness of the argument) depends on the degree of analogy or sharing of properties by x and S.

Analogical inference is undoubtedly common in everyday life and frequent among psychophysicists in practice. It requires justification, nevertheless, in the eyes of psychologists who are also logical behaviorists. Justification is required because the procedure involves the introduction of mentalistic terms from the referential base of the experimenter's own perceptual experience. It is in marked contradiction to Bergmann and Spence's (1944) dictum for psychophysics and psychology generally, that mentalistic terms must be introduced from a physicalistic meaning base. The contrasting positions of Bergmann and Spence (1944), and Rosner (1962) and Bridgman (1959) reflect certain developments in the philosophy of science with respect to the criterion of scientific meaningfulness or usefulness of statements. A shift has occurred from the doctrine that only conclusively verifiable statements be admissable as a part of science. The current widely held view is the only *confirmability* of hypotheses is necessary; any statement whose probability of truth can be increased or decreased by observations is considered scientifically meaningful. (For an introduction to this shift see Feigl, 1956, 1959, and references which he gave.) It is important to stress that Rosner's (1962) procedure for introducing terms referring to perceptual experience included confirmation of analogical inferences (made from one's own experience) by further observations of the behavior of subjects.

Finally, to illustrate some of these notions more concretely, an experiment on the visual perception of transformations of a shadow pattern by von Fieandt and Gibson (1959) will be discussed. Subjects were asked to report freely (to avoid suggesting what would be seen) concerning the "kind of movement" each saw under two conditions of stimulation, contraction of an elastic net versus rotation of the frame to which it was attached. For 20 of the 22 subjects, the descriptions fell into two categories corresponding to the two physical transformations of the shadow pattern, and the change from one to the other was "promptly noted and reported" by them. The subjects did not use, however, terms such as "rigid" and "elastic." They used words more familiar to them individually such as "wire fencing," "swinging toward me," "back and forth,"

"compression," "diagonal movement," and "horizontal movement," terms whose interpretation the authors were quick to admit is subject to error. In further tests, in which the subjects were instructed to continue using the same words for the same perceived motions, they showed consistency and the ability to report accurately the occurrence of transitions from one form of movement to the other.

The experimenters described in detail their own perceptions under the two conditions of stimulation, and they proposed that despite their subjects' use of less precise language, the excellent differentiations and consistency of the subjects suggested that they, too, saw a rigid and nonrigid surface-motion, although "the extent to which the abstract property of rigidity was induced in our experimental situation is not clear." The following implicit argument was being made: Given, on the one hand, the experimenters' own perceptual experiences, their own reports of these experiences, and the experiences' correspondence with the stimulating conditions, and, on the other hand, the subjects' reports, their consistent successful differentiations, and other numerous similarities between subjects and experimenters, it follows that *probably* the experiences of the subjects are as the experimenters describe their own. This is a form of probable reasoning that can be confirmed in its conclusions through the invention of further tests and the prediction of behavioral consequences but cannot achieve positivity.

Report Validity

An implicit goal of the discussion to this point has been to contribute to the refinement of psychology's use of report behavior. The ultimate goal should be the use of such reports in a way that can justifiably be considered an instance of "observation through causality" (Lenzen, 1938). The high value of this goal may become apparent. No less than the observation of the perceptual experiences *of others* in a direct, noninferential way is involved. "Report" has been distinguished from "response" in terms of its use as a relatively direct means of knowing about events unavailable to the experimenter for observation. Phenomenal reports were differentiated in terms of causality or functional relation to the phenomena of perceptual experience. *Inference* through causality can develop, as Lenzen (1938) indicated in discussing the observation of hidden physical processes, into *observation* through causality. Initially, certain macroscopic events are used as a basis for inferring their micro-causes. With confirmations of hypotheses or theories used as "constructive instruments of interpretation" of perceptible effects, the process of inference is short-circuited and transformed into a process of observation of what was unobservable and strictly inferential.

In a recent article on observation terms as used by scientists, Dretske (1964) clarified these ideas further. He argued that the observable in science is not limited, other than by the body of scientific knowledge and the observer's familiarity with it. All instances of so-called direct observation assume automatically and implicitly a certain set of beliefs. Similarly given the routine presumption of regularities relating an "unobservable" to an "observable," the "unobservable" is in fact *seen*. A friend observes one's depression, a meteorologist the impending cold front, a physicist certain light waves. The inference from effect to cause can become so immediate, automatic, and implicit that it is indistinguishable from those instances in which observation is ordinarily said to be "direct." The inability of some to see the same object, process, or event results from ignorance of a body of fact or relative unfamiliarity with it. It is not due to the absolute unobservability of the phenomena in question.

Responses truly become phenomenal reports as one becomes more capable of observing experience through them. In order to move any class of behaviors from the end of a continuum where its members are used in an indirect and intricate manner to yield by inference information concerning perceptual experience, to the other end of the continuum where, as true phenomenal reports, they become transparent means of observing perceptual experience, it is necessary in each case to confront and solve the problem of report validity: Whenever reports of perceptual experience are to be taken as informative, how can we determine that the subject's report is an accurate one? Surprisingly, Bergmann (1957) found this no problem at all: "assertions we make when we describe, as one says, the stream of consciousness by means of atomic statements of a 'phenomenalistic' language are incorrigible [p. 81]." Unless this statement is meant in a special philosophical sense which makes it irrelevant to psychological research, it is clearly false. Reports share with all behavior a susceptibility to influence by many factors other than the stream of consciousness. Perhaps Bergmann intended the "positiveness" of the experiences themselves, for, as soon as we make assertions about an experience or attempt other operations on it, error and uncertainty are possible and often likely. The latter point has been made by Price (1960).

APPROACHES TO REPORT VALIDITY

Several approaches to report validity, with examples, will be discussed next. It will become apparent that they are not, at a deeper level of analysis, unrelated. Their interrelations, similarities, and differences will be left, however, for another place. The approaches may be summarized briefly as follows: (*a*) positioning reports concerning perceptual experience in a theoretical network and testing deductions from it; (*b*) securing from subjects supplementary reports concerning their own report behavior; (*c*) applying a public criterion as a check on the accuracy of reports; and (*d*) eliminating by statistical and experimental means hypotheses alternative to report validity.

(a) The first approach to report validity listed can be illustrated through Carlson's experiments on size constancy. Previous research which presumably secured phenomenal size matches had often found underconstancy. Carlson (1960) proposed the factor responsible to be the subject's *belief* that distant objects look smaller than near ones of equal size ("the perspective attitude"). As a consequence of this belief, the subject undermatches with the nearer variable stimulus to represent the *supposed* smaller look of the more distant standard. Carlson's (1962b) phenomenal-size instructions made a particular point of the subject's ignoring actual, physical size: "Try to adjust the variable so that it appears equal to the standard to you visually, whether you think it is equal in actual size or not [p. 463]." Using such instructions, Carlson (1960, 1962a, 1962b; Carlson and Tassone, 1962) found repeatedly that the mean ratio of variable to standard size did not depart from unity to a statistically significant degree. Three exceptions appeared in his research, two of which are relevant to the present discussion. Carlson (1960) found that *over*constancy results when the task is difficult (90° angular separation of variable from standard, and phenomenal matches first in a series before objective matches). He interpreted the overconstancy as resulting from the subjects' automatic attempts to compensate for fancied errors; even under phenomenal-size instructions when conditions were difficult they made objective-size matches and applied the perspective attitude.[3] Support for this hypothesis comes in the form of a significant correlation (.64) of phenom-

enal-size with objective-size matches only under the difficult conditions. In another experiment (Carlson, 1961), a placebo taken with phenomenal instructions yielded significant overconstancy. The interpretation was motivational and similar to that for difficult conditions: The subject, believing that the placebo may reduce his accuracy, resorts to "the natural criterion for competent performance in the size-constancy situation" which is "the ability to make an accurate judgment of physical size."

The grounds for believing that Carson has elicited truly phenomenal-size matches is the empirical confirmation of a network of hypothetical and observed relationships. At the start, Carlson (1960) proposed that under natural perceptual conditions (when the person is not being tested), the perceived size of objects is constant with distance; "the most natural result of biological adaptation to the natural environment" is perfect size-constancy. Since the instructional attempt to remove interference by the subjects' beliefs yields perfect constancy on the average, it is likely that the instructions do elicit phenomenal matches. No independent check on this is available, other than that provided by the network of hypotheses and observed relationships. For example, Carlson (1961) hypothesized that a neutral, motivational state results in perfect constancy, and that high motivation to accomplish the task accurately produces overconstancy even with phenomenal-size instructions. The latter will occur because the perspective attitude is what the subject has at his disposal to improve his matches. Chlorpromazine was used to produce the neutral state; sleep deprivation appears to have been taken by subjects as a challenge with respect to producing a good performance. Observations of the subjects' attitudes and behaviors supported the assumption that these manipulations yield the respective motivational states. As expected, perfect constancy and significant overconstancy, respectively, resulted.

[3] The effect of the perspective attitude on objective-size matches might be expressed: Since more distant objects look smaller when equal in actual size to nearer objects, I must compensate for this appearance by adjusting the nearer variable so that it looks larger than the farther standard. When they look equal, the farther one must be bigger. (See, for example, Gilinsky, 1955, for findings of over-constancy with objective-size matches.)

Another example of the confirmation of this network of relationships is the experiment by Carlson and Tassone (1962) involving an independent measure of the perspective attitude by means of a kind of semantic differential. The perspective attitude was found to be positively and significantly correlated (.44 biserial) with matches under objective-size instructions, and nonsignificantly (.20) with phenomenal-size matches. On the other hand, Carlson (1962b) paradoxically predicted and found experimental support for his hypothesis that LSD results in *under*-constancy. The drug is said to shift the subject's orientation to the subjective. But how things look exemplifies subjectivity. Should one not expect, if LSD has such an effect, that *phenomenal-size matches* would occur, even under objective-size instructions?

Dulany (1962), in the context of reports about awareness in verbal conditioning studies, has discussed the above general basis for evaluating the reports of subjects as valid indicators of their perceptual experiences. As he sees it, the method involves "positioning the subject's report and what is reported in a theoretical network." This approach is distinct from an operationism in which all nonlogical terms must receive explicit definition in terms of observables. The relationship between the unobserved aspect of consciousness and the report about it is hypothetical rather than definitional. This relationship is embedded among others in a theory; "report validity takes the status of a hypothesis and we become concerned to see whether the reports behave as the theory holds they should [Dulany, 1962, p. 109]."

(*b*) The second means listed for determining the kind of report given, that is, whether the report does refer to perceptual experience, involves securing from subjects supplementary reports concerning their own report behavior. Joynson and Newson (1962) proposed the use initially of vague instructions, because precise instructions are believed to distort the relationships one seeks to observe. After the perceptual judgments are made, descriptions by the subject on the nature of his judgments are collected. In the experiment by Joynson and Newson (1962) on shape constancy with inclinations of the object from the frontal plane, the "vague" instructions asked for that member of a set of comparison stimuli which "looks most like" the standard. Despite such instructions, 62 (Group RO) of the 100 subjects did not indicate in their supplementary reports any other possible judgment than a selection based on actual shape. The (N) judgment mentioned spontaneously by the remaining subjects (Group RN), but always in contrast with (R) judgments of real shape, appears to be a kind of phenomenal-shape match which includes the deliberate discounting of the object's inclination. (As the angle of inclination increased, more subjects—15 of 20 at 80°—became aware of N judgments.) R judgments showed little if any departure from constancy; N judgments yielded compromise values between the true and the retinal shapes.

These two classes of judgments are unlikely to correspond to the present distinction between phenomenal and cognitive reports. R judgments were described by most as involving objects that "look the same [real] shape." Only one-fourth of Group RO could be made aware by discussion of the N judgment as distinct from R judgments. The rest of Group RO

> can see no important distinction between "looking the same shape" and "being the same," even when the distinction is explained to them. . . . So for these subjects, the R judgment seems to approximate closely to that quality of direct, visual impression which for Group RN characterized the N judgment [Joynson and Newson, 1962, pp. 10–11].

But the N judgments appear to involve, according to the subjects' reports, a conscious ignoring of the cues for inclination, as well as a departure from real shape. It would seem necessary to consider the following interpretation: Under conditions of this experiment the shapes look as they are; N judgments involve the analytic set which attempts to ignore all but projective size;[4] R judgments are either both phenomenal and cognitive or include some of each kind which in this experiment are the same; and the self-instructions that lead to N judgments may involve a counterpart to Carlson's perspective attitude, the assumption that what is immediately given ("the immediate impression of direct shape") must be two-dimensional, an attitude derived from the culturally common expression of shape in two dimensions on paper and canvas.

In a similar experiment on size judgments, Joynson and Kirk (1960) gave instructions for two different kinds of reports based on subjects' descriptions in earlier experiments (Joynson, 1958a, 1958b) of what kind of judgments they were making. The attempt to obtain N judgments involved these instructions:

> Do *not* try to make the rods the same real size. They are *not* to be adjusted so that, if measured with a ruler, they would be the same physical length. They are to be made *apparently* equal only. You are not to allow for the distance. Judge when they just look the same size, not when they *are* the same [Joynson and Kirk, 1960, p. 221].

The R instructions merely asked for judgments of equal real size. As would be expected from the results of Carlson and others, the N instructions produced marked underconstancy. The R instructions yielded slight (if any) underconstancy. It is clear from the instructions, these results, and the reports of subjects

following the N judgments that these judgments are not phenomenal reports; they are difficult analytic judgments in making which the subject must be vigilant not to take distance into account. The reports concerning the judgments further indicate that the R judgments are "intuitive," based on "appearance," and do not involve conscious calculation. The latter suggests that in large part such judgments of "real" size are phenomenal reports:

> We have argued that the R judgments obtained in these experiments correspond closely to our everyday perceptual impressions, and involve an active process [of allowing for distance] . . . usually carried out automatically [Joynson and Kirk, 1960, p. 229].

Whether subjects can tell what they did in an accurate and sufficiently detailed way is itself an open question. Joynson (1958b) expressed doubt as to the conclusions he drew from these supplementary reports: "It remains very difficult to know where observed fact ends, and interpretation creeps in [p. 145]." Schoenfeld and Cumming (1962), writing to the problem more generally, expressed stronger doubts. It is their belief that all perceptual reports refer to (are under the discriminative control of) perceptual responses; when someone says that he sees a bird, and then claims that what he is saying refers to the bird, he is mistaken. Despite the fact that the reporting response is under the control of an unobserved event, they saw room for further discriminative training to increase the accuracy with which the subject tacts (describes) the relation between his covert perceptual behavior and the overt report of it:

> Doubtless, further discriminative training, perhaps reminiscent of Titchener, could bring his report under the control of the actual properties of R [the perceptual response], so that he could tact his seeing behavior [Schoenfeld and Cumming, 1962, p. 236].

---

[4] Joynson and Newson referred to an experiment by Leibowitz, Waskow, Loeffler, and Glaser (1959), in which subjects were asked to adopt an analytic attitude, as resulting in compromise judgments (underconstancy) between retinal and real shape corresponding to the N judgments found by Joynson and Newson.

(c) When the question of report validity is raised, from time to time it is proposed informally that a public criterion is needed to determine whether the reports are accurately reflecting perceptual experiences. One seeks a response less susceptible to contaminating variables; involuntary, autonomic reactions are often suggested as criteria. However, if autonomic reactions are to be relied on as a check under problematical conditions, agreement must be found between the autonomic measure and the report under conditions in which there is no reason to suspect confounding variables. Poor correlations under the latter conditions would indicate that reports and autonomic reactions are not related to perceptual experience in a way simple and similar enough to permit the use of the autonomic response as a criterion.

Gunter's (1951) experiment on the binocular fusion of colors can serve as an example of the possible complexity of the relation between report and autonomic reaction. Following GSR conditioning to yellow spectral light presented to both eyes, subjects were tested with red to one eye and green to the other, as well as yellow, red, green, or blue to both. Yellow to both, and green to one and red to the other eye yielded GSRs of the greatest magnitude, while blue to both showed no response at all, and red or green to both eyes gave GSRs of intermediate magnitude. Of special importance is the fact that none of the eight subjects, all of whom showed the "fusion effect" according to the GSR, reported experiencing yellow when red and green were presented one to each eye. While the GSR supported the inference of experienced yellow, the subjects were reporting red and green rivalry. Replication with attention to eliciting complete reports is needed before much can be made of these results; however, there appears to be no reason to suspect the reports as inaccurate. The absence of correlation with autonomic readings forces the interpretation that the "yellow fusion" indicated by the GSR, at least in this experiment, does not occur in perceptual experience as commonly understood.

(d) The final approach to report validity to be discussed here requires the elimination of hypotheses competing with the assumption that the reports in question are providing an accurate portrayal of the attendant perceptual experience in some respect of interest. There are, in fact, parallel circumstances in both of which reports are solicited and given in the same way about similar perceptual experiences, yet these circumstances are distinguished with respect to whether or not the reports are taken at face value. To state that a check on the reports is necessary when results are controversial is to imply the existence of alternative accounts for the reports other than the having of the referred-to experience. It would be ideal if the means of eliminating alternative hypotheses could be made explicit in the form of a list of directives. This would serve to quell the critics who claim, in general, that one can never *know* about another's perceptual experience. However, a broad statement such as that of Garner, Hake, and Eriksen (1956) on converging operations is all that can be given *for the general case*. The approach called "strong inference" by Platt (1964) is similar to that of Garner, Hake, and Eriksen (1956) and involves the systematic listing and experimental elimination of alternative hypotheses. Platt (1964) argued that devising alternative hypotheses and crucial experiments to eliminate one or more of them is a matter of intellectual invention for which no recipe can be given. He quoted Bacon with favor to the effect that we can only progress in science "by negatives, and at last to end in affirmatives after exclusion has been exhausted," and Karl Popper, who argued against proof in science, since *later* explanation may turn out to be as good or better than the one that had resisted disproof until then. (The possibility of new hypotheses to account for the same results leaves the confirmed relationship between reports and perceptual experience at some level of probability of being true.)

When one turns to specific experiments and alternative hypotheses, specific recipes can be given for eliminating, statistically or experimentally, the effects of contaminating variables. This approach to report validity will be illustrated in three ways.

1. The first involves *statistical comparisons*. Landauer and Rodger (1964) asked whether matches made under reflectance or luminance instructions are different from apparent-brightness matches merely because in the latter case some subjects provide each of the former kinds of matches. If this were true, then the intersubject variance under instructions to match for apparent brightness would be greatest. Similarly, if individual subjects under apparent-brightness instructions vacillate between reflectance and luminance reports, then intrasubject variability would be greatest for this group. The apparent-brightness instructions asked subjects to "tell me when the two patches appear to you to look alike," to take "the normal, unsophisticated attitude of everyday life," to indicate "the way it appears to you at first sight, without any analysis of the situation." The reflectance instructions emphasized the matching of the exact shade of gray while disregarding the illumination, and the luminance instructions emphasized matching according to both the shade of gray and the illumination as would a photographer "who wants to get the correct brightness in his photograph, without shadows and highlights."

The apparent-brightness instructions yielded matches of intermediate luminance. The intersubject variance of this group was not significantly different from the variance of the group given luminance instructions. Although greater than the variance found for the reflectance group, the variance for the apparent-brightness group was significantly lower than expectations calculated on the assumption that some of the subjects in the phenomenal group would do exactly as those in the luminance group and the rest would make judgments of reflectance. These results eliminate the hypothesis that subjects in the phenomenal group are consistently using a reflectance or a luminance criterion. The log mean *intrasubject* variances for the three groups indicated that the phenomenal group was not vacillating between the other two kinds of judgments, since its log mean did not differ statistically from the reflectance group and was significantly less than that of the luminance group. Landauer and Rodger (1964) concluded that phenomenal reports of brightness which appear to be a compromise between objective (reflectance) and projective (luminance) judgments are distinct judgments rather than artifacts of averaging.

2. The second experimental illustration of this last approach to report validity represents Garner, Hake, and Eriksen's (1956) explication of the use of converging operations. Wallach, O'Connell, and Neisser (1953) studied the influence of memory on the perception as three-dimensional of shadows cast by stationary wire figures. Following the subjects' viewing the shadows of the wire figures rotating and thus providing abundant cues to their three-dimensional character, they were asked to describe what they saw when the wire figures were again, as before the rotation, stationary. While prior to rotation the static shadow figures were reported to be seen as two-dimensional, after the experience with rotation, the reports were nearly always of three-dimensional appearances. A converging operation was introduced to eliminate the hypothesis that the reports were directly dependent on knowing that the shadows were of three-dimensional figures. Some subjects were asked to continue looking at the stationary figure and to report what they saw. The spontaneous reports were of reversals of perspective, a perceptual experience requiring the perception of depth.

3. The third subcategory of this last approach to report validity seeks to eliminate experimentally the *relevance* of a competing hypothesis in accounting for the results. In the illustrative experiments the subject was acquainted, either prior to every trial or at the start of the experimental session, with the stimulus materials to be presented. This knowledge makes irrelevant the alternative hypothesis that differences in the reports given between experimental conditions reflect differences in the subjects' knowledge or hypotheses concerning the materials being presented to him.

Haber (1965) presented a series of tachistoscopic exposures (varying from 1 to 25 without the subject's prior knowledge), the same word at the same duration and intensity. Previous research (Haber and Hershenson, 1965; Hershenson and Haber, 1965) had shown that such repeated presentations, although separated by 8 or more seconds, resulted in better and better perception of the word. Haber (1965) presented half the words in his experiment for 5 seconds prior to the respective tachistoscopic series of exposures. This procedure was used to demonstrate that the course of development of the percept, as indicated by the subjects' reports of individual letters perceived completely, was not altered by prior knowledge of the identity of the word exposed. By eliminating, through the use of prior knowledge, the hypothesis that subjects were guessing the letters, Haber (1965) has a stronger case for phenomenal changes occurring with repeated, brief exposures.

A kind of prior knowledge has also been used by Natsoulas (1965; Natsoulas and Levy, 1965). Repeated auditory presentations over earphones of the identical utterance presented loudly and clearly by means of a loop of tape produces numerous and marked alterations in what is heard. Natsoulas (1965) explained precisely to all subjects the construction of the reel of tape from a loop containing a single

utterance, and that any changes heard would be perceptual, not on the tape. In informal interviews after their experimental sessions, a majority of subjects expressed concern over what they "should" have heard. This suggested the possibility of their withholding reports of perceptual change.

In a second experiment (Natsoulas and Levy, 1965), half the subjects knew the source of the transformations to be within their perceptual systems while the other half were led to believe the changes were occurring on the tape, that is, were "real." The group without knowledge of the experimental conditions reported more transformations and this difference grew within and across trials, as the transformations came more frequently. The intent of making the experiment transparent to some subjects was to eliminate reports about the tape, what was on it, etc. Knowledge of conditions affected the subject's expectations, however, concerning his own perceptual system under such conditions. "Hearing things" is not an admired ability among people of our culture. It is not surprising that subjects are more restrained in their reports when they know that the stimulus always remains constant.

This general method of acquainting subjects in advance with the stimulus materials is not without its sources of error. Knowledge of the stimulus may influence the reports indirectly through its effect on perception. The reports might remain phenomenal, but the expectation of seeing a particular form, for example, could alter the character of the perceptual process. Another source of error would be a consequence of the interaction between knowledge of the experimental conditions and the effects of the experimental conditions themselves. Certain experimental conditions may result in perceptions departing considerably from the subject's expectations based on his knowledge of the stimulus objects. Reports describing these perceptions may be withheld in favor of less extreme ones. Practice, training, and instructions may help to avoid this tendency. As Zener (Zener and Gaffron, 1962) has stressed, a good subject for an experiment requiring phenomenal reports needs "confidence in the reality of his own experiences."

Conclusions

This article is presented for purposes of opening important neglected issues to wider discussion. What a reporting response is, as distinguished from other responses, needs to be discussed. Then there is the psychological sense of reference, as when one says that the report referred to a certain stimulus object. Then, if one equates, following Schoenfeld and Cumming (1962), the referent of a reporting response (what it is about) with the discriminative stimulus that controls it, one is forced to ask how, and even whether, a private event can come to control a reporting response. For empirical purposes, one must also know how to determine whether a certain reporting response does, in fact, refer to perception rather than, say, the external stimulus object. Promising replies to these questions will raise further issues: the past training needed for a report to come under the control of perception and the present conditions necessary for this control to be exercised. Since the conditions for securing the proper reports from a subject seem often to involve instructions, the question of how instructions control or influence the subject's behavior will have to be faced.

References

ATTNEAVE, F. Perception and related areas. In S. Koch (Ed.), *Psychology: A study of a science.* vol. 4. New York: McGraw-Hill, 1962. pp. 619–659.

BAKAN, D. A reconsideration of the problem of introspection. *Psychological Bulletin,* 1954, *51,* 105–118.

BERGMANN, G. *Philosophy of science.* Madison: University of Wisconsin Press, 1957.

BERGMANN, G., and K. W. SPENCE. The logic of psychophysical measurement. *Psychological Review,* 1944, *51,* 1–24.

BLOUGH, D. S. A method for obtaining psychophysical thresholds from the pigeon. *Journal of the Experimental Analysis of Behavior,* 1958, *1,* 31–43.

BOLLES, R. C., and D. E. BAILEY. Importance of object recognition in size constancy. *Journal of Experimental Psychology,* 1956, *51,* 222–225.

BORING, E. G. The stimulus-error. *American Journal of Psychology,* 1921, *32,* 449–471.

BRIDGMAN, P. W. *The way things are.* Cambridge: Harvard University Press, 1959.

BURT, C. The concept of consciousness. *British Journal of Psychology,* 1962, *53,* 229–242.

CARLSON, V. R. Overestimation in size-constancy judgments. *American Journal of Psychology,* 1960, *73,* 199–213.

CARLSON, V. R. Effects of sleep-deprivation and chlorpromazine on size-constancy judgments. *American Journal of Psychology,* 1961, *74,* 552–560.

CARLSON, V. R. Size-constancy judgments and perceptual compromise. *Journal of Experimental Psychology,* 1962, *63,* 68–73. (a)

CARLSON, V. R. Underestimation in size-constancy judgments. *American Journal of Psychology,* 1962, *75,* 462–465. (b)

CARLSON, V. R., and E. P. TASSONE. A verbal measure of the perspective attitude. *American Journal of Psychology,* 1962, *75,* 644–647.

CARNAP, R. The methodological character of theoretical concepts. In H. Feigl and M. Scriven (Eds.), *Minnesota studies in the philosophy of science.* vol. 1. Minneapolis: University of Minnesota Press, 1956, pp. 38–76.

DRETSKE, F. I. Observational terms. *Philosophical Review,* 1964, *73,* 25–41.

DULANY, D. E., JR. The place of hypotheses and intentions: An analysis of verbal control in verbal conditioning. In C. W. Eriksen (Ed.), *Behavior and awareness: A symposium of research and interpretation.* Durham: Duke University Press, 1962. pp. 102–129.

FEIGL, H. Some major issues and developments in the philosophy of science of logical empiricism. In H. Feigl and M. Scriven

(Eds.), *Minnesota studies in the philosophy of science.* vol. 1. Minneapolis: University of Minnesota Press. 1956. pp. 3–37.

FEIGL, H. Philosophical embarrassments of psychology. *American Psychologist, 1959, 14,* 115–128.

FEIGL, H. Physicalism, unity of science, and the foundations of psychology. In P. A. Schlipp (Ed.), *The philosophy of Rudolf Carnap.* La Salle, Ill.: Open Court, 1963. pp.227–267.

GARNER, W. R., H. W. HAKE, and C. W. ERIKSEN. Operationism and the concept of perception. *Psychological Review, 1956, 63,* 149–159.

GIBSON, J. J. The useful dimensions of sensitivity. *American Psychologist, 1963, 18,* 1–15.

GILINSKY, A. S. The effect of attitude upon the percention of size and distance. *American Journal of Psychology, 1955, 68,* 173–192.

GRAHAM, C. H., and P. RATOOSH. Notes on some interrelations of sensory psychology, perception, and behavior. In S. Koch (Ed.), *Psychology: A study of a science.* vol. 4. New York: McGraw-Hill, 1962. pp. 483–514.

GUNTER, R. Binocular fusion of color. *British Journal of Psychology, 1951, 42,* 363–372.

HABER, R. N. Effect of prior knowledge of the stimulus on word-recognition processes. *Journal of Experimental Psychology, 1965, 69,* 282–286.

HABER, R. N., and M. HERSHENSON. Effects of repeated brief exposures on the growth of a percept. *Journal of Experimental Psychology, 1965, 69,* 40–46.

HEIDER, F. On Lewin's methods and theory. *Journal of Social Issues, 1960,* Supplement 13.

HERSHENSON, M., and R. N. HABER. The role of meaning in the perception of briefly exposed words. *Canadian Journal of Psychology, 1965, 19,* 42–46.

JOYNSON, R. B. An experimental synthesis of the Associationist and Gestalt accounts of the perception of size. Part I. *Quarterly Journal of Experimental Psychology, 1958, 10,* 65–76. (a)

JOYNSON, R. B. An experimental synthesis of the Associationist and Gestalt accounts of the perception of size. Part II. *Quarterly Journal of Experimental Psychology, 1958, 10,* 142–154. (b)

JOYNSON, R. B., and N. S. KIRK. An experimental synthesis of the Associationist and Gestalt accounts of the perception of size.

Part III. *Quarterly Journal of Experimental Psychology, 1960, 12,* 221–230.

JOYNSON, R. B., and L. J. NEWSON. The perception of shape as a function of inclination. *British Journal of Psychology, 1962, 53,* 1–15.

KOCH, S. Psychology and conceptions of knowledge. In T. W. Wann (Ed.), *Behaviorism and phenomenology.* Chicago: University of Chicago Press, 1964. pp. 1–41.

LANDAUER, A. A., and R. S. RODGER. The effect of "apparent" instructions on brightness judgments. *Journal of Experimental Psychology, 1964, 68,* 80–94.

LEIBOWITZ, H., I. WASKOW, N. LOEFFLER, and F. GLASER. Intelligence level as a variable in the perception of shape. *Quarterly Journal of Experimental Psychology, 1959, 11,* 108–112.

LENZEN, V. F. Procedures in empirical science. *International Encyclopedia of Unified Science, 1938, 1,* no. 5.

MacCORQUODALE, K., P. E. MEEHL, and EDWARD C. TOLMAN. In W. K. Estes et al. (Eds.), *Modern learning theory.* New York: Appleton-Century-Crofts, 1954. pp. 177–266.

NATSOULAS, T. A study of the verbal transformation effect. *American Journal of Psychology, 1965, 78,* 257–263.

NATSOULAS, T., and E. LEVY. A further study of the verbal transformation effect. Unpublished manuscript, University of California, Davis, 1965.

PAP, A. *An introduction to the philosophy of science.* New York: Free Press of Glencoe, 1962.

PERKINS, M. Intersubjectivity and Gestalt psychology. *Philosophy and Phenomenological Research, 1953, 13,* 437–451.

PLACE, U. T. Is consciousness a brain process? *British Journal of Psychology, 1956, 47,* 44–50.

PLATT, J. R. Strong inference. *Science, 1964, 146,* 347–353.

PRENTICE, W. C. H. The systematic psychology of Wolfgang Köhler. In S. Koch (Ed.), *Psychology: A study of a science.* Vol. 1. New York: McGraw-Hill, 1959. pp. 427–455.

PRICE, H. H. Some objections to behaviorism. In S. Hook (Ed.), *Dimensions of mind: A symposium.* New York: New York University Press, 1960. pp. 79–84.

QUINTON, A. M. The problem of perception. *Mind, 1955, 64,* 28–51.

ROSNER, B. S. Psychophysics and neurophysiology. In S. Koch (Ed.), *Psychology: A study of a science.* vol. 4. New York: McGraw-Hill, 1962 pp. 280–333.

SCHOENFELD, W. N., and W. W. CUMMING. Behavior and perception. In S. Koch (Ed.), *Psychology: A study of a science.* vol. 5. New York: McGraw-Hill, 1963. pp. 313–252.

SMART, J. J. C. Sensations and brain processes. *Philosophical Review,* 1959, 68, 141–156.

SMART, J. J. C. Sensations and brain processes: A rejoinder to Dr. Pitcher and Mr. Joske. *Australasian Journal of Philosophy,* 1960, 38, 252–254.

SMART, J. J. C. Further remarks on sensation and brain processes. *Philosophical Review,* 1961, 70, 406–407.

SMART, J. J. C. *Philosophy and scientific realism.* London: Routledge and Kegan Paul, 1963.

SMART, J. J. C. The identity thesis—A reply to Professor Garnett. *Australasian Journal of Philosophy,* 1965, 43, 82–83.

STEVENS, J. C., J. D. MACK, and S. S. STEVENS. Growth of sensation of seven continua as measured by force of handgrip. *Journal of Experimental Psychology,* 1960, 59, 66–67.

STEVENS, S. S. On the psychophysical law. *Psychological Review,* 1957, 64, 153–181.

STEVENS, S. S. Problems and methods of psychophysics. *Psychological Bulletin,* 1958, 55, 177–196.

STEVENS, S. S. The quantification of sensation. *Daedalus,* 1959, 88, 606–621.

STEVENS, S. S. The psychophysics of sensory function. In W. A. Rosenblith (Ed.), *Sensory communication.* Cambridge: MIT Press, 1961. pp. 1–33.

STEVENS, S. S. The basis of psychophysical judgments. *Journal of the Acoustical Society of America,* 1963, 35, 611–612.

STEVENS, S. S., and M. GUIRAO. Loudness, reciprocity, and partition scales. *Journal of the Acoustical Society of America,* 1962, 34, 1466–1471.

THOULESS, R. H. Individual differences in phenomenal regression. *British Journal of Psychology,* 1932, 22, 216–241.

TREISMAN, N. Psychological explanation: The "private data" hypothesis. *British Journal of the Philosophy of Science,* 1962, 13, 130–143.

VON FIEANDT, K., and J. J. GIBSON. The sensitivity of the eye to two kinds of continuous transformation of a shadow-pattern. *Journal of Experimental Psychology,* 1959, 57, 344–347.

WALLACH, H., D. N. O'CONNELL, and U. NEISSER. The memory effect of visual perception of three-dimensional form. *Journal of Experimental Psychology,* 1953, 45, 360–368.

WANN, T. W. (Ed.) *Behaviorism and phenomenalogy.* Chicago: University of Chicago Press, 1964.

WARREN, R. M. A basis for judgments of sensory intensity. *American Journal of Psychology,* 1958, 71, 675–687.

WARREN, R. M. Are loudness judgments based on distance estimates? *Journal of the Acoustical Society of America,* 1963, 35, 613–614. (a)

WARREN, R. M. Reply to S. S. Stevens. *Journal of the Acoustical Society of America,* 1963, 35, 1663–1665. (b)

WARREN, R. M., E. A. SERSEN and E. B. PORRES. A basis for loudness-judgments. *American Journal of Psychology,* 1958, 71, 700–709.

WARREN, R. M., and R. P. WARREN. Basis for judgments of relative brightness. *Journal of the Optical Society of America,* 1958, 48, 445–450.

WARREN, R. M., and R. P. WARREN. A critique of S. S. Stevens' "New Psychophysics." *Perceptual and Motor Skills,* 1963, 16, 797–810.

ZENER, K., and M. GAFFRON. Perceptual experience: An analysis of its relations to the external world through internal processings. In S. Koch (Ed.), *Psychology: A study of a science.* vol. 4. New York: McGraw-Hill, 1962, pp. 515–618.

Applications of Information Theory and Decision Theory to Human Perception and Reaction*

D. E. BROADBENT
Cambridge University

Since the publication of Wiener's *Cybernetics*, the application to psychology of conceptual techniques derived from the physical sciences has proceeded apace. One of the most stimulating developments of this sort has been the use of information theory in the study of human perception and choice reaction, and the present paper is intended to outline some of the ways in which this has happened. As will be familiar to my readers, information theory originated from considerations of the behaviour of physical communication systems. It deals with a set or ensemble of possible messages which are to be transmitted through a given channel, and the ways in which the signals in that channel may be encoded so as to convey the messages as fast as possible with a given amount of noise (unwanted disturbance) in the channel, and a specified degree of error. It can be shown, for example, that the average time taken per message in such a situation is proportional to

$$\sum_{i=1}^{i=n} - p_i \log p_i$$

where p_i is the probability of the ith message in an ensemble of size n. This expres-

* Wiener, N., and J. P. Schade (Eds.) *Cybernetics of the Nervous System*. Amsterdam: Elsevier Publishing Co., 1965, pp. 309–320.

sion is known as the average amount of information per message.

From one point of view we can regard a human being, who is perceiving or reacting, as a channel in the foregoing sense. When one of a set of alternative stimuli strikes his senses, he perceives one of a set of possible percepts or makes one of a set of reactions. The novelty of such an approach lay in the treatment of the whole set as relevant even although only one occurs on any particular occasion. Looking back, it seems likely that psychologists of earlier days were too inclined to concentrate upon the relationship between the present stimulus and its representation in experience: and thus to be taken by surprise by phenomena of the sort which are to be considered here.

The Relationship of Information Theory to Perception

(A) THE PROBABILITY OF WORDS

If we present a listener with speech over a noisy telephone channel, he may or may not hear correctly. Naturally the probability of perceiving a particular word varies with the signal-noise ratio, but it is greater for a given word as part of a sentence than it is for the same word in isolation (Miller *et al.,* 1951; Stowe *et al.,* 1963). This is surprising if the stimulus itself is regarded as determining perception; but to the information theorist the presence of the earlier words in the sentence can be regarded as changing the size of the ensemble from which the particular word is chosen, or at least the relative probabilities of the members. Some words do not occur in some contexts, and thus the same physical events at the senses may serve to select the correct word from the small set consistent with the context, when they are insufficient to do so from the large set of the whole dictionary.

Although the effect of context is important in everyday life, it is difficult to assign a number to the increase in objective probability of a word provided by a context, unless extra assumptions are made. Thus it is hard to apply quantitative predictions from information theory. A more tractable type of experiment is to use a fixed and known vocabulary of words and study intelligibility as a function of size of vocabulary. Another is to relate intelligibility of isolated words to the probability of those words as determined by counting their frequency of occurrence in natural samples of the language. In either case intelligibility does appear to be related to the negative logarithm of the probability of the word, at least approximately (Howes, 1957; Miller *et al.,* 1951). To this extent therefore the application of informational analysis seems valid.

(B) ABSOLUTE JUDGMENT OF SIMPLE STIMULI

An even more simplified approach is to abandon noisy telephone systems, and to construct a fixed vocabulary of simple artificial signals such as pure tones differing only in loudness. The listener is then asked to identify each tone as it is presented. Such an experiment may be carried out for varying sizes of vocabulary, so that the information input to the man is

varied: and the amount of information transmitted through him in his responses is then measured. (See Garner (1962) for the calculation of transmitted information.) It is found that the amount transmitted increases with the input up to a certain level, and then remains roughly constant as the input increases. That is, the listener can tell correctly which intensity of tone has been presented until the number of tones in the vocabulary becomes too great, and then he makes the right number of errors to keep the calculated information transmission constant. The critical level, when only one dimension such as loudness, pitch, or length is involved, usually corresponds to an information input of roughly 2.5 bits per signal, that is, correct identification of about five or six signals. The limit does not depend very much upon the physical spacing of the stimuli along the dimension, however, so that we may have the paradox that stimuli which are widely different in, say, pitch may be confused if they form part of a large widely spaced vocabulary, while reasonably discriminable when at the extremes of a small closely packed vocabulary. (Legge and Summerfield, 1964). If more than one stimulus dimension is involved, the number of discriminable alternatives is large but not as large as would be expected if each dimension was completely independent.

These findings certainly suggest a mechanism which is limited not by sensory factors but by informational ones, which has in fact an upper bound to its capacity for holding information. There is probably room for more research in this area, since information input seems usually to have been varied by changing the size of vocabulary rather than the relative probabilities of items or the conditional probability of one item following another. Such experiments would be relevant to the exact nature of the limited capacity mechanism. Nevertheless, there is here a clear indication of the value of the informational approach.

(c) SIMULTANEOUS PERCEPTION OF TWO SIGNALS

The notion of a limited capacity in human perception leads on to the application of this concept to division of attention. Highly complex signals, chosen from a large ensemble, such as spoken sentences are not easily perceived when more than one is presented at the same time. Two probable or familiar stimuli, however, can be perceived even though they arrive simultaneously. Evidence on this point has been reviewed by Broadbent (1958), and it seems that, in some situations at least, the ability of a man to perceive and react to two simultaneous stimuli can be shown to depend upon the size of the ensemble from which each is drawn.

Thus the difficulty found by most people in 'attending to two things at once' can plausibly be described as due to the information input exceeding the capacity in an informational sense. A particularly striking recent experiment by Baddeley (1962) for example required the subject to call out items such as letters of the alphabet in a random sequence. At the same time he had to sort a pack of cards into various categories such as red/black, the four suits, etc. The informational content of the sequence of letters, that is, its degree of randomness, became less as the number of categories in the card-sorting was increased.

In this latter experiment it appeared again to be the logarithm of the number of categories which gave the simplest relationship: but in general this area of application has not lent itself to quantitative use of information theory, and rather serves as an example of the use of the general conceptual framework.

(d) PATTERN PERCEPTION AND CONTOURS

If we consider every possible combination of states of all the sense organs feeding the brain, the ensemble is clearly exceedingly large and it is a priori likely that further stages in the system will suffer from difficulties due to limited capacity. The experimental results already quoted make this likely too. In fact however the world is so constructed that knowledge of the state of one sense-organ restricts the probabilities as regards other sense-organs. In general, each point in our visual field is adjacent to other points receiving similar stimulation, and it is only at contours, between one mass of colour or shade and another, that the state of the adjacent sense-organs becomes unpredictable. Thus the scenes which pass before a man's eyes in real life are partially redundant, that is, they are drawn from a smaller ensemble than the structure of the senses would permit. The point is similar to the effect of context in speech.

A line of experiment tending to support this approach stems from Attneave (1954). He asked people to guess whether each square in turn in a grid drawn over a black and white picture, was black or white. Subjects were informed of their results, so that they knew the picture up to the point they were now guessing. In general they made most of their errors at the contours. Thus they do appear to be aware of the probability structure of such pictures. Their ability to show this depends upon the sequence of guesses being arranged so that the results of earlier trials do provide evidence concerning later ones. (Courtis and Green, 1963). This does not seem unreasonable from our own point of view.

Another form of redundancy in visual patterns is symmetry or repetition, in which one part of a contour may be predicted from knowledge of another part.

Experiments showing that patterns with these characteristics are readily perceived go far back in psychology (Vernon, 1952) and have been developed in more quantitative form within the informational framework (Fitts *et al.*, 1956).

In general terms therefore this approach also has been fruitful, but there have been limits to its quantitative application. In most cases it is not easy to assign any numbers to the ensemble from which a given pattern is chosen, any more than one can do so in the case of context. When this difficulty is overcome by constructing artificial sets of patterns as in the work of Fitts *et al.* (1956), fresh complications emerge. When they displayed a sample pattern and asked men to find the same pattern in a number of others, the task actually became more difficult if the patterns presented for choice were sampled from a smaller rather than a larger ensemble. This is probably because the incorrect patterns then had more features in common with the correct one, so that more observations were necessary in order to reject them. A rather different type of task gave results supporting this interpretation (Anderson and Leonard, 1958).

(E) GENERAL CONCLUSIONS ON PERCEPTION

From what has been said it will be clear that considerable and widespread effects on perception have been shown from variations in the ensemble of stimuli which might have been present, and from which the actual one must be distinguished. More detailed quantitative application has not as yet however been sufficient to provide very rigorous uses of the theorems of information theory, rather than its descriptive measures and concepts. A hopeful line for the future is the study of different types of redundancy or dependence of one variable upon another. An analysis which will render such studies easier is that of Garner (1962), who, in addition to a far more detailed review of experiments than has been possible here, presents a conceptual framework for distinguishing different degrees and kinds of structure or interdependence between variables.

Information Theory and Reaction Time

(A) LAG AND WORKING RATE

We should first distinguish two concepts which are rather different and which do not always seem to have been kept separate in work on reaction time. By *'working rate'* we will indicate the information conveyed by the average number of messages which can be received at one end of a channel in a fixed time. The maximum value of working rate is of course essentially the concept of capacity as usually applied to physical systems. We give it a different name here however to distinguish it from the time taken on average between the beginning of the insertion of each message into the channel, and the end of its emergence at the far end. This latter concept we will call *'lag'*. It is in fact the lag which has usually been measured in most psychological experiments on reaction time, although these are sometimes described as measuring the channel capacity of the human being.

To clarify the distinction, think of a highway which is known to be carrying 3,600 cars per hour. It does not therefore follow that each car takes one second to travel the length of the highway. Confusion between the two measures may however arise because both can be expressed in seconds per car. It is only the former measure, which we are calling working rate, that corresponds to capacity in the usual informational sense. A typical psychological experiment however, as in the classic work of Hick (1952) or Hyman (1955), is to present a stimulus chosen from a prescribed set of alternatives and to measure the time elapsing before an appropriate response occurs. This is, in our present terms, a measure of lag. Even if we measure, as did Crossman (1955), the overall speed with which a man can sort a pack of cards by looking at each and placing it in an appropriate pile, the time taken is an index of the average lag between observing each card and placing it, so long as the subject is unable to see one card until he has dealt with the previous one.

Such measurements do show that the lag is linearly related to the information per response, whether that information is varied by changing the size of the ensemble of responses, changing the relative probability of demanding one response rather than another, changing the probability of sequences of responses, or changing the proportion of errors made by the subject. Where the time of arrival of the stimulus is certain, as in Crossman's experiment, the reaction time $= K \log n$, where n is the number of equiprobable alternative reactions and K is a constant. Where the time of arrival of the stimulus is uncertain, this relationship is not quite adequate: Hick (1952) suggested $K \log (n + 1)$, on the grounds that inaction is an extra alternative, and Welford (1960), in a substantial review, argues for this relationship. Possibly more investigators have preferred the alternative $k + K \log n$, where k is another constant representing those components of reaction time which are unaffected by response information. Such perhaps might be conduction times in nerves.

Whatever the best exact formulation, the uniformity of the relationship over a number of ways of varying information is striking, and tempts one to suggest that we are measuring an inherent limit to human performance due to the capacity of the nervous system. On this view, K would be an inverse measure of this capacity, and Welford (1960) follows Crossman in

assigning a value of 5–8 bits/sec to this value on the basis of a number of experiments. Such a view might be justified even although the measurements are of lag rather than working rate, because the lag might be supposed to increase with the duration of the coded signal sent down the channel, even though the lag also continued a fixed component. The duration of the coded signal would be related to capacity. In terms of our highway analogy, the time taken for a certain number of cars to pass completely through the highway (from the first entering to the last leaving) is made up of a fixed time taken by one car plus a time which varies directly with the number of cars in the group and inversely with the working rate of the highway.

If lag is an indirect measure of capacity, we should nevertheless expect working rate to be a direct measure. The type of experiment needed to show this is one in which stimuli are presented at varying speeds and the information per sec in the responses measured and compared with that in the stimuli. Since a stimulus may arrive before the response to the preceding stimulus has been made, any fixed time lag between stimulus and response should be unimportant and we might expect the information output to rise as the input is increased, until the maximum output is reached at the capacity of the system. This however does not appear to be the case. In the experiments of Alluisi et al. (1957), using stimuli drawn from ensembles of various sizes, the main limit on performance appeared to be simply the number of stimuli delivered per sec rather than the amount of information conveyed by them. For a constant rate of presentation of information in bits per sec, there was a higher rate of transmission through the man if the stimuli were drawn from a large ensemble and presented slowly rather than from a small ensemble and presented rapidly. Broadly similar results were found by

Klemmer and Muller and by Riesz and Deininger (quoted by Garner, 1962, p. 92). More such studies of working rate, rather than lag, are probably needed: especially using changes in the information per stimulus produced by means other than changes in ensemble size. Nevertheless it seems clear that a simple interpretation of changes in lag with stimulus information, as measuring the capacity of the system, cannot be adequate. Human beings must be limited in some other fashion independent of information, which restricts the number of separate actions per sec to two or three. The literature on the psychological refractory period, reviewed by Broadbent (1958, pp. 268–281) is relevant here.

(B) COMPATIBILITY AND DISCRIMINABILITY

One cannot of course predict the reaction time to a stimulus purely from the probability of that stimulus. Two very important variables are the physical difference between the stimulus and each of the other stimuli which may appear in the situation; and the ease or naturalness of the response which is appropriate to that stimulus. The former problem is that of "discriminability", and the latter of "compatibility".

Discriminability has been studied by a number of investigators from Crossman (1955) to Shallice and Vickers (1964). A particularly comprehensive review is by Welford (1960). It is universally agreed that reaction time, or lag, increases as the various stimuli in a set are made more similar to one another and that the changes are greater when the stimuli become more nearly equal. For a pair of stimuli, the most linear relationship is probably found by plotting response time against the inverse of the logarithm of the ratio of the stimuli. This may be regarded as a modern version of the Weber-Fechner Law, according to which the magnitude of a

sensation is a logarithmic function of its physical magnitude. It is interesting that, as yet, there appears to have been little exploration of the implications for reaction time of the Power Law advocated by Stevens (1957). On this view, sensation is an exponential function of physical magnitude. The two laws can be inter-related in various ways (Luce, 1959; Treisman, 1964), but it might nevertheless be possible to improve the prediction of reaction time by taking account of this development. It is clear, however, that attempts to relate reaction time to the difference between two stimuli expressed in informational terms have not, as yet, been as successful as the approach through magnitude of sensation.

The problem of compatibility is even less easy to handle in informational terms. Fitts and his co-workers (Fitts and Seeger, 1953; Fitts and Deininger, 1954) showed that faster reactions were obtained with natural combinations of stimuli and responses; if the left of two buttons is appropriate to the left of two lights, this is an easier task than the right button being appropriate to the left light. Later work has shown however that this advantage is not a constant: it increases for stimuli conveying more information. Thus prolonged practice or an exceptionally natural relationship between stimulus and response may make the usual dependence of reaction time on stimulus information disappear (Mowbray and Rhoades, 1959; Leonard, 1959). Certainly the value of K in the function $k + K \log n$ is reduced by increases in compatibility (Fitts et al., 1963; Broadbent and Gregory, 1965). Thus low compatibility may be compared to noise in the channel, requiring a more lengthy code and reducing the capacity. If K can indeed be reduced to zero, as some experiments show, this would mean that the capacity was now infinite; but as has previously been indicated, there are difficulties in accepting inferences from lag to capacity in any case, and we must therefore regard these experiments as additional evidence against the applicability of straight-forward theorems from information theory to data derived from lags.

(c) GENERAL CONCLUSIONS ON REACTION TIME

As in the case of perception, it is quite clear that marked effects on behaviour have been shown in reaction time experiments when the ensemble of possible stimuli has been varied. Furthermore, in this case quantitative relationships have been applied to a greater extent than in perception, and have been quite successful. When pressed to details, however, certain problems arise: performance seems to be limited by a rate of making successive responses independent of the information they convey, by difficulties of discriminating stimuli which are not so far reducible to informational terms, and by the particular mapping of stimuli onto responses which is employed in each experiment.

The Rise of Decision Theory

(a) THE DETECTION OF SIGNAL AS OPPOSED TO NON-SIGNAL

Since 1954 there has gradually developed another approach to the problems of perception and reaction, which is based primarily upon the analysis of rational decisions in statistical situations rather than upon information theory as originally interpreted. The usual point of origin is taken as the paper of Tanner and Swets (1954) on the detection of simple signals. They contended that a man who was watching or listening for a signal might be regarded as having within him a randomly varying process whose average value was changed by the occurrence of a signal, but which would still vary over a range which might overlap the range of its variation in the absence of a signal. Detection would

occur whenever the process exceeded some critical level, whose value was dependent upon the probability of a signal and the rewards or punishments to be expected for the various possible correct and incorrect decisions.

Such a theory places great emphasis on the occurrence of false detections, which are regarded as reflecting essential features of the process rather than the result of superimposed guessing or random events unconnected with detection. The relationship between correct and incorrect detections should, on the Tanner and Swets theory, be quite different from that expected on traditional approaches. In particular, at low rates of false detection, changes in that rate should result in very large changes in the frequency of correct detection. Results supporting this prediction were reported by Tanner and Swets (1954) and in general later work has supported the prediction (Green, 1960). It is particularly well-supported for the observation of signals under conditions resembling real-life tasks of monitoring or inspection work (Broadbent and Gregory, 1963). Possibly experiments under very sensitively controlled conditions may reveal effects of quantal discontinuities in the sensitivity of the senses (Norman, 1963), but even in such cases it is clear that the rate of reporting signals for a given sensory event does depend upon the probabilities and values of the situation.

In general, the more probable a signal is, the more likely are detections both true and false. Equally, the greater the gain from correct detections compared with the loss from false ones, the more detections occur. It is not quite clear however, that the actual performance of such human beings conforms to any suggested decision rule. Approximately, it seems to follow the performance that would arise from a strategy of maximising the average expected gain over a long series of trials (Green, 1960). There are however sizable remaining deviations from that prediction: people do not detect as many signals as they should when signals are probable, and they detect more than they should when signals are rare.

(B) CHOICE BETWEEN NUMEROUS ALTERNATIVE DETECTIONS

An extension of Tanner and Swets' analysis covers the situation in which there are several alternative signals of which the correct one has to be identified. In this case it may be supposed that each of the alternatives has its own randomly varying process within the man, but only for the correct alternative is the average value of the process shifted. If a sample is taken from each of the processes, the largest value found will probably be from the correct alternative. The larger the number of alternatives, the lower the probability of a correct answer from such a test (Swets, 1959).

This kind of analysis has usually been applied to experiments in which simple signals such as pure tones have been used. In such researches, the alternatives have been, for example, two closely successive time intervals, one of which contains a signal while the other does not. The subject is asked to identify which interval contains the signal. Such a technique is known to give more stable and reproducible results than the 'Yes or No' type of situation considered in the last section. Analysis of both situations by the model so far discussed gives much the same value in both cases for the shift, in the internal process, produced by a signal. It is the changes in the critical value required for a report of 'Yes' which produce the differences between different experiments using the 'Yes–No' method (Swets, 1959).

If changes in the number of alternatives are predicted to give changes in the number of correct reports, it is clear that this kind of model has some possible connection with the effects of vocabulary size on

perception, with which we began this paper. An analysis of a number of experiments in vocabulary size shows, that the effect of changes in vocabulary is indeed of approximately the form to be expected from the statistical decision model (Green and Birdsall, 1958). It is more difficult to perform an analysis in which one varies the probabilities of some items in a fixed vocabulary. A technique for doing this has however been developed by Luce (1959), using axioms which are rather different from those of Tanner and Swets but which normally lead to closely similar mathematical prediction. It will be interesting to see experimental data analysed in this way.

In general one would expect the number of detections of highly probable signals to be large compared with those of improbable signals, just as one would on the older informational analysis and as we have seen to be empirically the case. An interesting feature of the analysis based on decision or choice is that we would expect the errors to be predominantly choices of probable rather than improbable events: thus in listening to words over a noisy channel the incorrect perceptions should predominantly take the form of frequent rather than infrequent words. The proportion of common words amongst the errors is in fact related in a systematic way to the signal–noise ratio (Pollack, 1962).

(C) REACTION TIME IN CHOICE SITUATIONS

If a single sample of evidence in a multiple-choice situation, such as those considered in the last section, gives an undesirably high probability of error, a further series of samples will reduce that error. Since as already indicated, a larger ensemble gives a higher error probability, more samples will be needed for a fixed level of accuracy when the ensemble is large. By regarding the reaction time as spent in taking a series of samples, it is possible to produce hypothetical predictions about the change in reaction time with stimulus probability. Stone (1960) showed that the predicted relationship was in fact that reaction time will increase roughly with the logarithm of the size of the response ensemble. At the same time the rate of increase of reaction time depends upon the unreliability of the evidence available in each sample of evidence; if the probability of error is low even with few samples, the reaction time will not increase much as the response ensemble increases. Provided therefore that we regard conditions such as low compatibility as decreasing the reliability of the evidence in favour of any one response, this theory provides a way of explaining the changes in K with compatibility which are found in practice and have already been described.

Stone developed the relationship of reaction time to ensemble size only for the case of a fixed series of samples, the number being decided in advance to give a desired level of error. Such a model is unlikely to be true in this form, because of the fact already mentioned that improbable signals, when they do occur, gives responses that are slower than those to probable signals. If the number of samples were fixed in advance, this would not be so. An alternative model was suggested by Stone and developed by Laming (1962), in which each sample is followed by a decision either to react or to take a further sample. Thus the process of sampling continues until the evidence points, with a prescribed degree of confidence, to one reaction as correct. This will take longer for less probable reactions.

An interesting feature of such a model is that the time taken by a response should depend upon the nature of the response and not upon the stimulus which is objectively present. Thus if a man makes a very common reaction correctly to stimulus A and incorrectly to B, the reaction time should be the same. If on the other hand he makes two different reactions to the probable stimulus A, one correct and one both incorrect and improbable the two reaction times will be different. Broadly speaking, though not exactly, this prediction is verified. It is also predicted from the model, and found to be the case, that errors are predominantly of the form that probable responses occur to improbable stimuli rather than the reverse: so that the average reaction time for errors may well be faster than that for correct responses when one ignores the nature of the errors.

Conclusions

It will be clear from the last section that the introduction of statistical decision theory has allowed us to overcome certain difficulties in the application of information theory to perception and reaction. In particular, it has allowed a more quantitative approach to perceptual problems, and has provided a way round the difficulty of incorporating the effects of compatibility and similar variables into the analysis of reaction times. The two major advances of technique which it has entailed are the study of errors as an inherent part of the process under investigation, and the provision of a place for values and pay-offs. Both of these innovations are clearly justified by results, and the older-style analyses of information which paid little attention to them are thereby superseded.

At the same time this development should be regarded as a sophistication of the approach to human performance through information theory, and not as a discarding of that approach. The emphasis is still upon the man's task as a discrimination between different possible states of his environment, and upon probability as a major variable in deciding the outcome of that discrimination. Indeed, the battle for these causes has been won and no future approach to human performance can neglect them. In the general sense therefore the use of information theory has produced a revolution in psychological thought whose full consequences have not yet been digested; although experiment has disproved naive ideas of a simple representation of the nervous system as a single channel needing no further analysis.

Summary

Experimental work is reviewed on the efficiency of perception of stimuli conveying various amounts of information. Broadly speaking, the nature of the ensemble from which the particular stimulus is drawn has been proved beyond doubt to be an important variable; but quantitative applications of information theory have been less successful. Similarly, experiments on reaction time have established that time often varies with the amount of information being transmitted; in this area numerical predictions have been more successful but there are nevertheless some discrepancies and difficulties. A more recent development has been the application of decision theory as a model for human performance; and this, by emphasising the importance of errors in response, and by providing a place for rewards and losses, seems to be a hopeful line for further advance.

References

ALLUISI, E. A., P. F. MULLER, and P. M. FITTS. (1957): An information analysis of verbal and motor responses in a forced-paced serial task. *J. exp. Psychol.*, 53, 153–158.

ANDERSON, N. S., and J. A. LEONARD. (1958); The recognition naming and reconstruction of visual figures as a function of contour redundancy. *J. exp. Psychol.*, 56, 262–270.

ATTNEAVE, F., (1954); Some informational aspects of visual perception. *Psychol. Rev.*, 61, 183–193.

BADDELEY, A. D., (1962); *The Coding of Information*. Ph. D. Thesis, University of Cambridge.

BROADBENT, D. E., (1958); *Perception and Communication*. London. Pergamon Press.

BROADBENT, D. E., and M. GREGORY. (1963); Vigilance considered as a statistical decision. *Brit. J. Psychol.*, 54, 309–323.

BROADBENT, D. E., and M. GREGORY. (1965); On the interaction of S-R compatibility with other variables affecting reaction time. *Brit. J. Psychol.*, in press.

COURTIS, M., and R. T. GREEN. (1963); Information theory and figure perception: the metaphor that failed. *Bull. Brit. Psychol. Soc.*, 16, 4A (Abstract).

CROSSMAN, E. R. F. W., (1953); Entropy and choice time: the effect of frequency unbalance on choice response. *Quart. J. exp. Psychol.*, 5, 41–51.

CROSSMAN, E. R. F. W., (1955); The measurement of discriminability. *Quart. J. exp. Psychol.*, 7, 176–195.

FITTS, P. M., and R. L. DEININGER. (1954); S-R compatibility: correspondences among paired elements within stimulus and response codes. *J. exp. Psychol.*, 48, 438–492.

FITTS, P. M., J. R. PETERSON, and G. WOLPE. (1963); Cognitive aspects of information processing: II. Adjustments to stimulus redundancy. *J. exp. Psychol.*, 65, 507–514.

FITTS, P. M., and C. M. SEEGER. (1953); S-R compatibility: spatial characteristics of stimulus and response codes. *J. exp. Psychol.*, 46, 199–210.

FITTS, P. M., M. WEINSTEIN, M. RAPPAPORT, N. ANDERSON, and J. A. LEONARD. (1956); Stimulus correlates of visual pattern recognition. *J. exp. Psychol.*, 51, 1–11.

GARNER, W. R., (1962); *Uncertainty and Structure as Psychological Concepts*. London, Wiley.

GREEN, D. M., (1960); Psychoacoustics and detection theory. *J. acoust. Soc. Amer.*, 32, 1189–1202.

GREEN, D. M. and T. H. BIRDSALL. (1958); The effect of vocabulary size on articulation score. University of Michigan Electronics Defense Group. Technical Report No. 81.

HICK, W. E., (1952); On the rate of gain of information. *Quart. J. exp. Psychol.*, 4, 11–26.

HOWES, D., (1957); On the relation between the intelligibility and frequency of occurrence of English words. *J. acoust. Soc. Amer.*, 29, 296–305.

HYMAN, R., (1955); Stimulus information as a determinant of reaction time. *J. exp. Psychol.*, 45, 188–196.

LAMING, D. R. J., (1962); A statistical test of a prediction from information theory in a card-sorting situation. *Quart. J. exp. Psychol.*, 14, 38–48.

LEGGE, C. D., and A. SUMMERFIELD. (1964); in *Readings in Psychology*. J. M. Cohen, (Ed.). London. Allen and Unwin.

LEONARD, J. A., (1959); Tactual choice reactions. *Quart. J. exp. Psychol.*, 11, 76–83.

LUCE, R. D., (1959); *Individual Choice Behavior*. New York. John Wiley and Sons.

MILLER, G. A., G. A. HEISE, and W. LICH-TEN. (1951); The intelligibility of speech as a function of the context of the test materials. *J. exp. Psychol.*, 41, 329–335.

MOWBRAY, G. H., and M. V. RHOADES. (1959); On the reduction of choice reaction time with practice. *Quart. J. exp. Psychol.*, 12, 193–202.

NORMAN, D. A., (1963); Sensory thresholds and response bias. *J. acoust. Soc. Amer.*, 35, 1432–1441.

POLLACK, I., (1962); Incorrect responses to unknown messages restricted in word frequency. *Language and Speech*, 5, 125–127.

SHALLICE, T., and D. VICKERS. (1964); Theories and experiments on discrimination times. *Ergonomics*, 7, 37–50.

STEVENS, S. S., (1957); On the psycho-physical law. *Psychol. Rev.*, 64, 153–181.

STONE, M., (1960); Models for choice reaction time. *Psychometrika*, 25, 251–260.

STOWE, A. N., W. P. HARRIS, and D. B. HAMPTON. (1963); Signal and context components of word-recognition behaviour. *J. acoust. Soc. Amer.*, 35, 639–644.

SWETS, J., (1959); Indices of signal detectability obtained with various psycho-physical procedures. *J. acoust. Soc. Amer.*, 31, 511–513.

TANNER, W. P., and J. SWETS. (1954); A decision-making theory of visual detection. *Psychol. Rev.*, 61, 401–409.

TREISMAN, M., (1964); Sensory scaling and the psycho-physical law. *Quart. J. exp. Psychol.*, 16, 11–22.

VERNON, M. D., (1952); *A Further Study of Visual Perception*. Cambridge University Press.

WELFORD, A. T., (1960); The measurement of sensory-motor performance: Survey and reappraisal of twelve years progress. *Ergonomics*, 3, 189–229.

*A Theoretico-Historical Review of the Threshold Concept**

JOHN. F. CORSO

The Pennsylvania State University

This paper traces the concept of threshold from its classical beginnings and shows the relation of the concept to selected issues in contemporary psychology. Emphasis is placed on three main problems: the designation of the origin point on a psychological continuum; the interpretation of the sensory threshold as an intervening variable and the issue of sensory continuity-noncontinuity; and the specification of the response threshold as a dependent variable of behavior, rather than an index of organismic sensitivity. Reference is made to adaptation level theory and the theory of signal detection as possible approaches to the development of a complete psychophysics which does not start from the concept of threshold.

A few years ago, a symposium was sponsored by the American Psychological Association (Chicago, 1960) to honor Fechner (1860) for his monumental work and

* *Psychological Bulletin*, 1963, vol. 60, no. 4, pp. 356–370. The first draft of this paper was presented originally at the second annual meeting of the Psychonomic Society, Columbia University, New York City, September 2, 1961.

to celebrate the centennial anniversary of the birth of psychophysics. At the same time, however, some newer concepts were advanced to supplant those originally proposed by Fechner. One of these involved a revision of his logarithmic psychophysical law (Stevens, 1961a) and another raised a question concerning the existence of sensory thresholds (Swets, 1961). The purpose of the present paper is to provide a theoretico-historical review of the threshold concept as it relates to these and other selected problems in psychology.

The attempt of this paper is not to derive a new or revised version of the threshold concept, nor to abandon it, but to analyze the manner in which this concept has been used in the past and present history of psychology. It is believed that by reviewing the literature to ascertain the various meanings of the term, the issue of threshold should become clearer, thereby forestalling some irrelevant arguments which might otherwise be generated.

The Problem of Establishing the Beginning Point of Sensation

Although the doctrine of "degrees of consciousness," and of the "unconscious," can be traced as early as 1714 to Leibnitz (1890), the term "threshold" was introduced into psychology by Herbart (1824)[1] who defined the "threshold of consciousness" as that "boundary which an idea appears to cross as it passes from the totally inhibited state into some (any) degree of actual ideation." The general notion was advanced by Herbart that intensive ideas could be made to disappear below the threshold of consciousness by a process of inhibition. This could occur, however, in Herbart's formulation only to the weakest of three ideas of unequal strength. Given two simultaneous ideas of unequal strength, neither would be able to suppress the other below the threshold, or limen. While Herbart did not attempt to support his imaginary mechanics of ideas with experimental data, he proposed an equation for determining the rise time of ideas

which clearly anticipated the problem of the psychophysical measurement of sensation.

The Herbartian tradition was continued by Lotze (1852) but it remained for Fechner (1860) to establish the quantitative meaning of the term threshold by using it in his measurement formula. Fechner's major concern was the problem of ascertaining the functional relation between two series of phenomena (mind and body) and, in particular, to establish the law which would describe the manner in which the intensity of "mental" activity varied with changes in the intensity of its underlying physical activity. He approached the problem by establishing a metric principle of sensitivity in which sensitivity was related to organic irritability or excitability, i.e., the organism's capacity to respond to stimulation. Fechner reasoned that sensation (a mental magnitude) could not be measured directly and, therefore, had to be approached indirectly by way of sensitivity. In "measuring sensitivity," he distinguished between (a) absolute sensitivity, or the inverse of the stimulus magnitude sufficient to give rise to a particular sensation; and (b) differential sensitivity. Differential sensitivity was expressed in either of two ways: as simple or absolute differential sensitivity, by noting the inverse value of the absolute difference between two simuli which could arouse two (just noticeably) different sensations; or as comparative or relative differential sensitivity, by noting the inverse value of the ratio of these same two stimulus magnitudes.

From these fundamental psychophysical metrics and a few simplifying assumptions, Fechner proceeded to derive his measurement formula: $\gamma = K (\log \beta - \log b)$, in which γ is the magnitude of the sensation, K is a constant, β is the magnitude of the stimulus, and b is the absolute threshold value of the stimulus. Fechner believed that the sensation γ disappeared at the threshold value of the stimulus, i.e., when $\beta = b$, and that each sensation "is

---

[1] The term *Schwelle* (threshold) appears to occur initially in Herbart's *Psychologic Bemerkungen zur Tonlehre* published in 1811 and reprinted in 1889 (see Herbart, 1889). The *Psychologie* (Herbart, 1824), however, presents the threshold concept in detail and explains the methods of calculation.

built up (in equal increments) from the zero point of its existence." The issue at this time does not concern the validity of Fechner's law, but centers around the problem of the "zero-point"—the problem of establishing the beginning point of sensation.

Fechner was well aware of the difficulties present in measuring the absolute threshold (stimulus limen) and developed elaborate psychophysical methods for establishing the limen in statistical terms. The absolute threshold is now usually defined as "that low stimulus quantity that arouses a response 50 per cent of the time" (Guilford, 1954). This means, however, that stimulus values *lower* than the absolute threshold will also be able to arouse reportable responses; these will occur less than half the time but, nevertheless, a *measurable* percentage of the time. Hence, what value of the stimulus should be designated as corresponding to the beginning point of sensation? For Fechner, the answer was the absolute threshold; at the liminal value of the stimulus, sensation vanished. In this approach the threshold is defined arbitrarily in statistical terms; consequently, the problem which arises is that any change in the criterion percentage of response will change the zero point of the postulated psychological continuum in relation to the underlying physical continuum.

This problem has plagued contemporary psychologists, particularly those involved in scaling sensory magnitudes. For example, Steven (1961a) has proposed a psychophysical power function to replace Fechner's logarithmic relation between stimulus magnitude and sensation. The general form of the power law is $\Psi = K (\Phi - \Phi_0)^n$, where Ψ is subjective magnitude, Φ is stimulus magnitude, K is a constant, n is an experimentally determined exponent for a given perceptual continuum, and Φ_0 is the "effective threshold." Supposedly, Φ_0 is some finite stimulus magnitude which denotes the beginning point for the related scale of sensory magnitude; but, unfortunately, the meaning of Φ_0 ("effective threshold") has not as yet been given in terms of experimental operations. It would appear, however, that the procedure for establishing the value for Φ_0 should be related in some manner to one of the methods available for determining the conventional absolute threshold, with perhaps an adjustment of the criterion percentage to a value below 50%. Thus, as in Fechner's case, the sensation Ψ would reduce to zero at the "threshold" value of the stimulus, i.e., when $\Phi = \Phi_0$, and the beginning point of sensation would again be only an approximation.

As an additional point on Φ_0, it should be noted that for stimulus values well above the absolute threshold, the effect of small changes in Φ_0 will not significantly alter the values of the power function; however, the effect will be considerably more pronounced as the stimuli become smaller and approach Φ_0 in magnitude. The importance of specifying an empirically-derived value for Φ_0 is that it permits a more valid test of the "power law" hypothesis. It does *not* appear justifiable in attempting to test the hypothesis to "adjust" the value of Φ_0 to that "constant value whose subtraction from the stimulus values succeeds in rectifying the log-log plot of the magnitude function" (Stevens, 1961b). Psychophysical laws are matters of fact, not expediency.

Psychophysicists have yet to provide an adequate description of the events which occur on the assumed sensory continuum as the physical stimulus proceeds from zero to some particular value which produces the criterion percentage of responses; yet, the issue is clear. A distinction must be made between the zero point of sensation which represents the starting point for a given psychological dimension in accordance with some psychophysical law and the arbitrary beginning point of sensation conventionally defined by the absolute threshold. Barrell (1900) was aware of this problem and indicated that it would be desirable, if possible, "to bridge over the hiatus by a (psychophysical) formula which (would) extend down to the origin."

Several attempts in this direction have recently been made. Michels and Helson (1949) have proposed a restatement of Fechner's law which avoids the difficulties inherent in the specification of a value for Fechner's b and Stevens' Φ_0. In this formulation $S = K \log (R/A)$, where S is the magnitude of the sensation evoked by the stimulus R, K is a constant, and A is the adaptation level of the observer as determined in a given session by prior experience and other organismic factors, contextual stimuli, and experimental stimuli. It should be noted that while A is a constant in this formulation, it is derived "from the actual conditions of observation and varies with series stimuli, backgrounds, standards or anchors, etc." to which the subject is exposed in a given setting. This is probably the relativistic notion to which Stevens alludes in his term effective threshold. In this case, however, the adaptation level prevailing in a given experiment is not arbitrarily "adjusted," but can be determined from several experimental and computational operations. Another favorable consequence of the Michels and Helson interpretation of Fechner's law is that the problem of "negative" sensations is avoided; according to adaptation level theory, stimuli above the adaptation level arouse one kind of response, stimuli near the adaptation level evoke indifferent responses, and stimuli below the adaptation level elicit opposite types of response. Since the adaptation level is approximated as the weighted logarithmic mean of all stimuli affecting the organism at a given moment, the judgment of any stimulus is relative to (and depends upon) the adaptation level rather than the absolute threshold which is fixed for a given set of conditions. The developments of adaptation level theory (Helson,

1959) cover such a wide range of behavioral phenomena (sensory, psychophysical, social, cognitive, learning, and clinical) that a significant unifying principle seems to have been uncovered which can bridge the compartmentalization of problems so characteristic of contemporary psychology.

Ekman (1959), exploring the tenability of a psychophysical power function for various continua, proposed the form $S = c (R + a)^n$, where S is the magnitude of the sensation evoked by the stimulus R, c is a constant related to the unit of measurement, and a and n are constants to be experimentally determined. In an earlier statement of this function, $- R_0$ (the absolute threshold) was used in place of $+ a$; however, estimates based upon the treatment of fractionation data repeatedly yielded *negative* values for R_0. This destroyed the interpretation of R_0 as the absolute threshold. Consequently, the symbol R_0 was replaced by the arbitrary symbol a which is expected to be positive in most experiments. The point to be noted for purposes of this paper is that the subjective magnitude aroused by an external stimulus R is not measured from the value produced by a *threshold* stimulus, but is measured from the value produced by "some stimulus" with magnitude a.

It appears, therefore, that some progress is being made on the problem of relating the beginning point (or a neutral point) of the psychological continuum to some value of the physical stimulus other than the conventional absolute threshold. The conventional absolute threshold for a given stimulus dimension and the zero point of sensation for a specific logarithmic or power function for that dimension are based on two different sets of operational procedures. This means that two different concepts may be involved and the empirical results obtained from the two procedures need not be identical. In fact, the present statement of the problem precludes such a possibility, since the sensation at the absolute threshold (as conventionally defined) must have acquired a certain finite magnitude, i.e., must have passed the zero point for that particular sensory continuum.

The Sensory Threshold as an Intervening Variable and the Continuity-Noncontinuity Issue

The classical notion of threshold (stimulus limen) as held by Fechner (1860) referred to a point, not exactly constant but nearly so, above which sensory differences could be detected and below which the differences vanished into the "unconscious." Fechner postulated the existence of four continua: a stimulus continuum (physical process), an excitation continuum (physiological process), a sensory continuum (mental process corresponding to the excitation in a sensory center), and a judgment continuum (report of the observed comparison). The threshold was irretrievably imbedded somewhere between the excitation and the sensory continua. The incoming stimulus did not find the brain (in its waking state) physiologically empty, but already occupied by some sort of neurological excitations. To be sensed, the incoming stimulus and its corresponding excitations had to be sufficiently larger than the neurological activity residually present.

Thus, a liminal stimulus or a liminal stimulus difference was one which lifted the sensation or the sense-difference over the threshold of consciousness. This "barrier" notion of threshold reflected the thinking of Herbart (1824). It was perpetuated by Titchener (1905) who held a somewhat similar view and proposed that the "frictional resistance" characterizing each sense organ had to be overcome before the application of a stimulus would produce a corresponding change in sensation. Licklider (1951) contended that "in the simplest conceptual neurology, the

stimulus threshold owes its existence to the effect of a small barrier . . . between successive stages in the neurol processes. . . ." In this classical view, the threshold has a direct sensory reference, hence the notion of sensory threshold. Stated in current terminology, the classical concept of threshold may be considered as an *intervening variable* referring to a postulated sensory continuum. The concept of adaptation level falls in this same category (Helson, 1959).

The notion of residual neural activity which underlies the classical concept of threshold has recently been revived. Ekman (1959) appealed to sensory noise resulting from spontaneous neural activity when he found that in psychophysical scaling S (subjective magnitude) was greater than zero even though no external stimulation was present. This suggested another form of the power function: $S = S_0 + R^n$, where S_0 is the basic perceptual noise to which is added the subjective magnitude produced by an external stimulus R. The idea of a basic level of organismic activity is present in Helson's (1947) hypothesis of adaptation level, in which adaptation level is considered to shift along a given stimulus continuum as a function of all past and present factors influencing behavior. The results of a considerable number of human and animal electroencephalographic studies tend to support the Fechnerian notion of residual neural activity. For example, Jasper (1936) has shown that significant afferent stimuli will produce changes in the electrical activity of the cortex depending upon the excitatory state of the cortex at the time of arrival of the stimulus. In a study of single neurons in three cerebral regions of the cat, Evarts, Bental, Behari, and Huttenlocher (1962) have demonstrated that there is a greater variance of spontaneous discharge rates during waking than during sleep. Thus, the assumption of neural "noise" which is found in the development of several psychophysical theories seems reasonable when viewed from a neuro-physiological standpoint.

Fechner's concept of threshold gave rise to what may currently be called the sensory continuity-noncontinuity issue. Does sensory excitation increase in a smooth and continuous manner or is there an abrupt step-like change from no sensation to sensation, or from sensation to a difference in sensation, as the value of the physical stimulus is increased continuously along some specified dimension? Fechner (1860), Lotze (1884), and others, held to the non-continuity notion which embraced the threshold concept; but Delboeuf (1883), Pierce and Jastrow (1885), Müller (1896), and others, denied the supposed fact of threshold. Jastrow (1888) claimed that the threshold was a misconception introduced by Fechner's Method of Just Observable Difference. He argued that the sensory continuum consisted of "a continuous series of intermediate degrees of clearness and (that) there (was) no point on the curve with characteristics peculiar to itself, no threshold in any true sense." Jastrow believed that sensation and stimulation each formed a continuum and that applying discrete notions to them would lead to hopeless confusion.

The numerous experimental studies which followed on problems of sensory discrimination soon made it evident that the threshold at least was not a rigidly fixed point or line. The same stimulus, even when applied in the same manner, was sensed more or less strongly by one observer than by another, and by the same observer at different times. Consequently, attempts were made to define the various sources of sensory variability and to establish the form of the mathematical distribution of errors in psychophysical judgments.

Through the work of Jastrow, Cattell, Urban, Fernberger, Thomson, George, and others, several sources of variance were isolated. These included such factors as the observer's attitude, fatigue, attention, in-terest, and practice. As Cattell (1893) stated:

> these sources of variation sufficiently account for the fact that the same sensation does not occur [to the same stimulus]. They are, indeed, so numerous and to a certain extent so independent, that they justify . . . the assumption . . . [that an error is composed of a very large number of comparatively small and independent errors], and the results of experiments show that the errors are in a general way distributed as required by the theory of probability (p. 287).

This is the underlying principle of the classical theory of sensory discrimination.

The beginnings of the classical theory can be traced to Müller (1878) who started from the notion of a non-Fechnerian threshold which was subjected to chance variations. Müller and his followers assumed that the appropriate mathematical expression for the probabilities of these variations was the Gaussian exponential law, i.e., the frequency of these variations was a function of their size. Urban (1907), relating the threshold to experimental data, emphasized the notion of the probability of judgment (smaller, equal, or greater) and called the mathematical expression which gave the probability as a function of the comparison stimulus the psychometric function of that judgment (Urban, 1910). The classical form of the function resembles the integral of the normal curve and is known as the phi function of gamma ($\Phi\gamma$-hypothesis) (Urban, 1907). A complete description of the manner in which the psychometric function is generated according to the classical theory of sensory discrimination can be found in a paper by Boring (1917).

In the issue of sensory continuity-noncontinuity, the psychometric function is of paramount importance, since the specific form of the function is assumed to reflect the "inner workings" of the discriminatory mechanism. Any deviation of the psychometric function from its classical sigmoidal form opens the way for a new hypothesis about sensory discrimination. Since rectilinear psychometric functions were obtained by Stevens, Morgan, and Volkmann (1941), the neural quantum theory of sensory discrimination was offered as an alternative to the classical theory. A detailed treatment of the derivation of the theory has been published by Corso (1956b).

The characteristics of the psychometric functions as predicted by the neural quantum theory are that: (*a*) the percentage of responses between 0 and 100% will be a linear function of the size of the stimulus increments; (*b*) the slope of this function will be inversely proportional to its intercept; and (*c*) the smallest stimulus increment which elicits a response 100% of the time will be twice the size of the largest increment which elicits a response 0% of the time, provided the observer has adopted a "2 quanta" criterion of judgment. Some of the technical difficulties which have been encountered in testing these predictions have already been described (Corso, 1956b). It should also be pointed out that the tenability of Prediction *b* will be affected by the particular method which is adopted for obtaining the judgments. Miller and Garner (1944) have shown that in the quantal method a random order of presentation of stimuli will extend the psychometric function, since the observer cannot stabilize his criterion of judgment and, consequently, fluctuates from 1 to 3 quanta. Likewise, in the case of the phi gamma hypothesis, the slope of the psychometric function will be affected by the particular variant of the constant methods which is adopted, either for obtaining the required judgments or for computing the measure of precision, *h* (Guilford, 1954). Barlow (1961), who suggests that rectilinear psychometric functions may be approximations to (or distortions of) ogival functions, has developed a hypothesis in which both the slope

of the psychometric function and the associated threshold value on the stimulus intensity scale are dependent upon the variability of the instantaneous values of threshold and the rate of false positive responses. It seems, therefore, that any conclusions regarding the tenability of the quantal or phi gamma hypothesis and any generalizations concerning the basic discriminatory ability of the human observer which are derived from the slope of the psychometric function must be tempered with caution.

The two theories, the classical and the neural quantum, reflect the present status of the issue which originated with Fechner-Jastrow. The classical theory holds that sensation is a continuous function of stimulus magnitude, while the quantum theory holds that sensation is a discontinuous function of stimulus magnitude. The classical theory is derived from the assumption that the threshold of the human organism varies somehow (perhaps due to physiological and/or psychological factors) in accordance with the normal law of error; the quantum theory is derived from the basic assumption that the functional neural processes which mediate sensory discrimination operate in a step-wise or all-or-none fashion, once the threshold of the neural quantum is crossed. While the present paper is not an attempt to resolve the classical theory-quantum theory controversy, it perhaps should be noted that a review of the experimental evidence on the quantum theory has lead to the conclusion that "unequivocal support of the . . . theory is, for the most part, lacking" (Corso, 1956b).

The position which is usually taken by the quantum theorists, when negative evidence is obtained with respect to the three predictions, is that a sufficient reduction in the "noise" of the organism, the equipment, or the environment has not been achieved by the experimenter. Thus, the quantal step-function has not been allowed to manifest itself in the action of the sensory system. Regrettably, the successful experimenters have not been able to specify in advance the manner in which "the noise in a discrimination process (can be reduced) to a level enough to reveal the 'grain' in the sensory continuum." Stevens (1961c) has indicated that

> those experiments that have been successful have seemed to involve a carefully contrived arrangement designed to make the observer's task as easy as possible, plus a fortunate selection of observers capable of maintaining an unwavering attention over extended periods of time (p. 808).

Any complete treatment of the sensory continuity-noncontinuity issue must ultimately include the concept of the absolute threshold, as well as that of the differential threshold. Quantum theorists have suggested, however, that since their model assumes a continuous fluctuation in the overall sensitivity of the organism, rectilinear psychometric functions should not be obtained for the absolute limen. Here, it is said sigmoidal functions should be evidenced which reflect the time distribution of the organism's over-all sensitivity. This view opposes the fact that some of the earliest experimental data from which quantal notions were advanced were those of Békésy (1936) dealing with the absolute threshold of hearing at low frequencies. Other experiments on absolute thresholds (De Cillis, 1944) have not produced quantal functions and, in a replication and extension of the Békésy (1936) study, Corso (1961) has shown that when methodological artifacts are eliminated, the threshold of audibility assumes its usual continuous form. The problem of obtaining quantal data in experiments on absolute thresholds remains a real and significant challenge to the quantum theorists.

While the concepts of absolute threshold, differential threshold and psycho-

physical functions have in the present paper been treated in a somewhat isolated manner for purposes of exposition, their independence may be more superficial than real. In a penetrating analysis, Ekman (1959) has shown that starting from the interpretation of a in his power function, a common theoretical framework can be worked out which embodies both absolute and differential sensitivity, as well as the psychophysical relation between stimulus magnitude and subjective magnitude. These relationships have been described by a single mathematical expression. At least in principle, the concept of absolute sensitivity can be considered to be a special case of differential sensitivity. As substantive concepts, the two can be treated essentially without distinction; whether the underlying physiological mechanism for sensory discrimination is a single unitary process, however, remains to be determined.

Organismic Sensitivity and the Response Threshold as a Dependent Variable of Behavior

Up to this point, the concepts of absolute and differential thresholds have been considered primarily with respect to the continunity-noncontinuity issue. It was suggested that from this view thresholds should be approached as intervening variables of behavior. Since their introduction into psychology, threshold measures have also been used to provide an index of organismic sensitivity, i.e., of the least amount of energy required for a stimulus to be just detectable, or of the difference required between two stimuli in order for the two to be perceived as just noticeably different (Goodfellow, 1934). In practice, given an empirical set of data in the form of a psychometric function, the stimulus value corresponding to a particular point on this curve, e.g., 50% or 75% depending on the particular experimental procedure, is taken as the threshold (Boring, 1917). As Dunlap (1912) stated, "fifty percent of discrimination is taken as the conventional 'threshold' "; but other criteria have also been used. Volkmann defined his measure of sensitivity as one-half the interval of uncertainty—the distance on the stimulus scale between the upper and lower limens (Fernberger, 1914. Jastrow (1888) rejected the threshold concept and adopted the "standard ratio" as his index, i.e., the ratio of two stimuli which elicited one error in every four judgments.

Regardless of the specific method adopted by various investigators for computing the threshold value, two characteristics of the threshold were universally present: (a) the threshold was based on a probability of response—for Hunter (1924), a language response; and (b) the probability criterion was adopted arbitrarily—for Johnson (1930), a "social criterion." These considerations led to numerous objections to the use of the threshold measure as an index of sensitivity (the two measures are inversely related). Thomson (1920) objected to Volkmann's index by suggesting that the interval of uncertainty depended entirely on

the subject's readiness to give the answer undecided. It measures therefore rather a moral characteristic than a physical sensitivity . . . (p. 301) [the threshold] can be varied . . . at [the subject's] whim; and will vary with his mood at the moment (p. 307).

George (1917), Boring (1920), Guilford (1927), and others, wrote on the effect of attitude as it influenced psycho-physical judgments; but Fernberger (1914) made it explicitly clear that

one cannot measure sensitivity in absolute terms; one can only say that a given sensitivity has been found to exist under certain given experimental conditions (p. 542).

Newhall (1928) took a similar position and noted

that the observed . . . threshold is a variable depending for its value upon an unknown number of external and internal factors (p. 46).

Fernberger (1930) wrote:

the old idea that we are measuring the sensitivity of a particular sense organ has been abandoned. We now recognize that we are measuring the sensitivity of the entire psychophysical organism—his sense organs, his concentration, his attitude, his acceptance and understanding of instructions, his degree of practice, and what not besides . . . (p. 111).

High, Glorig, and Nixon (1961) have been concerned with the same problem and have enumerated about two dozen subclasses of variables which affect the threshold; these are grouped under four major categories: physical, physiological, psychological, and methodological.

Considerable experimental evidence is now available which supports the contention that psychophysical judgments, on which threshold measures (and, hence, sensitivity) are based, are affected by a wide range of manipulable conditions. Some of these relate to the physical stimulus, such as rate of onset (Goodfellow, 1946) in which higher thresholds were obtained with increased time delays; some relate to the physiological state of the observer such as sleeplessness, although Goodhill and Tyler (1947) found that 100 hours of experimental insomnia had no effect on hearing acuity. Among the psychological factors, Senders and Sowards (1952) have found that subjects yield proportions of judgments in accordance with their expectations based upon their knowledge of the experimental situation. The significance of methodological factors has been demonstrated, among others, by Corso (1956a) who found that the method of limits and the method of adjustment produced different auditory thresholds for the same group of subjects tested under both methods. In another methodological study, Newman (1933) was forced to reject the differential threshold—just noticeable difference (jnd)—as a unit of measurement when he showed that two stimuli equal in psychological magnitude are not reached by the same number of jnd's from the stimulus limen. This conclusion was found to hold for both brightness in vision and loudness in audition. In the latter case, for example, two frequencies, 80 and 1,900 cycles per second, were judged to have a loudness level of 70 phons, but the 80-cycle tone was only 8.3 jnd's above the stimulus limen while the 1,900-cycle tone was 115.9 jnd's above the stimulus limen. It may be concluded, therefore, that the classical notions of absolute sensitivity are no longer tenable; human judgments are relative and depend upon a wide number of factors which may be operating within a given experimental situation at a given time.

This view leads away from notions of threshold as substantive concepts—do thresholds exist or do they not—toward notions of threshold as conceptual tools. In this approach, the threshold measure is seen as a way of organizing data to arrive at the solution of a particular problem. The definitive statement of Graham (1950) exemplifies this position. He proposes that a psychophysical function is a special case of the general equation: $R = f$ $(a,b,c,d, \ldots h, \ldots t, \ldots x,y,z,)$, where a, b, c, and d refer to specified aspects of the stimulus, n is the number of stimulus presentations, t is time, and x, y, z are specified as conditions of the organism. For Graham (1958) any psychophysical function may be expressed as $R = f$ (a) where all the variables of the general equation are constant, except R and a:

> Such a function is a stimulus-response relation that shows how a measure of response varies with a controlling stimulus variable. From such a relation it is possible to obtain a new datum, a value of the stimulus variable that corresponds to a given probability of

response occurrence—for example, the 50% value . . . by virtue of this quantity, it is possible to treat as a single datum the outcome embodied in a total psychophysical function, and so derive . . . perceptual functions . . . functions obtained from a sequence of experiments concerned with finding thresholds under many different conditions (pp. 67–68).

The importance of this revised orientation is that it indicates a movement away from the concept of threshold as an index of sensitivity. Instead, the attempt is to determine how a critical value of the stimulus (the *response* threshold) varies as a function of a controlling variable. Furthermore, whether or not a *sensory* threshold "exists," the response threshold is established by means of its operational definition. Consequently, it is not appropriate to speak of threshold *measurements;* observations are collected on the probability of correct (positive) responses and the threshold is specified in terms of its operational definition. The definition, of course, contains an arbitrary selection of the probability criterion. In contemporary psychophysics, then, the concept of threshold is response oriented and is a *dependent variable* of behavior, unlike the classical sensory concept with its intervening variable connotation.

The concept of a response threshold has found wide applicability in psychology in areas other than psychophysics. For example, Martin, Paul, and Welles (1915) compared reflex and sensory thresholds; Hull (1917) compared the fluctuations of threshold in the formation and retention of associations among the insane; Williams (1918) calculated the associative limen in certain memory experiments; Wells (1919) reported a series of experiments involving the threshold of "conscious" learning; Oberly (1928) compared the "attention span" limen for ungrouped digits and the "memory span" limen for grouped digits; Irwin (1932) investigated the thresholds for the perception of differences in facial expression; Miller (1939) discussed the limen of awareness in the problem of discrimination without awareness; Postman, Bruner, and McGinnies (1948) treated the duration threshold in tachistoscopic presentations as an index of selective perception; Kissen, Gottesfeld, and Dicks (1957) determined the inhibition and tachistoscopic thresholds for sexually charged words; and Corso (1959) studied changes in auditory thresholds as a function of age and sex. In each of these investigations, recourse was taken to the threshold notion defined in a particular manner in order to determine the responsiveness of the human organism under a given set of conditions. The general utility of the response threshold as a criterion measure of performance and the specific meaning which can be ascribed to the term by its operational definition suggest that the notion of response threshold should not be abandoned, regardless of the outcome of the sensory threshold issue.

Although the present paper is not concerned directly with problems of perceptual defense and related topics, it should nevertheless be pointed out that in dealing with response thresholds (as with other behavioral indices) the question of reliability of measurement cannot be ignored. Byrne and Holcomb (1962) have reported that the coefficient of internal consistency was .00 when the "split-half reliability was determined by dividing hostile words into odd and even groups and computing the differential threshold scores for these two groups compared to their matching neutral words." Thus, while there was independent agreement among judges in terms of stimulus material and scoring procedures, the resulting scores were unreliable. This suggests that in studies of perceptual defense, where the differential recognition threshold has served as the dependent variable, some of the inconsistencies among findings may be attributable to unknown reliability coefficients rather than to theoretical inadequacies.

One final point remains to be mentioned before closing this section of the paper. It relates to the Tresselt and Volkmann (1942) hypothesis that psychophysical judgments and conditioning can be explained by the same set of psychological principles. The point of contact between these two concepts lies in the stimulus generalization gradient; specifically, given a range of stimulus magnitudes on a particular dimension, the same judgment category (or response) will occur to a set of stimuli within that range, with a particular stimulus magnitude from this set being associated most frequently with that judgment (or response). Guilford (1954) has shown that starting with two overlapping stimulus generalization gradients corresponding to two categorical judgments, it is possible to determine a threshold value expressed in stimulus units. The threshold is taken as that stimulus magnitude at which the probability of occurrence of that stimulus is the same for each of the two judgment categories. Cartwright (1941) has shown, as expected from learning principles, that continued practice reduces the range of equivalent stimuli that are capable of eliciting particular responses and Johnson (1949) has demonstrated that the shift in threshold values which accompanies changes in the set of judged stimuli tends to describe a learning function. These and other related studies suggest that further efforts in this direction may result in a rapprochement of psychophysical theory and learning theory, at least for those portions of learning theory related to problems of discrimination.

An Approach to Psychophysics without a Threshold Concept

In the presentation of the sensory continuity-noncontinuity issue, reference was made to the problem of noise in the psychophysical situation. While the quantum theorists have been busy trying to reduce noise in discrimination experiments, the proponents of the theory of signal detection (Tanner, Swets and Green, 1956) have introduced noise so that at least that part of it external to the observer can be appropriately measured. In this approach, noise is always present and the observer is faced with the task of reaching a decision stating whether or not a signal was present during a specified time interval. Only two assumptions are made about sensory discrimination in the derivation of the theory: it varies continuously due to the ever-present noise in the sensory system, and it is considered to be a unidimensional variable insofar as it affects the observer's report. The relevance of the theory of signal detection to the problems under consideration in this paper is that the variables of the theory do not contain a reference to threshold (Licklider, 1959).

The theory of signal detection provides an interesting and important innovation in the area of sensory discrimination since it apparently provides a method which permits the separation of the observer's criterion of response and his organismic sensitivity (Tanner and Swets, 1954). These two measures are extracted from an analysis of the observer's operating characteristic curve. This curve, for different levels of response certainty, is simply a plot of the proportion of "yes" reports made when the signal is present against the proportion of yes reports made when noise alone is present. As the observer is induced by instructions to change his response criterion from one set of trials to another, the plotted proportions will trace a single curve running from 0 to 1.0 on both coordinates. The curve is characterized by a single parameter, d, which is the difference between the means of the signal-plus-noise and noise-alone distributions divided by the standard deviation of the noise distribution. This parameter, d, is the measure of sensitivity.

The slope of the operating-character-istic curve at any point is equal to the value of the likelihood-ratio criterion which produces that point. According to the theory, the observer knows the probability with which each possible "excitatory state" will occur during an observation interval when noise-alone is present and during the interval when signal-plus-noise is present. The observer supposedly bases his report on the ratio of these two quantities; this ratio is called the likelihood-ratio. Some critical value of the likelihood-ratio is established by the observer as his response criterion, depending upon his detection goal and other relevant situational parameters. The observer says "yes" (a signal was present) whenever the likelihood-ratio measured in a given observation interval exceeds the response criterion, and "no" (only noise was present) whenever the likelihood-ratio is less than the criterion. If the observer follows this rule, then the two independent measures, sensitivity and response criterion, can be derived from the fourfold stimulus-response matrix which results in a "yes-no" experiment. It has been found that the sensitivity measure remains relatively constant in vision (Swets, Tanner, and Birdsall, 1955) and in audition (Tanner et al., 1956) regardless of changes in the observer's attitude and changes in the experimental procedures.

The approach of signal detection theory appears to circumvent many of the problems which were mentioned earlier in this paper and which are inherent in a psychophysics developed along classical lines. The theory makes it possible to define a problem and to resolve it in a manner which does not rely on the threshold concept. In reviewing the experimental data from several types of psychophysical experiments, Swets (1961) concluded that:

> the existence of a sensory threshold has not been demonstrated (p. 176) [and that] there is now reason to believe that sensory

excitation varies continuously . . . an apparent cut in the continuum results simply from restricting the observer to two categories of response (p. 169).

This is essentially what Jastrow (1888) had contended. A similar view was taken by Urban (1930) who stated that:

the threshold [is] a superfluous hypothesis, in itself not more than a [mere] metaphysical expression . . . All the [psychophysical] formulae may be obtained without it . . . the notion of the threshold is not needed for the foundation of psychophysics (pp. 99–100).

The theory of signal detection certainly seems to point in that direction, as does adaptation level theory.

Summary

The major content of the present paper may be summarized briefly by indicating that:

1. The conventional notion of threshold is inadequate for locating the beginning point of sensation on a postulated sensory continuum.

2. The classical notion of threshold is sensory in nature and, as such, should be treated as an intervening variable; this notion of threshold is implicit in the sensory continuity-noncontinuity issue which finds its current expression in the unresolved quantal-phi gamma controversy.

3. The tendency in contemporary psychophysics is to consider the threshold in terms of a response continuum; this permits an operational definition of the term on a probability basis and provides a dependent variable of performance which has applicability in a wide variety of experimental situations.

4. The notions of sensory and response thresholds are separate and distinct; thus the issue of the existence or non-existence of sensory thresholds has no bearing on the status of response thresholds.

5. The indications are, however, that the theory of signal detection may well supplant the classical threshold measure with its own measures of sensitivity and response criterion, thereby fulfilling Urban's (1930) prophesy of a "psychophysics which does not start from the threshold hypothesis."

6. Consideration is given to adaptation level theory as an alternative approach which has the potential of bridging a wide range of psychological problems without recourse to the threshold concept.

References

BARLOW, H. B. Comments on neural quanta. In W. A. Rosenblith (Ed.), Sensory communication. New York: Wiley, 1961.

BARRELL, F. R. The relation of stimulus to sensation: A reply to Mr. Max Meyer's criticisms on Prof. C. Lloyd Morgan's paper. Amer. J. Psychol., 1900, 12, 135–139.

BÉKÉSY, G. v. Uber die Horschwelle und Fuhlgrenze langsamer sinusformiger Luftdruckschwankungen. Ann. Phys., Leipzig, 1936, 26, 554–566.

BORING, E. G. A chart of the psychometric function. Amer. J. Psychol., 1917, 28, 465–470.

BORING, E. G. The control of attitude in psychophysical experiments. Psychol. Rev., 1920, 27, 440–452.

BYRNE, D., and J. HOLCOMB. The reliability of a response measure: Differential recognition-threshold scores. Psychol. Bull., 1962, 59, 70–73.

CARTWRIGHT, D. C. Relation of decision time to the categories of response. Amer. J. Psychol., 1941, 54, 174–196.

CATTELL, J. M. On errors of observation. Amer. J. Psychol., 1893, 5, 285–293.

CORSO, J. F. Effects of testing methods on hearing thresholds. AMA Arch. Otolaryngol., 1956, 63, 78–91. (a)

CORSO, J. F. The neural quantum theory of sensory discrimination. Psychol. Bull., 1956, 53, 371–393. (b)

CORSO, J. F. Age and sex differences in pure-tone thresholds. J. Acoust. Soc. Amer., 1959 31, 498–507.

CORSO, J. F. The quantal hypothesis and the threshold of audibility. Amer. J. Psychol., 1961, 74, 191–204.

DECILLIS, O. E. Absolute thresholds for the perception of tactual movement. *Arch. Psychol.*, 1944, 294, 1–52.

DELBOEUF, J. R. L. *Examen critique de la loi psychophysique: Sa base et sa signification.* Paris, France: G. Baillière, 1883.

DUNLAP, K. Difference-sensibility for rate of discrete impressions. *Psychol. Rev.*, 1912, 19, 32–59.

EKMAN, G. Weber's law and related functions. *J. Psychol.*, 1959, 47, 343–352.

EVARTS, E. E., E. BENTAL, R. BEHARI, and P. R. HUTTENLOCHER. Spontaneous discharge of single neurons during sleep and waking. *Science*, 1962, 135, 726–728.

FECHNER, G. T. *Elemente der Psychophysik.* Leipzig, Germany: Breitkopf & Härtel, 1860.

FERNBERGER, S. W. The effect of the attitude of the subject upon the measure of sensitivity. *Amer. J. Psychol.*, 1914, 25, 538–543.

FERNBERGER, S. W. The use of equality judgments in psychophysical procedures. *Psychol. Rev.*, 1930, 37, 107–112.

GEORGE, S. S. Attitude in relation to the psychophysical judgment. *Amer. J. Psychol.*, 1917, 28, 1–37.

GOODFELLOW, L. D. An empirical comparison of audition, vision, and touch in discrimination of short intervals of time. *Amer. J. Psychol.*, 1934. 46, 243–258.

GOODFELLOW, L. D. Significant incidental factors in the measurement of auditory sensitivity. *J. gen. Psychol.*, 1946, 35, 33–41.

GOODHILL, V., and D. B. TYLER. Experimental insomnia and auditory acuity. *Arch. Otolaryngol.*, 1947, 46, 221–224.

GRAHAM, C. H. Behavior, perception, and the psychophysical methods. *Psychol. Rev.*, 1950, 57, 108–120.

GRAHAM, C. H. Sensation and perception in an objective psychology. *Psychol. Rev.*, 1958, 65, 65–76.

GUILFORD, J. P. Fluctuations of attention with weak visual stimuli. *Amer. J. Psychol.*, 1927, 38, 534–583.

GUILFORD, J. P. *Psychometric methods:* New York; McGraw-Hill, 1954.

HELSON, H. Adaptation-level as frame of reference for prediction of psychophysical data. *Amer. J. Psychol.*, 1947. 60, 1–29.

HELSON, H. Adaptation level theory. In S. Koch (Ed.), *Psychology: A study of a science.* vol. 1. *Sensory, perceptual and physiological formulations.* New York: McGraw-Hill, 1959, pp. 565–621.

HERBART, J. F. *Psychologie als Wissenschaft,*

neu gegrundet auf Erfahrung, Metaphysik, und Mathematik. Könisburg, Germany: Unzer, 1824.

HERBART, J. F. Schriften zur Psychologie. In G. Hartenstein (Ed.), *Sammtliche Werke.* vol. 7. Leipzig, Germany: L. Voss, 1889.

HIGH, W. S., A. GLORIG, and J. NIXON. Estimating the reliability of auditory threshold measurements. *J. aud. Res.*, 1961, 1, 247–262.

HULL, C. L. The formation and retention of associations among the insane. *Amer. J. Psychol.*, 1917, 28, 419–435.

HUNTER, W. S. The problem of consciousness. *Psychol. Rev.*, 1924, 31, 1–31.

IRWIN, F. W. Thresholds for the perception of difference in facial expression and its elements. *Amer. J. Psychol.*, 1932, 44, 1–17.

JASPER, H. H. Cortical excitatory state and synchronism in the control of bioelectric autonomous rhythms. *Cold Spr. Harb. Symp. Quant. Biol.*, 1936, 4, 320–338.

JASTROW, J. A critique of psycho-physic methods. *Amer. J. Psychol.*, 1888. 1, 271–309.

JOHNSON, D. M. Learning function for a change in the scale of judgment. *J. exp. Psychol.*, 1949, 39, 851–860.

JOHNSON, H. H. Some properties of Fechner's intensity of sensation. *Psychol. Rev.*, 1930, 37, 113–123.

KISSEN, B., H. GOTTESFELD, and R. DICKS. Inhibition and tachistoscopic thresholds for sexually charged words. *J. Psychol.*, 1957, 43, 333–339.

LEIBNITZ, G. W. *Principles de la nature et de la grâce.* (Orig. publ. 1714) [The philosophical works of Leibnitz.] (Trans. by G. M. Duncan) New Haven, Conn.: Tuttle, Morehouse, and Taylor, 1890.

LICKLIDER, J. C. R. Basic correlates of the auditory stimulus. In S. S. Stevens (Ed.), *Handbook of experimental psychology.* New York: Wiley, 1951.

LICKLIDER, J. C. R. Three auditory theories. In S. Koch (Ed.), *Psychology: A study of a science.* vol. 1. *Sensory, perceptual and physiological formulations.* New York: McGraw-Hill, 1959, pp. 41–144.

LOTZE, R. H. *Medicinische Psychologie; oder, Physiologie der Seele.* Leipzig, Germany: Weidmann, 1852.

LOTZE, H. *Metaphysic; in three books, ontology, cosmology, and psychology.* (Trans. by B. Bosanquet, Ed.) London, England: Clarenden Press, 1884.

MARTIN, E. G., B. D. PAUL, and E. S. WELLS. A comparison of reflex thresholds with sensory thresholds: The relation of this comparison to the problem of attention. *Amer. J. Psychol.*, 1915, 26, 428–437.

MICHELS, W. C., and H. HELSON. A reformulation of the Fechner law in terms of adaptation-level applied to rating-scale data. *Amer. J. Psychol.*, 1949, 62, 355–368.

MILLER, G. A., and W. R. GARNER. Effect of random presentation on the psychometric function: Implications for a quantal theory of discrimination. *Amer. J. Psychol.*, 1944, 57, 451–467.

MILLER, J. G. Discrimination without awareness. *Amer. J. Psychol.*, 1939, 52, 562–578.

MÜLLER, G. E. *Zur Grundegung der Psychophysik.* Berlin, Germany: T. Grieben, 1878.

MÜLLER, G. E. Zur Psychophysik der Gesichtsempfindungen. *Z. Psychol.*, 1896, 10, 1–82, 321–413.

NEWHALL, S. M. An interpolation procedure for calculating thresholds. *Psychol. Rev.*, 1928, 35, 46–66

NEWMAN, E. The validity of the just noticeable difference as a unit of psychological magnitude. *Trans. Kan. Acad. Sci.*, 1933, 36, 172–175.

OBERLY, H. S. A comparison of the spans of "attention" and memory. *Amer. J. Psychol.*, 1928, 40, 295–302.

PIERCE, C. S., and J. JASTROW. On small differences of sensation. *Memoirs Nat. Acad. Sci.*, 1885, 3(pt. 1), 75–83.

POSTMAN, L., J. S. BRUNER, and E. McGINNIES. Personal values as selective factors in perception. *J. abnorm. soc. Psychol.*, 1948, 43, 142–155.

SENDERS, V. L., and A. SOWARDS. Analysis of response sequences in the setting of a psychophysical experiment. *Amer. J. Psychol.*, 1952, 65, 358–374.

STEVENS, S. S. To honor Fechner and repeal his law. *Science*, 1961, 133, 80–86. (a)

STEVENS, S. S. The psychophysics of sensory function. In W. A. Rosenblith (Ed.), *Sensory communication*. New York: Wiley, 1961. (b)

STEVENS, S. S. Is there a quantal threshold? In W. A. Rosenblith (Ed.), *Sensory communication*. New York: Wiley, 1961. (c)

STEVENS, S. S., C. T. MORGAN, and J. VOLKMANN. Theory of the neural quantum in the discrimination of loudness and pitch. *Amer. J. Psychol.*, 1941, 54, 315–335.

SWETS, J. A. Is there a sensory threshold? *Science*, 1961, 134, 168–177.

SWETS, J. A., W. P. TANNER, JR., and T. G. BIRDSALL. The evidence for a decision making theory of visual detection. Technical Report no. 40, 1955, University of Michigan, Electronic Defense Group.

TANNER, W. P., JR. and J. A. SWETS. A decision-making theory of visual detection. *Psychol. Rev.*, 1954, 61, 401–409.

TANNER, W. P., JR., J. A. SWETS, and D. M. GREEN. Some general properties of the hearing mechanism. Technical Report no. 30, 1956, University of Michigan, Electronic Defense Group.

THOMPSON, G. H. A new point of view in the interpretation of threshold measurements in psychophysics. *Psychol. Rev.*, 1920, 27, 300–307.

TITCHENER, E. B. *Experimental psychology.* Vol. II. Part II. Instructors' Manual. New York: Macmillan, 1905.

TRESSELT, M. E., and J. VOLKMANN. The production of uniform opinion by nonsocial stimulation. *J. abnorm. soc. Psychol.*, 1942, 37, 234–243.

URBAN, F. M. On the method of just perceptible differences. *Psychol. Rev.*, 1907, 14, 244–253.

URBAN, F. M. The method of constant stimuli and its generalizations. *Psychol. Rev.*, 1910, 17, 229–259.

URBAN, F. M. The future of psychophysics. *Psychol. Rev.*, 1930, 37, 93–106.

WELLS, F. L. V. Experiments concerning the threshold of conscious learning. *Psychol. Rev.*, 1919, 26, 382–388.

WILLIAMS, H. D. On the calculation of an associative limen. *Amer. J. Psychol.*, 1918, 29, 219–226.

Decision Processes in Perception*

JOHN A. SWETS

Massachusetts Institute of Technology

WILSON P. TANNER, JR., AND THEODORE G. BIRDSALL

University of Michigan

About five years ago, the theory of statistical decision was translated into a theory of signal detection.[1] Although the translation was motivated by problems in radar, the detection theory that resulted is a general theory for, like the decision theory, it specifies an ideal process. The generality of the theory suggested to us that it might also be relevant to the detection of signals by human observers. Beyond this, we were struck by several analogies between this description of ideal behavior and various aspects of the perceptual process. The de-

tection theory seemed to provide a framework for a realistic description of the behavior of the human observer in a variety of perceptual tasks.

The particular feature of the theory that was of greatest interest to us was the promise that it held of solving an old problem in the field of psychophysics. This is the problem of controlling or specifying the criterion that the observer uses in making a perceptual judgment. The classical methods of psychophysics make effective provision for only a single free parameter, one that is associated with the sensitivity of the observer. They contain no analytical procedure for specifying independently the observer's criterion. These two aspects of performance are confounded, for example, in an experiment in which the dependent variable is the intensity of the stimulus that is required for a threshold response. The present theory provides a quantitative measure of the criterion. There is left, as a result, a relatively pure measure of sensitivity. The theory, therefore, promised to be of value to the student of personal and social processes in perception as well as to the student of sensory functions. A second feature of the theory that attracted us is that it is a normative theory. We believed that having a standard with which to compare the behavior of the human observer would aid in the description and in the interpretation of experi-

* From *Psychological Review*, 1961, vol. 68, no. 5, pp. 301–320. This paper is based upon Technical Report No. 40, issued by the Electronic Defense Group of the University of Michigan in 1955. The research was conducted in the Vision Research Laboratory of the University of Michigan with support from the United States Army Signal Corps and the Naval Bureau of Ships. Our thanks are due H. R. Blackwell and W. M. Kincaid for their assistance in the research, and D. H. Howes for suggesting concerning the presentation of this material. This paper was prepared in the Research Laboratory of Electronics, Massachusetts Institute of Technology, with support from the Signal Corps, Air Force (Operational Applications Laboratory and Office of Scientific Research), and Office of Naval Research. This is Technical Report No. ESD-TR-61-20.

[1] For a formal treatment of statistical decision theory, see Wald (1950); for a brief and highly readable survey of the essentials, see Bross (1953). Parallel accounts of the detection theory may be found in Peterson, Birdsall, and Fox (1954) and in Van Meter and Middleton (1954).

mental results, and would be fruitful in suggesting new experiments.

This paper begins with a brief review of the theory of statistical decision and then presents a description of the elements of the theory of signal detection appropriate to human observers. Following this, the results of some experimental tests of the applicability of the theory to the detection of visual signals are described.

The theory and some illustrative results of one experimental test of it were briefly described in an earlier paper (Tanner and Swets, 1954). The present paper contains a more nearly adequate description of the theory, a more complete account of the first experiment, and the results of four other experiments. It brings together all of the data collected to date in vision experiments that bear directly on the value of the theory.[2]

The Theory

STATISTICAL DECISION THEORY

Consider the following game of chance. Three dice are thrown. Two of the dice are ordinary dice. The third die is unusual in that on each of three of its sides it has three spots, whereas on its remaining three sides it has no spots at all. You, as the player of the game, do not observe the throws of the dice. You are simply informed, after each throw, of the total number of spots showing on the three dice. You are then asked to state whether the third die, the unusual one, showed a 3 or a 0. If you are correct—that is, if you assert a 3 showed when it did in fact, or if you assert a 0 showed when it did in fact— you win a dollar. If you are incorrect— that is, if you make either of the two possible types of errors—you lose a dollar. How do you play the game? Certainly

[2] Reports of several applications of the theory in audition experiments are available in the literature; for a list of references, see Tanner and Birdsall (1958).

you will want a few minutes to make some computations before you begin. You will want to know the probability of occurrence of each of the possible totals 2 through 12 in the event that the third die shows a 0, and you will want to know the probability of occurrence of each of the possible totals 5 through 15 in the event that the third die shows a 3. Let us ignore the exact values of these probabilities, and grant that the two probability distributions in question will look much like those sketched in Figure 1.

Realizing that you will play the game many times, you will want to establish a policy which defines the circumstances under which you will make each of the two decisions. We can think of this as a *criterion* or a cutoff point along the axis representing the total number of spots showing on the three dice. That is, you will want to choose a number on this axis such that whenever it is equaled or exceeded you will state that a 3 showed on the third die, and such that whenever the total number of spots showing is less than this number, you will state that a 0 showed on the third die. For the game as described, with the a priori probabilities of a 3 and a 0 equal, and with equal values and costs associated with the four possible decision outcomes, it is intuitively clear that the optimal cutoff point is that point where the two curves cross. You will maximize your winnings if you choose this point as the cutoff point and adhere to it.

Now, what if the game is changed? What, for example, if the third die has three spots on five of its sides, and a 0 on only one? Certainly you will now be more willing to state following each throw, that the third die showed a 3. You will not, however, simply state more often that a 3 occurred without regard to the total showing on the three dice. Rather, you will lower your cutoff point: you will accept a smaller total than before as representing a throw in which the third die showed a 3. Conversely, if the third die has three

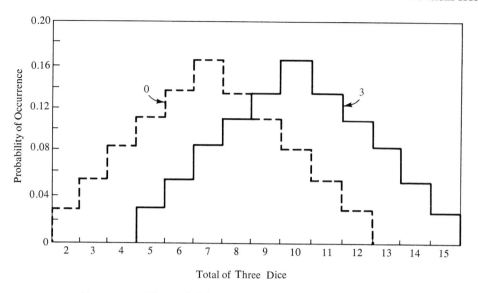

FIGURE 1   The probability distributions for the dice game.

spots on only one of its sides and 0's on five sides, you will do well to raise your cutoff point—to require a higher total than before for stating that a 3 occurred.

Similarly, your behavior will change if the values and costs associated with the various decision outcomes are changed. If it costs you 5 dollars every time you state that a 3 showed when in fact it did not, and if you win 5 dollars every time you state that a 0 showed when in fact it did (the other value and the other cost in the game remaining at one dollar), you will raise your cutoff to a point somewhere above the point where the two distributions cross. Or if, instead, the premium is placed on being correct when a 3 occurred, rather than when a 0 occurred as in the immediately preceding example, you will assume a cutoff somewhere below the point where the two distributions cross.

Again, your behavior will change if the amount of overlap of the two distributions is changed. You will assume a different cutoff than you did in the game as first described if the three sides of the third die showing spots now show four spots rather than three.

This game is simply an example of the type of situation for which the theory of statistical decision was developed. It is intended only to recall the frame of reference of this theory. Statistical decision theory—or the special case of it which is relevant here, the theory of testing statistical hypotheses—specifies the *optimal behavior in a situation where one must choose between two alternative statistical hypotheses on the basis of an observed event*. In particular, it specifies the optimal cutoff, along the continuum on which the observed events are arranged, as a function of (*a*) the *a priori* probabilities of the two hypotheses, (*b*) *the values and costs associated with the various decision outcomes,* and (*c*) *the amount of* overlap of the *distributions that constitute* the hypotheses.

According to the mathematical theory of signal detectability, the problem of detecting signals that are weak relative to the background of interference is like the one faced by the player of our dice game. In short, the detection problem is a problem in statistical decision; it requires testing statistical hypotheses. In the theory of signal detectability, this analogy is developed in terms of an idealized observer. It is our thesis that this conception of the detection process may apply to the human observer as well. The next several pages present an analysis of the detection process that will make the bases for this reasoning apparent.[3]

FUNDAMENTAL DETECTION PROBLEM

In the fundamental detection problem, an observation is made of events occurring in a fixed interval of time, and a decision is made, based on this observation, whether· the interval contained only the background interference or a signal as well. The interference, which is random, we shall refer to as *noise* and denote as N; the other alternative we shall term *signal plus noise*, SN. In the fundamental problem, only these two alternatives exist—noise is always present, whereas the signal may or may not be present during a specified observation interval. Actually, the observer, who has advance knowledge of the ensemble of signals to be presented, says

[3] It is to be expected that a theory recognized as having a potential application in psychophysics, although developed in another context, will be similar in many respects to previous conceptions in psychophysics. Although we shall not, in general, discuss explicitly these similarities, the strong relationship between many of the ideas presented in the following and Thurstone's earlier work on the scaling of judgments should be noted (see Thurstone, 1927a, 1927b). The present theory also has much in common with the recent work of Smith and Wilson (1953) and of Munson and Karlin (1956). Of course, for a new theory to arouse interest, it must also differ in some significant aspects from previous theories—these differences will become apparent as we proceed.

either "yes, a signal was present" or "no, no signal was present" following each observation. In the experiments reported below, the signal consisted of a small spot of light flashed briefly in a known location on a uniformly illuminated background. It is important to note that the signal is always observed in a background of noise; some, as in the present case, may be introduced by the experimenter or by the external situation, but some is inherent in the sensory processes.

REPRESENTATION OF SENSORY INFORMATION

We shall, in the following, use the term *observation* to refer to the sensory datum on which the decision is based. We assume that this observation may be represented as varying continuously along a single dimension. Although there is no need to be concrete, it may be helpful to think of the observation as some measure of neural activity, perhaps as the number of impulses arriving at a given point in the cortex within a given time. We assume further that any observation may arise, with specific probabilities, either from noise alone or from signal plus noise. We may portray these assumptions graphically, for a signal of a given amplitude, as in Figure 2. The observation is labeled x and plotted on the abscissa. The left-hand distribution, labeled $f_n(x)$, represents the probability density that x will result given

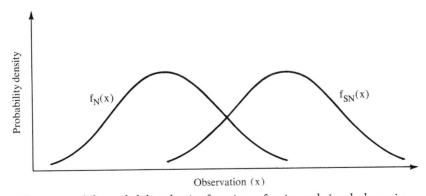

FIGURE 2   The probability density functions of noise and signal plus noise.

the occurrence of noise alone. The right-hand distribution, $f_{sn}(x)$, is the probability density function of x given the occurrence of signal plus noise. (Probability density functions are used, rather than probability functions, since x is assumed to be continuous.) Since the observations will tend to be of greater magnitude when a signal is presented, the mean of the SN distribution will be greater than the mean of the N distribution. In general, the greater the amplitude of the signal, the greater will be the separation of these means.

OBSERVATION AS A VALUE
OF LIKELIHOOD RATIO

It will be well to question at this point our assumption that the observation may be represented along a single axis. Can we, without serious violation, regard the observation as unidimensional, in spite of the fact that the response of the visual system probably has many dimensions? The answer to this question will involve some concepts that are basic to the theory.

One reasonable answer is that when the signal and interference are alike in character, only the magnitude of the total response of the receiving system is available as an indicator of signal existence. Consequently, no matter how complex the sensory information is in fact, the observations may be represented in theory as having a single dimension. Although this answer is quite acceptable when concerned only with the visual case, we prefer to advance a different answer, one that is applicable also to audition experiments, where, for example, the signal may be a segment of a sinusoid presented in a background of white noise.

So let us assume that the response of the sensory system does have several dimensions, and proceed to represent it as a point in an m-dimensional space. Call this point y. For every such point in this space there is some probability density that it resulted from noise alone, $f_N(y)$,

and, similarly, some probability density that it was due to signal plus noise, $f_{SN}(y)$. Therefore, there exists a likelihood ratio for each point in the space, $\lambda(y) = f_{SN}(y)/f_N(y)$, expressing the likelihood that the point y arose from SN relative to the likelihood that it arose from N. Since any point in the space, i.e., any sensory datum, may be thus represented as a real, nonzero number, these points may be considered to lie along a single axis. We may then, if we choose, identify the observation x with $\lambda(y)$; the decision axis becomes likelihood ratio.[4]

Having established that we may identify the observation x with $\lambda(y)$, let us note that we may equally well identify x with any monotonic transformation of $\lambda(y)$. It can be shown that we lose nothing by distorting the linear continuum as long as order is maintained. As a matter of fact we may gain if in particular, we identify x with some transformation of $\lambda(y)$ that results in Gaussian density functions on x. We have assumed the existence of such a transformation in the representation of the density functions, $f_{SN}(x)$ and $f_N(x)$, in Figure 2. We shall see shortly that the assumption of normality simplifies the problem greatly. We shall also see that this assumption is subject to experimental test. A further assumption incorporated into the picture of Figure 2, one made quite tentatively, is that the two density functions are of equal variance. This is equivalent to the assumption that the SN function is a simple translation of the N function, or that adding a signal to the noise merely adds a constant to the N function. The results of a test of this assumption are also described below.

To summarize the last few paragraphs,

---

[4] Thus the assumption of a unidimensional decision axis is independent of the character of the signal and noise. Rather, it depends upon the fact that just two decision alternatives are considered. More generally, it can be shown that the number of dimensions required to represent the observation is $M - 1$, where M is the number of decision alternatives considered by the observer.

we have assumed that an observation may be characterized by a value of *likelihood ratio*, $\lambda(y)$, *i.e., the likelihood that the response of the sensory system y arose from SN relative to the likelihood that it arose from N*. This permits us to view the observations as lying along a single axis. We then assumed the existence of a particular transformation of $\lambda(y)$ such that on the resulting variable, x, the density functions are normal. We regard the observer as basing his decisions on the variable x.

DEFINITION OF THE CRITERION

If the representation depicted in Figure 2 is realistic, then the problem posed for an observer attempting to detect signals in noise is indeed similar to the one faced by the player of our dice game. On the basis of an observation, one that varies only in magnitude, he must decide between two alternative hypotheses. He must decide from which hypothesis the observation resulted; he must state that the observation is a member of the one distribution or the other. As did the player of the dice game, the observer must establish a policy which defines the circumstances under which the observation will be regarded as resulting from each of the two possible events. He establishes a criterion, a cutoff x_c on the continuum of observations, to which he can relate any given observation x_i. If he finds for the ith observation, x_i, that $x_i > x_c$, he says "yes"; if $x_i < x_c$, he says "no." Since the observer is assumed to be capable of locating a criterion at any point along the continuum of observations, it is of interest to examine the various factors that, according to the theory, *will influence his choice of a particular criterion. To do so requires some additional notation.*

In the language of statistical decision theory the observer chooses a subset of all of the observations, namely the Critical Region A, such that an observation in this subset leads him to accept the Hypothesis SN, to say that a signal was present. All other observations are in the complementary Subset B; these lead to rejection of the Hypothesis SN, or, equivalently, since the two hypotheses are mutually exclusive and exhaustive, to the acceptance of the Hypothesis N. The Critical Region A, with reference to Figure 2, consists of the values of x to the right of some criterion value x_c.

As in the case of the dice game, a decision will have one of four outcomes: the observer may say "yes" or "no" and may in either case be *correct* or *incorrect*. The decision outcome, in other words, may be a *hit* ($SN \cdot A$, the joint occurrence of the Hypothesis SN and an observation in the region A), a *miss* ($SN \cdot B$), a *correct rejection* ($N \cdot B$), or a *false alarm* ($N \cdot A$). If the a priori probability of signal occurrence and the parameters of the distributions of Figure 2 are fixed; the choice of a criterion value x_c completely determines the probability of each of these outcomes.

Clearly, the four probabilities are interdependent. For example, an increase in the probability of a hit, $p(SN \cdot A)$, can be achieved only by accepting an increase in the probability of a false alarm, $p(N \cdot A)$, and decreases in the other probabilities, $p(SN \cdot B)$ and $p(N \cdot B)$. *Thus a given criterion yields a particular balance among the probabilities of the four possible outcomes;* conversely, the balance *desired by an observer in any instance will determine the optimal location of his criterion.* Now the observer may desire the balance that maximizes the *expected value of a decision in a situation where the four possible outcomes of a decision have individual values* as did the player of the dice game. In this case, the location of the best criterion is determined by the same parameters that determined it in the dice game. The observer, however, may desire a balance that maximizes some other quantity—i.e., a balance that is optimum according to some other definition of optimum—in which case a different criterion will be appropriate. He may, for example, want to maximize $p(SN \cdot A)$ while satisfying a restriction on $p(N \cdot A)$, as we typically do when as experimenters we assume an .05 or .01 level of confidence. Alternatively, he may want to maximize the number of correct decisions. Again, he may prefer a criterion that will maximize the reduction in uncertainty in the Shannon (1948) sense.

In statistical decision theory, and in the theory of signal detectability, the optimal criterion under each of these definitions of optimum is specified in terms of the likelihood ratio. That is to say, it can be shown that, if we define the observation in terms of the likelihood ratio, $\lambda(x) = f_{SN}(x)/f_N(x)$, then the optimal criterion can always be specified by some value β of $\lambda(x)$. In other words, the Critical Region A that *corresponds to the criterion contains all observations with likelihood ratio greater than or equal to β, and none of those with likelihood ratio less than β.*

We shall illustrate this manner of specifying the optimal criterion for just one of the definitions of optimum proposed above, namely, the maximization of the total expected value of a decision in a situation where the four possible outcomes of a decision have individual values associated with them. This is the definition of optimum that we assumed in the dice game. For this purpose we shall need the concept of *conditional probability as opposed to the probability of joint occurrence introduced above.* It should be stated that conditional probabilities will have a place in our discussion beyond their use in this illustration; the ones we shall introduce are, as a matter of fact, the fundamental quantities in evaluating the observer's performance.

There are two conditional probabilities of principal interest. These are the conditional probabilities of the observer saying "yes": $p_{SN}(A)$, the probability of a Yes decision *conditional upon,* or *given,* the occurrence of a signal, and $p_N(A)$, the probability of a Yes decision given the occurrence of noise alone. These two are sufficient, for the other two are simply

their complements: $p_{SN}(B) = 1 - p_{SN}(A)$ and $p_N(B) = 1 - p_N(A)$. The conditional and joint probabilities are related as follows:

$$p_{SN}(A) = \frac{p(SN \cdot A)}{p(SN)} \qquad [1]$$

$$p_N(A) = \frac{p(N \cdot A)}{p(N)}$$

where: $p(SN)$ is the a priori probability of signal occurrence and $p(N) = 1 - p(SN)$ is the a priori probability of occurrence of noise alone. Equation 1 makes apparent the convenience of using conditional rather than joint probabilities—conditional probabilities are independent of the a priori probability of occurrence of the signal and of noise alone. With reference to Figure 2, we may define $p_{SN}(A)$, or the conditional probability of a hit, as the integral of $f_{SN}(x)$ over the Critical Region A, and $p_N(A)$, the conditional probability of a false alarm, as the integral of $f_N(x)$ over A. That is, $p_N(A)$ and $p_{SN}(A)$ represent, respectively, the areas under the two curves of Figure 2 to the right of some criterion value of x.

To pursue our illustration of how an optimal criterion may be specified by a critical value of likelihood ratio β, let us note that the expected value of a decision (denoted *EV*) is defined in statistical decision theory as the sum, over the potential outcomes of a decision, of the products of probability of outcome and the desirability of outcome. Thus, using the notation V for *positive individual values* and K for *costs or negative individual values,* we have the following equation:

$$
\begin{aligned}
EV = &\, V_{SN} \cdot {}_A p(SN \cdot A) \\
&+ V_N \cdot {}_B p(N \cdot B) \\
&- K_{SN} \cdot {}_B p(SN \cdot B) \\
&- K_N \cdot {}_A p(N \cdot A) \quad [2]
\end{aligned}
$$

Now if a priori and conditional probabilities are substituted for the joint probabilities in Equation 2 following Equation 1, for example, $p(SN)p_{SN}(A)$ for $p(SN \cdot A)$, then collecting terms yields the result that maximizing EV is equivalent to maximizing:

$$p_{SN}(A) - \beta p_N(A) \qquad [3]$$

where

$$\beta = \frac{p(N)}{p(SN)} \cdot \frac{(V_N \cdot {}_B + K_N \cdot {}_A)}{(V_{SN} \cdot {}_A + K_{SN} \cdot {}_B)} \quad [4]$$

It can be shown that this value of β is equal to the value of likelihood ratio, $\lambda(x)$, that corresponds to the optimal criterion. From Equation 3 it may be seen that the value β simply weights the hits and false alarms, and from Equation 4 we see that β is determined by the a priori probabilities of occurrence of signal and of noise alone and by the values associated with the individual decision outcomes. It should be noted that Equation 3 applies to all definitions of optimum. Equation 4 shows the determinants of β in only the special case of the expected-value definition of optimum.

Return for a moment to Figure 2, keeping in mind the result that β is a critical value of $\lambda(x) = f_{SN}(x)/f_N(x)$. It should be clear that the optimal cut-off x_c along the x axis is at the point on this axis where the ratio of the ordinate value of $f_{SN}(x)$ to the ordinate value of $f_N(x)$ is a certain number, namely β. In the symmetrical case, where the two a priori probabilities are equal and the four individual values are equal, $\beta = 1$ and the optimal value of x_c is the point where $f_{SN}(x) = f_N(x)$, where the two curves cross. If the four values are equal but $p(SN) = \frac{5}{6}$ and $p(N) = \frac{1}{6}$, another case described in connection with the dice game, then $\beta = \frac{1}{5}$ and the optimal value of x_c is shifted a certain distance to the left. This shift may be seen intuitively to be in the proper direction—a higher value of $p(SN)$ should lead to a greater willingness to accept the Hypothesis SN, i.e., a more lenient cut-

off. To consider one more example from the dice game, if $p(SN) = p(N) = 0.5$, if $V_N \cdot {}_B$ and $K_N \cdot {}_A$ are set at 5 dollars and $V_{SN} \cdot {}_A$ and $K_{SN} \cdot {}_B$ are equal to 1 dollar, then $\beta = 5$ and the optimal value of x_c shifts a certain distance to the right. Again intuitively, if it is more important to be correct when the Hypothesis N is true, a high, or strict, criterion should be adopted.

In any case, β specifies the optimal weighting of hits relative to false alarms: x_c should always be located at the point on the x axis corresponding to β. As we pointed out in discussing the dice game, just where this value of x_c will be with reference to the x axis depends not only upon the a priori probabilities and the values but also upon the overlap of the two density functions, in short, upon the signal strength. We shall define a measure of signal strength within the next few pages. For now, it is important to note that for any detection goal to which the observer may subscribe, and for any set of parameters that may characterize a detection situation (such as a priori probabilities and values associated with decision outcomes), the optimal criterion may be specified in terms of a single number, β, a critical value of likelihood ratio.[5]

RECEIVER-OPERATING-
CHARACTERISTIC

Whatever criterion the observer actually uses, even if it is not one of the optimal criteria, can also be described by a single

[5] We have reached a point in the discussion where we can justify the statement made earlier that the decision axis may be equally well regarded as likelihood ratio or as any monotonic transformation of likelihood ratio. Any distortion of the linear continuum of likelihood ratio, that maintains order, is equivalent to likelihood ratio in terms of determining a criterion. The decisions made are the same whether the criterion is set at likelihood ratio equal to β or at the value that corresponds to β of some new variable. To illustrate, if a criterion leads to a Yes response whenever $\lambda(y) > 2$, if $x = [\lambda(y)]^2$ the decisions will be the same if the observer says "yes" whenever $x > 4$.

number, by some value of likelihood ratio. Let us proceed to a consideration of how the observer's performance may be evaluated with respect to the location of his criterion, and, at the same time we shall see how his performance may be evaluated with respect to his sensory capabilities.

As we have noted, the fundamental quantities in the evaluation of performance are $p_N(A)$ and $p_{SN}(A)$, these quantities representing; respectively, the areas under the two curves of Figure 2 to the right of some criterion value of x. If we set up a graph of $p_{SN}(A)$ versus $p_N(A)$ and trace on it the curve resulting as we move the decision criterion along the decision axis of Figure 2, we sketch one of the arcs shown in Figure 3. Ignore, for a moment, all but one of these arcs. If the decision criterion is set way at the left in Figure 2, we obtain a point in the upper right-hand corner of Figure 3: both $p_{SN}(A)$ and $p_N(A)$ are unity. If the criterion is set at the right end of the decision axis in Figure 2, the point at the other extreme of Figure 3, $p_{SN}(A) = p_N(A) = 0$, is obtained. In between these extremes lie the criterion values of more practical interest. It should be noted that the exact form of the curve shown in Figure 3 is not the only form which might result, but it is the form which will result if the observer chooses a criterion in terms of likelihood ratio, and the probability density functions are normal and of equal variance.

This curve is a form of the *operating characteristic* as it is known in statistics; in the context of the detection problem it is usually referred to as the *receiver-operating-characteristic*, or ROC, curve. The optimal "operating level" may be seen from Equation 3 to be at the point of the ROC curve where its slope is β. That is, the expression $p_{SN}(A) - \beta p_N(A)$ defines a utility line of slope β, and the point of tangency of this line to the ROC curve is the optimal operating level. Thus the theory specifies the appropriate hit probability and false alarm probability for any definition of optimum and any set of parameters characterizing the detection situation.

It is now apparent how the observer's choice of a criterion in a given experiment may be indexed. The proportions obtained in an experiment are used as estimates of the probabilities, $p_N(A)$ and $p_{SN}(A)$; thus, the observer's behavior yields a point on an ROC curve. The slope of the curve at this point corresponds to the value of likelihood ratio at which he has located his criterion. Thus we work backward from the ROC curve to infer the criterion that is employed by the observer.

There is, of course, a family of ROC curves, as shown in Figure 3, a given curve corresponding to a given separation between the means of the density functions $f_N(x)$ and $f_{SN}(x)$. The parameter of these curves has been called d', where d' is defined as the difference between the means of the two density functions expressed in terms of their standard deviation, i.e.:

$$d' = \frac{Mf_{SN}(x) - Mf_N(x)}{\sigma f_N(x)} \qquad [5]$$

Since the separation between the means of the two density functions is a function of signal amplitude, d' is an index of the detectability of a given signal for a given observer.

Recalling our assumptions that the density *functions* $f_N(x)$ *and* $f_{SN}(x)$ *are normal and of equal variance*, we may see from Equation 5 that the quantity denoted d' is simply the familiar normal deviate, or x/σ measure. From the pair of values $p_N(A)$ and $p_{SN}(A)$ that are obtained experimentally, one may proceed to a published table of areas under the normal curve to determine a value of d'. A simpler computational procedure is achieved by plotting the points $[p_N(A), p_{SN}(A)]$ on graph paper having a probability scale and a normal deviate scale on both axes.

We see now that the four-fold table of the responses that are made to a particular stimulus may be treated as having two independent parameters—the experiment yields measures of two independent aspects of the observer's performance. The variable d' is a measure of the observer's sensory capabilities, or of the effective signal strength. This may be thought of as the object of interest in classical psychophysics. The criterion β that is employed by the observer, which determines the $p_N(A)$ and $p_{SN}(A)$ for some fixed d', reflects the effect of variables which have been variously called the set, attitude, or motives of the observer. It is the ability to distinguish between these two aspects of detection performance that comprises one of the main advantages of the theory proposed here. We have noted that these two aspects of behavior are confounded in an experiment in which the dependent variable is the intensity of the signal that is required for a threshold response.

RELATIONSHIP OF D'
TO SIGNAL ENERGY

We have seen that the optimal value of the criterion, β, can be computed. In certain instances, an optimal value of d', i.e., the sensitivity of the mathematically ideal device, can also be computed. If, for example, the exact wave form and starting time of the signal are determinable, as in the case of an auditory signal, then the optimal value of d' is equal to $\sqrt{2E/N_o}$, where E is the signal energy and N_o is the noise power in a one-cycle band (Peterson, Birdsall, and Fox, 1954). A specification of the optimal value of d' for visual signals has been developed very recently.[6] Although we shall not elaborate the point in this paper, it is worth noting that an empirical index of detectability may be compared with ideal detectability, just as observed and optimal indices of decision

criteria may be compared. The ratio of the squares of the two detectability indices has been taken as a measure of the observer's sensory efficiency. This measure has demonstrated its usefulness in the study of several problems in audition (Tanner and Birdsall, 1958).

USE OF IDEAL DESCRIPTIONS
AS MODELS

It might be worthwhile to describe at this point some of the reasons for the emphasis placed here on optimal measures, and, indeed, the reasons for the general enterprise of considering a theory of ideal behavior as a model for studies of real behavior.[7] In view of the deviations from any ideal which are bound to characterize real organisms, it might appear at first glance that any deductions based on ideal premises could have no more than academic interest. We do not think this is the case. In any study, it is desirable to specify rigorously the factors pertinent to the study. Ideal conditions generally involve few variables and permit these to be described in simple terms. Having identified the performance to be expected under ideal conditions, it is possible to extend the model to include the additional variables associated with real organisms. The ideal performance, in other words, constitutes a convenient base from which to explore the complex operation of a real organism.

In certain cases, as in the problem at hand, values characteristic of ideal conditions may actually approximate very closely those characteristics of the organism under study. The problem then becomes one of changing the ideal model in some particular so that it is slightly less than ideal. This is usually accomplished by depriving the ideal device of some particular function. This method of attack has been found to generate useful hypotheses for

---

[6] W. P. Tanner, Jr. & R. C. Jones, personal communication, November 1959.

[7] The discussion immediately following is, in part, a paraphrase of one in Horton (1957).

further studies. Thus, whereas it is not expected that the human observer and the ideal detection device will behave identically, the emphasis in early studies is on similarities. If the differences are small, one may rule out entire classes of alternative models, and regard the model in question as a useful tool in further studies. Proceeding on this assumption, one may then in later studies emphasize the differences, the form and extent of the differences suggesting how the ideal model may be modified in the direction of reality.

ALTERNATIVE CONCEPTIONS
OF THE DETECTION PROCESS

The earliest studies that were undertaken to test the applicability of the decision model to human observers were quite naturally oriented toward determining its value relative to existing psychophysical theory. As a result, some of the data presented below are meaningful only with respect to differences in the predictions based upon different theories. We shall, therefore, briefly consider alternative theories of the detection process.

Although it is difficult to specify with precision the alternative theories of detection, it is clear that they generally involve the concept of the *threshold* in an important way. The development of the threshold concept is fairly obscure. It is differently conceived by different people, and few popular usages of the concept benefit from explicit statement. One respect, however, in which the meaning of the threshold concept is entirely clear is its assertion of a lower limit on sensitivity. As we have just seen, the decision model does not include such a boundary. The decision model specifies no lower bound on the location of the criterion along the continuous axis of sensory inputs. Further, it implies that any displacement of the mean of $f_{SN}(x)$ from the mean of $f_N(x)$, no matter how small, will result in a greater

value of $p_{SN}(A)$ than $p_N(A)$, irrespective of the location of the criterion.

To permit experimental comparison of decision theory and threshold theory, we shall consider a special version of threshold theory (Blackwell, 1953). Although it is a special version, we believe it retains the essence of the threshold concept. In this version, the threshold is described in the same terms that are used in the description of decision theory. It is regarded as a cutoff on the continuum of observations (see Figure 2) with a fixed location with values of x above the cutoff always evoking a positive response, and with discrimination impossible among values of x below the cutoff. This description of a threshold in terms of a fixed cutoff and a stimulus effect that varies randomly, it will be noted, is entirely equivalent to the more common description in terms of a randomly varying cutoff and a fixed stimulus effect. There are several reasons for assuming that the hypothetical threshold cutoff is located quite high relative to the density function $f_N(x)$, say at approximately $+3\sigma$ from the mean of $f_N(x)$. We shall compare our data with the predictions of such a "high threshold" theory, and shall indicate their relationship to predictions from a theory assuming a lower threshold. We shall, in particular, ask how low a threshold cutoff would have to be to be consistent with the reported data. It may be noted that if a high threshold exists, the observer will be incapable of ordering values of x likely to result from noise alone, and hence will be incapable of varying his criterion over a significant range.

If a threshold exists that is rarely exceeded by noise alone, this fact will be immediately apparent from the ROC curves (see Figure 3) that are obtained experimentally. It can be shown that the ROC curves in this case are straight lines from points on the left-hand vertical axis —$p_{SN}(A)$—to the upper right-hand corner

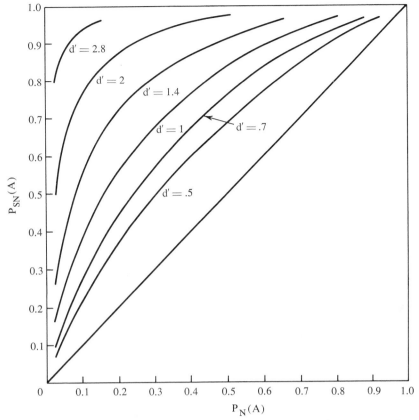

FIGURE 3   The receiver-operating-characteristic curves. (These curves show p_{SN} (A) vs. p_N (A) with d' as the parameter. They are based on the assumptions that the probability density functions, f_y (x) and f_{sn} (x), are normal and of equal variance.)

of the plot. These straight line curves represent the implication of a high threshold theory that an increase in $p_N(A)$ must be effected by responding "yes" to a random selection of observations that fail to reach the threshold, rather than by a judicious selection of observations, i.e., a lower criterion level. If we follow the usual procedure of regarding the stimulus threshold as the signal intensity yielding a value of $p_{SN}(A) = 0.5$ for $p_N(A) = 0.0$, then an appreciation of the relationship between d' and $p_N(A)$ at threshold may be gained by visualizing a straight line in Figure 3 from this point to the upper right-hand corner. If we note which of the ROC curves drawn in Figure 3 are

intersected by the visualized line, we see that the threshold decreases with increasing $p_N(A)$. For example, a response procedure resulting in a $p_N(A) = 0.02$ requires a signal of $d' = 2.0$ to reach the threshold, whereas a response procedure yielding a $p_N(A) = 0.98$ requires a signal of $d' < 0.5$ to reach the threshold. A graph showing what threshold would be calculated as a function of $p_N(A)$ is plotted in Figure 4. The calculated threshold is a strictly monotonic function of $p_N(A)$ ranging from infinity to zero.

The fundamental difference between the threshold theory we are considering and decision theory lies in their treatment of false alarm responses. According to the

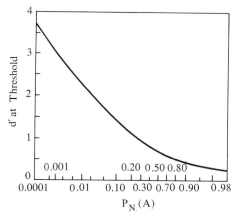

FIGURE 4   The relationship between d' and $p_N(A)$ at threshold.

threshold theory, these responses represent guesses determined by nonsensory factors; i.e., $p_N(A)$ is independent of the cutoff which is assumed to have a fixed location. Decision theory assumes, on the other hand, that $p_N(A)$ varies with the temporary position of a cutoff under the observer's control; that false alarm responses arise for valid sensory reasons, and that therefore a simple correction will not eliminate their effect on $p_{SN}(A)$. A similar implication of Figure 4 that should be noted is that reliable estimates of $p_{SN}(A)$ or of the stimulus threshold are not guaranteed by simply training the observer to maintain a low, constant value of $p_N(A)$. Since extreme probabilities cannot be estimated with reliability, the criterion may vary from session to session with the variation having no direct reflection in the data. Certainly, false alarm rates of 0.01, 0.001, and 0.0001, are not discriminable in an experimentally feasible number of observations; the differences in the calculated values of the threshold associated with these different values of $p_N(A)$ may be seen from Figure 4 to be sizeable. The experiments reported in the following were designed, in large measure, to clarify the relationship that exists between $p_N(A)$ and $p_{SN}(A)$, to show whether or not the observer is capable of controlling the location of his criterion for a Yes response.

Some Experiments

Five experiments are reported in the following. They are the first experiments that were undertaken to test the applicability of decision theory to psychophysical tasks, and it must be emphasized that they were intended to explore only the general relationships specified in the theory. We shall refer also to more recent experiments conducted within the framework of decision theory. The later experiments, although not focused as directly on testing the validity of the theory, support the principal thesis of this paper.

The experiments reported here are devoted to answering the two principal questions suggested by a consideration of decision theory. The first of these may be stated in this way: is sensory information (or the decision axis) continuous, i.e., is the observer capable of discriminating among observations likely to result from noise alone? The alternative we consider is that there exists a threshold cut, on the decision axis, that is unlikely to be exceeded by observations resulting from noise, and below which discrimination among observations is impossible. The second question has two parts: is the observer capable of using different criteria, and, if so, does he change his criterion appropriately when the variables that we expect will determine his criterion (probabilities, values, and costs) are changed?

Three of the five experiments to be described pose for the observer what we have called the fundamental detection problem, the problem that occupied our attention throughout the theoretical discussion. Of these, two test the observer's ability to use the criterion that maximizes the expected value of a decision. The a priori probability of a signal occurrence and the individual values associated with the four possible decision outcomes are varied systematically, in order to determine the range over which the observer can vary his criterion and the form of the resultant ROC curve. A third experiment tests the observer's ability to maximize the proportion of hits while satisfying a restriction on the proportion of false alarms. This experiment is largely concerned with the degree of precision with which the observer can locate a criterion.

The remaining two experiments differ in that the tasks they present to the observer do not require him to establish a criterion, that is, they do not require a Yes or No response. They test certain implications of decision theory that we have not yet treated explicitly, but they will be seen to follow very directly from the theory and to contribute significantly to an evaluation of it. In one of these the observer is asked to report after each observation interval his subjective probability that the signal existed during the interval. This response is a familiar one; it is essentially a rating or a judgment of confidence. The report of "a posteriori probability of signal existence," as it is termed in detection theory, may be regarded as reflecting the likelihood ratio of the observation. This case is of interest since an estimate of likelihood ratio preserves more of the information contained in the observation than does a report merely that the likelihood ratio fell above or below a critical value. We shall see that it is also possible to construct the ROC curve from this type of response.

The other experiment not requiring a criterion employs what has been termed the temporal forced-choice method of response. On each trial a signal is presented in exactly one of n temporal intervals, and the observer states in which interval he believes the signal occurred. The optimal procedure for the observer to follow in this case, if he is to maximize the probability of a correct response, is to make an observation x in each interval and to choose the interval having the greatest value of x associated with it. Since decision theory specifies how the proportion

of correct responses obtained with the forced-choice method is related to the detectability index d', the internal consistency of the theory may be evaluated. That is to say, if the observer follows the optimal procedure, then the estimate of the detectability of a signal of a given strength that is abused on forced-choice data will be comparable to that based on yes-no data. The forced-choice method may also be used to make a strong test of a fundamental assumption of decision theory, namely, that sensory information is continuous, or that sensory information does not exhibit a threshold cutoff. For an experiment requiring the observer to rank the n intervals according to their likelihood of containing the signal, the continuity and threshold assumptions lead to very different predictions concerning the probability that an interval ranked other than first will be the correct interval.

All of the experiments reported in the following employed a circular signal with a diameter of 30 minutes of visual angle and a duration of $\frac{1}{100}$ of a second. The signal was presented on a large uniformly illuminated background having a luminance of 10 foot-lamberts. Details of the apparatus have been presented elsewhere (Blackwell, Pritchard, and Ohmart, 1954).

MAXIMIZING THE EXPECTED
VALUE OF A DECISION—AN
EXPERIMENTAL ANALYSIS

A direct test of the decision model is achieved in an experiment in which the a priori probability of signal occurrence or the values of the decision outcomes, or both, are varied from one group of observations to another—in short, in which β (Equations 3 and 4) assumes different values. The observer, in order to maximize his expected value, or his payoff, must vary his willingness to make a Yes response, in accordance with the change in β. Variations in this respect will be indicated by the proportion of false alarms, $p_N(A)$. The point of interest is how $p_{SN}(A)$, the proportion of hits, varies with changes in $p_N(A)$, i.e., in the form of the observer's ROC curve. If the experimental values of $p_N(A)$ reflect the location of the observer's criterion, if the observer responds on the basis of the likelihood ratio of the observation, and if the density functions (Figure 2) are normal and of equal variance, the ROC curve of Figure 3 will result. If, on the other hand, the location of the criterion is fixed in such a position that it is rarely exceeded by noise alone, then the resulting ROC curve will be a straight line, as we have indicated above. We shall examine some empirical ROC curves with this distinction in mind.

This experiment can be made to yield another and, in one sense, a stronger test of these two hypotheses, by employing several values of signal strength within a single group of observations, i.e., while a given set of probabilities and values are in effect. For in this case stimulus thresholds can be calculated, and correlational techniques can be used to determine whether the calculated threshold is dependent upon $p_N(A)$ as predicted by decision theory, or independent of $p_N(A)$ as predicted by what we have termed the high threshold theory. We will grant that presenting more than one value of signal strength, within a single group of observations to which fixed probabilities and values apply, is not, conceptually, the simplest experiment that could have been performed to test our hypotheses. Nevertheless, a little reflection will show that this experimental procedure is entirely legitimate from any of our present points of view. We simply associate several values of $p_{SN}(A)$ with a given value of $p_N(A)$, and thereby obtain at once a point on each of several ROC curves and an estimate of the stimulus threshold that is associated with that value of $p_N(A)$.

First Expected-Value Experiment. The first of the two expected-value experiments

that were performed employed four values of signal strength.

Three observers, after considerable practice, served in 16 2-hour sessions. In each session, signals at four levels of intensity (0.44, 0.69, 0.92, and 1.20 foot-lamberts) were presented along with a "blank" or "no-signal" presentation. The order of presentation was random within a restriction placed upon the total number of occurrences of each signal intensity and the blank in a given session. Each of the signal intensities occurred equally often within a session. The proportion of trials on which a signal (of any intensity) was presented, $p(SN)$, was either 0.80 or 0.40 in the various sessions. In all, there were 300 presentations in each session—six blocks of 50 presentations, separated by rest periods. Thus each estimate of $p_N(A)$ is based on either 60 or 180 observations, and each estimate of $p_{SN}(A)$ is based on 30 or 60 observations, depending upon $p(SN)$.

In the first four sessions, no values were associated with the various decision outcomes. For the first and fourth sessions the observers were informed that $p(SN)=0.80$ and, for the second and third sessions, that $p(SN)=0.40$. The average value of $p_N(A)$ obtained in the sessions with $p(SN)=0.80$ was 0.43, and, in the sessions with $p(SN)=0.40$, it was 0.15—indicating that the observer's willingness to make a Yes response is significantly affected by changes in $p(SN)$ alone. In the remaining 12 sessions, these two values of $p(SN)$ were used in conjunction with a variety of values placed on the decision outcomes. In the fifth session, for example, the observers were told that $p(SN)=0.80$ and were, in addition, given the following payoff matrix:

	No	Yes
Signal	-1 $K_{SN \cdot B}$	$+1$ $V_{SN \cdot A}$
No Signal	$+2$ $V_{N \cdot B}$	-2 $K_{N \cdot A}$

A variety of simple matrices was used. These included, reading from left to right across the top and then the bottom row: $(-1, +1, +3, -3)$ and $(-1, +1, +4, -4)$ with $p(SN)=0.80$, and $(-1, +1, +2, -2)$, $(-1, +1, +1, -1)$, $(-2,$

+ 2, + 1, − 1), and (− 3, + 3, + 1, − 1) with $p(SN)=0.40$. By reference to Equation 4, it may be seen that these matrices and values of $p(SN)$ define values of β ranging from 0.25 to 3.00. The observers were actually paid in accordance with these payoff matrices, in addition to their regular wage. The values were equated with fractions of cents, these fractions being adjusted so that the expected earnings per session remained relatively constant, at approximately one dollar.

The obtained values of $p_N(A)$ varied in accordance with changes in the values of the decision outcomes as well as with changes in the a priori probability of signal occurrence. Just how closely the obtained values of $p_N(A)$ approached those specified as optimal by the theory, we shall discuss shortly. For now, we may note that the range of values of $p_N(A)$ obtained from the three observers is shown in Figure 5. The parts of this figure also show four values of $p_{SN}(A)$ corresponding to each value of $p_N(A)$; the four values of $p_{SN}(A)$, one for each signal strength, are indicated by different symbols. We have, then, in the parts of Figure 5, four ROC curves.

Although entire ROC curves are not precisely defined by the data of the first experiment, these data will contribute to our purpose of distinguishing between the predictions of decision theory and the predictions of a high threshold theory. It is clear, for example, that the straight lines fitted to the data do not intersect the upper right-hand corner of the graph, as required by the concept of a high threshold.

We have mentioned that another analysis of the data is of interest in distinguishing the two theories we are considering. As we have indicated earlier in this paper, and developed in more detail elsewhere (Tanner & Swets, 1954), the concept of a high threshold leads to the prediction that the stimulus threshold is independent of $p_N(A)$, whereas decision theory predicts a negative correlation between the

stimulus threshold and $p_N(A)$. Within the framework of the high threshold model that we have described, the stimulus threshold is defined as the stimulus intensity that yields a $p_{SN}(A) = 0.50$ for $p_N(A) = 0.0$. This stimulus intensity may be determined by interpolation from psychometric functions—$p_{SN}(A)$ vs. signal intensity—that are normalized so that $p_N(A) = 0.0$. The normalization is effected by the equation:

$$p_{SN}(A) \text{ corrected} = \frac{p_{SN}(A) - p_N(A)}{1 - p_N(A)} \quad [6]$$

commonly known as the "correction for chance success." The intent of the correction is to remove what has been regarded as the spurious element of $p_{SN}(A)$ that is contributed by an observer's tendency to make a Yes response in the absence of any sensory indication of a signal, i.e., to make a Yes response following an observation that fails to reach the threshold level. It can be shown that the validity of this correction procedure is implied by the assumption of what we have termed a high threshold. The decision model, as we have indicated, differs in that it regards sensory information as thoroughly probabilistic, without a fixed cutoff—it asserts that the presence and absence of some sensory indication of a signal are not separable categories. According to the decision model, the observer does not achieve more Yes responses by responding positively to a random selection of observations that fall short of the fixed criterion level, but by lowering his criterion. In this case, the chance correction is inappropriate; the stimulus threshold will not remain invariant with changes in $p_N(A)$.

The relationship of the stimulus threshold to $p_N(A)$ in this first experiment is illustrated by Figures 6 and 7. The portion of data comprising each of the curves in these figures was selected to be relatively homogeneous with respect to $p_N(A)$.

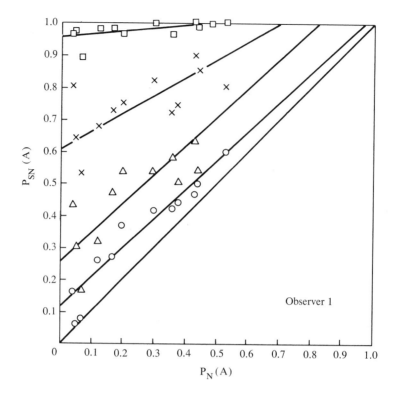

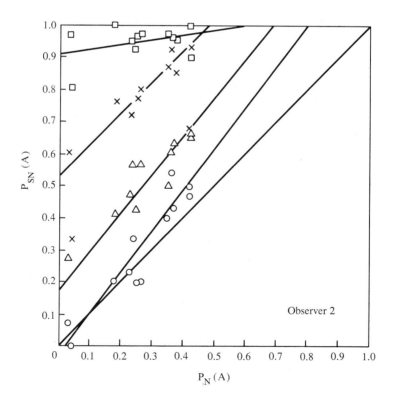

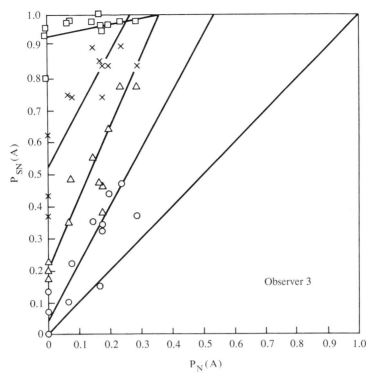

FIGURE 5   Empirical receiver-operating-characteristic curves obtained from three observers in the first expected-value experiment.

The curves are average curves for the three observers. Figure 6 shows $p_N(A)$ and $p_{SN}(A)$ as a function of the signal intensity, ΔI. The intercepts of the three curves may be seen to indicate values of $p_N(A)$ of 0.35, 0.25, and 0.04, respectively. Figure 7 shows the *corrected* value of $p_{SN}(A)$ plotted against signal intensity. It may be seen in Figure 7 that the stimulus threshold—the value of ΔI corresponding to a corrected $p_{SN}(A)$ of 0.50—is dependent upon $p_N(A)$ in the direction predicted by decision theory.[8]

Figures 6 and 7 portray the relationship in question in a form to which many of us

---

[8] ΔI is plotted in Figures 6 and 7 in terms of the transmission values of the filters that were placed selectively in the signal beam to yield different signal intensities. These values (0.365, 0.575, 0.765, 1.000) are converted to the signal values in terms of foot-lamberts that we have presented above, by multiplying them by 1.20, the value of the signal in foot-lamberts without selective filtering.

are accustomed; they are presented here only for illustrative purposes. We can, of course, achieve a stronger test by computing the coefficients of correlation between $p_N(A)$ and the calculated threshold. We have made this computation, and have in the process avoided the averaging of data obtained from different observers and different experimental sessions. The product-moment coefficients for the three observers are $-.37$ ($p = 0.245$), $-.60$ ($p = 0.039$), and $-.81$ ($p = 0.001$), respectively. For the three observers combined, $p = 0.0008$. The implication of these correlations is the same as that of the straight lines fitted to the data of Figure 5, namely, that a dependence exists between the conditional probability that an observation arising from SN will exceed the criterion and the conditional probability that an observation arising from N will exceed the criterion. Stated otherwise, the correlations indicate that the observer's decision function is

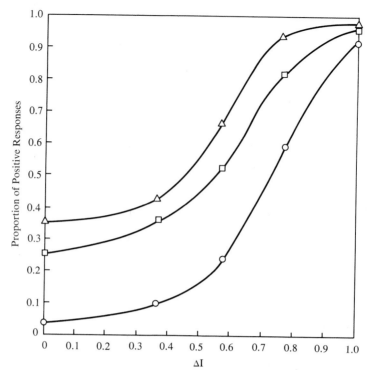

FIGURE 6 The relationship between the stimulus threshold and p_N (A) with the proportion of positive responses to four positive values of signal intensity, p_{SN} (A), and to the blank of zero-intensity presentation, p_N (A), at three values of p_N (A).

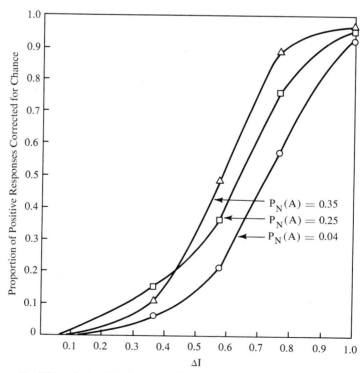

$P_N(A) = 0.35$
$P_N'(A) = 0.25$
$P_N(A) = 0.04$

FIGURE 7 The relationship between the stimulus threshold and p_N (A) with the three curves corrected for chance success, by Equation 6.

likelihood ratio or some monotonic function of it and that he is capable of adopting different criteria.

Second Expected-Value Experiment. A second expected-value experiment was conducted to obtain a more precise definition of the ROC curve than that provided by the experiment just described. In the second experiment greater definition was achieved by increasing the number of observations on which the estimates of $p_{SN}(A)$ and $p_N(A)$ were based, and by increasing the range of values of $p_N(A)$.

In this experiment only one signal intensity (0.78 foot-lamberts) was employed. Each of 13 experimental sessions included 200 presentations of the signal, and 200 presentations of noise alone. Thus, $p(SN)$ remained constant at 0.50 throughout this experiment. Changes in the optimal crite-

rion β, and thus in the obtained values of $p_N(A)$, were effected entirely by changes in the values associated with the decision outcomes. These values were manipulated to yield β's (Equation 4) varying from 0.16 to 8.00. A different set of observers served in this experiment.

The results are portrayed in Figure 8. In may be seen that the experimentally determined points are fitted quite well by the type of ROC curve that is predicted by decision theory. It is equally apparent, excepting Observer 1, that the points do not lie along a straight line intersecting the point $p_N(A) = p_{SN}(A) = 1.00$, as predicted by the high threshold model.

One other feature of these figures is worthy of note. It will be recalled that in our presentation of decision theory we tentatively assumed that the density functions of noise and of signal plus noise,

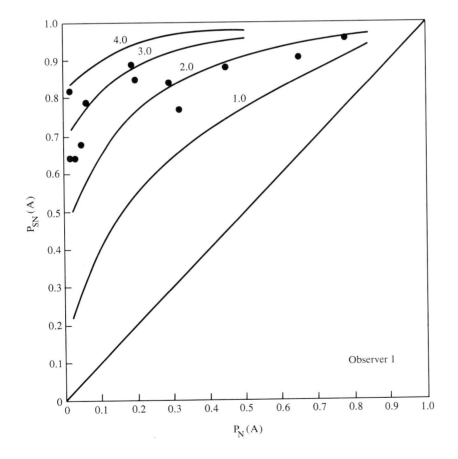

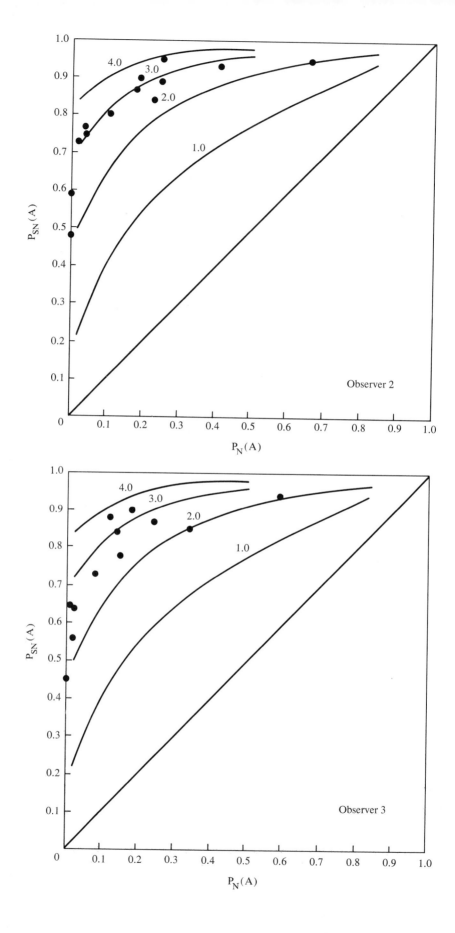

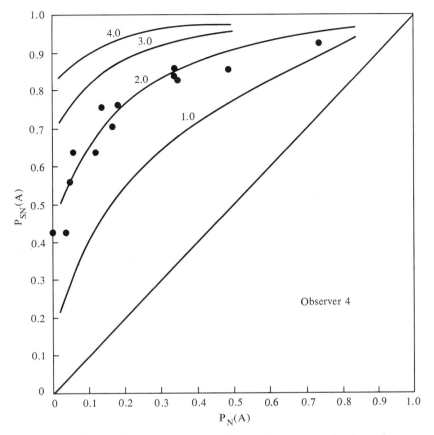

FIGURE 8   Empirical receiver-operating-characteristic curves for four observers
in the second expected-value experiment.

$f_N(x)$ and $f_{SN}(x)$, are of equal variance. Although we did not, in order to preserve the continuity of the discussion, we might have acknowledged at that point that the assumption of equal variance is not necessarily the best one. In particular, one might rather expect the variance of $f_{SN}(x)$ to be proportional to its mean. At any rate, the assumption made about variances represents a degree of freedom of the theory that we have not emphasized previously. We have, however, used this degree of freedom in the construction of the theoretical ROC curves of Figure 8. Notice that these curves are not symmetrical about the diagonal, as are the curves of Figure 3 that are predicated on equal variance. The curves of Figure 8 are based on the

assumption that the ratio of the increment of the mean of $f_{SN}(x)$ to the increment of its standard deviation is equal to 4, $\Delta M/\Delta\sigma = 4$. A close look at these figures suggests that ROC curves calculated from a still greater ratio would provide a still better fit. Since other data presented in the following bear directly on this question of a dependence between variance and signal strength, we shall postpone further discussion of it. We shall also consider later whether the exact form of the empirical ROC curves supports the assumption of normality of the density functions $f_N(x)$ and $f_{SN}(x)$. For now, the main point is that decision theory predicts the curvilinear form of the ROC curves that are yielded by the observers.

References

BLACKWELL, H. R. Psychophysical thresholds: Experimental studies of methods of measurement. *Bull. Eng. Res. Inst. U. Mich.*, 1953, no. 36.

BLACKWELL, H. R., B. S. PRITCHARD, and T. G. OHMART. Automatic apparatus for stimulus presentation and recording in visual threshold experiments. *J. Opt. Soc. Amer.*, 1954, 44, 322–326.

BORING, E. G. *A history of experimental psychology.* (2nd. ed.) New York: Appleton-Century-Crofts, 1950.

BRICKER, P. D., and A. CHAPANIS. Do incorrectly perceived tachistoscopic stimuli convey some information? *Psychol. Rev.*, 1953, 60, 181–188.

BROSS, I. D. J. *Design for decision.* New York: Macmillan, 1953.

CLARKE, F. R., T. G. BIRDSALL, and W. P. TANNER, JR. Two types of ROC curves and definitions of parameters. *J. Acoust. Soc. Amer.*, 1959, 31, 629–630.

DECKER, L. R., and I. POLLACK. Confidence ratings and message reception for filtered speech. *J. Acoust. Soc. Amer.*, 1958, 30, 432–434.

EGAN, J. P. Monitoring task in speech communication. *J. Acoust. Soc. Amer.*, 1957, 29, 482–489.

EGAN, J. P., and F. R. CLARKE. Source and receiver behavior in the use of a criterion. *J. Acoust. Soc. Amer.*, 1956, 28, 1267–1269.

EGAN, J. P., F. R. CLARKE, and E. C. CARTERETTE. On the transmission and confirmation of messages in noise. *J. Acoust. Soc. Amer.*, 1956, 28, 536–550.

EGAN, J. P., A. I. SCHULMAN, and G. Z. GREENBERG. Operating characteristics determined by binary decisions and by ratings. *J. Acoust. Soc. Amer.*, 1959, 31, 768–773.

GOLDIAMOND, I. Indicators of perception: I. Subliminal perception, subception, unconscious perception: An analysis in terms of psychophysical indicator methodology. *Psychol. Bull*, 1958, 55, 373–411.

HORTON, J. W. *Fundamentals of sonar.* Annapolis: United States Naval Institute, 1957.

HOWES, D. H. A statistical theory of the phenomenon of subception. *Psychol. Rev.*, 1954, 61, 98–110.

MILLER, J. G. *Unconsciousness.* New York: Wiley, 1942.

MUNSON, W. A., and J. E. KARLIN. The measurement of the human channel transmission characteristics. *J. Acoust. Soc. Amer.*, 1956, 26, 542–553.

OSGOOD, C. E. *Method and theory in experimental psychology.* New York: Oxford Univer. Press, 1953.

PETERSON, W. W., T. G. BIRDSALL, and W. C. FOX. The theory of signal detectability. *IRE Trans.*, 1954, PGIT-4, 171–212.

POLLACK, I., and L. R. DECKER. Confidence ratings, message reception, and the receiver operating characteristic. *J. Acoust. Soc. Amer.*, 1958, 30, 286–292.

SHANNON, C. E. The mathematical theory of communication. *Bell Sys. tech. J.*, 1948, 27, 379–423.

SMITH, M., and EDNA A. WILSON. A model of the auditory threshold and its application to the problem of the multiple observer. *Psychol. Monogr.*, 1953, 67(9, Whole No. 359).

SWETS, J. A. Indices of signal detectability obtained with various psychophysical procedures. *J. Acoust. Soc. Amer.*, 1959, 31, 511–513.

SWETS, J. A., and T. G. BIRDSALL. The human use of information: III. Decision-making in signal detection and recognition situations involving multiple alternatives. *IRE Trans.*, 1956, IT-2, 138–165.

SWETS, J. A., and D. M. GREEN. Sequential observations by human observers of signals in noise. In C. Cherry (Ed.), *Fourth symposium on information theory.* London: Butterworth, in press.

SWETS, J. A., ELIZABETH F. SHIPLEY, MARY J. McKEY, and D. M. GREEN. Multiple observations of signals in noise. *J. Acoust. Soc. Amer.*, 1959, 31, 514–521.

TANNER, W. J., JR. A theory of recognition. *J. Acoust. Soc. Amer.*, 1956, 28, 882–888.

TANNER, W. P., JR., and T. G. BIRDSALL. Definitions of d' and η as psychophysical measures. *J. Acoust. Soc. Amer.*, 1958, 30, 922–928.

TANNER, W. P. JR., and J. A. SWETS. A decision-making theory of visual detection. *Psychol. Rev.*, 1954, 61, 401–409.

TANNER, W. P. JR., J. A. SWETS, and D. M. GREEN. Some general properties of the hearing mechanism. Technical Report No. 30, 1956, University of Michigan, Electronic Defense Group.

THURSTONE, L. L. A law of comparative

judgment. *Psychol. Rev.*, 1927, 34, 273–286 (a)

THURSTONE, L. L. Psychophysical analysis. *Amer. J. Psychol.*, 1927, 38, 368–389. (b)

VAN METER, D., and D. MIDDLETON. Modern statistical approaches to reception in communication theory. *IRE Trans*, 1954, PGIT-4, 119–145.

WALD, A. *Statistical decision functions.* New York: Wiley, 1950.

CHAPTER 2

Perception of Movement

Problems in the Study of Visually Perceived Movement: An Introduction[*]

IRWIN M. SPIGEL
University of Toronto

Although the detection of movement is critical to the survival of many species, we have as yet no satisfactory conceptual framework within which to organize the mass of empirical data and theoretical speculation bearing on the problem. The crux of the difficulty appears to lie in the frequently paradoxical relationship between the phenomenal characteristics of movement perception and the physical characteristics of the visual stimuli which are correlated with it.

Since motion appears to be a quality conferred upon an object or objects by an observer, displacement of such stimuli in both time and place is implied. But physical displacement and perceived movement are not always correlated. Consider the motion of the moon in a cloudless sky, or the hands of a clock, or the shadows of fixed objects in the sun. Within some sufficiently long interval of time, these objects will be observed to have undergone some displacement in space, but the observer cannot report that he has seen them "move." Superficially, at least, the movement experience requires a perceptible rate of change in the position of some stimulus element with respect to another. The change may be of a figure with respect to

* *Readings in the Study of Visually Perceived Movement* by Irwin M. Spigel, pp. 1–32. Copyright © 1965 by Irwin M. Spigel. Reprinted by permission of Harper and Row, Publishers.

its ground, or to another figure, or to the bounding contours of the visual field.

It is for this reason that it is both tempting and convenient to give as a necessary condition for the perception of movement the successive stimulation of adjacent retinal loci. But any position which demands continuous displacement over a portion of the retinal mosaic as the necessary condition for movement perception is, to say the least, complicated by the existence of the phenomena of apparent movement. In the case of *phi* movement, for example, the appearance of continuous movement may be produced simply by the successive stimulation of discrete retinal loci, in the absence of continuous displacement of the stimulus upon the retina. Finally, while with *phi* movement there is at least a spatio-temporal succession of stimulus events, the apparent movement following exposure to the objective motion of repetitive patterns (the movement aftereffect) compounds the complexity. In these situations, movement is experienced in the absence of even discrete objective displacements during the interval of report. If such phenomena are to be explained as peripheral in origin, they would require analysis in terms somewhat different from those employed to account for the perception of either *real* or *phi* movement.

Although a score of specific questions are raised and discussed in the selections to follow, at last three general problems may be enumerated and allowed to serve as a conceptual framework for this volume:

1. What is the role of each of the different levels of the visual system in the processing of stimulus events underlying the movement experience?
2. To what degree does the organism respond to absolute or relational properties in the visual world with respect to motion? To what extent is the structure of the entire visual input a determinant of the movement experience with respect to any part?
3. What is the relationship between real and apparent movement? Are they correlated with different stimulus characteristics and mediated by different neural mechanisms? Or may one be seen as a special case of the other so that an understanding of one will shed light on the mechanisms underlying the other?

Real Movement

Part I of this volume deals with the perception of *real* movement, the traditional term reserved for the experiential correlates of objective displacement. As is the case with a great variety of perceptual phenomena, absolute thresholds for movement are a function of a number of situational variables, including the manner in which the limen is measured. In the early work of Brown (1931a, b) on such determinations, the minimal rate of perceptible movement was taken as the threshold and was found to vary inversely with the degree of the heterogeneity of the field. In other words, the absolute limen was highly determined by structural properties of the stimulus matrix—the more homogeneous the field, the greater the rate of motion required

for the emergence of perceived movement. Lower thresholds were also obtained with decreased size and brightness of the moving target. A number of investigations since that time have used, as the absolute threshold, the minimum angular distance traversed, with rate held constant. This was initially found to be less than the minimum angle for the resolution acuity for objects (Basler, 1906). Later work (Gordon, 1947) revealed that when measurements are taken at low levels of illumination, such a limen—more appropriately termed a displacement threshold—is quite similar to that obtained for resolution.

A more recent psychophysical examination of movement perception was undertaken by Ekman and Dahlbäck (1956), who constructed a subjective scale of velocity using the fractionation method. The positively accelerated function relating subjective and physical velocities was viewed as adequately represented by Guilford's n^{th} power law. The authors also collected data on discriminative sensitivity at a number of physical velocities and found the relationship of this sensitivity and subjective velocity to be linear.

Although a number of investigations have been aimed at determining the differential thresholds for velocity, differences in methodology make comparison of the obtained results difficult. Nine of these investigations and the procedures employed are summarized by Brown (1961), who also discusses the practical value of the Weber ratio as a convenient means by which velocity discriminations may be compared with sensitivity in other modalities as well as with tracking performance and prediction.

Mandriotta, Mintz, and Notterman (1962) report the effects of stimulus-related spatial and temporal cues on velocity discrimination, which appear to have a critical bearing on the differential threshold for angular speed. Within the range of velocities examined, these authors found the finest discrimination to occur in the presence of spatial cues, the next best with temporal cues, and the least sensitivity in the absence of either. Their conclusion that velocity judgments are at least in part dependent upon the systematic presence of such cues emphasizes the need for careful control of these influences in psychophysical studies of velocity discrimination.

It might be noted at this point that some comparative data on movement discrimination are available. An earlier paper by Kennedy (1936) summarizes a number of experiments relating to investigations of movement sensitivity in animals. Data on insects, birds, fish, rats, and cats are included. A further review of comparative data is found in the article by Smith in Part III of this collection. Ross (1943) found that thresholds for real movement as a function of illumination are higher for monkeys than for children, but that the obtained curves are parallel.

Further investigation by Brown into the perception of velocity has led to more exhaustive study of what has come to be known as the transposition phenomenon. Two rectangular movement fields in a darkened room were employed, the linear dimensions of one being one-half those of the other. Subjects, whose task it was to match the speed of a disk in the smaller field to the velocity of a moving disk in the larger field, judged the phenomenal velocities equal when the objective velocity in the larger field was nearly twice that of the phenomenal speed. Later work (Wallach, 1939) confirmed that phenomenal velocities appear equal when displacements per unit of time are proportional to the dimensions of their respective fields. Brown found the transposition effect to hold for velocities ranging from 2 to 10 inches per second. Although field size comparisons greater than 2:1 also produced the transposition effect, more severe departures of matched speeds from that of the ratio of the involved linear dimensions were evident when the differences in field size were extreme. It was also found that

transposition tended to break down when the laboratory was fully illuminated during the experiment.

These experiments have not only intrinsic interest as qualitative foundations of movement perception, but also wider implications for such enduring problems as size constancy and the more general question of the degree to which we respond to relational qualities in the visual world.

Whereas such demonstrations appear to emphasize relational determinants and field structure in the perception of movement, the investigations of Smith and Sherlock (1957) call attention to the need for careful control of both stimulus and subject variables if unambiguous results are to be obtained. In their study of the transposition effect, these authors concluded that subjects were matching apparent frequency rather than apparent velocity of the movement. In other words, subjects were judging the frequency with which objects left their bounded fields. They further demonstrated that with physical velocity held constant, frequency could be judged independently.

Induced Movement

The idea that motion is a quality conferred upon an object by an observer is clearly illustrated by the phenomenon of *induced* movement. With two objects or stimulus elements arranged such that one is the surround for the other, regardless of which is set in motion, it is the surrounded target that is inevitably perceived as the element which is moving. This highly compelling experience has been extensively studied by Duncker (1929). When three objective contours are given, each in turn surrounding the other, and the middle contour is set in motion, both this and the smallest target are observed as moving and the overall surround as remaining stationary. If the outermost surround is now eliminated, only the smallest target is observed as in motion. Furthermore, the perceived path of movement is rigidly determined by the specific direction of the objectively moving surround—should the latter be moved to the left, the perceived movement of the surrounded object will be to the right. The compelling nature of this experience is emphasized by the fact that the movement of the smaller target is observed even though the motion of the surround is at a suprathreshold velocity. In all cases, the perceived movement of the target is determined by its immediate surround, independent of the motion of this surrounding frame with respect to higher-order contours in the visual field. Such surround-induced movement constitutes still another illustration of the predominance of relational properties in the structure of perceptual experience. The question of imparted motion is also a substantial factor in the investigations of Michotte (1946) into perceived causality. In these experiments, complex and varied perceptual effects are imparted to one member of a pair of stimuli by its apparent contact with the other stimulus, and the conditions underlying these effects are explored.

Gibson (1958), in arguing for a stimulus-based position with reference to the perception of motion, suggests that problems in this area ought to be restated as problems of the perception of *change* in environmental events. He views motion perception as but one aspect of the more general problem of the sensory control of behavior by feedback stimulation. According to Gibson, research in the perception of motion cannot be separated from research in the visual perception of solid objects, space, and spatio-temporal relationships. Motion in the visual field is best conceived and analyzed in terms of the transformations undergone in the environmental structure by virtue of the objective movement. That is, the essential data is that involving changes in the configuration of contours and boundaries generated by the object in

motion. The results of a number of investigations have led Gibson to conclude that only a limited number of subsets of point velocities in a two-dimensional viewing field have any meaning for perception, and that the comprehension of motion perception will be facilitated by the isolation of these relevant subsets. From studies of the transformations of both regular and irregular patterns on the screen of a point-source shadow projector, Gibson concludes that changes in perspective seem to underlie a class of motions yielding the perception of a rigid object, constant in size and shape, moving in an apparently tridimensional space. Such experience is seen as suggesting that the pattern of the field of view must be more than a collection of individually moving points. The entire field, rather than points, is viewed as undergoing simultaneous transformation, and the perceived motion of a unitary surface can be most accurately understood from such configurational analysis rather than from principles derived from the study of point motion.

A critical implication for theoretical accounts of movement perception is treated by Ludvigh (1955), who addresses himself to the question of reduced visual acuity during pursuit movements of the eyes. Deterioration of visual acuity becomes more marked with increased angular velocity of the moving targets. Although Ludvigh attributes this loss of acuity in a general way to decreasing alignment between the eyes and target with greater objective speeds, he also explores a number of more profound considerations related to the ocular mechanisms involved. Pointing out that there is substantial evidence to indicate that the eye is virtually lacking in a position sense, Ludvigh raises the question of what constitutes the error signal for the eye, during tracking, in the absence of proprioception. In short, without articulation, how is physiological feedback mediated in the oculomotor system? He further cites the inadequacy of an hypothesized resort to exteroceptive feedback control of ocular motion, such as might accompany change of fixation from one point to another. Ludvigh holds that such a postulation is rendered inadequate by virtue of the fact that entire excursions of several degrees may be completed by the eye before there is time for any error signal of either an interoceptive or an exteroceptive nature to become effective. As an alternative, Ludvigh proposes that eye position is given almost exclusively by retinal information. Such information is suggested as a substitute for articular sensitivity in the operation of parametric feedback control. Inaccurate performance in any part of the visual system is viewed as resulting in image motion on the retina while the eye is pursuing a moving target—such motion resulting in the deterioration of visual acuity during objective movement.

Observations by MacKay (1961) further militate against attributing the movement experience to some intrinsic computer which selectively monitors the discrepancy between visual and kinesthetic input. MacKay found that stroboscopic illumination can seriously disturb the experiential continuity that normally follows continuous lighting of a movement sequence. Given a stroboscopically illuminated field in which both self-luminous and stroboscopically illuminated objects are in motion, the latter yield considerably lower thresholds of acuity for retinal image displacement. He further reported that with displacement of the entire field, the self-luminous targets appear to move independently of their stroboscopically illuminated background. Gregory (1964) views such phenomena as evidence to support the position that movement is directly coded in the nervous system rather than computed indirectly from changes in position with respect to time. He suggests that there may be two movement systems: one mediating velocity (which would underlie the experiences reported by MacKay), and the other subserving changes in the position of objects. This point will be raised again in connection with a discussion of the movement aftereffect.

The work of Smith and Gulick (1962) on dynamic contour perception is critically related to the more general problems of visual acuity and of the emergence and stability of contours in visual experience. Examining the effects of visual events preceding stimulus motion on the perception of the moving target, these authors found that the edges of a small stimulus object whose contours are not seen clearly at a particular velocity can be observed at that same velocity when the target is presented in a stationary position for a brief duration prior to its movement. That the involved processes are central in nature is suggested by interocular demonstration of the experience—the stationary stimulus presented to one eye and the moving target to the other. A neurostatistical theory based on the position of Marshall and Talbot (1942)—with reference to lateral summation of impulses resulting from reciprocal overlap of synaptic connections in the visual system—is offered to account for the enhanced dynamic acuity. These authors see neural activity in the visual cortex following cessation of the stationary stimulus condition as summating with the activity produced by the moving stimulus. The effect of this summation is viewed as maintaining the total level of neural excitation as sufficiently different from that of the surrounding cortical area to meet the necessary conditions for contour perception. Perception of the moving contour was held dependent upon the summation of neural excitation in the visual cortex from the two phases of the stimulation sequence. In the course of their more extensive discussion of the proposed statistical model, the authors cite experiments which suggest that neural excitation and/or summation at the retinal as well as at the cortical level may be involved, necessitating the possible inclusion of peripheral processes in the final explanation.

The last selection of Part I deals with the work of Johansson (1960) on *motion track enlargement*. This refers to the phenomenal distance traveled by a moving stimulus being greater than a nobjectively equal but stationary linear distance. Such determinations suggest that a simple geometric analysis of point-to-point relationships between objective and retinal distances may not be applicable when stimulus events involve motion. That the underlying processes are of central rather than peripheral origin is further suggested by a comparison of binocular and monocular findings reported by Johansson.

Apparent Movement

Representative investigations of several aspects of *apparent* movement are included in Part II of this collection. Three varieties of phenomenal displacement in the absence of physical movement are treated: *phi,* the autokinetic effect, and the aftereffect of seen movement. As suggested earlier, a critical question with regard to these phenomena concerns the degree to which they are mediated by processes identical to those which subserve real movement. Certainly much of the interest in apparent movement derives from the possibility that it offers a means by which movement experience in general may be explored. Implicit in such a position is the assumption that common processes or mechanisms are involved. The illusory nature of apparent movement is similarly of importance to those concerned with the more general problem of veridicality in perception and of the relationship of organization in phenomenal space to that in physical space.

PHI PHENOMENON

In addition to its theoretical implications, the *phi* phenomenon has an historical significance in connection with the emergence of Gestalt psychology. It was in reference to this variety of apparent movement that physiological continuity was inferred as underlying the perceptual continuity emphasized by this school. Early work with *phi* sought to delineate central excitatory processes underlying movement experience in general. Because successive, i.e., temporally and spatially discrete, physical stimulation produces as its phenomenal correlate the appearance of continuous displacement in space, it was hypothesized that the underlying physiological mechanism consisted of the generation and diffusion of excitatory fields in the visual cortex. Such excitatory processes were viewed as being generated at each of the cortical loci stimulated, and were conceived of as interacting in the manner of a short circuit to produce a flow of current in the space between the two loci. It was this current flow which was hypothesized as underlying the perceptual continuity experienced as apparent movement when two retinal areas were successively stimulated.

The fact that *phi* movement could be produced by varying a set of time, intensity, and distance parameters raised the question of whether appropriate adjustments of these parameters constituted the essential conditions for movement perception. Indeed, Korte's (1915) "laws," specifying the parametric control of the *phi* experience, emphasized the reciprocal interrelatedness of these factors, where change in one required predictable changes in one or both of the other variables in order to preserve optimal apparent movement. Korte's statements have served the experimental analysis of apparent movement with almost as much utility as has Weber's Law with respect to psychophysical investigation.

The various stages in the emergence and production of apparent movement are described by Boring (1942). *Phi* is reserved for the experience of movement which appears to connect the flashing targets. Such movement has direction but is not in itself perceived as having object quality. *Beta* movement is the name given to optimal apparent movement where a single object is perceived to be in motion. *Delta* movement, the reverse of *beta* movement, is movement whose direction is from the second stimulus to the first, and which may be produced by increasing the intensity of the later flash with reference to the earlier.

The manipulation of temporal and spatial factors in connection with *phi* movement has yielded a number of interesting phenomena which bear heavily on the theoretical aspects of apparent movement and its neural as well as psychological substrates. Early experiments by McConnell (1927) utilized simultaneous excitation by the two stimuli with varying degrees of initial or terminal overlap. It was found that the frequency of phenomenal movement reports under such conditions of simultaneous presentation was directly related to the amount of overlapping of one stimulus with the other. Initial overlap was found to be more productive of apparent movement than terminal overlap. Such demonstrations related to the general question of necessary conditions for apparent movement and the critical nature of temporal stimulus factors in the movement experience.

Zeeman and Roelofs (1953) projected stimuli at distances varying from 10 to 80 cm. and with time intervals ranging from 16 to 2,500 ms. Two rather pronounced phenomena were described: the apparent movement of afterimages from the stimuli, and the emergence of what was termed "tunnel movement." The latter consisted of the disappearance of one stimulus in the direction of the other. Tunnel movement was viewed not as a preliminary phase in the emergence of apparent movement, but as evidence of suppression by a competing process. This suggestion was also believed to account for the persistence of tunneling for longer periods of time with greater spatial separations of stimuli.

The experiments of Brown and Voth (1937) appeared to demonstrate a similarity between real and apparent movement. Four points of light, circularly arranged, were exposed successively. At speeds productive of apparent movement, a circular path of motion was observed which lay just within a locus passing through the objective points. This phenomenal shrinkage of the path of the lights was also obtained when a single light was objectively rotated. The authors attempted to explain this contracted movement locus as the resultant of directionally induced force vectors acting on the objective positions of the light. These "cohesive field forces" were seen as acting in the cortex, drawing the path of the light inward. The experiments of Brown and Voth are of interest on two accounts: first, as a purported demonstration of the similarity of real and apparent movement; and second, as a reflection of the advent of field theory and of the physicalistic bias which had been developing since the turn of the century.

Further investigation of *phi* movement by Gengerelli (1948) pointed to the central nature of the mechanisms involved. The interaction of both hemispheres in the production of *phi* was demonstrated, through the effect was less prominent than when unilaterally produced. The interhemispheric production of *phi* complicates the attempt to comprehend the nature of this phenomenon, as it would seem to imply some transcallosal connection between contralateral visual cortices. Anatomical demonstration of such direct callosal connection on a point-to-point basis has yet to be demonstrated in primates. The alternative, if direct neural interaction between contralateral events in the primary visual areas of each hemisphere is excluded, involves viewing such demonstrations of *phi* from a more elusive physiological framework, such as the diffusive spread of excitation through the mass of cortical tissue, as suggested by the Gestalt theorists. Smith (1948), however, views interhemispheric demonstration of apparent movement as evidence against the Gestalt position which utilized such a conceptualization of diffuse cortical induction.

A further argument against the classical Gestalt view of cortical "short-circuiting" may be inferred from a recent investigation by Rock and Ebenholz (1962). Their study was aimed directly at the question of whether apparent movement was dependent more upon retinal or phenomenal separation of stimuli. Using techniques allowing independent manipulation of both possibilities, it was found that phenomenal separation was the critical requirement for the perception of movement. The authors view their findings as implying that apparent movement need not depend on neural interaction.

Since the question of the identity of real and apparent movement remains a critical one, the results of some experiments by Kolers (1963) are particularly significant. It was found that the object in apparent movement fails to affect the detectability threshold for other objects in its path, whereas the real movement of such an object does so. Kolers views his findings as evidence against the identity of the mechanisms subserving real and apparent movement. Further support for this position is found in another study by Kolers (1964), in which qualitative differences were found in the perceptual experiences produced by a Necker cube in real movement and the same cube successively displaced so as to produce apparent movement. It is also of interest to note in this connection that transformations in the perspective of the cube were evident even in the interspace of a *phi* field. Kolers concludes that movement perception involves an orderly sequence of encodings at some level beyond the retina, and that the unity of percept may itself be an illusory end product of an organized series of separate operations rather than a point-to-point representation of the physical world in the visual system. The suggestion of a similar approach to the comprehension of the movement aftereffect is discussed later

when this form of apparent movement is considered.

AUTOKINETIC EFFECT

The role of environmental structure is once again the chief concern in the examination of the autokinetic effect. This phenomenon involves movement perception in the absence of displacement of the stimulus in either time or space. A fixed luminous source in an unarticulated surround—one which reduces to a minimum any frames of reference or stability—is seen as moving in an erratic, unpredictable fashion. Darkness has proved to be the most efficient contour-free situation for the production of autokinetic movement. Luchins (1954) studied the relationship between the perceived movement and the size of the luminous source. Generally, the larger the light, the weaker the autokinetic effect obtained. In addition, Luchins found a positive relationship between the size of the luminance and the movement latency, i.e., the time between light onset and the start of apparent movement. He also found an inverse relationship between the size of the light and the frequency of reported movements. One problem with Luchins's experiments, however, was the confounding of stimulus size and brightness. In fact, Edwards (1954), who obtained autokinetic movement with very large and very bright targets, suggested that if reference contours provided by the observer's nose and eyebrows could be eliminated, the magnitude of perceived movement may prove to be independent of stimulus size or luminosity. Spigel (1963), however, found that in the case of both steady and flickering photic sources, reduced illumination produced increased autokinetic movement, with most movement perceived at flash rates of 10 to 15 cps.

Although the results of several investigations (Gregory, 1959; Guilford and Dallenbach, 1928) are viewed by Gregory (1964) as ruling out eye movements as a necessary condition for autokinetic movement, alternative explanations of the phenomenon are equally unsatisfactory. Partly on the basis of experiments linking autokinetic movement to differential fatiguing of the extrinsic eye muscles, Gregory (1964) suggested that this variety of apparent movement could result from neural impulses directed toward the maintenance of fixation in the face of momentary changes in the efficiency of the ocular musculature. After finding that autokinetic movement is concentrated along the same meridian in which the eyes had previously been deviated, and often in the direction opposite to the deviation, Gregory and Zangwill (1963) hypothesized that the phenomenon is related to adaptational changes in the mechanisms of eye–head control.

MOVEMENT AFTEREFFECTS

The appearance of so many papers on the aftereffects of visually perceived movement reflects the increasing interest in this phenomenon in recent years. Since the movement aftereffect involves not only the experience of movement in the *absence* of either temporal or spatial displacement of the stimulus, but also a directionality *opposite* to that of the inducing movement which preceded it, one cannot so readily attribute the experience to erroneous judgment or momentary confusion. Although a number of theories have been offered to account for the aftereffect, none has achieved general acceptance. Recently, the phenomenon has proved useful in exploring the implications of contemporary theoretical and neurophysiological formulations.

Although the aftereffect may be brought about in several ways, the most frequently employed procedure calls for the continued observations of a stationary spiral following a period of rotation, or of a striped pattern following its linear motion.

Gates (1934) found that simultaneous monocular as well as binocular observation of two spirals rotating in opposite directions produced independent expansion or contraction aftereffects in the usual manner. In the binocular viewing condition, the two opposing aftereffects were obtained even when the two visual fields overlapped. Gates attempted to develop a refined motoric theory to account for these phenomena, suggesting that the internal musculature for accommodation and convergence were involved by way of sudden changes resulting from the cessation of rotation. The return of the tonicity of these muscles to a normal state was viewed as the correlate of the visual aftereffect. One of the chief problems for a muscular theory appeared to be the specification of processes by which muscle movements are translated into visual experience. Another involved explanation of the interocular transfer of the effect which had been demonstrated by several investigators (Ehrenstein, 1925; Durup, 1928).

A centrally oriented explanation of movement aftereffects was offered by Spitz (1958), who used as his theoretical framework the satiation theory of Köhler and Wallach (1944) and its application to figural aftereffects. Figural aftereffects involve the displacement of targets in the visual field following antecedent contour fixation. Köhler and Wallach suggested that fixation on a contour, called the inspection or "I" figure, led to the establishment of figural currents in the brain, analogous to currents set up in an electrolyte. According to this position the currents, viewed as isomorphic to the outline of the fixated figure, make for increased cortical resistance which tends to block or impede further stimulation of cerebral areas that are already the locus of spreading currents. The manifest result is the displacement of new contours to adjacent areas. (An excellent critical review of this as well as other accounts of figural aftereffect research and theory may be found in McEwen [1958].) Spitz presented a modification of this position, assigning a critical role to ionic processes, which were viewed as correlated with differential excitation of neighboring cortical areas isomorphic with the brightness differential of the stimulus. The aftereffect is explained as the correlate of a time course in the recovery of neural tissue following the cessation of the rotation which initially established the gradient. However, this position has been criticized by Deutsch (1959) as leading to a prediction of either no movement at all or movement in the wrong direction. Deutsch (1956) had also critized as inapplicable the statistical theory of figural aftereffects proposed by Osgood and Heyer (1952), which was based on the Marshall and Talbot position noted earlier. The statistical theory was applied by George (1953) to an explanation of movement aftereffects in terms of asymmetrical gradient of excitation established during objective rotation of the spiral. Spitz himself has noted that his own theoretical formulation is limited by its inability to explain why spiral rotation does not yield figural displacement outside its own border, whereas stationary fixation does.

The satiation position has been stated at some length because not only has it generated much research on perceptual problems in general, but it has also been a framework for many recent studies of apparent movement.

"Storage" of neural events underlying movement aftereffect phenomena is suggested by the results of investigations by Spigel (1962). Inhibition of the decay of the aftereffect was evident when either darkness or homogeneous illumination was interpolated during the postexposure period. It was inferred from the experiment reported in this volume that the absence of contour in the visual field during the postmovement period constituted the sufficient condition for this decay inhibition. Determinations reported elsewhere (Spigel, 1962a) revealed that only after subjects had experienced an interval in darkness equal to twice their mean aftereffect duration did

the decay reach 50 percent. Even after three times the subjects' mean aftereffect duration was spent in darkness, about 25 percent of the illusory movement remained. It would appear that this inhibitory effect makes available a perceptual probe for the examination of perseverative neural processes, previously explored at the behavioral level only within a learning paradigm. Elsewhere, Spigel (1962b) has proposed an elaboration of cell assembly theory augmented by processes of inhibitory interaction to account for the movement aftereffect and other motion phenomena. The illusion is viewed as the phenomenal correlate of a partial failure of the inhibitory mechanism under sudden changes in critical parameters of visual stimulation. The proposed model appears to resemble that implied in Kolers' speculation, noted earlier.

Using the stabilized retinal image technique, Sekuler and Ganz (1963) explored the implication of recent neurophysiological research (see below, Hubel and Wiesel, 1962). They proposed that sustained exposure to unidirectional stimulus movement produced differential adaptation of cortical cells sensitive to movement only in that direction. The authors predicted and found elevated movement thresholds for stimulus motion in the same direction as compared with thresholds obtained for motion in the reverse direction—the direction of the aftereffect. They conclude that the results support an explanation of the movement aftereffect in terms of adaptation of direction-specific cells in the visual cortex.

In this connection it may be well to return momentarily to Gregory's (1964) proposal that two systems—velocity and positional—subserve movement perception. He finds that the existence of movement aftereffects supports this position, and notes that such movement experience takes place wholly without an apparent change in position. He suggests that central adaptation of only one of the two systems—most likely the velocity system—occurs during the period of objective movement.

The experiments reported by Scott, Jordan, and Powell (1963) are of both theoretical and methodological importance. On the one hand, the authors sought to determine whether Gibson's theory of perceptual adaptation was applicable to phenomenal as well as objective velocities. Demonstration of the additivity of objective and apparent movement in human subjects was achieved, supporting the extension of Gibson's position to include the movement aftereffect experience, within the context of the experimental design. But of perhaps greater significance for further investigation of movement aftereffects is the successful use by these authors of a subhuman primate and appropriate operant methodology to demonstrate additivity with both real and apparent movement. In addition to providing comparative support for Gibson's position, the methodology developed may be employed in conjunction with recording techniques and/or systematic ablation in a more refined effort to ascertain neurophysiological bases for real and apparent movement perception.

Interrelationships

The interrelationship of apparent movement and figural aftereffect phenomena in a number of studies reflects, in part, the volume of research generated by the latter, and the usefulness of apparent movement as a device with which to examine the implications of a theoretical position. There are, at present, at least five theories which attempt to account for the perception of figural aftereffects. Although designed to explain the spatial displacement of stationary contours, an adequate theory must also be able to account for the effects of antecedent contour fixation on the perception of contours in motion—both real and apparent. To date, the greater number of such investigations have been undertaken within the context of satiation

theory, as noted earlier. The last two papers in Part II represent efforts to deal with the pertinent interrelational questions.

The effects of preinspection of a stationary figure on the path of apparent movement are reported by Weiskrantz (1950), such prior fixation leading to the lengthening or contraction of the pattern depending on whether the contours were placed outside of or within the physical space between the pair of stimuli. Although the findings are those predicted by satiation theory, a number of interesting questions requiring further study are raised by the author. For one thing, it cannot be determined from the experiment whether the figural preinspection actually altered the path of the movement or whether it was the distance between the targets that was phenomenally increased or decreased. The author also suggests the application of the experimental procedure to induced movement of the kind described by Duncker. The third and perhaps the most important, theoretical suggestion is Weiskrantz' proposal that the effects of satiation on thresholds for real movement be examined to determine whether similar influences will be evident.

Alterations in *phi* movement thresholds predictable from satiation theory were also found in experiments by Detherage and Bitterman (1952) and by Shapiro (1954). The former also noted changes in the path of apparent movement as a function of a laterally placed inspection contour. Both investigations relate the similarity of findings to the disturbances in apparent movement perception found in patients with cortical damage such as those reported by Bender and Teuber (1949). Shapiro, who noted that continuous stimulation may yield elevated apparent movement thresholds by increasing the apparent distance between targets, also suggests that the decrements in apparent movement perception by brain-damaged persons may be attributable to the inhibition of excitatory irradiation in the cortex. But a simple isomorphism such as is postulated in satiation theory is called into question by an investigation of Brenner (1953), who determined the effects of voluntary movement, mental arithmetic, and continuous auditory and visual stimulation on apparent movement thresholds. Significant alterations were obtained in all cases with respect to a control condition in the absence of stimulation. The influence of physical and mental activity and intersensory stimulation was viewed as suggesting that processes other than those of satiation, processes possibly involving the parastriate area of the cortex, underlie these perceptual phenomena as well as the interhemispheric demonstration of *phi* movement.

Predictions, based on satiation theory, concerning the effects of figural preinspection on the extent of autokinetic movement are made by Crutchfield and Edwards (1949). As anticipated, prior fixation resulted in an immediate, though transient, reduction in perceived autokinetic movement. Of special interest was the support offered for central mediation of the autokinetic phenomenon as inferred from the reduction in the apparent movement obtained even when the eyes were presented alternately with preinspection and autokinetic stimuli.

The central nature of both *phi* and the autokinetic effect as well as the underlying assumptions of satiation theory were the chief points of departure for a study by Livson (1953) which explores the effects of prior exposure to apparent movement upon magnitude of the autokinetic effect. His prediction of a reduction in autokinetic movement was confirmed.

Physiological Bases

A section devoted to physiological mechanisms is essential in a volume intended to provide a reasonably complete suggestion of the scope of research into visually perceived movement. To the extent that theoretical treatments are to be of something more than heuristic value, they must, at the very least, be compatible with neural determinations correlated with the movement experience.

The involvement of peripheral mechanisms is emphasized by Motokawa (1953), who concentrated on the use of phosphenes to explore the retinal excitation concurrent with moving stimuli. Phosphenes are visual experiences, such as flashes of light, produced by stimulation of the visual system by energy other than radiant (mechanical, electrical, etc.). Motokawa's position — termed retinal induction — acknowledges the embryological relationship of retina and brain and provides for the inclusion of processes of more central origin. Induction is the name given to the demonstrated spreading of excitation in the retina around the borders of a projected image. Excitation, as measured by least detectable electrically produced phosphenes, is seen to decrease monotonically from the borders of the figure—the rate of decrease depending on the brightness of the figure, its spatial characteristics, and the distortion of the retina itself. The locus of induction is placed in the retinal network distal to the ganglion cells. In the paper reprinted in this volume, Motokawa determines the physiological aftereffects of a moving retinal image. Using electrostimulation, the aftereffects at a series of points in the retinal pathway of the movement are measured and plotted as a function of distance, yielding "trace curves." Such "trace curves" appear to be set up in the direction of movement; and the higher the velocity, the higher the curve and the initial gradient. He notes further that the curve is higher for small figures. Perceived velocity is inferred as the resultant of interaction between the moving stimulus and the retinal trace behind it, such traces being viewed as continually subject to suppression by induction from the moving stimulus preceding it. Apparent velocity is little changed by reducing the linear dimensions of the moving field and the objective velocity to one-half the original, but the gradient becomes steeper. This view of what has come to be called the transposition phenomenon involves considering the trace itself as compensating for the loss of retinal velocity to keep apparent velocity constant. Retinal induction theory has also been applied to apparent movement by Motokawa and Ebe (1953).

Central Processes

Most physiological investigations of movement perception in higher animals, however, have focused on central rather than peripheral mechanisms. In his review of earlier experiments aimed at determining the role of the neocortex in the visual perception of movement in animals, Smith (1941) notes that bilateral destruction of the striate area produced deficits in this capacity but did not eliminate it. Evidence suggesting that cats could perceive only simple motions following such destruction is cited, as is the finding that partial bilateral lesions in the visual cortex yielded some elevation in the lower threshold of movement discrimination. In the experiments of Smith and his associates, a rotating striped pattern with the consequent optokinetic nystagmus was employed for the determination of movement thresholds. In the study reprinted in this volume, Smith used guinea pigs, noting that their maximum velocity thresholds, as measured by the optokinetic response, are comparable to those of cats and human beings. Four preparations were studied: occipital removals, hemidecorticates, hemidecorticates with contralateral occipital removals, and bilaterally decorticated animals. No change was found in the upper threshold for movement-induced fusion of the rotating stripes. Smith concludes that movement perception in guinea pigs is under multiple control, and that such perception is

mediated by subcortical centers in the absence of a cortex. He further concludes that the cortex is necessary for the perception of the movement of isolated patterns, but that subcortical processes suffice for responsiveness to the repetitive striations employed in the experiment. The author has also suggested that the nystagmic response in the absence of a cortex is further evidence against the earlier Gestalt conception of motion perception as dependent upon cortical induction. The possibility exists, however, that Smith's animals were not responding to movement stimulation *per se* but that the observed optokinetic nystagmus represented instead a reflex response to rapid and successive brightness discrimination ("flicker") induced by the rotating striations. This question will be considered again below in relation to data recorded from individual cortical cells in more recent microelectrode studies.

The investigations of Bender and Teuber (1949) into the experience of human patients with cerebral lesions provide some significant insights into the functions of the neocortex with respect to the perception of real and apparent movement. One of the most suggestive findings involves the occasional replacement of the continuous vision of a moving object by the appearance of a succession of stationary objects. Bender and Teuber also found that the path of movement in some patients with cerebral lesions at times appears curved rather than straight, and that to produce *phi* movement more rapid alternation of stimuli was required for these patients than for normal individuals. These observations lend plausibility to the speculation of such workers as Detherage and Bitterman and Shapiro about the relationship of satiation phenomena to cortical function when the findings of their own experimental work is considered.

In this connection, the investigation of Held and White (1959) and some relevant speculation by these authors appears to be of interest. They found that sensory deprivation in the form of prolonged patternless visual stimulation led to the underestimation by their subjects of the speeds of moving objects. Underestimation also followed exposure to "noisy" visual fields. Held and White suggested that spontaneous discharges dominate the visual system during the deprived period and that the normal perception of visual speed requires continuous exposure to the typical environment.

Weiskrantz (1961), however, emphasizes the difficulties inherent in the interpretation of evidence obtained in lesion studies with animals and in studies of brain injuries in man. With reference to Smith's determination that guinea pigs with striate cortex ablation cannot follow isolated moving objects, Weiskrantz notes that, in general, rodents do not display this particular behavior. Although he cites the findings of Rademaker and ter Braak (1941) that a destriate dog or monkey will respond to moving objects occupying "the greatest part of the visual field," but not to isolated objects, it ought to be noted that such a qualification continues to suggest that a gross change, or sharp gradient, in brightness might still be the adequate stimulus dimension underlying such reactivity. It should also be mentioned that more recent work by Meyer (1963) confirms that pattern discrimination in decorticate cats is severely impaired but not wholly eliminated. The entire question of residual capacities appears to require much additional research. From his review of the evidence, Weiskrantz concludes that there has been little alteration of the function of the striate cortex with phylogenetic development—the removal of this tissue appearing to have similar effects throughout the mammalian range. He further concludes that subtotal lesions in the visual cortex do not produce scotomata or general impairment of the extent that is predictable from a classical point-to-point projection theory, and suggests that other routes to the striate cortex are available for retinally elicited impulses.

To complicate matters even further, one must consider Doty's (1961) findings of apparently normal visual development in cats whose striate areas were removed at birth. Even in the absence of the geniculostriate system, shape discrimination was evident in these animals. Doty also cites the work of Blake (1959), which indicates that even with visual cortex intact, cats deprived of the superior colliculus lost pattern vision. Although Doty emphasizes caution in generalizing from cat to primate, he favors a theory of pattern discrimination which is based on statistical, "random net" principles rather than an approach requiring spatial contiguity of the involved nerve cells. This discussion has been carried on at some length, since the problems of movement perception are integrally related to the broader question of pattern perception.

Microelectrode Study

The advent of microelectrode study of individual cells at various levels of the visual system in animals has provided perhaps the most exciting of contemporary developments in visual neurophysiology. This technique involves recording with electrodes having a diameter smaller than a single cell so that the responses of individual neural units may be obtained while a stimulus is presented either to a portion of the retina or to all of the animal's eye. Changes in the firing patterns of single cells may thus be correlated with specific parameters of visual input. Although it is true that the dependent variable in these studies is neural activity, the investigator concerned with movement perception is primarily interested in the delineation and description of the receptive fields. The receptive field of a cell is taken as the portion or limits of retinal tissue which, when stimulated, affect the firing activity of the cell. Recordings so far have been made from cells at the levels of optic nerve, geniculate, tectum, and cortex, with peripheral stimulation ranging from that of a single ommatidium of the compound eye to the entire mammalian retina.

Neural specificity with regard to adequate stimulus parameters for the firing of individual units at the retinal, geniculate, and cortical levels has been demonstrated in several species. Recording from the ganglion cells of the frog and using dark and light objects of various sizes and shapes against equally varied backgrounds, Maturana, Lettvin, McCulloch, and Pitts (1960) determined five classes of stimulus-specific neural units. Three of these classes appeared to be directly concerned with the detection of movements: units which fired maximally in the presence of the movement of a small object darker than the background, units whose response frequency varied with the velocity of a moving edge, and cells which fired in response to moving objects that occupied portions of the visual field.

Hubel and Wiesel (1962), recording from the visual cortex of the cat, mapped the receptive fields of many cells in terms of their excitatory or inhibitory regions as given by the rate of "on" and "off" activity during retinal stimulation by stationary and moving stimuli. Cells with both "simple" and "complex" receptive fields were observed, the results having implications for both pattern and movement perception. The more defined and predictable responses of the "simple" fields, in which summation and mutual antagonism of excitatory and inhibitory components were reliably present, contrasted with the "complex" fields, whose cellular correlates responded in nowhere near such unqualified manner when stimulated by variously shaped moving or stationary targets. These investigators found not only predictable responses to movement on the basis of the excitatory and inhibitory regions, but also variation among cells in optimum rates of movement. Equally significant with respect to movement perception, Hubel and Wiesel noted a sustained response by some cells with complex fields to stimuli moved over a wide area of the retina. Such cells adapted rapidly to stationary targets and continued to discharge only with continued movement of the stimulus.

Recent studies of single neural units of the frog's optic tectum point to the likelihood that rather than continuous movement itself, it is the successive change in position within the receptive field which is the adequate condition for stimulation of "movement" detectors. How these determinations by Grüsser-Cornehls, Grüsser, and Bullock (1963) are to be reconciled with the behavioral data of Rock and Ebenholz (1962), pointing to phenomenal rather than retinal separation as the critical requirement for apparent movement, remains problematic. Equally interesting in this connection is the question of whether real movement is actually a special case of *phi*. Certainly, the identification in the mammalian visual system of units responsive to successive rather than continuous stimulus displacement would provide some support for this proposition. As yet, however, no such units have been reported, although facilitative and inhibitory interaction of neighboring cells seems to abound. In any case, the need for caution in any speculation is emphasized by the consideration of Kolers' findings, which do suggest underlying differences between real and apparent movement. Certainly, the fact that *phi* movement can be perceived across scotomata (Teuber, Battersby, & Bender, 1960) must be taken into account in conceptualizing a physiological substratum for movement perception. Although such evidence appears to be at least superficially incompatible with a position calling for the spread of excitation in the cortex as the correlated process, it could also be cited as evidence against the identity of the mechanisms subserving real and apparent movement.

One cannot help speculating on the relationship of these findings to earlier, more molar physiological investigation. For example, the series of stationary images reported by Bender and Teuber's brain-damaged patients may represent the response of intact cells capable of responding to a change in position. If this is the case, the absence of continuity in the perceptual experience may be due to a breakdown of the neural processes constituting Hebb's (1949) proposed supraordinate central mechanism. The Bender and Teuber findings take on even greater significance in the light of more recent speculation by Hebb (1960) and of the electrophysiological data from individual cells in the visual system. Hebb suggests that the entire concept of reality may be linked to some inhibitory mechanism. Stimulated by sensory impulses from the environment, these inhibitory processes are viewed as placing neural restraints on illusions and other perceptual distortions which are likely to accompany ongoing sequences of cerebral activity. Without such processes, Hebb noted, an object in motion might well be seen as a series of stills, with other more dramatic deterioration resulting in the case of more complex integrations of thought and experience. The operation of some supraordinate process for the preservation of continuity in experience, in the absence of which such deterioration as described by Hebb and noted by Bender and Teuber is conceivable, is rendered even more plausible by the recent micro-electrode studies cited above.

The role of peripheral kinesthetic stimulation in cell assembly theory is also brought into sharper focus. The possibility that central organizations may be developed directly by way of cortico-cortical stimulation even in the absence of proprioceptive facilitation must be considered, while the integration of such peripheral stimulation into a comprehensive schema would seem inevitably to be required.

Although the neural specificity for movement detection determined by Hubel and Wiesel in the mammalian visual cortex would seem superficially to be at variance with the findings of Smith and of some of the other investigators cited by Weiskrantz, it must be remembered that

perception of isolated pattern movement was apparently absent in the decorticate animals. The residual perception of very large object movement could conceivably constitute a special case of brightness discrimination whose mediation remains subcortical. Smith concluded that such processes further down in the nervous system did mediate responsiveness to repetitive pattern stimulation of large portions of the visual field. This, of course, touches on a critical methodological problem. If pattern is defined in terms of detectable brightness differences within the visual field, how may brightness and pattern discrimination be differentiated in experiments directed at movement perception? The investigations have been careful so far to describe the detection by decorticate animals of movement by objects occupying the greatest part of the visual field, but this leaves unanswered the question of what specific neural mechanisms mediate response to a moving brightness gradient, and whether these are identical to those in spared regions which appear to subserve residual pattern perception. In any case, it is clear that a satisfactory neural model for movement perception will have to incorporate subcortical as well as cortical processes.

Related Problems

Space, of course, does not begin to permit detailed examination of all aspects of research into movement perception. Although no separate studies of kinetic depth effects and dynamic visual acuity are included, the papers of Gibson and Ludvigh, respectively, draw liberally on research into these phenomena. The relationship between depth perception and motion is also discussed by Gibson. The continuing effort to study the correlates of movement perception at all levels of the visual system should, in time, help to throw new light on a number of phenomena that have been reported. Particularly, the emergence of movement accompanying fixation on a whole class of stationary figures described by MacKay (1961) deserves more intensive examination, as does his more recent demonstration of visual conditions which appear to impose order on what is otherwise random movement (visual "noise").

A tangentially related but important area of study concerns the problem of how the organism distinguishes between the visual input produced by the movement of objects in the environment and that visual input generated by its own movements. In order to make such distinctions possible, organismic movement must produce some information which is made available as feedback into the visual system. Such "reafferent" processes have been dealt with by von Holst and Mittlestädt (1950) in an extremely influential theoretical paper, and the problem has recently been discussed by Smith and Smith (1962). Although reafference theory is more generally applied to kinesthetic stimulation and organismic movement in space, its relationship to a more complete conception of the visual organization of the physical world has yet to be explored.

This, then, will introduce, at least in part, the pattern and scope of research—past and current—into problems of movement perception. They are complex and multidimensional, qualitative and parametric, elusive and challenging. They attract investigation at both molar and molecular levels, with implications for theory in broad areas of perceptual research.

References

BASLER, A. Über das Sehen von Bewegungen. I. Die Wahrnehmung kleinster Bewegungen. *Arch. ges. Physiol.*, 1906, *115*, 582–601.

BENDER, M. D., and H. L. TEUBER. Disturbance in visual perception following cerebral lesions. *J. Psychol.*, 1949, *28*, 223–233.

BLAKE, L. The effect of lesions of the superior colliculus on brightness and pattern discrimination in the cat. *J. comp. physiol. Psychol.*, 1959, *52*, 272–278.

BORING, E. G. *Sensation and perception in the history of experimental psychology.* New York: Appleton-Century Crofts, 1942. pp. 595–598.

BRENNER, N. W. Continuous stimulation and apparent movement. *Amer. J. Psychol.*, 1953, *66*, 494–495.

BROWN, J. F. The thresholds for visual movement. *Psychologische Forschung*, 1931, *14*, 249–268.

BROWN, J. F. The visual perception of velocity. *Psychologische Forschung*, 1931, *14*, 199–232.

BROWN, J. F., and A. C. VOTH. The path of seen movement as a function of the vector field. *Amer. J. Psychol.*, 1937, *49*, 543–563.

BROWN, R. H. Visual sensitivity to differences in velocity. *Psychol. Bull.*, 1961, *58*, 89–103.

CRUTCHFIELD, R. S., and W. EDWARDS. The effect of a fixated figure on autokinetic movement. *J. exp. Psychol.*, 1949, *39*, 561–568.

DETHERAGE, B. H., and M. E. BITTERMAN. The effect of satiation on stroboscopic movement. *Amer. J. Psychol.*, 1952, *65*, 108–109.

DEUTSCH, J. A. The statistical theory of figural aftereffects and acuity. *Brit. J. Psychol.*, 1956, *47*, 208–215.

DEUTSCH, J. A. The Köhler-Wallach theory and the aftereffect of seen movement. *Percept. mot. Skills*, 1959, *9*, 393–394.

DOTY, R. W. Functional significance of the topographical aspects of the retino-cortical projection. In R. Jung and H. Kornhuber (Eds.), Neurophysiologie und Psychophysik des visuellen Systems. *Sympos. Freiburg.* Berlin: Springer, 1961.

DUNCKER, K. Über induzierte Bewegung. *Psychol. Forsch.*, 1929, *12*, 180–259.

DURUP, G. Le probleme des impressions de mouvement consecutives d'ordre visuel. *Année Psychol.*, 1928, *29*, 1–56.

EDWARDS, W. Autokinetic movement of very large stimuli. *J. exp. Psychol.*, 1954, *48*, 493–495.

EHRENSTEIN, W. Versuch über die Beziehungen zwischen Bewegungs und Gestaltwahrnemungen. *Zsch. f. Psychol.*, 1925, *96*, 305–352.

EKMAN, G., and B. DAHLBÄCK. A subjective scale of velocity. *Reports from the Psychological Laboratory, The University of Stockholm*, February 1956, No. 31.

GATES, L. W. The after-effect of visually observed movement. *Amer. J. Psychol.*, 1934, *46*, 34–46.

GENGERELLI, J. A. Apparent movement in relation to homonymous and heteronymous stimulation of the cerebral hemispheres. *J. exp. Psychol.*, 1948, 38, 592–599.

GEORGE, F. H. On the theory of the figural aftereffect. *Canad. J. Psychol.*, 1953, 7, 167–171.

GIBSON, J. J. Research on the visual perception of motion and change. *Second Symposium on Physiological Psychology*, School of Aviation Medicine, Pensacola, Fla., March 19–21, 1958; sponsored by the Office of Naval Research, Department of the Navy.

GORDON, D. A. The relation between the thresholds of form, motion and displacement in parafoveal and peripheral vision at scotopic levels of illumination. *Amer. J. Psychol.*, 1947, 60, 202–225.

GREGORY, R. L. A blue filter technique for detecting eye movements during the autokinetic effect. *Puart. J. exp. Psychol.*, 1959, 11, 113.

GREGORY, R. L., and O. L. ZANGWILL. The origin of the autokinetic effect. *Quart. J. exp. Psychol.*, 1963, 15, 252.

GREGORY, R. L. Human perception. *Brit. med. Bull.*, 1964, 20, 21–26.

GRÜSSER-CORNEHLS, U., O.-J. GRÜSSER, and T. H. BULLOCK. Unit responses in the frog's tectum to moving and nonmoving visual stimuli. *Science*, Aug. 30, 1963, 141, No. 3583, 820–822.

GUILFORD, J. P., and K. M. DALLENBACH. A study of the autokinetic sensation. *Amer. J. Psychol.*, 1928, 40, 83.

HEBB, D. O. *The organization of behavior.* New York: Wiley, 1949.

HEBB, D. O. The American revolution. *Amer. Psychologist*, 1960, 15, 735–745.

HELD, R., and B. White. Sensory deprivation and visual speed. *Science*, 1959, 130, 860–861.

HOLST, E. VON, and H. MITTELSTÄDT. Das reafferenz-prinzip. *Naturwissenschaften*, 1950, 20, 464–476.

HUBEL, D. H., and T. N. WIESEL. Receptive fields, binocular interaction, and functional architecture in the cat's visual cortex. *Journal of Physiology*, 1962, 160, 106–154.

JOHANSSON, G. Binocular interaction in motion perception. *Scandinavian Journal of Psychology*, 1960, 1, 65–68.

KENNEDY, J. L. The nature and physiological basis of visual movement discrimination in animals. *Psychol. Rev.*, 1936, 43, 494–521.

KÖHLER, W., and H. WALLACH. Figural aftereffects: an investigation of visual processes. *Proc. Amer. phil. Soc.*, 1944, 88, 4.

KOLERS, P. A. Some differences between real and apparent visual movement. *Vis. Res.*, 1963, 3, 191–206.

KOLERS, P. Apparent movement of a necker cube. *Amer. J. Psychol.*, 1964, 77, 220–230.

KORTE, A. Kinematoskopische Untersuchungen. *Zsch. f. Psychol.*, 1915, 72, 193–206.

LIVSON, N. H. After-effects of prolonged inspection of apparent movement. *Amer. J. Psychol.*, 1953, 66, 66–72.

LUCHINS, A. The relation of size of light to autokinetic effect. *J. Psychol.*, 1954, 38, 439–452.

LUDVIGH, E. J. Visual and stereoscopic acuity for moving objects. *Symposium on Physiological Psychology*, School of Aviation Medicine, Pensacola, Fla., March 10, 11, 1955; sponsored by the Office of Naval Research, Department of the Navy.

MacKAY, D. M. Interactive processes in perception. In W. A. Rosenblith. (Ed.), *Sensory communication*. Boston: Mass. Inst. Tech. Press, 1961. pp. 339–355.

MANDRIOTA, F. J., D. E. MINTZ, and J. M. NOTTERMAN. Visual velocity discrimination: effects of spatial and temporal cues. *Science*, October 19, 1962, 138, No. 3538, 437–438.

MARSHALL, W. H., and S. A. TALBOT. Recent evidence for neural mechanisms in vision leading to a general theory of sensory acuity. In H. Klüver (Ed.), *Visual Mechanisms*. Biol. Symp., 7, Lancaster, Pa.: Cattrell, 1942.

MATURANA, H. R., J. Y. LETTVIN, W. S. McCULLOCH, and W. B. PITTS. Anatomy and physiology of vision in the frog *Rana pipiens*. *J. gen. Physiol.*, 1960, 43, 129–175.

McCONNELL, R. F. Visual movement under simultaneous excitations with initial and terminal overlap. *J. exp. Psychol.*, 1927, 10, 227–246.

McEWEN, P. Figural after-effects, *Brit. J. Psychol. Monogr. Suppl.*, 1958, 31.

MEYER, PATRICIA. Visual behavior in cats. *J. comp. physiol. Psychol.*, 1963, 56, 397–401.

MICHOTTE, A. *La perception de la causalité.* Louvain: Inst. Sup. de Philosophie, 1946.

MOTOKAWA, K. Retinal traces and visual perception of movement. *J. exp. Psychol.*, 1953, 45, 359–377.

MOTOKAWA, K., and M. EBE. The physiological mechanism of apparent movement. *J. exp. Psychol.*, 1953, 45, 378–386.

OSGOOD, C. E., and A. W. HEYER. A new interpretation of figural after-effects. *Psychol. Rev.*, 1952, *59*, 98–118.

RADEMAKER, G. G., and J. W. TER BRAAK. On the central mechanism of some optical reactions. *Brain*, 1941, *71*, 48–76.

ROCK, I., and S. EBENHOLZ. Stroboscopic movement based on change of phenomenal rather than retinal location. *Amer. J. Psychol.*, 1962, *75*, 193–207.

ROSS, S. Motion perception at various levels of illumination in monkeys and children. *Arch. Psychol., N.Y.*, 1943, no. 288, 1–31.

SCOTT, T. R., A. E. JORDAN, and D. A. POWELL. Does visual aftereffect of motion add algebraically to objective motion of the test stimulus? *J. exp. Psychol.*, 1963, *66*, 500–505.

SEKULER, R. W. and L. GANZ. Aftereffect of seen motion with a stabilized retinal image. *Science*, Feb. 1, 1963, *139*, No. 3553, 419–420.

SHAPIRO, M. B. A preliminary investigation of the effects of continuous stimulation in the perception of apparent movement. *Brit. J. Psychol.*, 1954, *45*, 58–67.

SMITH, K. U. Experiments on the neural basis of movement vision. *J. exp. Psychol.*, 1941, *28*, 199–216.

SMITH, K. U. Visual apparent motion in the absence of neural interaction. *Amer. J. Psychol.*, 1948, *61*, 73–79.

SMITH, K. U., and W. M. SMITH. *Perception and motion*. Philadelphia: Saunders, 1962.

SMITH, O. W., and C. SHERLOCK. A new explanation of the velocity transposition phenomenon. *Amer. J. Psychol.*, 1957, *70*, 102–105.

SMITH, W. M. and W. L. GULICK. A statistical theory of dynamic contour perception. *Psychological Review*, 1962, *69*, 91–108.

SPIGEL, I. M. Relation of movement aftereffect duration to interpolated darkness intervals. *Life Sci.*, 1962, *6*, 239–242. (a)

SPIGEL, I. M. The effects of differential postexposure stimulation on the decay of the aftereffect of visually perceived movement. *Doctoral dissertation*, Temple Univer. Library, 1962. (b)

SPIGEL, I. M. Contour absence as a critical factor in the inhibition of the decay of a movement aftereffect. *Journal of Psychology*, 1962, *54*, 221–228.

SPIGEL, I. M. Autokinetic movement of an intermittent luminance. *Psychol. Rec.*, 1963, *13*, 149–153.

SPITZ, H. H. Neural satiation in the spiral after-effect and similar movement aftereffects. *Percept. mot. Skills*, 1958, *8*, 207–213.

TEUBER, H. L., W. S. BATTERSBY, and M. B. BENDER. *Visual field defects after penetrating missile wounds of the brain*. Cambridge: Harvard Univer. Press, 1960.

WALLACH, H. On the constancy of visual speed. *Psychol. Rev.*, 1939, *46*, 541–552.

WEISKRANTZ, L. Figural after-effects in stroboscopic motion. *Quarterly Journal of Experimental Psychology*, 1950, *2*, 113–118.

WEISKRANTZ, L. Encephalization and the scotoma. In W. L. Thorpe and O. L. Zangwill (Eds.), *Current problems in animal behavior*. Cambridge Univer. Press, 1961. pp. 30–58.

ZEEMAN, W. P. C., and C. O. ROELOFS. Some aspects of apparent motion. *Acta Psychol.*, 1953, *9*, 158–181.

Some Differences between Real and Apparent Visual Movement*

PAUL A. KOLERS
Massachusetts Institute of Technology

Abstract—When a target stimulus is flashed in the path of an objectively moving line of light, threshold for the target increases with a decrease of the distance between the two forms. A parallel experiment was performed when the line of light was in apparent movement ("beta movement"); the target was flashed in its path. It was found that the "position" of the object in apparent movement did not affect the probability of detecting the target. The experiment was also performed of presenting supra-threshold objects in the path of apparent movement. These objects were found to affect the path, so that it curved into three dimensions. Thus an asymmetrical influence was revealed between the object in apparent movement and objects in its path. The results are taken to show that, the identity of appearance of the two perceptions notwithstanding, the mechanisms underlying real and apparent movement seem to be quite different. The asymmetrical influence between objects and the path of apparent movement is interpreted as evidence for sequential processing of visual information.

When two neighboring visual stimulus objects are alternated in place at an appropriate rate, the observer sees a single object in movement between them. This apparent movement is a compelling illusion: several investigators have reported that, given equivalent rates of apparent displacement, the observer is usually unable to distinguish apparent from real movement (WERTHEIMER, 1912; DIMMICK and SCAHILL, 1925; DESILVA, 1929; KENNEDY, 1936; GIBSON, 1954). The

* Vision Research, 1963, vol. 3, pp. 191–206. Preparation of this report was supported by Grant NSF G-16486 and Public Health Service Training Grant No. 2G-1011 Special to the Center for Cognitive Studies, Harvard University. Acknowledgments: The experimental work was performed at the U.S. Naval Medical Research Laboratory, with apparatus generously loaned by the Behavioral Sciences Laboratory, Wright-Patterson Air Force Base. I am grateful to C. A. Baker, J. M. Christensen, and H. L. Parris for that loan.

phenomenon, however, has not been studied much by investigators interested in quantitative relations between stimuli and response, but mostly in qualitative terms, particularly by the Gestalt psychologists. It is the cornerstone of the Gestalt theory of brain fields (WERTHEIMER, 1912; KOFFKA, 1931), but in fact there is no satisfactory theory that accounts for it. We may note that the phenomenon was of great interest to the sensory physiologists of an earlier day: HELMHOLTZ (1924) developed an apparatus to generate apparent movement, and EXNER (1875), his student, used the phenomenon to argue that movement was a "sensation" in its own right, since he was able to demonstrate with it that an image moving across the retina was not a condition necessary for a perception of movement. KOFFKA (1931), BORING (1942) and GRAHAM (1951) have summarized much of the vast, mostly qualitative, literature that has accumulated on this subject.

Many of the writers who have discussed the phenomenon seem to imply, or state outright, that since the perceptions of real and apparent movement are indistinguishable one from the other, the underlying mechanisms must similarly be identical (WERTHEIMER, 1912; DIMMICK and SCAHILL, 1925; DESILVA, 1929; KOFFKA, 1931; KENNEDY, 1936; GIBSON, 1954). In its literal, and trivial, sense this hypothesis can be rejected out of hand since, the stimulus conditions producing real and apparent movement being different, the mechanisms must be also. But, read generously, what these writers seem to be implying is that the perception of movement is determined only by the points of onset and offset of stimulation and the temporal relations between them. When these are of a certain kind, it does not matter, the argument seems to go, whether the "information" is provided by moving or merely by stationary but alternated stimuli. In this argument, stimulation by a physically moving image of the retinal regions *between* the termini is regarded as irrelevant for a perception of movement. GIBSON has pushed the argument farthest, asserting at one time that it was "unfortunate" (1954, p. 310) that a distinction was made between the two kinds of perception of movement. In view of the recent discovery that movement is "coded" at post-retinal regions of the visual nervous system (LETTVIN *et al.*, 1959; HUBEL and WIESEL, 1962), some support can be produced in behalf of these arguments. However, the extent of the similarity in processing of the two perceptions seems never to have been tested directly; nor has it been shown that stimulation of the inter-space between the termini is in fact irrelevant for a perception of movement. In this paper, we are concerned with the first of these, the question of similarity in processing of the two perceptions, the test to be made

by comparing the effects of an object seen to be moving upon the detection of a target in its path. The basis of the test is the masking effect.

Recent studies of visual masking show that when two stationary, concentric, temporally separated flashes of light are presented to the eye, threshold of the target flash varies with the luminance of the masking flash and with the temporal and spatial separation between them (KOLERS, 1962a; RAAB, 1963). The higher the luminance of the masking flash and the closer in time and space the two flashes occur, the higher the threshold of the target. This masking influence occurs irrespective of the order of presentation of the two flashes, although the quantitative relations are different for the two orders.

Several predictions can be made on the basis of these results for the case of a *moving* masking stimulus. Other things remaining equal, threshold for a brief fixed target should increase inversely with the spatio-temporal separations between the target and the moving stimulus, and directly with the luminance of the latter. If the target is a small luminous line flashed in the path of a larger, moving line, threshold of the target may be expected to be higher the brighter the moving line and the closer it is to the target. A preliminary report of results confirming these expectations has been presented (LURIA and KOLERS, 1962); a detailed account is still in preparation. For the sake of comparison with what is to follow, Figure 1 has been taken from the preliminary report. It shows the difference between two measures of threshold luminance of a target positioned at abscissa value 0, one measure made when the target was presented, briefly, alone, and the second when the target was presented during a sweep of a physically moving line, the line having reached one of the other positions marked on the abscissa. Data are shown for four luminances of the moving line, two speeds, and two directions of movement. They show that

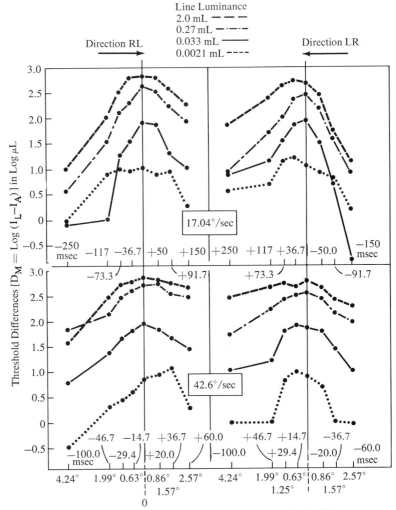

FIGURE 1   Inhibitory influence of a line in real movement. A line moved in the
direction and at the speeds and luminances shown in the legends. Once during
each sweep of the line a fixed target was presented briefly. The target is represented by abscissa value O, and the position reached by the moving line when
the target was presented is shown by the other values on the abscissas. The
difference in luminance threshold of the target when it was presented alone and
when the moving line was also presented is shown on the ordinates. Maximum
inhibition of the target occurs in the region of overlap of target and moving line.
(From Luria and Kolers, 1962).

the farther the moving line is from the
target, temporally and spatially, when the
target is presented, the less the effect the
moving line has upon threshold of the
target; and the brighter the moving line,
the greater its influence.

In the data reported below, a similar test
is made, but for the case of a line in *apparent* movement. The test examines the

effect of the "position" of a line in apparent movement upon the detection of a
target in its path.

In describing these experiments, the
following conventions will be used. "Real
movement" refers to a perception of movement arising from a continuous physical
displacement of a stimulus object. "Apparent movement" or "beta movement" (Bor-

ING, 1942; GRAHAM, 1951) refers to a perception of movement arising from the rapid alternation in place of two neighboring stimulus objects. "Optimal movement" (WERTHEIMER, 1912; KOFFKA, 1931; BORING, 1942) describes the appearance that a single object moves smoothly and continuously between the alternated forms.[1]

Method

APPARATUS

A six-channel electronic device controlled the duration and intensity of mercury–argon gas-discharge lamps which illuminated the stimulus forms from either the front or the rear. The forms were placed in chambers of a multifield Dodge-type viewing apparatus. The circuitry, viewing apparatus and methods for controlling the lamps have been described in detail elsewhere (KOLERS, 1962b). In brief, the apparatus can illuminate four different stimulus objects in sequence, each for its own predetermined duration and intensity. As many as two of the four can be re-illuminated in a single cycle of six presentations. Once begun, the device cycles automatically. A switch which disconnects a lamp permits timed intervals of darkness to be presented as readily as intervals of light. In addition, an ancillary circuit operates a warning bell 2 sec before the onset of a cycle.

Spectrophotometric measurements of the light output of a typical gas-discharge lamp were made prior to performing the experiments. Since such lamps have "lines" rather than "color temperature", the spectral composition of the light remained sub-

[1] Although the distinction is not always preserved, "phi movement" is different from "optimal movement". In the latter, an object is seen to be traversing the space between the termini whose alternation produces the illusion. In phi movement, no object is seen; only a sense of movement is derived from the rapid alternation of the two termini. Phi movement thus may be compared with the blurred impression of real movement derived from a rapidly moved target (VAN DEN BRINK, 1957).

stantially unchanged through a tenfold change in current through the lamps (25–250 mA). In the experiment itself the lamps were operated well within that range (50–90 mA). The halide phosphor in the lamps produced a "snow white" or "blue white" light. Amplitude and waveform of the current through the lamp for the target stimulus were monitored by means of an oscilloscope placed across a 10-ohm resistor in series with the lamp. No variations were noted during the course of the experiments.

MATERIALS

The stimulus materials for the experiments in Group I were transilluminated photographic negatives. That is, the negatives were between the light source and the observer's eye. The stimuli, therefore, appeared as lines of light on a dark background. The upper part of Figure 2 illustrates the appearance of one stimulus array used in the first group of experiments. The lines A and B were $0.9°$ long, the target stimulus or probe, P, $0.45°$, and all were approximately $0.05°$ wide. The lines appeared in a visual field $4°$ wide by $5.5°$ high, of 0.002 ft-L luminance. The intensity of A and B was 3 ft-L each, while P was set for each subject at such a level that $p(P)$, the probability of his seeing it in the absence of A and B, was 0.90 +. This value was found for each S in separate viewing sessions before the main experiments and was checked regularly during their course. The brightness of the target stimulus making $p(P) = 0.90 +$ ranged between 0.09 and 0.3 ft-L for the three Ss. In the second group of experiments, directly illuminated, high contrast photographs were presented to the light-adapted eye. The visual field was approximately the same size as for Group I, but of 4 ft-L brightness.

SUBJECTS

The principal subjects were two Naval enlisted men aged nineteen and the writer.

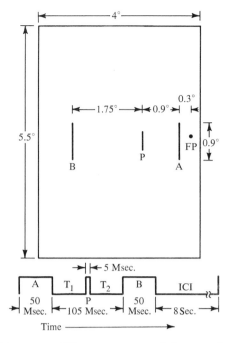

FIGURE 2 The arrangement of the stimulus forms. A, B and P were lines of light presented on a dark field. The time diagram shows one sequence of presentations.

Other observers were called in from time to time.

Procedure. The essential requirement of the procedure was to specify the "position" of the line in apparent movement. This was accomplished by fractionating the temporal interval between the offset of A and the onset of B, and presenting the target, P, at a known time during it. In a typical experiment of Group I, the two lines A and B were presented alternately each for 50 msec, with fixed pauses between them. One fixed pause was the inter-stimulus interval (ISI), between the offset of A and the onset of B; this was usually 105 msec. The other fixed pause, the inter-cycle interval (ICI), between the offset of B and the recurrence of A, was 8 sec. The probe, or target, P, was presented for 5 msec at some varied time during the first pause (ISI). One such arrangement is shown in the lower part of Figure 2. In that figure T_1 is the interval

between the offset of A and the onset of P, and T_2 is the interval between P and B. During the experiment, T_1 and T_2 were varied together while their sum was kept constant. For example, when T_1 was 5 msec, T_2 was 95 msec; when T_1 was 25 msec, T_2 was 75 msec, and so on. By keeping the duration $(T_1 + P + T_2)$ constant, P was presented when the line had appeared to have moved through various portions of the distance between A and B. All three Ss reported seeing a single line move smoothly and continuously between A and B (i.e. reported seeing "optimal movement") for the conditions used.

The data for the first group of experiments were collected with a modified quantal method described previously (KOLERS and ROSNER, 1960). In this method, S makes a large number of observations to a fixed set of stimulus conditions, and the relative frequency of detections of the target is computed for each condition. In the modification of the quantal method used, S made his report to eight identical presentations; conditions were then changed without S's knowledge and another eight presentations made, and so on. This procedure was followed until eight presentations were made at each of five pairs of T_1-T_2 values. Then a 1 min rest was given. This procedure was repeated four times in a single viewing session at each T_1-T_2 pair. Ss reported detecting the probe by sounding a buzzer twice, and reported a failure to detect by sounding it once.

Of the eight presentations of each T_1-T_2 pair, the reports to the first two were discarded in order to lessen the effect of S's response bias. A third presentation was made with the probe absent, in order to find the false alarm rate — the frequency of reporting the probe when it was in fact not present. This rate was always found to be less than 10 per cent with practiced Ss, a rate small enough to warrant eliminating all the data based on blank trials. The remaining five observations of each

T_1–T_2 pair are the data of interest. The curves below are based on the frequency of detecting P in 60–120 observations per plotted point, found in several viewing sessions in groups of five observations at each pair of T_1–T_2 values. These relative frequencies are plotted as $p(P)$.

The experiments on real movement, the data for which are shown in Figure 1, were collected using the method of limits. That method was used also in preliminary studies on apparent movement, but was found to be less sensitive than the modified quantal method. Note, however, that in Figure 1 the ordinate plots luminous energy, so that higher values on the ordinate mean that detectability is poorer. For the data based on the quantal method (Figures 3–7) *probabilities* are plotted, so that lower ordinate values are associated with poorer detectability.

All of the experiments of Group I were performed with transilluminated stimuli presented to S's dark-adapted eye. In the experiments of Group II, illuminated forms were presented to the light-adapted eye. For the first procedure, S was dark-adapted for 15 min. Presentations were then made approximately once every 8.2 sec (i.e. ICI = 8 sec), with the stimulus figures 75 cm from the eye. When the presentations were to the light-adapted eye (Group II), S was first dark-adapted for 3 min and then light-adapted for 1 min. Viewing distance was then 100 cm. In both cases S looked with his right eye only, through an artificial pupil 3 mm in diameter. A small (< 2′ visual angle) red light provided a fixation point.

Results

I. APPARENT MOVEMENT OF A LINE OF LIGHT

1. *Probe in the path of the moving line.*[2] The stimulus configuration for this experi-

[2] These results were previously reported in *Nature* (London), 1963, *197*, 271–272.

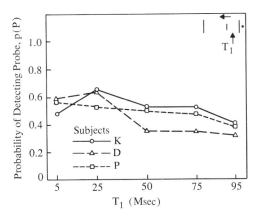

FIGURE 3   The abscissa shows the time between the offset of A and the onset of P; the ordinate plots probability of detecting the probe presented at a fixed duration and intensity. Probability of detecting the probe in the absence of the apparently moving line is 0.90+ for all Ss. The horizontal arrow in the inset shows the sequence of presentations, and thus the direction of apparent movement; the vertical arrow points to the temporal interval manipulated as T_1.

ment is shown in the inset of Figure 3, the horizontal arrow indicating the direction of apparent movement of the alternated forms. The probability of seeing the probe, $p(P)$, in this sequence is plotted on the ordinate of the figure, and T_1, the time between the offset of A and the onset of P, is plotted on the abscissa. The curves show the means for each of three Ss based on 80 or 100 observations/plotted point. For all three Ss a generalized inhibitory effect occurs in that $p(P)$ is always less than 0.90, its minimum value in the absence of A and B. However, within that effect, for two of the Ss $p(P)$ increases slightly with an increase in T_1, then decreases; for the third, $p(P)$ decreases only. For all Ss the probability of detecting the probe seems to vary with the "position" of the apparently moving line, although the variation is not large.

2. *Probe and line A only.* In this and the next experiment, $p(P)$ was found when A and B were each presented without the other. First, $p(P)$ was found at

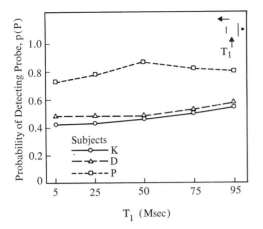

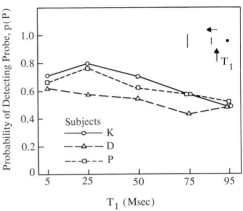

FIGURE 4   Effect of origin of apparent movement on the detectability of the test probe. Coordinates are the same as in Figure 3. B was a timed interval of darkness.

FIGURE 5   Effect of terminus of apparent movement on detectability of the test probe. Coordinates are the same as in Figure 3. A was a timed interval of darkness.

various times after the offset of A, with B absent. These probabilities are plotted on the ordinate in Figure 4, with T_1, the time between A and P, on the abscissa. Each point in the curves is a mean based on 80, 100 and 120 observations for Ss, P, K, and D, respectively. These means again describe a generalized inhibition ($p(P)$ is almost always <0.90), but without much trend. Although not shown in the figure, this stimulus sequence yielded more variable data than any other. The basis for the individual differences is not known.

3. *Probe and line B only.* The results of the reverse experiment, finding $p(P)$ at various times before the onset of B when A was absent, are shown in Figure 5. In this experiment A was a timed interval of darkness. The values of $p(P)$ are based on 60, 80 or 120 observations/point (K, P, D); the abscissa again shows the time after the "offset" of A. The means of Figure 5 show the generalized inhibition, but in addition reveal trends similar to those in Figure 3.

In Experiments 2 and 3 there was no apparent movement between A and B, as either the origin (A) or terminus (B) of movement was not shown. Occasionally, Ss reported movement between P and A

or B. More such reports occurred in Experiment 2 than in Experiment 3, so that these perceived movements may be the basis of the large amount of variability in Experiment 2.

4. *Reversal of sequence.* The sequence of stimulation was reversed with one subject, K, so that the line appeared to move from B to A. In Figure 6 the abscissa shows the time, T_1, between the offset of the first line (now B) and the onset of P. Three curves are shown, for three experiments identical, except for direction of apparent movement, with those described in Figures 3–5.

The relation between $p(P)$ and T_1 is shown in Figure 6: (1) when an apparent movement appeared between the termini (circles, 80 observations/point); (2) when only the first line, B, and the probe appeared (triangles, 60 observations/point); and (3) when only the second line, A, and the probe appeared (squares, 60 observations/point). The data of Figure 6 appear clearly to be related to those for subject K in Figures 3–5. Thus, the effect shown in the earlier figures seems not to depend much on whether the apparent movement is toward the fovea or away from it, any more than it does with real movement (Figure 1).

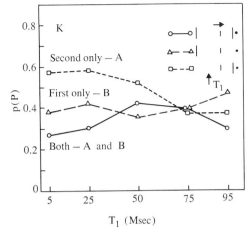

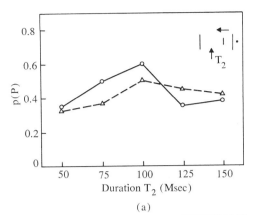

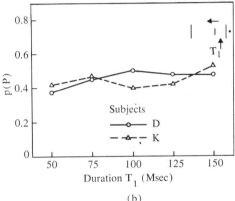

FIGURE 6   Probability of detecting the probe when the direction of movement was reversed. The three curves describe the condition when an apparent movement appeared (both—B and A); when only the origin and test probe appeared (first only—B); and when only the terminus and test probe appeared (second only—A). The vertical arrow shows the interval plotted as T_1.

5. *Extension of ISI.* In another experiment the interval T_1 between A and P was fixed at 25 msec, and interval T_2 between P and B was varied from 50 to 150 msec in steps of 25 msec. The total ISI $(T_1 + P + T_2)$ now ranged from 80 to 180 msec. As in the first experiments reported above, A preceded B, so that apparent movement was towards the periphery. Figure 7a shows the results of 80 observations/point for each of two Ss, with $p(P)$ on the ordinate and T_2, the interval between P and B, on the abscissa. Within the generalized inhibition, $p(P)$ is greater in the region $T_2 = 100$ msec than at intervals longer or shorter than that. The data thus show two different masking effects bracketing the point of maximum detectability, while that point itself is less than 0.90, the value of $p(P)$ in the absence of A and B.

The results of the converse experiment are shown in Figure 7b. For that experiment interval T_2, between P and B, was fixed at 25 msec while interval T_1, between A and P, was varied. Apparent

FIGURE 7   Probability of detecting the probe at different inter-stimulus intervals. The insets show the direction of apparent movement (horizontal arrows) and the intervals represented on the abscissas (vertical arrows).
(a) Interval between the offset of A and the onset of the probe was fixed at 25 msec. Interval between the offset of the probe and the onset of B is given on the abscissa.
(b) Converse experiment. Interval between the offset of the probe and the onset of B was fixed at 25 msec and interval between the offset of A and the onset of the probe is given on the abscissa.

movement was again from A to B. Figure 7b indicates that within the envelope of general inhibition $p(P)$ tends to increase, but only slightly, with an increase in the temporal separation between A and the probe.

The results described in Figure 7 reveal that $p(P)$ is almost independent of the time between the probe and the stimulus that precedes it, but varies markedly with the time between the probe and the stimulus that follows it. These results tend to confirm those in Figures 4 and 5, which also demonstrate that a stronger inhibitory effect is exerted upon the probe by the line following it temporally than by the line preceding it. Unrelated to this, but also of note, is the fact that Ss reported that the velocity of the apparently moving form varied with changes in the total duration of ISI.

The data of Experiments 2–5 indicate that the influence of the line upon the probe shown in Figure 3 is due principally to the effects of the alternated termini of apparent movement upon the probe, but not to any interaction between the object seen in movement and the probe: that is to say, the effects of the physical stimuli—A, B and the probe—interact in the visual system so that the presence of each modifies the perception of the other; but no interaction appears to occur between the *real* form, P, and the *apparent* form, the line seen in transverse movement.

II. APPARENT MOVEMENT OF
A BLACK DISK

The detectability of a brief, normally supra-threshold form is lessened when the form is followed by a neighboring one (Piéron, 1934; Alpern, 1958; Kolers and Rosner, 1960). In the extreme case, the normally supra-threshold target is made invisible by a subsequent stimulus exert-

ing a "retroactive" masking effect. Thus, when a black disk is followed at a proper interval by a concentric black ring, only the ring may be seen. Utilizing this masking effect, the question can be asked whether the illusion of movement depends upon *perceiving* the stimulus object, particularly at the origin of movement. In answer it will be shown that it does not: the physical (not the perceived) presence of a form is sufficient for a perception of movement.

6. *Disk–disk sequence.* This sequence was used to establish conditions yielding "optimal movement." Two black disks, D_1 and D_2, each of 0.5° angular subtense, were arranged as in Figure 8, but without the ring shown there. Each disk was presented for 30 msec, and optimal movement was reported when the intervals between them were each 100 msec. Observations were monocular and with a light-adapted eye. Under these conditions the ICI or re-cycling interval was very short, so that a continuous apparent oscillation of a single disk was perceived.

7. *Disk–ring–disk sequence.* This procedure differed from the preceding only in that a ring, R, was presented for 50 msec during the ISI, immediately after the offset of D_1. The ring was so placed that it appeared concentric with D_1, though presented after it. The remaining duration of the ISI, T_1, was taken up by a blank field. The sequence thus made was D_1–R–T_1–D_2–ICI, a sequence in which D_1 was invisible. (The experiment was made also with R following T_1 without essential change in the results.) The S was instructed to report the occurrence of optimal movement of the disk as T_1 and ICI were increased in 10 msec steps. ICI, to begin with, was 50 msec. Table 1 outlines the results of five trials for each condition with one S. It shows, for each of the stimulus sequences given in the rows of the table, the ISI–ICI values at which optimal

FIGURE 8   Black disks alternated to produce apparent movement. A separation subtending to 10′ visual angle was made between the border of D_1 and the inner border of R; the wall of R subtended to 15′ visual angle. The distance from FP to the right edge of D is 2.29° (*see* Figure 2).

TABLE 1

Minimum Value of ISI Required for a Report of Optimum Movement in Various Sequences of Stimulation. (The Numbers in the Body of the Table Refer to Time in Msec. Each Row is a Separate Sequence)

TEST	A	ISI	B	ICI
1	$D_1 = 30$	100	$D_2 = 30$	100
2	R $= 30$	100	$D_2 = 30$	100
3	$D_1 = 30$	R $= 50$ $T_1 = 50$	$D_2 = 30$	100*
4	$D_1 = 30$	$T_1 = 50$ R $= 50$	$D_2. = 30$	100*

* If R is not presented, so that ISI = 50 and ICI = 100 mesc, the temporal disparity is resolved as a three-dimensional display: the path of movement appears to be curved in depth during the ICI phase.

movement was first reported. Tests 3 and 4 in the table are the critical ones; they indicate, first, that with R = 50 msec, T_1 had to be increased until the duration of $(R + T_1)$ or $(T_1 + R)$ equalled the previously found ISI of 100 msec for optimal movement. Since D_1 was made invisible by R in these tests, the results show that apparent movement depends upon the occurrence of a stimulus, not upon its being perceived.[3]

Secondly, the time between the offset of A and the onset of B has a unit quality. Rows 3 and 4 of Table 1 show that presenting another form during part of the ISI does not affect the toal value of ISI required for optimal movement. Thus, presenting D_1 appears to start some timing mechanism in the visual system which is relatively insensitive to the occurrence of other stimulation within its "period", a process very different from that characterizing the formation time of simple figures (McCONNELL, 1927; STROUD, 1956; BOYNTON, 1961; KOLERS, 1962a). One may thus note the dependence of apparent move-

ment upon transients in the visual nervous system since we have found in many experiments that no apparent movement is reported when one stimulus is continuous and the other is flickered. Both must be flickered for apparent movement to be seen.

Thirdly, it is worth noting that a temporal disparity, wherein ISI is different from ICI, is resolved as a three-dimensional display. This seems to reflect a bias in the visual system, for the disparity could as readily be resolved as changes in rate, the form seen to be moving slower in one direction than in the other. Why a perception of depth is preferred to that of a change in rate is not clear.

From the results of the preceding seven experiments, one might infer that apparent movement is perceived as the direct result of a given order and timing of stimulation; and, further, that it is coded at some level of the visual system at which no interaction occurs between nervous events reporting movement and those reporting other elements in the visual field. WERTHEIMER (1912), for example, in Section 16 of his great paper, reports that a segment of a line placed to be perpendicular to the arc made by another, apparently moving, line, did not summate with the latter to make it appear even momentarily longer. However, this inference of no interaction would be wrong, for complex inter-

[3] Since D_1 was invisible, its path of movement was reported to be from near the outside border of R to D_2 and back. If another ring were presented, to mask D_2, making the sequence D_1–R_1–D_2–R_2, with pauses added as needed, two distinct movement impressions might well occur, one of partly visible disks and the other of fully visible rings. Our apparatus could not readily be adapted to create this display.

actions do occur, some of which are briefly described below.

8. *Other sequences.* Experiment 7 demonstrates also that a form placed in the inter-space, in this case the ring around the disk, does not prevent the occurrence of movement across that space. This apparent absence of an interaction between the object seen in movement and the space traversed by it was investigated more fully using two disks as the stimulus forms. The disks were presented for 30 msec each, and a variety of other forms were presented in the inter-space, singly, each for 50 msec. A blank field was presented for the remainder of the ISI. The forms used were solid and outline rectangles, grids, spikes, and the like. The maximum width of these forms was always less than the width of the inter-space. Under these conditions, apparent movement of a disk was always reported. The most common form of this movement, however, was an elliptical path or orbit in depth around the forms in the inter-space. A few subjects reported that the black disk in orbit appeared to be paler than when the forms were not present in the inter-space.

Finally, since the observer's attitude and past experience are known to affect the perception of apparent movement (WERTHEIMER, 1912; NEUHAUS, 1930; TOCH and ITTELSON, 1956; SCHURECK, 1960), various efforts were made to see a sinuous movement between the spikes shown in Figure 9. The Ss reported that they could not; only an elliptical path was ever seen.

FIGURE 9   A suprathreshold form presented between D_1 and D_2. The figure is drawn to the same scale as Figure 8.

Discussion

Figure 2 shows that P, the probe, was positioned about one-third of the distance between A and B. If the line in apparent movement in Figure 3 had constant velocity across the interspace, it would have been closest to P at the measured value $T_1 = 25$ msec. This would correspond to a separation from overlap no greater than 10 msec in time or 15′ visual angle of space. Overlap is shown for real movement in Figure 1 as abscissa values of 0; and for two lines, one of which moved faster, the other slower than the calculated rate of the line in apparent movement. (The calculated rate is for a spatial separation of 2.65° between A and B, and a temporal one of 105 msec, or 25°/sec.) Inspection of Figure 1 shows that at such spatio-temporal separations, a line in real movement exerts a very powerful inhibitory effect upon the detectability of the probe in its path. Therefore, if the effect of a line in apparent movement were similar to that of a line in real movement, the curves of Figure 3 would all be U-shaped: the probe would be maximally detectable at the onset and offset of stimulation, and would be at a minimum in the region $T_1 = 25$ msec. Clearly the curves are not U-shaped. Clearly, then, the line in apparent movement has different effects from a line in real movement.

However, some inhibition in the detection of P does occur. This is of two kinds. First, $p(P)$ is always less than 0.90, its "absolute threshold", when either A or B is also presented (Figures 3–7). Secondly, there is a tendency for $p(P)$ to be less at longer durations of T_1 (Figure 3). No reason is readily apparent to account with certainty for the first of these, the overall decline in the probability of seeing P. The decline may be due to changes in sensitivity attributable to contrast with the line seen as moving, or equally to a change in adaptation induced by the physical presence of A and B. Further experiments are required to identify the basis of this effect. On the other hand, the change in the shape of the detection function of P found with changes in T_1 is easily explained as due to the "retroactive" masking effect one visual contour exerts upon another, neighboring, one (ALPERN, 1953; KOLERS and ROSNER, 1960). Presumably, the physical stimulus B exerts such a retroactive inhibitory effect upon P; while, consistent with the earlier findings just cited, very little "proactive" effect of A on P is found (Figure 4). In no case is there any evidence, however, that the line in apparent movement itself exerts any influence upon the detection of the target in its path. Rather, the effects that are found seem to be attributable to the alternation of the physical stimuli, A and B, but not to the illusory line seen in apparent movement between A and B.

Although the "position" of the line in apparent movement does not markedly affect the detectability of objects in its path, an effect in the opposite direction occurs. When suprathreshold objects are placed in the path of movement, the path curves into depth (Group II): Thus there is an asymmetry of effects: an object in apparent movement does not affect objects in its path, but the latter affect the path of movement. One difference distinguishes the stimulus conditions that produce real and apparent movement: no image moves across the retina in the latter case. An image moving across the retina thus seems to be a necessary condition for inhibition of the brightness threshold of objects in the path of movement. It would seem to follow, then, that brightness thresholds are coded principally at the retina, while depth and movement are coded beyond the retina. And since it has also been reported that curvature and three-dimensionality of the path of an object in apparent movement occurs when only strong after-effects of stimulation are present in the path (DETHERAGE and BITTERMAN, 1952; SHAPIRO,

1954), the question arises whether induced spatial displacement of contours is processed earlier or later than movement and depth.

The theories available to account for beta movement are unsatisfactory. The best-known is the Wertheimer–Köhler hypothesis that two neighboring regions of nervous excitation building up within the proper spatio-temporal bounds discharge into each other, and that this "short-circuit" is the correlate of the object seen as moving (WERTHEIMER, 1912; KOFFKA, 1931). This hypothesis assumes that perceptual experience (i.e. the "picture in the head") is unitary, and that in processing information the visual cortex acts as a homogeneous medium. Two facts, however, constitute objections to the hypothesis of a short circuit in a homogeneous visual cortex. The first is that beta movement "completes" across acquired scotomata, which is inconsistent with it (TEUBER et al., 1960). A second objection is to the assumption that stimulation results in some sort of spatial spread of excitation. Experiment shows to the contrary that the principal influence a briefly stimulated region exerts upon its neighbors is inhibitory, not excitatory (FRY, 1934; ALPERN, 1953; RATLIFF and HARTLINE, 1959; KOLERS, 1962 a). Thus, two neighboring visual regions stimulated alternately would inhibit each other both "retroactively" and "proactively" in the temporal intervals studied. Since beta movement is perceived at ISIs equal to or greater than those at which such a spatial spread is stopped by inhibitory masking effects, it cannot be due to such a spread. Rather, the mechanism of apparent movement seems to be principally a temporal one, with only a limited spatial component to it. As Experiments 6 and 7 and Table 1 showed, stimulation by neighboring forms did not influence the occurrence of apparent movement determined by other stimuli. That is to say, the presence of other forms in interspace did not prevent S from seeing movement across that space, nor did those forms change the values of ISI required for the perception of movement. Such a temporal mechanism would seem to be sensitive to a "bucking" of on and off processes that would result from the rapid on and off alternation of neighboring stimuli (RATLIFF, 1961).

Therefore, if two visual experiences appear alike, but are produced by different stimulus conditions, we may speak of "a final common percept", but one produced by different "paths" in the nervous system. The fact that identical perceptions have different processes, according to which stimulus conditions produced them, argues that different interactions in the nervous system occur at different places. The question arises whether these different interactions—between contours, brightnesses, depths, and others—occur simultaneously or serially in the visual system. This may be answered by finding other perceptions whose component "parts" can be identified, for both the present results and recent electrophysiological evidence (LETTVIN *et al.*, 1959; HUBEL and WIESEL, 1962) imply that there is an order or sequence to the neural processing of a percept. Rather than in a "weighted average of influences" from nervous system, body tonus, experience and the like (ALLPORT, 1955), a percept may be processed in isolatable parts.

Another way to state the case is that stimulation from physically co-planar objects is not necessarily processed in coplanar regions of the nervous system. Therefore, the "unity" of a perceptual experience may itself be illusory; it may be but an end-product, organized from a series of separable operations, rather than an isomorphic representation of the physical field based on strict retino–topical projection.

Summary

The perceptions of real and apparent movement are usually reported to be indistinguishable, suggesting to some writers that the underlying mechanisms for the two perceptions are identical. To test this hypothesis the question was asked whether an object seen in apparent movement affects the detection threshold for objects in its path, a known property of real movement.

1. The "position" of a line in apparent movement did not affect the threshold for a target line in its path. The variations in the latter that were found were attributable to masking effects produced by the alternated termini of movement upon the target, but not to an influence of the object in apparent movement upon the real test line.

2. Physical occurrence of the stimulus was found to be sufficient for a report of apparent movement; a form masked to the point of invisibility at the origin of movement was still reported to be seen in movement.

3. The pause needed between two stimuli of constant duration for a perception of movement to be reported was not affected by interposing other forms between them, spatially or temporally. The entire temporal sequence had a unit quality to it, apparently initiated by the onset of the first form.

4. While an object in apparent movement did not affect the detectability of objects in its path, supra-threshold objects affected the path, so that it curved in depth. This depth effect was in turn found to be insensitive to experimentally induced attitudes and wishes: sinuous movement of a form between spikes in its path could not be seen as a willed alternative to depth.

The results are taken to mean that different aspects of a percept are processed in different parts of the visual nervous system. Rather than representing a mélange of "influences", a percept may be thought to result from a series of separately encoded events. One task of the psychology of perception may be taken to be the plotting of the "flow chart" that describes the timing and loci of these processes.

References

ALLPORT, F. H. (1955). *Theories of perception and the concept of structure.* John Wiley, New York.

ALPERN, M. (1953). Metacontrast. *J. opt. Soc. Amer. 43,* 648–657.

BORING, E. G. (1942). *Sensation and Perception in the History of Experimental Psychology.* Appleton-Century-Crofts, New York.

BOYNTON, R. M. (1961). Some temporal factors in vision; pp. 739–756 in *Sensory Communication:* ROSENBLITH, W. A. (Ed.). M.I.T. Press and John Wiley, New York.

VAN DEN BRINK, G. (1957). *Retinal summation and the visibility of moving objects,* Institute for Perception, Soesterberg, The Netherlands.

DESILVA, H. R. (1929). An analysis of the visual perception of movement. *Brit. J. Psychol. 19,* 268–305.

DETHERAGE, B. H., and M. E. BITTERMAN. (1952). The effect of satiation on stroboscopic movement. *Amer. J. Psychol. 65,* 108–109.

DIMMICK, F. L., and H. G. SCAHILL. (1925). Visual perception of movement. *Amer. J. Psychol. 36,* 412–417.

EXNER, S. (1875). Ueber das Sehen von Bewegungen und die Theorie des zusammengesetzen Auges. *S.B. Akad. Wiss. Wien 72,* 156–190.

FRY, G. A. (1934). Depression of the activity aroused by a flash of light by applying a second flash immediately afterwards to adjacent areas of the retina. *Amer. J. Physiol. 108,* 701–707.

GIBSON, J. J. (1954). The visual perception of objective motion and subjective movement. *Psychol. Rev. 61,* 304–314.

GRAHAM, C. H. (1951). Visual Perception; pp. 868–920 in *Handbook of Experimental Psychology:* STEVENS, S. S. (Ed.). John Wiley, New York.

VON HELMHOLTZ, H. (1924). *Treatise on Physiological Optics,* Vols. II and III. Optical Society of America, New York.

HUBEL, D. H., and T. N. WIESEL. (1962). Receptive fields, binocular interaction and functional architecture in the cat's visual cortex. *J. Physiol. 160,* 106–154.

KENNEDY, J. L. (1936). The nature and phys-iological basis of visual movement discrimination in animals. *Psychol. Rev. 43,* 494–521.

KOFFKA, K. (1931). Die Wahrnehmung von Bewegung, vol. 12, pt. 2, pp. 1166–1214, in *Handbuch der normalen und pathologischen Physiologie,* BETHE, A. *et al.* (Ed.). Springer, Berlin.

KOLERS, P. A. (1962 a). Intensity and contour effects in visual masking. *Vision Res. 2,* 277–294.

KOLERS, P. A. (1962 b). Multi-field electronic apparatus for studies of visual perception. MRL–TDR–62–33, Wright-Patterson Air Force Base, Ohio.

KOLERS, P. A., and B. S. ROSNER. (1960). On visual masking (metacontrast): dichoptic observation. *Amer. J. Psychol. 73,* 2–21.

LETTVIN, J. Y., H. R. MATURANA, W. S. McCULLOCH, and W. H. PITTS. (1959). What the frog's eye tells the frog's brain. *Proc. Inst. Radio Engrs, N.Y. 47,* 1940–1951.

LURIA, S. M., and P. A. KOLERS. (1962). Interaction of moving and stationary visual stimuli. *J. opt. Soc. Amer. 52,* 1320 (Abstract).

McCONNELL, R. F. (1927). Visual movement under simultaneous excitations with initial and terminal overlap. *J. exp. Psychol. 10,* 227–246.

NEUHAUS, W. (1930). Experimentelle Untersuchungen der Scheinbewegung. *Arch. ges. Psychol. 75,* 315–458.

PIÉRON, H. (1935). Le processus du métacontraste. *J. Psychol. norm. path. 32,* 1–24.

RAAB, D. H. (1963). Backward masking. *Psychol. Bull., 60,* 118–129.

RATLIFF, F. (1961). Inhibitory interaction and the detection and enhancement of contours; pp. 183–203 in *Sensory Communication:* ROSENBLITH, W. A. (Ed.). M.I.T. Press and John Wiley, New York.

RATLIFF, F., and H. K. HARTLINE. (1959). The responses of *Limulus* optic nerve fibers to patterns of illumination on the receptor mosaic. *J. gen. Physiol. 42,* 1241–1255.

SCHURECK, P. J. (1960). Studies in the perception of apparent visual movement. *Aust. J. Psychol. 12,* 101–116.

SHAPIRO, M. B. (1954). A preliminary investigation of the effects of continuous stimulation on the perception of "apparent motion". *Brit. J. Psychol. 45,* 58–67.

STROUD, J. M. (1956). The fine structure of psychological time; pp. 174–207 in *Information theory in Psychology:* QUASTLER, H. (Ed.). Free Press, Glencoe, Illinois, U.S.A.

TEUBER, H-L., W. S. BATTERSBY, and M. B. BENDER. (1960). *Visual field defects after penetrating missile wounds of the brain.* Harvard University Press, Cambridge, Mass., U.S.A.

TOCH, H. H. and W. H. ITTELSON. (1956). The rôle of past experience in apparent movement: a revaluation. *Brit. J. Psychol.* 47, 195–207.

TRAIN, L. E. and W. J. WALTHALL, Jr.

(1958). A comparison of figural after-effects from the perception of real and apparent movement. *J. gen. Psychol.* 59, 157–166.

WERTHEIMER, M. (1912). Experimentelle Studien über das Sehen von Bewegung. *Ztschr. Psychol.* 61, 161–265. Translated in large part in *Classics in Psychology:* SHIPLEY, T. (Ed.). Philosophical Library, New York, 1961.

Autokinetic Movement: Selective Manipulation of Directional Components by Image Stabilization[*]

LEONARD MATIN

Columbia University

G. ERNEST MacKINNON

University of Waterloo (Ontario)

Abstract. With the retinal image of a 35-minute circular target stabilized against horizontal eye movements, horizontal autokinesis is markedly reduced. It is suggested that this result is consistent with an eye movement interpretation of autokinetic movement, and further, that the response patterns reported here are similar to those that might be expected from recent work describing cortical single unit movement detectors.

In 1879 Hoppe (*1*) suggested that the autokinetic phenomenon, or the apparent movement of a fixated light in an otherwise dark field, was the result of fluctuations in the retinal location of the target image produced by involuntary eye movements. Since then, only two attempts at directly testing the eye movement interpretation have been reported (*2*, *3*). In both studies, a search was made for a correlation between measurements of eye movements and autokinesis, but essentially

* *Science,* 1964, vol. 143, pp. 147–148. Copyright © 1964 by the American Association for the Advancement of Science. This work was supported by grants G-18120 and GB-944 from the National Science Foundation.

opposite conclusions were reached. However, due largely to limitations in the techniques of measurement available at the times the studies were performed, both have numerous methodological inadequacies which make it difficult to accept the conclusions drawn from either of them. Even in experiments in which the methodological requirements for meaningful measurements are met, failure to find a correlation between measured eye movements and autokinesis may mean that the appropriate parameters of the eye movements were not chosen for comparison. On the other hand, any correlation that might be obtained would need to be further analyzed with regard to the alternative possibility that the appearance of subjective movement may result in pursuit eye movements.

A straightforward test of the eye movement interpretation of autokinesis would be performed if, independently of eye movements, one directional component of variation in retinal location could be removed. If the eye movement approach had any merit, the identical component of autokinetic movement ought also to be attenuated. This report describes such a test in which autokinesis viewed under conditions of image stabilization (4) is compared with autokinesis viewed normally.

Two subjects were used, each of whom wore an individually fitted scleral contact lens with a front-surfaced plane mirror embedded in its temporal margin; the mirror's normal was set at approximately 40 degrees to the subject's fixation axis and in the same horizontal plane. The subject saw in Maxwellian view a circular 35-minute target at optical infinity with luminance about 1 log unit above the dark-adapted foveal absolute threshold. Under the stabilized viewing condition a beam incident on the contact lens mirror was returned to the subject's pupil after passing through a telescopic system with slightly less than 0.5 angular magnification. The stabilized condition was thus arranged so that a horizontal eye movement of 1 degree resulted in a horizontal shift in the location of the retinal image of less than 1 minute; the effect of vertical eye movements was demagnified so that a 1-degree vertical movement resulted in a vertical shift in the location of the retinal image of about 15 minutes. The normal, unstabilized view of the same target could be instantaneously substituted by moving two mirrors into a position which deflected the incident beam through the same optical path without striking the contact lens mirror. For stabilized viewing these mirrors were rotated out of the way, permitting the incident beam to strike the contact lens mirror (5).

During experimental sessions the light source was electronically interrupted every 7 seconds for 0.5 second, and the subject reported the direction of the first autokinetic drift (6) which occurred during each period when the light was on by pressing one of a ring of eight switches which signalled north, northeast, east, southeast, south, southwest, west, or northwest; no movement was signalled with a ninth switch. In experiments (a), (b), and (d) (Figure 1), a block of ten measurements in the stabilized condition was regularly alternated with a block of ten in the normal condition throughout each session; in experiment (c), random alternation of blocks of three measurements for each condition was employed.

Three features of the results shown in Figure 1 are of significance here. (i) Both east and west responses were markedly reduced in frequency under stabilized viewing as compared to frequencies under normal viewing. (ii) The overall frequency of diagonal responses was reduced under stabilized viewing, although this was due mainly to reduction in northeast and northwest responses; southeast and southwest response frequencies either showed no marked change or increased under stabilization. (iii) The frequency of "no movement" responses increased under stabilization. These results strongly support the view that autokinesis is due to the occurrence of involuntary eye movements which continually shift the target image across the retina, and are consistent with the notion that local sign is involved in the perception of visual direction.

It might be expected from this interpretation that the normal and stabilized frequency distributions would be similar in each experiment, with the exception that (concurrent with the decrement in east and west frequencies) the "no movement" frequency for the stabilized condition be approximately equal to the sum of the east, west, and "no movement" frequencies for the corresponding normal viewing condition. Such is not the case, however.

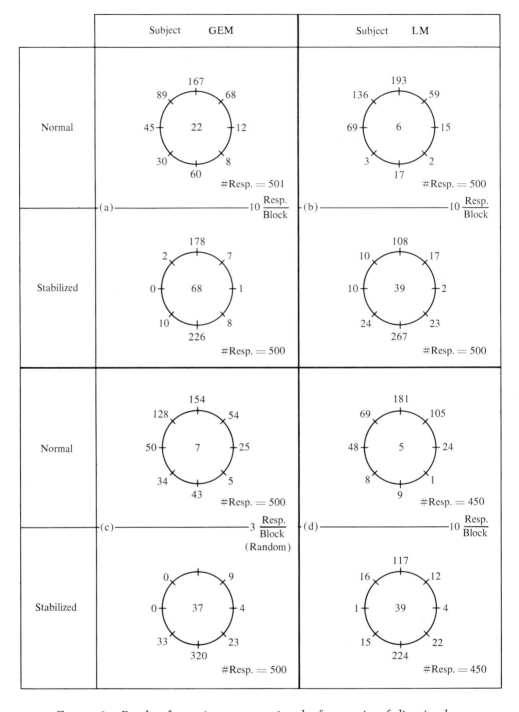

FIGURE 1   Results of experiments comparing the frequencies of directional response under stabilized and normal viewing. Each number outside the circumference of a circle refers to the frequency of movement in a given direction, for
example, in experiment (a) there were 167 north responses and 12 east responses in the normal viewing condition; frequency of "no movement" is given
at the center of the circle. Experiment (d) was essentially a replication of (b)
performed at a later date.

In each experiment in Figure 1, northerly responses predominated in the normal viewing condition and southerly responses predominated in the stabilized condition. This result has been analyzed and its basis established in several further experiments which are described elsewhere (7). It is also shown there that the result is consistent with the eye movement interpretation for autokinesis.

A neurophysiological basis for our results is suggested by recent work in which electrical recordings were made from single units in the striate cortex of cats (8). This work shows that some cortical cells are differentially sensitive to different directions of movement of a pattern across their receptive fields. Thus, for example, some units which are stimulated most effectively by movement in either direction along a given retinal meridian do not respond at all to movement along the meridian perpendicular to the given one and yield small responses to movement along intermediate meridians. A unit of this type may be most sensitive to vertical movement, horizontal movement, or movement along a particular diagonal meridian. Further, some units may be least sensitive to movement at 180 degrees from the direction of movement to which they are most sensitive (see also 9).

The reduction of horizontal movement during our stabilized viewing condition may be related to the fact that those neural units sensitive to horizontal movement are not being adequately stimulated, while those sensitive to movements in other meridians are still being stimulated. The response of the group sensitive to diagonal movement would be expected to be attenuated, however, since its stimulation now results mainly from vertical movements rather than from movement in those directions to which it is most sensitive. This interpretation of our results, of course, depends on the existence, as yet undemonstrated, of single unit movement detectors

in the human visual system, similar to those in cats, and also on the requirement that the output of such detectors be coded in perception so as to retain direction-specific information in the sense of a modern version of specific nerve energies.

References and Notes

1. HOPPE, J. I. *Die Scheinbewegung*, 1879, p. 23, cited in (2).
2. GUILFORD, J. P., and K. M. DALLENBACH. *Am. J. Psychol.* 40, 83 (1928).
3. SKOLNICK, A. *J. Exptl. Psychol.* 26, 373 (1940).
4. RIGGS, L. A., F. RATLIFF, J. C. CORNSWEET, and T. N. CORNSWEET. *J. Opt. Soc. Am.* 43, 495 (1953).
5. Preliminary work showed that two alignment criteria were essential: (i) it was necessary that the stablized view be foveally centered; (ii) when the stabilized view was substituted for the normal view, it was necessary that no shift of target location be observed by the subject. These criteria will be discussed more fully in a paper by L. Matin, G. E. MacKinnon, and D. Pearce, in preparation.
6. The autokinetic movements we observed could, without difficulty, be separated into (i) small, short-lasting, jerky, or oscillatory movement which appeared to be of considerably lesser magnitude than the diameter of the fixation target, and (ii) prolonged, slower drifts of larger apparent magnitude. We did not attempt to obtain information on the first type—when such movements do occur, changes in direction are too rapid for the subject to record. The data reported here concern the drifts.
7. MATIN, L., G. E. MACKINNON, and D. PEARCE. Paper read at a meeting of Psychonomic Society in Bryn Mawr, Pa., August 1963, manuscript in preparation; G. E. MacKinnon, in preparation.
8. HUBEL, D. H., and T. N. WIESEL. *J. Psysiol.* 148, 574 (1959); *ibid.*, 160, 106 (1962).
9. BARLOW, H. B., and R. M. HILL. *Science* 139, 412 (1963); U. Grusser-Cornehls, O. Grusser, and T. H. Bullock, *ibid.* 141, 820 (1963); H. R. Maturana and S. Frenk, *ibid.* 142, 977 (1963).

The Influence of Eye Movements on a New Type of Apparent Visual Movement*

When the sides of a contour triangle are sequentially presented, Ss report a sequential "flow" of brightness within the sides or a sequential "growth" of the sides. Modal report of this movement occurs in all three sides when the interside intervals are equal and 100 msec. Increasing the probability of contour scanning eye movements leads to an increase in this type of apparent visual movement.

From studies dealing with beta and gamma movement, it has been argued that eye movements do not influence apparent visual movement (Bartley, 1963; Guilford and Helson, 1929; Hulin and Katz, 1934; Wertheimer, 1912). A type of apparent visual movement is reported here which is influenced by eye movements. This type of apparent visual movement, similar to both beta and gamma, was noted by Ss in a number of studies which employed a method of sequentially presenting the sides of a contour triangle (McFarland, 1963, 1964a,b, 1965). Ss frequently reported "flow" or "growth" in one or several of the lines, viz., "the line appears in its entirety all at once but within the line there is a brightness which flows from one end to the other" or "one end of the line appears and then grows into the complete line." Ss also reported that "flow" and "growth" occurred from both ends toward the middle of a line or the reverse.

Method

To test whether eye movements affect this type of movement, one of three ob-

servation instructions is employed for each of three independent groups of eight Ss. These instructions are selected on the assumption that they differentially affect the probability of contour scanning eye movements during observation: (a) "fixate the small red light," (b) "try and look straight ahead," (c) "try and scan the lines."

The stimulus is an equilateral, contour triangle (Figure 1a). Sides are presented for 10 msec each in CCW sequence, 1, 2, 3. The two interside intervals are maintained equal and varied on different trials from 0 – 300 msec in 25 msec steps. Ss are dark adapted for 10 min and receive five trials on both an ascending and a descending series at each interside interval, a total of 130 trials for each S (see Mc-Farland, 1965, for details).

Results

There were reports of "flow" or "growth" on 20% of the total 3,120 trials for the three groups. Movement was reported in one, two, and three sides, either unidirectional or bidirectional. Three types of unidirectional movement occurred: CCW, movement commenced at the left end of side 1 and proceeded to the right, or commenced at the bottom of side 2 and pro-

* *Psychonomic Science*, 1966, vol. 4, pp. 51–52. This study was supported in part by National Institutes of Health Grant M6403(A), U.S. Public Health Service.

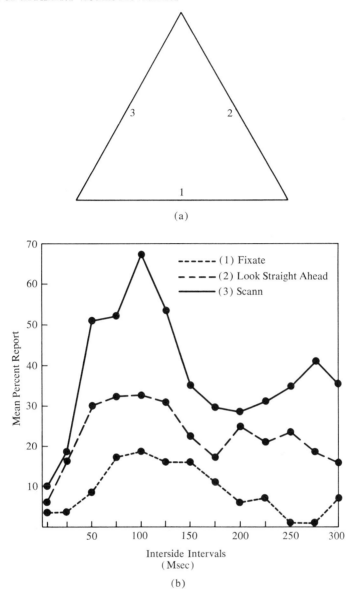

FIGURE 1a The stimulus is presented straight ahead, at eye-level, in a fronto-parallel plane, 17 in. from the S. Each side is 1 degree in length and approximately .44 ft. lamberts. For group 2, the red fixation light appears at the center of the triangle. 1b: Mean percent movement report for the three observation groups as a function of interside intervals.

ceeded up, or commenced at the top of side 3 and proceeded down; CW, the reverse of CCW; and CCW and CW, a combination. Two types of bidirectional movements occurred: from the center of the line to the ends; from the ends of the line to the center. Bidirectional movement was always, when reported in more than one line, CCW and CW.

The modal report was CCW, unidirectional movement (F = 59.58, p < .01) in all three sides (F = 2.97, p < .01) at an interside interval of 100 msec (F = 2.86, p < .01). At this interside interval, over

TABLE 1

Types of Movement Reports as a Function of Observation Instruction (Frequency)

| | UNIDIRECTIONAL MOVEMENT | | BIDIRECTIONAL MOVEMENT | |
| | | | CCW AND CW | COMBINED CENTER-ENDS AND ENDS-CENTER |
	CCW	CW		
Fixate	84	10	4	0
Straight ahead	167	7	5	56
Scan	158	99	9	22

50% of the reports from other Ss are that some of the sides appear unjoined at their ends and the sides appear in perfect succession (McFarland, 1965).

Effects of observation instructions on all movement reports can be seen throughout the range of interside intervals tested ($F < 1.00$) (Figure 1B). Instructions have their particular effect on the direction and type of movement (Table 1). Both "try and look straight ahead" and "try and scan the lines" increases the report of CCW, unidirectional movement ($F = 5.21$, $p < .01$). Instructions to "try and scan the lines" also increases the report of CW, unidirectional movement ($F = 6.80$, $p < .01$).

Discussion

In considering these effects of observation instructions, it is evident there are two avenues whereby an increase in contour scanning eye movements could lead to the observed increases in this type of apparent visual movement. First, eye movements could displace the stimuli on the retina; and, second, signals from central efferent and/or peripheral afferent structures of the extra-ocular motor system could interact with retinal signals (Grüsser and Grüsser-Cornehls, 1961). As eye movements are not monitored in the present experiment, however, a clear-cut decision

in this regard is not possible. On the basis of the present experiment, it can only be said that, since the modal frequency of this type of movement occurs when interside intervals approximate the latency for a saccadic eye movement (Bartz, 1962; Ditchburn and Ginsborg, 1953; Nachmias, 1959; Ratliff and Riggs, 1950; Tinker, 1953; Westheimer, 1954), it is likely that when eye movements do occur, they occur during the interside intervals when no side is visible. If future work shows that this is indeed the case, then it would seem plausible to argue that signals from central efferent and/or peripheral afferent structure of the extra-ocular motor system are interacting with retinal signals at some site within the nervous system to produce the increase in this type of movement. The plausibility of such an argument is enhanced by the fact that interaction of extra-ocular motor and retinal signals has already been found to affect the visibility of retinal signals (McFarland, 1964c).

References

BARTLEY, S. H. *Vision*. Hafner: New York, 1963, 176–177.
BARTZ, A. Eye-movement latency, duration, and response time as a function of angular displacement. *J. exp. Psychol.* 1962, *64*, 318–324.

DITCHBURN, R. W., and B. L. GINSBORG. Vision with a stabilized retinal image. *Nature*, 1952, *170*, 36–37.

GUILFORD, J. P., and H. HELSON. Eye movements and the phi phenomenon. *Amer. J. Psychol.*, 1929, *51*, 595–606.

GINSBORG, B. L. Small involuntary movements of the eye. *Brit. J. Ophthal.*, 1953, 37, 746–754.

GRÜSSER, O. J., and URSULA GRÜSSER-CORNEHLS. Reaktionsmuster einzelner Neurone in Geniculatum laterals und visuellen Cortex der Katze bei Reisung mit optokinetischen Streifenmustern. In R. Jung and H. Kornhuber (Eds.). *The visual system: neurophysiology and psychophysics.* Springer-Verlag: Berlin, 1961.

HULIN, W. S., and D. KATZ. Eye movements and the phi phenomenon. *Amer. J. Psychol.*, 1934, *46*, 332–334.

MCFARLAND, J. H. Some evidence bearing on visual form perception as a process of temporal integration. Eastern Psychological Association Meetings, April 11–13, 1963, New York.

MCFARLAND, J. H. The effect of stimulus-guided eye movements on visual form recognition. Eastern Psychological Association Meetings, April 16–18, 1964a, Philadelphia.

MCFARLAND, J. H. Some evidence bearing on operations of "analysis" and "integration" in visual form perception by humans. *Symposium on Models for the Perception of Speech and Visual Form.* November 11–14 1964b, Boston, Mass. MIT Press, 1967.

MCFARLAND, J. H. Extra-ocular feedback: a factor in binocular rivalry. *Percept. mot. Skills*, 1964c, *19*, 56.

MCFARLAND, J. H. Sequential part presentation: A method of studying visual form presentation. *Brit. J. Psychol.*, 1965.

NACHMIAS, J. Two dimensional motions of the retinal image during monocular fixations. *J. Opt. Soc. Amer.*, 1959, *49*, 901–908.

RATLIFF, F., and L. A. RIGGS. Involuntary motions of the eye during monocular fixation. *J. exp. Psychol.*, 1950, *40*, 687–701.

TINKER, M. A. Recent studies of eye movements in reading. *Psychol. Bull.*, 1958, *55*, 215–231.

WERTHEIMER, M. Experimentelle Studien über das Sehen von Bewegung. *Z. Psychol.*, 1912, *61*, 161–265.

WESTHEIMER, G. Mechanisms of saccadic eye movements. *Amer. Med. Ass. Arch. Ophthal.*, 1954, *52*, 710–724.

Visual Acuity when Eyes Are Pursuing Moving Targets*

NORMAN H. MACKWORTH

IRA T. KAPLAN

Harvard University

Abstract. *Acuity for a stationary test object decreased when the eye followed a moving fixation target. This effect became larger with increased target speed, with decreased illumination, and with longer exposure of the acuity object. The acuity object's orientation also influenced the results.*

A person maximizes the resolution of a moving object by following it with his eyes (1). The effectiveness of this process

* *Science*, 1962, vol. 136, pp. 387–388. Copyright © 1962 by the American Association for the Advancement of Science.

has been studied by measuring visual acuity with a moving test object (2). Visual tracking has a side effect, however, for the clarity gained by fixating a moving object is accompanied by blurring of the stationary environment. The present experiment (3) was intended to determine the effects of pursuit eye movement upon acuity for a motionless test object.

Ocular pursuit was elicited by a moving target which the subject was instructed to fixate. This target was a small white rectangle that moved horizontally across a large black screen. Target speed was varied from 0° to 120° of visual angle per second. An acuity object in the middle of the screen was briefly illuminated when the target passed directly beneath it. The center of the test object was 54 min above the target. The brightness and duration of the illuminating flash was varied.

The acuity object was a pattern of three parallel white stripes on a black background. Minimum resolvable size of the pattern was determined by the method of

limits. An increase in threshold stripe width indicated a decrease in visual acuity.

The relationship between target speed and acuity was found to be influenced by the orientation of the stripes (horizontal or vertical) and by the brightness and duration of the flash that illuminated them. Figure 1 shows minimum stripe width in minutes plotted against target speed in degrees of visual angle per second. Exposure duration was 99 msec. When the acuity object was brightly illuminated, target speed had little effect. When the light was dimmer, however, ocular pursuit raised thresholds. Acuity was reduced more for vertical stripes than for horizontal ones. Also, the rise in threshold produced by a given increment in target speed became

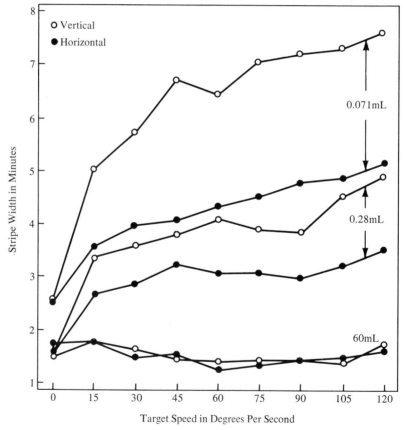

FIGURE 1   Minimum resolvable stripe width in minutes of visual angle as a function of target speed in degrees of visual angle per second. Thresholds for horizontal and vertical stripes were obtained at three luminance points. Each point is the average of eight determinations on one subject.

less at the higher speeds.

With the luminance of the stripes equal to 60 mlam, minimum resolvable stripe width did not increase as target speed increased. In fact, threshold width was somewhat below its initial value when the target moved at 60° per second. When the target was at rest, minimum width was 1.53 min for vertical stripes and 1.75 min for horizontal ones. At this luminance the flash looked glaringly bright against the dark background and the stripes seemed to spread. Eye movement made the light appear less bright. The slight improvement in acuity produced by ocular motion was about equal to the improvement produced by dimming the light to eliminate glare. Vertical stripes were as visible as horizontal ones at all speeds.

At 0.28 mlam pursuit movement raised threshold. When the fixation target was stationary, horizontal and vertical thresholds were both 1.61 min—about what they were at 60 mlam. But target motion raised vertical threshold to almost 5 min and horizontal threshold to about 3.5 min. The rise in threshold was even greater with the luminance decreased to 0.071 mlam, as was the disparity induced between vertical and horizontal thresholds. Thus the uppermost pair of curves in Figure 1 begins at about 2.5 min, and the horizontal threshold rises above 5 min while the vertical exceeds 7.5 min at 120° per second. Each of the four highest curves is steeper at the lower speeds. More than half their overall rise occurs in the first 30° of the 120° range of target speeds.

Ocular pursuit had little effect on acuity when the test object was illuminated by a very brief stroboscopic flash. A 99-msec flash of 7.9 μlam yielded thresholds of about 5 min for both horizontal and vertical stripes under steady fixation. The same light energy concentrated into a 1-μsec strobe flash gave approximately the same thresholds, for within certain limits a constant product of luminance and duration results in a constant acuity level (4). This relation between energy and acuity held with steady fixation, but it did not hold with a moving fixation target. Thresholds obtained with the 99 msec flash were greatly increased during visual tracking, and vertical thresholds became much higher than horizontal ones. In contrast, when the 1-μsec flash was used there was a maximum increase of less than 1 min with no separation between horizontal and vertical thresholds.

Tracking the target naturally causes motion of the acuity object's image on the retina. Since there is a lag in the visual response to the changing pattern of retinal illumination, the acuity object looks blurred. Horizontal movement makes the horizontal stripes appear longer and dimmer. Resolution of vertical stripes is affected more than that of horizontal ones because light from the vertical stripes is spread, in effect, over the dark spaces between them, thereby reducing contrast as well as brightness.

The smaller effect of ocular pursuit at higher luminances may be related to the fact that the acuity loss caused by a given decrement in brightness is smaller at high luminances than at lower ones (5). Over a certain range of high brightness, visual acuity is not altered by varying luminance. Faster discrimination of the moving image may also reduce the effect of eye movement at higher brightnesses. The perception of flicker presents a similar case of improved temporal resolution accompanying increased luminance (6).

The stroboscopic flash minimizes the effect of eye movement by virtually stopping motion of the retinal image. During the 1-μsec exposure the acuity object's image moves hardly any distance at all on the retina. Hence threshold was constant under varied target speed.

The reason that equal increments in target speed have less effect at higher speeds is probably that they do not produce corresponding increments in speed of eye movement. The eye can make smooth following movements at velocities up to about 30° per second, but at higher target speeds sustained pursuit motion becomes increasingly slower than target speed (7).

References

1. WOODWORTH, R. S., and H. SCHLOSBERG, *Experimental Psychology* (Holt, Rinehart and Winston, Inc., New York, 1954), p. 510.
2. LUDVIGH, E. J., *Science* 108, 63 (1948); ——, *A.M.A. Arch. Ophthalmol.* 42, 14 (1949); —— and J. W. Miller, *J. Opt. Soc. Am.* 48, 799 (1958); J. W. Miller, *ibid.* 48, 803 (1958).
3. This research was supported by a contract (C-180) from the National Science Foundation.
4. GRAHAM, C. H., and C. COOK, *Am. J. Psychol.* 49, 654 (1937).
5. SHLAER, S. *J. Gen. Physiol.* 21, 165 (1937).
6. BARTLEY, S. H., in *Handbook of Experimental Psychology*, S. S. Stevens, Ed. (Wiley, New York, 1951), p. 960.
7. WESTHEIMER, G., *A.M.A. Arch. Ophthalmol.* 52, 932 (1954).

Selective Sensitivity to Direction of Movement in Ganglion Cells of the Rabbit Retina*

HORACE B. BARLOW

University of California, Berkeley

RICHARD M. HILL

Ohio State University

Abstract. *Among the ganglion cells in the rabbit's retina there is a class that responds to movement of a stimulus in one direction, and does not respond to movement in the opposite direction. The same directional selectivity holds over the whole receptive field of one such cell, but the selected direction differs in different cells. The discharge is almost uninfluenced by the intensity of the stimulus spot, and the response occurs for the same direction of movement when a black spot is substituted for a light spot.*

The great sensitivity of retinal ganglion cells to movement of a pattern of light over the retina has been recognized since Hartline's work on the frog (1). Hubel and Wiesel presented evidence that certain cells in the cat's cortex respond, not to any movement, but only to movement in a particular direction (2). Reports of similar directional selectivity have been made on the retina and optic tectum of frog (3), on the cortex of cat (4), on the lateral geniculate of rabbit (5), and most recently on the retina of pigeon (6) and the tectum of rabbit (7). The extraction of information as to direction of motion is a surprisingly complex task for a few synaptic layers to perform, and some doubt remained in our minds as to whether a simpler explanation of apparent directional selectivity had been adequately excluded.

Hartline showed that "off" units in the frog responded to any diminution in the total contribution from all parts of the

* *Science*, 1963, vol. 139, pp. 412–414. Copyright © 1963 by the American Association for the Advancement of Science. This work was supported by U.S. Public Health Service Grants B-3843 and B-3154.

receptive field to the ganglion cell (1). As well as responding to dimming of a uniform light, they also responded to movement of a spot of light away from the most sensitive central zone of the receptive field. In such a unit, if a stimulating spot is moved to and fro over the edge of the receptive field one may easily obtain records showing a discharge to movement in one direction, and not in the opposite direction. It would be misleading, however, to call this directional selectivity, for if other regions of the receptive field are explored the direction of movement giving the maximum discharge will not be constant; it will always tend to lie on a line away from the center of the receptive field. On the other hand, a unit showing true selectivity for direction should show the same direction of preference in all parts of its receptive field. A similar argument applies to contrast; a unit which is genuinely selecting out direction of motion should show the same preference regardless of contrast, whereas Hartline showed that the frog's "off" units discharged when a shadow moved towards the center of the receptive field, not away from it as with bright stimulus spots.

The receptive fields of most of the cells for which directional sensitivity has been reported are more complex than those of the "off" units investigated by Hartline, and we originally felt that an explanation in terms of a change in the pooled excitatory and inhibitory contributions from all parts of the receptive field had not been excluded except for certain cortical neurones (2). However, we have found that about one-third of the units isolated in the rabbit's retina show a movement sensitivity in which the direction of preferential response is invariant in different parts of the receptive field, and is invariant for changes in contrast. We think this excludes simple explanations of the type outlined above, and shows that retinal units can be genuinely directionally selective.

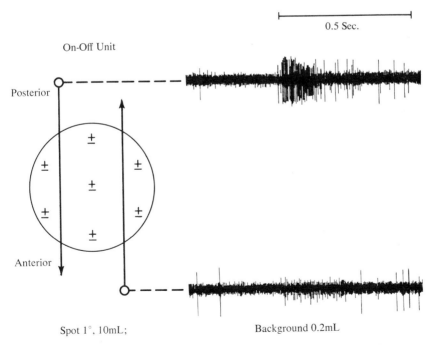

FIGURE 1   A spot of light is moved right across the receptive field of an "on-off" unit. It responds to movement from posterior to anterior, but not to movement from anterior to posterior. Thus it shows directional selectivity. A second unit is visible which responds to antero-posterior movement.

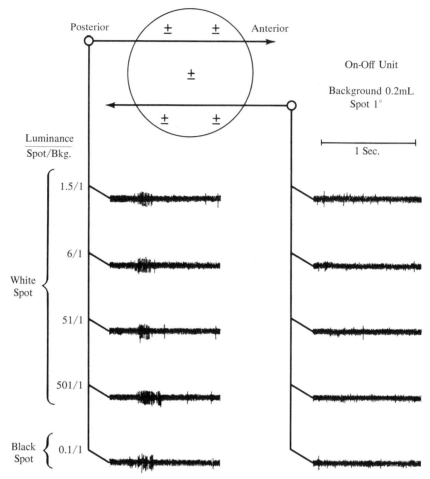

FIGURE 2   Effect of intensity and reversal of contrast on response to movement. The spot is moved through the field of an "on-off" unit first from posterior to anterior, then in the reverse direction. For the top four records the spot was brighter than the background, the ratio of luminances being indicated on the left. The ratio just eliciting a discharge was about 1.2 to 1. However, when the spot was darker than the ground a response was again obtained and occurred for the same direction of motion as with a bright spot.

Single retinal units were isolated by a technique similar to that of Kuffler (8). The rabbits were lightly anesthetized with urethane, or in some cases decerebrated under ether. Figure 1 shows the response of a unit to movement of a spot of light all the way across its receptive field. It is clear that movement in a posterior-anterior direction evokes a vigorous discharge, whereas movement from anterior to posterior evokes none. We were sure that the spot traversed the whole receptive field because this had previously been explored by turning on and off the same stimulus spot (10 millilamberts, 1° diameter, background illumination 0.2 mlam). As in most units showing directional selectivity, discharges were obtained at both "on" and "off," even at the center of the receptive field. They are thus similar to the "on-off" units in the frog (9). However directional selectivity is not only found in association with this type of field; we have occasionally found it in units for which "on" and "off" thresholds differed greatly.

Many units in the rabbit have concentric "on" and "off" zones, as in the cat (8). These are sensitive to movement, but the greatest discharge tends to occur for centrifugal or centripetal motion. The receptive fields of the units shown in Figures 1 and 2 were approximately 5° in diameter.

It has been suggested that the asymmetry of the directionally selective units was caused by damage or optical effects of the electrode itself. This is excluded by the fact that we have observed it when recording from fibers, in which case the field is some distance from the electrode.

Figure 1 shows an expected, smaller, second set of action potentials which appear for movements that cause little activity in the larger unit. This is important for it shows that the selected direction of sensitivity is diversified, and is not the same in all units.

Figure 2 shows invariance of response for changes in contrast. Changing the intensity of the moving spot over a range of 1000 : 1 has little influence on the discharge. The lowest line shows the response when a black dot on a large white card is moved through the receptive field. Reversing the contrast only reduces the discharge in the favored direction by a small amount and does not result in a greater discharge in the opposite direction.

In summary, four main characteristics differentiate units that have genuine directional selectivity from other types of units. First, movements of a spot of light completely across their receptive fields produce a discharge from certain directions only. Second, the same directional preference is shown for spots darker or brighter than the background. Third, the discharge varies little for big changes in intensity of a bright spot. And fourth, these units commonly (but not invariably) yield both "on" and "off" responses at all points within their borders.

We believe these observations exclude simple explanations of movement sensitivity in terms of pooled effects from "on" and "off" zones of the receptive field. Exploration with a stationary spot turned on and off, and noting the phase at which a discharge occurs, does not provide a sufficient basis for predicting the response to a moving spot. In addition it is clear that two synaptic layers can abstract direction of motion from the spatio-temporal pattern of light falling on the retina, and that the rabbit possesses such a system of directionally selective ganglion cells in its retina (10).

References

1. HARTLINE, H. K., Am. J. Physiol. 130, 690 (1940).
2. HUBEL, D. H., and T. N. WIESEL, J. Physiol. 148, 574 (1959); 160, 106 (1962).
3. LETTVIN, J. Y., H. R. MATURANA, W. S. McCULLOCH, and W. H. PITTS, Proc. I.R.E. (Inst. Radio Engrs.) 47, 1940 (1959).
4. GRÜSSER, J. O. Personal communication (1962).
5. ARDEN, G. Personal communication (1962).
6. MATURANA, H. Information Symposium Proceedings of the XXIII International Union of Physiological Sciences, Leiden (1962).
7. SCHAEFFER, K. P. Proc. Intern. Union Physiol. Sci. Part 2, 1, 496 (1962).
8. KUFFLER, S. W., J. Neurophys. 16, 37 (1953).
9. HARTLINE, H. K., Am. J. Physiol. 121, 400 (1938); H. B. Barlow, J. Physiol. 119, 69 (1953).

Receptive Fields, Binocular Interaction, and Functional Architecture in the Cat's Visual Cortex*

D. H. HUBEL   T. N. WIESEL

Harvard Medical School

Organization of Receptive Fields in Cat's Visual Cortex: Properties of "Simple" and "Complex" Fields

The receptive field of a cell in the visual system may be defined as the region of retina (or visual field) over which one can influence the firing of that cell. In the cat's retina one can distinguish two types of ganglion cells, those with "on"-center receptive fields and those with "off"-center fields (Kuffler, 1953). The lateral geniculate body also has cells of these two types; so far no others have been found (Hubel and Wiesel, 1961). In contrast, the visual cortex contains a large number of functionally different cell types; yet with the exception of afferent fibers from the lateral geniculate body we have found no units with concentric "on"-center or "off"-center fields.

When stimulated with stationary or moving patterns of light, cells in the visual cortex gave responses that could be interpreted in terms of the arrangements of excitatory and inhibitory regions in their receptive fields (Hubel and Wiesel, 1959). Not all cells behave so simply, however; some responded in a complex manner which bear little obvious relationship to the receptive fields mapped with small spots. It has become increasingly apparent to us that cortical cells differ in the complexity of their receptive fields. The great majority of fields seem to fall naturally into two groups, which we have termed "simple" and "complex." Although the fields to be described represent the commonest subtypes of these groups, new varieties are continually appearing, and it is unlikely that the ones we have listed give anything like a complete picture of the striate cortex. We have therefore avoided a rigid system of classification, and have designated receptive fields by letters or numbers only for convenience in referring to the figures. We shall concentrate especially on features common to simple fields and on those common to complex fields, emphasizing differences between the two groups, and also between cortical fields and lateral geniculate fields.

Results

SIMPLE RECEPTIVE FIELDS

The receptive fields of 233 of the 303 cortical cells in the present series were classified as "simple." Like retinal ganglion and geniculate cells, cortical cells with simple fields possessed distinct excitatory and inhibitory subdivisions. Illumination of part or all of an excitatory region in-

* Excerpted from an article of the same title in the *Journal of Physiology*, 1962, vol. 160, pp. 106–154.

creased the maintained firing of the cell, whereas a light shone in the inhibitory region suppressed the firing and evoked a discharge at "off." A large spot confined to either area produced a greater change in rate of firing than a small spot, indicating summation within either region. On the other hand, the two types of region within a receptive field were mutually antagonistic. This was most forcefully shown by the absence or near absence of a response to simultaneous illumination of both regions, for example, with diffuse light. From the arrangement of excitatory and inhibitory regions it was usually possible to predict in a qualitative way the responses to any shape of stimulus, stationary or moving. Spots having the approximate shape of one or other region were the most effective stationary stimuli; smaller spots failed to take full advantage of summation within a region, while larger ones were likely to invade opposing regions, so reducing the response. To summarize: these fields were termed "simple" because like retinal and geniculate fields (1) they were subdivided into distinct excitatory and inhibitory regions; (2) there was summation within the separate excitatory and inhibitory parts; (3) there was antagonism between excitatory and inhibitory regions; and (4) it was possible to predict responses to stationary or moving spots of various shapes from a map of the excitatory and inhibitory areas.

While simple cortical receptive fields were similar to those of retinal ganglion cells and geniculate cells in possessing excitatory and inhibitory subdivisions, they differed profoundly in the spatial arrangements of these regions. The receptive fields of all retinal ganglion and geniculate cells had one or other of the concentric forms shown in Figure 1A, B. (Excitatory areas are indicated by crosses, inhibitory areas by triangles.) In contrast, simple cortical fields all had a side-to-side arrangement of excitatory and inhibitory areas with separation of the areas by parallel straight-line

boundaries rather than circular ones. There were several varieties of fields, differing in the number of subdivisions and the relative area occupied by each subdivision. The commonest arrangements are illustrated in Figure 1C–G. Table 1 gives the number of cells observed in each category. The departure of these fields from circular symmetry introduces a new variable, namely the orientation of the boundaries separating the field subdivisions. This orientation is a characteristic of each cortical cell, and may be vertical, horizontal, or oblique. There was no indication that any one orientation was more common than the others. We shall use the term *receptive-field axis* to indicate a line through the centre of a field, parallel to the boundaries separating excitatory and inhibitory regions. The *axis orientation* will then refer to the orientation of these boundaries, either on the retina or in the visual field. Axes are shown in Figure 1 by continuous lines.

Two common types of fields, shown in Figure 1C, D, each consisted of a narrow elongated area, excitatory or inhibitory, flanked on either side by two regions of the opposite type. In these fields the two flanking regions were symmetrical, i.e., they were about equal in area and the responses obtained from them were of about the same magnitude. In addition there were fields with long narrow centers (excitatory or inhibitory) and asymmetrical flanks. An example of an asymmetrical field with an inhibitory center is shown in Figure 1E. The most effective stationary stimulus for all of these cells was a long narrow rectangle ("slit") of light just large enough to cover the central region without invading either flank. For maximum center response the orientation of the slit was critical; changing the orientation by more than 5–10° was usually enough to reduce a response greatly or even abolish it. Illuminating both flanks usually evoked a strong response. If a slit having the same size as the receptive-field center was shone

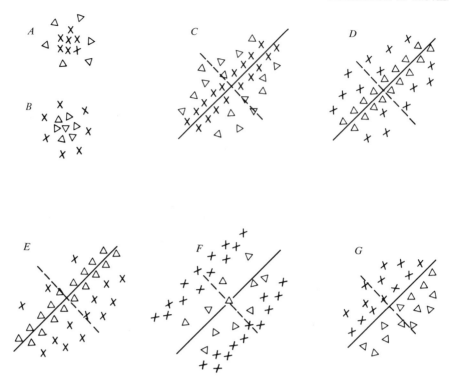

FIGURE 1   Common arrangements of lateral geniculate and cortical receptive fields. (*A*) "On"-center geniculate receptive field. (*B*) "Off"-center geniculate receptive field. (*C-G*) Various arrangements of simple cortical receptive fields. X, areas giving excitatory responses ("on" responses); △, areas giving inhibitory responses ("off" responses). Receptive-field axes are shown by continuous lines through field centers; in the figure these are all oblique, but each arrangement occurs in all orientations.

in either flanking area it evoked only a weak response, since it covered only part of one flank. Diffuse light was ineffective, or at most evoked only a very weak response, indicating that the excitatory and inhibitory parts of the receptive field were very nearly balanced.

In these fields the equivalent but opposite-type regions occupied retinal areas that were far from equal; the centre portion was small and concentrated whereas the flanks were widely dispersed. A similar inequality was found in fields of type *F*, Figure 1, but here the excitatory flanks were elongated and concentrated, while the centre was relatively large and diffuse. The optimum response was evoked by simultaneously illuminating the two flanks with two parallel slits (see Hubel and Wiesel, 1959, Figure 9).

Some cells had fields in which only two regions were discernible, arranged side by side as in Figure 1*G*. For these cells the most efficient stationary stimulus consisted of two areas of differing brightness placed so that the line separating them fell exactly over the boundary between the excitatory and inhibitory parts of the field. This type of stimulus was termed an "edge." An "on" or an "off" response was evoked depending on whether the bright part of the stimulus fell over the excitatory or the inhibitory region. A slight change in position or orientation of the line separating the light from the dark area was usually enough to reduce greatly the effectiveness of the stimulus.

Moving stimuli were very effective, probably because of the synergistic effects of leaving an inhibitory area and simultaneously entering an excitatory area (Hubel and Wiesel, 1959). The optimum stimulus could usually be predicted from the distribution of excitatory and inhibitory regions of the receptive field. With moving stimuli, just as with stationary, the orientation was critical. In contrast, a slit or edge moved across the circularly symmetric field of a geniculate cell gave (as one would expect) roughly the same response regardless of the stimulus orientation. The responses evoked when an optimally oriented slit crossed back and forth over a cortical receptive field were often roughly equal for the two directions of crossing. This was true of fields like those shown in Figure 1C, D, and F. For many cells, however, the responses to two diametrically opposite movements were different, and some only responded to one of the two movements. The inequalities could usually be accounted for by an asymmetry in flanking regions of the type shown in Figure 1E (see also Hubel and Wiesel, 1959, Figure 7). In fields that had only two discernible regions arranged side by side (Figure 1G), the difference in the responses to a moving slit or edge was especially pronounced.

Optimum rates of movement varied from one cell to another. On several occasions two cells were recorded together, one of which responded only to a slow-moving stimulus (1°/sec or lower), the other to a rapid one (10°/sec or more). For cells with fields of type F, Figure 1, the time elapsing between the two discharges to a moving stimulus was a measure of the rate of movement (see Hubel and Wiesel, 1959, Figure 5).

If responses to movement were predictable from arrangements of excitatory and inhibitory regions, the reverse was to some extent also true. The axis orientation of a field, for example, was given by the most effective orientation of a moving slit or edge. If an optimally oriented slit produced a brief discharge on crossing from one region to another, one could predict that the first region was inhibitory and the second excitatory. Brief responses to crossing a very confined region were characteristic of cells with simple cortical fields, whereas the complex cells to be described below gave sustained responses to movement over much wider areas.

Movement was used extensively as a stimulus in experiments in which the main object was to determine axis orientation and ocular dominance for a large number of cells in a single penetration, and when it was not practical, because of time limitations, to map out every field completely. Because movement was generally a very powerful stimulus, it was also used

TABLE 1

Simple Cortical Fields

	FIGURE	NUMBER OF CELLS
(a) Narrow cencentrated centers		
(i) Symmetrical flanks		
Excitatory centers	2C	23
inhibitory centers	2D	17
(ii) Asymmetrical flanks		
Excitatory centers		28
inhibitory centers	2E	10
(b) Large centers; concentrated flanks	2F	21
(c) One excitatory region and one inhibitory	2G	17
(d) Uncategorized		117
Total number of simple fields		233

in studying cells that gave little or no response to stationary patterns. In all, 117 of the 233 simple cells were studied mainly by moving stimuli. In Table 1 these have been kept separate from the other groups since the distribution of their excitatory and inhibitory regions is not known with the same degree of certainty. It is also possible that with further study some of these fields would have revealed complex properties.

COMPLEX RECEPTIVE FIELDS

Intermixed with cells having simple fields, and present in most penetrations of the striate cortex, were cells with far more intricate and elaborate properties. The receptive fields of these cells were termed "complex." Unlike cells with simple fields, these responded to variously-shaped stationary or moving forms in a way that could not be predicted from maps made with small circular spots. Often such maps could not be made, since small round spots were either ineffective or evoked only mixed ("on-off") responses throughout the receptive field. When separate "on" and "off" regions could be discerned, the principles of summation and mutual antagonism, so helpful in interpreting simple fields, did not generally hold. Nevertheless, there were some important features common to the two types of cells. In the following examples, four types of complex fields will be illustrated. The numbers observed of each type are given in Table 2.

The cell of Figure 2 failed to respond to round spots of light, whether small or large. By trial and error with many shapes of stimulus it was discovered that the cell's firing could be influencecd by a horizontally oriented slit $\frac{1}{8}°$ wide and 3° long. Provided the slit was horizontal, its exact positioning within the 3°-diameter receptive field was not critical. When it was shone anywhere above the centre of the receptive field (the horizontal line of Figure 2) an "off" response was obtained; "on" responses were evoked throughout the lower half. In an intermediate position (Figure 2C) the cell responded at both "on" and "off." From experience with simpler receptive fields one might have expected wider slits to give increasingly better responses owing to summation within the upper or lower part of the field, and that illumination of either half by itself might be the most effective stimulus of all. The result was just the opposite: responses fell off rapidly as the stimulus was widened beyond about $\frac{1}{8}°$, and large rectangles covering the entire lower or upper halves of the receptive field were quite ineffective (Figure 2F, G). On the other hand, summation could easily be demonstrated in a horizontal direction, since a slit $\frac{1}{8}°$ wide but extending only across part of the field was less effective than a longer one covering the entire width. One might also have expected the orientation of the slit to be unimportant as long as the stimulus was wholly confined to the region above the

TABLE 2

Complex Cortical Receptive Fields

	FIGURE	NUMBER OF CELLS
(a) Activated by slit–non-uniform field	3	11
(b) Activated by slit–uniform field	4	39
(c) Activated by edge	5–6	14
(d) Activated by dark bar	7–8	6
Total number of complex fields		70

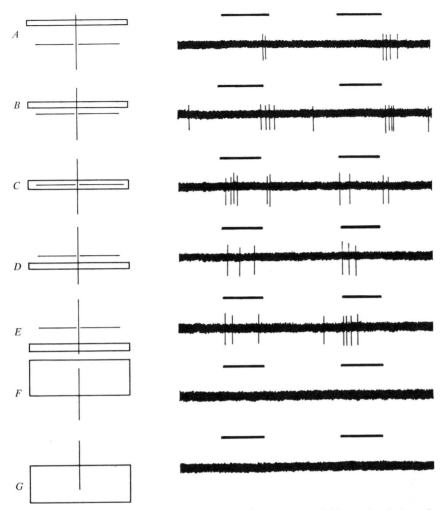

FIGURE 2   Responses of a cell with a complex receptive field to stimulation of the left (contralateral) eye. Receptive field located in area centralis. The diagrams to the left of each record indicate the position of a horizontal rectangular light stimulus with respect to the receptive field, marked by a cross. In each record the upper line indicates when the stimulus is on. A-E, stimulus $\sqrt{3\frac{1}{3}}° \times 3°$, F-G, stimulus $1\frac{1}{2}° \times 3°$ ($4°$ is equivalent to 1 mm on the cat retina). For background illumination and stimulus intensity see Methods section of original report. Cell was activated in the same way from right eye, but less vigorously (ocular-dominance group 2, see Part II of original report). An electrolytic lesion made while recording from this cell was found near the border of layers 5 and 6, in the apical segment of the post-lateral gyrus. Positive deflexions upward; duration of each stimulus 1 sec.

horizontal line or the region below. On the contrary, the orientation was critical, since a tilt of even a few degrees from the horizontal markedly reduced the response, even though the slit did not cross the boundary separating the upper and lower halves of the field.

In preferring a slit specific in width and orientation, this cell resembled certain cells with simple fields. When stimulated in the upper part of its field it behaved in many respects like cells with "off"-center fields of type D, Figure 1; in the lower part it responded like "on"-center fields of Figure

1C. But for this cell the strict requirements for shape and orientation of the stimulus were in marked contrast to the relatively large leeway of the stimulus in its ordinate position on the retina. Cells with simple fields, on the other hand, showed very little latitude in the positioning of an optimally oriented stimulus.

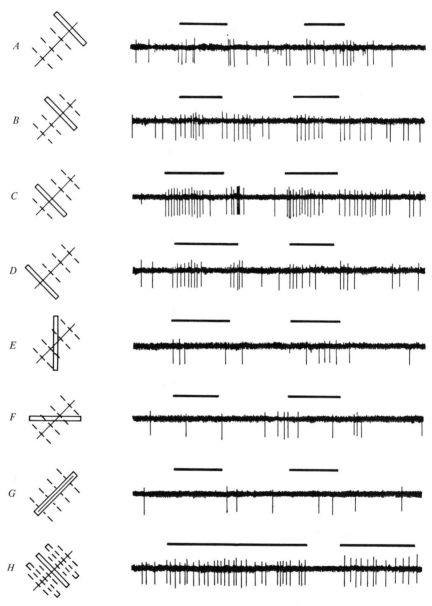

FIGURE 3   Responses of a cell with a complex field to stimulation of the left (contralateral) eye with a slit $\frac{1}{8} \times 2\frac{1}{2}°$. Receptive field was in the area centralis and was about $2° \times 3°$ in size. A-D, $\frac{1}{8}°$-wide slit oriented parallel to receptive field axis, E-G, slit oriented at 45° and 90° to receptive-field axis H, slit oriented as in A-D, is on throughout the record and is moved rapidly from side to side where indicated by upper beam. Responses from left eye slightly more marked than those from right (Group 3, see Part II of original report). Time 1 sec.

The upper part of this receptive field may be considered inhibitory and the lower part excitatory, even though in either area summation only occurred in a horizontal direction. Such subdivisions were occasionally found in complex fields, but more often the fields were uniform in this respect. This was true for the other complex fields to be described in this section.

Responses of a second complex unit are shown in Figure 3. In many ways the receptive field of this cell was similar to the one just described. A slit was the most potent stimulus, and the most effective width was again ⅛°. Once more the orientation was an important stimulus variable, since the slit was effective anywhere in the field as long as it was placed in a 10 o'clock–4 o'clock orientation (Figure 3A–D). A change in orientation of more than 5–10° in either direction produced a marked reduction in the response (Figure 3E–G). As usual, diffuse light had no influence on the firing. This cell responded especially well if the slit, oriented as in A–D, was moved steadily across the receptive field. Sustained discharges were evoked over the entire length of the field. The optimum rate of movement was about 1°/sec. If movement was interrupted the discharge stopped, and when it was resumed the firing recommenced. Continuous firing could be maintained indefinitely by small side-to-side movements of a stimulus within the receptive field (Figure 3H.) The pattern of firing was one characteristic of many complex cells, especially those responding well to moving stimuli. It consisted of a series of short high-frequency repetitive discharges each containing 5–10 spikes. The bursts occurred at irregular intervals, at frequencies up to about 20/sec. For this cell, movement of an optimally oriented slit was about equally effective in either of the two opposite directions. This was not true of all complex units, as will be seen in some of the examples given below.

Like the cell of Figure 2, this cell may be thought of as having a counterpart in simple fields of the type shown in Figure 1C–E. It shares with these simpler fields the attribute of responding well to properly oriented slit stimuli. Once more the distinction lies in the permissible variation in position of the optimally oriented stimulus. The variation is small (relative to the size of the receptive field) in the simple fields, large in the complex. Though resembling the cell of Figure 2 in requiring a slit for a stimulus, this cell differed in that its responses to a properly oriented slit were mixed ("on-off") in type. This was not unusual for cells with complex fields. In contrast, cortical cells with simple fields, like retinal ganglion cells and lateral geniculate cells, responded to optimum restricted stimuli either with excitatory ("on") responses or inhibitory ("off") responses. When a stimulus covered opposing regions, the effects normally tended to cancel, though sometimes mixed discharges were obtained, the "on" and "off" components both being weak. For these simpler fields "on-off" responses were thus an indication that the stimulus was not optimum. Yet some cells with complex fields responded with mixed discharges even to the most effective stationary stimuli we could find. Among the stimuli tried were curved objects, dark stripes, and still more complicated patterns, as well as monochromatic spots and slits.

A third type of complex field is illustrated in Figures 4 and 5. There were no responses to small circular spots or to slits, but an edge was very effective if oriented vertically. Excitatory or inhibitory responses were produced depending on whether the brighter area was to the left or the right (Figure 4A, E). So far, these are just the responses one would expect from a cell with a vertically oriented simple field of the type shown in Figure 1G. In such a field the stimulus placement for optimum response is generally very critical. On the contrary, the complex unit responded to vertical edges over an unusually large region about 16° in length (Figure 5).

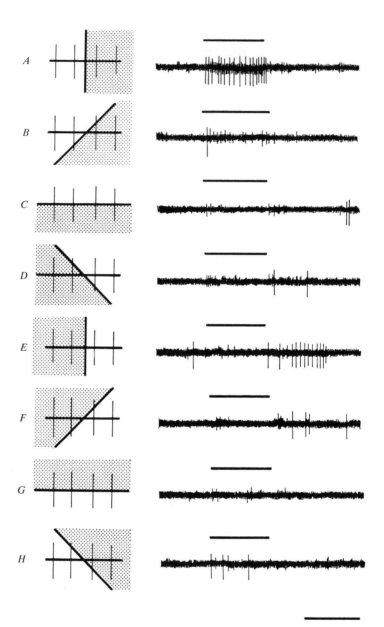

FIGURE 4 Responses of a cell with a large (8° × 16°) complex receptive field to an edge projected on the ipsilateral retina so as to cross the receptive field in various directions. (The screen is illuminated by a diffuse background light, 0.0 $\log_{10}$ cd/m². At the time of stimulus, shown by upper line of each record, half the screen, to one side of the variable boundary, is illuminated at 1.0 $\log_{10}$ cd/m², while the other half is kept constant.) A, vertical edge with light area to left, darker area to right. B-H, various other orientations of edge. Position of receptive field 20° below and to the left of the area centralis. Response from ipsilateral eye stronger than those from contralateral eye (group 5, see Part II of original report). Time 1 sec.

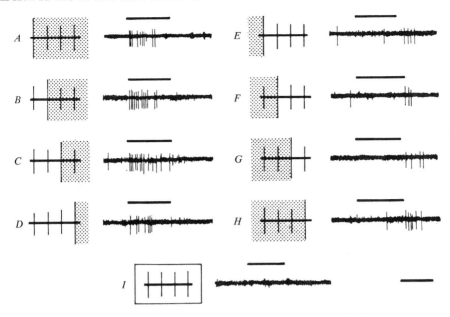

FIGURE 5 Same cell as in Figure 4. A-H responses to a vertical edge in various parts of the receptive field; A-D, brighter light to the left; B-H, brighter light to the right; I, large rectangle, 10° × 20°, covering entire receptive field. Time 1 sec.

"On" responses were obtained with light to the left (A–D), and "off" responses with light to the right (E–H), regardless of the position of the line separating light from darkness. When the entire receptive field was illuminated diffusely (I) no response was evoked. As with all complex fields, we are unable to account for these responses by any simple spatial arrangement of excitatory and inhibitory regions.

Like the complex units already described, this cell was apparently more concerned with the orientation of a stimulus than with its exact position in the receptive field. It differed in responding well to edges but poorly or not at all to slits, whether narrow or wide. It is interesting in this connection that exchanging an edge for its mirror equivalent reversed the response, i.e., replaced an excitatory response by an inhibitory and vice versa. The ineffectiveness of a slit might therefore be explained by supposing that the opposite effects of its its two edges tended to cancel each other.

As shown in Figure 5, the responses of the cell to a given vertical edge were con-

sistent in type, being either "on" or "off" for all positions of the edge within the receptive field. In being uniform in its response-type it resembled the cell of Figure 3. A few other cells of the same general category showed a similar preference for edges, but lacked this uniformity. Their receptive fields resembled the field of Figure 2, in that a given edge evoked responses of one type over half the field, and the opposite type over the other half. These fields were divided into two halves by a line parallel to the receptive-field axis: an edge oriented parallel to the axis gave "on" responses throughout one of the halves and "off" responses through the other. In either half, replacing the edge by its mirror image reversed the response-type. Even cells which were uniform in the response-types, like those in Figures 3–5, varied to some extent in the magnitude of their responses, depending on the position of the stimulus. Moreover, as with most cortical cells, there was some variation in responses to identical stimuli.

A final example is given to illustrate the

wide range of variation in the organization of complex receptive fields. The cell of Figures 6 and 7 was not strongly influenced by any form projected upon the screen; it gave only weak, unsustained "on" responses to a dark horizontal rectangle against a light background, and to other forms it was unresponsive. A strong discharge was evoked, however, if a black rectangular object (for example, a piece of black tape) was placed against the brightly illuminated screen. The receptive field of the cell was about 5 × 5°, and the most effective stimulus width was about ⅓°. Vigorous firing was obtained regardless of the position of the rectangle, as long as it was horizontal and within the receptive field. If it was tipped more than 10° in either direction no discharge was

evoked (Figure 6D, E). We have recorded several complex fields which resembled this one in that they responded best to black rectangles against a bright background. Presumably it is important to have good contrast between the narrow black rectangle and the background; this is technically difficult with a projector because of scattered light.

Slow downward movement of the dark rectangle evoked a strong discharge throughout the entire 5° of the receptive field (Figure 7A). If the movement was halted the cell continued to fire, but less vigorously. Upward movement gave only weak, inconsistent responses, and left-right movement (Figure 7B) gave no responses. Discharges of highest frequency were evoked by relatively slow rates of down-

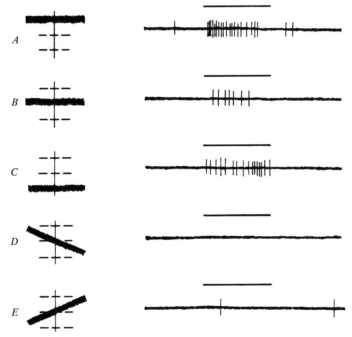

FIGURE 6 Cell activated only by left (contralateral) eye over a field approximately 5° × 5°, situated 10° above and to the left of the area centralis. The cell responded best to a black horizontal rectangle, ⅓° × 6°, placed anywhere in the receptive field (A-C). Tilting the stimulus rendered it ineffective (D-E). The black bar was introduced against a light background during periods of 1 sec, indicated by the upper line in each record. Luminance of white background, 1.0 $\log_{10}$ cd/m²; luminance of black part, 0.0 $\log_{10}$ cd/m². A lesion, made while recording from the cell, was found in layer 2 of apical segment of postlateral gyrus.

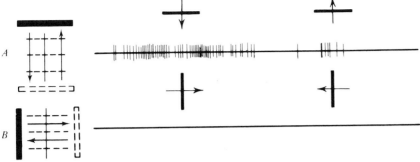

FIGURE 7   Same cell as Figure 6. Movement of black rectangle ⅓° × 6° back and forth across the receptive field: *A*, horizontally oriented (parallel to receptive-field axis); *B*, vertically oriented. Time required to move across the field 5 sec. Time, 1 sec.

ward movement (about 5–10 sec to cross the entire field); rapid movement in either direction gave only very weak responses.

Despite its unusual features this cell exhibited several properties typical of complex units, particularly the lack of summation (except in a horizontal sense), and the wide area over which the dark bar was effective. One may think of the field as having a counterpart in simple fields of type *D*, Figure 1. In such fields a dark bar would evoke discharges, but only if it fell within the inhibitory region. Moreover, downward movement of the bar would also evoke brisker discharges than upward, provided the upper flanking region were stronger than the lower one.

In describing simple fields it has already been noted that moving stimuli were often more effective than stationary ones. This was also true of cells with complex fields. Depending on the cell, slits, edges, or dark bars were most effective. As with simple fields, orientation of a stimulus was always critical, responses varied with rate of movement, and direction asymmetries of the type seen in Figure 7 were common. Only once have we seen activation of a cell for one direction of movement and suppression of maintained firing for the opposite direction. In their responses to movement, cells with complex fields differed from their simple counterparts chiefly in re-

sponding with sustained firing over substantial regions, usually the entire receptive field, instead of over a very narrow boundary separating excitatory and inhibitory regions.

RECEPTIVE-FIELD DIMENSIONS

Overall field dimensions were measured for 119 cells. A cell was included only if its field was mapped completely, and if it was situated in the area of central vision (see p. 135 of original report). Fields varied greatly in size from one cell to the next, even for cells recorded in a single penetration (see Figure 15 of original report). In Figure 8 the distribution of cells according to field area is given separately for simple and complex fields. The histogram illustrates the variation in size, and shows that on the average complex fields were larger than simple ones.

Widths of narrow subdivisions of simple fields (the centres of types *C*, *D*, and *E* or the flanks of type *F*, Figure 1) also varied greatly: the smallest were 10–15 minutes of arc, which is roughly the diameter of the smallest field centres we have found for geniculate cells. For some cells with complex fields the widths of the most effective slits or dark bars were also of this order, indicating that despite the greater overall field size these cells were able to convey detailed information. We wish to

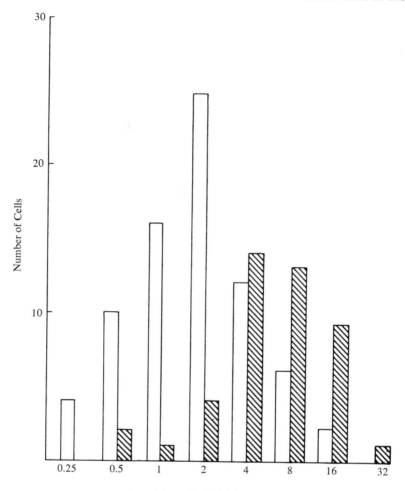

Area of Receptive Fields in (degrees of arc)²

FIGURE 8   Distribution of 119 cells in the visual cortex with respect to the approximate area of their respective fields. White columns indicate cells with simple receptive fields; shaded columns, cells with complex fields. Abscissa: area of receptive fields. Ordinate: number of cells.

emphasize that in both geniculate and cortex the field dimensions tend to increase with distance from the area centralis, and that they differ even for a given location in the retina. It is consequently not possible to compare field sizes in the geniculate and cortex unless these variations are taken into account. This may explain the discrepancy between our results and the findings of Baumgartner (see Jung, 1960), that "field centres" in the cortex are one-half the size of those in the lateral geniculate body.

RESPONSIVENESS OF
CORTICAL CELLS

Simple and complex fields together account for all of the cells we have recorded in the visual cortex. We have not observed cells with concentric fields. Except for clearly injured cells (showing extreme spike deformation or prolonged high-frequency bursts of impulses) all units have responded to visual stimulation, though it has occasionally taken several hours to find the retinal region containing the receptive field and to work out the optimum stimuli. Some cells responded only to stimuli which were optimum in their retinal position and in their form, orientation, and rate of movement. A few even required stimulation of both eyes before a response could be elicited. But there is no indication from our studies that the striate cortex contains nerve cells that are unresponsive to visual stimuli.

Most of the cells of this series were observed for 1 or 2 hr, and some were studied for up to 9 hr. Over these periods of time there were no qualitative changes in the characteristics of receptive fields: their complexity, arrangements of excitatory and inhibitory areas, axis orientation, and position all remained the same, as did the ocular dominance. With deepening anaesthesia a cell became less responsive, so that stimuli that had formerly been weak tended to became even weaker or ineffective, while those that had evoked brisk responses now evoked only weak ones. The last thing to disappear with very deep anaesthesia was usually the response to a moving form. As long as any responses remained the cell retained the same specific requirements as to stimulus form, orientation, and rate of movement, suggesting that however the drug exerted its effects, it did not to any important extent functionally disrupt the specific visual connections. A comparison of visual responses in the anaesthetized animal with those in the unanaesthetized, unrestrained preparation (Hubel, 1959) shows that the main differences lie in the frequency and firing patterns of the maintained activity and in the vigour of responses, rather than in the basic receptive-field organization. It should be emphasized, however, that even in light anaesthesia or in the attentive state diffuse light remains relatively ineffective; thus the balance between excitatory and inhibitory influences is apparently maintained in the waking state.

COMPLEX RECEPTIVE FIELDS

The method of stimulating the retina with small circular spots of light and recording from single visual cells has been a useful one in studies of the cat's visual system. In the pathway from retina to cortex the excitatory and inhibitory areas mapped out by this means have been sufficient to account for responses to both stationary and moving patterns. Only when one reaches cortical cells with complex fields does the method fail, for these fields cannot generally be separated into excitatory and inhibitory regions. Instead of the direct small-spot method, one must resort to a trial-and-error system, and attempt to describe each cell in terms of the stimuli that most effectively influence firing. Here there is a risk of over- or underestimating the complexity of the most effective stimuli, with corresponding lack of precision in the functional description of the cell. For this reason it is encouraging to find that properties of complex fields can be interpreted by the simple supposition that they receive projections from simple-field cells, a supposition made more likely by the anatomical findings of Part III of the original report.

Compared with cells in the retina or lateral geniculate body, cortical cells show a marked increase in the number of stimulus parameters that must be specified in order to influence their firing. This apparently reflects a continuing process which has its beginning in the retina. To obtain an optimum response from a retinal ganglion cell it is generally sufficient to specify the position, size, and intensity of a circular spot. Enlarging the spot beyond the size of the field centre raises the threshold, but even when diffuse light is used it is possible to evoke a brisk response by using an intense enough stimulus. For geniculate cells the penalty for exceeding optimum spot size is more severe than in the retina, as has been shown by comparing responses of a geniculate cell and an afferent fibre to the same cell (Hubel and Wiesel, 1961). In the retina and lateral geniculate body there is no evidence that any shapes are more effective than circular ones, or that, with moving stimuli, one direction of movement is better than another.

In contrast, in the cortex effective driving of simple-field cells can only be obtained with restricted stimuli whose position, shape, and orientation are specific for the cell. Some cells fire best to a moving stimulus, and in these the direction and even the rate of movement are often critical. Diffuse light is at best a poor stimulus, and for cells in the area of central representation it is usually ineffective at any intensity.

An interesting feature of cortical cells with complex fields may be seen in their departure from the process of progressively increasing specificity. At this stage, for the first time, what we suppose to be higher-order neurones are in a sense less selective in their responses than the cells which feed into them. Cells with simple fields tend to respond only when the stimulus is both oriented and positioned properly. In contrast, the neurones to which they supposedly project are concerned predominantly with stimulus orientation, and are far less critical in their requirements as regards stimulus placement. Their responsiveness to the abstraction which we call orientation is thus generalized over a considerable retinal area.

The significance of this step for perception can only be speculated upon, but it may be of some interest to examine several possibilities. First, neurophysiologists must ultimately try to explain how a form can be recognized regardless of its exact position in the visual field. As a step in form recognition the organism may devise a mechanism by which the inclinations of borders are more important than their exact visual-field location. It is clear that a given

form in the visual field will, by virtue of its borders, excite a combination of cells with complex fields. If we displace the form it will activate many of the same cells, as long as the change in position is not enough to remove it completely from their receptive fields. Now we may imagine that these particular cells project to a single cell of still higher order: such a cell will then be very likely to respond to the form (provided the synapses are excitatory) and there will be considerable latitude in the position of the retinal image. Such a mechanism will also permit other transformations of the image, such as a change in size associated with displacement of the form toward or away from the eye. Assuming that there exist cells that are responsive to specific forms, it would clearly be economical to avoid having thousands for each form, one for every possible retinal position, and separate sets for each type of distortion of the image.

Next, the ability of some cells with complex fields to respond in a sustained manner to a stimulus as it moves over a wide expanse of retina suggests that these cells may play an important part in the perception of movement. They adapt rapidly to a stationary form, and continuous movement of the stimulus within the receptive field is the only way of obtaining a sustained discharge (Figure 3H). Presumably the afferent simple-field cells also adapt rapidly to a stationary stimulus; because of their staggered fields the moving stimulus excites them in turn, and the higher-order cell is thus at all times bombarded. This seems an elegant means of overcoming a difficulty inherent in the problem of movement perception, that movement must excite receptors not continuously but in sequence.

Finally, the above remarks apply equally well to displacements of retinal images caused by small eye movements. The normal eye is not stationary, but is subject to several types of fine movements. There is psychophysical evidence that in man these may play an important part in vision, transforming a steady stimulus produced by a stationary object into an intermittent one, so overcoming adaptation in visual cells (Ditchburn and Ginsborg, 1952; Riggs, Ratliff, Cornsweet, and Cornsweet, 1953). At an early stage in the visual pathway the effect of such movements would be to excite many cells repeatedly and in turn, rather than just a few continuously. A given line or border would move back and forth over a small retinal region; in the cortex this would sequentially activate many cells with simple fields. Since large rotatory movements are not involved, these fields would have the same axis orientations but would differ only in their exact retinal positions. They would converge on higher-order cells with complex fields, and these would tend to be activated continuously rather than intermittently.

References

DITCHBURN, R. W., and B. L. GINSBORG. Vision with stabilized retinal image. *Nature, Lond.,* 1952, *170,* 36–37.

HUBEL, D. H. Single unit activity in striate cortex of unrestrained cats. *J. Physiol.,* 1959, *147,* 226–238.

HUBEL, D. H., and T. N. WIESEL. Receptive fields of single neurones in the cat's striate cortex. *J. Physiol.,* 1959, *148,* 574–591.

HUBEL, D. H., and T. N. WIESEL. Integrative action in the cat's lateral geniculate body. *J. Physiol.,* 1961, *155,* 385–398.

JUNG, R. Microphysiologie corticaler Neurone: Ein Beitrag zur Koordination der Hirnrinde und des visuellen Systems. In D. B. Tower and J. P. Schadé (Eds.), *Structure and function of the cerebral cortex.* Amsterdam: Elsevier, 1960.

KUFFLER, S. W. Discharge patterns and functional organization of mammalian retina. *J. Neurophysiol.,* 1953, *16,* 37–68.

RIGGS, L. A., F. RATLIFF, J. C. CORNSWEET, and T. N. CORNSWEET. The disappearance of steadily fixated visual test objects. *J. opt. Soc. Amer.,* 1953, *43,* 495–501.

Aftereffect of Seen Motion with a Stabilized Retinal Image*

ROBERT W. SEKULER

Northwestern University

LEO GANZ

New York University

Abstract. *Prolonged inspection of uniformly moving contours affects differentially the luminance threshold for the detection of test contours as a function of the direction of motion of the test contours. This finding supports a new explanation of the well-known aftereffect.*

If one views a train of contours moving steadily across the visual field and then turns to a nonmoving scene, the stationary scene appears to be in motion. The direction of the movement aftereffect is opposite to the movement of the contours that was initially seen. This widely known and easily observed phenomenon has never been satisfactorily explained (1).

Recently, Hubel and Wiesel (2) have reported neural cells in the visual cortex of the cat which respond to stimuli moving in a single direction within the visual field. Such a finding offers a new basis of explanation of the movement aftereffect. It may be that extended viewing of stimuli moving in one direction can produce differential adaptation at the cortex, affecting only cells sensitive to movement in that direction. Such an explanation has been proposed by Sutherland (3): "the direction in which something is seen to move might depend upon the ratios of firing in cells sensitive to movement in different directions, and after prolonged movement in one direction a stationary image would

produce less firing in the cells which had just been stimulated than normally, hence apparent movement in the opposite direction would be seen to occur." If the perception of motion depends upon the action of these direction-specific cells, it follows that prolonged viewing of a stimulus moving in one direction will elevate the threshold for the subsequent detection of stimulus patterns moving in that direction. We made a study (4) to find whether a threshold elevation exists and, if it does, whether it is related to movement aftereffect. According to the theory, magnitude of the movement aftereffect and magnitude of threshold elevation should be covariant.

To obtain maximal differential adaption to motion it is necessary to present a subject with a stimulus having truly unidirectional motion. This is ordinarily impossible, since involuntary movements of the eye, present even during "steady" fixation, superimpose a random spectrum of eye motions upon the motion of the physical stimulus (5). We eliminated the effect of involuntary eye movements and rendered our stimulus unidirectional by presenting the targets as stabilized retinal images. This technique optically "locks" a stimulus onto one retinal area (6).

The subject focused upon a black point on a luminous circular field subtending a visual angle of 4°30′ (luminance 1.19 millilambert). The stabilized target, a rectangle with sides subtending visual angles of 2°14′ and 1°35′, respectively, was centered within this field. It comprised bright vertical stripes, 6 minutes of arc wide, separated by areas of background field 32 minarcs wide. These stripes could be made to move either to the right or to the left within the rectangle. The stimulus was presented in a 15-second repeating cycle with three phases. (i) Inspection: for 5.0 second the subject viewed the moving stripes (stripe luminance, 1.48 mlam). (ii) Interval: for 2.8 seconds the subject viewed the circular background field; no stripes were presented. (iii) Test: for 7.2 seconds the subject "tracked" his threshold for stripe detection. "Tracking" is a psychophysical procedure in which the subject diminishes the intensity of the stimulus when he detects the target and increases the intensity when he does not detect it (7). During the test phase the subject kept the intensity of the stimulus just above or just below his luminance threshold for stripe detection. Key presses on either of two keys moved a photometric wedge interposed in the optical path of the stimulus so as to modulate intensity either up or down. Recording equipment provided a record of the intensity of the stimulus as a function of time. Catch trials, in which no stripe target was presented, were interspersed during the test phase.

Luminance thresholds for the detection of moving stripes were measured under two conditions. In the "reverse" (R) condition, the direction of motion during the inspection phase was opposite to that during the test phase; in the "nonreverse" (NR) condition, the direction of motion during the inspection and test phases was the same. According to the prediction, the luminance threshold would be higher in the NR than in the R condition. Threshold elevation was determined in three sub-

jects for various velocities of the stripes. The velocity ranged from 10′50″ visual angle per second, where motion is just perceptible, to 15° per second, where the observer reports a blur in which the individual stripes are not discernible. A typical session required 32 minutes of observations. Blocks of tests under conditions R and NR were presented alternately in a balanced design. The same velocities were used for the inspection and the test phases.

For velocities between 4° and 9° visual angle per second, the luminance threshold under the NR condition was, in every determination, higher than that under the R condition. Figure 1 is a record showing the variations in threshold for seen motion through one session. At each introduction of the NR condition the threshold rose abruptly. At lower and higher speeds the same effect occurred, though less markedly. Figure 2 (a–c) shows the percentage of threshold elevation, $100 [(\overline{NR}-\overline{R})/\overline{R}]$, as a function of velocity for the three subjects. Since conditions R and NR are indistinguishable at angular velocity of 0° per second, we can assume the absence of threshold elevation at that point. The relationship between velocity and percentage of rise in threshold is curvilinear, with a maximum in the 4- to 9-degree region. In addition, we found, as did other investigators (8), the luminance threshold to be an increasing function of the velocity of the stripes.

To assess the relationship between threshold elevation and motion aftereffect, a measure of motion-aftereffect strength was obtained. The subject viewed the

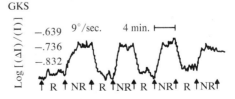

GKS

$Log [(\Delta I)/(I)]$

−.639   9°/sec.   4 min. ⊢————⊣

−.736

−.832

↑ R ↑ NR ↑ R ↑ NR ↑ R ↑ NR ↑ R ↑ NR ↑

FIGURE 1   A continuous record of luminance threshold values during one session. Changes of condition, between R and NR, are shown at the bottom of the record.

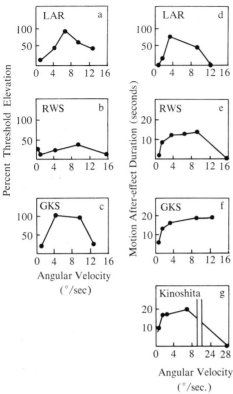

Percent Threshold Elevation

Motion After-effect Duration (seconds)

Angular Velocity (°/sec)

Angular Velocity (°/sec.)

FIGURE 2 (*a-c*) Threshold elevation, 100 $[(\overline{NR}-\overline{R})/\overline{R}]$, as a function of stimulus velocity. Each point is based on the mean of 170 to 300 measurements. (*d-f*) Duration of motion aftereffect as a function of stimulus velocity for the three subjects of *a-c*. (*g*) Comparable data of Kinoshita on the duration of motion aftereffect, for one subject.

stripes in motion, retinally stabilized, for 1 minute. He then shifted his focus to a stationary textured field (at luminance of 39 mlam) and reported when he no longer saw motion. The field was at the same distance for the inspection and test phases. There was a period of 2 minutes between trials. A number of tests for motion aftereffect were made with the three subjects of the earlier tests, and at a number of velocities.

Figure 2 (*d-f*) depicts the mean duration of motion aftereffect at the velocities studied. Figure 2g shows comparable data from the work of Kinoshita (9). Motion aftereffect occurs over a broad range of velocities; the relationship is approximately

curvilinear, not unlike the threshold-elevation function shown in Figure 2 (*a-c*). Inter- and intrasubject variability in motion aftereffect makes it necessary to view this last conclusion with caution.

Our results definitely support an explanation of motion aftereffect on the basis of direction-specific cortical adaption, such as Sutherland has proposed. In accordance with this explanation, it has been shown that the threshold for motion perception changes as a function of the direction of motion. The change in threshold shows peaking and curvilinearity with velocity, much like the motion aftereffect itself.

References

1. This phenomenon was first correctly reported by J. Purkinje, *Medizinisches Jahrbuch des K. K. Öest. Staates* (Vienna, 1820); for reviews of theories of motion aftereffect and their shortcomings see A. Wohlgemuth, *Brit. J. Psychol. Monographs Suppl. 1* (1911); L. W. Gates, *Am. J. Psychol.* 46, 34 (1934).
2. HUBEL, D. H., and T. N. WIESEL, *J. Physiol. London* (1959) 148, 574; *ibid.* 160, 106 (1962).
3. Sutherland, N. S., *Quart. J. Exptl. Psychol.* 13, 222 (1961); see also R. S. Woodworth and H. Schlosberg, *Experimental Psychology* (Holt, Rinehart and Winston, Inc., New York, 1954), pp. 515–516.
4. This investigation was supported in part by the National Institutes of Health (PHS fellowship MF–10, 244 to L.G.). We thank Lorrin A. Riggs for continued advice and encouragement.
5. RATLIFF, F., and L. A. RIGGS, *J. Exptl. Psychol.* (1950) 40, 687.
6. RIGGS, L. A., F. RATLIFF, J. C. CORNSWEET, and T. N. CORNSWEET, *J. Opt. Soc. Am.* (1953) 43, 495. The optical system is described in G. K. Shortess, *ibid.* (1962) 51, 555.
7. BÉKÈSY, G. V., *Acta Oto-Laryngol.* (1947) 35, 411.
8. CROOK, M. N., *J. Psychol.* (1937) 3, 541; R. H. BROWN, *J. Opt. Soc. Am.* (1958) 48, 125.
9. KINOSHITA, T., *Z. Sinnesphysiol.* (1909) 43, 434.

Factors in
the Immediate Processing
of Visual Stimulation

Some Temporal Factors in Vision*

ROBERT M. BOYNTON

University of Rochester

Reciprocity

Probably the most fundamental relation in vision involving time is the reciprocity between time and intensity, known as Bloch's law, which is said to hold for short light flashes. Although there is some difference of opinion about the generality of the reciprocity law,[1] let us assume that it holds for some conditions at least and consider its significance.

The explanation of Bloch's law is certainly not simple. To dismiss it by stating that under certain conditions the eye responds to energy alone (without regard to its distribution in time) is not to offer an explanation but merely to restate the law. When a relation holds even as precisely as Bloch's law, one is tempted to suppose that the responsible mechanism must be located at or near the beginning of the chain of events between stimulus and response. By this reasoning, one might hope to show that the photochemical changes produced by flashes of equal energy but differing time distributions were identical. This position, however attractive, is blatantly impossible. The reasons are at the least the following:

1. Experiments by Wulff et al. (1958a, b) show that the largest part of the density changes of rhodopsin in solution that follow the onset of a very brief (20-microsecond) illuminating flash occurs within 0.5 millisecond of the flash. This suggests that if successive flashes were administered to the same receptor, within the critical duration of Bloch's law, the speed of the reaction would be sufficient to allow two discrete photochemical changes to occur. A suitable mechanism in the eye could theoretically respond to these as separate events and transmit a double signal to the brain.

2. At threshold, the probability that two or more quanta will be absorbed in the same receptor is negligible; at threshold, then, summation[2] cannot be photochemical.

3. Much work has been done by Bouman (1955a, b) and his co-work-

* *Sensory Communication*, W. A. Rosenblith (Ed.), Cambridge, Mass.: The M.I.T. Press, 1961, pp. 739–756.

[1] Whereas, for example, LeGrand (1957) states that Bloch's law holds exactly at all levels, Piéron (1952) insists that "the technical difficulties of experimentation and of obtaining measurements endowed with the necessary extreme precision have not enabled the question to be given a definite answer."

[2] The term "summation" is used since, within the critical duration in which intensity-time reciprocity holds, the system summates (or integrates) the light output without regard to its distribution in time. Neural summation is not necessarily implied.

ers presenting double flashes separated in space as well as time. They found that complete summation occurs if two flashes are within a certain critical small distance and short time; it is perhaps even clearer in these experiments that separate receptors are involved and that summation cannot take place at a photochemical level alone.

Reciprocity, then, seems generally to involve a neural summation, and the fact that the relationship breaks down after a certain duration is reached (in the case of a single flash), or a time interval exceeded (in the case of two very brief flashes) may mean that the limit of temporal neural summation has been reached for the conditions being explored. This has been the usual view, and at threshold it is probably substantially correct.

Above threshold, however, certain interesting effects occur which do not seem to admit of such a simple interpretation. I would like now to describe an experiment by Katz (1959) which relates to this point.

Intensity-Time Interactions above Threshold

The subject is presented with a haploscopic view of two semicircular fields which appear juxtaposed in space. One of these fields, the comparison field, is always presented to the left eye. The other, the test field, is seen by the right eye. For a given experiment, the luminance of the comparison field is set at a standard value, and its duration is set at 200 msec. Successive presentations of the comparison field—and of the test field as well—are spaced in time to eliminate the adaptive effects of previous flash pairs. The experiments consist of an adjustment by the subject of the luminance of the test flash—whose duration is equal to or shorter than that of the comparison flash—until an equal brightness sensation is elicited. Thus in

the usual case, the match involves an equal-brightness match of two flashes of light of unequal duration.[3] Since the 200-msec flash of standard luminance is always delivered to the left eye, with the luminance of each shorter right-eye flash adjusted in turn to match, one may conclude that the luminances so obtained for the shorter flashes are those required to produce flashes of equal brightness; this involves only the assumption that flashes equal in brightness to a standard flash would themselves seem equally bright if compared with one another in turn.

A typical result from Katz is shown in Figure 1. This figure is for a single subject, field size, and luminance level, and though it represents only about 3 percent of the data collected by Katz the results are typical for moderately high luminances, any area (from 0.5 to 5 degrees), and either a haploscopic or monocular comparison. We should note in Figure 1 that reciprocity fails slightly between 8 and 25 msec. (Over the experiment as a whole, about 10 percent more energy is required for the longer of these two short flashes. Unfortunately, 25 msec is on the border of the neural-summation range, so that the meaning of this is not unequivocal.) Further increases in time cause a still greater departure from reciprocity (much as occurs for threshold), but still further increases cause a given flash to grow dimmer, as revealed by the need to increase the luminance of the test flash to maintain equal brightness. Adding more light thus reduces brightness.

The most plausible explanation would seem to have something to do with the on-

[3] The results are little altered by varying in time the two extreme positions of the test flash relative to the comparison flash. When the two begin together under monocular presentation, the longer comparison flash produces a noticeable inhibition near the border of the short test flash; though only a part of the test flash is visible, the match is about the same as when the flashes terminate together. The condition of co-termination was used in most of the experiments.

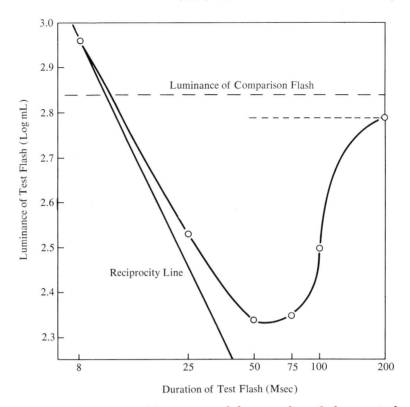

FIGURE 1   Combinations of luminance and duration of test flashes required to match a 200-msec flash of 2.84 log mL in the opposite eye. The graph shows that, between 50 and 75 msec, the luminance of the test flash need be only about one-third that of the comparison flash in order for the two to appear equally bright. The reciprocity line has been drawn from the point at 8 msec to show that the efficiency of the eye is maximal for very short flashes despite the so-called "enhancement" effect (data from Katz, 1959; field size, 5 degrees; white light).

discharge that is characteristic of many of the neural units carrying the message about the flash to the brain. If the brightness sensation were related to the average number of impulses per unit time received during the flash, the obtained result would be expected. It should be pointed out in this regard that if time were quantized somehow in the input, and if brightness were related to the average input per time quantum, the same result would be expected.

Some readers will recognize this as a variation of the classical Broca-Sulzer (1902, 1903) experiment, which it is. We feel that the method is superior to those used previously because of the haploscopic presentation (used also by Alpern, 1950,

1953) and the use of a constant reference stimulus. Haploscopic presentation rules out monocular retinal interaction effects, whereas the use of a constant reference stimulus negates the importance of sensitivity differences between the two eyes and permits unambiguous comparison between these data and the classical reciprocity data. Broca and Sulzer and their followers (for example, Stainton, 1928) had the subject adjust the luminance of a steady light for brightness, and there was therefore no constant reference stimulus.

The usual view that the Broca-Sulzer effect is an "enhancement" phenomenon is shown by Katz's study to be incorrect, in that very short flashes require the least energy for their perception.

Apparatus Required for Binocular Experiments

The apparatus required for an experiment like Katz's is illustrated in Figure 2, which is taken from Kandel's (1958) dissertation. In general, it consists of a two-channel optical system, each channel of which has a source image at the plane of the shutters and another image in the

pupil of the subject. By means of beam-splitting cubes, the Maxwellian view thus provided by each system may be brought into the separate eyes or superimposed in a right-eye view. The perceived areas of the fields are determined by apertures A, A', A'' at appropriate planes. Wedges and filters shown in solid black are used to control the luminance of the stimuli, and precautions are taken to monitor carefully the output of the stimulus lamp. Since the

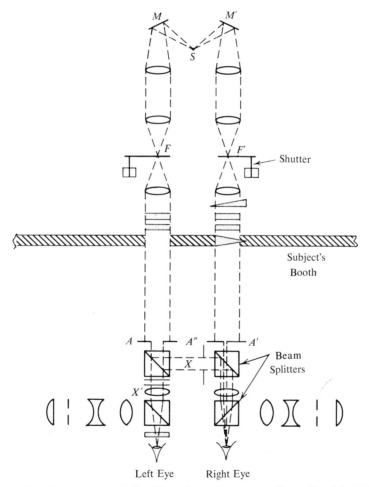

FIGURE 2 Apparatus used for binocular experiments (from Kandel, 1958). Light from source lamp S is delivered by mirrors M and M' to two separate optical channels. Light is collimated and focused at F and F', where shutters are located. Light is recollimated and passed through neutral filters and wedges into subject's booth. With an opaque shield at X (between the two anterior beam splitters), the output of the two systems is delivered to the separate eyes. With an opaque shield at X', the outputs are superimposed and delivered only to the right eye. Auxiliary systems, projecting to left and right at bottom of diagram, provide adapting fields and/or fixation targets for the separate eyes.

shutters cut each beam at a focal point, adequate (about 3 to 5 msec) rise-time characteristics are obtained. Katz used a large rotating motor-driven disc with auxiliary electromagnetic shutters for his work. The experiments of Kandel, to be described, involved electromagnetic shutters alone. The proper alignment of such systems is extremely difficult, and it is usual, therefore, to finish an experiment on one subject before starting to collect data on the next.

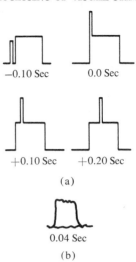

Transitional Thresholds

Until the late 1940s, most studies of light and dark adaptation ignored events occurring within the first few seconds following a sudden change in illumination. Two exceptions are the "instantaneous threshold" study of Blanchard (1918), in which an attempt was made to measure thresholds just at the offset of an adapting light, and the "alpha adaptation" reported by Schouten and Ornstein (1939). The latter study involved a binocular matching technique and indicated very rapid changes in "apparent brightness" (as evaluated by such a match) at the onset of an adapting stimulus. In 1947 Crawford reported that very abrupt threshold changes occurred at the onset and offset of a "conditioning" (adapting) stimulus. Later Baker (1953) investigated this more thoroughly for the offset condition—the beginning of dark adaptation—and although we at Rochester did one preliminary study along this line (Boynton and Bush, 1953) we have concentrated our attention upon the onset. In New York Battersby and Wagman (1959) have been working along similar lines, and in Holland Bouman (1955b) has conducted relevant experiments. It is gratifying to report that, since the agreement among laboratories is good, it will not be misleading if I confine my remarks to a description of some of the important aspects of our work.

The experiments consist of delivering

FIGURE 3   Stimulus sequence used for transitional thresholds. (a) Four conditioning intervals; these are tracings of records produced by placing a phototube in the position of the eye and photographing the result on a cathode-ray oscillograph. (b) The test-flash characteristics on an expanded scale. (From Bush, 1955.)

to the eye (or eyes) a "conditioning-stimulus—test-flash (CS-TF) sequence," as illustrated in Figure 3. The experiment begins with the subject adapted to some prevailing level (usually total darkness). A sequence is then delivered to the subject. A sample condition might involve a conditioning stimulus of a visual angle of 5 degrees, fixated centrally, with a duration of 0.5 sec, with a superimposed 1/50-sec test flash appearing, say, 0.05 sec following the onset of the conditioning stimulus. By manipulating the temporal position of the superimposed test flash, the threshold changes that occur as the eye goes from a dark-adapted state toward the light-adapted state can be investigated. A given threshold may be determined by any desired psychophysical method; we have most often used a descending method of limits while exploring one conditioning interval[4] at a time. Enough time must be allowed

[4] "Conditioning interval" is defined as the time between the onset of the conditioning stimulus and the onset of the test flash.

between each sequence to permit the eye to return to its original state of adaptation.

Results are plotted as the log increment threshold versus conditioning interval. Some representative data are shown in Figure 4 from Kandel (1958).

1. Threshold elevations occur at negative conditioning intervals up to at least 100 msec. This means that the threshold of a test flash may be elevated by a subsequent conditioning stimulus. Although I incline (Boynton and Triedman, 1953; Boynton, Bush, and Enoch, 1954) toward the

view originally expressed by Crawford (1947) that differences in transmission time allow interference to occur between the coded representation of the two stimuli, this could be true only if the latency of response to the test flash were longer than that to the conditioning stimulus. Ordinarily the test flash at threshold is both smaller and of lower luminance than the conditioning stimulus, and the explanation is plausible. However, Kandel (1958) has recently found conditions under which a leading test flash must be of higher lumi-

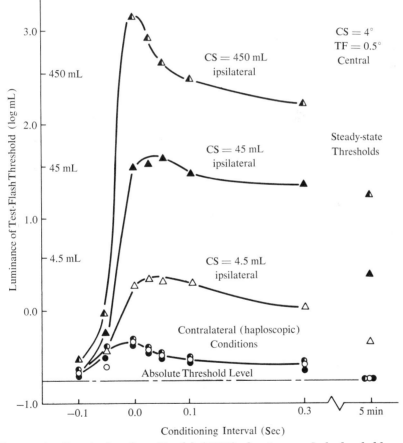

FIGURE 4 Sample data from Kandel (1958) showing test-flash threshold as a function of conditioning interval (time between onset of conditioning stimulus and onset of test flash) for three luminances of conditioning stimulus and for ipsilateral and contralateral (haploscopic) conditions. In the ipsilateral case, the conditioning stimulus and test flash were delivered to the same eye, in the contralateral case to the separate eyes. Note that the effect under the contralateral condition is largely independent of the luminance of the conditioning stimulus.

nance than the following conditioning stimulus in order to be visible at threshold. The explanation in terms of transmission time is definitely ruled out in this case and may indeed be of secondary importance in some of the more typical cases. If time is handled by the nervous system in discrete packages rather than as a continuous variable, any two stimuli that occur wholly or in part within the same "time frame" or information-processing period would be expected to interfere with one another as separately perceptible events. This has been called "quantization" of time by Stroud (1956).

2. The test-flash threshold just after the onset of the conditioning stimulus is as much as 100 times higher than it becomes after adaptation to the conditioning stimulus is complete. During the first few minutes following the onset of the conditioning stimulus, the threshold required for test-flash visibility drops. It seems likely that the transient elevation of the threshold is caused by some kind of masking effect produced by the burst of on-activity associated with the onset of the conditioning stimulus. As this on-activity subsides, the threshold drops, despite the decrease in receptor photosensitivity that must be occurring at the same time. The latter, if operating alone, would tend to drive the threshold in the opposite direction.

One consequence of this kind of thinking was the prediction that preadaptation of the eye, despite its known photodesensitization effect, could *reduce* the threshold of a test flash, provided the test flash in each case followed the onset of a constant conditioning stimulus. In an experiment to test this point (Boynton and Kandel, 1957; Boynton, 1958), it was found, for a conditioning stimulus of about 40 millilamberts, that increases

in the level of preadaptation of the eye up to about 100 millilamberts resulted in a lowering of the test-flash threshold. The prediction, thus verified, involves the idea that light-adapting the eye will reduce the burst of on-activity to a given conditioning stimulus and thus the amount of masking.

3. The question of where, in the visual system, this transient masking takes place has been investigated. An early experiment (Boynton and Triedman, 1953) that at least indicated the plausibility of a peripheral locus showed that if the electroretinogram to CS-TF sequences is recorded, there is an interference between the response to each which makes it difficult to discriminate, in the graphic record, whether the test flash was present or not. This argued in favor of a peripheral locus. Recent experiments by Kandel (1958) involving ipsilateral and contralateral (haploscopic) presentation of the test and conditioning stimuli have clarified the issue to at least this extent: for the conditions that we have most often used, where the test flash is smaller than the conditioning stimulus, only a small interaction occurs between the visual systems associated with the separate eyes. When the conditioning stimulus and test flash are delivered to contralateral eyes, no more than a two- or threefold rise in test-flash threshold is producible, *regardless of the intensity of the conditioning stimulus*. In experiments where the eye is completely adapted to the conditioning stimulus, no bilateral interaction occurs, which suggests a total independence of left- and right-eyed visual nervous systems. That we do find a significant effect is of importance because it shows that the two systems are not independent during the transient phase: the sensitivity of one can

be momentarily altered by stimulation of the other. On the other hand, the small magnitude of the effect compared to the ipsilateral case indicates that the two systems are indeed largely independent so far as sensitivity is concerned. Furthermore, although the locus of the ipsilateral effect is largely peripheral, the contralateral experiments show that masking can also take place higher in the visual system. Thus a fraction of the ipsilateral interference may occur at higher levels—most likely at the visual cortex.

In order for the entire ipsilateral effect to be cortical, a much larger signal-to-noise ratio would seem to be required for discriminability at the cortex than at the periphery. This implies that, although a "discriminable" signal is sent from the eye to the brain, the visual brain is not able to make use of that signal. It appears most unlikely that the visual system, which seems peculiarly adapted to preserve and enhance small differences in contrast, could operate in such a way.

4. The relative size of the conditioning stimulus compared to the test flash is very important. A small test flash upon a large conditioning field allows discrimination to be made between the brightness of the test spot and the surround, even if the two are flashed simultaneously. However, if the conditioning stimulus is of the same size and retinal position as the test spot, the discrimination can be made only by successive comparisons in time. In experiments Kandel (1958) has found that thresholds become higher and more variable. The experimental differences between ipsilateral and contralateral conditions become smaller and may disappear altogether for stimulation of the peripheral retina when the onsets are near one another in time.

The implications of these results are as follows: although the ability of the higher visual centers (presumably the visual cortex) to mediate spatial discriminations based on intensive differences is very good, these centers are relatively poor at mediating discriminations based upon time alone.

An important and very significant exception is the contralateral equal-area condition in which one eye is completely adapted to the conditioning stimulus. In this case, the test-flash threshold is no different from the threshold for complete dark adaptation of the two eyes, regardless of the areas involved. One interpretation is that under steady-state conditions of adaptation, the prevailing rate of activity in the cortex produced by the conditioning stimulus is so low as to exert a negligible effect upon the perceptibility of the contralateral test flash.

Some of the results of the transient adaptation studies are summarized in Table 1.

Quantization of Time

It has been thrice suggested in the preceding discussion that the notion of an input quantization of time in vision is compatible with the results. The basic idea is that the visual input may be packaged in successive time frames, and that, therefore, any two events that occur within a given time frame and that depend upon a temporal discrimination alone for their perception cannot be discriminable. This idea has been mentioned by previous speakers on this program (perhaps most elegantly by Dr. Rushton) and has been expounded in some detail by Stroud (1956). It accords with the familiar fact that the visual presentation of sixteen still pictures each second, the standard rate for "motion" picture projection, provides a rather satisfactory illusion of continuous time-flow. Such time packages also appear consistent with what might be expected,

TABLE 1

Factor by which Threshold to Test Flash is Elevated above Threshold for the Dark-Adapted and Otherwise Unstimulated Eye

Data are from the experiment of Kandel (1958) for his eye and are for a conditioning stimulus having a diameter subtending 4 degrees at a luminance of 4.5 mL. The transient condition refers to thresholds obtained 0.05 sec following onset of conditioning stimulus; thresholds for the steady condition were taken after at least 5-min exposures to the conditioning stimulus. For the ipsilateral condition, the conditioning stimulus and test flash were each delivered to the right eye; for the contralateral condition, the conditioning stimulus was delivered to the left eye and the test flash to the right. Threshold contrast is also given.

CONDITION OF LATERALITY	DIAMETER OF TEST FLASH (DEGREES)	TEMPORAL CONDITION	FACTOR OF ELEVATION	CONTRAST AT THRESHOLD (PERCENTAGE)*
Ipsilateral	0.5	Transient	12	45
Contralateral	0.5	Transient	1.8	6.7
Ipsilateral	0.5	Steady	2.2	8.5
Contralateral	0.5	Steady	0.9†	3.7
Ipsilateral	4	Transient	1100	91
Contralateral	4	Transient	28	1.7
Ipsilateral	4	Steady	75	6.2
Contralateral	4	Steady	1	0.1

* Threshold expressed as a percentage of 4.5 mL. The concept *contrast* does not apply strictly to the contralateral condition.
† Not significantly different from 1.0.

from the standpoint of communication theory, of an efficient detection-transmission system. Numerous questions are raised by this theory, such as whether and how the time frames are triggered, and to what extent they are synchronized among the various components of the visual system handling information from different parts of the visual field. There would seem to be many important psychophysical and electrophysiological experiments that might be addressed to this question.

Flicker

One of the most intensively investigated areas in vision has been flicker. Of the thousands of studies done on this time-related subject, most have involved critical flicker frequency (cff) as the dependent variable. Perhaps the most fundamental relations involving flicker are the follow-

ing: (1) the increase in cff associated with an increase in stimulus intensity; (2) variations in cff as a function of various complex temporal arrangements of a periodic stimulus in time. The latter range from the classical, often-investigated light-time fraction to very recent studies involving the interlacing of two frequencies within a single, repetitive pattern (Forsyth and Brown, 1959). The cff-versus-intensity function is so basic that one is surprised to find that no really satisfactory theoretical account exists, though several have been suggested. So far as the second class of phenomena is concerned, a plausible explanation exists in the theory of de Lange Dzn (1954), based on his own experiments and some early ideas of Ives and Kingsbury (1914). According to de Lange Dzn, the visual system performs a Fourier analysis on the stimulus pattern and then pays attention only to the fundamental frequency, ignoring the harmonics. In addition, the system is assumed to have a "filtering action," which causes the amplitude of the output, for a given amplitude of input, to decrease with increasing frequency. The behavior of a variety of complex stimulus patterns at a given intensity level may be accounted for in this manner. Also, the cff-intensity relation may be explained as a special case of intensity discrimination. Although why intensity discrimination itself improves with increasing luminance is still the subject of controversy, the principle of de Lange Dzn at least reduces the problem of flicker discrimination to a familiar domain.

There is, however, little hint in the theory of de Lange Dzn concerning how the alleged Fourier analysis is performed by the visual mechanisms. We have recently begun to turn our attention to this and other related problems, in a new kind of experiment that grew out of the conditioning-stimulus-test flash type of study already described.

Our technique is to superimpose upon a flickering stimulus, a small test flash once each second. The test flash may fall in any part of either the light or dark phase of the cycle. It should be noted that the time intervals involved are of a different order of magnitude than those previously studied, and for this reason extremely brief test flashes must be used. A threshold is determined by the up-and-down method using a complex apparatus which records automatically and permits responses to be made to each flash (once per second). These measurements are repeated for other points in the cycle of the flickering stimulus. As many as thirty thresholds of the test flash, each based upon more than fifty yes-no judgments, may be determined in this way during a one-hour session. The apparatus, which took two years to build, has just recently been completed, and we are in the early stages of data collection.

A sample result is shown in Figure 5. This is a record of the waxing and waning of the threshold of the test flash in response to a 30-cps flickering light. In this example, two flashes have been removed from each thirty to produce, once per second, a dark period five times longer than usual. The record shows a substantial recovery of

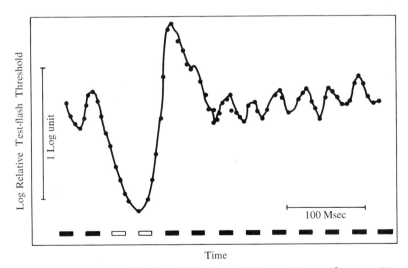

FIGURE 5   Variations in the threshold of a test flash superimposed upon a 30-cps flickering light at various precisely timed points in the flickering-light cycle. Solid bars indicate the light phase of the flickering light; unfilled bars show the position of two flashes in each thirty that are omitted to cause a longer-than-usual dark period.

sensitivity during this extra-long dark period, followed by an unusually large "on-response" to the first flash following the period of darkness. Then one sees a near obliteration of the "response" to the second flash, after which the system begins to return to normal.

It would seem that we have succeeded, by this technique, in providing an indirect picture of the visual *response* to a flickering light in the human subject. In time, we should be able to analyze such records to show the interrelations among the factors of photosensitivity and neural masking that seem clearly to be involved.

That we are able to obtain significant differences in the thresholds for test flashes separated by only two or three milliseconds bears discussion in terms of the time quantization idea previously mentioned. This result indicates that the sensitivity of the visual system is very precisely specifiable at a given moment. Variability of thresholds obtained under these transient conditions is not unduly large. These results would not be expected if the input were being quantized at the receptoral level. The results are, however, consistent with the idea of time quantization at some higher level of the visual system.

It should be noted in this connection that an observer will report a flicker of 30 cps as appearing substantially slower; further, if asked to count the number of flashes perceived in response to a finite number of flashes at this rate, he will report a substantially smaller number than actually presented (Cheatham and White, 1952; White and Cheatham, 1959; Forsyth and Chapanis, 1958). Our results also appear to confirm those of electroretinographic studies (Armington, White, and Cheatham, 1953) which indicate that the peripheral visual system is capable of following a flickering stimulus at a faster rate than can the central visual nervous system, although the peripheral mechanism does attenuate the amplitude of response to a progressively higher degree as flicker rate increases.

Summary

Three psychophysical experiments involving temporal relations in vision have been reported. The first shows that, even with improved experimental technique, high-intensity short flashes can indeed look brighter than longer flashes of the same intensity, thus indicating that the classical Broca-Sulzer effect is not an artifact. The second experiment was a study of the transitional fraction of a second between dark adaptation and the beginning of light adaptation, using the conditioning-stimulus—test-flash technique. From this second experiment it is clear that the nature of the discrimination involved may vary, depending on whether the eye has just been subjected to an increased level of stimulation or whether it has been allowed to adapt to it. The third experiment concerns the successful measurement of test-flash thresholds in the presence of a 30-cps flickering stimulus. Each of these experiments raises a number of questions regarding the neurophysiological organization, function, and interactions of the visual systems serving the two eyes. A common unifying principle, apparently consistent with the data, is the idea of temporal quantization of the visual input by the higher visual nervous system, so that the input is "packaged" into discrete time frames within which a purely temporal discrimination is not possible.

Addendum

If I may be permitted a few additional remarks, I should like to speak as a psychophysicist addressing those of you who are electrophysiologists.

We who are interested in psychophysics from the standpoint of a curiosity about underlying mechanisms are interested, I think, in the relation between conscious experience and neural events—and please note that I frankly say experience and not behavior. To a large degree, many of you seem to be interested in the same thing. Both of us are bothered, no doubt, by the realization that conscious experience is, by its private nature, outside the bounds of science; yet this stops neither of us from doing what we are doing, though it may prevent us from achieving ultimate answers.

But how can we best help one another toward a better understanding? The most precise information available about experience has been gained by using the observer as a null instrument—by finding combinations of physical variables that combine to produce the same response, be it threshold, brightness match, or what have you. There is no richness of experience in such results. In fact they tell us nothing about the subject's experience—directly. Nevertheless, psychophysical data obtained by treating the human observer as a null instrument have provided a framework within which many sensory physiologists operate, and have in themselves occupied a substantial portion of many textbooks on sensory physiology. The very indirection of the null-instrument approach is what gives it its scientific validity and makes it useful.

We use this technique in psychophysics because, until recently at least, it seemed the only possible one to use on the nonlinear, drifting, and uncalibrated device called the eye. The psychological scaling techniques described by Stevens also look promising, but at the moment the null-instrument results are much more precise. In attempting to relate our data to yours, however, we are often frustrated by the following two related factors:

1. A relatively casual attention to stimulus control. After the achievement of a truly remarkable state of the art as regards surgical and recording technique, it seems a shame to use whistles, hand claps, casual jabs, and unspecified lights as physical stimuli. It is those experiments in which wave length, energy, spatial distribution, and time are carefully specified that are likely to be most useful to us.

2. The very rare use of the null-instrument technique in your work. Take the matter of the interaction of intensity and time, for example, which has been worked out, so far as I know, only in *Limulus,* though I stand to be corrected. With your electrodes buried in the visual system, it would seem a relatively simple thing to determine where, and under what conditions, and with what response measures such a relation holds. The chances are good that flashes of equal time *times* intensity look the same to many animals, as well as to man. By following a program such as I suggest, you could at least establish the neural correlates of equivalent experiences. Surely this kind of work should antedate any serious efforts to find neural correlates for such things as form recognition, since the latter probably involves the comparison of equivalents also—between the coded representation of input, and that of past experience. These equivalents must be considerably more complex, however.

I offer these suggestions with a feeling of humility and a real appreciation for the magnificent work that you are doing. For our part, those of us in psychophysics who share your goals must do our best to keep abreast of your concepts, and to restrict our serious speculations to those that are not contrary to the facts that you have so far discovered.

References

ALPERN, M. A study of some aspects of metacontrast. Doctoral dissertation, Ohio State University, 1950.

ALPERN, M. Metacontrast, *J. opt. Soc. Amer.,* 1953, 43, 648–657.

ARMINGTON, J. C., C. T. WHITE, and P. G. CHEATHAM. Evidence for central factors influencing perceived number. *J. exp. Psychol.,* 1953, 46, 283–287.

BAKER, H. D. The instantaneous threshold and early dark adaptation. *J. opt. Soc. Amer.*, 1953, 43, 798–803.

BATTERSBY, W. S., and I. W. WAGMAN. Neural limitations of visual excitability, I: The time course of monocular light adaptation. *J. opt. Soc. Amer.*, 1959, 49, 752–759.

BLANCHARD, J. The brightness sensibility of the retina. *Phys. Rev.*, 1918, 11, 81–99.

BOUMAN, M. A. The absolute threshold conditions for visual perception. *J. opt. Soc. Amer.*, 1955a, 45, 36–43.

BOUMAN, M. A. On foveal and peripheral interaction in binocular vision. *Optica Acta*, 1955b, 1, 177–183.

BOYNTON, R. M. On-responses in the visual system as inferred from psychophysical studies of rapid-adaptation. *Arch. Ophthalmol.*, 1958, 60, 800–810.

BOYNTON, R. M., and W. R. BUSH. Dark adaptation and the instantaneous threshold. *Amer. Psychologist*, 1953, 8, 324 [Abstract].

BOYNTON, R. M., W. R. BUSH, and J. M. ENOCH. Rapid changes in foveal sensitivity resulting from direct and indirect adapting stimuli. *J. opt. Soc. Amer.*, 1954, 44, 56–60.

BOYNTON, R. M., and G. L. KANDEL. On-responses in the human visual system as a function of adaptation level. *J. opt. Soc. Amer.*, 1957, 47, 275–286.

BOYNTON, R. M., and M. H. TRIEDMAN. A psychophysical and electrophysiological study of light adaptation. *J. exp. Psychol.*, 1953, 46, 125–134.

BROCA, A., and D. SULZER. La sensation lumineuse en fonction des temps. *J. Physiol.*, 1902, 4, 632–640.

BROCA, A., and D. SULZER. La sensation lumineuse en fonction des temps. *C. R. Acad. Sci.*, 1903, 137, 944–946; 977–979; 1046–1049.

BUSH, W. R. Foveal light adaptation as affected by the spectral composition of the test and adapting stimuli. *J. opt. Soc. Amer.*, 1955, 45, 1047–1057.

CHEATHAM, P. G., and C. T. WHITE. Perceived number as a function of flash number and rate. *J. exp. Psychol.*, 1952, 44, 447–451.

CRAWFORD, B. H. Visual adaptation to brief conditioning stimuli. *Proc. roy. Soc.*, 1947, B134, 283–302.

FORSYTH, D. M., and C. R. BROWN. Flicker contours for intermittent photic stimuli of alternating duration. *J. opt. Soc. Amer.*, 1959, 49, 760–763.

FORSYTH, D. M., and A. CHAPANIS. Counting repeated light flashes as a function of their number, their rate of presentation, and retinal location stimulated. *J. exp. Psychol.*, 1958, 56, 385–391.

IVES, H. E., and E. F. KINGSBURY. The theory of the flicker photometer. *Phil. Mag.*, 1914, 28, 708–728.

KANDEL, G. L. A psychophysical study of some monocular and binocular factors in early adaptation. Doctoral dissertation, University of Rochester, 1958.

KATZ, M. S. The perceived brightness of light flashes. Doctoral dissertation, University of Rochester, 1959.

DE LANGE DZN, H. Relationship between critical flicker-frequency and a set of low-frequency characteristics of the eye. *J. opt. Soc. Amer.*, 1954, 44, 380–389.

LEGRAND, Y. *Light, Colour, and Vision.* New York: Wiley, 1957.

PIÉRON, H. *The Sensations.* New Haven: Yale University Press, 1952.

SCHOUTEN, J. F., and L. S. ORNSTEIN. Measurements on direct and indirect adaptation by means of binocular vision. *J. opt. Soc. Amer.*, 1939, 29, 168–192.

STAINTON, W. H. The phenomenon of Broca and Sulzer in foveal vision. *J. opt. Soc. Amer.*, 1928, 16, 26–37.

STROUD, J. M. The fine structure of psychological time. In H. Quastler (Ed.), *Information Theory in Psychology*. Glencoe, Ill.: Free Press, 1956. pp. 174–207.

WHITE, C. T., and P. G. CHEATHAM. Temporal numerosity, IV: A comparison of the major senses. *J. exp. Psychol.*, 1959, 58, 441–444.

WULFF, V. J., R. G. ADAMS, H. LINSCHITZ, and E. W. ABRAHAMSON. Effect of flash illumination on rhodopsin in solution. *Ann. N. Y. Acad. Sci.*, 1958a, 74, 281–290.

WULFF, V. J., R. G. ADAMS, H. LINSCHITZ, and D. KENNEDY. The behavior of flash-illuminated rhodopsin in solution. *Arch. Ophthalmol.*, 1958b, 4, 695–701.

Visual Perceptive Simultaneity and Masking of Letters Successively Presented*

PAUL FRAISSE

Sorbonne, University of Paris

Two sets of letters S_1 and S_2 when presented successively are perceived as simultaneous if the total duration of time from the beginning of S_1 to the end of S_2 is kept constant, whatever the duration of S_1, S_2, or the interval. The same law applies in the case of dots arranged to form geometrical figures. On the other hand, the phenomena of meta contrast with letters are modified when the relative duration of S_1, S_2, and the interval vary. Thus perceptive integration and masking depend upon different processes.

Under what temporal conditions are letters successively presented seen as simultaneous or successive? This problem has not received much attention. Using four dots or lights arranged in such a way as to form a diamond, Lichtenstein (1961) found that, when flashed successively, the four dots were perceived as forming the diamond if the total duration between the lighting of the first and fourth dot did not exceed 125 msec, variations in the temporal intervals having no effect within these limits. Results are not so precise when letters or words are used as stimuli; however, Hylan (1903) had noticed that six letters are viewed as simultaneous, whatever the order of presentation may be, provided the total duration does not exceed 80 msec. Stein (1928) showed that the letters of a word when flashed successively, in direct or in reverse order, were perceived in the same way as if the letters were presented simultaneously, provided the total duration of successive flashes did not exceed 100 msec.

* *Perception and Psychophysics*, 1966, vol. 1, pp. 285–287.

The purpose of this work is to verify and render more precise these results, and particularly: (a) to compare the laws of this phenomenon with letters or dots in a geometrical pattern; (b) to compare the laws of perceptive integration to those of lateral masking (or metacontrast) between letters themselves, when we change the duration of the stimuli and of the interval.

Method

With a three channel tachistoscope (Scientific Prototype model) the subject is presented with a preliminary stimulus (followed by a light interval of the same luminance) after which a second follows.

Six-letter words of which letters 1-3-5 form a word and letters 2-4-6 another, were chosen. Example: F L E U R I formed with F E R and L U I. The first and the second words are respectively the first and the second stimuli. Letters are presented in such a way that in simultaneous presentation both stimuli are perceived as forming only one word. Capital letters are used (letters were 4 mm high and 3 to 4 mm thick). We used eight words of the same type as FLEURI. Each subject was presented with two different words in order to neutralize the structural and frequency effects of the words.

For figurative material we used black dots in a diamond pattern divided into two stimuli (S_1: two vertical dots; S_2: two horizontal dots) and in an hexagon pattern divided into two triangles of 3 points each.

The durations of S_1, S_2, and the interval determined four experimental situations:

Experiment 1: $S_1 = S_2 = 15$ msec, with a varying interval from 0 to 320 msec.

Experiment 2: $S_1 = S_2$, varying simultaneously from 20 to 180 msec; interval $= 0$

Experiment 4: $S_1 = 20$ msec; S_2 varies msec; $S_2 = 20$ msec; interval $= 0$

Experiment 4: $S_1 = 20$ msec; S_2 varies from 20 to 320 msec; interval $= 0$

In each situation there were eight different subjects (male and female students). The presentation order (figures or words) was counterbalanced in each situation. For four subjects the variable duration was presented first in increasing order and then in decreasing order; the inverse order was used for the other four. Words and figures were presented twice at each step of duration.

As a result of our experimental design (eight subjects by two orders—increasing

and decreasing—by two presentations), we obtained 64 values for letters and figures.

The subject was asked to say: (a) whether or not he perceived the stimuli successively; (b) the letters viewed in each stimulus.

Results

We have classified the responses of the subjects according to two categories: simultaneous perception or successive perception, even in the case of the content of the stimuli being partly perceived, or the case of interference (letters from the second stimulus being given as ones of the first or inversely).

The results show that experimental situations are comparable only if the total duration of the stimulation, from the beginning of S_1 to the end of S_2, is taken into account. The longer the duration, the more often there is perception of succession (Figure 1a).

The phenomenon develops in the same way, whether or not there is an interval between the stimuli and whether or not the first stimulus is shorter, equal or longer than the second. It appears, however, that the situation where both stimuli have the same length, without an interval, is more favorable than the others. Results with

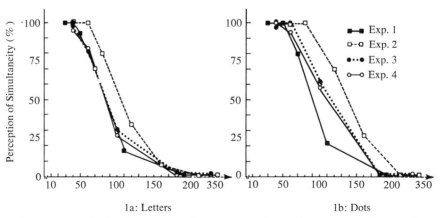

1a: Letters   1b: Dots

FIGURE 1a and 1b   Percentage of perception of simultaneity according to the total duration (from the beginning of S_1, to the end of S_2).

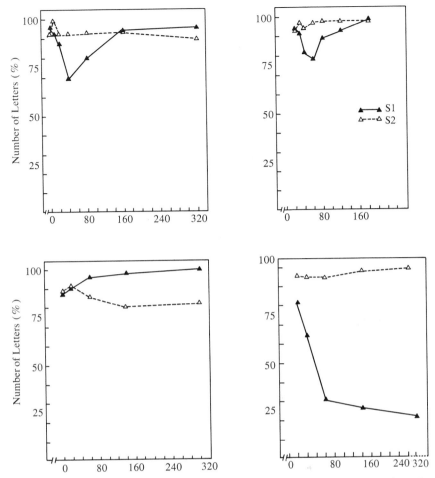

FIGURES 2, 3, 4, 5   Percentage of recognized letters according to the variation of the duration of the interval (Figure 2, *top left*), of S_1 S_2 (Figure 3, *top right*), of S_1 (Figure 4, *bottom left*), of S_2 (Figure 5, *bottom right*).

dots are the same (Figure 1b). This is true provided the duration of exposure of S_1 or S_2 is sufficient (here from 15 to 20 msec). We must add that individual differences are important though for any subject numerical values obtained with letters and dots are almost the same. It can be concluded that in the case of durations less than 80–120 msec simultaneity rather than succession will be perceived.

In order to study the masking effect we have taken the number of perceived letters belonging to the first or the second stimulus, irrespective of the order in which they were given by the subjects, whether

forming a word or isolated, and whether or not perceptive simultaneity occurred.

The rate of perceived letters related to the total duration of presentation $S_1 + i + S_2$ is given in Figures 2, 3, 4, 5. Lateral masking effects are closely linked to the particular situations. In Experiment 1 (Figure 2) there is a maximum backward masking for a total duration of 70 msec, i.e., for a duration of 55 msec between the beginning of S_1 and the beginning of S_2. In Experiment 2 (Figure 3) the masking has the same nature with a maximum for a duration of 60 msec between the beginning of S_1 and the beginning of S_2. In Experiment 3

(Figure 4), S_1 increases and there is a forward masking which increases with the duration of S_1. In Experiment 4 there is a backward masking which increases with the increase of duration of S_2.

Discussion

Visual perceptive simultaneity appears within the same temporal limits, be the stimuli letters or geometric figures. Results are not affected by the meaning of the stimuli. On the other hand, the relative duration of the stimuli and the interval play an almost insignificant role.

These results confirm those obtained by the above-mentioned authors and lend fresh support to the theses of those who believe in the existence of a psychological moment (Stroud, 1955; Lichtenstein, 1961; White, 1963).

However, specific modes of masking of the letters correspond to the diverse temporal conditions of the stimulation. We confirmed (a) the curve in U reported by Kolers (1962) and J. Blanc-Garin (1965), Weisstein and Haber (1965) and (b) an increasing effect of the masking when S_2 increased, S_1 being constant and an increasing forward masking when S_1 increased, S_2 being constant.

These phenomena of masking cannot be explained as a result of the processes which determine perceptive simultaneity, even if they take place in the same scale of duration.

In some more recent and yet unpublished experiments, it has been found that the role of the total duration of S_1, S_2 *and* the interval remains predominant when those varibles are varied in a wide range. However, it appeared that within a total duration of 100 msec the perception simultaneity varies as a function of the duration of S_1 and S_2. There are great individual differences. However, it seems that perception of simultaneity is more frequent when the duration of S_1 is superior to the value of S_2 with an optimum for the structure $S_1 : 60$ ms $i = 20$ ms $S_2 = 20$ ms. In this case it is also found that the number of letters perceived in S_1 is equal to the number of letters perceived in S_2.

References

BLANC-GARIN, J. Quelques problèmes posés par l'étude du métacontraste visuel. *Psychol. Franc.*, 1965, 65, 147–154.

BLANC-GARIN, J. Les relations temporelles dans le masquage latéral visuel. *Année Psychol.*, 1966, 66/2, in press.

HYLAN, J. P. The distribution of attention. I. *Psychol. Rev.*, 1903, 10, 373–403.

KOLERS, P. A. Intensity and contour effects in visual masking. *Vis. Res.*, 1962, 2, 277–294.

LICHTENSTEIN, M. Phenomenal simultaneity with irregular timing of components of the visual stimulus. *Percept. mot. Skills*, 1961, 12, 47–60.

STEIN, W. Tachistoskopische Untersuchungen über das Lesen. *Archiv. ges. Psychol.*, 1928, 64, 301–346.

STROUD, J. M. The fine structure of psychological time. In H. Quastler (Ed.), *Information theory in psychology*. Glencoe, Ill. The Free Press, 1955. pp. 174–207.

WEISSTEIN, N., and R. N. HABER, A U-shaped backward masking function in vision. *Psychon. Sci.*, 1965, 2, 75–76.

WHITE, C. T. Temporal numerosity and the psychological unit of duration. *Psychol. Monogr.*, 1963, no. 575.

The Magical Number Seven, Plus or Minus Two: Some Limits on Our Capacity for Processing Information*

GEORGE A. MILLER

Harvard University

My problem is that I have been persecuted by an integer. For seven years this number has followed me around, has intruded in my most private data, and has assaulted me from the pages of our most public journals. This number assumes a variety of disguises, being sometimes a little larger and sometimes a little smaller than usual, but never changing so much as to be unrecognizable. The persistence with which this number plagues me is far more than a random accident. There is, to quote a famous senator, a design behind it, some pattern governing its appearances. Either there really is something unusual about the number or else I am suffering from delusions of persecution.

I shall begin my case history by telling you about some experiments that tested how accurately people can assign numbers to the magnitudes of various aspects of a stimulus. In the traditional language of psychology these would be called experiments in absolute judgment. Historical accident, however, has decreed that they should have another name. We now call them experiments on the capacity of people

to transmit information. Since these experiments would not have been done without the appearance of information theory on the psychological scene, and since the results are analyzed in terms of the concepts of information theory, I shall have to preface my discussion with a few remarks about this theory.

Information Measurement

The "amount of information" is exactly the same concept that we have talked about for years under the name of "variance." The equations are different, but if we hold tight to the idea that anything that increases the variance also increases the amount of information we cannot go far astray.

The advantages of this new way of talking about variance are simple enough. Variance is always stated in terms of the unit of measurement—inches, pounds, volts, etc.—whereas the amount of information is a dimensionless quantity. Since the information in a discrete statistical distribution does not depend upon the unit of measurement, we can extend the concept to situations where we have no metric and we would not ordinarily think of using the variance. And it also enables us to compare results obtained in quite different experimental situations where it would be meaningless to compare variances based on

* *The Psychological Review*, 1956, vol. 63, pp. 81–97. This paper was first read as an Invited Address before the Eastern Psychological Association in Philadelphia in 1955. Its preparation was supported by the Harvard Psycho-Acoustic Laboratory under Contract N5ori-76 between Harvard University and the Office of Naval Research.

different metrics. So there are some good reasons for adopting the newer concept.

The similarity of variance and amount of information might be explained this way: When we have a large variance, we are very ignorant about what is going to happen. If we are very ignorant, then when we make the observation it gives us a lot of information. On the other hand, if the variance is very small, we know in advance how our observation must come out, so we get little information from making the observation.

If you will now imagine a communication system, you will realize that there is a great deal of variability about what goes into the system and also a great deal of variability about what comes out. The input and the output can therefore be described in terms of their variance (or their information). If it is a good communication system, however, there must be some systematic relation between what goes in and what comes out. That is to say, the output will depend upon the input, or will be correlated with the input. If we measure this correlation, then we can say how much of the output variance is attributable to the input and how much is due to random fluctuations or "noise" introduced by the system during transmission. So we see that the measure of transmitted information is simply a measure of the input-output correlation.

There are two simple rules to follow. Whenever I refer to "amount of information," you will understand "variance." And whenever I refer to "amount of transmitted information," you will understand "covariance" or "correlation."

The situation can be described graphically by two partially overlapping circles. Then the left circle can be taken to represent the variance of the input, the right circle the variance of the output, and the overlap the covariance of input and output. I shall speak of the left circle as the amount of input information, the right circle as the amount of output informa-

tion, and the overlap as the amount of transmitted information.

In the experiments on absolute judgment, the observer is considered to be a communication channel. Then the left circle would represent the amount of information in the stimuli, the right circle the amount of information in his responses, and the overlap the stimulus-response correlation as measured by the amount of transmitted information. The experimental problem is to increase the amount of input information and to measure the amount of transmitted information. If the observer's absolute judgments are quite accurate, then nearly all of the input information will be transmitted and will be recoverable from his responses. If he makes errors, then the transmitted information may be considerably less than the input. We expect that, as we increase the amount of input information, the observer will begin to make more and more errors; we can test the limits of accuracy of his absolute judgments. If the human observer is a reasonable kind of communication system, then when we increase the amount of input information the transmitted information will increase at first and will eventually level off at some asymptotic value. This asymptotic value we take to be the *channel capacity* of the observer: it represents the greatest amount of information that he can give us about the stimulus on the basis of an absolute judgment. The channel capacity is the upper limit on the extent to which the observer can match his responses to the stimuli we give him.

Now just a brief word about the *bit* and we can begin to look at some data. One bit of information is the amount of information that we need to make a decision between two equally likely alternatives. If we must decide whether a man is less than six feet tall or more than six feet tall and if we know that the chances are 50–50, then we need one bit of information. Notice that this unit of information does not refer in any way to the unit of length that we use—feet, inches, centimeters, etc. However you measure the man's height, we still need just one bit of information.

Two bits of information enable us to decide among four equally likely alternatives. Three bits of information enable us to decide among eight equally likely alternatives. Four bits of information decide among 16 alternatives, five among 32, and so on. That is to say, if there are 32 equally likely alternatives, we must make five successive binary decisions, worth one bit each, before we know which alternative is correct. So the general rule is simple: every time the number of alternatives is increased by a factor of two, one bit of information is added.

There are two ways we might increase the amount of input information. We could increase the rate at which we give information to the observer, so that the amount of information per unit time would increase. Or we could ignore the time variable completely and increase the amount of input information by increasing the number of alternative stimuli. In the absolute judgment experiment we are interested in the second alternative. We give the observer as much time as he wants to make his response; we simply increase the number of alternative stimuli among which he must discriminate and look to see where confusions begin to occur. Confusions will appear near the point that we are calling his "channel capacity."

Absolute Judgments of Unidimensional Stimuli

Now let us consider what happens when we make absolute judgments of tones. Pollack (17) asked listeners to identify tones by assigning numerals to them. The tones were different with respect to frequency, and covered the range from 100 to 8000 cps in equal logarithmic steps. A tone was sounded and the listener responded by giving a numeral. After

the listener had made his response he was told the correct identification of the tone.

When only two or three tones were used the listeners never confused them. With four different tones confusions were quite rare, but with five or more tones confusions were frequent. With fourteen different tones the listeners made many mistakes.

These data are plotted in Figure 1. Along the bottom is the amount of input information in bits per stimulus. As the number of alternative tones was increased from 2 to 14, the input information increased from 1 to 3.8 bits. On the ordinate is plotted the amount of transmitted information. The amount of transmitted information behaves in much the way we would expect a communication channel to behave; the transmitted information increases linearly up to about 2 bits and then bends off toward an asymptote at about 2.5 bits. This value, 2.5 bits, therefore, is what we are calling the channel capacity of the listener for absolute judgments of pitch.

So now we have the number 2.5 bits. What does it mean? First, note that 2.5 bits corresponds to about six equally likely alternatives. The result means that we can-

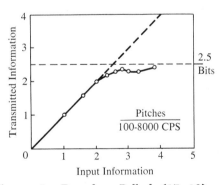

FIGURE 1   Data from Pollack (17, 18) on the amount of information that is transmitted by listeners who make absolute judgments of auditory pitch. As the amount of input information is increased by increasing from 2 to 14 the number of pitches to be judged, the amount of transmitted information approaches as its upper limit a channel capacity of about 2.5 bits per judgment.

not pick more than six different pitches that the listener will never confuse. Or, stated slightly differently, no matter how many alternative tones we ask him to judge, the best we can expect him to do is to assign them to about six different classes without error. Or, again, if we know that there were N alternative stimuli, then his judgment enables us to narrow down the particular stimulus to one out of N/6.

Most people are surprised that the number is as small as six. Of course, there is evidence that a musically sophisticated person with absolute pitch can identify accurately any one of 50 or 60 different pitches. Fortunately, I do not have time to discuss these remarkable exceptions. I say it is fortunate because I do not know how to explain their superior performance. So I shall stick to the more pedestrian fact that most of us can identify about one out of only five or six pitches before we begin to get confused.

It is interesting to consider that psychologists have been using seven-point rating scales for a long time, on the intuitive basis that trying to rate into finer categories does not really add much to the usefulness of the ratings. Pollack's results indicate that, at least for pitches, this intuition is fairly sound.

Next you can ask how reproducible this result is. Does it depend on the spacing of the tones or the various conditions of judgment? Pollack varied these conditions in a number of ways. The range of frequencies can be changed by a factor of about 20 without changing the amount of information transmitted more than a small percentage. Different groupings of the pitches decreased the transmission, but the loss was small. For example, if you can discriminate five high-pitched tones in one series and five low-pitched tones in another series, it is reasonable to expect that you could combine all ten into a single series and still tell them all apart without error. When you try it, however, it does not

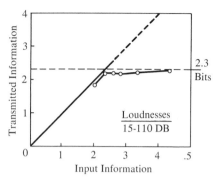

FIGURE 2   Data from Garner (7) on the channel capacity for absolute judgments of auditory loudness.

work. The channel capacity for pitch seems to be about six and that is the best you can do.

While we are on tones, let us look next at Garner's (7) work on loudness. Garner's data for loudness are summarized in Figure 2. Garner went to some trouble to get the best possible spacing of his tones over the intensity range from 15 to 110 db. He used 4, 5, 6, 7, 10, and 20 different stimulus intensities. The results shown in Figure 2 take into account the differences among subjects and the sequential influence of the immediately preceding judgment. Again we find that there seems to be a limit. The channel capacity for absolute judgments of loudness is 2.3 bits, or about five perfectly discriminable alternatives.

Since these two studies were done in different laboratories with slightly different techniques and methods of analysis, we are not in a good position to argue whether five loudnesses is significantly different from six pitches. Probably the difference is in the right direction, and absolute judgments of pitch are slightly more accurate than absolute judgments of loudness. The important point, however, is that the two answers are of the same order of magnitude.

The experiment has also been done for taste intensities. In Figure 3 are the results obtained by Beebe-Center, Rogers, and O'Connell (1) for absolute judgments of

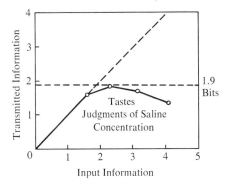

FIGURE 3   Data from Beebe-Center, Rogers, and O'Connell (1) on the channel capacity for absolute judgments of saltiness.

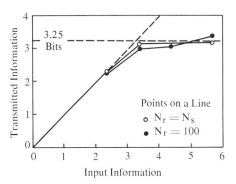

FIGURE 4   Data from Hake and Garner (8) on the channel capacity for absolute judgments of the position of a pointer in a linear interval.

the concentration of salt solutions. The concentrations ranged from 0.3 to 34.7 gm. NaCl per 100 cc tap water in equal subjective steps. They used 3, 5, 9, and 17 different concentrations. The channel capacity is 1.9 bits, which is about four distinct concentrations. Thus taste intensities seem a little less distinctive than auditory stimuli, but again the order of magnitude is not far off.

On the other hand, the channel capacity for judgments of visual position seems to be significantly larger. Hake and Garner (8) asked observers to interpolate visually between two scale markers. Their results are shown in Figure 4. They did the experiment in two ways. In one version they let the observer use any number between zero and 100 to describe the position, although they presented stimuli at only 5, 10, 20, or 50 different positions. The results with this unlimited response technique are shown by the filled circles on the graph. In the other version the observers were limited in their responses to reporting just those stimulus values that were possible. That is to say, in the second version the number of different responses that the observer could make was exactly the same as the number of different stimuli that the experimenter might present. The results with this limited response technique are shown by the open circles on the graph. The two functions are so similar

that it seems fair to conclude that the number of responses available to the observer had nothing to do with the channel capacity of 3.25 bits.

The Hake-Garner experiment has been repeated by Coonan and Klemmer. Although they have not yet published their results, they have given me permission to say that they obtained channel capacities ranging from 3.2 bits for very short exposures of the pointer position to 3.9 bits for longer exposures. These values are slightly higher than Hake and Garner's, so we must conclude that there are between 10 and 15 distinct positions along a linear interval. This is the largest channel capacity that has been measured for any unidimensional variable.

At the present time these four experiments on absolute judgments of simple, unidimensional stimuli are all that have appeared in the psychological journals. However, a great deal of work on other stimulus variables has not yet appeared in the journals. For example, Eriksen and Hake (6) have found that the channel capacity for judging the sizes of squares is 2.2 bits, or about five categories, under a wide range of experimental conditions. In a separate experiment Eriksen (5) found 2.8 bits for size, 3.1 bits for hue, and 2.3 bits for brightness. Geldard has measured the channel capacity for the skin by placing vibrators on the chest region. A good observer can identify about four intensities, about five durations, and about seven locations.

One of the most active groups in this area has been the Air Force Operational Applications Laboratory. Pollack has been kind enough to furnish me with the results of their measurements for several aspects of visual displays. They made measurements for area and for the curvature, length, and direction of lines. In one set of experiments they used a very short exposure of the stimulus—$\frac{1}{40}$ second—and then they repeated the measurements with a 5-second exposure. For area they got 2.6 bits with the short exposure and 2.7 bits with the long exposure. For the length of a line they got about 2.6 bits with the short exposure and about 3.0 bits with the long exposure. Direction, or angle of inclination, gave 2.8 bits for the short exposure and 3.3 bits for the long exposure. Curvature was apparently harder to judge. When the length of the arc was constant, the result at the short exposure duration was 2.2 bits, but when the length of the chord was constant, the result was only 1.6 bits. This last value is the lowest that anyone has measured to date. I should add, however, that these values are apt to be slightly too low because the data from all subjects were pooled before the transmitted information was computed.

Now let us see where we are. First, the channel capacity does seem to be a valid notion for describing human observers. Second, the channel capacities measured for these unidimensional variables range from 1.6 bits for curvature to 3.9 bits for positions in an interval. Although there is no question that the differences among the variables are real and meaningful, the more impressive fact to me is their considerable similarity. If I take the best estimates I can get of the channel capacities for all the stimulus variables I have mentioned, the mean is 2.6 bits and the standard deviation is only 0.6 bit. In terms of distinguishable alternatives, this mean corresponds to about 6.5 categories, one standard deviation includes from 4 to 10 categories, and the total range is from 3 to 15 categories. Considering the wide variety of different variables that have been studied, I find this to be a remarkably narrow range.

There seems to be some limitation built into us either by learning or by the design of our nervous systems, a limit that keeps our channel capacities in this general range. On the basis of the present evidence it seems safe to say that we possess a finite and rather small capacity for making such unidimensional judgments and that this capacity does not vary a great deal from one simple sensory attribute to another.

Absolute Judgments of Multidimensional Stimuli

You may have noticed that I have been careful to say that this magical number seven applies to one-dimensional judgments. Everyday experience teaches us that we can identify accurately any one of several hundred faces, any one of several thousand words, any one of several thousand objects, etc. The story certainly would not be complete if we stopped at this point. We must have some understanding of why the one-dimensional variables we judge in the laboratory give results so far out of line with what we do constantly in our behavior outside the laboratory. A possible explanation lies in the number of independently variable attributes of the stimuli that are being judged. Objects, faces, words, and the like differ from one another in many ways, whereas the simple stimuli we have considered thus far differ from one another in only one respect.

Fortunately, there are a few data on what happens when we make absolute judgments of stimuli that differ from one another in several ways. Let us look first at the results Klemmer and Frick (13)

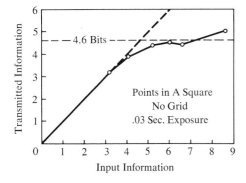

FIGURE 5   Data from Klemmer and Frick (13) on the channel capacity for absolute judgments of the position of a dot in a square.

have reported for the absolute judgment of the position of a dot in a square. In Figure 5 we see their results. Now the channel capacity seems to have increased to 4.6 bits, which means that people can identify accurately any one of 24 positions in the square.

The position of a dot in a square is clearly a two-dimensional proposition. Both its horizontal and its vertical position must be identified. Thus it seems natural to compare the 4.6-bit capacity for a square with the 3.25-bit capacity for the position of a point in an interval. The point in the square requires two judgments of the interval type. If we have a capacity of 3.25 bits for estimating intervals and we do this twice, we should get 6.5 bits as our capacity for locating points in a square. Adding the second independent dimension gives us an increase from 3.25 to 4.6, but it falls short of the perfect addition that would give 6.5 bits.

Another example is provided by Beebe-Center, Rogers, and O'Connell. When they asked people to identify both the saltiness and the sweetness of solutions containing various concentrations of salt and sucrose, they found that the channel capacity was 2.3 bits. Since the capacity for salt alone was 1.9, we might expect about 3.8 bits if the two aspects of the compound stimuli were judged inde-

pendently. As with spatial locations, the second dimension adds a little to the capacity but not as much as it conceivably might.

A third example is provided by Pollack (18), who asked listeners to judge both the loudness and the pitch of pure tones. Since pitch gives 2.5 bits and loudness gives 2.3 bits, we might hope to get as much as 4.8 bits for pitch and loudness together. Pollack obtained 3.1 bits, which again indicates that the second dimension augments the channel capacity but not so much as it might.

A fourth example can be drawn from the work of Halsey and Chapanis (9) on confusions among colors of equal luminance. Although they did not analyze their results in informational terms, they estimate that there are about 11 to 15 identifiable colors, or, in our terms, about 3.6 bits. Since these colors varied in both hue and saturation, it is probably correct to regard this as a two-dimensional judgment. If we compare this with Eriksen's 3.1 bits for hue (which is a questionable comparison to draw), we again have something less than perfect addition when a second dimension is added.

It is still a long way, however, from these two-dimensional examples to the multidimensional stimuli provided by faces, words, etc. To fill this gap we have only one experiment, an auditory study done by Pollack and Ficks (19). They managed to get six different acoustic variables that they could change: frequency, intensity, rate of interruption, on-time fraction, total duration, and spatial location. Each one of these six variables could assume any one of five different values, so altogether there were 5^6, or 15,625 different tones that they could present. The listeners made a separate rating for each one of these six dimensions. Under these conditions the transmitted information was 7.2 bits, which corresponds to about 150 different categories that could be absolutely identified without error. Now we are beginning to

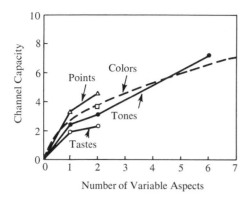

FIGURE 6   The general form of the relation between channel capacity and the number of independently variable attributes of the stimuli.

get up into the range that ordinary experience would lead us us to expect.

Suppose that we plot these data, fragmentary as they are, and make a guess about how the channel capacity changes with the dimensionality of the stimuli. The result is given in Figure 6. In a moment of considerable daring I sketched the dotted line to indicate roughly the trend that the data seemed to be taking.

Clearly, the addition of independently variable attributes to the stimulus increases the channel capacity, but at a decreasing rate. It is interesting to note that the channel capacity is increased even when the several variables are not independent. Eriksen (5) reports that, when size, brightness, and hue all vary together in perfect correlation, the transmitted information is 4.1 bits as compared with an average of about 2.7 bits when these attributes are varied one at a time. By confounding three attributes, Eriksen increased the dimensionality of the input without increasing the amount of input information; the result was an increase in channel capacity of about the amount that the dotted function in Figure 6 would lead us to expect.

The point seems to be that, as we add more variables to the display, we increase the total capacity, but we decrease the accuracy for any particular variable. In

other words, we can make relatively crude judgments of several things simultaneously.

We might argue that in the course of evolution those organisms were most successful that were responsive to the widest range of stimulus energies in their environment. In order to survive in a constantly fluctuating world, it was better to have a little information about a lot of things than to have a lot of information about a small segment of the environment. If a compromise was necessary, the one we seem to have made is clearly the more adaptive.

Pollack and Ficks's results are very strongly suggestive of an argument that linguists and phoneticians have been making for some time (11). According to the linguistic analysis of the sounds of human speech, there are about eight or ten dimensions—the linguists call them *distinctive features*—that distinguish one phoneme from another. These distinctive features are usually binary, or at most ternary, in nature. For example, a binary distinction is made between vowels and consonants, a binary decision is made between oral and nasal consonants, a ternary decision is made among front, middle, and back phonemes, etc. This approach gives us quite a different picture of speech perception than we might otherwise obtain from our studies of the speech spectrum and of the ear's ability to discriminate relative differences among pure tones. I am personally much interested in this new approach (15), and I regret that there is not time to discuss it here.

It was probably with this linguistic theory in mind that Pollack and Ficks conducted a test on a set of tonal stimuli that varied in eight dimensions, but required only a binary decision on each dimension. With these tones they measured the transmitted information at 6.9 bits, or about 120 recognizable kinds of sounds. It is an intriguing question, as yet unexplored, whether one can go on adding dimensions indefinitely in this way.

In human speech there is clearly a limit to the number of dimensions that we use. In this instance, however, it is not known whether the limit is imposed by the nature of the perceptual machinery that must recognize the sounds or by the nature of the speech machinery that must produce them. Somebody will have to do the experiment to find out. There is a limit, however, at about eight or nine distinctive features in every language that has been studied, and so when we talk we must resort to still another trick for increasing our channel capacity. Language uses sequences of phonemes, so we make several judgments successively when we listen to words and sentences. That is to say, we use both simultaneous and successive discriminations in order to expand the rather rigid limits imposed by the inaccuracy of our absolute judgments of simple magnitudes.

These multidimensional judgments are strongly reminiscent of the abstraction experiment of Külpe (14). As you may remember, Külpe showed that observers report more accurately on an attribute for which they are set than on attributes for which they are not set. For example, Chapman (4) used three different attributes and compared the results obtained when the observers were instructed before the tachistoscopic presentation with the results obtained when they were not told until after the presentation which one of the three attributes was to be reported. When the instruction was given in advance, the judgments were more accurate. When the instruction was given afterwards, the subjects presumably had to judge all three attributes in order to report on any one of them and the accuracy was correspondingly lower. This is in complete accord with the results we have just been considering, where the accuracy of judgment on each attribute decreased as more dimensions were added. The point is probably obvious, but I shall make it anyhow, that the abstraction experiments did *not* demonstrate that people can judge only one attribute at a time. They merely showed what seems quite reasonable, that people are less accurate if they must judge more than one attribute simultaneously.

Subitizing

I cannot leave this general area without mentioning, however briefly, the experiments conducted at Mount Holyoke College on the discrimination of number (12). In experiments by Kaufman, Lord, Reese, and Volkmann random patterns of dots were flashed on a screen for $\frac{1}{5}$ of a second. Anywhere from 1 to more than 200 dots could appear in the pattern. The subject's task was to report how many dots there were.

The first point to note is that on patterns containing up to five or six dots the subjects simply did not make errors. The performance on these small numbers of dots was so different from the performance with more dots that it was given a special name. Below seven the subjects were said to *subitize*; above seven they were said to *estimate*. This is, as you will recognize, what we once optimistically called "the span of attention."

This discontinuity at seven is, of course, suggestive. Is this the same basic process that limits our unidimensional judgments to about seven categories? The generalization is tempting, but not sound in my opinion. The data on number estimates have not been analyzed in informational terms; but on the basis of the published data I would guess that the subjects transmitted something more than four bits of information about the number of dots. Using the same arguments as before, we would conclude that there are about 20 or 30 distinguishable categories of numerousness. This is considerably more information than we would expect to get from a unidimensional display. It is, as a matter of fact, very much like a two-dimensional display. Although the dimensionality of the random dot patterns is not entirely clear, these results are in the same range as Klemmer and Frick's for their two-dimensional display of dots in a square. Perhaps the two dimensions of numerousness are area and density. When the subject can subitize, area and density may not be the significant variables, but when the subject must estimate perhaps they are significant. In any event, the comparison is not so simple as it might seem at first thought.

This is one of the ways in which the magical number seven has persecuted me. Here we have two closely related kinds of experiments, both of which point to the significance of the number seven as a limit on our capacities. And yet when we examine the matter more closely, there seems to be a reasonable suspicion that it is nothing more than a coincidence.

The Span of Immediate Memory

Let me summarize the situation in this way. There is a clear and definite limit to the accuracy with which we can identify absolutely the magnitude of a unidimensional stimulus variable. I would propose to call this limit the *span of absolute judgment,* and I maintain that for unidimensional judgments this span is usually somewhere in the neighborhood of seven. We are not completely at the mercy of this limited span, however, because we have a variety of techniques for getting around it and increasing the accuracy of our judgments. The three most important of these devices are (*a*) to make relative rather than absolute judgments; or, if that is not possible, (*b*) to increase the number of dimensions along which the stimuli can differ; or (*c*) to arrange the task in such a way that we make a sequence of several absolute judgments in a row.

The study of relative judgments is one of the oldest topics in experimental psychology, and I will not pause to review it now. The second device, increasing the

dimensionality, we have just considered. It seems that by adding more dimensions and requiring crude, binary, yes-no judgments on each attribute we can extend the span of absolute judgment from seven to at least 150. Judging from our everyday behavior, the limit is probably in the thousands, if indeed there is a limit. In my opinion, we cannot go on compounding dimensions indefinitely. I suspect that there is also a *span of perceptual dimensionality* and that this span is somewhere in the neighborhood of ten, but I must add at once that there is no objective evidence to support this suspicion. This is a question sadly needing experimental exploration.

Concerning the third device, the use of successive judgments, I have quite a bit to say because this device introduces memory as the handmaiden of discrimination. And, since mnemonic processes are at least as complex as are perceptual processes, we can anticipate that their interactions will not be easily disentangled.

Suppose that we start by simply extending slightly the experimental procedure that we have been using. Up to this point we have presented a single stimulus and asked the observer to name it immediately thereafter. We can extend this procedure by requiring the observer to withhold his response until we have given him several stimuli in succession. At the end of the sequence of stimuli he then makes his response. We still have the same sort of input-output situation that is required for the measurement of transmitted information. But now we have passed from an experiment on absolute judgment to what is traditionally called an experiment on immediate memory.

Before we look at any data on this topic I feel I must give you a word of warning to help you avoid some obvious associations that can be confusing. Everybody knows that there is a finite span of immediate memory and that for a lot of different kinds of test materials this span is about seven items in length. I have just shown you that there is a span of absolute judgment that can distinguish about seven categories and that there is a span of attention that will encompass about six objects at a glance. What is more natural than to think that all three of these spans are different aspects of a single underlying process? And that is a fundamental mistake, as I shall be at some pains to demonstrate. This mistake is one of the malicious persecutions that the magical number seven has subjected me to.

My mistake went something like this. We have seen that the invariant feature in the span of absolute judgment is the amount of information that the observer can transmit. There is a real operational similarity between the absolute judgment experiment and the immediate memory experiment. If immediate memory is like absolute judgment, then it should follow that the invariant feature in the span of immediate memory is also the amount of information that an observer can retain. If the amount of information in the span of immediate memory is a constant, then the span should be short when the individual items contain a lot of information and the span should be long when the items contain little information. For example, decimal digits are worth 3.3 bits apiece. We can recall about seven of them, for a total of 23 bits of information. Isolated English words are worth about 10 bits apiece. If the total amount of information is to remain constant at 23 bits, then we should be able to remember only two or three words chosen at random. In this way I generated a theory about how the span of immediate memory should vary as a function of the amount of information per item in the test materials.

The measurements of memory span in the literature are suggestive on this question, but not definitive. And so it was necessary to do the experiment to see. Hayes (10) tried it out with five different kinds of test materials: binary digits, decimal digits, letters of the alphabet, letters

plus decimal digits, and with 1,000 monosyllabic words. The lists were read aloud at the rate of one item per second and the subjects had as much time as they needed to give their responses. A procedure described by Woodworth (20) was used to score the responses.

The results are shown by the filled circles in Figure 7. Here the dotted line indicates what the span should have been if the amount of information in the span were constant. The solid curves represent the data. Hayes repeated the experiment using test vocabularies of different sizes but all containing only English monosyllables (open circles in Figure 7). This more homogeneous test material did not change the picture significantly. With binary items the span is about nine and, although it drops to about five with monosyllabic English words, the difference is far less than the hypothesis of constant information would require.

There is nothing wrong with Hayes's experiment, because Pollack (16) repeated it much more elaborately and got essentially the same result. Pollack took pains to measure the amount of information transmitted and did not rely on the traditional procedure for scoring the responses.

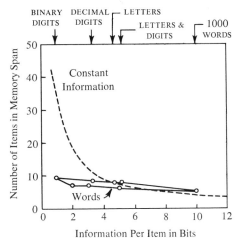

FIGURE 7 Data from Hayes (10) on the span of immediate memory plotted as a function of the amount of information per item in the test materials.

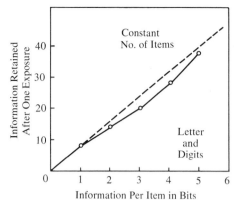

FIGURE 8   Data from Pollack (16) on the amount of information retained after one presentation plotted as a function of the amount of information per item in the test materials.

His results are plotted in Figure 8. Here it is clear that the amount of information transmitted is not a constant, but increases almost linearly as the amount of information per item in the input is increased.

And so the outcome is perfectly clear. In spite of the coincidence that the magical number seven appears in both places, the span of absolute judgment and the span of immediate memory are quite different kinds of limitations that are imposed on our ability to process information. Absolute judgment is limited by the amount of information. Immediate memory is limited by the number of items. In order to capture this distinction in somewhat picturesque terms, I have fallen into the custom of distinguishing between *bits* of information and *chunks* of information. Then I can say that the number of bits of information is constant for absolute judgment and the number of chunks of information is constant for immediate memory. The span of immediate memory seems to be almost independent of the number of bits per chunk, at least over the range that has been examined to date.

The contrast of the terms *bit* and *chunk* also serves to highlight the fact that we are not very definite about what constitutes a chunk of information. For example, the memory span of five words that Hayes

obtained when each word was drawn at random from a set of 1,000 English monosyllables might just as appropriately have been called a memory span of 15 phonemes, since each word had about three phonemes in it. Intuitively, it is clear that the subjects were recalling five words, not 15 phonemes, but the logical distinction is not immediately apparent. We are dealing here with a process of organizing or grouping the input into familiar units or chunks, and a great deal of learning has gone into the formation of these familiar units.

Recoding

In order to speak more precisely, therefore, we must recognize the importance of grouping or organizing the input sequence into units or chunks. Since the memory span is a fixed number of chunks, we can increase the number of bits of information that it contains simply by building larger and larger chunks, each chunk containing more information than before.

A man just beginning to learn radiotelegraphic code hears each *dit* and *dah* as a separate chunk. Soon he is able to organize these sounds into letters and then he can deal with the letters as chunks. Then the letters organize themselves as words, which are still larger chunks, and he begins to hear whole phrases. I do not mean that each step is a discrete process, or that plateaus must appear in his learning curve, for surely the levels of organization are achieved at different rates and overlap each other during the learning process. I am simply pointing to the obvious fact that the dits and dahs are organized by learning into patterns and that as these larger chunks emerge the amount of message that the operator can remember increases correspondingly. In the terms I am proposing to use, the operator learns to increase the bits per chunk.

In the jargon of communication theory, this process would be called *recoding*. The input is given in a code that contains many chunks with few bits per chunk. The operator recodes the input into another code that contains fewer chunks with more bits per chunk. There are many ways to do this recoding, but probably the simplest is to group the input events, apply a new name to the group, and then remember the new name rather than the original input events.

Since I am convinced that this process is a very general and important one for psychology, I want to tell you about a demonstration experiment that should make perfectly explicit what I am talking about. This experiment was conducted by Sidney Smith and was reported by him before the Eastern Psychological Association in 1954.

Begin with the observed fact that people can repeat back eight decimal digits, but only nine binary digits. Since there is a large discrepancy in the amount of information recalled in these two cases, we suspect at once that a recoding procedure could be used to increase the span of immediate memory for binary digits. In Table 1 a method for grouping and renaming is illustrated. Along the top is a sequence of 18 binary digits, far more than any subject was able to recall after a single presentation. In the next line these same binary digits are grouped by

pairs. Four possible pairs can occur: 00 is renamed 0, 01 is renamed 1, 10 is renamed 2, and 11 is renamed 3. That is to say, we recode from a base-two arithmetic to a base-four arithmetic. In the recoded sequence there are now just nine digits to remember, and this is almost within the span of immediate memory. In the next line the same sequence of binary digits is regrouped into chunks of three. There are eight possible sequences of three, so we give each sequence a new name between 0 and 7. Now we have recoded from a sequence of 18 binary digits into a sequence of 6 octal digits, and this is well within the span of immediate memory. In the last two lines the binary digits are grouped by fours and by fives and are given decimal-digit names from 0 to 15 and from 0 to 31.

It is reasonably obvious that this kind of recoding increases the bits per chunk, and packages the binary sequence into a form that can be retained within the span of immediate memory. So Smith assembled 20 subjects and measured their spans for binary and octal digits. The spans were 9 for binaries and 7 for octals. Then he gave each recoding scheme to five of the subjects. They studied the recoding until they said they understood it—for about 5 or 10 minutes. Then he tested their span for binary digits again while

TABLE 1

Ways of Recoding Sequences of Binary Digits

BINARY DIGITS (BITS)		1 0 1 0 0 0 1 0 0 1 1 1 0 0 1 1 1 0							
2:1	Chunks	10	10	00	10	01	11	00	11	10
	Recoding	2	2	0	2	1	3	0	3	2
3:1	Chunks	101		000		100	111	001		110
	Recoding	5		0		4	7	1		6
4:1	Chunks	1010			0010		0111		0011	10
	Recoding	10			2		7		3	
5:1	Chunks	10100				01001		11001		110
	Recoding	20				9		25		

they tried to use the recoding schemes they had studied.

The recoding schemes increased their span for binary digits in every case. But the increase was not as large as we had expected on the basis of their span for octal digits. Since the discrepancy increased as the recoding ratio increased, we reasoned that the few minutes the subjects had spent learning the recoding schemes had not been sufficient. Apparently the translation from one code to the other must be almost automatic or the subject will lose part of the next group while he is trying to remember the translation of the last group.

Since the 4:1 and 5:1 ratios require considerable study, Smith decided to imitate Ebbinghaus and do the experiment on himself. With Germanic patience he drilled himself on each recoding successively, and obtained the results shown in Figure 9. Here the data follow along rather nicely with the results you would predict on the basis of his span for octal digits. He could remember 12 octal digits. With the 2:1 recoding, these 12 chunks were worth 24 binary digits. With the 3:1 recoding they were worth of 36 binary digits. With the 4:1 and 5:1 recodings, they were worth about 40 binary digits.

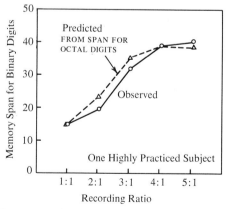

FIGURE 9   The span of immediate memory for binary digits is plotted as a function of the recoding procedure used. The predicted function is obtained by multiplying the span for octals by 2, 3 and 3.3 for recoding into base 4, base 8, and base 10, respectively.

It is a little dramatic to watch a person get 40 binary digits in a row and then repeat them back without error. However, if you think of this merely as a mnemonic trick for extending the memory span, you will miss the more important point that is implicit in nearly all such mnemonic devices. The point is that recoding is an extremely powerful weapon for increasing the amount of information that we can deal with. In one form or another we use recoding constantly in our daily behavior.

In my opinion the most customary kind of recoding that we do all the time is to translate into a verbal code. When there is a story or an argument or an idea that we want to remember, we usually try to rephrase it "in our own words." When we witness some event we want to remember, we make a verbal description of the event and then remember our verbalization. Upon recall we recreate by secondary elaboration the details that seem consistent with the particular verbal recoding we happen to have made. The well-known experiment by Carmichael, Hogan, and Walter (3) on the influence that names have on the recall of visual figures is one demonstration of the process.

The inaccuracy of the testimony of eyewitnesses is well known in legal psychology, but the distortions of testimony are not random—they follow naturally from the particular recoding that the witness used, and the particular recoding he used depends upon his whole life history. Our language is tremendously useful for repackaging material into a few chunks rich in information. I suspect that imagery is a form of recoding, too, but images seem much harder to get at operationally and to study experimentally than the more symbolic kinds of recoding.

It seems probable that even memorization can be studied in these terms. The process of memorizing may be simply the formation of chunks, or groups of items that go together, until there are few enough chunks so that we can recall all the items. The work by Bousfield and Cohen

(2) on the occurrence of clustering in the recall of words is especially interesting in this respect.

Summary

I have come to the end of the data that I wanted to present, so I would like now to make some summarizing remarks.

First, the span of absolute judgment and the span of immediate memory impose severe limitations on the amount of information that we are able to receive, process, and remember. By organizing the stimulus input simultaneously into several dimensions and successively into a sequence of chunks, we manage to break (or at least stretch) this informational bottleneck.

Second, the process of recoding is a very important one in human psychology and deserves much more explicit attention than it has received. In particular, the kind of linguistic recoding that people do seems to me to be the very lifeblood of the thought processes. Recoding procedures are a constant concern to clinicians, social psychologists, linguists, and anthropologists and yet, probably because recoding is less accessible to experimental manipulation than nonsense syllables or T mazes, the traditional experimental psychologist has contributed little or nothing to their analysis. Nevertheless, experimental techniques can be used, methods of recoding can be specified, behavioral indicants can be found. And I anticipate that we will find a very orderly set of relations describing what now seems an uncharted wilderness of individual differences.

Third, the concepts and measures provided by the theory of information provide a quantitative way of getting at some of these questions. The theory provides us with a yardstick for calibrating our stimulus materials and for measuring the performance of our subjects. In the interests of communication I have suppressed the technical details of information measurement and have tried to express the ideas in more familiar terms; I hope this paraphrase will not lead you to think they are not useful in research. Informational concepts have already proved valuable in the study of discrimination and of language; they promise a great deal in the study of learning and memory; and it has even been proposed that they can be useful in the study of concept formation. A lot of questions that seemed fruitless twenty or thirty years ago may now be worth another look. In fact, I feel that my story here must stop just as it begins to get really interesting.

And finally, what about the magical number seven? What about the seven wonders of the world, the seven seas, the seven deadly sins, the seven daughters of Atlas in the Pleiades, the seven ages of man, the seven levels of hell, the seven primary colors, the seven notes of the musical scale, and the seven days of the week? What about the seven-point rating scale, the seven categories for absolute judgment, the seven objects in the span of attention, and the seven digits in the span of immediate memory? For the present I propose to withhold judgment. Perhaps there is something deep and profound behind all these sevens, something just calling out for us to discover it. But I suspect that it is only a pernicious, Pythagorean coincidence.

References

1. BEEBE-CENTER, J. G., M. S. ROGERS and D. N. O'CONNELL. Transmission of information about sucrose and saline solutions through the sense of taste. *J. Psychol.*, 1955, 39, 157–160.
2. BOUSFIELD, W. A., and B. H. COHEN. The occurrence of clustering in the recall of randomly arranged words of different frequencies-of-usage. *J. gen. Psychol.*, 1955, 52, 83–95.
3. CARMICHAEL, L., H. P. HOGAN, and A. A. WALTER. An experimental study of the effect of language on the reproduction of visually perceived form. *J. exp. Psychol.*, 1932, 15, 73–86.
4. CHAPMAN, D. W. Relative effects of determinate and indeterminate *Aufgaben*. *Amer. J. Psychol.*, 1932, 44, 163–174.

5. ERIKSEN, C. W. Multidimensional stimulus differences and accuracy of discrimination. *USAF, WADC Tech. Rep.*, 1954, No. 54–165.

6. ERIKSEN, C. W., and H. W. HAKE. Absolute judgments as a function of the stimulus range and the number of stimulus and response categories. *J. exp. Psychol.*, 1955, 49, 323–332.

7. GARNER, W. R. An informational analysis of absolute judgments of loudness. *J. exp. Psychol.*, 1953, 46, 373–380.

8. HAKE, H. W., and W. R. GARNER. The effect of presenting various numbers of discrete steps on scale reading accuracy. *J. exp. Psychol.*, 1951, 42, 358–366.

9. HALSEY, R. M., and A. CHAPANIS. Chromaticity-confusion contours in a complex viewing situation. *J. Opt. Soc. Amer.*, 1954, 44, 442–454.

10. HAYES, J. R. M. Memory span for several vocabularies as a function of vocabulary size. In *Quarterly Progress Report*, Cambridge, Mass.: Acoustics Laboratory, Massachusetts Institute of Technology, Jan.–June, 1952.

11. JAKOBSON, R., C. G. M. FANT, and M. HALLE. *Preliminaries to speech analysis.* Cambridge, Mass.: Acoustics Laboratory, Massachusetts Institute of Technology, 1952. (Tech. Rep. No. 13.)

12. KAUFMAN, E. L., M. W. LORD, T. W. REESE, and J. VOLKMANN. The discrimination of visual number. *Amer. J. Psychol.*, 1949, 62, 498–525.

13. KLEMMER, E. T., and F. C. FRICK. Assimilation of information from dot and matrix patterns. *J. exp. Psychol.*, 1953, 45, 15–19.

14. KÜLPE, O. Versuche über Abstraktion. *Ber. ü. d. I Kongr. f. exper. Psychol.*, 1904, 56–68.

15. MILLER, G. A., and P. E. NICELY. An analysis of perceptual confusions among some English consonants. *J. Acoust. Soc. Amer.*, 1955, 27, 338–352.

16. POLLACK, I. The assimilation of sequentially encoded information. *Amer. J. Psychol.*, 1953, 66, 421–435.

17. POLLACK, I. The information of elementary auditory displays. *J. Acoust. Soc. Amer.*, 1952, 24, 745–749.

18. POLLACK, I. The information of elementary auditory displays. II. *J. Acoust. Soc. Amer.*, 1953, 25, 765–769.

19. POLLACK, I., and L. FICKS. Information of elementary multi-dimensional auditory displays. *J. Acoust. Soc. Amer.*, 1954, 26, 155–158.

20. WOODWORTH, R. S. *Experimental psychology.* New York: Holt, Rinehart and Winston, Inc. 1938.

Short-Term Storage of Information in Vision*

E. AVERBACH AND G. SPERLING

Bell Telephone Laboratories

There have been numerous estimates of human ability to extract information from

* *Symposium on Information Theory.* C. Cherry (Ed.) London: Butterworth, 1961, pp. 196–211.

This paper is a joint presentation of two separate lines of research. The theory and methods of Part I are due to G. Sperling, those of Part II to E. Averbach.

brief visual presentations. The greatest information intake has been observed with exposures of items having high information content as compared to items of low information content, e.g. decimal digits and letters as opposed to binary digits. The limit of performance in these experiments, called the "span of perception" or "span of immediate memory", seems to be a limit on the number of items recalled rather than a limit on amount of information. A subject can report only about a half dozen items regardless of the ensemble from which these items were chosen.

"Span" experiments are very gross. They treat the observer as a transmission link without indicating where or how, information is lost between exposure of the stimulus and the subject's report. This paper describes some experiments that attempt to measure the characteristics of the early stages of the perceptual process. In the first part (by G. S.) the classical "span" technique of dealing with brief exposures is contrasted with a "sampling" technique. It is shown that humans are able to store rather large amounts of information for short time periods. Experimental estimates are given of the amount and duration of the visual storage and of the rate at which visually stored information can be utilized. The second part of the paper (by E. A.) presents a slightly different sampling experiment, two kinds of "erasure" experiments and a model which relates observed storage time, true storage time, erasure and read-out rate.

Part One

The span type of experiment is an old one, and it is not surprising that it has many names. It has been called the span of apprehension, span of attention, span of perception, and span of immediate-memory experiment. In this kind of experiment the subject is briefly shown a stimulus containing a number of letters. He is asked to report as many letters as he can; that is, to make a *whole* report of the visual stimulus.

This whole report procedure was tried with a variety of different stimulus arrays. Figure 1 shows some typical stimuli. These arrays vary in the number of items, in their spatial arrangement, and in their composition; that is, some arrays have letters alone, others have letters and numbers.

```
        R N F              K L B
                           Y N X


                           X M R J
      X V N K H            P N K P


                           T D R
      L Q D K K J          S R N
                           F Z R


                           7 I V F
      Z Y V V F F          X L 5 3
                           B 4 W 7
```

FIGURE 1

The various stimuli were exposed for 50 msec ($\frac{1}{20}$th sec) individually to five highly trained subjects. Figure 2 shows the average number of letters that subjects were able to report correctly. The subjects reported nearly all the letters correctly so long as the number of letters in the stimulus did not exceed five. When stimuli contained five or more letters, subjects were able to report only about $4\frac{1}{2}$ letters correctly on the average. These are the classical results. We would say that the span of immediate-memory for these stimuli is about four to five letters.

In order to find out if this five letter limit was determined by the short exposure time that was used, the exposure duration was systematically varied from 15 to 500 msec at the same intensity. Figure 3 shows

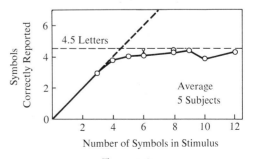

FIGURE 2

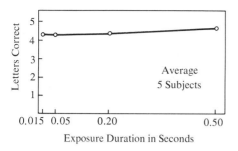

FIGURE 3

the results. Apparently, within the limits of the conditions used, exposure duration does not influence the number of letters reported.

The span type of experiment may be summarized as follows: when the subjects are asked to report all the letters of a stimulus, they can report only about five letters on the average; this limit of "immediate-memory" holds for a wide range of visual arrays and exposure durations.

In the whole report procedure observers often assert that they could *see* more letters than they were able to *report* later. They say that while they are reporting some letters, they forget others. This suggests that the immediate-memory span sets a limit on a process that is otherwise rich in available information. In other words, although an observer can correctly report only about five letters from the brief visual stimulus, he may nevertheless have chosen these five letters from a larger store of letters which were momentarily available to him. In the sampling type of experiment an attempt was made to ascertain how much information does, in fact, become available to the observer as a result of the stimulus.

In this experiment a sampling procedure which does not require a whole report is used in order to circumvent the immediate-memory span. This method requires the observers to report only a part (designated by location) of a letter array exposed for $\frac{1}{20}$th sec. The part to be reported consists of just one out of three rows of letters. It is small enough (3–4 letters) to lie within

the memory span. A tonal signal (high, medium or low frequency tone) was used to indicate which of the rows was to be reported. The subject did not know which signal to expect, and the indicator signal was not sounded until after the visual stimulus had been turned off. In this way, information available for report was sampled immediately after the termination of the stimulus.

There is an important procedural difference in the two kinds of experiments. In the first kind, the observer is required to report all the letters of the stimulus. He must give a "whole" report. In the sampling experiment the observer reports only one row of letters of the stimulus, but he does not know which row of letters will be called for until after the stimulus has been turned off. We call this a "partial" report.

Each observer, for each set of material tested (stimuli of 6, 8, 9 and 12 symbols), gave partial reports that were more accurate than whole reports for the same material (5). These results are illustrated in Figure 4. The lower curve is the same immediate-memory data as that illustrated in Figure 2. These are obtained by a *whole* report. The upper curves represent the accuracy of *partial* reports. For example, following the exposure of stimuli consisting of 12 letters, 76 per cent of the letters called for in the partial report were given correctly by the observers. It is possible to calculate the total information available to the observer from which he draws his

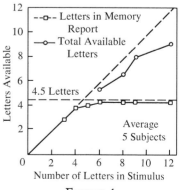

FIGURE 4

partial report. It is about 9.1 letters; namely, 76 per cent of 12 letters. The 9.1 randomly chosen letters are equivalent to 40.6 bits of information. This estimate of the information available in a brief exposure is considerably more than previous experimental estimates (20 to 25 bits) which were obtained using a whole report. Apparently, the subject's memory span was the limiting factor in these experiments. Further experiments with stimuli containing more than 12 letters showed that the 40-bit figure observed using partial report experiments was limited by the small amount of information in the stimuli rather than by the capacity of the observers.

These results show that immediately after the stimulus is turned off, observers have available at least two to three times more information than they can give in a whole report. In order to determine how this available information decreases with time, the instruction signal which indicates the row of the stimulus to be reported was delayed by various amounts.

Figure 5 shows data obtained with stimuli having 12 letters each. The light flash is schematically indicated at the lower left. The span of immediate-memory for this material is indicated by the bar at the right. Note that information in excess of the memory span is stored for less than a second. Both the whole report and the partial report procedure give exactly the *same* estimate of the number of available letters (namely four to five) when the instruction to report is delayed by more than a second. Only when the instruction is given within a second of the exposure do the results obtained by the two methods differ. That is why the results of this experiment are different from those of previous ones; in this experiment, unlike earlier ones, the instruction to give a partial report was coded so that it could be given at a precisely determined time, *within* one second of the exposure.

One of us (E. A.) has recently completed a similar experiment, to be described

in detail below, in which a visual arrow rather than a tonal instruction was used to indicate the letters to be reported. The results are quite similar to those shown in Figure 5. It seems to make little difference whether a tone (which calls for three letters) or an arrow (which calls for only one letter) is used. The important thing is the use of a sample, the partial report, which consists of fewer letters than the memory span.

Once it is established that subjects can retain much stimulus information for a brief time, the question naturally arises: how do they do it? The title of this paper suggests that they do it visually, i.e. that they can utilize a visual image of the stimulus, which persists for a brief time after the exposure before it fades. Subjects say, for example, that they can still "read" the stimulus even when the instruction tone comes several hundred milliseconds after termination of the stimulus. In fact, naïve subjects sometimes think that the physical light source is a slowly fading one.

A good way to show that stimulus information can be retained as a persisting visual image is to show how the persistence depends on the kind of visual stimulation. Figure 6 indicates two possible kinds of presentations. In each case, the stimulus is exposed for 50 msec at an intensity of 31 ft.-lamberts. In the first type of presentation the pre- and post-exposure fields are dark. This presentation is thought to favor persisting after-images. In the second type

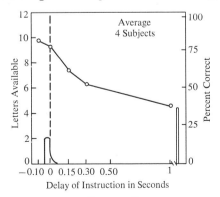

FIGURE 5

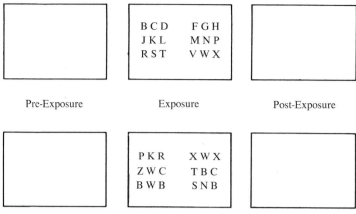

Pre-Exposure　　　　　　　　Exposure　　　　　　　　Post-Exposure

FIGURE 6

of presentation the pre- and post-exposure fields are about equal in intensity to the stimulus. An experiment using stimuli of 18 letters was performed in order to compare these two kinds of presentation. Figure 7 shows the results for one representative subject. The persistence of stimulus information is clearly different in the two kinds of presentation. When the pre- and post-exposure fields are dark, a legible image of the stimulus persists for longer than two seconds after the exposure, whereas, in the light pre- and post-exposure presentation the persistence is definitely less than one half second.

Figure 7 also shows immediate memory data (whole report) for each of the two conditions of presentation. In these immediate-memory experiments the subject was either allowed to report "immediately" or he was required to wait for 5.0 sec after the exposure before beginning to report. Subjects can delay an "immediate-memory" report for much longer than 5 sec without any loss of information, but 5 sec is the largest delay plotted in Figure 7. This kind of experiment shows that so-called "immediate-memory" is virtually a permanent memory. Note that despite the great differences in partial reports, the whole reports

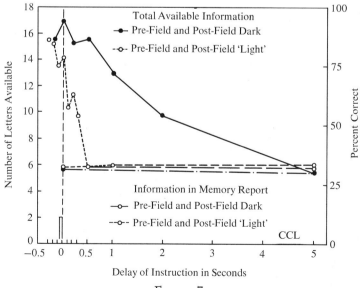

FIGURE 7

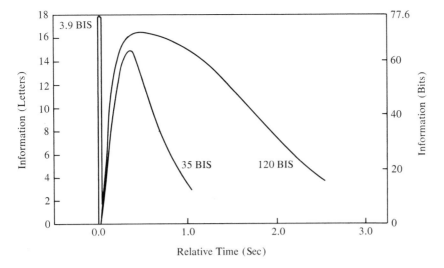

Information (Letters) [y-axis left]
Information (Bits) [y-axis right]
Relative Time (Sec) [x-axis]

FIGURE 8

are the same for the two kinds of presentation and for the two different delays.

In Figure 8 these data are abstracted. The rise and fall of visual information following a brief exposure is schematically illustrated. It is assumed the rise begins at the onset of the exposure, and that decay of information follows the curve shown in Figure 7. However, exact values are not important for the inferences that will be drawn; they obtain for any reasonable model. In fact, one such model will be presented below.

The stimulus consists of 18 letters or 77.6 bits of information, counting each letter as 4.3 bits. Since it is exposed for $\frac{1}{20}$th sec, there are $\frac{1}{20} \times 77.6$ or 3.9 bit-sec of stimulus information. (In Figure 8 the contraction "bis" is used for bit-second.)

In the presentation with dark pre- and post-exposure fields there are about 120 bit-sec. This means that, on the average, stimulus information is stored for approximately 30 times longer than it was presented. This is certainly information storage; in this case, it is "visual information storage".

Even in the presentation with light pre- and post-exposure fields, which is the traditionally "good" tachistoscopic presenta-

tion, stimulus information is, on the average, visually available for about nine times longer than it is presented.

These considerations show that in ordinary tachistoscopic presentations the time for which the stimulus is visually available may greatly exceed the exposure duration. Therefore, if the rate at which visual information can be utilized is computed on the basis of exposure duration (as it usually is), then this computed rate is likely to be wildly erroneous.

In order to find out how fast information can be utilized or "read-out" of visual storage, we use a masking method in which the persisting image is masked or "erased" by a subsequent interfering field (1). In our procedure, the stimulus exposure is followed immediately by a visual "noise" field, which consists of parts of letters spread randomly over the field. The noise field would effectively mask the stimulus even if both fields were on simultaneously; therefore, it is assumed to stop any possible persistence of the stimulus. The subject's task is to report as many letters as possible, and the exposure duration (delay of the noise field) is varied in successive blocks of trials. Although this procedure has its pitfalls, we have found the following generalization to hold over a wide range of exposure conditions. Each 10 msec increment in exposure duration enables the subject to report about one additional letter, provided that the total number of letters reported is not greater than four. The fifth and sixth letters, if they are reported, require a relatively longer exposure. This experiment shows that information can be read-out of storage rapidly in bursts of about five letters. During such a reading burst the rate can be as high as 100 letters per sec.

Part Two

In this section we will outline four experiments[1] aimed at elucidating some of the erasure properties of the visual storage and at estimating the visual storage time for a fixed and constant background brightness. The first experiment is essentially like the sampling experiment in Part I, except that a visual signal is used instead of a tone to designate part of a briefly exposed array.

1. RETENTION

A 2 × 8 array of randomly chosen letters is exposed for 50 msec. Then, after a variable delay, a black bar marker of 50 msec duration is presented either above one of the letter positions of the upper row, or below one of the letter positions of the lower row. The subject's task is to name the letter designated by the marker. Figure 9 shows a typical array and bar marker. Also shown is a black circle that is used

[1] Mr. A. S. Coriell of Bell Telephone Laboratories assisted with the experimental work of Part II.

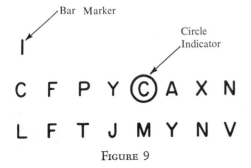

Bar Marker

Circle Indicator

C F P Y Ⓒ A X N

L F T J M Y N V

FIGURE 9

as a marker in the second experiment to be described later.

The experimental sequence is illustrated in Figure 10. A uniform field of 70 ft.-lamberts, having a dark fixation point in the centre, was maintained constantly. The black letters and marker appeared briefly against this background. The letter size and contrast were such that single letters, exposed for 50 msec in any of the 16 letter positions, were perfectly legible when the eyes were fixed on the centre. The experiment involved three sessions during each of which 128 different arrays were exposed. The markers appeared randomly in each of the 16 array positions at each of eight time intervals between array and marker. An additional session was run later in which array and marker were presented simultaneously.

Figure 11 shows the average performance of our three well-practiced subjects as a function of the time between onsets of array and marker. The vertical lines indicate the onset and offset of the array. The curve obtained is very much like that reported in Part 1 (cf. Figure 7) with similar exposure conditions (light after-field).

Although it might be assumed that this experiment yields a reasonably good description of the time decay of the short term visual storage, the curves obtained cannot be said to represent this decay, for two reasons. First, the true storage would be expected to decay to zero for long enough time intervals; these results decay to a final level of about 30 per cent indicating that the measured performance contains components of more permanent memory as well as the short term memory component we would like to measure. Second, because the process of detecting a marker and reading a letter undoubtedly takes time, the measured performance should not give a true indication of the storage decay. As will be shown, it is possible to measure and correct for these factors in arriving at an estimate of the storage time.

It is somewhat surprising that even

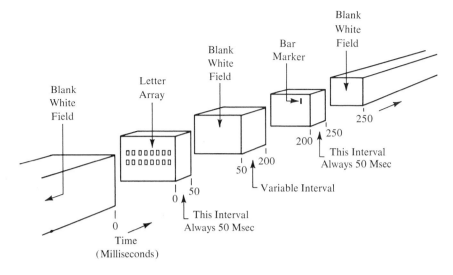

FIGURE 10   Sequence presented in a typical trial.

when marker precedes the array by over 100 msec, performance does not reach 100 per cent. The explanation seems to lie in the fact that letters, although perfectly legible by themselves, are not legible in the context of the array. This is shown in Figure 12 by a plot of performance as a function of position. The numbers 1 to 8 represent, from left to right, the positions of the upper line of the array, and 9 to 16 the positions of the lower line.

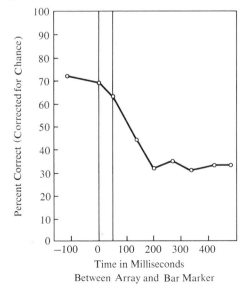

FIGURE 11   Retention.

The percentage is based on the pooled data of the three subjects taken across all time intervals. All subjects show the same distribution in which performance is better at the centre and ends and poorer in between. Performance on the upper line is consistently better than performance on the lower.

An estimate of the amount of information stored, based on performance measured, when bar marker follows immediately after array yielded the figure of 37 bits for one subject and 54 bits each for the other two.

2. ERASURE

If persistence were the only property of the visual storage, it would be difficult to understand how we see at all in our normal continually changing visual environment. A storage process ordinarily involves erasure also, to assure that old information is out of the store before new information is put in. Otherwise new information and old would be inextricably merged in the store.

The visual erasure process is nicely illustrated by an experiment that is identical in every respect to the experiment just described, except for the replacement of

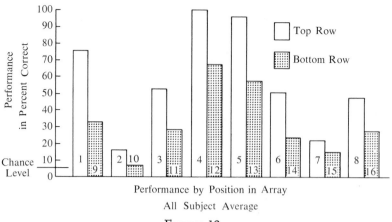

Performance by Position in Array

All Subject Average

FIGURE 12

the black bar marker by a black circle like that shown in Figure 9. The effect of such a circle on the letter it follows is very different from that of the bar. This effect, which we call erasure, is illustrated in Figure 13 where performance with bar and circle may be compared. It is seen that the curves begin together and end together, with performance in the "circle" experiment significantly poorer between.

What is the essential difference between the circle and bar that results in such a great difference in performance? It is primarily a matter of distance. If the bars were placed close to the letters, parts

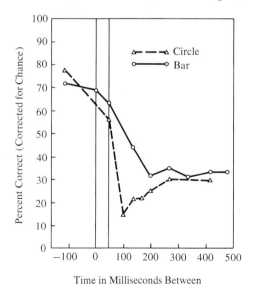

Time in Milliseconds Between

Array and Marker

FIGURE 13   Erasure (first example).

of the letters near the bar would be rendered illegible. In the retention experiment, the bar was carefully set far enough away to avoid this unwanted effect.

We are inclined to consider the effect of the circle on a preceding letter—space does not allow elaboration—as a quick substitution of the circle for the stored letter. The shape of the erasure curve may then be interpreted as follows:

(1) High performance when circle follows immediately after array is due to simple temporal averaging. This results in letter and circle being effectively superimposed which should not affect letter legibility.

(2) Lower performance at slightly longer delays can be attributed to the change from the superposition (averaging) condition to the erasure condition.

(3) The slow rise from the minimum with further increases in delay of the circle is attributable to the increased time available to read the letter before it is erased.

(4) At the longest delays the circle arrives after the storage has decayed. Therefore it no longer erases, but acts only as a marker. Performance at these times simply measures the number of letters in the more permanent memory.

The suggestion that two closely-

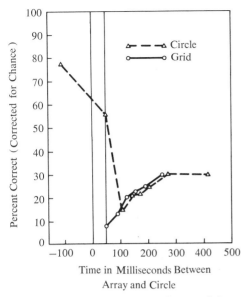

FIGURE 14   Erasure (second example).

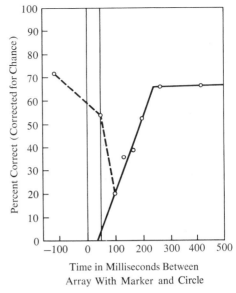

FIGURE 15   Read-out.

timed stimuli are perceived as super-posed was verified by repeating the erasing experiment using a circle filled with grid lines. As shown in Figure 14, such an "eraser" is more disturbing than an unfilled circle for times when superposition might hold (<100 msec), but not more disturbing with longer time separations.

We should mention that prelimin-ary work has been done in which eight letters are exposed to one eye and an unfilled circle is delivered to the other. Erasure clearly occurs under these conditions, but we have not de-termined how binocular erasure com-pares with monocular.

3. READ-OUT

As we have already pointed out in dis-cussing the bar-marker experiment, the process of detecting the presence of a marker and reading the marked letter un-doubtedly takes some time. If the time required for this process can be measured, we shall have a more accurate idea of the time duration of the storage. A method for measuring this time is available provided that our conclusions about the action of the circle in erasing are correct. Suppose

we present simultaneously an array and a bar marker pointing to one letter in the array, and then a short time afterwards present a circle around the marked letter. If the circle indeed removes the marked letter from the subject's storage, his per-formance under these conditions will measure how well he can detect the marker and read the letter given only the time interval between the onset of the array and marker, and the onset of the circle. The results of such an experiment are shown in Figure 15. It is seen that when circle follows by more than 100 msec, per-formance rises rapidly as a function of the time allowed for detecting the marker and reading the designated letter. This task clearly takes a significant amount of time, as much as 250 msec before maximum performance is attained. Performance when circle follows by less than 100 msec is very much like that obtained in the erasure ex-periment using circle without marker.

4. STORAGE TIME

In discussing the bar-marker experiment we offered two reasons why it would not be correct to interpret the bar-marker per-formance curve as representing the short term storage decay: (a) the measured decay contains components of permanent memory, and (b) the curve does not take into account the detection and read-out time that we have just measured. In this section we shall return to our analysis of the bar-marker experiment and attempt, by correcting for these two factors, to arrive at an estimate of the effective visual storage time.

Performance in the bar-marker experiment is undoubtedly the result of two different kinds of performance on the part of the subject as shown by the fact that the decay curve does not fall to zero. First, there is a non-selective read-out which occurs when the array is exposed but *before* the marker is perceived; second, a selective process which occurs *after* the marker is perceived when the subject has been cued to direct his attention to the single required letter. Although we did not point it out earlier, we have already measured this "before-marker" component, for in the erasure experiment (Figure 13), the circle plays the peculiar role of both "marker" and "eraser"; it erases the letter it marks. Performance in that experiment must represent only what has been read into the permanent memory *before* appearance of the marker (circle) because read-out from the short term memory is impossible after appearance of the marker.

The "after-marker" component can be derived by subtracting out the "before-marker" component from the whole (bar-marker curve). This derivation is illustrated in Figure 16. In Figure 16a the bar-marker curve is shown together with the erasing curve which has been extrapolated to zero. Figure 16b shows the curve derived by subtracting one from the other. The subtraction used is not a simple algebraic one. If, by chance, the subject reads the correct letter before appearance of the marker, designation by the marker cannot improve performance. Therefore it seemed more reasonable to solve for P_A (the after-marker component) from the equation $P_T = P_B + (1 - P_B)P_A$ where

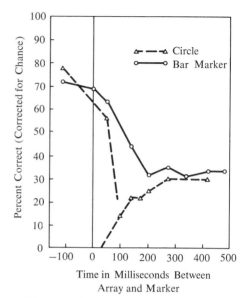

FIGURE 16a   Retention and erasure.

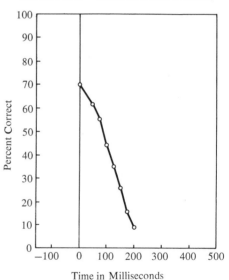

FIGURE 16b   Derived "after-marker" performance.

P_B is the before-marker performance component and P_T is the total, the performance measured in the bar-marker experiment.

If it be assumed that the derived decay curve in Figure 16 represents the "after-marker" component of performance, and that this component of performance is limited by the time available to detect the marker and read the letter before decay of

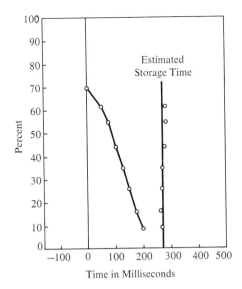

FIGURE 17   Storage time.

the storage, the storage time can be obtained by adding the experimentally determined read-out times for each level of performance (Figure 15) to the times corresponding to the same level of performance in Figure 16. The result of this operation is shown in Figure 17. The points shown on the right, each of which is an independent estimate of the storage time, approximate a vertical line surprisingly well. The estimated storage time is 270 msec.

Summary and Conclusions

The work described in this paper shows that the visual process involves a buffer storage of relatively high capacity that can take in information virtually instantaneously and retain it to permit its relatively slow utilization. By making use of sampling techniques and the erasure characteristics of the storage, the following properties were demonstrated:

(1) The capacity of the storage is high compared to the 20–25 bits obtained in span of immediate memory. The experiments showed that 70 bits could be stored, but this is still only a lower bound on the capacity since different arrangements might well have produced higher figures.

(2) The decay time depends upon pre- and post-exposure conditions as well as on the exposure itself. The measured decays varied from ¼ sec to several seconds.

(3) The spatial resolution of the storage is disturbed when too many letters are put in. A 2×8 array is enough to demonstrate this effect.

(4) The storage is erasable; new information erases previously stored information.

(5) The storage may be read out rapidly up to about five items, the initial rate during such a reading burst being of the order of 100 items per sec.

Discussion

N. M. BLACHMAN: What is the effect of eye movement in between presentation of the letters and presentation of the marker?

J. O. ACKROYD: In everyday life we can remember numbers of 5, 6 or 7 digits which have been seen or heard quite briefly, for example telephone numbers or sums of money. Can this be reconciled with the authors' finding that the number of symbols memorized is asymptotic to approximately 4.5? In their experiments they employed a larger alphabet; perhaps also the motivation was less than in real life situations.

E. AVERBACH in reply to Dr. Blachman: Although we did not study their effect systematically, we know from casual observation that eye movements between presentation of the letters and presentation of the marker can have a very disturbing influence on observer performance in this kind of experiment. The effect of such movements, from the observer's point of view, is to displace the marker relative to the letters. In fact, if the movement is just right, it appears to the observer that the marker is pointing to a different letter from the one designated by the experiment. We eliminated these eye movements from our experiments by having the observer fix his eyes just before each exposure on a fixation point in the centre of the screen. It is well established that trained observers can maintain fairly accurate fixation for a great deal longer than the half-second fixation required in these experiments.

G. SPERLING in reply to Dr. Ackroyd: I should first like to point out that the finding that only 4 or 5 letters can be reported after a brief exposure dates back to the last century (2, 4). My contribution has been, I think, to show that these few letters can be arbitrarily selected from a considerably larger number of letters which are available momentarily during and shortly after the exposure. The reason that, in everyday situations, the number of items remembered seems to be larger than four is that everyday situations usually do not represent brief exposures. For example, Deininger (3) found that in order to remember a seven digit telephone number correctly, most people actually require two glances, in each of which they learn three or four digits. In the text, I pointed out that while four items can be read and remembered in a fraction of a second, the learning of additional items requires substantially more time and effort. In contrast to the extremely rapid learning of the first few items, the slow learning of additional items probably depends on complicated coding and/or association processes. These mnemonic processes are undoubtedly markedly influenced by motivation, as is all difficult learning. However, the 4·5 item limit (individual differences ranged from four to six items) seems to be quite independent of motivation.

References

1. BAXT, N. "Ueber d. Zeit welche nötig ist, damit ein Gesichtseindruck zum Bewusstsein kommt," *Pflug. Arch. ges. Physiol.*, 4 (1871), 325–336.
2. CATTELL, J. McK. "Ueber die Zeit der Erkennung und Benennung von Schriftzeichen, Bildern und Farben 1885," *Philos. Stud.*, 2, 635–650.
3. DEININGER, R. L. "Human Factors Engineering Studies of the Design and Use of Pushbutton Telephone Sets", *Bell System Tech. J.*, 1960, 39, 995–1012.
4. ERDMANN, B. and R. DODGE. *Psychologische Untersuchung ueber das Lesen*, Halle, M. Niemeyer, 1898.
5. SPERLING, G. "The Information Available in Brief Visual Presentations." *Psychol. Monogr.* 74, No. 11, Whole No. 498 (1960).

Temporal Factors in Perception and Short-Term Memory*

DORIS AARONSON
Harvard University

The temporal course of perception may be an important determinant of errors that occur in immediate recall tasks. The studies reviewed suggest that the following factors play an important role in perception and short-term memory: (a) The rate at which stimuli are presented, (b) the duration of the stimuli, (c) pre- and poststimulus events. Further, the S's strategies may in part determine (a) the time elapsing before the various perceptual processes are performed on an item or (b) the order in which items are processed.

In most short-term memory experiments, the extent to which errors arise during perception, rather than during subsequent retention or retrieval of the information, cannot be determined directly. Indeed it is usually implicitly assumed that perception of the items presents no problem in sequential recall tasks. At first glance this appears to be a reasonable assumption; there is generally little difficulty in perceiving the individual items in the sequence of stimuli (Aaronson and Sternberg, 1964). However, the requirement to remember the items may induce perceptual difficulties. The requirement to recall may increase the time needed for perception (Aaronson, 1965).

* *Psychological Bulletin*, 1967, vol. 73, pp. 130–144. Preparation of this paper was supported in part by United States Public Health Service predoctoral fellowship MH–14,589 from the National Institutes of Health to the University of Pennsylvania and by United States Public Health Service postdoctoral fellowship MH–14,589 and grant MH–05,120–05 from the National Institutes of Health to Harvard University, Center for Cognitive Studies. The author wishes to thank Saul Sternberg and Charles Harris who read various drafts of this paper.

The processes performed during a short-term memory task might be classified into three categories: perception, retention, and retrieval. For the purpose of this review, all processes up to and including identification or encoding of a stimulus item, based on a meaning or name, are classified as perceptual processes, and all subsequent processes are classified as mnemonic.

Several investigators have recently proposed that in immediate recall tasks, perception occurs in two stages. For example, some of the recent studies of Pollack (1959), Mackworth (1959), Sperling (1960, 1963), Sternberg (1964), and Broadbent (1957a, 1957b, 1958) provide evidence for two such stages. According to their research, Stage 1 can be characterized as having the following properties: (a) Perceptual processing during the first stage is not at a high level; the stimulus representations are "unidentified sensations" or "direct representations" of the physical stimulus attributes. (b) These representations, or traces, are relatively unstable; with the passage of time or the occurrence of intervening events they may easily become degraded. (c) During Stage 1, representations are held in a relatively large-capacity perceptual storage system. This buffer or "perceptual" storage can receive items in parallel, that is, two or more items can enter the system simultaneously.

Stage 2 differs from Stage 1 in several respects: (a) Processing at this stage is at a higher level than at Stage 1. Items are identified or encoded on the basis of a meaning or a name of some sort. (b) Representations are more permanent after Stage 2 than during Stage 1. Their *rate* of decay has decreased, even though some of the initial information was sacrificed in the abstraction of properties that occurred in identification. (c) At Stage 2, representations are handled by a limited-capacity system. This system can receive items only in series, that is, only one item at a time can enter the system, additional items being delayed until the "single-channel" is free.

Some of the evidence for a relatively large-capacity, rapid-decay buffer storage and for a limited-capacity, slow-decay storage system comes from Sperling (1960, 1963). Either before or at various intervals after a tachistoscopic presentation, subjects were cued to recall a randomly determined part of a visual display. Recall accuracy indicated that about 9 of the 12 stimulus letters were available when the earliest cues occurred. As the cue was delayed, this number decreased rapidly to about 4.5 letters in .3 second. Little difference in accuracy occurred between partial recall cued .3 second after the display, and total recall cued several seconds later. Sperling reported that "in fact, he [the subject] can delay his report for an additional 30 seconds or more without any loss of accuracy." Sperling hypothesized that the visual stimuli initially go to a rapid-decay "visual information store," but that items lasting for about .3 second are encoded for an "auditory information store" whose contents decay more slowly. As evi-

dence for an auditory representation of the visual stimulus, both Sperling (1962) and Conrad (1962, 1963, 1964) have shown that errors in the written recall of visually presented items are often attributable to acoustic confusions: The errors are letters that sound rather than look similar to the correct items. Mackworth (1959) also suggested that the stimulus representation undergoes two stages of processing. Using a running memory span task, she obtained evidence for a "direct perceptual trace" taking about .25 second to form, and a more durable "verbal trace" taking up to 1 second to become established.

The perceptual systems proposed by Broadbent and Pollack for auditory inputs are similar in structure to those suggested by Sperling and Mackworth for visual inputs. On the basis of evidence from tasks involving immediate recall of dichotic stimuli, Broadbent (1957a, 1957b, 1958) argued that auditory information goes first to a large-capacity, rapid-decay parallel processor, the S system (sensory storage system), and then to a P system (perceptual system) that handles items one at a time. Broadbent questioned whether all stimulus representations must be processed by the S system prior to the P system. He suggested that in some situations, the S system may function only as an overflow storage unit to handle items when processing in the P system is delayed because (a) several items have arrived simultaneously or (b) items have arrived at a rate exceeding the P system processing rate.

The studies considered in this review provide evidence that stimulus factors, and strategies developed by the subject, affect the temporal course of perceptual processing at an initial sensing or detection stage and at a subsequent identification or encoding stage. These studies suggest that in short-term memory tasks, the temporal course of perceptual processing can have an important influence on errors occurring in the subsequent recall of the items. The following sections are concerned with variables that influence the temporal course of perception in short-term memory tasks.

Rate at which Stimuli are Presented

Presentation rate may be important in short-term memory experiments for at least two reasons. First, reducing the rate may allow more time for decay, and therefore result in lower recall accuracy. Second, reducing the rate may allow more time for perception, and therefore result in higher accuracy. Empirical results provide evidence for both of these possibilities. To date there has been little success in determining the critical factors responsible for the conflicting rate effects in short-term memory.

Experiments showing greater accuracy at slower rates were performed by Pollack, Johnson, and Knaff (1959) and by Pollack and Johnson (1963), using running memory span paradigms with rates ranging from .125 to 4 items per second. In another study, Pollack (1952) found that both the percentage of items recalled correctly and the amount of information transmitted increased as the presentation rate of auditory sequences of digits and letters was decreased from 4 to .25 items per second. Pollack suggested that subjects performed better at the slow rates because they could use the extra time for encoding and organizing the stimulus information. Limiting the amount of time available between the items by increasing the rate would restrict the range of encoding strategies that the subjects could employ, perhaps preventing them from using an optimal strategy. As evidence consistent with this hypothesis, Pollack showed that the variability in performance among subjects decreased as rate increased.

In addition to Pollack and his colleagues, other experimenters finding better performance at slow rather than fast rates in short-term memory tasks were the following: Yntema, Wozencraft, and Klem (1964), using sequential auditory presentations; Mackworth (1962c), studying recall of sequentially presented visual digits; Melton, Sameroff, and Schubot (1963), studying recognition of visually presented three-digit numbers; Murdock (1960), studying free recall of visually presented words; Norman (1966), studying recognition and recall of auditory and visual sequences; and Aaronson (1966b, 1966c), studying the recall of auditory sequences. Other studies showing similar results were reviewed by Blankenship (1938) and by Posner (1963).

On the other hand, accuracy increased as rate was increased in at least three short-term memory studies. For eight-digit auditory sequences, Fraser (1958) found higher recall accuracy for a 120-per-minute than for a 40-per-minute presentation rate with both old and young subjects. Conrad and Hille (1958) presented auditory sequences at 30 or 90 digits per minute. In accord with their memory-trace-decay hypothesis, more errors were found with slower rates of presentation. In addition to varying the presentation rate, Conrad and Hille paced their subjects' recall at 30 or 90 digits per minute. Variations in presentation rate and in recall rate would consequently produce variations in the retention intervals for the items. Regardless of recall rate, the normalized serial curves of recall errors were more negatively skewed for fast than for slow presentation rates. But, recall rate had no effect on the shape of the serial curve for either presentation rate.[1] That is, the *shape* of their curves was determined by the presentation rate, and therefore by the time available for perception, and *not* by the recall rate or by the retention interval between presentation and recall.

---

[1] The author wishes to thank R. Conrad for making these data available to her.

Posner (1964) attempted to account for the conflicting results on presentation rate in terms of the constraints on the order of recall. "Increasing the rate of presentation will only show improved recall because of decreased time in storage in tasks which tend to reduce the use of recall strategies." To test this hypothesis, he presented eight-digit auditory sequences at either 30 or 96 digits per minute. The subjects were instructed to recall first either serial positions 1–4 or 5–8. Posner found higher accuracy for the fast than for the slow rate for ordered recall, in agreement with Conrad and Hille's data. But no rate effect was found when subjects recalled the last half of the series first. Posner stated: "These data resolve previous conflicting results and tend to support a decay factor in immediate memory. With presentation at the slow rate, rehearsal during the first 4 items preserves them during the subsequent presentation and recall of the last four."

Posner's experiment, however, did not resolve all of the problems regarding rate. First, for his slow rate, accuracy was higher for positions 1–4 with reversed recall than for positions 5–8 with ordered recall. According to his rehearsal-decay hypothesis, it is difficult to understand why the digits that must endure a greater time interval and greater interference from rehearsal were recalled best. Second, Posner's hypothesis does not completely account for the effects of rate on recall accuracy, as demonstrated in the following studies. Mackworth's (1962c) study used ordered and unordered recall, and found accuracy for the slow presentation rates to be superior in both conditions. Also, Pollack et al. (1959) allowed subjects to recall in any order in their running memory span study, whereas Pollack and Johnson's (1963) running memory paradigm required subjects to recall the items in order; and accuracy was best for the slow rates in both experiments. These experimenters did not present data on the order of recall

actually used by the subject in the free recall conditions. However, it has been found that subjects generally recall the last part of the list first, the first part next, and the middle items last in a free recall situation (Deese and Kaufman, 1957).

A comparison of short-term memory experiments in which presentation rate was varied shows that the conflicting results cannot be attributed solely to any one of the following variables: recall order, stimulus modality (auditory or visual), methods of responding (Posner used both spoken and written and found no difference), range of presentation rates used (the range used by Conrad was a subset of that used by Pollack), type of material, or method of testing (recall or recognition).

It is possible that variations in perceptual factors can in part account for the conflicting results regarding presentation rate. For example, in most previous short-term memory experiments, stimulus duration, stimulus intensity, stimulus intelligibility, and other factors that may affect perception were not carefully controlled or measured. As Pollack and Rubenstein's (1963) data suggest, decreasing the intelligibility, and thereby increasing the time needed to perceive the stimuli, may have some effects similar to those of increasing the rate. Indeed, other stimulus factors may interact with rate in affecting recall accuracy. For example, Aaronson and Sternberg (1964) found greater recall accuracy for slow than for fast rates at high signal-to-noise ratios and the reverse at low ratios. Their results suggest that stimulus intelligibility is important in determining the effects of rate on recall.

One way in which presentation rate has been varied is by compressing the speech: that is, by uniformly deleting small sections of .01 to .1 second from tape recordings of natural speech and compressing the remainder (Fairbanks, Guttman and Miron, 1957a, 1957b, 1957c; Fairbanks and Kodman, 1957; Garvey, 1953a, 1953b; Klumpp and Webster, 1961). Immediately after subjects heard messages of natural speech or of speech compressed by 50% (i.e., double the original rate), Fairbanks et al. (1957b) questioned them on the factual content of the messages. Accuracy was lower for the compressed than for the original messages. Fairbanks et al. hypothesized that the decreased accuracy was not due to a decrease in intelligibility of the *single* stimulus words, but that subjects had difficulties with "comprehension" rather than with the intelligibility of single items. Supporting evidence for this hypothesis has been given by other studies using "intelligibility" or "articulation" paradigms in which the subject hears one word at a time and identified what he has heard. In these studies, single words were compressed to as much as 50% to 20% of their original duration without intelligibility scores dropping below 95% (Fairbanks et al., 1957c; Garvey, 1953a, 1953b). Over wide ranges of speech compression, the critical factor affecting comprehension and subsequent recall may be the decrease in rate or in the silent intervals between words, rather than the decrease in the word durations themselves. If subjects use the intervals between words to identify or encode items for memory, then one might expect that comprehension of sequences (or sentences) could decrease while the intelligibility of single items remained constant.

In summary, the effects of rate on immediate recall have not been entirely accounted for. Most short-term memory experiments in which rate was varied showed that faster rates, which reduce the time available for perception, produce lower accuracy. However, a few experiments show that slower rates, which allow more time for trace decay, result in lower accuracy. Further experiments are needed to determine more precisely the critical factors which cause rate to have each of these effects.

Duration of the Stimuli

The presentation rate in short-term memory experiments can be increased either by decreasing the duration of the stimulus items themselves or by decreasing the time intervals between stimuli. In many studies, the experimental designs have not varied these factors separately in a systematic way. For example, when rate was increased by speech compression, temporal segments were usually deleted in a uniform pattern from the stimulus material, from both the words and the intervals between words. In the studies using visual presentations, there was frequently no blank interval between stimuli, and rate was decreased by decreasing the stimulus exposure time. (Indeed, the confounding of duration and presentation rate may in part account for the conflicting data on presentation rate.)

Variations in the stimulus duration and in the intervals between stimuli may have different effects on the perceptual processes in short-term memory tasks. For example, the stimulus duration might determine the amount of stimulus information that goes into a "buffer" storage, while the duration of the interstimulus interval might affect the time available to identify or encode the representations. In order to obtain maximum recall accuracy for any given presentation rate, there may be an optimal ratio of stimulus duration to interstimulus interval.

Bergstrom (1907) reported studies by Herrington in which the use of a memory drum permitted independent variation of the exposure duration and the interstimulus interval for visual stimuli. In the first experiment, the total time from the beginning of one stimulus to the beginning of the next was held constant at 768 milliseconds, but exposure durations were varied from 41 to 318 milliseconds. Recall accuracy was unaffected by duration. Bergstrom concluded,

> the apprehension of a syllable is so nearly purely a performed apperceptive process that the longer duration of the visual image seems to affect the result but little. In fact, the process appears to have a period of its own so that the duration of the objective stimulus beyond a certain point is felt to be disagreeable [p. 224].

However, in Herrington's second experiment, when the stimulus exposure time was held constant, recall accuracy improved as the interstimulus interval was increased, allowing more time for encoding.

Sperling (1960, 1963) reported studies in which the duration of simultaneous visual displays was varied. When the availability of the internal representation for subsequent perceptual processing was not controlled, the physical stimulus duration had little effect on recall accuracy. (His experiments are considered in greater detail in the next section.) Sperling (1960, 1963), Averbach and Coriell (1960), and Mackworth (1962a, 1962b, 1962c, 1962d, 1963) presented evidence that a visual image can be formed and maintained in a buffer storage system. Even after the physical stimulus is terminated, the items in buffer storage can be scanned and identified.

There is little published work with auditory stimuli on the effect of stimulus duration per se. As is the case for visual presentations, experimenters have generally confounded rate and duration in their experimental designs. For example, when presentation rate is increased by a natural speaker speeding up his own vocalizations, the durations of both the words and the intervals between them are decreased (Hutton, 1954). Yntema, Wozencraft, and Klem (1964) and Aaronson and Sternberg (1964) examined rate effects on recall when the stimulus duration was held constant. Rate was varied by using electronic timing equipment to vary only the silent intervals between items; therefore, their results show that the decreased accuracy, when rate is increased, cannot be attributed simply to a decrease in stimulus duration.

Two unpublished studies varied auditory stimulus duration while holding presentation rate constant. Therefore, when speech duration was increased, the duration of the silent intervals between stimuli was correspondingly decreased. The first study dealt with the perception of compressed speech. Hutton (1954) had a natural speaker read a message at each of eight rates, and he then produced five degrees of compression of each of the eight readings. Although Hutton did not systematically vary speech duration while keeping rate fixed, the compression ratios he used permit one to find six triples of presentations such that all members of the triple had identical presentation rates but the ratio of speech time to total message time varied within a triple. Hutton had subjects rank their preference for and the effectiveness of the various messages. The data showed that for a fixed presentation rate, preference and effectiveness were lower for longer stimulus durations. For a fixed speech rate, subjects preferred a longer silent interval between words, at the cost of reducing the stimulus length. The subject may use the silent interval between words for identification or encoding.

Aaronson (1966a) conducted a study in which auditory stimulus duration was varied for a fixed presentation rate. Spoken digits having an initial mean duration of 225 milliseconds were compressed by about 35%. Using electronic timing equipment, seven-digit sequences were recorded at a 3-digits-per-second rate with both the original and the compressed stimuli. Subjects memorized each sequence and tried to recall it a few seconds after the presentation ended. Recall accuracy was *higher* for the shorter stimulus duration. For a fixed presentation rate, subjects produced fewer errors when the ratio of speech to silent time was decreased. The silent time, during which the stimulus presentation may undergo perceptual processing, is important for accurate recall. Within limits, the stimulus duration can be reduced without an increase in recall errors.

In summary, experiments using either visual or auditory stimuli provide evidence that the amount of time between stimuli, during which the stimulus representation is available to the subject for perceptual processing, may be a more important factor than physical stimulus duration in determining recall accuracy.

Pre- and Poststimulus Events that Restrict Perception Time

POSTSTIMULUS EVENTS: TERMINATION OF PERCEPTUAL PROCESSES

For both visual and auditory presentations, techniques that restrict the subject's perception time have been developed. Sperling (1963) hypothesized that postexposure fields of "visual noise" (made of jumbled pieces of letters) "erased" the initial visual stimulus information from buffer storage. When he increased the effective exposure duration of tachistoscopic stimuli by increasing the delay of onset of the postexposure noise field, recall accuracy improved. The improvement was rapid as delays increased from 10 to 100 milliseconds, but only a slight additional gain was obtained when the delay was increased to 200 milliseconds. Averbach and Coriell (1960) obtained similar results with a slightly different technique. However, Eriksen and Steffy (1964) and Eriksen and Hoffman (1963) have questioned whether the noise field "erases" information from a "buffer storage."

Mackworth (1962a, 1962b, 1962c, 1963) found that recall accuracy increased with stimulus duration for both simultaneous and sequential presentations. Her experiments were such that the perceptual processing time could have been restricted

in two ways. First, each stimulus presentation was followed by a blank bright area of motion picture screen—a homogeneous bright field functions as an "erasing stimulus" according to Sperling (1960, 1963) and Averbach and Sperling (1961). Second, having to perceive the next item in a sequence may terminate perception of the previous item if the subject cannot process two items simultaneously. Mackworth's data, as well as Sperling's, indicated that performance improves rapidly at first and then levels off as the effective time available for perception increases. Once an item has been identified or encoded, the additional time (which may be used for rehearsal), does not significantly improve recall accuracy.

When auditory presentations are used, poststimulus events may restrict perception time. For example, Conrad (1958) found lower accuracy when subjects preceded their immediate recall of eight-digit sequences by a vocalized "naught" than when this additional response was not required of the subject. Conrad concluded that the interpolated "naught" decreased accuracy because it interfered with immediate postpresentation rehearsal.[2] A vocal response immediately after the presentation and before recall may interfere with perceptual processes occurring after the stimulus presentation is terminated.

Brown (1955) conducted two experiments that provide additional support for Conrad's hypothesis. He varied the delay between presentation of the last stimulus item and the interpolated event, keeping the total interval between presentation and recall constant. He found significantly higher recall accuracy for greater delays,

[2] The hypothesis that subjects treat the prefix as an extra digit was rejected by Conrad because the shapes of the serial curves of accuracy were the same with or without the prefix. He rejected the hypothesis that the prefix causes a long delay during which decay occurs. The delay was much shorter when subjects recalled with a key-set than with a dial, yet there was little difference in recall accuracy between the two response conditions.

and also that the effect of delay on accuracy was nonlinear. Interpolated events occurring within about 1 second after the presentation caused large decrements in recall accuracy, but decrements decreased and leveled off with further increases in the interpolated delay. Interpolated events occurring immediately after the presentation may interfere with the perception of the stimuli, while later interpolated events would interfere only with rehearsal.

Conrad (1960) also varied delay of the interpolated event. In his experiment, the interpolation impaired recall and the effects of delay were in the same direction as those found by Brown. However, the differences in accuracy as a function of delay were not significant. Aaronson and Sternberg's (1963) study suggested that the interpolated delay was less effective, partly because the subject's response delay was not controlled. Subjects were cued to say a predetermined letter 1/6, 3/6, or 5/6 second after a tape-recorded sequence. Recall accuracy for the sequence differed little with *cue delays*. However, an examination of the *response delays* showed that subjects delayed their interpolated response longer with early than with late stimulus cues. The critical factor determining the effect of interpolation on recall appeared to be the response delay (which was not controlled or measured by Conrad), rather than the stimulus delay. Recall accuracy was lower when subjects responded within 300 milliseconds of the cue than when response times were between 300 and 400 milliseconds, as would be predicted by hypotheses of post-presentation encoding, or rehearsal of the items (as suggested by Conrad).

In summary, experimental evidence indicates that perceptual processes continue to occur after the physical stimulus presentation—either auditory or visual—is terminated. Interference with or termination of these post-presentation perceptual processes can lead to decreased recall accuracy in short-term memory tasks.

Prestimulus Events: Delay of Initiation of Perceptual Processes

Several experiments suggest that events preceding the stimulus presentation can restrict perception time: the initiation of perceptual processes can be delayed. For example, if two stimuli occur in close succession, perception of the second may be delayed until the first is perceived.

In studies of the "psychological refractory period," when subjects responded to two successive stimuli, the response to the second stimulus was delayed when the stimuli occurred in close temporal proximity (Davis, 1957, 1959). Some explanations for this observation are based on response mechanisms (Broadbent, 1958; Welford, 1952). However, experimental results suggest that the longer response time may be due partly to a delayed perception of the second stimulus. Davis (1959) found that even when no response was required to the first stimulus, its mere presentation (and presumably its perception) was sufficient to delay the second response. The response latency for the second stimulus decreased when the interstimulus interval was increased.

Physiological evidence supports the present perceptual hypothesis. Electrical stimuli applied to the cochlea of dogs resulted in an absolute refractory period of 20 to 100 milliseconds in the auditory cortex, the auditory radiations, and the medial geniculate bodies; followed by gradual recovery during 100 to 250 milliseconds (Tunturi, 1946). Although the cortical response latency to a single cochlear stimulation was 7 to 10 milliseconds, when a prior stimulation occurred at the same location the neural response latency was greatly increased. These delays are closer in order of magnitude to delays found in "psychological refractory period" experiments than to refractory periods of .5 to 2 milliseconds usually found for conduction in single nerve fibers. The psychological refractory period studies suggest that perceptual difficulties should arise when stimuli are presented at rapid rates for perception and immediate recall.

Broadbent (1957a, 1958), as well as Davis (1959), has hypothesized that the psychological refractory period is a result of delays in the perceptual processing of stimuli. If stimulus information arrives while the single-channel central processor is already occupied, the new arrivals are delayed in a preperceptual store until the processor is free. The results of Broadbent's (1956, 1957b) and Moray's (1960) memory experiments in which presentation rate and number of stimulus "input channels" were of interest, are consistent with this theory.

In an immediate memory task with visual stimuli, Sperling (1963) showed that perceptual processes could be delayed when a prestimulus exposure field consisted of "visual noise" rather than the usual dark field. The data provided evidence that with the noise field, initiation of scanning from the visual image was delayed by an additional 20 milliseconds, although the rate of scanning remained constant for the two prestimulus conditions.

The experiments considered in this section indicate that a critical factor affecting perceptual processes is the time available for these processes to occur, rather than the duration of the physical stimulus presentation itself. In short-term memory experiments with sequential presentations, the perception time for any individual item may be restricted by the preceding and succeeding items of the series.

Perception of Temporal Order

When a short list is memorized and recalled a few seconds later, we recall the items in the order of presentation more often than in other orders. If a different recall order were required, more errors would result. For example, recall accuracy is often lower when subjects must recall the last half of a list first, rather than vice versa (Kay and Poulton, 1951). However, Conrad (1959) showed that our ability to recall items in order is often poor. In his experiment, at least 50% of the recall errors for eight-digit auditory sequences were "order errors." Is there any evidence that these order errors in recall are a consequence of an incorrect order of perceiving the items? This section reviews experimental results suggesting that we may indeed perceive the items to occur in an order different from their presentation.

In 1822, Bessel pointed out that we are poor at discriminating whether an auditory or a visual stimulus occurred first, when the stimuli occurred in close succession (Boring, 1950). Since that date, many experiments, often classified as experiments on "prior entry," have further demonstrated that our ability to discriminate temporal order is poor when the events occur in close succession. As an explanation, many researchers have suggested that inaccurate temporal discrimination arises because "psychological time" is quantal and we are unable to attend to more than a single event within a quantal unit of time. Titchener's (1908) law of prior entry states that "the stimulus for which we are predisposed requires less time than a like stimulus, for which we are unprepared, to produce its full conscious effect." William James (1890) wrote "there is thus a certain difficulty in perceiving the exact date of two impressions when they do not interest our attention equally." He cited anecdotes of a surgeon seeing blood flow before he saw the instrument penetrate the patient's skin, and of a smith seeing sparks fly before he saw the hammer hit the iron.

Stone's (1926) subjects, who were instructed to attend to one of two stimulus modalities (auditory or tactile), often reported that the stimulus to which they attended was presented first when, in fact, the two were presented simultaneously or in the reverse order. The experiments on prior entry lead one to suspect that order errors in sequential memory tasks can be attributed partly to perceptual processes rather than to forgetting.

Psychologists studying prior entry were concerned with the effects of specific instructions about attention on judgments of successiveness. However, recent psychophysical studies of the discrimination of successiveness suggest that even without specific biasing instructions, our ability to judge temporal order is influenced by attention processes. For example, Needham (1934, 1936), and Hirsh and Sherrick (1961) conducted experiments showing that even within the same sensory modality, perception of temporal order is imperfect.

Schmidt and Kristofferson (1963) developed a quantal theory for the discrimination of successiveness of two events. According to their theory, imperfect discrimination of temporal order is a consequence of "psychological time" being quantal. They argued that we can switch our attention only at the end of a "moment" and cannot discriminate the order of events occurring within a moment. Their experimental data for judging successiveness between a light and a sound were consistent with the predictions of their model, although these data are not sufficient to disconfirm continuous models of attention. Stroud (1955) also proposed a quantal model of "psychological time," and presented data from which he estimated the duration of a "moment" to be about 100 milliseconds. Hirsh (1959), using a multiple-look procedure, varied the onset time between two auditory events (tones, clicks, or noises) and asked subjects to report which was initiated first. The 95% point on the psychophysical function corresponded to a separation of about 60 milliseconds between stimulus onsets.

Psychologists concerned with prior entry would discuss the above experiments in terms of attention and perception hypotheses. However, one might question whether the order errors resulted from misperceiving the stimulus order rather than from forgetting the order by the time of the response. The following evidence suggests that the order errors were a consequence of perceptual rather than mnemonic factors: (a) The errors occur only when the time between stimuli is short. With longer durations between stimuli, the frequency of order errors approaches zero: There is no difficulty in remembering the order of two events when they do not occur in close temporal proximity. (b) Theories of forgetting would predict that order errors should increase with the time between presentation and response. Needham's (1936) data suggest that this is not the case. Needham (1936) used conditions in which the time between the stimulus events being judged and the end of the trial (and therefore the time of the response) was varied over 12 values (a range of about 3 seconds). Accuracy did not decrease with the time between events to be judged and end of trial, as would be predicted according to theories of forgetting. (c) Finally, in Ladefoged and Broadbent's (1960) study, subjects judged the location of a click or an "s" in relation to an auditory sequence of words. One group of subjects listened to each recorded sequence and wrote down the word at which the click or s occurred. A second group had been familiarized with the sequences, had read them aloud before the stimulus recording was played, and had a written copy of the sequences before them during the experimental task. The memory demands were greater for the first group of subjects: They had to remember the words as well as the temporal order between the words and the click or s. A mnemonic theory would predict that greater memory demands should lead to a greater frequency or order errors. However, the difference between groups in judgment of temporal order was not statistically significant (even though both groups were highly inaccurate in their judgments). This result provides evidence that the errors in judgment of temporal order were in large part perceptual.

The studies on prior entry and discrimination of succession indeed show that our ability to perceive the order of two events is imperfect. But the data indicate that we are rather good at this task when the separation between two events becomes as large as 100 milliseconds, a duration less than the separation between stimulus items in most short-term memory tasks. However, the studies of Needham (1934) and of Ladefoged and Broadbent (1960) indicate that when the stimuli being judged are not simply pairs of items, but items embedded in a sequence (as is usually the case in short-term memory studies), our ability to judge temporal order becomes worse. Needham (1934) showed that when subjects judge the temporal location of an auditory event (a buzz) in a sequence of auditory events (pure tones) the difference between the judged location and the true location is frequently about 250 milliseconds, and sometimes as much as 500 milliseconds.

Ladefoged and Broadbent (1960), studying the perception of speech, reported experiments in which the temporal location of an event in a sequence was sometimes misjudged by more than a second. Their experimental task was closer to the usual short-term memory task than most of the experiments concerned with the perception of temporal order: (a) their stimuli were presented sequentially, (b) their stimuli were spoken words, and (c) the subject was required to identify the words. When the subjects heard sentences or sequences of digits with a click or an s superimposed on one word or between words, they usually reported hearing the click or the s earlier than it actually occurred. Ladefoged and Broadbent interpreted their results in terms of selective attention hypotheses similar to the early

prior entry hypotheses. Subjects listened selectively for an s or a click. Their greater attention for the s or click than for the words caused the sound to be perceived earlier than its actual occurrence relative to the words. In memory experiments with sequential stimuli, the fluctuation of the subject's attention from word to word may lead to an incorrect perception of their order.

In short-term memory studies, the subject's task of perceiving the order of events is even more difficult than in the above experiments. First, subjects in the above studies were required to report only which of two possible events occurred first, or the temporal location of a single event in a sequence. In most short-term memory tasks, the subject must perceive which of several events occurred in each of several sequential locations. Second, the difficulties of order perception may be magnified by the requirement to retain the sequence of items for later recall. Thus these studies on perception of temporal order provide only lower bounds for the frequency of order errors in short-term memory tasks and lower bounds for the temporal separation between adjacent items needed for accurate perception of order.

Broadbent's (1957b, 1958) theory and data also suggest that the requirement to recall may increase the difficulties of order perception. He hypothesized that items arrive and are stored in parallel in an S system (sensory storage) and then are identified or encoded sequentially by a P system (perceptual system). If the order in which items enter the P system is determined by a probability distribution over the items in the S system, then order errors in perception may increase with the number of items accumulated in the S system. If the recall order depends in part on the P system processing order, then accumulations in the S system should lead to order errors in recall. The faster the presentation rate relative to the encoding rate, the greater the number of items accumulating in the S system, and therefore the greater the number of order errors expected in recall. In support of this hypothesis, Aaronson and Sternberg (1964) found in an auditory serial-recall task that the number of order errors (and the percentage of all errors that were order errors) was greater for a fast (3 digits per second) than for a slow (1.5 digits per second) presentation rate.

In summary, the studies in this section suggest (a) that order errors in short-term memory may be due in part to misperception of the stimulus order, (b) that embedding items in a sequence increases the difficulties of order perception, and (c) that the requirement to recall the items may further increase the difficulties of order perception.

However, it is certainly not the case that all order errors in short-term memory tasks can be attributed to the perceptual stages. Conrad (1965), Wickelgren (1965), and Yntema and Trask (1963) have presented evidence for the occurrence of order errors during retention and retrieval. Conrad has shown that some order errors may be due to mutual auditory confusions (that is, pairs of item errors) arising during retention. Yntema and Trask have shown that accuracy in the judgment of order decreases with the number of items that intervene between the events to be compared and the response. Finally, Wickelgren has presented evidence suggesting that order errors can arise during retention as a function of strengths of associations between items.

Temporal Factors and Perceptual Strategies

Many of the experimental results discussed in the preceding sections suggested that stimulus information may initially be received by a buffer storage system before undergoing additional perceptual processing. It is possible that the temporal delay of some perceptual operations is not determined strictly by the stimulus conditions,

but that (a) the time elapsing before the various perceptual processes are performed on an item or (b) the order in which items are processed is in part determined by the subject (not necessarily consciously). That is, the subject may be able to use alternative strategies of perceiving the stimulus items, and the choice of strategy may affect performance. Because we cannot directly observe the subject's perceptual processing, evidence concerning the strategy he may be using is necessarily indirect. We make inferences about strategies based on various aspects of the observed data. Five types of data might be considered in the investigation of strategies: (a) the pattern of times at which the responses occur, (b) the order in which the responses are made, (c) the patterns of errors in responding, (d) the results of verbal reports from subjects, and (e) the effects of training on response patterns.

PATTERN OF TIMES AT WHICH THE RESPONSES OCCUR

Miller (1962) suggested that the time used to perceive speech may be decreased by delaying certain perceptual operations:

> In order to comprehend messages spoken at 150 words/min, we would presumably have to make about a dozen phonemic decisions every second and perhaps 100 phonetic decisions. . . . A single delayed decision would require far less time than would a series of immediate decisions [p. 81, 82].

Whereas Miller has pointed out an advantage of a delayed strategy, Moray and Taylor (1958) have pointed out that it also has a disadvantage: With long delays, sufficient information may be lost from the representation to result in response errors.

Moray and Taylor have shown that when subjects shadow one of two dichotic messages, the temporal aspects of the responses are influenced by the stimulus uncertainty.

> Our subjects' responses could be divided into two clearly distinguishable groups, which we call the "continuous" and "dis-

continuous" type of response. The former appear to show no pauses in speaking longer than the pause between adjacent words, while the latter spoke groups of words with a silent period extending over several words between each output [p. 107].

They reported that with uncertain stimulus materials (i.e., low sequential constraints) the continuous strategy was more efficient, and that subjects often changed to the discontinuous stragedy for more redundant stimulus materials. They suggested that subjects deal with the more redundant materials in groups of words. One interpretation of their results is the following: If subjects cannot simultaneously utter some words while identifying new ones, then their identification of some items may be delayed while they are overtly responding to other items. The data suggest that with highly uncertain material, the subject may identify one word at a time and then respond immediately after its identification, thereby delaying identification of the next word slightly while making the shadowing response to the preceding word. However, with redundant materials, the subjects may identify several words and make the shadowing responses to the entire group of words, thereby delaying identification of many subsequent words for a longer period of time than they would with the uncertain materials.

The Moray and Taylor study suggests an alternative interpretation of the Ladefoged and Broadbent (1960) results discussed earlier. If subjects lagged behind the presentation in their identification of the words, then when the click or s occurred they might still be identifying an earlier word, rather than that presented simultaneously with the click or the s. If the time of identification affects the time a word appears to have occurred, subjects should report hearing the click or the s earlier than it actually occurred. Ladefoged and Broadbent's data are consistent with this prediction. Subjects generally reported hearing the click or s earlier than it actu-

ally occurred, and this trend increased toward the end of the sequence or sentence. Further, the response data suggest that subjects delayed their identification less when the speech consisted of isolated digits (that had fewer sequential constraints) than when the speech consisted of meaningful sentences.

In summary, the patterns of response times in the above studies could have occurred because the subject's listening strategy varied with stimulus redundancy: The greater the redundancy, the greater the delay between presentation and identification of the stimulus and the larger the group of stimuli identified when identification occurs.

ORDER OF RESPONSES

If the order in which items are recalled in an immediate memory task is in part determined by the order in which they are identified, then we might make inferences about the identification order from the response data.

Bryden (1962) analyzed in detail the patterns in which subjects recalled items in a dichotic experiment with presentation rates from .5 pair per second to 2 pairs per second. He found that at slow rates, subjects recalled the digits in the temporal order of arrival (they recalled the first pair first, the second pair next, and so on). As rate increased, subjects used the temporal order of report less, and tended to recall all of the digits presented to one ear before those presented to the other. Perhaps at slow rates there was enough time between stimuli to identify one pair before the next was presented. At fast rates, the time between stimuli may have been insufficient to identify two items. Therefore, subjects would delay the identification of items presented to one ear until after the presentation (storing the later items in an S-system buffer, according to Broadbent's theory). Further, at rapid rates, when subjects did use the temporal order of report, more errors occurred than when "ear-by-ear" recall was used. This may indicate that when a temporal strategy rather than an ear-by-ear strategy of identification is used at rapid rates, it is less efficient.

PATTERNS OF ERRORS
IN RESPONDING

In their sequential recall experiment, Aaronson and Sternberg (1964) presented evidence that subjects receiving a slow presentation rate used an "immediate" listening strategy: They actively identified the digits during the presentation. But subjects receiving a fast rate used a "delayed" strategy: They delayed identifying the digits until the presentation was completed. With an immediate strategy, the probability of mishearing should be higher later in the series because

> the encoding of one digit may not have been completed by the time the next digit was presented. With a delayed strategy, subjects could reduce the item errors resulting from interference between successive digits, but delayed encoding should increase the number of order errors [p. 6].

In agreement with their hypothesis, more item errors were found for the slow than for the fast rate, and item errors increased over serial positions. Also, there were relatively more order errors and fewer item errors for the fast than for the slow rate.

RESULTS OF VERBAL
REPORTS FROM SUBJECTS

After subjects memorized and recalled seven-digit auditory sequences presented at 3 digits per second or 1.5 digits per second, Aaronson (1963) asked them to assign scale values to statements about strategies (the more frequently they used the strategy, the higher the scale value). The four statements relevant to perception were:

> 1. You passively waited for all 7 digits to be presented and then actively listened to them.
> 2. You passively waited for the first few digits to be presented and then actively lis-

tened to those as a group. You passively waited for the rest of the digits to be presented and actively listened to them.
> 3. You actively listened to one digit at a time at a slight delay after its presentation.
> 4. You actively listened to each single digit as it was presented.

As indicated in Table 1, from items 1 to 4, the scores, in general, decreased for the 3-per-second group and increased for

TABLE 1

Results from Strategy Questionnaire*

STATEMENT	PRESENTATION RATE	
	3/SEC	1.5/SEC
1	1.7	0.9
2	1.2	1.0
3	0.1	1.2
4	0.4	1.7

* From Aaronson (1963).

the 1.5-per-second group. These questionnaire results give additional support to the hypothesis that the subject's perceptual strategy depends in part on the presentation rate at which he is trained.

EFFECTS OF TRAINING
ON RESPONSE PATTERNS

The above studies suggest that the pattern of errors in recalling digit sequences may be in part determined by the subject's listening strategy. Therefore, when rate is changed, if subjects continue to use the same listening strategy, one would expect to find that the shape of the serial curve at the new rate was in part determined by the rate the subject originally experienced. In the above Aaronson and Sternberg experiment, when subjects participated in a second session a week later, the presentation rates for the two groups were reversed. They found that the rate the subjects experienced during Session 1 influenced the shape of the distributions of errors over serial positions in Session 2. Aaronson (1966b, 1966c) trained subjects to recall sequences presented at one of three rates. The three groups were all tested at the intermediate rate a week later. The serial curves of recall errors during the test were more negatively skewed for subjects who had been previously trained on the slower rates. The rate on which subjects are trained may influence the perceptual strategy they develop, and this strategy may persist during a second session when the rate is changed.

Harris and Haber (1963) found that subjects spontaneously used two encoding strategies in short-term memory of tachistoscopic presentations. They then systematically trained two groups of subjects to encode the attributes of pairs of geometric forms in one of those two temporal orders: by an "objects code" (e.g., two red circles; four blue stars) or by a dimensions code (e.g., two-four; red-blue; circles-stars). On test trials, subjects were given attention instructions regarding the emphasis to be placed on each stimulus dimension. Harris and Haber presented three types of evidence that subjects persisted in using the training strategy during the test trials.

1. Verbal reports. Judges (who did not know how any given subject was trained) determined on the basis of questionnaire data which code subjects used during the test. The questionnaire data indicated a strong persistence of the training strategy during the test.

2. Report order. In general, the order in which subjects responded, when they were free to report the stimulus attributes in any order, corresponded to the temporal order of their training code.

3. Error patterns. When subjects were forced to recall in a given order, "the code S used determined whether or not his accuracy was affected selectively by attention instructions." The "dimensions-coders" made fewer errors on emphasized than unemphasized dimensions. However, "objects-

coders" did *not* recall emphasized dimensions better than unemphasized dimensions and continued to persist in their object-encoding strategy even though it was not optimal for the task at hand. Harris and Haber presented some time data that may explain the above recall results. The silent naming of the figures took an average of 2.9 seconds and 4.2 seconds with the objects and dimensions codes, respectively. "Since the visual image of a briefly presented stimulus fades considerably within 2 sec. (Sperling, 1960), the slower dimensions coders are unable to encode it completely before it fades [Harris and Haber, 1963]."

The experiments discussed in the above subsections suggest that subjects may develop strategies regarding (*a*) the delay of perception and (*b*) the temporal order of perception of stimulus items or attributes. These strategies may in part determine the subjects' performance in short-term memory experiments.

Summary

The experiments reviewed here suggest that in short-term memory tasks, the temporal course of the perceptual processes can have an important influence on errors occurring in the subsequent recall of the items. Increasing the presentation rate of the stimulus sequences, which restricts the time available for perception between items, frequently results in poorer recall accuracy. It appears that the physical stimulus duration per se is not a crucial factor in determining recall accuracy. Instead, the critical factor is the time during which the stimulus information is available to the subject for perception, which may be longer than the physical stimulus duration. A few experimental techniques have been developed that use various pre- and post-stimulus events to restrict the amount of time the stimulus information is available for processing by the subject. When the stimulus availability is controlled in these ways, the recall accuracy does increase with exposure duration. The results from studies of "prior entry" and discrimination of temporal order suggest that order errors may be attributed partly to the perceptual stages in short-term memory tasks. Finally, there is some evidence that subjects may develop perceptual strategies that can influence their performance in short-term memory tasks.

References

AARONSON, D. Effects of presentation rate and recall delay in short-term memory. Unpublished manuscript, University of Pennsylvania, 1963.

AARONSON, D. Perception and immediate recall of auditory sequences. Paper read at Eastern Psychological Association, Atlantic City, 1965.

AARONSON, D. Immediate recall of compressed speech. Unpublished manuscript, Harvard University, Center for Cognitive Studies, 1966. (a)

AARONSON, D. Perception and immediate recall of auditory sequences. Unpublished doctoral dissertation, University of Pennsylvania, 1966. (b)

AARONSON, D. The temporal course of perception in a short-term memory task. Paper read at the Eastern Psychological Association, New York, 1966. (c)

AARONSON, D., and S. STERNBERG. Effects of a post-stimulus interference on the immediate recall of auditory sequences. Unpublished manuscript, University of Pennsylvania, 1963.

AARONSON, D., and S. STERNBERG. Effects of presentation rate and signal-to-noise ratio on immediate recall. Paper read at Eastern Psychological Association, Philadelphia, 1964.

AVERBACH, E., and A. S. CORIELL. Short-term memory in vision. Bell Telephone System Technical Publication, 1960, Monogr. no. 3756.

AVERBACH, E., and G. SPERLING. Short-term storage of information in vision. In C. Cherry (Ed.), Information theory. London: Butterworth, 1961.

BERGSTROM, J. A. Effects of changes in time variables in memorizing together with some discussion of the techniques of memory experimentation. American Journal of Psychology, 1907, 18, 206–238.

BLANKENSHIP, A. B. Memory span: A review of the literature. Psychological Bulletin, 1938, 35, 1–25.

BORING, E. G. A history of experimental psychology. New York: Appleton-Century-Crofts, 1950.

BROADBENT, D. E. Successive responses to simultaneous stimuli. Quarterly Journal of Experimental Psychology, 1956, 8, 145–152.

BROADBENT, D. E. Immediate memory and simultaneous stimuli. Quarterly Journal of Experimental Psychology, 1957, 9, 1–11. (a)

BROADBENT, D. E. A mechanical model for human attention and immediate memory. Psychological Review, 1957, 64, 205–215. (b)

BROADBENT, D. E. Perception and communication. New York: Pergamon Press, 1958.

BROWN, J. An experimental study of immediate memory. Unpublished doctoral dissertation, University of Cambridge, 1955.

BRYDEN, M. P. Order of report in dichotic listening. Canadian Journal of Psychology, 1962, 16, 291–299.

CONRAD, R. Accuracy of recall using key set and telephone dial, and the effect of a prefix digit. Journal of Applied Psychology, 1958, 42, 285–288.

CONRAD, R. Errors of immediate memory. British Journal of Psychology, 1959, 50, 349–359.

CONRAD, R. Very brief delay of immediate recall. Quarterly Journal of Experimental Psychology, 1960, 12, 45–47.

CONRAD, R. An association between memory errors and errors due to acoustic masking of speech. Nature, 1962, 193, 1314–1315.

CONRAD, R. Acoustic confusions and memory span for words. Nature, 1963, 197, 29–30.

CONRAD, R. Acoustic confusions in immediate memory. British Journal of Psychology, 1964, 55, 75–84.

CONRAD, R. Order error in immediate recall of sequences. Journal of Verbal Learning and Verbal Behavior, 1965, 4, 161–169.

CONRAD, R., and B. HILLE. The decay theory of immediate memory and paced recall. Canadian Journal of Psychology, 1958, 12, 1–6.

DAVIS, R. The human operator as a single channel information system. Quarterly Journal of Experimental Psychology, 1957, 9, 119–129.

DAVIS, R. The role of "attention" in the psychological refractory period. Quarterly Journal of Experimental Psychology, 1959, 11, 211–220.

DEESE, J., and R. A. KAUFMAN. Sequential

effects in recall of unorganized and sequentially organized material. *Journal of Experimental Psychology,* 1957, 54, 180–187.

ERIKSEN, C. W., and M. HOFFMAN. Form recognition at brief durations as a function of adapting field and interval between stimulations. *Journal of Experimental Psychology,* 1963, 66, 485–499.

ERIKSEN, C. W., and R. A. STEFFY. Short-term memory and retroactive interference in visual perception. *Journal of Experimental Psychology,* 1964, 68, 423–434.

FAIRBANKS, G., N. GUTTMAN, and M. S. MIRON. Auditory comprehension in relation to listening rate and selective verbal redundancy. *Journal of Speech and Hearing Disorders,* 1957, 22, 23–32. (a)

FAIRBANKS, G., N. GUTTMAN, and M. S. MIRON. Auditory comprehension of repeated high-speed messages. *Journal of Speech and Hearing Disorders,* 1957, 22, 20–22. (b)

FAIRBANKS, G., N. GUTTMAN, and M. S. MIRON. Effects of time compression upon the comprehension of connected speech. *Journal of Speech and Hearing Disorders,* 1957, 22, 10–19. (c)

FAIRBANKS, G., and F. KODMAN. Word intelligibility as a function of time compression. *Journal of Acoustical Society of America,* 1957, 29, 636–641.

FRASER, D. C. Decay of immediate memory with age. *Nature,* 1958, 182, 1163.

GARVEY, W. D. The intelligibility of abbreviated speech patterns. *Quarterly Journal of Speech,* 1953, 39, 296–306. (a)

GARVEY, W. D. The intelligibility of speeded speech. *Journal of Experimental Psychology,* 1953, 45, 102–107. (b)

HARRIS, C. S., and R. N. HABER. Selective attention and coding in visual perception. *Journal of Experimental Psychology,* 1963, 65, 328–333.

HIRSH, I. Auditory perception of temporal order. *Journal of the Acoustical Society of America,* 1959, 31, 759–767.

HIRSH, I., and C. E. SHERRICK. Perceived order in different sense modalities. *Journal of Experimental Psychology,* 1961, 62, 423–432.

HUTTON, C. L. A psychophysical study of speech rate. Unpublished doctoral dissertation, University of Illinois, 1954.

JAMES, W. *The principles of psychology.* New York: Holt, 1890.

KAY, H., and E. C. POULTON. Anticipation in memorizing. *British Journal of Psychology,* 1951, 42, 34–41.

KLUMPP, R. G., and J. C. WEBSTER. Intelli-

gibility of time-compressed speech. *Journal of the Acoustical Society of America,* 1961, 33, 265–267.

LADEFOGED, P., and D. E. BROADBENT. Perception of sequence in auditory events. *Quarterly Journal of Experimental Psychology,* 1960, 12, 162–170.

MACKWORTH, J. F. Paced memorizing in a continuous task. *Journal of Experimental Psychology,* 1959, 58, 206–211.

MACKWORTH, J. F. The effect of display time upon the recall of digits. *Canadian Journal of Psychology,* 1962, 16, 48–54. (a)

MACKWORTH, J. F. The effect of the response upon the immediate memory span. *Canadian Journal of Psychology,* 1962, 16, 120–127. (b)

MACKWORTH, J. F. Presentation rate and immediate memory. *Canadian Journal of Psychology,* 1962, 16, 42–47. (c)

MACKWORTH, J. F. The visual image and the memory trace. *Canadian Journal of Psychology,* 1962, 16, 55–59. (d)

MACKWORTH, J. F. The relation between visual image and post-perceptual immediate memory. *Journal of Verbal Learning and Verbal Behavior,* 1963, 2, 75–85.

MELTON, A. W., A. SAMEROFF, and E. SCHUBOT. Short-term recognition memory. Paper read at Psychonomic Society, Bryn Mawr, 1963.

MILLER, G. A. Decision units in the perception of speech. *IRE Transactions on Information Theory,* 1962, IT–8, 81–83.

MORAY, N. Broadbent's filter theory: Postulate H and the problem of switching time. *Quarterly Journal of Experimental Psychology,* 1960, 12, 214–220.

MORAY, N., and A. TAYLOR. The effect of redundancy in shadowing one of two dichotic messages. *Language and Speech,* 1958, 1, 102–109.

MURDOCK, B. B. The immediate retention of unrelated words. *Journal of Experimental Psychology,* 1960, 60, 222–234.

NEEDHAM, J. G. Prior entry within a single sense department. *Journal of Experimental Psychology,* 1934, 17, 400–411.

NEEDHAM, J. G. Some conditions of prior entry. *Journal of General Psychology,* 1936, 14, 226–240.

NORMAN, D. A. Acquisition and retention in short-term memory. *Journal of Experimental Psychology,* 1966, 72, 369–381.

POLLACK, I. The effect of rate of presentation of information. Report no. 25, 1952, Human Factors Operations Research Laboratories. (AD 140)

POLLACK, I. Message uncertainty and message

reception. *Journal of the Acoustical Society of America,* 1959, *31,* 1500–1508.

POLLACK, I. and L. B. JOHNSON. Continuing memory span for digits. *Perceptual and Motor Skills,* 1963, *17,* 731–734.

POLLACK, I., L. B. JOHNSON, and P. R. KNAFF. Running memory span. *Journal of Experimental Psychology,* 1959, *57,* 137–146.

POLLACK, I., and H. RUBENSTEIN. Response time to known message sets in noise. *Language and Speech,* 1963, *6,* 57–62.

POSNER, M. I. Immediate memory in sequential tasks. *Psychological Bulletin,* 1963, *60,* 333–349.

POSNER, M. I. Rate of presentation and order of recall in immediate memory. *British Journal of Psychology,* 1964, *55,* 303–306.

SCHMIDT, M. W., and A. B. KRISTOFFERSON. Discrimination of successiveness: A test of a model of attention. *Science,* 1963, *139,* 112–113.

SPERLING, G. The information available in brief visual presentations. *Psychological Monographs,* 1960, *74* (11, Whole No. 498).

SPERLING, G. Auditory interference with a visual memory task. Paper read at Eastern Psychological Association, Atlantic City, 1962.

SPERLING, G. A model for visual memory tasks. *Human Factors,* 1963, *5,* 19–31.

STERNBERG, S. Two operations in character recognition: Some evidence from reaction

time measures. In *Models for the perception of speech and visual form.* AFRCL Symposium, Boston, 1964.

STONE, S. A. Prior entry in the auditory-tactual complication. *American Journal of Psychology,* 1926, *37,* 284–287.

STROUD, J. M. The fine structure of psychological time. In H. Quastler (Ed.), *Information theory in psychology.* Glencoe, Ill.: Free Press, 1955.

TITCHENER, E. B. *The psychology of feeling and attention.* New York: Macmillan, 1908.

TUNTURI, A. R. A study in the pathway from the medial geniculate body to the acoustic cortex in the dog. *American Journal of Physiology,* 1946, *47,* 311–319.

WELFORD, A. T. The "physiological refractory period" and the timing of high-speed performance: A review and a theory. *British Journal of Psychology,* 1952, *43,* 2–19.

WICKELGREN, W. A. Short-term memory for repeated and non-repeated items. *Quarterly Journal of Experimental Psychology,* 1965, *17,* 14–25.

YNTEMA, D. B., and F. P. TRASK. Recall as a search process. *Journal of Verbal Learning and Verbal Behavior,* 1963, *2,* 65–74.

YNTEMA, D. B., F. T. WOZENCRAFT, and L. KLEM. Immediate serial recall of digits presented at very high rates. Paper read at Psychonomic Society, Niagara Falls, Ontario, 1964.

Decision-time without Reaction-time: Experiments in Visual Scanning[*]

ULRIC NEISSER
Cornell University

It has become common to regard human beings as processors of information, but not

* *American Journal of Psychology,* 1963, vol. 76, pp. 376–385. This research was supported by the Lincoln Laboratory of the Massachusetts Institute of Technology, operated with support from the U.S. Army, Navy, and Air Force.

much is known about the underlying functions. Accurate measurement of the *time required* to execute cognitive operations may help us to interpret them. In the classical reaction-time experiment, processing-time is confounded with the time used to prepare and execute the physical response itself. In the present experiments, a procedure involving visual scanning was used to circumvent this problem. An S who scans a list of items, to find one of a certain kind, must examine each item he encounters, but he makes no response until he comes upon the particular item for which he is searching. The rate at which he scans measures the time he uses to analyze the items that elicit no response.

The five experiments reported here serve two purposes. First, they "calibrate" the scanning method, which can be considered trustworthy to the extent that different Ss in different experiments produce comparable results. Secondly, they provided preliminary information about the depth, breadth, and flexibility of the processes involved in recognizing printed letters.

The experiments are designed and interpreted on the assumption that the process of recognition is hierarchically organized. Before an S "decides" that the letter Z, for example, is present in the input, he must make prior "decisions" about subordinate features such as parallel lines and angles; these in turn are probably based on processes of a still lower order. We should expect processing-times to depend on the depth of the hierarchy required by a problem. If, however, several operations are at the same level in the hierarchy, S may be able to execute them simultaneously.[1] The scanning method may enable us to determine whether simultaneity actually is possible. It may also provide information about the flexibility with which S can shift from one mode of processing to another, to take advantage of altered circumstances.

METHOD

A list of 50 items arranged in a single-spaced column is presented to S. Each item is a string of letters. As soon as the list is

exposed, a clock starts, and S begins to scan down the list from the top. When he finds the single item that has the *critical property*, he turns a switch which stops the clock. If the critical property is the absence of Z, for example, the list might contain 49 items like *JZTXVB, DQFJHZ, MBZJSV, ZXLSMT, RLZQXS,* and one critical item like *VXRLFH.* A series of 15 such trials (lists) with the same critical property usually is given; the critical item appears in an unpredictably different position on each trial. Afterwards, scanning-time is plotted as a function of the position of the critical item, i.e. of the number of items scanned. These graphs usually are fitted fairly well by straight lines. An example appears in Figure 1. Linearity implies that the time taken to scan each item does not change from one end of the list to the other. The most important property of such a line is its *slope:* the average time per item scanned. The slope represents the time S needs to assure himself that each item does *not* have the critical property. In the example above, he must identify a Z in each item.

The slope is unaffected by the time required to begin scanning, to decide upon a response, or to turn the switch. There is no reason to believe that any of these response-factors varies with the position of the critical item on the list. They affect only the intercept of the fitted line—its height above the X-axis.[2] The slope, or time-per-item, therefore is a relatively pure measure of the time required to process the information. If S scans at the fastest rate consistent with relatively error-free performance, his rate (in the example) should be limited only by the speed with which he can analyze the items for the presence of Z. (Physiological limitations on eye-movements may limit the speed to some maximum, but would not affect the

---

[1] The theoretical significance of such simultaneity is explored in Ulric Neisser, "The Multiplicity of Thought," *British Journal of Psychology,* 1963, vol. 54, pp. 1–14.

[2] Some non-linearity is to be expected at the beginning of the list, as S begins to scan. For this reason, the y-intercepts of the fitted lines do not provide reliable information.

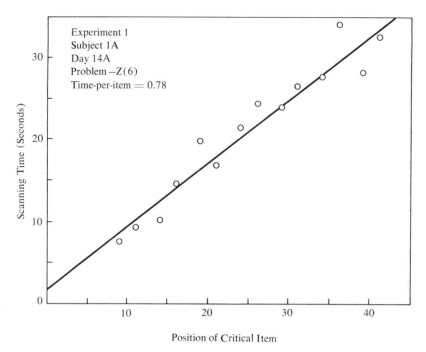

FIGURE 1   Scanning-time as a function of the position of the critical item: A typical graph.

conclusions drawn here.) In some problems (*i.e.* with some types of critical property), S may process the items in groups rather than individually. In this case "time-per-item" is a fiction, but a convenient one; it still enables us to compare "processing-time" for different tasks.

The Ss were college students, paid for their services. The lists were exposed in a device which activated a Standard Electric Timer (calibrated in 0.01 sec) when E opened a spring-loaded door, and stopped it when S turned a hand-held rotary switch in either direction. To discourage premature responses, alternate items on all lists were flanked by a pair of dots; S was instructed to turn his switch clockwise if the critical item had these dots, and counterclockwise if it did not. (Signal lights informed E of the direction of the response chosen.) S was urged to scan as fast as possible, consistent with making relatively few errors. If he failed to find the critical item on his first time through the list, or mistakenly turned the switch without reaching the critical item, an error was

noted and the same list was later presented again. All items in all lists were permutations of a certain set of letters called the "context," which was varied in some of the experiments. The permutations were random except with respect to the critical property. All the lists, made up of randomized strings of letters having the desired properties, were prepared by a suitably programmed IBM 7090 computer, and printed on an ANELEX high-speed printer. They were taped to strips of cardboard for ease in handling.

In the first three of the five experiments, S worked on two different problems (critical properties) in each daily session. Twenty trials were devoted to each problem, but the first six trials were considered practice, and were not used in the determination of slope. A daily session took from 30–45 min. The critical items actually occurred at list-positions 5, 6, 25, 30, 45, and 46 (randomly ordered) during practice, and at 9, 11, 14, 16, . . . , 39, 41 (randomly ordered) during the experiment proper, but S did not know this. In Experiments 4 and 5, only 15 trials were given for each problem, the first three being practice. The position of the critical item in each trial was randomly chosen from the integers 1, 2, . . . , 50, except that it was never the same twice for any one problem on one day. In these experiments, S worked on 4–5 problems in each daily session.

In every case, the points were plotted and a straight line was visually fitted to them. The data reported here, however, are not taken from these visual fits but from lines fitted mathematically by the method of least squares. Slopes and intercepts of the best-fit lines, as well as standard errors of estimate around the lines, were calculated by an IBM 7090 computer. The computer-program disregarded any isolated points which deviated greatly from the line determined by the others. (Actually, the program discarded points which deviated from the line at 5% level by a *t*-test. This criterion was used for the sake of simplicity; it is not fully satisfactory because search-times are markedly more variable when the critical item is near the bottom of the list than when it is near the top.)

Experiment I: Preliminary

The first experiment was a preliminary study of the effects of the following variables:[3] the identity of the target-letter (Q vs. Z); the number of letters in each item (2 vs. 6); the complexity of processing required (scanning items *without* the target-letter to find an item that contains it versus scanning items *containing* a letter to find an item without it); the number of acceptable alternative target-letters (1 vs. 2).

[3] Experiment 1 has been described earlier: Neisser, Time-analysis of logical processes in man (*Proc. West, Joint Computer Conf.*, 1961, 579–585). Since the results presented in that paper are based on visually fitted lines, they differ slightly from those appearing here.

PROCEDURE

The design of the experiment involved 14 conditions: 7 critical properties, each embedded in two sets of lists. In one set, each item was two letters wide (*e.g.* ZD, JZ, LR, ZQ), while in the other set each was six letters wide (*e.g.* JZLXSH, QVZ MXL, FDRVQH). The critical properties were Z, Q, ZvQ, −Z, −Q, −ZvQ, and −QvZ. These terms are to be interpreted as follows. In Problem Z, the critical item alone contains a Z, which may be considered the target of the search; in ZvQ the critical item may contain either Z or Q or both, and S does not know which until he encounters it (parallel scanning); in −Z, all the items *except* the critical one contain a Z; in a problem like −ZvQ, all items except the critical one have a Z and no Q, while the critical one may lack a Z, may have a Q, or both. The lists were made up of J, P, S, T, V, and X in addition to Z and Q.

Three Ss were used.[4] Each was given 2 practice sessions, 7 experimental sessions in which the 14 problems were presented (in a different order to each S), and 7 additional sessions in which the 14 problems were presented again in the opposite order.

RESULTS

Since data for the different Ss are very similar, only mean times-per-item appear in Table 1. We may draw certain tentative conclusions. (1) −Z takes longer than Z, and −Q takes longer than Q; (2) QvZ takes no longer than Z alone; (3) six-letter lists take longer than two-letter lists, but generally not three times as long; (4) Z

[4] The assistance of Miss Emily Carota, Mr. Arthur Warmoth, and Mr. Norman Goldberg, who served as E in Experiments I, II, and III, of Mr. Robert Greenway, who served as E in Experiments IV and V; and of Mr. Paul Weene, who assisted in the construction of the apparatus is gratefully acknowledged. Experiments III and V were carried out at the Harvard Center for Cognitive Studies.

takes longer than Q, and −Z takes longer than −Q; (5) in the two-letter lists, all problems involving the absence of a letter take about equally long. While many of these findings will be extended or confirmed in the four experiments to follow, we will pause at this point to consider their implications for the depth, breadth, and flexibility of the cognitive processes involved.

When S is looking for a particular letter (e.g. Z), each noncritical item gets only scant attention. S need only view each item long enough that the lower-order recognitive systems could (for the individual features of Z) be activated by the right input. That input does not appear, and the Z-recognizer as a whole is not activated, until the critical item is reached. This analysis is substantiated by introspective report: S does not "see" the letters he passes; he "sees" only a blur until the Z "jumps out at him." The situation is different when S looks for an item without a Z. Now the Z in each item must be identified; the full depth of the recognizer for Z is used on each line. Because of this greater depth, problems in which S looks for the absence of a letter take longer than those in which he need only find the letter. The effect of practice in this difference will be examined in Experiment IV.

Even in the rapid search for a target, Z, elementary analyses of the stimulus-input are being carried out. The elementary operations that could detect a Z, if it were to occur, must be different from those which could detect Q. Since Ss can be alert for *both* letters without slowing their scanning-rate, it seems that the different operations can be carried out simultaneously. (It may be argued that the operations for Q are somehow interleaved with those for Z, instead of being simultaneous with them, a point which will be considered further in the light of the data of Experiment V.) This evidence for the breadth of the processes involved is in contrast to a finding which seems to emphasize the opposite: wider lists take more time to scan. One might easily imagine a six-channel device able to handle two- and six-letter widths with equal speed, but no S behaves like such a device. In experiment II, we shall consider whether this effect is due to the defects of peripheral vision; in Experiment IV, whether it disappears with practice.

The difference in speed between Z and Q may be an unchangeable property of the recognitive systems for these two letters. If, however, these systems are flexibly organized, we should expect the difference to be eliminated or reversed in a different letter-context or a different experimental situation. The first of these predictions is tested in Experiment III. The second is borne out, rather unexpectedly, by the

TABLE 1

Mean Time-per-Item (Sec) in Experiment I

Each entry is the mean of the slopes of the 3 Ss, each slope based on about 14 measurements.

NO. OF LETTERS	DAY	PROBLEM						
		Q	−Q	Z	−Z	QvZ	−QvZ	Qv−Z
6	1	0.14	0.42	0.50	0.70	0.60	0.98	0.82
	2	0.08	0.42	0.55	0.64	0.45	0.72	0.65
2	1	0.09	0.32	0.23	0.37	0.21	0.30	0.34
	2	0.05	0.27	0.20	0.29	0.20	0.31	0.34

observation that $-Z$, $-Q$, $-ZvQ$, and $-QvZ$ are equally fast in two-letter lists. A glance at the lists themselves provides an explanation. In these problems, there is a Z in every non-critical item; the result is a *column* of Zs which switches haphazardly from one side of the list to the other. Following such a column with the eye is very different from inspecting individual items. Evidently the Ss discovered this, and promptly used it to increase the speed of their scan. No such columns are formed in six-letter lists.

Experiment II: Horizontal Spacing

Two reasons might be advanced for the fact that it takes less time to process a two-letter item than a six-letter item. First, the six-letter item extends farther horizontally, and thus may encourage real or incipient eye-movement, or may require parafoveal vision. (The six-letter item occupies about 5° of visual angle.) Secondly, the increase in amount of information to be processed may be the important variable. To decide this issue, horizontal spacing itself was varied in Experiment II.

PROCEDURE.

There were four conditions. In each case the target was Z, and the letter-context was identical with that of Experiment I. The conditions were Z(2) (items two letters wide as in Experiment I); Z(4) (items four letters wide); Z(4w) (items composed of four letters, but with two inserted dashes to increase the width of the item, as *P-TX-Q*); Z(6) (items six letters wide, as in Experiment I). Each of 4 Ss scanned in each condition five times (two per day).

RESULTS.

Mean times-per-item appear in Table 2. It is evident that Condition Z(4w) is just as fast a Condition Z(4), and systematically faster than Z(6). In other words, the critical factor is the number of letters per item, rather than their horizontal spread. Note that, on the first two trials, times-per-item for Z(2) and Z(6) are comparable with those of Experiment I, but that practice causes sharp decreases in time. The effects of practice will be considered further in Experiments IV and V.

Experiment III: Context

The difference in time-per-item between problems involving Z and those involving Q was one of the most striking results of Experiment I. The difference might ascribed to the two letters as such or to the letter-contexts in which they were embedded. The other letters in Experiment I were J, P, S, T, V, and X. Perceptually,

TABLE 2

Mean Time-per-Item (Sec) in Experiment II

Each entry is the mean of the slopes of the 4 Ss, each slope based on about 14 measurements.

DAY	PROBLEM			
	Z(2)	Z(4)	Z(4w)	Z(6)
1	0.22	0.41	0.48	0.79
2	0.20	0.30	0.30	0.51
3	0.17	0.27	0.25	0.34
4	0.14	0.20	0.21	0.29
5	0.11	0.16	0.16	0.25

the Q seems to stand out vividly from this assortment because of its roundness. For experiment III, two letter-contexts were selected. One was intended to make Z even harder to see, the other to obscure the Q. The first, called the "angular" context, consisted of the letters E, I, M, V, W, and X; the second, called the "round" context, consisted of C, D, G, O, R, and U. Six-letter items were used.

PROCEDURE.

The 3 Ss worked on six different problems, doing each problem twice in each context. In addition to studying the context-effect, we wished to confirm and extend the finding of Experiment I that it takes no longer to scan for two letters in parallel than for one alone. The problems used were, therefore, Q, Z, QvZ, −Q, −Z, and −Qv−Z. The last of these represents a list in which every item except the critical one has both a Q and a Z (in either order, not necessarily adjacent), while one or both of these letters are absent from the critical item. In other respects the design was like that of Experiment I.

RESULTS.

Mean times-per-item appear in Table 3. It is evident that contextual background is of great importance in determining processing-time. In the angular context, problems involving Q take much less time than those involving Z, while the opposite is true in the round context. Indeed, the Ss found the search for Q or for −Q very difficult against the round background, and made frequent errors based on confusions between Q and O, or Q and G.

The results confirm Experiment I in showing that it takes no longer per item to scan in parallel for Q or Z than for one of these targets alone: no longer than to scan for Q in the round context, and no longer than Z in the angular context. No such parallelism is demonstrable, however, at the more complicated level represented by −Q, −Z, and −Qv−Z. Here S must assume himself that each item he scans does contain the critical letter, or letters. To check for both takes consistently longer than to check for one alone.

Experiment IV : Extended Practice

The results of Experiment II demonstrated that scanning time decreases with practice, at least with a simple problem like Z. It is particularly important to determine whether the relation between the time-per-item for different types of problems is also altered. Experiments I and II showed that wider items take longer to analyze; will this remain true after extended practice? Experiments I and III

TABLE 3

Mean Time-per-Item (Sec) in Experiment III

Each entry is the mean of the slopes of the 3 Ss, each slope based on about 14 measurements.

LETTER-CONTEXT	DAY	PROBLEM					
		Q	−Q	Z	−Z	QvZ	−Qv−Z
Angular	1	0.08	0.36	0.24	0.45	0.13	0.74
	2	0.07	0.35	0.22	0.49	0.17	0.61
Round	1	0.58	0.68	0.11	0.34	0.60	0.82
	2	0.46	0.61	0.09	0.32	0.56	0.77

showed that problems involving letter-absence, which require S to identify the critical letter on each line, take longer than problems in which a single instance of a letter is to be located. Will this also remain true after extended practice?

PROCEDURE.

Each of 3 Ss was given 17 or 18 sessions on more or less consecutive weekdays. Four problems were used: Z and −Z, each in two-letter and six-letter widths. The letter-context included B, D, F, H, J, L, M, Q, R, S, T, V, and X as well as Z. Usually, all four problems were presented each day, with the order of presentation varied from one day to the next.

RESULTS.

The results for one S, plotted in Figure 2, show that items six letters wide take at least twice as long as those two letters wide, even after three weeks, and that −Z takes much longer than Z in items of both widths. The results for the other two Ss (which cannot be presented for lack of space) substantiate these conclusions.

There were, however, pronounced individual differences in the effect of practice. One of the other two Ss began with times-per-item from 50–200% longer than those of the S, whose data are plotted, and much larger day-to-day variation. The third S began more slowly still, but improved dramatically, and attained speeds comparable to those of the first S by the third week. These differences are comparable to those stressed by Bryan and Harter in their classical study of telegraphy as a cognitive skill.[5]

Experiment V: Extended Practice with Parallel Scanning

Experiments I and III demonstrated that one scans for either of two targets as quickly as for a single target. It seemed important to determine whether this parallelism extends to more than two targets, and also whether it survives prolonged practice. Three Ss served for 30 or 31

[5] W. C. Bryan and Noble Harter, Studies in the physiology and psychology of the telegraphic language, *Psychol. Rev.* 1897, *4*, 27–53.

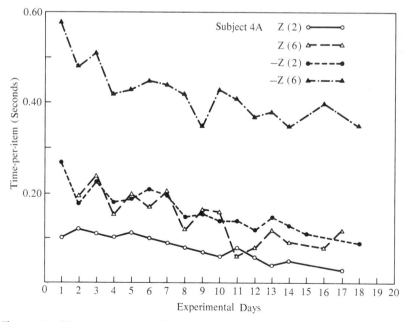

FIGURE 2   Time-per-item as a function of day of practice. Each point represents a single slope, based on about 12 measurements.

weekdays, more or less consecutively, in an attempt to answer these questions.

PROCEDURE.

All items were six letters wide (with a minor exception noted below), and the letter-context was the same as that of Experiment 4. On each of the first seven days, every S worked on four single-target problems: H, M, Q, and Z. These four problems also were presented later, on four different days interspersed in the later portion of the experiment, to provide a baseline with which parallel scanning could be compared. Beginning on the eighth day, each S was presented regularly with three two-target problems instead: HvM, HvZ, and QvZ. On the thirteenth day, a four-target problem, HvMvQvZ, was introduced and became a regular part of the procedure. In this problem, the critical item might contain *any* of the four target letters, and S did not know which until he found it. Of course, no non-critical item contained any of the four letters. On the last few days of the experiment (Day 26 or later), another problem was introduced for exploratory purposes. This was HvMv

QvZ in a format *eight* letters wide instead of six. After 4–6 days of practice with this problem, none of the Ss has achieved the speed with which they were doing HvMvQvZ (6). As far as it goes, this finding seems to confirm the results of Experiment IV, but we will not consider it further here.

RESULTS.

The results for one of the Ss are plotted in Figure 3. The other two Ss produced very similar data. It is evident that parallel scanning can be sustained and that it applies to situations involving four targets. All three Ss were scanning the two- and four-target problems with about equal speed in the last week. This speed was generally within the range of speeds used on the single-target problems, although slightly above the mean of the speeds on the four single targets. It appears consistently possible to be on the lookout for several things at once.

It would be difficult to maintain that these results are due to interleaving. There might indeed be enough dead time between analyses for slanting lines, say, to

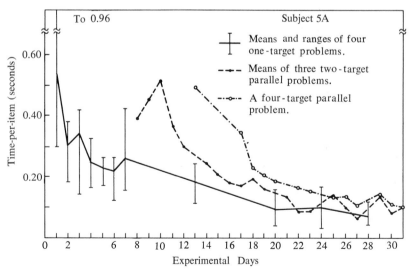

FIGURE 3   Time-per-item as a function of day of practice. For the one-target problems, each point is based on four slopes; for the two-target problems each is based on three; there is a single four-target problem. Each slope is based on about 12 measurements.

carry out the detection of roundness, but one would expect these dead times to diminish with practice; Z should gain more from practice than ZvQ. The data contradict this prediction, because times-per-item for the different problems converge with practice instead of separating. The finding with HvMvQvZ also argues for simultaneity rather than for interleaving. How much dead time can there be?

Summary

The method of visual scanning was employed in five experiments to obtain direct measures of the processing time of human information. The results indicate that the method is reliable and permit several tentative conclusions about the organization of cognitive processes in the identification of printed letters. (1) At simple levels, several distinct processes of recognition can function simultaneously in the analysis of a single stimulus-configuration. (2) No such simultaneity appears in the analysis of *spatially distinct* parts of the input, even after extended practice. (3) The recognitive hierarchy for a given task can be altered to take advantage of different contextual or other conditions. (4) Positive indentification of a letter (such as is necessary when a response is contingent on its absence) takes longer than the simple search made when the response is to be contingent on its presence.

High-Speed Scanning in Human Memory*

SAUL STERNBERG
Bell Telephone Laboratories

Abstract. *When subjects judge whether a test symbol is contained in a short memorized sequence of symbols, their mean reaction-time increases linearly with the length of the sequence. The linearity and slope of the function imply the existence of an internal serial-comparison process whose average rate is between 25 and 30 symbols per second.*

How is symbolic information retrieved from recent memory? The study of short-term memory (1) has revealed some of the determinants of failures to remember, but has provided little insight into error-free performance and the retrieval processes that underlie it. One reason for the neglect of retrieval mechanisms may be the implicit assumption that a short time after several items have been memorized, they can be immediately and simultaneously available for expression in recall or in other responses, rather than having to be retrieved first. In another vocabulary (2), this is to assume the equivalence of the "span of immediate memory" (the number of items that can be recalled without error) and the "momentary capacity of consciousness" (the number of items immediately available). The experiments reported here (3) show that the assumption is unwarranted.

* *Science*, 1966, vol. 153, pp. 652–654. Copyright © 1966 by the American Association for the Advancement of Science.

Underlying the paradigm of these experiments is the supposition that if the selection of a response requires the use of information that is in memory, the latency of the response will reveal something about the process by which the information is retrieved. Of particular interest in the study of retrieval is the effect of the number of elements in memory on the response latency. The subject first memorizes a short series of symbols. He is then shown a test stimulus, and is required to decide whether or not it is one of the symbols in memory. If the subject decides affirmatively he pulls one lever, making a positive response; otherwise he makes a negative response by pulling the other lever. In this paradigm it is the identity of the symbols in the series, but not their order, that is relevant to the binary response. The response latency is defined as the time from the onset of the test stimulus to the occurrence of the response.

Because they are well learned and highly discriminable, the ten digits were used as stimuli. On each trial of experiment 1, the subject (4) saw a random series of from one to six different digits displayed singly at a fixed locus for 1.2 seconds each. The length, s, of the series varied at random from trial to trial. There followed a 2.0-second delay, a warning signal, and then the test digit. As soon as one of the levers was pulled, a feedback light informed the subject whether his response had been correct. The trial ended with his attempt to recall the series in order. For every value of s, positive and negative responses were required with equal frequency. Each digit in the series occurred as a test stimulus with probability $(2s)^{-1}$, and each of the remaining digits occurred with probability $[2(10-s)]^{-1}$.

Each subject had 24 practice trials and 144 test trials. Feedback and payoffs were designed to encourage subjects to respond as rapidly as possible while maintaining a low error-rate. The eight subjects whose data are presented pulled the wrong lever on 1.3 percent of the test trials (5). Recall was imperfect on 1.4 percent of the trials. The low error-rates justify the assumption that on a typical trial the series of symbols in memory was the same as the series of symbols presented.

Results are shown in Figure 1. Linear regression accounts for 99.4 percent of the variance of the overall mean response-latencies (6). The slope of the fitted line is 37.9 ± 3.8 msec per symbol (7); its zero intercept is 397.2 ± 19.3 msec. Lines fitted separately to the mean latencies of positive and negative responses differ in slope by 9.6 ± 2.3 msec per symbol. The difference is attributable primarily to the fact that for $s = 1$, positive responses were 50.0 ± 20.1 msec faster than negative responses. Lines fitted to the data for $2 \leqslant s \leqslant 6$ differ in slope by an insignificant 3.1 ± 3.2 msec per symbol.

The latency of a response depends, in part, on the relative frequency with which it is required (8). For this reason the fre-

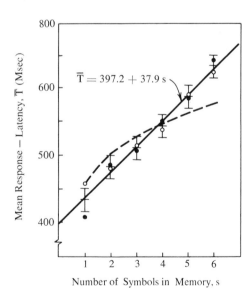

FIGURE 1   Relation between response latency and the number of symbols in memory, s, in experiment 1. Mean latencies, over eight subjects, of positive responses (filled circles) and negative responses (open circles). About 95 observations per point. For each s, overall mean (heavy bar) and estimates of $\pm \sigma$ are indicated (6). Solid line was fitted by least squares to overall means. Upper bound for parallel process (broken curve.)

quencies of positive and negative responses and, more generally, the response entropy (8), were held constant for all values of s in Experiment 1. However, the test-stimulus entropy (predictability) was permitted to co-vary with s.

Both response and test-stimulus entropies were controlled in Experiment 2, in which the retrieval process was studied by an alternative method similar to that used in more conventional experiments on choice-reaction time. In Experiment 1, the set of symbols associated with the positive response changed from trial to trial. In contrast to this varied-set procedure, a fixed-set procedure was used in Experiment 2. In each of three parts of the session, a set of digits for which the positive response was required (the positive set) was announced to the subject (4); there followed 60 practice trials and 120 test trials based on this set. The subject knew that on each trial any of the ten digits could appear as the test stimulus, and that for all the digits not in the positive set (the negative set) the negative response was required. Each subject worked with non-intersecting positive sets of size $s = 1$, 2, and 4, whose composition was varied from subject to subject.

Stimulus and response entropies were both held constant while s was varied, by means of specially constructed populations of test stimuli. Let x_1, y_1, y_2, z_1, . . . , z_4 and w_1, . . . , w_3 represent the ten digits. Their relative frequencies in the population were x_1, 4/15; each y, 2/15; each z, 1/15; and each w, 1/15. The three sequences of test stimuli presented to a subject were obtained by random permutation of the fixed population and assignment of x_1, the y_1, or the z_1 to the positive response. Thus, the population of test stimuli, their sequential properties, and the relative frequency of positive responses (4/15) were the same in all conditions (9).

A trial consisted of a warning signal, the test digit, the subject's response, and a feedback light. Between a response and the next test digit, 3.7 seconds elapsed. As

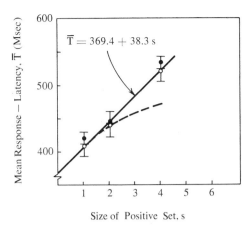

FIGURE 2   Relation between response latency and the size of the positive set, s, in experiment 2. Mean latencies, over six subjects, of positive responses (filled circles) and negative responses (open circles). About 200 (positive) or 500 (negative) observations per point. For each s, overall mean (heavy bar) and estimates of $\pm\,\sigma$ are indicated (6). Solid line was fitted by least squares to overall means. Upper bound for parallel process (broken curve).

in Experiment 1, feedback and payoffs were designed to encourage speed without sacrifice of accuracy. The six subjects whose data are presented pulled the wrong lever on 1.0 percent of the test trials (5).

The results, shown in Figure 2, closely resemble those of experiment 1. A positive set in Experiment 2 apparently played the same role as a series of symbols presented in Experiment 1, both corresponding to a set of symbols stored in memory and used in the selection of a response. As in Experiment 1, linear regression accounts for 99.4 percent of the variance of the overall mean response-latencies (6). The slope of 38.3 $\pm$ 6.1 msec per symbol is indistinguishable from that in experiment 1; the zero intercept is 369.4 $\pm$ 10.1 msec. In Experiment 2, the relation between latencies of positive and negative responses when $s = 1$ is not exceptional. Lines fitted separately to latencies of the two kinds of response differ in slope by an insignificant 1.6 $\pm$ 3.0 msec per symbol.

The linearity of the latency functions suggests that the time between test stimulus and response is occupied, in part, by a serial-comparison (scanning) process. An internal representation of the test stimulus is compared successively to the symbols in memory, each comparison resulting in either a match or a mismatch. The time from the beginning of one comparison to the beginning of the next (the comparison time) has the same mean value for successive comparisons. A positive response is made if there has been a match, and a negative response otherwise.

On trials requiring negative responses, s comparisons must be made. If positive responses were initiated as soon as a match had occurred (as in a self-terminating search), the mean number of comparisons on positive trials would be $(s + 1)/2$ rather than s. The latency function for positive responses would then have half the slope of the function for negative responses. The equality of the observed slopes shows, instead, that the scanning process is exhaustive: even when a match has occurred, scanning continues through the entire series. This may appear surprising, as it suggests nonoptimality. One can, however, conceive of systems in which a self-terminating search would be inefficient. For example, if the determination of whether or not a match had occurred were a slow operation that could not occur concurrently with scanning, self-termination would entail a long interruption in the scan after each comparison.

On the basis of the exhaustive-scanning theory, the zero intercept of the latency function is interpreted as the sum of the times taken by motor response, formation of the test-stimulus representation, and other unknown processes whose durations are independent of the number of symbols in memory. The slope of the latency function represents the mean comparison-time. The two experiments, then, provide a measure of the speed of purely internal events, independent of the times taken by sensory and motor operations. The average rate of between 25 and 30 symbols per second is about four times as high as the

maximum rate of "subvocal speech" when the words are the names of digits (11). This difference suggests that the silent rehearsal (12) reported by subjects in both experiments should probably not be identified with high-speed scanning, but should be thought of as a separate process whose function is to maintain the memory that is to be scanned.

In view of the substantial agreement in results of the two experiments, one difference in procedure merits particular emphasis. A response in Experiment 1 was the first and only response based on a particular series, made about three seconds after the series had been presented. In contrast, the positive set on which a response was based in experiment 2 had been used on an average of 120 previous trials. Evidently, neither practice in scanning a particular series nor lengthening of the time it has been stored in memory need increase the rate at which it is scanned.

In accounting for human performance in other tasks that appear to involve multiple comparisons, theorists have occasionally proposed that the comparisons are carried out in parallel rather than serially (13, 14). (This perhaps corresponds to the assumption mentioned earlier that the momentary capacity of consciousness is several items rather than only one. Are the present data inconsistent with such a proposal? Parallel comparisons that begin and also end simultaneously (14) are excluded because the mean latency has been shown to increase with s. A process in which multiple comparisons begin simultaneously is more difficult to exclude if the comparison times are independent, their distribution has nonzero variance, and the response is initiated when the slowest comparison ends. A linear increase in mean latency cannot alone be taken as conclusive evidence against such a process. The magnitude of the latency increase that would result from a parallel process is bounded above, however (15); it is possible to apply the bound to these data (16). This was done for the negative responses in both experiments, with the results shown by the broken curves in Figures 1 and 2. Evidently, the increase in response latency with s is too great to be attributed to a parallel process with independent comparison times (17).

Other experiments provide added support for the scanning theory (16). Two of the findings are noted here: (i) variation in the size, n, of the negative set ($n \geqslant s$) had no effect on the mean latency, indicating that stimulus confusability (10, 18) cannot account for the results of Experiments 1 and 2; (ii) variation in the size of a response-irrelevant memory load had no effect on the latency function, implying that the increase in latency reflects the duration of retrieval and not merely the exigencies of retention.

The generality of the high-speed scanning process has yet to be determined, but there are several features of Experiments 1 and 2 that should be taken into account in any comparison with other binary classification tasks (14, 19): (i) at least one of the classes is small; (ii) class members are assigned arbitrarily; (iii) relatively little practice is provided; (iv) high accuracy is required and errors cannot be corrected; and (v) until the response to one stimulus is completed the next stimulus cannot be viewed.

References

1. MELTON, A. W. *J. Verbal Learning Verbal Behavior* 2, 1 (1963).
2. MILLER, G. A. *Psychology, the Science of Mental Life* (Harper and Row, New York, 1962), p. 47.
3. These experiments were first reported by S. Sternberg, "Retrieval from recent memory: Some reaction-time experiments and a search theory," paper presented at a meeting of the Psychonomic Society, Bryn Mawr, August 1963.
4. Subjects were undergraduates at the University of Pennsylvania.
5. These trials were excluded from the analysis. Three other subjects in experiment 1 (two in experiment 2) were rejected because they exceeded an error criterion. Their latency data, which are not presented, resembled those of the other subjects.
6. For both experiments the data subjected to analysis of variance were, for each subject, the mean latency for each value of s. So that inferences might be drawn about the population of subjects, individual differences in mean and in linear-regression slope were treated as "random effects." Where quantities are stated in the form $a \pm b$, b is an estimate of the standard error of a. Such estimates were usually calculated by using variance components derived from the analysis of variance.
7. The analyses of variance for both experiments provided a means of testing the significance of differences among slopes. Significance levels are .07 (experiments 1) and .09 (experiment 2), suggesting true inter-subject differences in slope; the population distribution of slopes has an estimated standard deviation of 8.0 msec per symbol.
8. GARNER, W. R. *Uncertainty and Structure as Psychological Concepts* (Wiley, New York, 1962).
9. A result of this procedure is that other factors in choice-reaction time were also controlled: stimulus discriminability (10); information transmitted (8); and information reduced, M. I. Posner, *Psychol. Rev.* 71, 491 (1964); P. M. Fitts and I. Biederman, *J. Exp. Psychol.* 69, 408 (1965).
10. SHEPARD, R. N. and J. J. CHANG, *J. Exp. Psychol.* 65, 94 (1963); M. Stone, *Psycholmetrika* 25, 251 (1960).
11. LANDAUER, T. K. *Percept. Mot. Skills* 15, 646 (1962).
12. BROADBENT, D. E. *Perception and Communication* (Pergamon, New York, 1958), p. 225.
13. CHRISTIE, L. S. and R. D. LUCE, *Bull. Math. Biophys.* 18, 89 (1956); A Rapoport, *Behavioral Sci.* 4, 299 (1959).
14. NEISSER, U. *Amer. J. Psychol.* 76, 376 (1963); *Sci. Amer.* 210, 94 (1964).
15. HARTLEY, H. O. and H. A. DAVID, *Ann. Math. Stat.* 25, 85 (1954).
16. S. Sternberg, in preparation.
17. Exponentially distributed parallel comparisons (13) and other interesting theories of multiple comparisons (18) lead to a latency function that is ap-

proximately linear in log s. Deviations of the overall means from such a function are significant ($P < .03$) in both experiments.

18. WELFORD, A. T. *Ergonomics* 3, 189 (1960).

19. POLLACK, I. J. *Verbal Learning Verbal Behavior* 2, 159 (1963); D. E. Broadbent

and M. Gregory, *Nature* 193, 1315 (1962).

20. Supported in part by NSF grant GB-1172 to the University of Pennsylvania. I thank D. L. Scarborough for assistance, and J. A. Deutsch, R. Gnanadesikan, and C. L. Mallows for helpful discussions.

Supplementary Report: The Effect of Stimulus Duration and Luminance on Visual Reaction Time*

DAVID RAAB   ELIZABETH FEHRER

Brooklyn College

Raab, Fehrer, and Hershenson (1961) found that simple reaction time (RT) was independent of stimulus duration over the range of 10 to 500 msec. Luminance, on the other hand, was found to be an important determiner of RT. Since intensity rather than total energy (intensity times duration) determined RT, it is obvious that the critical duration (CD) for RT is 10 msec. or less for the three luminance levels (3000, 30, and 0.3 ft-L) investigated.

The term critical duration has been borrowed from visual threshold studies, which have shown reciprocity (Bunsen-Roscoe law) up to a CD of aproximately 100 msec., beyond which temporal integration ceases and the threshold is defined solely in terms of luminance.

It seemed worthwhile to determine the CDs in the mediation of RT for the luminances previously studied and the relation between RT and stimulus duration below these critical values. In the experiment to be reported, the six durations ranged from 0.5 to 20 msec., and thus overlapped the range used previously. Two additional intermediate luminances were included.

Method

Target flashes were generated and RTs measured by the same equipment as that employed in our previous study. A single Tektronix wave-form generator provided the gating pulses for the glow modulator tube; pulse durations were switched between trials, as required.

In order to generate flashes having wave forms as rectangular as possible, the driving pulses were shaped to "overvolt" the glow modulator tube, and the tube itself was placed next to an ultraviolet source. With these arrangements, flash energy was found to be proportional to flash duration within

* *Journal of Experimental Psychology*, 1962, vol. 64, pp. 326–327. This research was supported by grants from the National Science Foundation (G-6456) and from the National Institute of Neurological Diseases and Blindness (B-1028) and by funds provided by Brooklyn College. The data were gathered by Carlos Goldberg and Naomi Maizel as part of an honors course.

0.5 db. from 0.5 to 20 msec. The circular target, 1 cm. in diameter, subtended 1° 10′ of arc and was viewed binocularly.

Two senior honors students and the 2 authors served as Ss. Each S served in 30 experimental sessions. Computations are based on data of the last 25 sessions. Only one luminance was used in a given session; the five luminances were counterbalanced over test days for each S. Each session consisted of four blocks of 18 trials each, in which each combination of the six durations and three foreperiods appeared once in random order. Only the four longer durations could be explored for the 0.3 ft-L luminance, since this light was below foveal threshold when presented for 0.5 or 1 msec.

Each session began with 5 min. of dark adaptation. Four practice trials preceded the recorded trials. The four blocks were separated by 1-min. rest periods.

The 12 RTs obtained in a session for each of the six durations were reduced to 10 by discarding the longest and the shortest RT. Testing over 25 days (5 at each luminance) thus yielded means for each luminance-duration combination based on 50 trials.

Results and Discussion

Mean RTs for the 4 Ss combined are plotted in Figure 1. Each data point is thus based on 200 RTs.

For the two higest luminances, duration is unrelated to RT over the range studied. For the 30 ft-L flash, there was a 10-msec. increase in RT when its duration was reduced from 5 to 0.5 msec. For the two lowest luminances, stimulus duration has a far more marked effect on RT, RT being obviously an accelerated function of flash briefness.

Our results show that the CD for moderately intense stimuli (3000 and 300 ft-L) is remarkably brief, being less than 0.5 msec. At 30 and at 3 ft-L, CD lies between 2 and 5 msec. For the weakest target, the

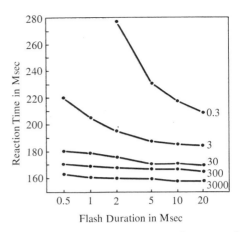

FIGURE 1   Reaction time as a function of stimulus duration. (The parameter is flash luminance in ft-L. Each data point is the mean for 4Ss).

CD lies between 10 and 25 msec. The present study shows a small decrease in RT as duration increased from 10 to 20 msec. In the previous study, a smaller decrease occurred between 10 and 25 msec., but there was no further decrease when this stimulus was prolonged beyond 25 msec.

These CDs for RT are far shorter than the 100-msec. value previously reported for absolute threshold (e.g., Baumgardt & Hillmann, 1961) or the minimal value of 30 msec. reported by Graham and Kemp (1938) for the incremental threshold at their highest background luminance. The three dependent variables, RT, RL, and DL, are thus differently related to stimulus duration, with the CD being obviously shortest for RT.

Although luminance differences are confounded with test days (i.e., only one luminance was studied in a given test session), the effect of luminance on RT is pronounced and is apparent at all durations studied. That RT decreases when luminance is increased is consistent with earlier findings (see Woodworth & Schlosberg, 1954). But the form of the relation between luminance and RT will depend on stimulus duration *unless* each stimulus duration is greater than the CD. In other words, our data could be replotted to display six different luminance-RT functions, one for each flash duration.

Our results show that although the overt response to a target flash may not appear until much later, the minimal latency of that response is determined very shortly after stimulus onset. The finding that increasing duration may cease to be effective long before the criterion response appears parallels the classical observation of this fact made by Hartline (1934). The fact that RT is determined by so brief a "package" of luminous energy is consistent with our earlier finding that RT is independent of the growth (with duration) of phenomenal brightness. In addition, it helps to explain why retroactive (metacontrast) masking of a flash does not affect its RT (Fehrer & Raab, 1962).

References

BAUMGARDT, E., and B. HILLMANN, Duration and size as determinants of peripheral retinal response. *J. Opt. Soc. Amer.*, 1961, *51*, 340–344.

FEHRER, E., and D. RAAB, Reaction time to stimuli masked by metacontrast. *J. exp. Psychol.*, 1962, 63, 143–147.

GRAHAM, C. H., and E. H. KEMP, Brightness discrimination as a function of the duration of the increment in intensity. *J. gen. Psysiol.*, 1938, *21*, 635–650.

HARTLINE, H. K. Intensity and duration in the excitation of single photoreceptor units. *J. cell. comp. Physiol.*, 1934, 5, 229–247.

RAAB, D., E. FEHRER, and M. HERSHENSON, Visual reaction time and the Broca-Sulzer phenomenon. *J. exp. Psychol.*, 1961. *61*, 193–199.

WOODWORTH, R. S., and H. SCHLOSBERG, *Experimental psychology.* (Rev. ed.) New York: Holt, Rinehart and Winston, Inc. 1954.

Visual Evoked Potentials as a Function of Flash Luminance and Duration*

J. D. WICKE   E. DONCHIN
D. B. LINDSLEY
University of California, Los Angeles

Abstract. *Computer-averaged evoked potentials were recorded to visual stimuli of constant duration and varying luminance, as well as to flashes whose luminance and duration varied reciprocally. With constant duration, the latency, amplitude, and waveform of the evoked response varied as a function of luminance. The effects of decreasing the luminance on amplitude and waveform of the responses can be balanced by increasing the duration of the flash. This reciprocity between luminance and duration suggests a relationship between apparent brightness and evoked potentials.*

The data from several studies of visual evoked potentials in humans, in which light flashes of constant duration were

* *Science*, 1964, vol. 146, pp. 83–85. Copyright © 1964 by the American Association for the Advancement of Science.

used, suggest that the wave-form of the potentials varies as a function of stimulus luminance (*1*). The use of flashes of constant duration, however, makes it difficult to separate the effect of the physical parameter, luminance, from that of the psychological parameter, apparent brightness, since the latter may vary as a function of both luminance and duration (2). It is therefore of interest to relate these physical and psychological dimensions to electrophysiological data.

One method of holding brightness constant while changing physical parameters is suggested by Bloch's law, sometimes referred to as the Bunsen-Roscoe law (2, 3). According to this law, the apparent brightness of flashes shorter than some critical period C depends on both luminance and duration. In other words, flashes which vary in these physical parameters can be made to have the same apparent brightness as long as the product of their luminance and duration remains constant, and C is not exceeded. The exact value of the critical period, C, varies with the conditions of observation, but it is usually given at about 100 msec. Using this method, we have investigated the average visual evoked potentials elicited by light flashes varied in both luminance and duration and thereby related to apparent brightness.

Two different stimuli were presented to the fovea of the right eye in Maxwellian view: a semi-circle of 1° 22′ visual angle along its diameter, and a full circle of 2° 6′ visual angle. The light sources were Sylvania R1131C glow modulator tubes, whose luminous intensities were initially equated by means of a photomultiplier display on a cathode ray oscilloscope. The maximum luminance of the circular stimulus and that of the semicircular stimulus was 9000 mlam. Flash duration was controlled by two Grass-S4B stimulators monitored by an electronic counter. The subjects fixated four dim red lines converging upon the stimulus area and pressed a key to trigger each flash arrhythmically about once every 2 seconds (4). When sufficient stimulations had accumulated, the experimenter terminated that series. Electrical potentials were amplified by a Grass model 6 electroencephalograph and recorded on magnetic tape. The average evoked poten-

tials were obtained with a Mnemotron Computer of Average Transients, a 1-second epoch being used, with a sampling rate of 400 per second. All records presented here are from the scalp over the visual area, 2.5 cm above the inion and 2.5 cm to the right of the midline, with reference to the left ear lobe.

Figure 1 shows the average evoked potentials obtained from one of seven subjects exposed to flashes of constant duration (10 msec) and varying luminance [see Donchin (5) for further details]. As flash luminance was reduced over a range of 4 log units, changes occurred in the number, amplitude, and latency of the components of the average evoked potential as well as in the overall waveform. With the stimulus of greatest luminance, namely 9000 mlam, two diphasic waves appear in the average evoked potential (abc and cde in Figure 1). Negative peak latencies occur at about 80 and 175 msec (b, d); positive peak latencies, at about 120 and 210 msec (c, e).

In the average evoked potentials elicited by the circular stimulus, the peak-to-trough amplitude of the first diphasic component (b–c) decreases as the luminance is reduced and eventually disappears into the background activity. The peak-to-trough amplitude of the second diphasic component (d–e) initially increases as luminance is decreased and reaches a maximum approximately when the first diphasic wave disappears. With further reduction in luminance, the amplitude of this component sharply diminishes, and a long positive wave of 200 to 400 msec develops when the luminance approaches threshold values. The negative peak latencies of both diphasic waves increase with reduced luminance, by approximately 40 msec over 5 log units.

These same trends are apparent when the luminance of the semicircular stimulus is reduced. The wave-forms tend to be similar when the stimuli are approximately the same number of log units above threshold. Thus the differences in contour and retinal area play a small role in determining the waveform of the average evoked potential for these stimuli. Confirming a previous suggestion (6), we may conclude that stimuli of relatively high luminance (at least 3 log units above threshold) elicit average evoked potentials with at least two diphasic components, whereas dimmer flashes evoke a response in which only the second diphasic component is apparent.

An indication of the stability of the evoked potential patterns (general form, amplitude, and latency of components) is shown, for three of seven subjects, in Figure 2. Here, the average evoked potential tracings, resulting from a number of replications in which the same stimulus was employed, have been superimposed to show that the intra-subject variability is small. Inter-subject variability is greater but there is sufficient similarity in the pattern, and latency of the component peaks, to identify them relative to the stimulus parameters. Similar results in terms of intra- and inter-

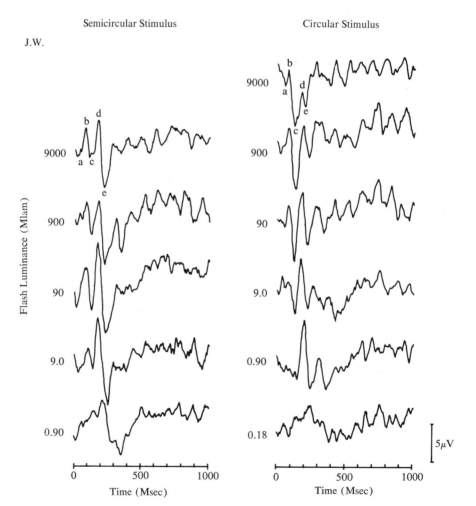

FIGURE 1   Effect of flash luminance on average evoked potentials for subject J. W., with semicircular and circular stimulus flashes of constant duration (10 msec). Flash onset occurs at the start of each trace. Each average is based on 100 stimulations. Negativity at visual area in this and subsequent figures is upward. The bottom traces in both columns are responses to stimuli just above subjective threshold; areal differences account for their different luminance values.

subject variability are reported by Dustman and Beck (7). In this connection, it would appear to be better to study the evoked potentials of a few individual subjects intensively rather than many subjects more superficially.

To determine the extent to which the waveform is related to the apparent brightness of the flashes, the luminance and duration of the semicircular stimulus were varied reciprocally so that their product (mlam × msec) was constant. Three such product-values were investigated, 900, 9000 and 90,000: stimulus duration varied from 1 msec to 150 msec. Figure 3 shows the results for two of three subjects.

Two general trends are apparent. Within rows, where luminance is varied for flashes of constant duration, changes in the form, amplitude, and latency of the evoked potentials are seen. These changes correspond with those indicated in Figure 1, where luminance was varied over 5 log units for a 10-msec flash. On the other hand, the waveform and amplitude of the average evoked potentials within most columns, where the luminance-duration product is constant, show a striking similarity.

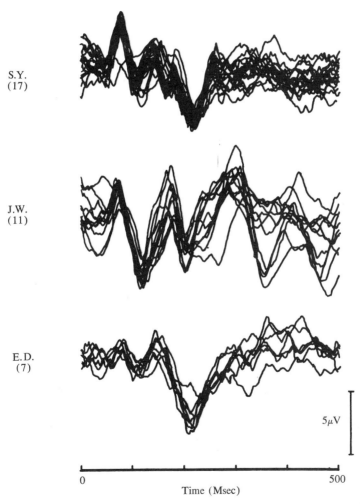

FIGURE 2   Reliability of average evoked potentials for given stimulus conditions for subjects S. Y., J. W., and E. D. The number of superimposed traces, each of which is based on 100 stimulations, is indicated below the subject's initials. Circular stimulus: 9000 mlam, 10 msec.

(a)

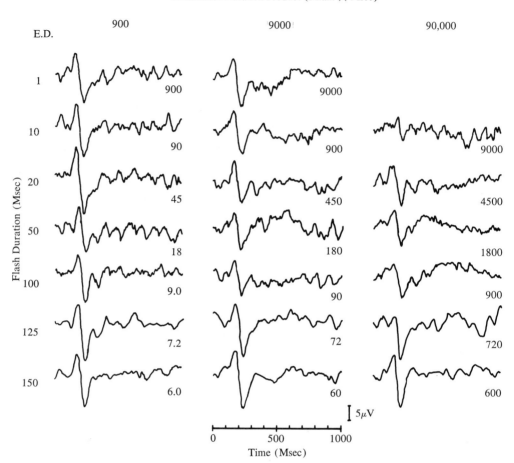

FIGURE 3   Average evoked potentials from visual area for subjects E. D. (A) and J. W. (B) for different luminance-duration products, with the semicircular stimulus. Each trace is based on 100 stimulus flashes; onset of flash at start of trace. Number beneath each trace indicates luminance in millilamberts.

In other words, increased duration of the flashes compensates for decreased luminance. These data indicate that the waveform and amplitude of the average evoked potentials depend on the total luminous energy of apparent brightness, in accordance with Bloch's law.

It will be noted within a given column that the latency of the negative peaks of both diphasic waves increases as luminance is decreased to compensate for increasing duration. A similar increase in latency as a function of luminance is shown in Figure 1. Thus the latency of the evoked potential components appears to be determined

largely by the luminance of the flash. Prolongation of the flash tends to preserve the pattern of the response but has no appreciable effect on the latency of its components.

The data presented here suggest that the waveform and amplitude of average evoked potentials recorded from the occipital area of the cortex are systematically related to the luminance-duration product and therefore to the apparent brightness of the eliciting flashes. In addition, the latency of the response to the flashes appears to be related to the luminance of the flash independently of its duration.

(b)

Luminance-Duration Product (Mlam × Msec)

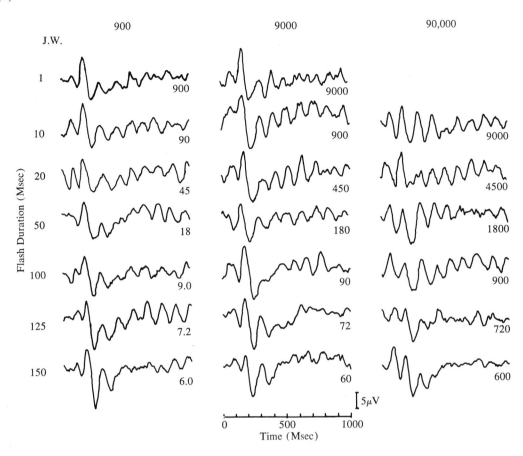

Time (Msec)

References

1. TEPAS, D. I., and J. C. ARMINGTON, *Vision Res.* 2, 449 (1962); M. Ebe and T. Mikami, *Tohoku J. Exptl. Med.* 78, 17 (1962); F. Contamin and H. P. Cathala, *Electroencephalog. Clin. Neurophysiol.* 13, 674 (1961).

2. LEGRAND, Y., *Light, Colour and Vision* (Wiley, New York, 1957).

3. BRINDLEY, G. S., *Physiology of the Retina and Visual Pathway* (Arnold, London, 1960), p. 177.

4. For a detailed description of apparatus used in stimulus presentation and control, see R. C. Boyle, "An investigation of perceptual interference resulting from successive visual presentations," dissertation, University of California, Los Angeles (1963).

5. DONCHIN, E., "Cortical evoked potentials and retroactive masking and enhancement effects with brief paired flashes of light," dissertation, University of California, Los Angeles (1964).

6. DONCHIN, E., J. D. WICKE, D. B. LINDSLEY, *Science* 141, 1285 (1963).

7. DUSTMAN, R. E., and E. C. BECK, *ibid.* 142, 1480 (1963)

8. Supported by Army contract DA-49-007-MD-722 and aided by Navy contract Nonr 233(32). We gratefully acknowledge use of facilities and equipment of the Data Processing Laboratory of the Brain Research Institute, UCLA. We thank Gary Galbraith and Stephen Young for their assistance.

Tendencies to Eye Movement and Perceptual Accuracy*

HERBERT F. CROVITZ

Veterans Administration Hospital, Durham, N. C.

WALTER DAVES

Duke University

The present study deals with one possible role of sensory-motor factors in perception. While the movement of the eyes leads to new visual stimulation which may be relevant in perceiving, the neural activity responsible for an eye movement may itself play a role in perceptual integration whether or not an eye movement occurs and whether or not the sensory feedback effects of an eye movement are supplied to the locus of perceptual integration. This neural state tending to produce an eye movement and having a possible role in perceptual processing will be called a "tendency to eye movement."

The postulated process may be related to the process underlying the use of the term tendencies to eye movement as used previously in psychology. For example, Woodworth (1938) cites a theory relating eye movements to the Müller-Lyer illusion which ". . . admits that actual movements do not occur in all cases, but assumes that a tendency to such movement is sufficient to give the impression of length" (p. 645). Recently the term has been used in perceptual theory by Gaffron (1950), Heron (1957), and Crovitz (1960).

In normal visual experience, perception may be affected by both the feedback supplied by eye movement and by the neural state which initiated the movement. Using a tachistoscope, however, when exposure time is shorter than the latency of eye movement, the eye movements which occur lead to the fixation of the blank post-exposure field. The *first* eye movement which occurs must be the result of the tendency to eye movement existing at the initiation of the movement. If, as assumed, there is a relationship between the tendency to eye movement qua neural state, and perception, a relationship should exist between some property of the initial eye movement, as an index of the tendency, and some property of perception. It would appear reasonable that a property in which a relationship could be shown would be the directionality of eye movement and perceptual accuracy; i.e., a congruence might be expected between the direction of the initial eye movement and the direction of the more accurate field.

Method

STIMULUS MATERIALS

The stimulus material[1] consisted of three sets of eight cards, each card with

* *Journal of Experimental Psychology*, 1962, vol. 63, pp. 495–498. The authors are indebted to Karl Zener for his valued advice in the formulation and execution of this study; to Robert L. Green who made available part of the eye movement recording apparatus used, and to Paul G. Daston for critical reading of the report.

[1] The perceptual situation chosen was determined by requirements of a replication of an unpublished study on perceptual anisotropies and laterality done by Hilborn at Duke University. The present report, however, does not relate to the specifics of Hilborn's problem.

numerals appearing at 3°, 5°, and 7° of visual angle of both the left and right stimulus fields of a Gerbrands mirror tachistoscope. The tachistoscope was fitted with an eye aperture occluder such that the line of numerals across the whole field could be viewed binocularly or with the left or the right eye alone. Each set of eight cards used in the three viewing conditions (both eyes, left eye alone, right eye alone) had each of the numerals (2–9) in each of the six positions once. Otherwise the positions for the numerals were randomly selected. The numerals, executed in India ink using a Zephyr lettering kit, stood about ³⁄₁₆ in high, and subtended a visual angle of about 30′.

PROCEDURE

Cards were presented in a fixed random order, binocular and monocular trials intermixed. On each trial S adjusted the eye aperture occluder according to E's instructions, viewing with both eyes, left eye alone, and right eye alone for a total of eight trials each. A constant exposure time of 100 msec was used, and since the latency of voluntary eye movements is somewhat longer than this (Woodworth, 1938) such post-exposure eye movements could not lead to fixation of a numeral.

RECORDING TECHNIQUES

An electro-oculograph technique was used to record initial postexposure eye movements. Eye movement potentials were amplified by a Grass Model III-D high efficiency EEG machine equipped with converter-demodulators (Grass Model CD-3) in order to provide dc voltage input to the pen. Electrodes were made of jeweler's "high fine" silver disks, 1 mm. thick by 8 mm. diameter, plated with silver chloride and encased in silver cups, in general agreement with the method suggested by Ford and Leonard (1958).

TABLE 1

Frequency of Occurrence of Each Combination of Accuracy Difference and Eye Movement Direction for Each Viewing Condition

VIEWING CONDITION	MORE ACCURATE FIELD	EYE MOVEMENT DIRECTION			
		RIGHT	LEFT	NO.	TOTAL
Both eyes	Right	30	3	10	43
	Left	2	32	7	41
	Equal	5	14	9	28
	Total	37	49	26	
Right eye	Right	39	4	12	55
	Left	6	8	13	27
	Equal	8	11	11	30
	Total	53	23	36	
Left eye	Right	18	8	11	37
	Left	4	26	13	43
	Equal	3	17	12	32
	Total	25	51	36	

Electrodes were placed bitemporally for recording the horizontal components of the eye movements. A second channel was connected to the tachistoscope timer such that a sharp spike was produced on the moving paper record each time the stimulus field was flashed on and each time it was flashed off allowing for and leading to a check that the initial eye movement recorded began after the stimulus material flashed off. Paper speed was 30 mm/sec.

Before the electrodes were taped into position, the skin sites were washed with acetone and lightly sanded with fine grade sandpaper in order to reduce the resistance between the pair of electrodes. While the resistance was not measured directly (an extremely low voltage ohmmeter was not available and the phosphene effect of passing a current through the electrodes might have produced undue anxiety in the naive Ss) the resistance was considered sufficiently low when a calibration eye movement of 7° produced a pen deflection of at least 5 mm. on the eye movement channel with the gain setting used.

INSTRUCTIONS

The instructions to S were to fixate a centrally placed dot in the fixation field upon a "ready" signal, to refrain from moving his eyes until the stimulus appeared, to move his eyes to whatever numeral or numerals he pleased when the stimulus appeared.

The S was told to write on an answer sheet after each trial the numerals he had seen in the positions in which they had appeared.

SUBJECTS

Fourteen naïve college students served as Ss.

Results

The data support the hypothesis that a congruence in direction exists between the initial postexposure eye movement and the more accurate field on trials in which there was both an eye movement and an accuracy difference between the fields. There were more congruent than noncongruent trials ($t = 5.05$, $P < .01$), and this relationship held for 13 of the 14 Ss (a binomial test giving $P < .01$).

This congruence also appears in each viewing condition individually. Table 1 presents the frequency of occurrence of trials with each combination of eye movement direction and accuracy difference for each viewing condition.

Disregarding perceptual accuracy, in both monocular sets of trials there are twice as many initial eye movements in the direction of the viewing eye than in the opposite direction; i.e., with right eye alone there are more initial eye movements to the right than to the left ($t = 4.12$; $P < .01$) and with left eye alone there are more initial eye movements to the left than to the right ($t = 5.36$; $P < .01$).

Scorable initial postexposure eye movements (in a latency range of from 150 msec. to 1000 msec. after stimulus onset) did not occur on about 30% of the trials. This can, in part, be attributed to the electro-oculograph method used. It was found to be subject to interference from eye blinks and occasional galvanic skin response potentials when such occurred in the latency range chosen.

Perceptual accuracy (defined as correct numeral reported in its correct location) was moderately high, with 52.9% of all reported numerals correct. However, Ss recorded only 35.8% of all reportable numerals.

Discussion

The results of the present experiment reveal a relation between relative accuracy of perception of numerals on either side of the fixation point and the direction of the initial postexposure eye movement.

The conditions of the experiment effectively precluded any visual feedback from eye movement which could lead to differential accuracy on the two sides of the field.

The significance of the present finding lies in the clear indication that other processes than visual feedback are significantly related to accuracy of report of visual material. However, the design of the study does not permit differentiation between the effects of tendencies to eye movements and the effects of possible kinesthetic feedback from the initial eye movement, a task for later empirical determination. Further, one explanation of the findings of a visual nature might lie in the possibility that the clearer perception of numerals on one side of the field, for whatever reason, might lead to an actual eye movement in that direction of relatively short latency. Congruence occurred on 85% of the trials in which the latency of initial post-exposure eye movements was from 150 to 175 msec. Whether such short latencies are consistent with an alternative explanation in terms of an underlying visual discrimination process is a question for more discriminating empirical determination.

The clear demonstration of an association between accuracy of report and eye movement direction urgently raises the need for clarification of the detailed ways in which tendencies to movement or other relevant variables may affect perception and calls for tests of alternative hypotheses. For instance, one problem is whether the motor tendency directly affects properties of the visual reaction itself or is more intimately related to the process of accurate report.

A secondary positive finding which also invites specific explanation is that initial postexposure eye movements tend to be made to the left when viewing with the left eye and to the right when viewing with the right eye. At a physiological level, the movement of the viewing eye is re-lated to action of the external rectus muscle, and movements are made toward stimuli exciting nasal retina; while at a psychological level a possible relevant fact might be that S adjusted the eye aperture occluder and was "aware" that he viewed with a given eye alone, eye movements being in the direction away from the occluded aperture. Again an experimental determination between alternative explanations might give insight into the details of the processes involved.

Regardless of ultimate explanation, the findings of the present experiment indicate the necessity of taking into account direction of initial postexposure eye movements as related to accuracy differences between the fields in tachistoscopic studies, and gives evidence that the presentation of stimuli at exposure times short enough to rule out fixation eye movements does not eliminate the possible effects of eye movements, or tendencies to eye movements, upon the subsequent report.

Summary

The direction of initial postexposure eye movements was studied in a tachistoscopic situation in which a row of numerals appeared across the visual field and no eye movement occurred until the cessation of stimulation. A congruence was found between the direction of the initial eye movement and the side of the visual field more accurately perceived. This finding supports the hypothesis that differential tendencies to eye movement are associated with differential accuracy. A secondary finding was that, in monocular viewing, there were more eye movements to the side of the viewing eye.

References

CROVITZ, H. F. Patterns of relative localization of an odd element within a visua-

grouping as a function of laterality characteristics and tendencies to eye movement. Unpublished doctoral dissertation, Duke University, 1960.

FORD, A., and J. L. LEONARD, Techniques for recording surface biolectric direct currents. *USN Electron. Lab. Rep.*, 1958, No. 839.

GAFFRON, M. Right and left in pictures. *Art Quart.*, 1950, *13*, 312–331.

HERON, W. Perception as a function of retinal locus ,and attention. *Amer. J. Psychol.* 1957, *70*, 38–48.

WOODWORTH, R. S. *Experimental psychology.* New York: Holt, 1938.

Selective Attention in Man[*]

ANNE M. TREISMAN

Oxford University

Fifty years ago psychologists thought of attention as "the focalization of consciousness" or "the increased clearness of a particular idea". But these and other definitions in terms of mental faculties or subjective experience proved sterile for empirical research and ended in a series of inconclusive controversies. Recently interest in this problem has revived, prompted both by the urgent practical need, with the increasing use of machines in industry, to define man's characteristics as an information-handling system, and by two conceptual advances: the rejection of introspective reports as a source of explanation, and the development of scientific models dealing not with the conservation and transmission of energy but with control and communication. There has been a parallel development of interest in the neurophysiological bases of attention and selectivity of response, and the prospect is that the neural structures underlying the functional processes inferred from psychological studies will ultimately be identified; but this paper is confined to behavioural research.

* *British Medical Bulletin,* 1964, vol. 20, pp. 12–16.

1. Methods, Problems and Approach

Various experimental methods have been used to investigate behaviour in tasks requiring selective attention. Our examples are mainly of human subjects responding to passages of speech. A subject is presented with two or more messages which can differ in physical characteristics such as intensity, frequency or spatial localization, in features of the language such as similarity, meaningfulness, importance to the subject or contextual probability, and finally in the degree to which the messages overlap or are separated in time. He may be asked to respond to one message or to several, or to monitor all messages and respond only to some. The response required may be immediate or delayed; it may coincide with further messages or alternate with them; and it may vary in complexity, for example it may be repeating back the message or replying to questions—the two most common tasks—or translating, writing, summarizing or recalling the message.

Examples of problems which arise are the nature of the limits in man's ability to respond to competing messages; the form

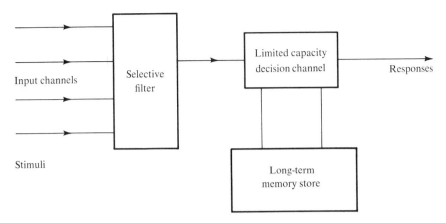

FIGURE 1 Broadbent's "Filter" and "Information Flow" model for selective attention (Broadbent, 1958). The diagram illustrates a model in which man is represented as an information-handling system. The successive parts of the model are discussed in the text.

of selective system used by the brain and the stage at which irrelevant data are discarded; finally, the way in which incoming data are analysed from sound to word and meaning, stored in short-term or long-term memory and used to determine the appropriate response. A useful approach is to start with a general descriptive model, making it more precise as evidence accumulates. The alternatives at this level are usually qualitative and the evidence relates to the type of function rather than to the actual mechanisms which carry it out, and to the order in which the processes occur rather than to their spatial lay-out. Broadbent (1958) made an important contribution with his "filter" and "information flow" theory (Figure 1), which provides the basis and starting-point for this paper. Some alternative accounts of attention are given by Hebb (1949), Sutherland (1959), Berlyne (1960) and Deutsch and Deutsch (1963).

2. Limits to Performance with Competing Inputs

Many experiments (Broadbent, 1952; Cherry, 1953; Mowbray, 1953; Poulton, 1953; Webster and Thompson, 1954) have shown that if a man must deal with competing messages there is a limit at which his performance will break down. For example, Broadbent asked his subjects to answer questions about a changing visual display and found that their efficiency was lower if two questions (in different voices) were given simultaneously. Cherry showed that subjects who repeated back a passage of prose heard through one ear were unable to report any of the verbal content of another passage presented at the same time to the other ear. They were aware of its general physical characteristics—that it was speech in a man's voice—but they failed to notice when the English changed to German or to speech played in the reverse direction.

What sets the limits to performance in tasks like these? Peripheral masking is unlikely to be the whole answer, since subjects are quite able to handle either of the two messages if no response is required to the other. Moreover, very similar results are obtained when one message is visual and one auditory (Mowbray, 1953). Competition between motor responses may be avoided by requiring successive responses to simultaneous messages, for instance asking subjects to repeat one, then recall the other, as in Cherry's experiment. Thus part at least of the interference must occur at some central stage, either in identification of the words or in memory storage.

An important finding is that this central limit is set not primarily by the number of messages but by their predictability or information content (see Crossman, p. 32 of this number of the Bulletin). Subjects can respond to two simultaneous callsigns chosen from a small set of alternatives, but to only one message chosen from a wider range (Webster and Thompson, 1954). The sound of a buzzer produces more interference with a simultaneous speech task if it requires one of two responses than if a fixed response or no response must be made (Broadbent, 1956a).

3. Broadbent's "Filter" and "Information Flow" Model

To summarize these findings, Figure 1 shows the relevant parts of Broadbent's model. A number of messages may reach the receptors together and pass along different input "channels" to a selective system which he calls the "filter". This blocks some and passes others to a single decision channel of limited capacity, which has access to information in a long-term memory store and which determines the appropriate response. The next problem is to specify the parts of the model and their interrelations in more detail.

A. INPUT CHANNELS

The word "channel" normally implies a discrete physical system with defined properties, and might be used to describe different sense organs, like eye and ear. However, many experiments have shown that messages can be selected or rejected on the basis of characteristics other than the receptors at which they arrive. Subjects can respond efficiently to one of two auditory messages if these differ in spatial position, whether real (Broadbent, 1954) or apparent (Broadbent, 1954; Treisman, 1961), in frequency range (Spieth and Webster, 1955, in intensity (Egan, Carterette and

Thwing, 1954)—in short, in any general physical feature. The efficiency of selective response declines as the difficulty of discrimination between selected and irrelevant messages is increased along any of these dimensions (Broadbent, 1958). Thus, in terms of the model, the input channels are functionally defined as carrying classes of sounds distinguished by one or more physical features which allow the filter to select between them.

Broadbent originally suggested that classes of words distinguished by their meaning might also be thought of as coming in different channels; for example, the filter might select names of food or reject taboo words. Cherry (1953) has shown that subjects can use the contextual probabilities of words to pick out one of two messages in the absence of any other cue. But this type of selection is much less efficient than that based on general physical features, for Cherry's subjects needed many trials to separate the two messages completely. If bilingual subjects are presented once only with two messages in different languages, they are hardly more efficient in repeating back one of the two than when both are in the same language, and do much worse than when the two are in different voices, despite the extreme difference at the linguistic level (Treisman, 1961). Since no message can be discarded on the basis of features still to be discriminated, rejection of classes of words could occur only during or after word identification. This allows much less economy in analysis than selection by a physical feature in the sounds of the messages, which may be discriminated at an earlier stage.

This leaves the problem of how the brain separates out the single, complex sound-wave reaching both ears into two or more channels, of which it can select one for further analysis. There have been some attempts to specify in more detail how these discriminations are carried out. For example, Cherry and Sayers (1956) have put forward a model for auditory localization in which the signals reaching the two ears are cross-correlated to determine which constitute the same message; the delay interval giving maximum correlation for each message then indicates the apparent position of each source of sound. Another example is the suggestion by Broadbent and Ladefoged (1957) that the cue distinguishing different voices is the larynx tone or pulse modulation rate of the frequency spectrum. When this is the same, different frequencies in the same or opposite ears are heard as one "sound"; when it differs, two "sounds" are heard. This pulse rate may be coded by the nervous system as a rate of firing, so that the channels are not necessarily identifiable with separate neural pathways.

B. STAGES OF INPUT ANALYSIS AND LEVEL OF FILTER

It is plausible to suppose that different features of the input messages are discriminated successively, and that the filter selects on the basis of past analyses which inputs will be passed on for further processing and which discarded. Both the order in which the different features are analysed and the stage at which the selection is made could be fixed or variable. There is some evidence that in human selective listening the channel discriminations based on general physical features are always made, and that the filter can operate only at a later stage; Cherry's subjects could report all these features of the message to which they were not attending (Cherry, 1953). I have shown that the interference with response to a selected message was determined not by the number of irrelevant messages or verbal sequences but by the number of channels in which they were presented, although the minimum physical difference between selected and irrelevant channels was kept constant (Treisman, 1961). This suggests that all the physical features distinguishing the irrelevant channels were being discriminated, whether they were needed for the task or not.

On the other hand, there is little evidence that differences in the purely verbal content of irrelevant messages are noticed or produce differences in interference, provided that they arrive in separate channels from the selected message. For example, Moray's subjects showed no trace of recognition of a repeated series of words presented in an irrelevant channel, and failed to recall digits that they had specifically been told to listen for (Moray, 1959). To ensure that this was not a limit in memory only, I asked subjects to make an immediate manual response to any digit on either channel while repeating back one message only (Treisman, 1961). The information in the manual response was the same for both channels, but subjects responded only to digits in the selected message. I also failed to produce any change in efficiency of selective response by varying the information content, the meaningfulness or the similarity of irrelevant messages, provided that no consistent differences were produced in non-linguistic features of the sounds (Treisman, 1961). (This last factor was not controlled in experiments by Webster and Thompson (1953) or by Peters (1954), who claimed to find effects on performance of the content of competing messages.)

However, there are a few interesting exceptions to the rule that the verbal content is never reported. Moray (1959) showed that subjects sometimes noticed their own names if these occurred in the irrelevant message, and suggested that there might be a specific system, before the filter, for analysing patterns and for identifying highly important signals. I found that subjects occasionally repeated a word from the irrelevant mesage if it was made highly probable in the context of the message to which they had been attending (Treisman, 1960). This is more difficult to attribute to a specific pattern-analyser, since the range of words which could be made highly probable is very large. Cherry (1953) showed that if identical messages were presented to the two ears a few seconds out of step, subjects became aware that the two were the same. To determine at what level the identity was recognized, I presented the same messages in different voices and also two messages with the same meaning in different languages, using bilingual subjects in the latter case (Treisman, 1961). In both conditions subjects still noticed the identity. Deutsch and Deutsch (1963) argue that these examples of recognition of the verbal content of "rejected" messages imply that selection is made only after full analysis of all inputs. As further support for this idea they quote studies of habituation by Sharpless and Jasper (1956) and by Sokolov (1960).

4. Habituation

If the same stimulus is presented repeatedly, the response originally made tends to decrease or disappear; this change is known as habituation. Like selective attention to competing messages, it implies some form of selectivity or filtering, and Broadbent originally attributed both to the same filter system. He postulated that this had an intrinsic bias for passing novel stimuli ("novel" implying both stimuli which had not been present before and those which had not recently been selected by the filter). As the stimuli to which the subject is being habituated are repeated, they become less novel, and the filter will shift to new channels.

Sokolov (1960) reports some interesting studies of habituation in the arousal response or "orienting reflex". He examined the decrease or disappearance of alpha blocking in the electroencephalogram and the galvanic skin response in human subjects on repeated presentations of the same stimulus. He then altered the stimulus in various ways, and found that the arousal response reappeared not only when the intensity or duration of the habituated

stimulus increased but also when they decreased. This makes it unlikely that the habituation is due to perceptual blocking or attenuation of the stimulus, and he concluded that the recurrence of the arousal response was produced not by the stimulus as such, but by a mismatch between the new stimulus and a neural record representing the features of the habituated stimulus. He found, moreover, that this mismatch could imply complex levels of analysis, such for instance as a change in meaning with words. Deutsch points out that selection in these experiments must follow more complex analysis of the signals than discrimination of the simple features which distinguish functional input channels. Broadbent's original account is probably not inconsistent with Deutsch's, since his concepts both of "novelty" and of "filtering" were very general and flexible. However, it does not follow that selection must always be made at this late stage, and a different system may control habituation from that which controls selective attention with competing and highly informative inputs.

5. Word Identification and Selective Response

I have suggested an alternative explanation of the few occasions when the verbal content is identified (Treisman, 1960, 1961). It may be that the channel filter attenuates irrelevant messages rather than blocks them completely. If so, words which were highly important or relevant to the subject could be picked out when the threshold for identifying them was permanently or temporarily lowered within the word-identification system itself, in spite of their reduced signal-to-noise ratio. A possible system for identifying words is a hierarchy of tests carried out in sequence and giving a unique outcome for each word or other linguistic unit. The decision at each test point could be thought of as a signal detection problem (cf. Tanner &

Swets, 1954): a certain adjustable cut-off or criterion point is adopted on the dimension being discriminated, above which signals are accepted and below which they are rejected as "noise". The criteria determining the results of the tests would be made more liberal for certain outcomes if favoured by contextual probabilities, by recent use or by importance. Messages attenuated by the filter would pass the tests only if the criteria had been lowered in their favour and, if not, would pass no further through the hierarchy. This would be more economical than Deutsch's full analysis, since most irrelevant words would fail tests early in the hierarchy. Broadbent & Gregory (1963) recently showed that the auditory threshold of one ear is raised if subjects are asked to attend to simultaneous digits in the other ear, and that this change is in the internal signal-to-noise ratio, not in the decision criterion. The complementary test is to show that thresholds are lowered for particular important or probable words and that this change is in the decision criterion, not the signal-to-noise ratio. There is certainly considerable evidence that, with a single message masked by noise, the threshold is lowered both for contextually probable words (Miller, Heise & Lichten, 1951) and for one's own name (Howarth & Ellis, 1961); moreover when two competing messages are presented in the same channel, selection is determined by the transition probabilities between words (Cherry, 1953; Treisman, 1961). But it has not yet been determined whether this is owing, as predicted, to a change in decision criterion.

It seems likely that the channel filter will be used only when two or more competing inputs would together overload the central decision channel. If so, it would not be brought into play in the usual restricted and monotonous environment of an habituation experiment. Habituation could then be attributed not to attenuation of certain input channels but to a change in the criteria for particular test outcomes

at any level in the identification hierarchy, depending on the common features of the habituation stimuli used. This change could thus be as specific as the effects found by Sokolov, leaving the criteria for all other features unaffected.

6. Shifting of Attention

The final problems raised relate to the setting and shifting of the filter from one channel to another and to the retrieval of temporarily "rejected" messages. Does the filter take time to shift to a new channel, and can one message be held temporarily in store while another is handled? In an ingenious series of experiments Broadbent (1954, 1956b, 1957; Broadbent and Gregory, 1961) reached an affirmative answer to both questions. He presented subjects with three pairs of simultaneous digits to be recalled, one of each pair in a different input channel (either the two ears; or ear and eye; or a frequency-filtered and a normal voice). He found that at rates faster than one digit per ear per second, subjects always recalled the digits from one channel first, followed by the other, rather than alternating between the channels to approximate the correct temporal order. The alternating order was possible only when the presentation rate was reduced to half a digit per ear per second where different sense organs were used, and two-thirds of a digit per ear per second with voices differing in frequency spectrum. Two conclusions can be drawn: (i) there is a limit to the rate at which the filter can shift from one input channel to another, which is probably faster the less distinct the channels; (ii) there is a short-term store prior to the filter in which the digits from the second channel are held while those from the first are identified.

Moray (1960) questioned the first conclusion: he showed that if the digits were staggered in time, his subjects could alternate between their ears at rates much higher than those in Broadbent's experiments. But his own results also show that the subjects did worse when the digits alternated between the ears than when all were given to one ear. This again implies a limit in switching rate, although the shifts appear to be faster for staggered than for simultaneous digit pairs. Perhaps the filter shifts are facilitated by the presence of an external stimulus rather than a stored trace (as with the simultaneous digits). Gray & Wedderburn (1960) also raise a difficulty for Broadbent's account by their finding that when the words of a common phrase such as "Who goes there?" are used instead of digits, subjects are as likely to group their responses by meaning as by input channel. In this case, subjects appear to select at a later stage, perhaps to take advantage of the transition probabilities between the words and thus to compensate for any extra intereference in identifying them.

7. Short-Term Storage

Two main questions arise about the nature of the short-term store: (i) whether it is limited primarily by decay of items with time, or by interference between items held in it; (ii) whether it is used only to cope with temporary overloading caused by momentary peaks of information or as a normal stage through which all inputs must pass. Broadbent varied both the time for which the digits in the second channel had to be stored before recall (by increasing the number given in the first channel) and the number of items to be held in store (by increasing the number in the second channel). Both these changes impaired recall, suggesting that the store is limited both by a short decay time (of the order of one or two seconds) and by a small capacity. He also compared recall when subjects were told in advance which series of digits they were to repeat first and when they were told only after presentation of the digits. If all digits were auto-

matically held in store, there should be no difference between these conditions, while if digits in one channel were sent straight through, advance knowledge of the order of recall would allow subjects to choose which to send first and should thus give better results. Broadbent (1957) found that his subjects could perform in either way, but tended to change from an initial strategy of storing all digits to one of sending some through immediately, perhaps because it proves less efficient to hold all digits in the limited peripheral store.

Other recent findings may throw more light on this relatively peripheral "buffer" storage. Rabbitt (1962) has shown that two aspects of a single visual stimulus (its shape and its colour) may be treated in the same way as the digits sent to right and left ears in Broadbent's experiment on the order of recall. Thus the model for storage and selection can apply to any feature of the input which is as yet uncategorized as well as to inputs coming from one particular channel or source. Sperling (1960) reports an ingenious method of estimating the information available in a temporary store immediately after presentation of a visual display, and of measuring its decay with time. He used a sampling technique to see whether the normal limit of five or six items in the span of apprehension is set by the initial intake capacity or by a central selection. At different intervals after a short exposure he gave a signal to instruct subjects which one of several rows of items they should recall; then used the partial recall to estimate the total number of items available. He found that this was initially two or three times the number in the normal span, but declined rapidly in less than a second to the normal limit. His finding seems closely related to the change from multi-channel to single-channel functioning in Broadbent's model, although the decay time for vision may be more rapid than for hearing. Finally I compared the storage time for selected and rejected auditory messages: I repeated Cherry's experiment, presenting identical speech messages to the two ears, separated by a variable time interval, and noted the interval at which subjects recognized the identity, both with the selected message leading in time and with the rejected one leading (Treisman, 1961). In the first case the selected message had to be stored for comparison with the rejected one, and the interval for recognition was 5 sec; in the second case the rejected message was stored, and the interval fell to 1 or 2 sec. This result is consistent with Broadbent's estimate of the decay time for as yet uncategorized signals, and shows that identification of the sounds as words may treble their memory survival time.

8. Conclusion

The traditional model of attention has become both more general and more precise: it has been related to the mechanisms of perception as such and has been defined in the language of channels, information, filtering processes and storage. This clarification may open the way to a more exact linking of behavioural concepts with underlying physiological mechanisms which are now being investigated, and some of which are discussed elsewhere in this number of the Bulletin. Developments of great interest are to be expected from the convergence of these two approaches.

References

BERLYNE, D. E. (1960) Conflict, arousal and curiosity. McGraw-Hill, London.

BROADBENT, D. E. (1952) J. exp. Psychol. 43, 267.

BROADBENT, D. E. (1954) J. exp. Psychol. 47, 191.

BROADBENT, D. E. (1956a) Brit. J. Psychol. 47, 51.

BROADBENT, D. E. (1956b) Quart. J. exp. Psychol. 8, 145.

BROADBENT, D. E. (1957) Quart. J. exp. Psychol. 9, 1.

BROADBENT, D. E. (1958) Perception and communication. Pergamon Press, Oxford.

BROADBENT, D. E. and M. GREGORY. (1961) Quart. J. exp. Psychol. 13, 103.

BROADBENT, D. E. and M. GREGORY. (1963) Proc. roy. Soc. B, 158, 222.

BROADBENT, D. E. and P. LADEFOGED. (1957) J. acoust. Soc. Amer. 29, 708.

CHERRY, E. C. (1953) J. acoust. Soc. Amer. 25, 975.

CHERRY, E. C. and B. M. SAYERS. (1956) J. acoust. Soc. Amer. 28, 889.

DEUTSCH, J. A. and D. DEUTSCH. (1963) Psychol. Rev. 70, 80.

EGAN, J. P., E. C. CARTERETTE, and E. J. THWING. (1954) J. acoust. Soc. Amer. 26, 774.

GRAY, J. A. and A. A. I. WEDDERBURN. (1960) Quart. J. exp. Psychol. 12, 180.

HEBB, D. O. (1949) The organization of behavior: a neuropsychological theory. Chapman and Hall, London.

HOWARTH, C. I. and K. ELLIS. (1961) Quart. J. exp. Psychol. 13, 236.

MILLER, G. A., G. A. HEISE, and W. LICHTEN. (1951) J. exp. Psychol. 41, 329.

MORAY, N. (1959) Quart. J. exp. Psychol. 11, 56.

MORAY, N. (1960) Quart. J. exp. Psychol. 12, 214.

MOWBRAY, G. H. (1953) J. exp. Psychol. 46, 365.

PETERS, R. W. (1954) Competing messages: the effect of interfering messages upon the reception of primary messages. U.S. Naval School of Aviation Medicine, Naval Air Station, Pensacola, Florida, Joint Project Report No. 27.

POULTON, E. C. (1953) J. exp. Psychol. 46, 91.

RABBITT, P. M. (1962) Nature, Lond. 195, 102.

SHARPLESS, S. and H. JASPER. (1956) Brain, 79, 655.

SOKOLOV, E. N. (1960) In: Brazier, M. A. B., ed. The central nervous system and behavior. Transactions of the Third Conference, February 21, 22, 23, and 24, 1960, Princeton, N.J., p. 187. Josiah Macy, Jr. Foundation, New York.

SPERLING, G. (1960) Psychol. Monogr. 74, No. 11.

SPIETH, W. and J. C. WEBSTER (1955) J. acoust. Soc. Amer. 27, 866.

SUTHERLAND, N. S. (1959) In: Mechanisation of thought processes. Proceedings of a symposium held at the National Physical

Laboratory on 24th, 25th and 27th November 1958, vol. 2, p. 577. (National Physical Laboratory Symposium No. 10.) HMSO, London.

TANNER, W. P., Jr. and J. A. SWETS. (1954) Psychol. Rev. 61, 401.

TREISMAN, A. M. (1960) Quart. J. exp. Psychol. 12, 242.

TREISMAN, A. M. (1961) Attention and speech. (Thesis for D. Phil. degree) University of Oxford.

WEBSTER, J. C. and P. O. THOMPSON (1953) J. audio Engng. Soc. 1, 171.

WEBSTER, J. C. and P. O. THOMPSON (1954) J. acoust. Soc. Amer. 26, 396.

Discrimination of Successiveness: A Test of a Model of Attention*

MARIANNE W. SCHMIDT
University of Cincinnatti

ALFRED B. KRISTOFFERSON
McMaster University

Abstract. Interpreting attention as a periodic phenomenon, we show its relevance to discriminating the successiveness of signals presented to separate sense modalities. Experiments confirm the expected linear relation between the probability of discriminating pairs of successive from pairs of simultaneous signals and make it possible to infer the period of attention.

A study was made to develop and test the hypothesis that the sensory systems consist of independent channels which can be attended only one at a time. Attention is conceived of as a periodic phenomenon. The period of attention, M, is assumed to be a fixed value. When attention is directed at one channel it may be signaled to switch to a second channel by an input arriving over the second channel. Attention can switch only at the end of a period, although it may remain on a channel for multiples of M. The periodicity of attention is internally controlled; it is independent of sensory input.

Along with these assumptions, which

* Science, 1963, vol. 139, pp. 112–113. Copyright 1963 by the American Association for the Advancement of Science.

already imply that some inputs may have some effects when they are not attended, it can be asserted further that the temporal ordering of input signals in experience or behavior, or both, will be influenced by the switching order of attention. Let us consider vision (V) and audition (A) and assume that they, at least, cannot both be attended during a single period of attention. If attention is directed at V and inputs arrive simultaneously in the "display areas" of V and A, they will be coded in order VA—that is, in adjacent periods of attention, even when the individual asserts that the signals were perceived simultaneously. To be discriminated as successive they would have to arrive in the display areas sufficiently separated in time to be attended in nonadjacent periods. The probability that this will occur will depend upon the degree of difference in time of arrival of the inputs in relation to M. The symbol t refers to the difference in time of arrival of the V and A inputs in the display areas. If, under ideal conditions, attention switches reliably after the first input is scanned, then the probability that the inputs will be scanned in non-adjacent periods will be a linear function of t. The probability will be zero when $t = 0$ and will be unity when $t = M$, under the condition that attention is directed initially to the channel over which the first input arrives. If attention is directed to the channel of the second input when the first arrives, then for all values of t between zero and M the inputs will be scanned in adjacent periods.

The difference in times of arrival at the receptor surface (T) for auditory and visual stimuli should not be the same as the difference in times of arrival at the display areas (t), since conduction times differ for different modalities. There is some non-zero value of T, called x, for which $t = 0$. Positive values of T mean that the visual stimulus precedes the auditory, and negative values mean that the auditory precedes. Many lines of evidence suggest that conduction is more rapid in the auditory system, at least for stimuli of moderate intensity. Hence, for the inputs to arrive simultaneously in the display areas the light stimulus should precede the sound—that is, x would be expected to be positive.

Measurement of the probabilities of discriminating successiveness is accomplished by presenting two light-sound pairs on each trial and requiring the subject to indicate the pair for which the likelihood is greatest that the light preceded the sound. In one pair, the standard pair, T is the same for all trials and is set at a value less than x by an amount less than M. Since attention is directed to light, the signals should be attended always in adjacent periods for the standard pair. The other pair on each trial, the variable, may have any of several values of T greater than x. Under these conditions the function relating the probability of indicating the variable as the successive pair to T should be linear, intersecting the chance level (.50) at $T = x$ and rising to 1.00 at $T = x + M$.

In the experiments reported here, values of x and M were first estimated by means of a method of limits. The value of T for the standard pair in the forced-choice procedure was determined from these estimates. The forced-choice data were then obtained in daily sessions of 120 trials each, 24 for each of five values of the variable.

A neon lamp provided the visual signal, and a pure tone, delivered over a speaker, was the auditory signal. The observer was instructed to indicate the pair in which the likelihood was greatest that the light terminated before the sound. Termination rather than onset was used in order to define the relevant channels as unequivocally as possible for the observer. The stimuli came on together and remained on for about 2 seconds before termination of the first one.

The data obtained are presented in Figure 1. Two experiments, each consisting of 12 sessions, were completed for each of two observers. The number of responses determining each point in the graphs is 288.

Experiment 1 for observer R.C. provided only two data points within the range of primary interest. Least-square lines were fitted to each of the other three sets of data; omitted from the analysis was one point which did not exceed chance expectancy for observer E.H. in Experiment 2.

These data are clearly consistent with the hypothesis in that they are described adequately as linear functions. The mean absolute deviation of the points from the lines in the vertical direction is 0.74 percentage unit. Testing goodness of fit by chi-square yields values of chi-square

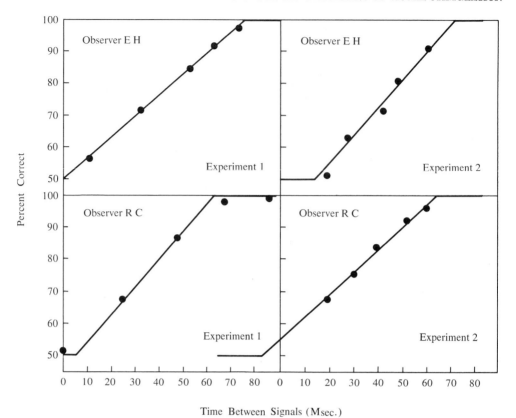

FIGURE 1   Percentage of trials on which the variable pair, rather than the standard pair, was designated "more successive" plotted against the time interval between the terminations of the light and of the sound that comprise the variable pair.

having associated probabilities of .55 to .90.

The inferred difference in conduction time x for auditory and visual stimuli averages 6.9 msec for observer E.H. and −1.1 msec for observer R.C. Positive values of x imply more rapid conduction in the auditory channel.

The mean period of attention, M, calculated for observer E.H. is 66.4 msec; for observer R.C. it is 63.8 msec. There is no indication of a directional change in M from Experiment 1 to Experiment 2 in these limited data. For E.H. the values are 74.5 and 58.3, respectively; for R.C. they are 56.5 and 72.2. The difference in M for the two experiments is fairly large for both observers, but the differences are of opposite sign.

Psychophysical data are almost invari-

ably described by cumulative normal distribution functions. The data presented here do not appear to require any hypothesis more complex than the linear hypothesis. However, it is extremely difficult to choose between these types of function (see, for example, 1), and the data obtained so far are not adequate for that purpose.

The theory discussed has much in common with theories proposed by several other workers in recent years (2). It has frequently been suggested, by us and by others, that a physiological correlate of periodic attention may be the alpha rhythm of the electroencephalogram. If this is so, M would be expected to fall within a range of 77 to 110 msec. Results for the two observers in this study do not satisfy that expectation, but experiments are being conducted with additional observers to establish this point more convincingly (3).

References and Notes

1. BLACKWELL, H. R. *Am. J. Psychol.* 66, 397 (1953).
2. PITTS, W. and W. S. McCULLOCH, *Bull. Math. Biophys.* 9, 127 (1947); W. G. Walter, *The Living Brain* (Norton, New York, 1953); J. Stroud, in *Information Theory in Psychology*, H. Quastler, Ed. (Free Press, Glencoe, Ill., 1956). Pp. 174–205; P. McReynolds, *Psychol. Rev.* 60, 319 (1953).
3. This report summarizes part of a doctoral dissertation to be submitted to the Graduate School of the University of Cincinnati by one of us (M.W.S.). We thank the Graduate School for its support of parts of this research.

The Span of Apprehension as a Function of Exposure Duration *

EMANUEL AVERBACH
Bell Telephone Laboratories

The concept of the span of apprehension derives from the assumption that visual information is processed in parallel, but there are a limited number of independent inputs that can be processed simultaneously, the limit being defined as the span. According to this notion, when a group of objects are exposed briefly and the S is required to ascertain their number, if the number of objects is below his span, the number will be perceived immediately, essentially in parallel. If the number is greater than his span, he will have to process them in sequence, by counting or otherwise.

To measure the span, experimenters briefly exposed groups of dots or other objects, varying the number from trial to trial, and determined the maximum number that could be ascertained reliably by their Ss. The brevity of the exposures was considered to be important to assure that

* *Journal of Verbal Learning and Behavior,* 1963, vol. 2, pp. 60–64. Judith B. Perkins assisted in the preparation of the stimulus materials and in running the experiment.

the exposed items were not available for processing for longer than an instant, so that the Ss would be obliged to process them simultaneously. Spans obtained in this way have an average of about 8 (Woodworth and Schlosberg, 1954).

There is little in the way of experimental justification for the assumption that the brevity of the exposures used in span experiments prevents sequential processing of the exposed material. Careful measurement of the span over a wide range of brightness levels and exposure times indicates that when brightness and contrast are adequate, changes in exposure time in what is normally taken to be the tachistoscopic range—4 to 150 msec—have little effect on the span (Hunter and Sigler, 1940). Recent studies of visual information storage (Sperling, 1960; Klemmer, 1963; Averbach and Coriell, 1961) show, in fact, that tachistoscopic information is normally available to the S for considerably longer than the duration of the exposure, unless it is erased as a consequence of the presentation and storage of "new" information

270 FACTORS IN THE PROCESSING OF VISUAL STIMULATION

(Sperling, 1960; Averbach, 1961). The Sperling, Klemmer, and Averbach studies also demonstrate, by the fact that their Ss were successfully able to utilize information presented *after* a brief test exposure in processing the previously exposed test material, that sequential processing can be performed on briefly exposed material.

Some support for the assumption that number is ascertained by a parallel process comes from reaction time studies (Kaufman, Reese, Lord, and Volkman, 1949). Using a fixed exposure time of 200 msec, they exposed groups of dots, ranging in number from 1 to 210, and measured reaction time as a function of the number of dots presented. Their results indicate that two different processes are involved in ascertaining the number of dots in a brief exposure, one for numbers of dots less than six and one for numbers greater than six. Since their Ss' accuracy was greater for groups having six or less than from from groups having more dots, and since they found reaction time—in their view, a correlate of processing time—to be about the same for the smaller numbers of dots, they concluded that small numbers are ascertained in about the same amount of time, essentially in parallel.

Complete acceptance of these conclusion is difficult for a number of reasons. For one thing, the question of the relationship between reaction times and processing times is still in question (Mowbray, 1960). Secondly, because Kaufman *et al.* used only two samples of each number of dots—two configurations with 1 dot, two with 2 dots, etc.—it is quite likely that their Ss became familiar with many of the patterns. Recognition of patterns might be a parallel process even if ascertaining number is not. Finally, it should be mentioned, a similar reaction time experiment (Saltzman and Garner, 1948) yielded negative results.

The experiment to be described aims at answering the question of whether, and within what range, the time required to ascertain the number of dots in a group is independent of the number of dots in

the group. This is done by determining how the "span" changes as a function of exposure time. This experiment differs from that of Hunter and Sigler (1940), who also measured the span as a function of exposure duration, in the following ways: (1) The exposure conditions used here—luminance, contrast, size, etc.—are such as to maximize the visability of the dots in order to assure that S's performance is limited by his ability to ascertain number and not by his ability to detect; (2) a large number of different dot arrangements are used to reduce the number of repetitions of the same arrangement and, thereby, to reduce the opportunity for S to become familiar with individual patterns; (3) an erasing field is presented immediately after the test field to assure that processing of the stimulus does not continue internally after the end of the exposure (Averbach and Coriell, 1961).

Method

To begin with, S saw a uniform white field with a fixation point in the center. Once fixated, he pressed a switch and a test field containing anywhere from 1 to 13 dots appeared for a pre-set time interval. Just as the test field went off, an erasing field, having a large number of dots that were randomly positioned, was turned on for 5 sec. The S's task was to report the number of dots in the test field. The sequence of fields is illustrated in Figure 1. A three channel, electronically controlled

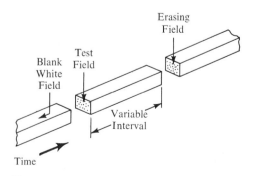

FIGURE 1 Exposure sequence.

mirror tachistoscope was used to illuminate and sequence the fields.

Twelve test-field exposure times were used in the experiment: 40, 50, 60, 75, 100, 125, 150, 175, 225, 300, 400, and 600 msec. A single session involved exposing three different test fields having the same number of dots, for each number of dots from one through 13, at each of the 12 exposure times. The exposure time was not changed after each trial but after blocks of 39 trials, each block having three fields of from one through 13 dots in random sequence. Thirty-three experimental sessions were run in all, in which the author and another Bell Telephone Laboratories employee alternated as S and E.

The test fields were produced by mounting black dots on 5×8 file cards. The dots were assigned at random to positions in a 30-position rectangular matrix—5 vertical by 6 horizontal—except that positions were balanced for each number within the limits of commensurability of the numbers. Sets of 60 different fields with the same number of dots were made for each of the numbers from 2 to 13. These were presented upside-down 50% of the time in order to vary the patterns further. A different set was used during the 15 practice sessions that preceded the experiment proper.

The tachistoscope field subtended 10° vertical by 16° horizontal at a viewing distance of 29 in. The dot matrix was centered in this field. It subtended 4.5° by 5.5°. The diameter of the dots and the edge-to-edge separation of the dots along the rows and columns was 0.5°. The background luminance was kept constant from field to field at a level of 50 ft-L. The contrast ratio was 94% so the dots were easily visible in the absence of an erasing field, even at the 40-msec exposure.

Results

Each of the 12 exposure times yields a curve relating the number of dots presented to the frequency with which that

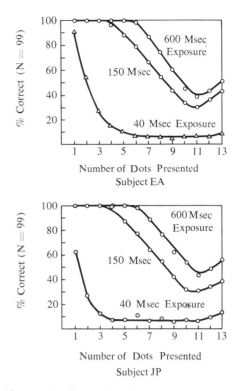

FIGURE 2   Proportion of correct reports as a function of the number of dots presented.

number was reported correctly. Figure 2 shows three such curves for each of the S's. Since the obtained curves are smooth and the changes in the curves as a function of exposure time were found to be regular, this sample illustrates the main features of the data.

It is readily apparent in the 40-msec curve that performance is better for one dot than for two, better for two dots than for three, and so forth. This might be taken as evidence that larger numbers of dots cannot be processed in the same amount of time as smaller numbers. It has been argued, however, that the span is not constant, but varies from moment to moment (Woodworth and Schlosberg, 1954, p. 98). These differences in performance, from that point of view, are due not to differences in processing time, but due to fluctuations in the span about its mean.

It is noteworthy that with a 600-msec exposure Ss did not perform perfectly with seven, or even six dots. This performance is considerably poorer than that obtained by Hunter and Sigler (1940, p. 168). Considering that the Ss were well practiced and that the display used here was highly superior in legibility, it seems reasonable to relate the poorer performance obtained here to the fact that the Ss did not have as much opportunity to become familiar with the individual patterns.

The books (Woodworth and Schlosberg, 1954) suggest that the curves relating the number of dots presented to the frequency with which they are reported correctly have an ogive shape and drop to zero or chance level for larger numbers of dots. It does not appear difficult to explain ad hoc why these do not. The S is given a limited set of response alternatives, the numbers 1 to 13, and a task in which ascertaining the smaller numbers is less difficult than ascertaining the larger ones. As exposure time is increased and performance improves—even reaching 100% on the smaller numbers—improvement would be expected on the larger numbers simply on the assumption that S guesses from a more restricted set of alternatives. What seems more difficult to explain is the consistant superiority of 12 over 11 and 11 over 10 with longer exposures. These are superior, not only in terms of more correct, but in having fewer false alarms as well.

Figure 3 shows the relationship between exposure time and the span of apprehension for the two Ss. The spans represent the 50% correct point on the curves that relate the number of dots presented to the

frequency with which the number was reported correctly (Figure 2). The span rises rapidly with increasing exposure time, at first. Then, it bows and almost levels off. On the assumption that for small numbers of dots the processing time is independent of the number of dots to be processed, one would expect the initial rise to be vertical. The obtained deviation from verticality shows clearly that if S is given less time, he processes fewer dots. If given more time, he processes more dots. The S's efficiency at utilizing this time decreases markedly when the exposure time is increased above 100 msec.

Discussion

Throughout this paper parallel and sequential processing have been identified with different processing-time characteristics. Sequential processing has been identified with processing smaller numbers of inputs in less time than larger numbers; parallel processing has been identified with processing different numbers of inputs in the same amount of time. It may be argued that the definition of parallel used here is too restrictive, that the term parallel should apply as well to all systems that accept parallel inputs in spite of the fact that their processing times increase with increases in the number of inputs (Woodworth and Schlosberg, 1954, p. 98). Such a broad definition, however, renders any distinction between parallel and sequential processing meaningless. The broad definition implies that any sequential system can be made parallel by the mere introduction of a buffer storage that takes parallel inputs and stores them long enough for them to be processed in sequence.

Although the results of this experiment show clearly that the span involves sequential processes, it would be incorrect to infer from the data presented here that ascertaining number is purely a sequential process. The stimuli used in the experiment dif-

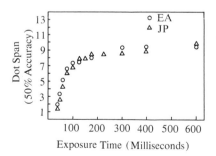

FIGURE 3   The span of apprehension as a function of exposure duration.

fered from each other, not only in number, but in their average brightness, in the perimeter of the dot areas, in the size of the areas containing the dots, etc. It would hardly be surprising if Ss made use of these additional cues in making their judgments of number.

The obtained bow-shaped relation between exposure time and the span presents a problem. Why does efficiency fall so rapidly with increases in exposure time above 100 msec? One possible explanation (Woodworth and Schlosberg, 1954, p. 98) is that ascertaining number, like other forms of judgment, is limited by discrimination. The difference between the presented number and the adjacent numbers —from which the presented number must be discriminated—remains fixed in the experiment. But the ratio of this difference to the presented number, upon which discrimination presumably depends, becomes smaller as the number presented is increased. When this ratio is equal to the hypothetical Weber fraction for number, performance reaches a maximum.

An alternative hypothesis to explain the bow-shape—also unsupported by experimental evidence—assumes that the limiting factor is short-term memory of the kind described by Miller (1956). For, although counting a regular arrangement of objects in a predetermined sequence requires a minimum of memory, in the case of a random arrangement, memory is required for identifying which dots have been counted and which have not been counted. Since only a limited number of items can be stored in immediate memory, the positions and the status—already counted versus not counted—of only a limited number of dots can be retained. The span will accordingly be limited to the maximum number of position-counting status combinations that can be held in short-term memory. Thus, there occurs a leveling off of performance with increasing exposure time.

Further experimentation is needed to shed light on the relationship between exposure duration and the span of apprehension.

References

AVERBACH, E., and A. S. CORIELL. Short term memory in vision. *Bell System Tech J.,* 1961, *40,* 309–328.

HUNTER, W. S., and M. SIGLER. The span of visual discrimination as a function of time and intensity of stimulation. *J. exp. Psychol.,* 1940, *26,* 160–179.

KAUFMAN, E. L., M. W. LORD, T. W. REESE, and J. VOLKMAN. The discrimination of visual number. *Amer. J. Psychol.,* 1949, *62,* 498–525.

KLEMMER, E. T. Perception of linear dot patterns. *J. exp. Psychol.,* 1963, *65,* 468–473.

MILLER, G. A. The magical number seven, plus or minus two. *Psychol. Rev.,* 1956, *63,* 81–97.

MOWBRAY, G. H. Choice reaction times for skilled responses. *Quart. J. exp. Psychol.,* 1960, *12,* 193–202.

SPERLING, G. The information available in brief visual presentations. *Psychol. Monogr.,* 1960, *74,* no. 11.

WOODWORTH, R. S., and H. SCHLOSBERG. *Experimental psychology,* rev. ed. New York: Holt, Rinehart and Winston, Inc., 1954.

Perceived Number and Evoked Cortical Potentials*

M. RUSSELL HARTER and C. T. WHITE

U.S. Navy Electronics Laboratory
San Diego, California

Abstract. *Evoked cortical potentials and the number of flashes perceived were compared when subjects were presented with short trains of flashes under conditions where each presented flash could not be counted individually, but the train of flashes appeared to be flickering (1 to 14 flashes at 33.3 flashes per second). The rate at which each successive perceived flash was added appeared to correspond with the rate at which the successive components of the evoked response pattern were added. The temporal nature of this pattern was similar for both single flashes and trains of flashes. The results suggest that the onset of stimulation triggers a process which has a marked effect on both the cortical and perceptual response to subsequent stimulation.*

The perceived number of flashes has been compared to the actual number of flashes presented (*1–4*). In these studies, short trains of flashes (0 to 1000 msec) were presented at a rapid rate (20 to 50 flashes/sec) under conditions where the flashes appeared to be flickering but where each presented flash could not be counted individually. The flashes were somehow grouped into perceptual units of approximately 100 msec, the perceived number of flashes being much less than the actual number of flashes presented. For example, when 14 flashes were presented at 30 flashes/sec (a flash-train duration of 430 msec) subjects most frequently reported seeing four flashes, a perceived flash being added for approximately each 100 msec of stimulation (*1, 2*).

* *Science*, 1967, vol. 156, pp. 406–408. Copyright © 1967 by the American Association for the Advancement of Science. We thank R. G. Eason for assistance. Supported in part of NSF grants GB-4067 and in part by the Navy Electronics Laboratory.

In working with averaged cortical potentials evoked by stimulus conditions similar to those used in the above experiments, we noted (i) that the temporal nature of visually evoked cortical potentials appeared to be related to the number of flashes perceived, and the occurrence of each successive perceived flash appeared to correspond with the occurrence of the successive components of the evoked response pattern, and (ii) that the temporal characteristics of cortical responses evoked by trains of flashes appeared to be similar to those evoked by single flashes. These observations suggest that "the onset of stimulation in some way initiates a process (or processes) which can have a marked influence on the perceptual response to any succeeding stimulation" (*3*). We investigated the relation between the temporal nature of evoked cortical potentials initiated by single flashes and trains of flashes and the number of flashes that were perceived.

Four subjects were presented trains of flashes containing from 1 to 14 flashes.

Longer trains were not used because the variability in judgment becomes too great for our present purposes. The flashes were presented at 33.3 flashes/sec (there was an interval of 30 msec between flashes) and, therefore, the flash-train duration varied from 0 to 390 msec. Since the subjects did not always report the same perceived number of flashes to a given number of flashes presented, the subjects reported their perceptual response after each flash-train presentation. Each subject participated in three experimental sessions; in every session each of the 14 flash-trains was presented 50 times. A given flash-train was randomly selected and presented 25 times; then, another flash-train was randomly selected from those remaining and presented 25 times; this procedure was continued until all the flash-trains were presented. Therefore, the three sessions, four subjects, 14 flash-trains, and 50 flash-train presentations resulted in a total of 7000 observations.

The light flashes (4 mm in diameter and 10 μsec in duration) were viewed binocularly with the subject's eyes 60 cm from the flash source. The subjects fixated a point 5 mm above the flash source. The number (1 to 14) and frequency (33.3 flashes/sec) of flashes within each flash-train, as well as the time interval between flash-trains (1.5 second), were controlled with an American Electronic Laboratory model 104A laboratory stimulator which triggered a model PS-2 Grass photostimulator set on intensity 2. The flashes were approximately 2.5 log intensity units above threshold and were surrounded by a white homogeneous field (18.3 mlam). These conditions elicited a simple sinusoidal evoked cortical potential wave form and a clear perception of flicker.

Evoked cortical potentials were obtained in response to the same flash-trains used to elicit the perceptual judgments. The procedure used for recording evoked cortical potentials has been described (5). Briefly, potentials were recorded monopo-larly from the occipital region of the scalp, the active electrode being placed 2.5 cm above the inion and 2.5 cm to the right of the midline. The reference electrode was attached to the right ear lobe. The potentials were amplified by an Offner type R dynograph and averaged with a Mnemotron model 400C computer of average transients. The averaged potentials were recorded on graph paper with a model 135C Moseley autograph (X-Y plotter).

The effects of the number of flashes in the flash-train on the resulting evoked cortical potential are illustrated in Figure 1. Consistent with past findings (3), the number of flashes of this size and intensity had no apparent differential effect on the evoked potential wave form. Although Figure 1 contains data from only one subject (C.W.) and four flash-trains (containing 1, 4, 8, and 12 flashes), these data are typical of all the flash-trains and subjects investigated. Therefore, in the remaining figure, the responses elicited by all the flash-trains are combined into a single average potential for each subject and each session.

The relation between evoked potential wave form and the number of flashes perceived is illustrated in Figure 2. The solid lines show the oscillations in the averaged evoked cortical potential wave form and the dotted lines show the frequency that each perceived number of flashes (N_s) was reported. For example, subject C.W. most frequently reported seeing one flash when one to four flashes were presented, two flashes when four to seven flashes were presented, three flashes when seven to ten flashes were presented, and so forth.

The results indicate that there was an initial fusion period, after the onset of stimulation, when the short flash-trains were perceived as fused (the subjects most frequently reported seeing one flash). The duration of the fusion period varied between subjects, ranging from 50 to 100 msec (flash-trains containing three to five flashes). In all cases, this period ended

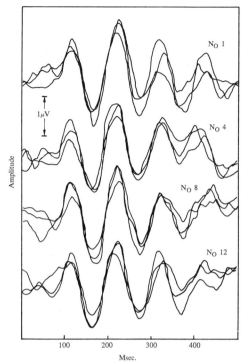

FIGURE 1   Evoked cortical potentials elicited by flash-trains containing 1, 4, 8, and 12 flashes. Flashes were presented at 33.3 flashes/sec. Background illumination 602.6 mlam and fixation point directly on flash source. Each of the three superimposed evoked cortical potential traces represents the summation of responses to 100 flash-trains. Negativity downward. Subject is C. W.

after the first major deflection in the evoked cortical potential wave form. Otherwise, there was no apparent relationship between the evoked potential wave form and the perception of number during this period.

After the initial fusion period, that is, when the subjects most frequently reported seeing two or more flashes, the periodicity of the averaged evoked potentials appears to reflect the rate at which the successive perceived counts were added up to 350 msec after the onset of the flash-train. This relationship did not hold for subjects M.L. and R.H. when flash-trains longer than 350 msec were presented. To compare the rates at which the successive evoked po-

tential components and the successive perceived counts were added, the average interval between the points in time when each N_s was maximally perceived was compared to the average interval between the corresponding evoked cortical potential peaks or troughs (whichever the case may be). The respective average between count and between component intervals for each subject (in msec) were 103 and 107 (C.W.), 95 and 102 (M.L.), 97 and 90 (R.H.), and 102 and 103 (J.A.). If the similarity of these two average periods is a coincidence, it is indeed a striking one. Furthermore, the fact that both measures have 10 counts per second has considerable generality in view of the number of studies which have reported evoked potential data (3, 6) and perceptual data (1–4) similar to that reported here.

Our results may be summarized as follows: (i) the temporal nature of averaged evoked cortical activity was similar for potentials evoked by both single flashes and trains of flashes; (ii) the first large deflection in the averaged evoked cortical potential wave form appeared to reflect the minimal period of time required for the perception of two flashes, assuming a conduction-time latency of 35 msec; and (iii) after the initial fusion period, the periodicity of the averaged evoked cortical potential wave form appeared to reflect the frequency at which additional perceptual flashes were added for flash-trains up to 350 msec in duration. (Sufficient data were not collected to speculate on this relationship for longer flash-train durations.) These and other results suggest that the onset of stimulation initiates a central process which may have a marked effect on both the cortical and perceptual response to subsequent stimulation.

In conclusion, the findings of our study possibly are related to those of other studies concerned with cortical excitability cycles in humans (7, 8). In these studies, the excitability of the cortex was shown to

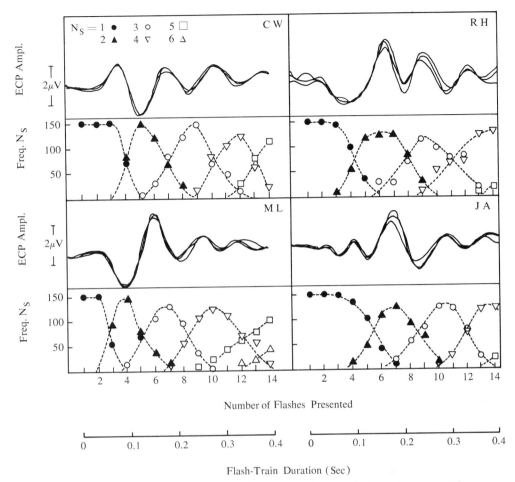

FIGURE 2   Effects of number of flashes presented on evoked cortical potentials
(ECP) and perceived number of flashes (Ns). Flashes were presented at 33.3
flashes sec. Each of the three superimposed evoked cortical potential traces represents the summation of responses to all flash-trains within a single session (700
flash-trains consisting of 1 to 14 flashes). Negativity downward. Frequency of Ns
reflects the number of times each flash-train was perceived as 1, 2, 3, 4, 5, or 6
flashes, each flash-train being presented 150 times. Due to conduction time-lag,
flash-train onset is displaced 35 msec after trace onset.

fluctuate rhythmically after stimulation by
a brief flash of light; when a pair of flashes
was presented, the amplitude of the evoked
cortical potential resulting from the second
flash varied as a function of the time between the two flashes. The evoked cortical
potential wave form elicited by the first
flash may reflect the periodicity of the
excitability cycle (8). In humans, a complete excitability cycle had a duration of
approximately 100 msec, which is in accord

with the duration of each perceived flash
and evoked potential oscillation in our
experiment. Apparently the flashes presented within a single excitability cycle
(possibly reflected by the periodicity of the
evoked cortical potential wave form) were
grouped into a single perceptual unit and
were perceived as a single flash. These
findings are relevant to the current theoretical interest in the concept of central
intermittency in perception (2, 9).

References

1. FORSYTH, D. M. and A. CHAPANIS, *J. Exp. Psychol.* 56, 385 (1958).
2. WHITE, C. T., *Psycholog. Monogr.* 77, Whole No. 575 (1963).
3. WHITE, C. T. and R. G. EASON, *ibid.* 80, Whole No. 632 (1967).
4. CHEATHAM, P. G. and C. T. WHITE, *J. Exp. Psychol.* 44, 447 (1952); C. T. White and P. G. Cheatham, *ibid.* 58, 441 (1959).
5. EASON, R. G., L. R. AIKEN, C. T. WHITE, and M. LICHTENSTEIN, *Perceptual Motor Skills* 19, 875 (1964).
6. EASON, R. G., D. ODEN, and C. T. WHITE, *Electroencephalog. Clin. Neurophysiol.*, in press.
7. CIGANEK, L., *Ann. N.Y. Acad. Sci.* 112, Art. 1, 241 (1964).
8. GASTAUT, H., A. ROGER, J. CORRIOL, and R. NAQUET, *Electroencephalog. Clin. Neurophysiol.* 3, 401 (1951).
9. BERTELSON, P., *Quart. J. Exp. Psychol.* 18, 153 (1966); M. R. HARTER, *Psychol. Bull.*, in press; D. B. LINDSLEY, *Electroencephalog. Clin. Neurophysiol.* 4, 443 (1952); J. M. Stroud, in *Information Theory in Psychology*, H. Quastler, Ed. (Free Press, Glencoe, Ill., 1955), p. 174; N. Wiener, *Cybernetics* (Wiley, New York, 1948), pp. 156–167.

CHAPTER 4

Form and Pattern Perception

Stabilization of the Retinal Image:
A Review of Method, Effects, and Theory[*]

E. G. HECKENMUELLER
University of Cincinnati

A summary is presented of 3 basic methods used in reducing or stopping involuntary eye movements in order to produce a stable retinal image. This stabilization produces some degree of fading or disappearance of the target being viewed. Additional effects on such factors as acuity and contrast thresholds are considered, as well as the effects of such variables as exposure time, flicker, attention, meaning, and target complexity on the nature and extent of target disappearance. Some explanations for the phenomenon are presented, and the theoretical implications of invariant stimulation on the perceptual process are discussed.

It has been known for some time that the eye is always in motion. Even under conditions where steady fixation is attempted, small, involuntary movements of the eye are always present. Knowledge of these movements has generated considerable experimentation in an attempt to understand their role in the visual process. This experimentation, most of which has been conducted within the past 12 years, has included investigations on both physiological and psychological levels. The questions which the experimentation has attempted to answer are: (*a*) What are the nature and extent of these involuntary eye movements? (*b*) What effect do these movements have on the visual process? A historical summary of the answers to the first question is presented by Ratliff and Riggs (1950), together with their own experimentation on the problem. Their results indicate that the involuntary movements

consist of: a slow drift of the eye; a rapid, jerking movement (saccadic); and a small, rapid tremor superimposed on the drift. In view of the general nature of the methods which have been used in attacking the problem, the second question might better be stated as: What are the effects on the visual process of reducing or stopping the involuntary movements of the eye?

The purpose of this paper, therefore, is to summarize the attempts to answer this second question. The summary will proceed by considering: the methods of producing a stabilized image, the perceptual effects of a stabilized image, a summary of effects and comments, some relevant physiological evidence, and the theoretical implications of the stabilized image phenomenon.

Methods of Producing a Stabilized Retinal Image

A summary of relevant studies gives an indication of the extent of the movements. The drift movements are of a magnitude

[*] *Psychological Bulletin*, 1965, vol. 63, pp. 157–169. The author would like to thank W. N. Dember and R. J. Senter for their critical reading of this paper.

of approximately 1 minute arc per second. The saccadic movements occur with magnitudes between 2 and 50 minutes of arc with an average somewhere around 5–6 minutes of arc. These saccades occur irregularly at intervals ranging from .2 to .5 second intervals. The small tremor movements occur with a magnitude of less than .5 minute of arc at a rate up to 150 cycles per second. An interesting finding regarding these tremor movements (Riggs and Ratliff, 1951) is that they are not coordinated between the two eyes in binocular fixation. So-called "corresponding points" on the two retinas, therefore, are not actually corresponding points.

One effect of these involuntary movements, of course, is to keep the retinal image constantly in motion. It has been shown (Riggs, Armington, and Ratliff, 1954) that the retinal image is virtually stationary for exposures up to .01 second. Exposures as long as .10 second result in an average displacement of the retinal image of 25 seconds of arc which is approximately equal to the diameter of one foveal cone. In an exposure of 1.00 second, the average displacement is 3 minutes of arc. Thus a retinal image will traverse an average of 10 receptors during a 1.00-second exposure. The question then becomes one of stabilizing these movements to observe whether or not they are a necessary condition for normal vision.

One method of producing a stabilized image on the retina would be simply to stop the movements of the eye. The resulting discomfort and possible dire consequences to the subject, however, make this method the least likely of all. An alternate approach would be to present the visual stimulus in such a way that its image remains in the same position relative to the retina regardless of any movement of the eye. In other words, the visual stimulus must move with a direction and magnitude exactly opposite that of the eye movements so that the effect is one of cancelling out the movements so far as the retina is con-

cerned. Many techniques have been developed to achieve this compensation, but all of them can be classified under one of the following three basic methods: methods in which the internal structure of the eye is imaged on the retina, methods which use an optical lever system, and methods in which the target is attached directly to the eye. Each of these methods, together with their variations, will be discussed in turn.

Internal Structure of the Eye

The first of these methods, those in which the internal structure of the eye is imaged on the retina, exploits well-known entoptic phenomena. For example, shadows of the retinal capillaries can be produced by moving a pinhole in front of the pupil while viewing a uniformly illuminated surface. Another type of entoptic phenomenon is known as "Haidinger's brushes" (Ratliff, 1958). These images have an hour-glass shape and can be seen by viewing a field of blue light through a polarizer. In all of these phenomena, the image which is being observed is a part of the eye structure itself and therefore remains stationary relative to the retina. The advantages of such methods are the very stable images which they afford and the absence of distortions (to be discussed later) which are sometimes introduced in methods using attachments to the eye. The disadvantages of these methods are mainly that the variety of targets which can be viewed is extremely limited and that there is no way to manipulate the degree of movement of the retinal image.

Optical Lever System

The second general class of methods involves the use of optical lever systems. These methods are fairly complex in design, but they are, in some ways, very versatile. They consist essentially of a system which projects the target on a small mirror mounted on a contact lens worn by the subject. The image is then viewed by the subject in one of two ways. Either the image from the mirror is directed onto a screen, or it is fed through a system of lenses focusing the image directly on the pupil. The latter method produces what is called a Maxwellian view. In both cases, the position of the image on the retina is made dependent on the position of the eye. As the eye moves, the mirror which is mounted to the contact lens worn on the eye also moves. Since the target is being projected from this mirror, then the target itself moves. The direction of eye movement is thus compensated for, but not the magnitude of movement. This is due to the difference in the angular displacement of the projected image relative to the angular displacement of the eye. By altering the length of the optical path through which the projected image reaches the eye, these differences in angular displacement can be exactly compensated. This alteration is accomplished through the use of suitably arranged mirrors and/or prisms placed in the optical path of the system (see Ratliff and Riggs, 1950, for a description of such a system).

A disadvantage of these systems is that the mirror from which the target is reflected is mounted in the contact lens on the temporal side of the pupil. The resulting geometry is such that only the eye movements in the horizontal direction can be compensated. An improved system was later developed (Clowes and Ditchburn, 1959) which alleviates this problem to a considerable degree. In this system, the mirror is mounted on a stalk which is attached to the contact lens. This type of mounting permits alignment of the mirror so that it is normal to the visual axis with the incidence of the light normal to the mirror. This arrangement allows for compensation in both the horizontal and vertical planes, and also compensates for slight translational movements of the head. The measurements by Clowes and Ditchburn

indicate that 99.7% of the natural movements of the eye is eliminated.

An additional characteristic of these systems concerns the positioning of the subject's head. This is obviously an important consideration in such methods since any movement of the head naturally imposes additional movements on the eye. The usual technique for controlling the position of the head is to have the subject place his head against a rest while grasping a dental biting-board with his teeth.

The major advantages of these optical lever methods are the increased range of targets which can be used compared to the methods using entoptic phenomena, the capability of manipulating certain characteristics of the target, and the possibility of varying the degree of stabilization of the retinal image. Certain disadvantages are introduced, however, mainly as a result of the physical attachments on the eye which are required. These disadvantages would include slippage of the contact lens relative to the eye and the possibility of changes in the shape or movement of the lens especially when the eye engages in the relatively large flick movements. In addition, the torsional movements of the eye are not controlled which, among other things, limits the size of the field which can be used.

Targets Mounted Directly to Eye

The third general class of methods of producing a stabilized image consists of attaching the target directly to the eye. Ditchburn and Pritchard (1956) placed a calcite crystal, 6 millimeters in diameter, between two polaroid sheets and attached this to a stalk mounted on a contact lens. Illumination of the assembly produced interference fringes that resulted in the subject's seeing a pattern of rings. As the eye engaged in its involuntary motions, the target, being attached to the eye by way of the contact lens, moved with it, thus producing a stabilized image on the retina.

This method yielded a large field, but the variety of targets was restricted.

A later step in the development of this method (Yarbus, 1957) was to mount a target onto a stalk which was attached to a high-power contact lens. The high-power lens, however, produced problems with regard to the quality of the retinal image. These problems were alleviated somewhat by improving the quality of the lens, but the lens also presented difficulties with regard to the subject's comfort. It was necessary to use a local anesthetic and also to tape back the eyelids of the subject.

Pritchard (1961a) presented a design which offered further improvements. A miniature light collimator was constructed and attached to a stalk on the contact lens. A target was inserted in the end of the collimator and was illuminated by a tiny grain-of-wheat light bulb. The resulting collimated light from the illuminated target thus appeared at optical infinity with the eye in a relaxed state. The advantages to this design are: stabilization of vertical, horizontal, and torsional movements over a large field is attained; focusing is required only when the system is constructed and none thereafter; anesthetics and retraction of the eyelids are not required; and the target can be changed during the experiment. The disadvantages compared to the optical lever systems are mainly that variations in the degree of stabilization cannot be achieved. It also possesses the other disadvantages to be discussed later which are associated with techniques involving physical contact with the eye.

Several investigators have used the techniques described under the third general class of methods of producing a stabilized image. Certain discrepancies which appeared among their results led Barlow (1963) to conduct a series of experiments designed to determine more precisely the amount of stabilization actually being achieved by the different methods. His study centered primarily on the problem of the slippage of the contact lens.

Barlow notes that two types of contact lens have been used in previous studies. One is the full-fitting type which covers the entire cornea. This type seats on the conjunctiva which is attached to the sclera only at the limbus. The second one is a suck-on type which seats near the limbus and is held in place by suction. The second type is, therefore, much less subject to slippage, although it does produce discomfort to the subject which can become quite painful with some of the more vigorous eye movements. By simultaneously comparing the stabilized images produced by each of these techniques with afterimages which presented true stabilized images, Barlow was able to determine the amount of slippage of both types of lens. It was found that the full-lens type yielded an average movement of $\pm 3\frac{1}{2}$ minutes of arc while the suck-on type yielded an average of ± 40 seconds of arc with a maximum of about 2 minutes of arc.

Perceptual Effects of a Stabilized Image

A question might now be raised: If the normal perception of a target involves eye movements, what happens to the perception of a stabilized target in which eye movements have, in effect, been canceled? The first attempts to answer this question were undertaken independently by Ditchburn working in England and by Riggs working in the United States.

Ditchburn and Ginsborg (1952) conducted a study in which they stabilized the image using an optical lever system. Stabilization was acomplished only in the horizontal plane, and the subject viewed the stabilized image projected on a screen. Ditchburn mentions that he had carried out preliminary experimentation in Dublin in 1945, but he was unable to repeat the experiment or to check on the degree of stabilization obtained. In the 1952 experiment, a circular patch of light covering a 1-degree visual field was presented as the target. The patch was divided vertically into two halves by making one half of the field either 30, 40, or 60% brighter than the other half. It was found that, after a few seconds of viewing, the demarcation line disappeared and the two halves appeared to be of equal brightness. This condition would persist for 2–3 seconds and would recur at intervals of about 1 minute. It was also observed that the contrast threshold was higher under the stabilized condition than it was under normal viewing conditions. Ditchburn proposed as a possible explanation that the eye recognizes the abnormality of the stabilized condition and temporarily makes an adjustment such as accommodation which would cause the image to reappear.

Riggs, Ratliff, Cornsweet, and Cornsweet (1953), also using an optical lever system, compared the effects as studied under three conditions of viewing: with eye movements compensated, with normal eye movements, and with exaggerated eye movements. The target consisted of a circular test field containing a fine, vertical line. Several different fields were used, each containing lines of different widths. These test fields were viewed as stabilized images (stabilization in the horizontal plane only) and were displayed inside a nonstabilized annulus which was also in the visual field. The subjects viewed the image for 1-minute periods and indicated the presence or absence of the vertical line by releasing a telegraph key. The results showed that, under the compensated condition, the vertical lines disappeared after a few seconds of viewing. After continued viewing, the lines would reappear and then fade out again, at a rate which was a function of the width of the line; that is, the finer the line, the less time it remained visible. Under the normal condition, fine lines disappeared and reappeared, but heavy lines remained constant, while under conditions of exaggerated motion, scarcely any lines disappeared.

In view of these findings, Riggs considered the possible function that the eye movements serve in the visual process. One function might be for purposes of acuity. The ability of the eye to make the increasingly finer brightness discriminations implied by acuity may be enhanced by eye movements. Another possibility arises from consideration of a physiological process proposed by Hecht (1937). This process hypothesizes that under conditions of constant illumination, the photoreceptor process in the retinal receptor cells reaches a stationary state in which opposing reaction rates become equal and the cells then fail to emit further neural impulses. Hartline (1940) mentions that few neural fibers respond to constant illumination—most fibers respond to "on-off" or "off" states of illumination only. Eye movements, then, might be required to maintain neural firing in general and may not be concerned primarily with acuity.

A second part of Riggs' study involved the same viewing conditions and the same targets, but the targets were presented for very brief durations so that disappearance did not occur and only the subject's ability to detect the lines was measured. Four exposure times were used: .034, .110, .213, and .472 second. The results indicate little difference in acuity as a function of stabilized, normal, or exaggerated viewing conditions. The stabilized condition was slightly superior at the shorter exposure times, and the exaggerated condition was better at .2-second exposures and over. The normal condition yielded results in between the other two conditions. Riggs' conclusion was that eye movements did not enhance acuity but rather seemed to function primarily to overcome loss of vision due to constant stimulation.

Ratliff (1952) conducted another study which also investigated the role of eye movements in visual acuity. A circular target with a grid of either vertical or horizontal striations was presented to the subject under normal viewing conditions. Records of the subject's eye movements were made by an optical lever arrangement in an attempt to correlate amount of movement with acuity. No evidence was found which would indicate an enhancement of acuity by eye movements; in fact, large amounts of tremor and drift were found to be detrimental to acuity.

Cornsweet (1956), again using an optical lever system with the same type of vertical-line target used previously, introduced a controlled rate of flicker in the illumination of the target. The rate of flicker was varied from .8 to 4.4 cycles per second. At the slower rates of flicker, the stabilized image remained visible for periods of time resembling those of normal viewing conditions. As the flicker rate increased, however, disappearance time increased until at 4.4 cycles per second the amount of time that the target was visible returned to values resembling those of the stabilized image. These results suggest that change in stimulation is at least one factor involved in maintaining perception of an image, and is consistent with the notion that the involuntary movements of the eye provide this change under normal conditions of viewing.

Using, as a measuring device, the phenomenon observed when flicker is imposed upon the target, Cornsweet then investigated the stimulus conditions which might initiate the involuntary drifts and saccadic movements of the eye. Three possible conditions which might trigger such movements seemed likely: the disappearance of the target, the displacement of the target from the retinal "center of best vision," or an inherent instability of the oculomotor system. The reasoning proceeded as follows: If the disappearance is the primary stimulus condition, then, as flicker rate increases, thereby increasing disappearance time, the eye movements should also increase. If, on the other hand, displacement is the stimulus condition, then stopping the image and thereby stopping displacement should decrease eye movements. If neither result is observed, the movements could be

attributed to an inherent instability of the oculomotor system.

The results indicated that the drift movements of the eye are not influenced by either the disappearance or the displacement of the target. Drift movements might therefore be attributed to the instability of the oculomotor system. The saccadic movements, on the other hand, were not affected by disappearance, but they were affected by displacement of the target. This implies that saccadic movements are adjustive in function. The data indicate that the adjustments are corrective in both magnitude and direction. An interesting observation in this study is the finding that a fixation point must be provided if the corrective function is to be accomplished; otherwise the eye moves further and further away from the original position. This would suggest, as Cornsweet observes, that the saccadic movements are under visual rather than proprioceptive control.

Ditchburn and Fender (1955) also investigated the effects of flicker on the stabilized image. Using the improved type of optical lever system in which both horizontal and vertical movements are compensated, they varied the flicker rate from 0 to 60 cycles per second, and noted a gradual decrease in disappearance time up to approximately 20 cycles per second where the target remained visible for about 97% of the time or approximately equal to normal viewing conditions. The point of 20 cycles per second coincides with the critical flicker frequency under these conditions. As the flicker rate was further increased, a gradual increase in disappearance time occurred until, at 60 cycles per second, the visibility was about equal to that of a stabilized image.

The striking difference in these results compared to those obtained by Cornsweet (1956) should be observed. Cornsweet found a sudden increase in visibility at slow rates of flicker with a decrease up to 4.4 cycles per second, whereas Ditchburn found a gradual increase throughout the range of 0 to 20 cycles per second. One source of difference between the two studies lies in the method of producing flicker. Cornsweet flickered only the line within the visual field, while Ditchburn turned the entire field off and on.

A further finding by Ditchburn (Ditchburn and Fender, 1955) was that the brightness of the visual field under high flicker rates was greatly overestimated by the subject. A brightness of 10 millilamberts was estimated as high as 1,000 millilamberts. Ditchburn offers as a possible explanation the idea that the retina is receiving repeated strong bursts of impulses from the continued turning on of the light. This idea, however, does not seem to be consistent with the assumption that rapid flicker approximates steady illumination in which case the fibers should be incapable of repeated response. This inconsistency, together with the inconsistency with Cornsweet's data, presents a provocative problem for further research. Such research should bear importantly on the concept of changing stimulation as a factor in perception.

Krauskopf (1957) conducted a study in which the effects of retinal image motion on contrast thresholds were measured. An optical lever system with a Maxwellian view was used. The targets were vertical lines varying in width as follows: 10 seconds, 1, 4, and 8 minutes of arc. Various degrees of movement were induced in the targets by rotating one of the mirrors in the system. These movements were 1, 2, 5, 10, 20, and 50 cycles per second in frequency. The magnitude of the movements was also varied so that amplitudes of 30 seconds, 1, 2, and 4 minutes of arc were incorporated.

The results of these studies indicate that for all bar widths, lower contrast thresholds were obtained under high amplitude, low frequency motions than under stopped conditions. With narrow bars, high frequency motions raised thresholds relative to the stopped condition. Krauskopf observes that

this suggests the disappearance of an image under stabilized viewing conditions is probably due to the removal of the low frequency components of normal retinal image motion. Frequencies below 10 cycles per second with an amplitude of 1 minute of arc or greater seemed particularly effective in maintaining target visibility. High frequency motions either have detrimental effects or, if the amplitude is less than 1 minute of arc, have no measurable effect at all. It would seem, therefore, that the drift and saccadic movements of the eye lower contrast thresholds while the small, high frequency tremor motions are ineffective so far as these thresholds are concerned.

A later study by Ditchburn, Fender, and Mayne (1959) makes necessary some qualification of these conclusions. Considering the suggestion of Marshall and Talbot (1942) that the most important characteristics of change in stimulation is the generation of "on" and "off" responses in the neural fibers, Ditchburn attempted to manipulate the degree of change by controlling the degree of the three types of eye movements. The improved model of the optical lever system as described by Clowes and Ditchburn (1959) was used together with an apparatus that could impose motion of any of the three types in any degree. The target was again a vertical black line.

It was found that the drift movements of the eye had some, but very little effect on visibility of the target. The saccadic movements produced a very sharp image, but the image would then fade out again. The tremor movements of the eye seemed to be a factor in maintaining vision, but their effects varied with different frequencies of the tremor. There also seemed to be important effects of the amplitude of the tremor movements as indicated by the finding that movements up to .3 minute of arc produced a decrease in the time in which the target remained visible, while movements that reached this .3 minute of arc magnitude produced a sudden increase in visibility time.

Riggs and Tulaney (1959) regulated the extent of motion by varying the degree of compensation of eye movements. By means of an optical lever system, the ratio of the length of the viewing path to the length of the projection path was varied. A 2 : 1 ratio produced a stabilized image, and any deviation from this ratio introduced some degree of movement. The target was a circular path of light divided vertically into two halves of different brightnesses. This target was presented within a nonstabilized annular ring. The results show that as the degree of motion was increased, the amount of disappearance of the target decreased.

Using the same kind of bipartite field with the improved (Clowes and Ditchburn, 1959) type of optical lever system, Clowes (1961) studied the subject's ability to make brightness discriminations under conditions of exaggerated, normal, and stabilized movements of the retinal image. The ability to make such discriminations was found to increase as retinal image movement increased.

Keesey (1960), in another attempt to evaluate the effects of eye movement on visual acuity, used the improved (Clowes and Ditchburn, 1959) type of optical lever system with three different kinds of targets: a vernier offset between two vertical lines, a single line, and a grating. Seven exposure times were used in viewing each target. These exposure times varied from .020 to 1.280 seconds. No differences were found in acuity threshold values between the stabilized and the unstabilized conditions of viewing. The main factor seemed to be the exposure time, with threshold values decreasing to an asymptotic value as exposure time was increased. Acuity appears to be mainly a matter of discriminating spatial differences of intensity in the stimulation of the retina. For a given value of contrast, therefore, the ability to make such discriminations seems to be independent of the eye movements involved, and is primarily a function of exposure time.

Other findings of considerable interest were the observations (Pritchard, 1958; Pritchard and Vowles as cited in Pritchard, Heron, and Hebb, 1960) that the part of the image to which the subject's attention was directed remained in view longer than other parts, and that stimulation of other sensory modalities, such as a sudden noise or the operation of the telegraph key used in recording, would cause regeneration of an image that had disappeared. Stabilization of a field containing three colors (Pritchard, 1961b) resulted in disappearance of the three colors after the first few seconds of viewing so that only three brightnesses were observed. With continued viewing, these three brightnesses gave way to an achromatic field of homogeneous brightness. These results are analogous to those of experiments that involve viewing colors in a Ganzfeld (Cohen, 1958).

Attention should also be given to some findings from experiments in which stabilization of the retinal image was complete or as near complete as possible. Such findings are those from studies in which the internal structure of the eye is imaged on the retina (Campbell and Robson, 1961; Doesschate, 1954). Campbell, for instance, found that the shadows or images viewed in this manner disappear in a few seconds and never return. Besides the problem of lens slippage, these methods also preclude effects due to changes in accommodation, pupil area variations, vignetting in the optical pathways, and changes in intraocular tension. Near-complete stabilization was also achieved by Yarbus (1957) using the suck-on type contact lens. Although some distortions occurred in image quality, the extremely stable image achieved produced the same kind of result mentioned above—that is, the target remained visible for about 3 seconds and then disappeared permanently.

Barlow (1963) presents a detailed phenomenological description of the events that follow stabilization of an image. He used the suck-on type of lens similar to that of Yarbus, but with improved image quality. The target was perceived with full clarity for 1 to 2 seconds which was followed by a loss of contrast and detail. The target then began to fluctuate for approximately 1 minute whereupon it disappeared, leaving a cloudy, indistinct field with a vague resemblance to the target contours. No further changes ocurred as long as the conditions were not altered. If the image was moved such as by flicking the target mount, it was immediately regenerated, but sharp changes were produced only at the borders of the image with the area within the borders remaining unchanged. During the period of fluctuation, it was also observed that the regenerated image was never as good as the original in contrast and detail.

All of the studies which have been discussed thus far have investigated the effects of a stabilized image on the retina of one eye only. Several experiments have been reported on the effects of binocular stabilization.

Krauskopf and Riggs (1959) studied interocular transfer in the disappearance of stabilized images. Two optical lever systems were used, both with a projected target image. One system was used for each eye. A nonstabilized fixation field was also presented stereoscopically to both eyes. This fixation field consisted of an annular ring with a small dot in the center. Three conditions of stabilized viewing were used: the experimental condition, the control condition, and the test condition. In the experimental condition, a target consisting of a circular patch of light containing a small vertical bar in the left-hand side of the field was presented. This patch was presented within the annular fixation field to one eye only. In the control condition, the same kind of target was presented to the same eye except that now the vertical

bar was positioned in the right-hand side of the field. In the test condition, exactly the same kind of target as the one used in the experimental condition was presented to the other eye. The sequence of presentation was, therefore, either the experimental condition for 30 seconds followed by the test condition for 30 seconds or control followed by test. These sequences resulted in the test bar's falling on either the same position of the retina in the second eye as compared to the first, or on a different position of the retina. The results indicate the disappearance of the stabilized image occurred significantly faster in the experimental condition as compared to the control. This demonstrates that the effects of the stabilized image are apparently transferred between eyes, thus supporting the idea that something other than purely retinal effects are at work.

In order to control for the possibility of the effect being due to afterimages, a separate set of experiments was run in which it was found that the subject failed to get an afterimage after 3 seconds of viewing. The effect of the transfer, however, lasted the full 30 seconds of viewing.

Krauskopf offers two possible explanations for the stabilized image phenomenon. One explanation would incorporate a neural mechanism involving centrifugal control of peripheral activity as proposed by Granit (1955). The other explanation suggests that some kind of neural adaptation is occurring in addition to the retinal photochemical adaptation process.

Cohen (1961) investigated the effects of contralateral visual stimulation on the disappearance of stabilized images. Three conditions of contralateral stimulation were used: a dark patch worn over one eye, half of a ping-pong ball placed over one eye to produce diffuse light, and a patterned stimulation produced by fixating a spot on the wall. Visibility of the stabilized image was found to increase in the order of contralateral stimulation presented above, thus offering further evidence in support of the idea that central factors are involved in the phenomenon.

Organization of the Disappearance Phenomenon

The emphasis of the studies cited thus far has been primarily on the disappearance and reappearance of a stimulus target which produces a constant stimulation of the retina. Several variables have been investigated in an attempt to discover the causal factors of this phenomenon. The question, it might be said, has been: Why does disappearance of an image occur under stabilized conditions of viewing? During the course of these studies, however, it was observed that not only does disappearance of the target occur, but it occurs in what seems to be an orderly fashion. For instance, in those studies in which a thin vertical line was viewed, the line not only disappeared, but it disappeared as a unit. The line did not gradually fade with first some parts disappearing and then others, but rather it followed an "all-or-none" principle—that is, it was either wholly visible or wholly invisible. These observations might be considered to present a second question: Why does the disappearance of a stabilized image occur in the way that it does? The following studies will present some attempts which have been made to answer this question.

Studies were conducted (Pritchard, 1961b; Pritchard, Heron, and Hebb, 1960) using a light-collimating system attached directly to the contact lens worn by the subject through which targets of varying shapes and complexity were projected. Many findings of interest were made. One general statement is that the length of time that a target remains visible is at least partly a function of the complexity of the figure. (Complexity here refers to an increase in the number of elements and/or an increase in meaningfulness.) A simple target such as a straight line may be visible only 10% of the total viewing time while a more complex figure might be visible 80% of the time. Second, a simple line vanishes completely as a unit and reappears the same way while the lines comprising a more complex figure behave independently of each other. Each separate element of the more complex figure, however, disappears and regenerates as a unit.

These two general principles of visibility as a function of complexity and the unitary action of elements are basic to the phenomenon. There are, however, other rules which the activity of the figures seems to follow. For instance, the profile of a face (a meaningful figure) will remain visible longer than an irregularly shaped curved line. If the profile is viewed alone, certain parts of the face appear and disappear as a unit; that is, the front of the face or the top of the head may remain visible while the rest disappears. A letter over which a jagged line has been superimposed will act independently of the jagged line in its disappearance, and will remain visible longer. While viewing a square, a common perception is one in which either the two horizontal or the two vertical lines appear and disappear together. Another aspect of the importance of linear organization can be seen while viewing a matrix of squares arranged in rows and columns. Whole rows or columns act together. Thus the entire matrix may disappear leaving a single row, column, or diagonal of squares remaining in view. Another illustration is the superiority of smooth, rounded figures (the "good" figures of Gestalt psychology) over jagged, irregular figures in maintaining visibility. A word such as "beer" when viewed may, due to fragmentation of the image, be seen as other words such as "peep," "peer," "be," or "beep." Finally, in considering field effects, it has been found that, while viewing a triangle and a circle placed side by side, the parts of the triangle and circle nearest to each other remain visible while the other parts disappear; or, if some other side of the triangle remains visible, an arc portion of the circle which is approximately parallel to that side also remains visible.

These field effects seem to be important aspects of the stabilized image phenomenon. An experiment was performed by Cohen (1961) in which two lines were presented to the subject with a separation between the lines of 25, 75, or 150 minutes of arc. One of the lines was presented as a stabilized image while the other was presented normally. It was found that an increase in separation produced a decrease in the amount of time that the stabilized line remained visible. Cohen suggests a field effect to account for this change in visibility as a function of distance.

These conclusions, however, require some modification in light of an experiment performed by Tees (1961). Two parallel lines (A and B) were presented with a diagonal line (C) positioned between them. The measurement of interest is the percentage of time that any given line (such as A) is accompanied by either of the other two lines (B and C) when disappearance occurs. It was found that Line A was accompanied by C 22% of the time and by B 73% of the time. If the only factor involved was a field effect, then such an effect should be stronger for the intervening line. Apparently a field effect is at work, but it must be more complex than previously supposed, or it must work in conjunction with some other mechanism.

A final observation (Pritchard, 1961b) should be mentioned regarding the activity of a "filled-in" figure, such as a blackened square, when presented as a stabilized image. Here it is observed that disappearance of the square is gradual rather than sudden. The center portion of one of the sides will begin to fade with the fade-out spreading first toward the middle of the figure and then outwards toward the other

sides. An important comment made by Hebb (1963) concerning this activity is that it demonstrates that a gradual fading can occur, thus strengthening the notion that the all-or-none type of activity observed with other figures is probably due to the failure of a system or systems.

Summary of Effects and Comments

The rather large number of effects associated with stabilization of the retinal image as presented in the preceding section can probably best be appreciated in summary. When the image of a visual target is stabilized on the retina, the image disappears and gives way to a homogeneous field. This condition remains so long as nothing else is changed. In most instances, however, the image will periodically reappear with a frequency determined by several factors. One of these factors is the degree of stabilization which is achieved. Any slippage of the contact lens, for instance, will cause the image to be regenerated. Assuming the amount of slippage to be constant, another factor which causes regeneration seems to be stimulation of another sensory modality. Also, if the attention of the subject is directed to a certain portion of the image, that portion will remain visible longer than others. The relative complexity of the image further determines the extent of disappearance, with more complex images remaining visible longer than simple ones. In addition, the disappearance of the image occurs in an all-or-none manner, and, in the case of more complex figures, seems to be subject to the classical Gestalt principles of organization.

Other important effects of a stabilized image were also discussed. As might be expected, any movement of the image once it has disappeared will result in restoration of the image. If the image is held stationary, the introduction of flicker in the illumination of the target enhances visibility depending on the rate of flicker. The apparent brightness of a stabilized image is greatly overestimated, and contrast thresholds were found to be considerably higher than in normal viewing conditions. A finding of considerable importance is the fact that, for exposure times sufficiently short to preclude disappearance of the image, visual acuity is apparently not affected by stabilization of the image.

These results imply that the involuntary movements of the eye are importantly related to the perception of a retinal image. In general, the low frequency, high amplitude components of these movements seem to be most effective. The effect of the movements seems to be primarily one of overcoming the loss of vision resulting from constant stimulation of the retina. Stated another way, the effect of the movements is to provide changing sensory stimulation of a spatial variety.

Finally, it was observed that the effects of a stabilized retinal image are transferred between eyes--that is, there are central as well as peripheral factors involved. This implies, at the very minimum, that neural adaptation processes are involved in addition to the photochemical adaptation processes of the retina.

As is always the case, observations which have been described are not exempt from some criticism. The criticism, however, does not reflect on the quality of the studies nor on the general nature of the results, but rather it is directed towards more precise quantifications in the effects which result from the many variables uncovered by the studies themselves. For instance, Barlow's (1963) discussion of the problems introduced by lens slippage does not invalidate the studies which were conducted, but simply means that the results must be considered as an expression of reduced image motion instead of stopped image motion. This implies further that studies in which motion was experimentally manipulated contain observations that resulted from the manipulated motions

and motions due to slippage. Ideally, these effects should be separated.

Barlow also discusses other artifacts which can produce misleading results, but which either have been or can be controlled. Some of the factors include other possible sources of movement such as movement of the lens of the eye, pupil changes, and changes in accommodation. Retinal ischaemia (a local anemia produced by local obstacles to the arterial flow) and fading of vision due to distortion of the eyeball by the lens and increases in intraocular pressure are also possible factors, as are distortions in the image due to poor optical conditions (e.g., smearing of lens, corneal misting, etc.). The already present chromatic aberration of the eye may be even further increased by the use of short focus lens. If the entrance pupil to the eye is narrowed, the increase in diffraction which results mars resolution. A small pupil diameter also renders the eye more sensitive to trans-scleral light, thus reducing contrast in the image and mimicking fading. Finally, the quality of the image as seen through the contact lens must be carefully controlled by observing the image under conditions of natural eye movements.

Another problem for consideration would be the control of stimulation or lack of stimulation of the area of the retina not being subjected to the stabilized image. If there is any interaction between these areas and the area being stimulated, this control would seem to be quite important.

The knowledge that intersensory stimulation has effects on the visibility of the image introduces some methodological problems. In those studies using an optical lever system of stabilization, for instance, the use of a dental biting-board to control head movements may produce variations in the effects. The irritation which usually accompanies the wearing of the contact lens and the use of anesthetics are other sources of stimulation. In addition, the recording technique of pressing or releasing a telegraph key to signal the disappearance of the image is itself a source of stimulation known to effect visibility. A possible alternate method of recording might be to have the subject press the key after a given number of regenerations of the image and then compare these records with those obtained with individual regenerations recorded. A useful complementary recording technique might be the use of electroencephalogram records of the occipital alpha rhythm. If the alpha rhythm, which is suppressed under normal visual stimulation, recurs under conditions of stabilization of the retinal image, then the use of EEG recordings would not only be a valuable recording technique, but would also yield additional evidence regarding concomitants of the stabilized image phenomenon. Such a technique has been successfully used in experiments that involved viewing targets in a Ganzfeld (Cohen and Cadwallader, 1958).

Relevant Physiological Considerations

Electrophysiological studies have yielded much evidence concerning the structure of the visual system which is of particular interest so far as the stabilized image phenomenon is concerned. Since most of the evidence was obtained in animals, a cautious approach must be taken in extending such evidence to man. With this caution in mind, some of the findings of several investigators (Granit, 1955; Hubel, 1963; Kennedy, 1963) will be presented in synthesis.

The path from the retina to the cortex contains at least six different types of nerve cells. Three of these cells are the receptors, the bipolars, and the ganglion all of which are located in the retina. The other three are the cells of the lateral geniculate body, simple cortical cells, and complex cortical cells. All of these cell types are organized into receptive fields, the shape and structure of which differ for each type. Activity in each cell is either of an excitatory or an

inhibitory nature and is produced by either the onset or offset of stimulation by light. If a large number of cells is subjected to stimulation, the differential excitatory and inhibitory activity from all of them summates to produce resultant "on" or "off" discharging systems. These resultant systems are superimposed upon a variable level of spontaneous activity (noise) already present in the system, so that detection of the stimulus depends upon whether or not the resultant activity is above the noise level. When a group of cells is subjected to invariant stimulation, as is the case with a stabilized image, the inhibitory components exceed the excitatory and the resultant discharging system drops below the noise level, thus resulting in a cessation of neural firing. Either a movement of the image or a change in the noise level could produce detectable activity in the resultant discharging system.

The shape and structure of the receptive fields associated with the six different cell types suggest that each cell type may be specialized to evaluate only a limited number of dimensions of the visual stimulus. These dimensions include the frequency, intensity, pattern, orientation, position, and movement of the visual stimulus. Another possible effect of invariant stimulation, therefore (i.e., invariant on one or more of these dimensions), might be a loss of information concerning the dimensions in question. Thus, while complete invariance of stimulation would result in disappearance of an image, invariance on only a few dimensions might explain the ordered fragmentation of an image which is so typically observed.

Theoretical Implications of the Stabilized Image Phenomenon

The perceptual effects associated with the stabilized image phenomenon bear importantly on more general theories of perception. The ideas contained within some theories seem to be untenable in view of certain findings. Hebb (1963) discusses several of these ideas. The all-or-none disappearance of an image, for instance, makes unlikely any explanation by fatigue in independently functioning cells. Equally unlikely are explanations involving local areas of satiation, or those based on the activity of inhibitory cells. Fatigue or inhibition within the cells would require a precise coordination in time of thousands of cells to yield the sudden cessation of activity. Satiation effects would produce a fading of an image rather than the abrupt disappearance. Pritchard, Heron, and Hebb (1960) discuss as another unlikely explanation the idea of random fluctuation of thresholds in various parts of the visual field. Such random fluctuations could not account for the ordered activity which has been observed.

Two major theories that receive considerable support from the stabilized image phenomenon are Gestalt theory (Köhler, 1929) and cell-assembly theory (Hebb, 1949). In Gestalt theory, the notion of field effects can be applied to some of the organized activity which has been observed, such as the activity of adjacent figures (Pritchard, Heron, and Hebb, 1960). The holistic approach of Gestalt theory is also supported by the principles of closure, contiguity, and similarity which seem to be present in the organization of the disappearance of the stabilized image. On the other hand, cell-assembly theory finds support in the sudden, all-or-none kind of disappearance of separate elements, and also in the differential activity in meaningful versus meaningless figures. These observations make tenable the idea of specific assemblies of cells acting as perceptual elements that operate as a unit or not at all, and the idea that complex assemblies (i.e., meaningful) can remain active longer than less complex assemblies (i.e., meaningless). Both of these theories, however, have difficulty in explaining some effects. The work of Tees (1961), for instance, has demonstrated that, while Gestalt field effects may be present, they cannot completely account for the phenomenon found in the interaction between certain line patterns. Likewise, cell-assembly theory cannot account for the failure of angles to behave as separate elements, the completion noted in incomplete figures, and the nature of the disappearance of solid figures.

The stabilized image phenomenon also has relevance with respect to the role of learning in perception. The evidence indicates that some innate organization seems to be present but that this organization is modifiable as a result of experience. Although this view is certainly not new, it receives additional strong support.

A final consideration is related to the general notion of the role of changing stimulation in perception. Dember (1960) discusses this aspect of stimulus change with respect to the stabilized image phenomenon, and also relates it to findings of studies involving exposure to homogeneous fields and the phenomenon associated with the viewing of blurred images. The results of these studies all demonstrate that changing stimulation is necessary to both form and maintain a visual image.

References

BARLOW, H. B. Slippage of contact lenses and other artifacts in relation to fading and regeneration of supposedly stable retinal images. *Quarterly Journal of Experimental Psychology*, 1963, *15*, 36–51.

CAMPBELL, F. W., and J. G. ROBSON. A fresh approach to stabilized retinal images. *Journal of Physiology*, 1961, *158*, 1–11.

CLOWES, M. B. Some factors in brightness discrimination with constraint of retinal image movement. *Optica Acta*, 1961, *8*, 81–91.

CLOWES, M. B., and R. W. DITCHBURN. An improved apparatus for producing a stabilized retinal image. *Optica Acta*, 1959, *6*, 128–133.

COHEN, H. B. The effect of contralateral visual stimulation on visibility with stabilized retinal images. *Canadian Journal of Psychology*, 1961, *15*, 212–219.

COHEN, W. Color perception in the chromatic

Ganzfeld. *American Journal of Psychology*, 1958, *71*, 390–394.

COHEN, W., and T. C. CADWALLADER. Cessation of visual experience under prolonged uniform visual stimulation. Paper read at American Psychological Association, Washington, D. C., 1958.

CORNSWEET, T. N. Determination of the stimuli for involuntary drifts and saccadic eye movements. *Journal of the Optical Society of America*, 1956, *46*, 987–993.

DEMBER, W. N. *Psychology of perception.* New York: Holt, Rinehart and Winston, Inc., 1960.

DITCHBURN, R. W., and D. H. FENDER. The stabilized retinal image. *Optica Acta*, 1955, *2*, 128–133.

DITCHBURN, R. W., D. H. FENDER, and S. MAYNE. Vision with controlled movements of the retinal image. *Journal of Physiology*, 1959, *145*, 98–107.

DITCHBURN, R. W., and B. L. GINSBORG. Vision with a stabilized retinal image. *Nature*, 1952, *170*, 36–38.

DITCHBURN, R. W., and R. M. PRITCHARD. Stabilized interference fringes on the retina. *Nature*, 1956, *177*, 434.

DOESSCHATE, J. T. A new form of physiological nystagmus. *Ophthalmologica*, 1954, *127*, 65–73.

GRANIT, R. *Receptors and sensory perception.* New Haven: Yale University Press, 1955.

HARTLINE, H. K. The receptive field of the optic nerve fibers. *American Journal of Physiology*, 1940, *130*, 690–699.

HEBB, D. O. *The organization of behavior.* New York: Wiley, 1949.

HEBB, D. O. The semiautonomous process: Its nature and nurture. *American Psychologist*, 1963, *18*, 16–27.

HECHT, S. Rods, cones, and chemical basis of vision. *Physiological Review*, 1937, *17*, 239–290.

HUBEL, D. H. The visual cortex of the brain. *Scientific American*, 1963, *209*(5), 54–62.

KEESEY, U. K. Effects of involuntary eye movements on visual acuity. *Journal of the Optical Society of America*, 1960, *50*, 769–774.

KENNEDY, D., Inhibition in visual systems. *Scientific American*, 1963, *209*(1), 122–130.

KÖHLER, W. *Gestalt psychology.* New York: Liveright, 1929.

KRAUSKOPF, J. Effect of retinal image motion on contrast thresholds for maintained vision. *Journal of the Optical Society of America*, 1957, *47*, 740–747.

KRAUSKOPF, J., and L. A. RIGGS. Interocular transfer in the disappearance of stabilized images. *American Journal of Psychology*, 1959, *72*, 248–252.

MARSHALL, W. H., and S. A. TALBOT. Recent evidence for neural mechanisms in vision leading to a general theory of sensory acuity. *Biological Symposium*, 1942, *7*, 117–164.

PRITCHARD, R. M. Visual illusions viewed as stabilized retinal images. *Quarterly Journal of Experimental Psychology*, 1958, *10*, 77–81.

PRITCHARD, R. M. A collimator stabilizing system. *Quarterly Journal of Experimental Psychology*, 1961, *13*, 181–183. (a)

PRITCHARD, R. M. Stabilized images on the retina. *Scientific American*, 1961, *204*(6), 72–78. (b)

PRITCHARD, R. M., W. HERON, and D. O. HEBB. Visual perception approached by the method of stabilized images. *Canadian Journal of Psychology*, 1960, *14*, 67–77.

RATLIFF, F. The role of physiological nystagmus in monocular acuity. *Journal of Experimental Psychology*, 1952, *43*, 163–172.

RATLIFF, F. Stationary retinal images requiring no attachments to the eye. *Journal of the Optical Society of America*, 1958, *48*, 274–275.

RATLIFF, F., and L. A. RIGGS. Involuntary motions of the eye during monocular fixation. *Journal of Experimental Psychology*, 1950, *40*, 687–701.

RIGGS, L. A., E. C. ARMINGTON, and F. RATLIFF. Motions of the retinal image during fixation. *Journal of the Optical Society of America*, 1954, *44*, 315–321.

RIGGS, L. A., and F. RATLIFF. Visual acuity and the normal tremor of the eyes. *Science*, 1951, *114*, 17–18.

RIGGS, L. A., F. RATLIFF, J. C. CORNSWEET, and T. N. CORNSWEET. The disappearance of steadily fixated visual test objects. *Journal of the Optical Society of America*, 1953, *43*, 495–501.

RIGGS, L. A., and S. U. TULANEY. Visual effects of varying the extent of compensation for eye movements. *Journal of the Optical Society of America*, 1959, *9*, 741–745.

TEES, R. C. The role of field effects in visual perception. *Undergraduate Research Projects in Psychology, McGill University*, 1961, *3*, 87–96.

YARBUS, A. L. A new method of studying the activity of various parts of the retina. *Biofizika*, 1957, *2*, 165–167.

Vision in the Ganzfeld*

LLOYD L. AVANT

Johns Hopkins University

A summary of the evidence on exposure to structureless visual fields is presented. The data show the experience of such fields to be characterized by reports of: immersion in a "sea of light" which separates into figure and ground as brightness is increased, chromatic adaptation in colored fields, loss of efficiency in detecting the presence and movement of inhomogeneities introduced into the field, disorientation of the observer, an increased and fluctuating state of accommodation, and the occasional joint occurrence of an apparent cessation of function of the visual mechanism and increased alpha activity in the brain.

The advent of high-altitude supersonic flight and space travel have added to the theoretical concern for the Ganzfeld a practical interest in the effects of a structureless field upon vision. The loss in efficiency of the visual mechanism in the Ganzfeld is similar to that of high-altitude flight. This similarity is exemplified by the fluctuation and increase in accommodation characteristic of "empty field" myopia for the Ganzfeld observer and "sky" myopia in the case of high altitude flying. The purpose of this paper is to review and discuss available evidence on the effects of exposure to structureless visual fields.

In 1930 Metzger seated observers 1.25 meters distant from a carefully white-washed 4×4 meter square surface from which wings extended toward the observer on three sides. He illuminated the field with a neutral light and asked the observ-ers to verbalize their experience on this field. Metzger termed this field the Ganzfeld. Gestalt theory, holding that primitive vision is binocular rather than monocular, would predict for Metzger's observers an experience of tridimensional, rather than bidimensional, space. Metzger's data favored this Gestalt prediction, and the contribution of Metzger's work to Gestalt theory is reflected in Koffka's (1935) statement of Gestalt thinking.

Metzger's results did not, however, completely support the Gestalt position, and Metzger's query, as well as his new method of studying visual perception, went unnoticed for some years. The revival of interest in the experience of the Ganzfeld has occurred largely during the last decade. More recent research has shown that, with regard to a number of visual functions or skills, the Ganzfeld produces an experience markedly different from the experience of structured fields. Varying the brightness and/or chromaticity of the field or the introduction of spots differing in brightness or chromaticity from the remainder

* *Psychological Bulletin*, 1965, vol. 64, pp. 246–258. The author wishes to thank Henry Helson and William Bevan for their critical reading of this paper.

295

of the field produces responses to such variations which differ from responses to these variables in structured fields. The observer's accommodation and orientation are affected in the Ganzfeld situation, and the visual mechanism even appears at times to cease functioning without field structure.

Phenomenal Characteristics of the Ganzfeld

Illuminating the Ganzfeld with neutral light, Metzer (1930; cited by Koffka, 1935) found that the observer felt "himself swimming in a mist of light which becomes more condensed at an indefinite distance." Practically all subsequent investigators have reported a like experience for the observer in the Ganzfeld. Impressions reported by Hochberg, Triebel, and Seaman (1951) were such as to be subsumed under the term "fog" or "cloud." According to Gibson and Waddell (1952) the experience was that of a "sea of light," with some observers at times sensing something vaguely surfacelike in front of the face. Cohen's (1956, 1957) observers found it difficult to apply to the empty field experience the language usually adequate to express visual experience of structured fields; "sea of light" seemed most descriptive for most of these observers.

Atypical experience includes surfaces and a "cone-shaped three-dimensional surface" concave toward the observer (Hochberg, Triebel, and Seaman, 1951), a "cracked ice effect" or a "web-like structure" (Cohen, 1957), and awareness of vitreous opacities and retinal blood vessels (Miller and Hall, 1962). Miller and Ludvigh (1960) reported gradations of light and shade, rings of different sizes and shapes, and when homogeneous stimulation of other sense modalities was added to the experience of the Ganzfeld, extensive hallucinations resulted (Bexton, Heron, and Scott, 1954).

The location, or distance, of the fog produced by the Ganzfeld is not accurately determined. Cohen's (1957) observers described the homogeneous field as "close at hand," although the meaning of "close" varied among observers. Only one of these observers consistently described the field as being more than 6 inches away, and the modal distance was 2 inches. However, the fog extended for an indefinite distance. Gibson and Waddell (1952) pointed out the voluminous nature of the experience of the fog. Their report is in agreement with other investigators and is the basis for Gibson and Waddell's tentative agreement with Metzger's findings in support of the Gestalt belief in the tridimensional nature of primitive visual experience. However, Gibson and Waddell stressed caution in such a conclusion because observers agree that the experience is indefinite, indeterminate, or ambiguous. Neither Metzger nor Gibson and Waddell have given definitive evidence of the two-dimensional or three-dimensional nature of primitive visual experience.

Various aftereffects of exposure to homogeneous stimulation for a period of 20 minutes were found in one study (Cohen, 1960). The observers of this study experienced extreme fatigue and a feeling of great lightness of body. Motor coordination was reportedly poor, and observers had difficulty maintaining balance. Time perception was disturbed. Subjects often complained of dizziness and sometimes appeared to be intoxicated. One observer experienced temporary states of depersonalization, a condition which Cohen did not define.

Brightness Variations in the Ganzfeld

The "mist of light" experience described by Metzger's observers prevailed as long as the illumination of the whitewashed surface remained "below a certain level." Increasing the illumination produced new experiences. As the illumination was increased the fog became condensed into a regularly curved surface which surrounded the observer on all sides; its appearance was filmy like the sky, not surfacy, and, similar to the sky, it was slightly flat in the center [Metzger, 1930, p. 13; cited by Koffka, 1935].

Further increase in the illumination caused the surface to straighten out into a plane, the apparent distance of which was definitely greater than that of the real one. The explanation of this result offered by Koffka was that the increased illumination allowed the observer to accommodate to the microstructure or "grain" of the surface, and there was no longer homogeneous stimulation. Under Metzger's conditions, these results are not surprising. It is of interest to note, however, that Metzger's results tend to support Ittelson and Ames' (1950) contention that accommodation is to apparent rather than to objective distance. Metzger's observers, given sufficient illumination to accommodate to the microstructure of the viewed surface, saw it as farther away than was actually the case. Ittelson and Ames varied the apparent distance of playing cards by changing the size of the cards; they found, with a constant distance for cards of different sizes, that accommodation and convergence varied with apparent distance.

Cohen (1956, 1957, 1958a, 1958b) produced the Ganzfeld differently from Metzger and obtained different indications of the effects of brightness variations. His Ganzfeld was produced by two adjoining spheres, A and B, 1 meter in diameter, which, at their juncture, produced an 8-centimeter aperture. Wearing a special mask which also formed a removable section of the wall of Sphere A, these observers looked monocularly into Sphere A. By controlling the chromaticity, purity, and luminance of the two spheres independently, the experimenter could produce a homogeneous field or a field containing a background (Sphere A) and an 8-centimeter spot (the juncture of Spheres A and B). In the homogeneous field Cohen found

that variations in the intensity of the field did not consistently alter the appearance of the field. There was, however, some tendency for the fog of brighter fields to appear denser and closer.

With a field made inhomogeneous by the introduction of the spot, he found that variations in brightness differences between field and spot within the range 1.8 to 4.9 millilamberts produced no statistical evidence of a relation between intensity of illumination and the density or closeness of the fog. This lack of agreement with Metzger's findings Cohen attributes to the microstructure of Metzger's field which was absent in his own. With regard to the separation of field and spot, Cohen found that when the gradient between field and spot is not steep the fog seems nearer but the spot seems farther away. Further increase in the intensity gradient between field and spot reverses this appearance; the fog recedes, and the spot is seen in front of the field fog. At a maximum intensity difference between field and spot, judgments of *figural* distance ranged from "next to the eye" to 3 feet away with a median of 6 inches. The ground was usually judged a few inches behind the spot. Cohen reports great individual differences between, but consistency within, distance judgments of his observers. In addition to these effects of independent variation of brightness, this investigator found that when inhomogeneity was initially produced by chromatic differences the figure-ground separation thus established was enhanced by the addition of a brightness gradient. Cohen concluded that the phenomenal characteristics of the Ganzfeld are not independently determined. He maintained that any change in the stimulus distribution that modifies one aspect of experience produces concomitant changes in other phenomenal characteristics of the Ganzfeld. The most recent study of the Ganzfeld (Weintraub, 1964) indicates that Cohen's conclusion is incorrect, and that intensity of stimulation and the colorimetric purity of the Ganzfeld are independent dimensions. Weintraub's results appear to disagree with the well-established principle of color conversion (Helson, 1938), certainly with regard to the chromatic effect of brightness variation. This conflict is discussed in the following section.

Chromatic Effects in the Ganzfeld

Questioning the necessity of the experience of a mid-gray as the end result of prolonged homogeneous stimulation, as required by Hering's opponent processes theory of vision, Helson and Judd (1932) constructed an "adaptation sphere" of Hering paper, suspended a 100-watt Mazda lamp in its center, and had observers sit with the sphere encircling their heads for as long as 75 minutes. They report that whatever chromatic adaptation took place occurred during the first few minutes, but at no time, even after 75 minutes, did the color of the surface of the sphere disappear. The paper of which the inner surface of the sphere was constructed was an orange-red, and the authors state that the red component tended to be reduced, making the orange surface more yellowish. Only during very brief periods lasting no more than a few seconds when the eyes were held fixed did a fairly good gray appear. These authors interpret their results as evidence against the Hering theory of vision with its concept of a mid-gray as the end result of adaptation. They concluded that "eye-movements alone, all other factors held constant, are sufficient to arrest the course of adaptation so that complete adaptation with total loss of chroma does not occur [p. 397]." Hochberg, Triebel, and Seaman (1951) criticized Helson and Judd's results on the basis that they were obtained in a field of definite structure. However, Helson[1] reported an unpublished confirmation of his and Judd's find-

ings and pointed out (Helson, 1964) that complete adaptation is not found with very intense stimulation.

The results obtained by Hochberg, Triebel, and Seaman (1951) concerning chromatic effects in the Ganzfeld contrast sharply with those obtained by Helson and Judd (1932). In the first of a series of studies, Hochberg, Triebel, and Seaman produced a homogeneous field by taping halved table-tennis balls over the eyes of their observers; they stimulated one group by a 100-watt light passed through a red Wratten filter (no. 70) and another by the same light passed through a green Wratten filter (no. 54). In the group stimulated by red light, 5 out of 6 observers initially reported a red-colored surfaceless field followed by the disappearance of the color within the first 3 minutes. The remaining observer of this group reported a three-dimensional surface which remained a "very dark, brownish magenta." All the observers of the group stimulated with green light initially reported a green surfaceless field followed within a maximum of 6 minutes by total disappearance of the green. The one point on which the Helson and Judd and the Hochberg, Triebel, and Seaman studies agree is that the final state of chromatic adaptation is not the mid-gray postulated by Hering. Whereas Helson and Judd reported little color loss, Hochberg, Triebel, and Seaman reported final adaptation to range from black (or "nothingness") to dark gray.

In further phases of their work, Hochberg, Triebel, and Seaman covered the right eye while the left was adapted to either a red or a green light. They stated that when the covering was removed from the right eye the observer reported the perception of the illuminant color and three fifths of their observers localized this perception in the nonadapted right eye. Again, they reported the loss of color perception with the right eye after prolonged stimulation, although this adaptation was not as satisfactory as that obtained with

[1] Personal communication, 1965.

simultaneous stimulation of both eyes or of one eye alone. The movement of a finger so as to cast a shadow on the lower portion of the field of the adapted eye produced the experience of a black shadow with a halo of the color of the illuminant. Eye movements, after the loss of color was reported by the observer, produced no reappearance of color for half the observers and fleeting flashes of either red or blue-green for the other half. Accordingly, the authors concluded that eye movements have only limited ability to restore color perception. Interruption of the red light for approximately 2 seconds produced a complementary blue-green for 9 out of these 10 observers, and reestablishment of the red illuminant produced a brief flash of red.

Hochberg, Triebel, and Seaman's use of halved table-tennis balls to produce homogeneous stimulation deserves notice. Other investigators have used this technique (e.g., Weintraub, 1964). It is highly likely that this technique produces a different field from that produced by a larger stimulus field at a greater distance from the eyes.

Producing the homogeneous field by a technique different from that of either Metzger, Helson, and Judd, or Hochberg, Triebel, and Seaman, Cohen (1956, 1957, 1958b) also found a loss of chroma within an adaptation period of 3 minutes for 80% of his observers, the remaining 20% reporting only a "trace of color." As previously noted, Cohen produced either a homogeneous or inhomogeneous field by varying the chroma and/or luminance of two adjoining spheres. The observer looked into one of these spheres, and both the luminance and chromaticity of each sphere were independently controlled. The observer's visual field could be made either homogeneous or inhomogeneous by the presence or absence of color or brightness gradients between the two spheres.

The reports from Cohen's (1957, 1958b) observers are largely in agreement with the results obtained by Hochberg, Triebel, and Seaman (1951). The most noticeable difference in the results of these studies is that Cohen's results would support the medium gray end state of color adaptation called for by the Hering theory, whereas Hochberg, Triebel, and Seaman reported an end state of too dark a gray to be in accord with Hering's position. Cohen suggested that this difference may be attributable to the fact that Hochberg, Triebel, and Seaman used a lower intensity of illumination and longer periods of adaptation. Cohen also reported that dominant, long wavelength illumination made the Ganzfeld fog appear closer and denser than did dominant, short wavelength illumination. His observers reported feeling less "immersed" in the "blue" field, and to Cohen this suggested that the receptors sensitive to long wavelengths are more densely concentrated than those sensitive to short wavelengths.

Cohen's introduction of a differentiated area into the field changed its phenomenal characteristics. When this differentiation was due only to chromatic differences between the field and the 8-centimeter spot, the field was described as more saturated than was the homogeneous field. The addition of an intensity difference to the chromatic difference reduced the saturation of the field to the level reported for the homogeneous field. This was true except when the difference in intensity was such as to make the spot achromatic and black; in this case, the saturation of the field surrounding the spot was increased. And, as might be expected by classical contrast, most of the saturation enhancement occurred in the area of the spot figure. Cohen (1958b) stated that the presence of a *chromatic* difference within the field does not radically change most of the phenomenal characteristics of the Ganzfeld, that its principal effect is on the experience of hue. It is noteworthy, however, that a chromatic difference produces a separation of figure and ground, albeit a relatively

indefinite one. With a chromatic difference, observers described a well-saturated
figure in a poorly saturated ground, even
when the stimulation from the spot was
achromatic. Again, Cohen pointed out that
this separation is primarily in one dimension of experience only, that is, color. With
larger intensity gradients between figure
and field, separation of the two becomes
possible on other dimensions as well; such
aspects as spatial separation, differences of
contour, and textural differences between
figure and ground become more pronounced, and a reduction of saturation in
the field occurs. As noted above, with moderate intensity gradients Cohen's observers
reported the fog of the field nearer and the
differentiated figure farther away, while an
increased intensity gradient reversed this
relation, causing the field fog to recede and
the figure to approach the observer.

The most characteristic effect of adaptation to inhomogeneity in the field Cohen
(1958b) found to be the formation of a
halo, usually involving desaturation and
darkening of the field, immediately following the formation of a small, bright, highly
saturated area encircling the spot. This
halo may consist of a mixture of colors
which are not fused, but appear to exist
independently in different planes. Although spatial characteristics of the halo
vary, it was most often seen as being in
a plane behind the figure but in front of
the field, appearing, thus, to facilitate the
separation of figure and ground.

Although it was performed in a structured field, a study reported by Helson
and Jeffers (1940) provides an interesting
comparison with Cohen's findings in a
chromatic field. Cohen reported the effects
of chromatic inhomogeneity to be restricted
largely to the color dimension of experience. Helson and Jeffers found that object
colors lose their individuality to a great
extent when the illuminant changes from
daylight to strongly chromatic. With such
a change they said that colors retreat into
the plane of the background, that they

become softer and filmier, that demarcation
between object and background colors is
not sharp, and contours almost disappear.
In addition, the observer seems to be
bathed in the illumination which takes on
a strong affective character. Chromatic illumination results in perceptions approaching those of Ganzfeld conditions.

In two additional studies, cessation of
the experience of color after prolonged exposure to an empty field was found. An
abstract of a study unavailable to this
writer by ten Doesschate (1961) stated
that, "When the empty field is viewed
through colored glasses, the perception of
chroma gradually diminishes and is often
followed by a sensation of dark grey . . .
[and in two cases] periods of apparent
darkness [p. 565]."

The most recent study conducted under
empty field conditions (Weintraub, 1964)
produced results apparently conflicting with
the well-established principle of color conversion (Helson, 1938). Helson's statement of this principle is that in every
viewing situation an adaptation level (AL)
is established such that objects having reflectances above the AL will be tinged with
the hue of the illuminant, objects having
reflectances below the AL will be tinged
with the hue of the afterimage complement
of the illuminant, and objects having reflectances at or near the AL will be either
achromatic or weakly saturated and of
uncertain hue. Weintraub's observers
adapted to a Ganzfeld which had either a
dominant wavelength of 648 mμ, colorimetric purity of 1.00, and luminance of
.30 footlambert or a field having the
same dominant wavelength and luminance
but a colorimetric purity of .50. After 6
minutes exposure to one of these two
fields, his observers were exposed to postadapting fields of 648 mμ, 441 mμ, 493
mμ, or 568 mμ, varying in colorimetric
purity by steps of .25 between .0 and 1.00,
at various luminance levels ranging from
.00 to .60 footlambert.

Weintraub stated that with an adapting red of 100% purity, 8 out of 10 observers adapted completely, adaptation times ranging from 2 seconds to 12 minutes. Seven of these observers reported a dark field; the others reported brightness but no hue. With a red-adapting field of 50% purity, 6 out of 10 observers adapted chromatically, times ranging from 2 minutes to 40 minutes. All observers who adapted to the red field of 50% purity also adapted to the red field of 100% purity, and adaptation to the stimulus of lower purity always required more time.

The color experiences initiated by the successive contrast of the postadapting field Weintraub reported to be a function of colorimetric purity but not of luminance: "A change in luminance from adapting field to postadapting field affected perceived brightness, but not perceived hue [p. 559]." Postadapting fields of colorimetric purity equal to or greater than the purity of the adapting field were reported as red; postadapting fields of colorimetric purity less than that of the adapting field were perceived as a complementary blue-green hue.

In view of previous evidence clearly demonstrating the applicability of the principle of color conversion with its emphasis on the luminance dimension as a determinant of perceived hue, Weintraub's results call for additional evaluation. Note, for example, Helson (1938) and Judd's (1960) handling of the Land (1959) phenomenon by color conversion. The present writer is of the opinion that a closer examination of Weintraub's training procedure may change the interpretation of his results. Weintraub exposed observers to a red (648 mμ) adaptation field followed by an achromatic postadaptation field and trained these observers to describe their experience in terms of hue, saturation, and brightness, for example, "hue, red; saturation, 50%; brightness, 10." The investigator did this to teach his observers the judging procedure and to establish a stable color reference system. The color reference system

thus established suggests itself as at least a partial explanation of the divergence of Weintraub's results from previous ones. After exposure to one of two red adaptation fields, Weintraub introduced an achromatic field and trained his observers to call the color thus produced by successive contrast "blue-green," an afterimage complement of the red adapting field. Helson (see Footnote 1) suggested as one possible reason for the conflict between his and Weintraub's results the fact that the differences in luminance between the latter's adaptation and postadaptation fields were not great enough to yield afterimage colors. For Weintraub's observers the change was from .30 footlambert to .20 footlambert, whereas the nonselective patches of Helson's 1938 study had reflectance values ranging from .80 to .03. Thus, for Helson's observers the light reaching the eye varied by a ratio of approximately 27–1, whereas the ratio of change for Weintraub's observers was 1.5–1. Also, Weintraub's results might have been different had the shift from adaptation to postadaptation fields been gradual rather than abrupt. The effect of rate of change in illumination is best noted in the dimming phenomenon in which the complementary color response to a chromatic spot on a nonselective background is facilitated by slow, rather than rapid, dimming of the illumination of the spot. Illuminating a nonselective ground with chromatic illuminants, Higbee (1947) found that apertures centrally located in the background showed conversion toward the afterimage complementary of the surround as the ratio of aperture luminance to surround luminance decreased. These results, coupled with those of Helson and Self (1961; cited by Helson, 1964) showing the complementarity of colored shadows to be a function of the ratio of the luminances of the two light sources, support the principle of color conversion and present an explanatory challenge which Weintraub's work fails to meet. At present there remains the challenging research opportunity of demonstrating that Weintraub's results, rather than denying the operation of the principle of color conversion, indicate its operation when the purity of the Ganzfeld is varied.

Orientation in the Ganzfeld

Upon exposure to the Ganzfeld, observers search hurriedly for something on which to focus the eyes in an effort to orient themselves to the visual field (Miller and Hall, 1962). These investigators found that observers, finding no fixation objects, become aware of vitreous opacities and retinal blood vessels, report gradations of light and shade and, in extreme cases, hallucinations. In addition to these phenomena, the observer soon becomes conscious of an uncertainty as to *where* he is looking. This uncertainty becomes a serious problem if the observer's task is to locate a single object. The observer not only does not know where he is looking, he also does not know where he has been looking previously. Miller and Ludvigh (1960) have shown that it may take as long as 20 seconds to locate an object as large as 6 times the threshold size when no external cues are available. Ludvigh (1936; cited by Miller and Hall, 1962) obtained evidence that with a small section of the cornea anesthetized the eye can be moved mechanically without arousing any sensation of eye movement. He also found (1952; cited by Miller and Hall, 1962) that using false cues can cause an observer to feel that his eyes are in violent motion when they are in fact stationary. From such evidence Ludvigh attributes disorientation in the Ganzfeld to the lack of proprioceptive feedback from the extraocular muscles.

Miller and Hall prefer to interpret orientation in the Ganzfeld as due to the fact that the individual orients himself in relation to some sort of internal bodily coordinate system. They define a displacement threshold as the ability of the individual to place a single test object in the center of the visual field in the absence of all visible detail other than facial features. These investigators produced homogeneous stimulation by means of a clear Plexiglas cylindrical annulus containing a fogging solution through which the observer viewed a uniformly illuminated white field. A test object subtending a visual angle of 25 minutes at the nodal point of the eye was moved in a horizontal arc approximately 11 feet from the observer. This test object was randomly positioned across a 34-degree horizontal path, and observers were instructed to return it to the center of the field. Subjective center was found to be to the left of true center for half the observers and to the right for the other half, average displacements being 2.37 and 2.94 degrees, respectively. Seventy-five percent of the time these observers moved the test object in the appropriate central direction when it was displaced as little as 2.7 degrees from true center. Miller and Hall also provided reference positions at various points in the field to which observers returned test objects. The appropriate reference was presented before each displacement of the test object, and under these conditions the displacement thresholds for different positions averaged 2.0 degrees. These investigators concluded that although the eye may lack an extremely accurate proprioceptive mechanism, the individual appears to possess surprisingly accurate spatial orientation in the absence of retinal cues. Subjective reports of methods used by their observers in locating the center of the field indicate that they resorted to orientation cues from various parts of the body, for example, neck, shoulders, trunk, and hips.

Form Perception in the Ganzfeld

The most primitive level of form perception in the Ganzfeld is that reported by Cohen (1957) who found that the introduction of a brightness gradient into the

Ganzfeld at first reversed the usual figure-ground relationship, putting the ground before the figure. Increases in the steepness of the gradient reversed this relationship, producing the usual relation of figure to ground. Cohen also found the spot was judged about 1½ times as large as its real size.

Prolonged homogeneous stimulation seems to result in the failure of the perceptual mechanism to produce a phenomenal field. Cohen (1960) terms this phenomenon "blank out" and says it is best described as a temporary cessation of vision. This investigator tested observers' ability to discriminate forms during blank out by tachistoscopically presenting (for $\frac{1}{25}$ second) figures varying in complexity such as a circle and a star. Time of presentation of the forms coincided with the observer's indication that he was experiencing blank out. With these observers the less complex figures were usually correctly identified during periods of no blank out, but in no case was the observer able to recognize any of the forms during blank out. This lack of ability to recognize the objects persisted even with repeated presentations of the same figure during blank out. At best, observers could describe only a "flash." However, the presence of the forms did, in many instances, seem to terminate the blank out. In the most extreme cases of blank out such a brief presentation of the figures did not produce even the report of a flash. Presentation of the figures for as long as 2 seconds did, however, terminate even the extreme cases of blank out.

Extending his investigation of the effects of homogeneous stimulation, Cohen (1960) presented a series of 16 figures to observers immediately upon their entry into the homogeneous field, after a 90-second adaptation to the homogeneous field, or in a field with a homogeneous center portion and a structured periphery. He found that even a 90-second exposure to a homogeneous field interferes with form recognition. The extent of this interference is somewhat ameliorated by presentation of the series of figures; accuracy of recognition for the first 2 figures is considerably lower than for the remaining 14. This facilitative effect of series presentation is maintained even if exposure of the figures is as short as $\frac{1}{100}$ of a second, unless the interval between presentations is extended from 10 to 30 seconds. The most easily recognized figures were the circle, square, diamond, and equilateral and right triangles; most difficult to recognize were the star, pentagon, hexagon, octagon, cross, and the letter X. Rectangles, parallelograms, the letter T, the letter L, and the inverted letter T were of moderate difficulty. Cohen noted that the detrimental effects of the uniform field are most pronounced in the recognition of the more difficult figures; although prolonged exposure to the uniform field reduced the accuracy of recognition for all figures, the greatest loss in accuracy occurred with the more complex figures.

Miller and Ludvigh (1960) investigated the effects of homogeneous stimulation on the acquisition of both stationary and moving test objects. Their Ganzfeld was produced by the cylindrical annulus described previously, and their 5 test objects subtended visual angles of 10.00, 12.34, 17.45, 29.55, and 59.13 minutes of arc at the nodal point of the eye. Stationary targets could be positioned at any one of 29 positions within the field. Moving targets were moved horizontally from one or another of these 29 positions at a rate of .14 degrees per second, a rate previously determined to be below threshold for moving objects. They found that the same general relationship held for all their experimental conditions; length of time required to locate a test object was inversely related to the size of the test object. Acquisition time increased over a range of approximately 3 to 120 seconds, with the increase becoming quite rapid when test-object size was less than approximately 20 minutes of arc. This result was unanticipated in view of the fact that visual acuity previously measured through the fogging solution of the Ganzfeld was found to average 3 minutes of arc for the 3 observers in this study. These authors pointed out the observer's lack of awareness of where he is presently searching or where he has previously searched in the Ganzfeld and noted that this introduces an element of chance into visual search in the Ganzfeld. Calculating probability of acquisition as a function of target size, these authors indicated that the probability of target acquisition does not reach a range of approximately .82 to .92 until target size has increased to approximately 60 minutes of arc. Using as a base the previously determined average visual acuity of 3 degrees, Miller and Ludvigh found it necessary to increase the angular subtense of the target by a factor of 10 over the measured visual acuity in order for acquisition to occur within a relatively short time (approximately 3–5 seconds).

Movement Perception in the Ganzfeld

Cohen (1958a) reasoned that if autokinetic movement under conditions of darkness results from an inadequate visual framework, then similar movement of a figure in an illuminated uniform visual field should occur. Using the adjoining spheres described previously, he exposed observers monocularly to a field containing an 8-centimeter-diameter spot. His subjects observed a series of situations in which differences between the figure and field were systematically varied and, in about 40% of these situations, reported spontaneous autokinetic movement of the spot. The predominance of movement to the right is probably attributable to the fact that Cohen's observers viewed the field monocularly with the right eye. The frequency of reports of movement was not wholly dependent upon the kind of difference between figure and ground, that is, either

chromatic differences or intensity differences produced movement. When intensity was gradually increased the previously noted phenomenon of receding ground and approaching figure occurred.

In a subsequent publication, Cohen (1960) reported blurring of contours, transformations of shape, and disappearance of stationary figures in the Ganzfeld Observers were also found to be relatively insensitive to the movement of objects slowly rotated in the uniform field. When objects were moved at near threshold speeds, movement was often perceived in the direction opposite to the real movement, an extremely confusing effect for the observer when he found that the phenomenal displacement of the object was in a direction opposite to that of his experience of it.

Miller and Ludvigh (1961) noted Aubert's 1886 estimate that the absolute threshold for movement increased by about a factor of 10 when the subject was without a satisfactory frame of reference and Brown's experimental demonstration (1931; cited by Miller and Ludvigh, 1961) that as the background became less and less structured, the phenomenal velocity of a test object decreased. Miller and Ludvigh also reported an experiment in which observers were placed in a Ganzfeld with eyes closed, given a signal to open their eyes, and asked to indicate the cessation of movement of test objects within the field. Two targets, subtending 19.1 and 51.7 minutes of arc at the nodal point of the eye, were exposed for either 5, 10, or 15 seconds and were moved both to the right and left at angular velocities of .30, .56, .71, 1.08, 1.56, and 2.96 degrees per second. "Time delay," the elapsed time between actual stoppage of the target and the observer's report that it had stopped, was the measure of performance. Time delay approached about .5 second for all three durations of movement, for all higher angular velocities. This .5-second value is probably a limiting reaction time since less than .5% of the responses occurred with shorter time delays. As stimulus velocity decreased time delay increased—to a maximum of approximately 6.5 seconds for 5-second exposures, 10.0 seconds for 10-second exposures, and 15.5 seconds for 15-second exposures. No statistical difference was found between delay times as a function of direction of movement. Reported in terms of target size rather than exposure time, the data showed that the larger target produced shorter time delays than the smaller one at angular velocities below 1.50 degrees per second. These authors discussed their results in terms of a hypothesis of "contrast of velocity" whereby the sudden cessation of high apparent speed is held to be more obvious than the sudden cessation of lower apparent speeds. They found, by a chi-square test, that the following formula described their data: $t = (r + 1/av^2)$, where t is time delay in seconds, r is reaction time in seconds, v is the velocity of the test object in angular degrees per second around the nodal point of the eye, and a is the parameter of inverse proportionality. The adequacy of this formula in describing their data lends mathematical support to Miller and Ludvigh's "contrast of velocity" hypothesis.

Accommodation in the Ganzfeld

An empty visual field produces a condition of increased refractive state of the eye similar to the phenomenon known as night myopia. The presence of an empty field also produces fluctuations in the refractive state of the eye. Westheimer and his fellow workers (Campbell and Westheimer, 1959; Westheimer, 1957, 1960; Westheimer, Campbell, and Robson, 1958) have reported a series of studies of fluctuating levels of accommodation produced by empty visual fields. Westheimer (1957, 1960) flashed a beam of .05-second duration into the subject's eye, the beam passing through two fixed positions in the sub-

ject's pupil every 10 seconds over a period of 30 to 40 minutes and giving information concerning the refractive state of the eye. The subject's field was either a dark empty field, a bright empty field, or a red fixation spot at optical infinity. The observer was asked to indicate, by pressing the appropriate button or combination of buttons, which of four response categories applied to the presentation of two vertically aligned or misaligned measuring light bars: over accommodation, under accommodation, correct accommodation, or unable to say. These stimulus conditions brought into play positive accommodation usually of the order of .75–1.75 diopters. The accommodative level did not remain fixed throughout an experimental run. Most runs showed no long-term trends, but there were prominent cycle lengths of 1.25 and 2 minutes, and peak to trough amplitudes sometimes ranged up to 1 diopter. Harmonic analysis showed the accommodation time curves had strong components of some frequency bands, but no frequencies characteristic of an observer or a stimulus condition. From these results, Westheimer (1960) concluded that since the refractive state of the eye is unsteady in the presence of a structureless field, it does not seem possible to correct this myopia with a single lens. Flyers have noted that high-altitude flight presents empty field conditions ("sky" myopia) and, consequently, an unstable refractive state. For such conditions Westheimer (1960) noted the probability that an observer, even when wearing the best "average" correction for the task of target detection, may be out of focus by perhaps .5 diopter or more. Brown (1957), working from the hypothesis that optical devices that would produce focus at optical infinity could perhaps correct the unstable refractive state, employed collimated reticles and obtained negative results. He suggested selection of normally hyperopic persons for high altitude target-detection tasks.

According to Koomen, Scolnik, and Tousey (1951), the phenomenon of night

myopia was noticed as early as 1883 by
Lord Rayleigh. This is nearsightedness developed by the eye in dim illumination,
necessitating negative lenses to counteract
the decrement in visual acuity. Chin and
Horn (1956) mention several bases for
this phenomenon: accommodation, increased positive spherical aberration due to
pupil dilation in dim illumination, the
combination of chromatic aberration and
the Purkinje shift, and the fact that a
point is not imaged on the retina as a
point but forms a caustic along the visual
axis near the retina due to spherical aberration.

The magnitude of night myopia is a
matter of some dispute; values vary from
nearly zero to more than 2 diopters. For
example, Otero and Duran (1942), according to Koomen, Scolnik, and Tousey
(1951), reported values of 1.5 to 2.0 diopters, while Wald and Griffin (1947) found
much more variation from subject to subject. These investigators found for their
subjects changes in the power of the eye
ranging from +1.4 to −3.4 diopters with
an average of .59 diopter. Both Koomen,
Scolnik, and Tousey (1951) and Helson
(1952) drew attention to the fact that such
conflicting results are more than likely
because various experiments have been
carried out at widely differing levels of
illumination using a variety of measures.

Paralleling the lack of agreement as to
the magnitude of night myopia is the disagreement as to its cause or causes. This
disagreement has been largely between
Koomen, Scolnik, and Tousey on the one
hand, and Otero on the other. The former
based their conclusion largely on the fact
that night myopia persisted after accommodation was prevented by optical methods
and by the use of homatropine, and that
it could be produced by means of a lens
system having the spherical aberration
properties of the eye. Otero (1951) said
of his work that ". . . experimental evidence is presented proving that the main
cause of night myopia is closely related to

the mechanism of accommodation [p.
942]." This experimenter, using a light
flash too brief to change the accommodative state of a completely dark-adapted
eye, photographed Purkinje images to obtain a measure of the state of accommodation of the eye corresponding to its state
of rest. For 3 observers this state proved
to be 1.12, 1.22, and 1.24 diopters. Otero
maintained that spherical aberration and
chromatic aberration contribute .3 and .4
diopter, respectively, to the 1.5 to 2.0 diopters of night myopia he observed. Adding the contributions of these 3 factors to
night myopia gives totals approximately
equal to the observed night myopia, and
Otero concluded that accommodation is its
main cause. More recently Chin and Horn
(1956) measured the refractive state of the
eye in dim illumination and in darkness
using an infrared skiascope, and they concluded that the contribution of accommodation to night myopia was generally small.

Helson (1952) pointed out that the Koomen, Scolnik, and Tousey conclusion, emphasizing the role of spherical aberration,
is difficult to accept in view of the fact that
these authors failed in at least 3 instances
to produce spherical aberration in the eyes
of subjects. The conflicting results from
Otero and Chin and Horn likewise leave
uncertain the role of accommodation.
Helson's conclusion in 1952 that the problem was not closed is equally applicable
at this time.

Ganzfeld "Blank Out" and Its Electrophysiological Correlates

In a series of 3 studies of vision in the
Ganzfeld, Cohen (1956, 1957, 1960) reported for some observers a temporary cessation of visual experience; this phenomenon he termed "blank out." It was found
in 5 out of 16 observers, 2 of whom reported it almost every time they were
exposed to the uniform field. The experience was not simply the presence of a dark,
undifferentiated field, but rather a "com-

plete disappearance of the sense of vision for short periods of time." Cohen (1960) found various degrees of blanking out. For example, the observer may experience a feeling of light with no external reference. Or, in the most extreme cases, he may experience a "complete absence of seeing," this latter extreme generally occurring only after exposures of 10–20 minutes. Observers reported uncertainty as to whether or not their eyes were open; they were also unable to control their eye movements. Although blinking and eye movement usually brought about the return of the visual field, this did not occur with the most extensive losses of vision.

Cohen (1960) suggested that persistent uniform stimulation without a structured field results in the failure of the perceptual mechanism to produce a phenomenal field, a possibility supported by the fact that reports of blank out were found to be associated with the return of bursts of alpha activity. Cohen pointed out that alpha patterns in the EEG record are usually associated with the absence of visual stimulation. The return of alpha activity during blank out, he suggested, would indicate a functional similarity between no stimulation and prolonged uniform stimulation. Individual differences in susceptibility to blank out Cohen found to be correlated with individual EEG records; high alpha activity in the absence of visual stimulation was associated with more susceptibility to blank out. Cohen and Cadwallader (1958) found supporting data for this conclusion.

Cohen's suggestion generated further research by Tepas (1962), who exposed 3 subjects with normal vision and normal EEG's to a white, uniformly illuminated sphere for 5-minute periods followed by 3-minute rest periods. Electrical activity was recorded from six standard EEG electrodes. Subjects were initially instructed to describe what they saw as accurately as possible. Once the subject verbalized experiencing blank out, he was instructed to close a microswitch which produced a signal on the EEG record. On all experimental sessions, alpha scores were obtained at the beginning and end of the session under "eyes closed" and "eyes open" conditions. Tepas found that all subjects experienced blank out and that the alpha present during Ganzfeld viewing was intermediate between "eyes closed" and "eyes open" conditions for all observers. There was a significant absence of saccadic eye movement or blinking just prior to onset of blank out and during the experience, but the end of the experience coincided with eye movements or blinking to a statistically significant degree. Also, an increase in the number of viewing trials increased the amount of alpha present but did not alter the blank-out/non-blank-out alpha difference.

Data from a typical high alpha subject indicated that, irrespective of the general level of ongoing alpha activity in the brain, there was significantly more alpha during blank out than when blank out was not reported. There was also a general increase in the level of alpha activity as the experimental session progressed; however, the amount of blank out reported had become relatively stable at 10 to 15% by the middle experimental session and did not increase thereafter with the level of alpha activity. This finding indicates that amount of blank-out time need not be merely a function of the general level of alpha activity. Tepas' data showed a negative relationship between amount of eye-movement potentials and amount of blank out reported, causing him to conclude that the hypothesis that high alpha activity is an important indicant of blank-out susceptibility was not strongly supported.

More detailed specification of the factors contributing to the relationship between blank out and alpha activity deserves the continued interest of physiological psychologists, as do the relationships between the factors contributing to night myopia. These two problems, along with the possibility of

demonstrating the operation of the principle of color conversion when colorimetric
purity is varied, are likely to be rewarding
ones for interested researchers.

References

BEXTON, W. H., W. HERON, and T. H.
SCOTT. Effects of decreased variation in the
sensory environment. *Canadian Journal of
Psychology,* 1954, 8, 70–76.

BROWN, J. F. The visual perception of velocity.
Psychologische Forschung, 1931, 14, 199–
232.

BROWN, R. H. "Empty-field" myopia and visibility of distant objects at high altitudes.
American Journal of Psychology, 1957, 70,
376–385.

CAMPBELL, F. W., and G. WESTHEIMER.
Factors influencing accommodation responses of the human eye. *Journal of the
Optical Society of America,* 1959, 49, 568–
571.

CHIN, N. B., and R. E. HORN. Infrared skia-
scopic measurements of refractive changes
in dim illumination and in darkness. *Journal of the Optical Society of America,* 1956,
46, 60–66.

COHEN, W. Comparisons of homogeneous
Ganzfelds with Ganzfelds containing simple figures. *Dissertation Abstracts,* 1956,
16, 1510–1511.

COHEN, W. Spatial and textural characteristics
of the Ganzfeld. *American Journal of Psychology,* 1957, 70, 403–410.

COHEN, W. Apparent movement of simple
figures in the Ganzfeld. *Perceptual and Motor Skills,* 1958, 8, 32. (a)

COHEN, W. Color perception in the chromatic
Ganzfeld. *American Journal of Psychology,*
1958, 71, 390–394. (b)

COHEN, W. Form recognition, spatial orientation, perception of movement in the uniform visual field. In A. MORRIS and E. P.
HORNE (Eds.), *Visual search techniques.*
(Pub. 712) Washington: National Academy of Science-National Research Council, 1960. pp. 119–123.

COHEN, W., and T. C. CADWALLADER. Cessation of visual experience under prolonged
uniform visual stimulation. *American Psychologist,* 1958, 13, 410. (Abstract)

GIBSON, J. J., and D. WADDELL. Homogeneous retinal stimulation and visual perception. *American Journal of Psychology,*
1952, 62, 263–270.

HELSON, H. Fundamental problems in color
vision: I. The principle governing changes
in hue, saturation, and lightness of nonselective samples in chromatic illumination.
Journal of Experimental Psychology, 1938,
23, 439–476.

HELSON, H. Vision. *Annual Review of Psychology,* 1952, 3, 55–84.

HELSON, H. *Adaptation level theory.* New
York: Harper and Row, 1964.

HELSON, H., and V. B. JEFFERS. Fundamental problems in color vision: II. Hue, lightness, and saturation of selective samples in
chromatic illumination. *Journal of Experimental Psychology,* 1940, 26, 1–27.

HELSON, H., and D. B. JUDD. A study of photopic adaptation. *Journal of Experimental
Psychology,* 1932, 15, 380–398.

HELSON, H., and H. C. SELF. A study of
coloured shadows. Paper read at Maxwell
Color Centenary, London, 1961.

HIGBEE, R. V. Hue and saturation of aperture
colors as a function of the composition and
luminance of the surrounding field. Unpublished doctoral dissertation, Bryn Mawr
College, 1947.

HOCHBERG, J. E., W. TRIEBEL, and G. SEA-
MAN. Color adaptation under conditions of
homogeneous visual stimulation (Ganzfeld). *Journal of Experimental Psychology,*
1951, 41, 153–159.

ITTELSON, W. H., and J. A. AMES. Accommodation, convergence, and apparent distance. *Journal of Psychology,* 1950, 50,
43–62.

JUDD, D. B. Appraisal of Land's work on two-
primary color projections. *Journal of the
Optical Society of America,* 1960, 50, 254–
268.

KOFFKA, K. *Principles of gestalt psychology.*
New York: Harcourt, Brace, and World,
1935.

KOOMEN, M., R. SCOLNIK, and R. A. TOUSEY.
A study of night myopia. *Journal of the
Optical Society of America,* 1951, 41, 80–
90.

LAND, E. H. Experiments in color vision. *Scientific American,* 1959, 200, 84–94, 96, 99.

LUDVIGH, E. J. Is ocular proprioceptive sense
concerned in vision? *Archives of Ophthalmology,* 1936, 15, 1037–1049.

LUDVIGH, E. J. Possible role of proprioception
in the extraocular muscles. *Archives of Ophthalmology,* 1952, 48, 436–441.

METZGER, W. Optische Untersuchungen am
Ganzfeld: II. Zur phanomenologie des
homogenen Ganzfelds. *Psychologische Forschung,* 1930, 13, 6–29.

MILLER, J. W., and R. J. HALL. The problem
of motion perception and orientation in the
Ganzfeld. In M. A. WHITCOMB (Ed.),

Visual problems of the armed forces. Washington: National Academy of Science-National Research Council, 1962. pp. 14–20.

MILLER, J. W., and E. LUDVIGH. Time required for detection of stationary and moving objects as a function of size in homogeneous and partially structured visual fields. In A. MORRIS and E. P. HORNE (Eds.), *Visual search techniques.* (Pub. 712) Washington: National Academy of Science-National Research Council, 1960. pp. 170–180.

MILLER, J. W., and E. LUDVIGH. The perception of movement persistence in the Ganzfeld. *Journal of the Optical Society of America,* 1961, 51, 57–60.

OTERO, J. M. Influence of the state of accommodation on the visual performance of the human eye. *Journal of the Optical Society of America,* 1951, 41, 942–948.

OTERO, J. M., and A. DURAN. Continuación del estudio de la miopía nocturna. Notas II y III. *Anales de física y química,* 1942, 38, 236–244.

TEN DOESSCHATE, G. Vision in an empty field. *Psychological Abstracts,* 1961, 35, 565.

TEPAS, D. L. The electrophysiological correlates of vision in a uniform field. In M. A. WHITCOMB (Ed.), *Visual problems of the armed forces.* Washington: National Academy of Science-National Research Council, 1962. pp. 21–25.

WALD, G., and D. R. GRIFFIN. The change in refractive power of the human eye in dim and bright light. *Journal of the Optical Society of America,* 1947, 37, 321–336.

WEINTRAUB, D. J. Successive contrast involving luminance and purity alterations of the Ganzfeld. *Journal of Experimental Psychology,* 1964, 68, 555–562.

WESTHEIMER, G. Accommodation measurements in empty visual fields. *Journal of the Optical Society of America,* 1957, 47, 714–718.

WESTHEIMER, G. Accommodation levels in empty visual fields. In E. P. HORNE and M. A. WHITCOMB (Eds.), *Vision research reports.* (Pub. 835) Washington: National Academy of Science-National Research Council, 1960. pp. 21–23.

WESTHEIMER, G., F. W. CAMPBELL, and J. B. ROBSON. Significance of fluctuations in accommodation. *Journal of the Optical Society of America,* 1958, 48, 669.

In the Mind's Eye*

JULIAN HOCHBERG
New York University

Introduction

I'm going to talk today about some current attempts to analyze the structure of visually perceived form, and to identify those com-

* This paper is a slightly revised version of an Invited Address read at the September, 1966 meetings of the American Psychological Association, Division 3. The unpublished research referred to herein was variously supported by Off. Educ., S–407; by A.F. contr. 19 (628) 5830, with Sperry Rand Res. Center; and by NSF GB 5270. I am indebted to Fred Attneave, Lloyd Kaufman, and Harry Blum for discussion of many of the questions to which this paper is addressed.

ponents of perceptual processing that mediate the known effects of set, of knowledge and of learning. Most of the work is unpublished, and some is only starting, so what I will say is tentative and groping, and the implications are much less well-thought through than I would wish.

First, a question that would not have been necessary forty years ago, and would not have been possible twenty years ago: When should we talk about *form perception,* let alone analyze it? I am raising this question because we'll need an answer to it that we can use, not merely as a definitional exercise.

The question was unnecessary forty years ago because a formal definition in terms of introspective observation was available and acceptable. In Structuralist terms, "perception" could be analyzed into fundamental mental units, and there was good reason to do so, since what one perceived was itself used to predict other mental events.

The question would have been impossible, or at least in bad taste, twenty years ago, because by then two points were well established. They were the following:

(1) The Gestaltists' point: the basic introspective units—the *sensations* and *images* into which it was once thought *percepts* could be reduced, and in terms of which they were to be defined—turned out to be useless for that purpose, even in principle.

(2) The Behaviorists' point: no causal status could be attributed to a mental event; and in any case, introspective reports about what one perceives are only verbal responses, not mental events. They are dependent variables, not independent variables.

Now we cannot ignore all that history. Structuralist introspection *won't* work, the old definitions are *not* consistent with the rest of present-day psychology, and the behaviorist arguments, philosophically motivated though they may have been, remain methodologically sound as far as they go. Yet some psychologists continue to talk about "perception," even though they no longer have the original introspective definition, nor do they have the original purposes within which to use it as an independent variable. New definitions in terms of converging operations can and have been devised—Postman (1952); Garner, Hake and Eriksen (1956); Hochberg (1956). But if it's only an "effect," never a "cause," why pick these particular responses for special definition and for present study?

The answer is that there is clearly a large and important set of problems, important both in and out of psychology, in which this particular dependent variable—"perception"—does in fact seem to have some kind of causal status. Thus, when perception psychologists wish to check whether or not a subject *really* sees some object or event, they usually ask him a question that they do not expect him to be able otherwise to answer. And this means using "perception" as a *construct*, based conjointly on the subject's reports and on the physical stimulus, with which we can more simply predict the subject's behavior than we can by measures taken on the stimulus alone—a use for the construct, "perception," which surely should be taken into account in our attempts at definition (Hochberg, 1956). Thus, the general answer to the question of when we should talk about form perception, is this: *When we can predict and explain the subject's responses to the world that confronts him more simply and elegantly with the aid of such a construct than without it.*

What criteria are thereby implied for perceptual responses? Before explicating this point in the area of form perception, in which the relevant stimulus measures are still largely unknown, let us first look at an analogous example in the field of color perception, where we are fairly certain of the relevant physical variables.

A primary fact of color perception is this: a single perceived hue may be produced by a great many different sets of wavelengths. However, where *metamerism* holds, it doesn't matter what stimuli we have used to elicit a given color. A yellow may be produced by light of 580 mμ or by a mixture of 530 and 650 mμ, but no matter how it is produced, all lights of that yellow hue will mix with a given perceived blue to produce the same perceived gray, and will mix with a perceived red to produce the same perceived orange. And, where metamerism holds, *laws of color mixture can be stated and used without*

 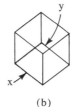 

(a)   (b)   (c)

(d)   (e)   (f)

FIGURE 1   Reversible-perspective figures:

	A	B	C	D	E	F
Apparent tridimensionality:	1	2	3	1	2	3
Gestalt complexity, 2D (Kopfermann, 1930):	1	2	3	1	2	3
Measured pattern complexity:	1	2	3	1	2	3

knowing what wavelengths are employed. When the painter or photographer uses the "color circle," he is using *perceived color,* which is a dependent variable, a response—as a *cause,* as an independent variable.

Similar response-response relationships have been proposed in the study of perceived distance, of perceived size, and of perceived shape. From Berkeley, through Helmholtz to Woodworth, perceived size has been explained in terms of perceived distance (that is, as though it were causally dependent on perceived distance); perceived shape has been explained in terms of perceived slant, and so on. To illustrate: if you really see the cube's lower face as nearer, as in Figure 1B, you will probably see line X as shorter than line Y; if you see the upper face nearer, line Y will probably look shorter than line X. Your responses are not independent of the stimulus, or of each other.

It seems to me that the following are minimum requirements for calling any set of responses "perceptual" (Hochberg, 1956): If the responses were completely independent of the stimuli, we would be dealing with imagination, with memory, with hallucination; if the responses were dependent only on the stimuli (that is, if there were no inter-response constraints, no perceptual

organization or *structure*), then talking about a "percept" would be gratuitous, since a simple psychophysical (S-R) correlation would then suffice. But we may in fact gain something by talking about the perceived cube in Figure 1A, as we just saw in the line-length example, and there are in fact a great many similar questions that one could ask the subject about what he sees in that figure, to which his answers could be predicted better once we know which alternative arrangement of the cube —which organization—he perceives. This is true because there are many attributes of the specific perceptual structure, "cube-with-lower-face-forward," that are different from those of "cube-with-upper-face-forward," and it is the coupling between such attributes that defines the perceptual structure.

In order for such a construct—a "perceived structure"—to be useful, we need to know in advance which attributes are coupled to each other, and how. What determines the inter-attribute coupling in any perceived structure?

Imagine that you are playing a game somewhat similar to Twenty Questions, and that you have to decide whether someone *really* is looking at some object in front of him. You ask him questions about the object—questions which he can answer only while looking at the object. Some of your questions require answers depending simply on the *physical* structure (for example that the diagonal of a square is 1.4 times the length of a side), but other questions depend on the observer's visual system. Some, *but not all,* of the consistencies and couplings of the real physical world are more or less reflected in the perceived structure (that is, in the interresponse constraints) of objects and scenes; some attributes are quite different (as in the geometrical illusions); and some couplings and consistencies of objects in the physical world are, as we shall see, missing from their perceived form. Whether or not it's worthwhile to talk about the subject's "perception," in any specific case, seems to me to be a local, empirical quesion—a matter of how much it simplifies our description, not a general philosophical issue.

Let me now apply these abstract considerations to the study of form perception. Various problems have been pursued under this name for various reasons. First, of course, the structuralist attempt—by Helmholtz, by Wundt and Titchener—to analyze form into two kinds of content: (1) local *sensations* of color—innate, visual, and meaningless; and (2) associated to each familiar pattern or sub-pattern by the results of past experience, the *images* (memory) of previous movement-produced tactual and kinesthetic sensations which, because they are the results of commerce with the real world and its physical consistencies, provide structure to the percepts in which they participate. I will not review the reasons for abandoning this attempt, except to note that a major factor was the Gestaltist argument that a form comprises a unit which cannot be analyzed into more elementary parts or elements—an argument which I will seriously dispute.

A second and more neutral set of problems consists of pattern-discrimination and pattern-recognition. I can't see the point of

this enterprise *unless we expect some consequences to follow from the fact that the subject identifies one pattern rather than another.* And, of course, although students of pattern-recognition rarely seem concerned with such matters, there are many phenomena that *do* seem to depend on the configuration of the pattern, and/or on its perceived form. These are the phenomena of the geometrical illusions, and the Gestalt phenomena of apparent motion, figure-ground reversal, and ambiguous depth.

This is, to me, the most significant set of problems in the field of form perception. Which form a subject reports seeing apparently makes a difference. In fact, in this area perceived form is important in three ways:

(1) Because we don't have a single physical dimension of stimulation by which to define the stimulus configuration to which a subject is responding, or by which we can decide what it is that two different patterns, which both produce the same form percept, have in common. In fact, we don't even have a limited set of dimensions that we know are relevant to perceived form. Nothing analogous to the physical dimensions of luminance and wavelength with which S-R treatments of color perception can be attempted. So, in most non-trivial cases, we have to use human observers to define the stimulus configuration. We can say, of course, that we're merely doing this for convenience and not from permanent necessity, and that we'll surely be able to define the relevant physical stimulus characteristics objectively when we really want to—but *even* if that were true (and I'm no longer all that certain that it is true), the fact at present is that *we need someone's form perceptions (whether experimenter's or subject's) to define our independent variable.*

(2) Because the subject can perceive very different forms in response to the same physical stimulus, and which form he perceives critically determines the other

answers he gives to questions about shape, motion, size, depth, and so on.

(3) Because of a third, and more subtle, involuted way in which form perception has causal status in this research area.

These form-dependent phenomena have been studied primarily by Gestalt psychologists, motivated by the belief that effects of a given stimulus pattern all depend upon, and therefore reveal, the underlying physiological processes set up by the physical stimulus acting on the sensory system— underlying physiological processes that are different in configuration from the physical stimulus pattern, and which mediate between the physical stimulus and the final perception. The determinants of the form-dependent phenomena were presumably the "laws of organization" of the underlying physiological process. Since the underlying physiological process is not known, and since the perceived forms' phenomenal attributes were presumed to be *isomorphic* with that underlying process, the alternative percepts that could be obtained with a given physical stimulus pattern were used in effect as measures of the alternative physiological processes that a given physical stimulus could arouse and, thereby, a means of predicting *which* such process and which percept *would* occur.

This point is obscure but important. Consider Kopfermann (1930): Using ambiguous drawings (Figure 1), which can readily be perceived in either of two very different ways—that is, as flat two-dimensional shapes or as tridimensional reversible-perspective objects, she demonstrated that *one obtains the flat percept when that is "simpler" in some sense than the tridimensional percept, and vice versa.* Note that prediction (and explanation) of which alternative percept will be obtained was given in terms of the attributes of the alternative percepts themselves (or of their mythical underlying physiological distributions), not in terms of any stimulus measure. The *independent variable* was essentially this: the degree of difference

between the simplicities of the two alternative percepts that could be obtained with each stimulus; the *dependent variable* was the relative strengths of the two alternative percepts.

In principle, of course, it must be possible, in any specific case, to replace such a mentalistic explanation with one couched in physical terms. Brooks and I did this in 1960, by finding, empirically, a function of objective measures of pattern complexity (for example, number of angles, number of continuous line segments, and so on) that predicts the judged tridimensionalities of Kopfermann's ambiguous forms. This function sidesteps the subjective variables of "perceived complexity" or "perceived simplicity" as predictors of the subjects' tridimensionality rating and form-naming responses. This start at constructing a *psychophysics of form-perception*, in S-R terms, seemed at the time to be moderately successful. We could predict subjects' reports about relative tridimensionality, and about which alternative form he sees, from measurable features of the physical stimulus configuration. We seemed, therefore, on our way to breaking out of the mentalistic circle. But these hopes were premature for two reasons:

(1) It turns out that we cannot yet really define the physical stimulus configurations whose measured attributes we are using as predictive variables.

(2) The function found is wrong, not in detail but in principle.

Let us see first why I say that we can't at present define what the effective stimuli are for form perception; then let us see why the specific psychophysical attempt is basically wrong.

Exotic Stimuli for Presenting Forms to the Mind's Eye

Most form perception research uses luminance-difference contours as stimuli. We cannot, with such displays, decide which form-dependent phenomena occur at

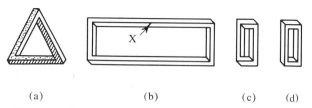

(a)   (b)   (c)   (d)

FIGURE 2 "Impossible" and consistent pictures. A: Adapted from Penrose and Penrose, 1958. B, C, D: Hochberg and Brooks, 1962.

the same level in the nervous system, are tied to each other, and therefore have to be explained together. What we did, therefore, was to produce each form in whose relative apparent tridimensionality we were interested, by three very different classes of physical stimulus display, some of which bypassed any possible retinal contributions to perceived structure:

(1) BINOCULAR ENTRY

Forms can be presented postretinally by using stereograms in neither field of which is the form visible (cf. Julesz, 1960): Two identical random matrices of dots were viewed stereoscopically, one by each eye. In one eye's view, a region of dots, corresponding to one of the reversible-perspective figures, was cut out of the matrix and displaced slightly (20 min. of arc); since this produces a binocular disparity for those dots, the figure thereby delineated seems to float in front of the remaining dots. This is schematized in Figure 3A, with the displaced region opposite in colour from its surround; in actual use, of course, the figure is set off only via stereopsis, not by color.

(2) MOMENTARY DISPLACEMENT

Take a single regular matrix of dots, and *briefly* displace a subset which delineates a reversible-perspective pattern, as in Figure 3D. If a 50 msec displacement of that pattern relative to the rest of the matrix is repeated regularly, with an inter-displacement interval of about 500 msec, a form is "sensed" which displays most of the form-dependent phenomena. Charles

Eriksen (1966) is using a very similar technique to study form storage, a field of inquiry to which we shall return shortly.

(3) SUCCESSIVE APERTURE VIEWING

This last method places the entire problem at a different level, and may wipe out at one stroke most of the Gestalt physiological models, and the various diffusion models of form perception that have been offered at different times by Köhler; by Hochberg, Gleitman, MacBride; by Sickles; and most recently, by Harry Blum.

In 1965, Parks reported an immensely interesting phenomenon: if a pattern is moved behind a stationary slit so that its parts appear successively in the same place, the entire pattern can be recognized. To Parks, this demonstrates the existence of post-retinal visual storage. One might dismiss this phenomenon as the result of eye movements that spread the entire pattern out on adjacent regions of the retina, making Parks' effect a case of parallel stimulation within sensory integration time, that is, not different in principle from any brief exposure. Even were this argument completely true, however, which seems very unlikely to me, it misses an exceedingly important point raised by the Parks effect: that the visual perceptual system can, under the proper conditions, assemble a set of partial views that fall on the same retinal area over a period of time into a single simultaneous form or scene; and that such scenes synthesized in space out of time must comprise a large part of the normal visual experience on which our attempts at perceptual laws are based. We

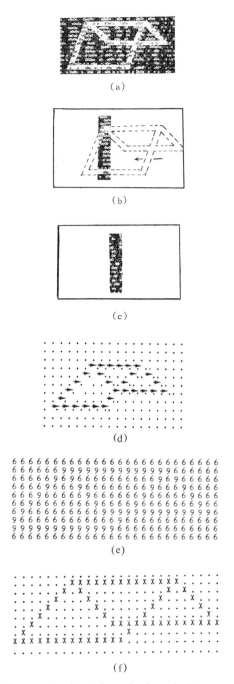

FIGURE 3   Exotic form displays. A: Representation of a binocularly-entered (Julesz-pattern) reversible-perspective figure. B: How the stereogram of (A) is moved behind a (binocular) aperture. C: What a monocular view of (B) looks like. D: Figure produced by momentary displacement of subset in dot-matrix. E: The same figure outlined in 9s. F: The same figure outlined in Xs.

shall discuss research explicitly directed to this point later on.

Our variation of Parks' procedure was this: Instead of outline drawings pulled behind a slit, the Julesz-pattern dot-matrix stereograms, described under binocular entry, above, were moved (via motion picture) back and forth behind a pair of binocular slits (Figures 3B, C). Overall figure width was 18° to 23°, slit width was 3°, and time for the entire figure to traverse the slit was 1.5 seconds. Reversible-perspective figures, Muller-Lyer patterns, and so on were clearly recognizable to each of 5 Ss when so presented. Coordinated tracking and "binocular retinal painting" is a barely conceivable explanation for the apprehension of such displays, but (considering the long elapsed times and large excursions, which would place the figure's trailing edge some 20° off the fovea if the latter were tracking the leading edge after it passed behind the slit) to me, a very strained one.

I have tested two families of reversible-perspective figures with each of the above three procedures and, with all of them, subjects rank the apparent tridimensionalities of the figures in the same way that they do with conventional displays. However, these procedures are remarkably abstract ways of getting a form into the CNS. Let me describe what our dot-matrix aperture-views look like to me: In the aperture itself, a clearly *sensory* vertical ribbon of dots, with some parts clearly nearer in stereospace; the ribbon of dots—still quite clearly—is part of an entire (largely *unseen*) surface of dots that is moving back and forth *behind* the aperture, and the raised regions are the exposed parts of a shape that is raised from, or floating in front of, the background. Now, unlike what Parks reports for his arrangement, there is no real sensory quality to either the shape or its background, where these are occluded by the mask. I'm completely certain that I only *see* those portions of the shape that are behind the aperture at any moment, but I'm equally certain of the extension of the shape behind the mask. Is this "perception," "apprehension," "imagination?" Perhaps we're not dealing with perception at all, in these situations. Maybe merely *knowing* what the pattern is, is sufficient to elicit the different tridimensionality ratings, regardless of how that knowledge is gained.

How, in short, can we decide whether the observer really perceives these forms as tridimensional, using these exotic display conditions?

This is why I spent so much time before on the matter of defining form perception. We will say that the subject has perceived a tridimensional form if the structure implied in such a statement lets us make predictions that we otherwise cannot. In the present case, characteristic and appropriate *spontaneous reversals* and *apparent motions* are obtained. In all three methods of display, any form which was reported to appear tridimensional rather than flat, was also reported to undergo spontaneous depth reversal, which is what we have come to expect from such percepts. And this does not happen, as far as I can tell, with knowledge alone. Consider, for example, the reversible-perspective figure outlined in 9s against a background of 6s in Figure 3E, and in Xs against a background of dots in Figure 3F. In 3F, the pattern is clearly perceptible as a figure, and its relative tridimensionality, when compared to other patterns presented in this manner, is what it should be. Spontaneous depth reversal occurs with prolonged inspection. In 3E,

however, while the subject can name or identify the reversible-perspective pattern by tracing out the 9s with his gaze, the pattern is not perceived as a figure, it does not appear tridimensional and, of course, patterns presented in this way do not display the expected rank-order of relative tridimensionality. Nor does spontaneous reversal occur.

A second converging operation: If I view the successive figures in Figure 4A, each of which maintains one tridimensional orientation, in sequence, one direction of apparent tridimensional motion appears to occur; if the figures each show the other tridimensional orientation, Figure 4B, the other direction of motion appears to occur. I have indicated the motions in profile at the bottom in each column. If these successions of figures are presented by any of the three procedures described above (including our modified Parks method, that is, by moving a succession of stereograms behind a binocular slit while the succession itself is proceeding), the appropriate directions of tridimensional motion are reported (although with the Parks procedures the motion—which is taking place largely "offstage", *behind* the slit—appears to me to be qualitatively different from normal *phi*, being "paler" and less compelling).

It seems reasonable, therefore, to accept subjects' ratings of relative tridimensionalities of ambiguous figures as obtained with these displays on the same terms as their ratings obtained with normal displays. If these relative tridimensionalities

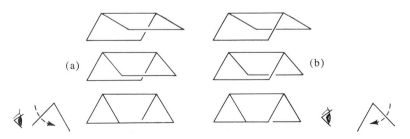

FIGURE 4   Direction of apparent motion as a function of depth "cues." A: Motion away from the observer. B: Motion toward the observer.

reflect organizational factors, Gestalt or otherwise, such organization must be characteristic of the way in which successive glimpses are stored in the nervous system, rather than (or perhaps in addition to) being a characteristic of the interactions between simultaneously-entered sensory processes—that is, Gestalt organization may be a characteristic of immediate memory, rather than of sensory projection (a point that Attneave, 1959, and I, 1957, have suggested for other reasons, anyway).

Before we consider this matter of organization and storage, however, let's turn to a curious class of figures which I think are very relevant to this question.

"Impossible Pictures" and Their Implications

Figure 2A is an "impossible picture" published by Penrose and Penrose in 1958. Modified as in Figure 2B, C, D, the pattern permits parametric study, by keeping constant the informative regions while varying the distance over which the integration proceeds. Since the corners are inconsistent in three dimensions, any reasonable application of the Hochberg and Brooks algorithm or, in fact, of Kopfermann's Gestalt formulation, should predict that the figure would appear flat. As we reported in 1962, with small distance between inconsistent corners (Figure 2C), the figures do appear inconsistent and, relatively often, as a flat nested pattern. However, with increased distance (Figure 2B), tridimensionality judgments are about as high as with completely consistent figures of the same dimensions.

Such figures have been "explained" as being examples of the inherent difficulties of presenting tridimensional objects by two-dimensional drawings, but this misses some very important implications: First, in what sense is Figure 2B "impossible?" In one sense: as an integrated 3-dimensional object, line x must be seen (discontinuously, one would think) as the apex of one di-

hedral angle at the left corner, and as the apex of a different dihedral at the right corner. As a flat pattern, on the other hand, it involves us in no such inconsistencies. Nevertheless, we see a tridimensional picture and, with sizable intercorner distance, do not even initially note its impossibility. Our perceptual systems seem more tolerant of inconsistency than they would if they mirrored faithfully the couplings found in the real world. To me, this phenomenon suggests one minor point and two major ones.

The minor point: our algorithm for ambiguous pictures (and Kopfermann's, as well) doesn't fit inconsistent pictures. In Figures 2B and 2C, apparent tridimensionalities change merely with changing separation between inconsistent corners, leaving unaltered the criteria of simplicity —for example, number of angles, number of line segments, and so on.

Next, two major points: (A) The stimulus determinants of depth are not given by the whole configuration, but only by certain features (in Figure 2, by the corners) which act as *local depth cues,* and which exert their effects only over some limited distance. (B) Form perception must be broken down into at least two very different components of processing: one, the input of a single glance; the other, the perceived structure or *schematic map* (which has only limited interresponse coupling or consistency constraints) within which the separate glimpses take their place. I shall propose that the former components are relatively independent of learning, or of set, or of knowledge, while the latter are more susceptible to, and dependent on, such factors.

I shall try to explicate these two points in turn.

1. Local Depth Cues: Indirect Evidence

The idea of local depth cues is, of course, the more difficult to incorporate in any Gestaltish model. I suggest that, at least with line-drawn figures, any indication of depth effects the relevant lines only in its immediate neighborhood. I can not prove this point, but I can bring a number of indirect arguments to bear.

First. As we've already seen, it's perfectly possible to incorporate two incompatible depth cues in a single picture and, if they're not too close to each other, each

continues to maintain its appropriate depth in its immediate vicinity. This is probably related to the fact that line-drawn depth cues are ineffective away from the fovea (perhaps because of the detail-loss in the periphery). This isn't surprising. But consider what it implies about your normal viewing of such a drawing: not all of the potential indicators of depth are simultaneously effective, and the uniformly tridimensional appearance that the object seems to

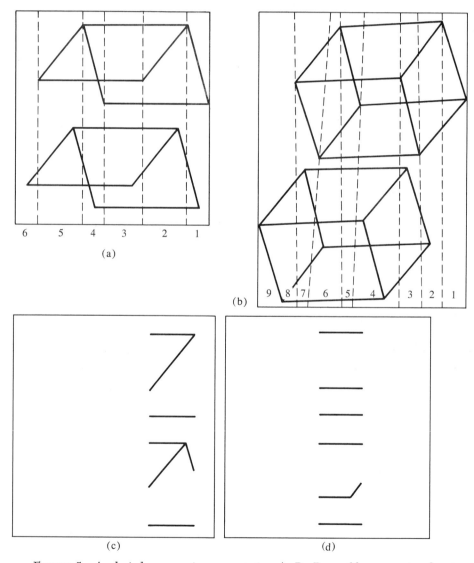

FIGURE 5   Analysis by successive presentation A, B: Reversible-perspective figures presented in single vertical slices (as numbered). C: Slice 2 of display (A). D: Slice 3 of display (A).

present must result from the integration of the various cues as they are successively fixated.

Second. Consider the stimuli in Figures 5A and 5B. Each total pattern is presented to the observer by means of a succession of strips, as indicated by the vertical dotted lines that show how the pattern is "cut up" for successive presentation. (The second and third strips of Figure 5A are shown at Figures 5C and 5D respectively.) In the lower patterns appearing in Figures 5A and 5B, each local depth cue is presented as a unit, simultaneously, for parallel processing; in the upper patterns, the cuts are made so as to minimize the depth cues in each strip. Note that these patterns are presented to adjacent regions of the retina, so that the eye knows where each strip falls relative to the adjacent strips. We have sidestepped the question of whether retinal "painting" is responsible for any effects we obtain—the opportunity for such "painting" is provided for in both conditions of "cutting up" the pattern.

If we present all of the strips simultaneously, or in such rapid succession that they fall on adjacent regions of the retina with dwell times below 120 msec, the upper and the lower patterns appear about equally tridimensional. This is not surprising, of course, since the information contained in the total assemblage of strips is the same, regardless of where the pattern is cut.

With slower succession however—with rates of the order of 300 to 960 msec per strip—the two methods of cutting have different results. Although the shapes are identifiable in both cases, the upper patterns look flat, and no spontaneous depth reversal occurs, while the lower patterns look tridimensional and often display appropriate spontaneous depth reversal despite their fragmented presentation. I think the reversal may be keyed to the presentation of certain cues, but I am not sure.

What I think we have in this demonstration is a display of the action of local depth cues as minimum chunks or features. Figures can be subdivided into these features and still display appropriate tridimensionality. But the features themselves cannot be subdivided, or entered serially, and still maintain perceived depth. Although the technique is reminiscent of McFarland's (1965), we are not concerned, as he was, with judgments of simultaneity, but with obtaining a method for isolating local depth cues—and this one looks promising. Parenthetically, this phenomenon is also obtained binocularly with Julesz patterns, as well as with the line contours of Figure 5.

These then are my arguments for *local depth cues*: that different parts of a figure, when fixated, can elicit different depth responses; that the effects of (outline) depth cues are spatially restricted; and that breaking up a pattern so as to prevent parallel processing of the local depth cues, as in Figure 5, makes those cues relatively ineffective.

Now, let us consider the other question raised by the Penrose figures—how successive glances are integrated into a single perceptual structure.

2. The Integration of Successive Glimpses: Perceptual Storage and Schematic Maps

I will first describe a technique currently being used to study the stored structure of impossible pictures, and some preliminary findings; I will then discuss more general questions about perceptual structure.

Consider the pair of patterns in Figures 6A and B. Figure 6A is a Necker cube; Figure 6B is a very simple sort of "impossible" figure derived from it. Move this pattern around behind a hole whose diameter is such that we can see at most one *corner at a time* through the hole. With the pattern moved through positions 1–7 in Figure 7, with about ½ sec dwell

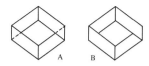

FIGURE 6 A: Reversible perspective cube. B: Inconsistent cube.

time at each of the corners (that is, at fields 4 and 7), five of five adult observers correctly reported the figure as "impossible". (Note that the subjects were set to detect inconsistency, not like the naive subjects who cannot initially pinpoint what's wrong with the Penrose figure.) How do they do this?

Look at the corner in field 4, Figure 7. Its orientation is ambiguous: either the apex of a convex dihedral (Figure 8A) or a concave one (Figure 8B). After the sequence, fields 1 through 3 (Figure 7), the corner in field 4 looks concave; starting at the other end of the sequence, it appears convex. In looking at the sequence, 1–7 (Figure 7), given this kind of after-effect, the observer will have to reverse the depth relationships between the upper and lower edge of the cube's side when fields 6–7 appear. This depth reversal can reveal to the observer that the pattern is inconsistent. But does this imply visual storage of the entire pattern? If it is merely the effect of one local depth cue on a successively viewed local region, then we should be able to interfere with this restricted form of storage by an equally restricted kind of visual confusion. I think we can, by merely interposing the concave dihedral, shown in Figure 8B, in the sequence of views immediately after field 4 in Figure 7. Since there is no conflict between the

convex corner and the subsequent view of the next corner in fields 6 and 7, the local cue to inconsistency has been removed. Of course, that in turn introduces a noticeable reversal between the previously determined orientation of corner 4, and the interposed convex corner, but we can cause the subject to lose track of these simply by alternating, at random, some number of times, between the two non-ambiguous views of the corner shown in Figures 8A and B. When we do this (cf. Figure 9), the ability to detect whether the figure is possible or impossible seems to disappear for a while. But the observer has other resources. He can, for instance, ignore the corner at field 4 entirely, and merely encode the corner at field 1 as "down", and then remember that verbal cue until he gets to field 7 which he might encode as "up." These verbal crutches can, in turn, be interfered with. For example, I tried having one subject solve an imaginary visual maze which required responses of "up" and "down" in an irregular order, imposing this task while the sequence (abbreviated in Figure 9) was presented. Performance again dropped, until still another encoding strategy was devised.

These are preliminary findings with few subjects, and limited by the fact that I have not yet been able to devise a suitable control for any possible effects due to sheer distraction. The subjects' resourcefulness, and the multiplicity of possible cues and strategies, makes this a messy line of research, reminiscent of the old work on objective tests of imagery (Woodworth, 1938). Yet the technique does seem to have some promise, and it raises two sub-

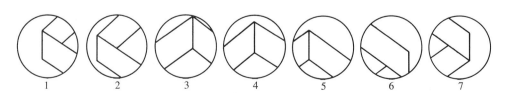

FIGURE 7   Views of Figure 6B being moved around behind an aperture.

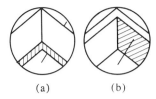

(a)   (b)

FIGURE 8   Unambiguous corners. A: Convex.
B: Concave.

stantive points to which we can bring other evidence. (1) We can interfere with the detection of inconsistency by visual means, interfering with the continuity of depth-meaning attributed to an ambiguous line. (2) We can interfere with the detection of inconsistency by verbal means, interfering with the way in which the subject stores the two critical corners. Are there two kinds of storage providing the integration of successive glances in normal form perception, visual and verbal?

One simplifying assumption would be that, aside from a rapidly fading afterimage, there is no visual storage, only verbal coding, and that the visual interference described above functioned merely as a distractor, or via the medium of the verbal encodings that accompanied the alternations between corners 4a and 4b. Conversely, we might argue that, normally, the succession of glimpses is almost continuous, and that the context of such succession removes the need for most or all of the "verbal loop" storage, in Glanzer's

term, by which gaps in visually determined integration seemed to be bridged, when necessary (and by which the inadequate glance presented by tachistoscopic exposures is eked out), that is, we might argue that the "verbal loop" determines perceptual organization (cf. Glanzer and Clark, 1963, 1964) only under the abnormal demands of tachistoscopic recognition experiments (and perhaps under the normal demands of rapid reading saccades; cf. Hochberg, in press).

Of these two alternatives, I think the first one—that organization rests solely on verbal storage—quite unlikely. There is clearly also something visual that the subject stores, as we will see when we consider how he builds up a schematic map of a cross (Figures 10–12).

Two types of visual storage have received attention recently, but neither would seem to account for the integration of successive views into perceived objects or scenes. (1) Eidetic imagery seems to be complete visual storage of the world, and the result of successive integration, since it apparently preserves the distribution of spatial relationships between objects, not their retinal traces (Haber and Haber, 1964). This ability is not widely available, and most probably doesn't explain normal form perception. (2) The short-term storage demonstrated by Sperling (1960) and Averbach and Coriell (1961): essentially

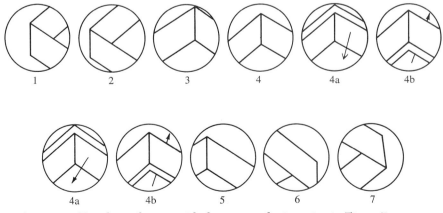

1   2   3   4   4a   4b

4a   4b   5   6   7

FIGURE 9   Visual interference with the storage of orientation in Figure 7.

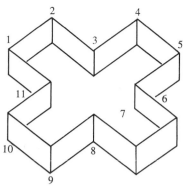

FIGURE 10   Form showing the mind's eye, using the same elements as those of Figure 7.

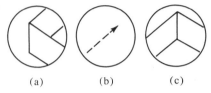

(a)   (b)   (c)

FIGURE 11   Part of the sequence in Figure 10. A:Corner six. B: Blank (view 7), seen as motion across the southeast arm. C: Corner 8.

an after-image, tied to retinal locus. This certainly contributes to retrieval of tachistoscopically presented material, by prolonging the effective duration of any momentary glimpse, but it cannot normally help and should more usually hinder the integration of successive glimpses of forms and scenes. Look from corner 1 to corner 2 on the square in Figure 13B, C. Since retinally tied persistence could not discount the eyemovement (or the figure's traverse, if the eye is stationary and the figure moves), what we should perceive in consequence is a stick cross (Figure 13D).

What we need is a set of operations for defining and studying the kind of visual storage that will build up the structures of perceived forms out of momentary glimpses, not simply add them up in overlapping persistence.

If we move the block outline crosses shown in Figures 10 or 12 around behind a hole at a reasonably slow pace and with good cues as to the motion (ca. 500 to 1000 msec between corners), and follow the order indicated in each case by the

small numbers, we have no difficulty in recognizing the shape as a cross. In fact, when the sequence reaches the gaps—the blank spaces between corners 6 and 8 in Figure 10A, and between corners 8 and 9 in Figure 12, most uninstructed subjects (13 of 15) *report the arm of the cross as moving behind the window, even though the view is blank at the moment.* A more objective measure of this "jump" is perhaps this: angles 8 in Figure 10, and 9 in Figure 12, are seen appropriately as 270° rather than 90°, even though the same view is seen as 90° in the first field in each sequence.

This looks much more like visual than verbal storage (although I think that some formal statements of the properties of each had best be worked out and agreed on); certainly the times involved place it beyond the short-term storage of Sperling and others. How might we study such visual *schematic maps*, as I will tentatively call them, and determine their properties?

We can build different shapes out of the corners and lines shown in Figures 12 to 15 by varying the sequence in which we present these elements in *direct* succession (that is, with *no* actual intervening motion or motion cues) through the stationary hole. With very rapid succession of the corners in Figure 12, of course, sensory fusion occurs, producing a "+": with somewhat slower rates (such as 8 cps), a pretty straightforward set of apparent mo-

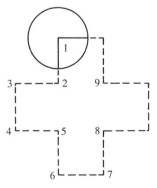

FIGURE 12   Form presented to the mind's eye by sequential views of right angles.

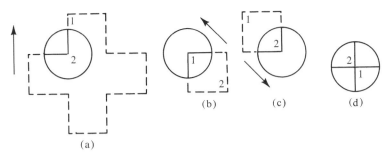

FIGURE 13   Succession of two right angles. A: Second view in Figure 12. B, C: Sampling a square. D: Results of persistence of the first view.

tions occur (such as an "L" flipping over in space or a pair of clock hands skipping from one quadrant to another). Presented at moderate rates, for example, with dwell times of ca. 140 msec and ISIs of 45 msec, a most peculiar kind of *phi* may result. I usually perceive a square moving around behind the window with whatever motions are appropriate—along a lateral, between corners 6 and 7 in Figure 12, or a diagonal between corners 1 and 2; cf. Figure 13C, D. This effect does not seem to be subject to set or to knowledge. Views taken successively around the cross, in the order shown in Figure 12, start out with the mask transparent so that the cross is initially entirely visible, then make the mask opaque so that the occluded parts of the cross gradually fade out as we continue to move it around behind the hole. When only the part seen through the hole remains visible, the motion again becomes that of a square. This effect is new to me, and I know next to nothing about it. But whatever it is, the important point here is that set and knowledge do not seem to contribute to what is seen when the succession of views is rapid.

Let us now slow down the presentation rate to a dwell time of about 400 to 1000 msec duration. This will also help to introduce a line, as shown, between the presentation of the corners, as in the sequence of views shown in Figure 15. What we see then *is* a function of set and knowledge. Told that he is being shown a square, the subject recognizes a square,

making the appropriate motions; told he is being shown a cross, and he reports a cross, again with the appropriate motions.

Thus, with rapid succession, set seems incapable of eliciting the perception of the cross; with slow succession, set and knowledge do appear more capable of affecting which shape, executing its appropriate motions, is seen.

This suggests to me something about the mechanism by which such factors normally influence form perception, and I shall explore this suggestion in the next section of this paper.

But first, as I have tried to ask throughout this paper, how do I know that the subject really perceived what he says he does? Let us return to what the defining characteristics of such visual storage, of such a schematic map, should be. In Figure 12 if I have such a map, when I look at point 1, I should expect to see a 90° angle, and when I look at point 9, I should see a 270° angle. *The program of possible samplings of an extended scene, and of contingent expectancies of what will be seen as a result of those samplings, is what I mean by a schematic map.*

With this in mind, the obvious measurement technique suggests itself: if we *did* perceive the sequence of views in Figure 15 as the successive glimpses of a square, the individual displacements that would appear to connect the views would not fall into any simple pattern (cf. Figure 14). Since they exceed in number what we can hold in immediate memory span,

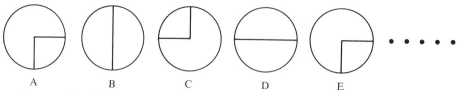

FIGURE 14   Successive views of Figure 12. A: Corner 1. B: Vertical side. C: Corner 2. D: Horizontal side. E: Corner 3.

we shouldn't be able to distinguish that sequence from another sequence which begins and ends similarly but which is very different in between. But when told the object is a cross, we see that the sequence forms a simple predictable pattern, and it is then easy to tell, on the very first trial, that some other sequence which does not follow a simple path around the cross, is different. (I have tried this demonstration on some dozen observers, and the effect seems to be clear and usable; but I have not yet undertaken formal experiment and there may be unforeseen difficulties with the method.)

"To apprehend a pattern is to discern the principle on which its elements are ordered. To see the elements only will not suffice, for the pattern does not reside in the elements . . . [but] in the rule which governs their relations to each other. . . . Stereotyped vision sees only those patterns which its stereotypes have permitted it to anticipate." I'm quoting from *Design and Expression in the Visual Arts,* by J. F. A. Taylor (1964). For "apprehended pattern" say "schematic map", and we are talking about the integrative component in visual processing, the "glue" by which successive glimpses are joined into a single perceptual structure. If I have the right schematic map, successive glimpses fit together so

well into the perceptual structure that the stable form is easy to see and the component glances are difficult to detect. With the wrong schematic map, I have only momentary glimpses, erratic and disorganized *sensations,* and no *perceptual* structure emerges, no form is *perceived.* The schematic map is thus not merely a variety of visual storage, or aftereffect; the passive aftereffects, like the familiar afterimage, are tied to retinal locus and, except in the special conditions of tachistoscopic information retrieval (cf. Sperling, 1960), can only degrade and confuse the perceptual process. In contrast, the storage effected by these schematic maps is contingent on direction of gaze, or on the *clearly indicated motion of an object, viewed by a stationary eye, that apparently can be substituted for the exploratory movements of the glance over a stationary object in building up a perceived structure.* These facts place the map's locus much higher in the nervous system than anything like an afterimage.

(A) Schematic maps have local visual consequences, that is, they contain visual information or structure. A schematic map is a matrix of space-time expectancies (or assumptions).

These expectancies are revealed by the couplings or constraints which they impose on otherwise ambiguous shapes and motions, but I presume them to be responsible for the integration of successive glimpses, and for perceptual structure in general, *whether the stimuli are ambiguous or not.*

(B) A schematic map is not a completely detailed counterpart of the total pattern—it is not like an eidetic image (cf. Haber and Haber, 1964)—else the "impos-

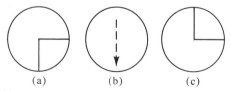

FIGURE 15   Part of the sequence in Figure 12. A: Corner 8. B: Blank, seen as motion across the right-hand arm. C: Corner 9.

sible picture" problem would not arise. Remember that verbal encoding was used to detect the "impossibility" in Figure 7. Perhaps such directional information can be added to the schematic map by practice, so that unmediated visual detection of "impossibility" could be made despite the interference between frames 4 and 5 of sequence in Figure 9, but I have no evidence to this point at present.

(C) I have not been able to produce the "cross" response, in Figure 12, by furnishing appropriate set or knowledge, with *rapid* succession of inputs. There might well be several reasons for this; for example, perhaps with rapid succession, stimuli might be present that produce unambiguous *phi*, that is, that produce an apparent motion peripherally determined and resistant to central intrusions. But I propose that the explanation is at least partly that schematic maps are ways in which successive sensory input is stored, and storage probably takes substantial time for read-in and read-out, so that *rapid succession rates prevent retrieval of the relevant expectations in time to affect the next glimpse.*

These schematic maps seem closely related to what Hebb calls phase sequences (1949). It seems most plausible to me that they are built up not only from the successive views of a given object or scene, but from *previous* experiences as well. I say this only because it seems most unlikely that the completion phenomena involved in the perception of crosses in Figures 10 and 12 (that is, the "filling in" of the gap where the cross's arms were jumped over) are innate, rather than learned. If schematic maps, which are a form of short-term storage, are thus also vehicles of long-term storage, they suggest a very simple approach to one of the fundamental questions of perceptual learning.

Clearcut examples of the effects of learning on visual form perception are not easy to come by. But one seems clear enough at first glance—the effects of *having*

learned to read on the tachistoscopic recognition of letters. Such effects *must* be the result of learning and, what's more, they seem to effect rapidly presented displays, which here seemed to be resistant to the effects of knowledge. Let us consider this research area, therefore, in the context of the preceding discussions.

3. Short-Term Storage as the Site of Perceptual Learning: Maps and Plans

While only a few unrelated letters can be recognized in a brief tachistoscopic exposure, a great many more can be recognized if they form some familiar or pronounceable word. After we learn to read, the letters in familiar words are processed in larger chunks (cf. Miller, 1956). These old observations seem to offer clear evidence of learning in perception, as does the fact that legible letters have lower tachistoscopic thresholds for recognition than do their illegible mirror images (Henle, 1942). But does learning affect the way we *see* the words—that is, the way we pick up their forms initially—or does learning to read only alter the ways in which those forms are stored and remembered? There are two extreme alternatives to this issue:

(1) The basic receptive processes themselves might alter, and thereby the nature of what will be an adequate visual stimulus might change. That is, I think, characteristic of such otherwise diverse theorists as Hebb, Hayek, and J. J. Gibson.

(2) The receptive processes, and at least some associated *perceptual* phenomena, might remain untouched by perceptual learning (there might be basic and relatively inalterable form-perception mechanisms, inherited or established early in the individual's life; surely, today the facts of sensory physiology can no longer be marshalled to oppose such a proposal—cf. Hubel and Wiesel, 1962). Any changes in form-perception that do occur through

learning would then consist, on the one hand, only of changes in the organism's deployment of attentional eyemovements; on the other hand, of changes in the ways in which each glimpse of the world is remembered and integrated with other glimpses into schematic maps.

I shall argue here that what little evidence there is more closely supports the second alternative, that is, that *the effects of perceptual learning consist of changes in where you look, and of how you remember what you saw, but not of changes in what you see in any momentary glance.*

The proposal is not a really new one, of course; it is an aspect of the old and complex nativism-empiricism issue and, characteristic of that domain of problems with its multiple goals and criteria (Hochberg, 1962), it is not clear how it could be put to direct test. But as a general strategy one can try to show two things: First, that phenomena very similar to those effects that others have offered as examples of the influences of learning on perception can be obtained by what looks more like manipulations of memory. Second, that other form-dependent phenomena normally accompanying the recognition of a particular form with a given display, remain unaffected by the presumed effects of learning or past experience on that form.

Thus, several of us argued some years ago that most of the New Look attempts to demonstrate the effects of motivation and of set on perception, usually by means of tachistoscopic recognition experiments, were memorial rather than perceptual. For example, the perceptual defence findings (that negative words require longer tachistoscopic exposures to recognize than do neutral ones) could be explained this way: Emotional response to the momentarily presented word interferes with the fragile memory of what has just been seen and, since all perceptual report has to be retrospective to a greater or lesser degree if it is to be made at all, the subject is left with nothing to report (Hochberg, Haber and Ryan, 1955; Hochberg and Brooks, 1958). The classic work on the effects of set on tachistoscopic recognition stems from Kulpe's finding that subjects seemed to see better, under tachistoscopic exposures, those stimulus attributes which they had been set to attend. Harris and Haber showed recently that these effects could well be accounted for as the results of encoding processes, rather than as effects on sensitivity (1963; cf. also Haber, 1964; Haber, 1966). What all these explanations have in common is their stress on the strong involvement of short-term memory processes in perceptual reports and, thereby, the possibility that the effects of emotion, needs, set, and so on might be mediated entirely by the memorial processes.

Let us return to the interpretation of the effects of learning on the tachistoscopic recognition of letters and words. Henle (1942) had shown longer exposures to be needed for unfamiliar (reversed) letters than for familiar ones; is this changed sensitivity a result of perceptual learning? Not if Hayes, Robinson, and Brown (1961) are right, because they reported that when subjects' task was to report whether two tachistoscopically presented forms were the same or different—that is, when the task didn't by its very nature require that the subject compare his fading memory of the vanished stimulus display with his memories of how the various letters appeared—then no difference was obtained between normal and reversed letters. Is it, therefore, the same with the effects of having learned to read as with the effects of set, that in both cases the change is due to having a set of encoding responses by which the observer can better store the fading trace left by the momentary glance (cf. Haber, 1966)? I have two series of demonstrations to this point, done with Robert Keen and Virginia Brooks. The first series does for words pretty much what Hayes *et al.* did for letter forms—it sets up a condition under which a form-dependent phenomenon, namely same-difference judgments, is no better for familiar words than it is for unfamiliar or illegible ones. The second series shows that with the same procedures, but with more involvement of short-term memory, the characteristic differences between familiar and unfamiliar material reappears. These experiments were performed in two different versions. The first time through the stimuli were all printed on pages which were handed to the subject, who responded "same" or "different" to each pair of words in turn; here the dependent variable was the total time taken to read each page of word-pairs (cf. Hochberg, 1966). The findings by this method were, for the most part, replicated in a completely new set of experiments with Robert Keen (cf. Hochberg, in press), using tachistoscopic exposures (ca. one sec) of each word-pair, with the dependent variable being the number of times the exposure had to be repeated to make the same-difference judgment of that pair. In all of these experiments, adequate numbers of subjects were used, and the differences that I shall describe were statistically significant at the .05–.01 level.

(a) *Direct or Simultaneous Comparison.* In this condition, the two words were close together in a double column, the corresponding letters in each word being immediately adjacent. This demanded least of subjects' memories, and minimized possible responses to over-all familiar word-forms. Each word might be either meaningful or pronounceable or meaningless and unpronounceable, printed in normal orientation, or in reversed or inverted arrays (cf. Figure 16A, B, C). Both members might be in upper case, or one in upper and one in lower case, as in Figure 16C. (This last condition has not yet been replicated via tachistoscopic exposure.)

In this direct condition, familiarity has no measurable effect. Whether the words were meaningful or not, whether in illegible mirror images or in normal type, the comparison time and the number of tachistoscopic glances needed in order to decide whether the words were the same or different, both measures were unchanged. (Only one condition made a difference in performance: when one word was printed in capitals, the other in lower case—as in Figure 16A—performance time increased. That is, if the two words differed in *form*, even though they had the same spelling, the comparison task took longer [as noted above, this last condition has not yet been replicated]. The letters now had to pass through a decoding stage, in which different shapes have equivalent meaning, before the subject could decide whether they were the same or different, and *now* familiarity helped.)

(b) *Indirect or Successive Comparison.* Subject compared two words which were separated horizontally, as in Figure 16D,

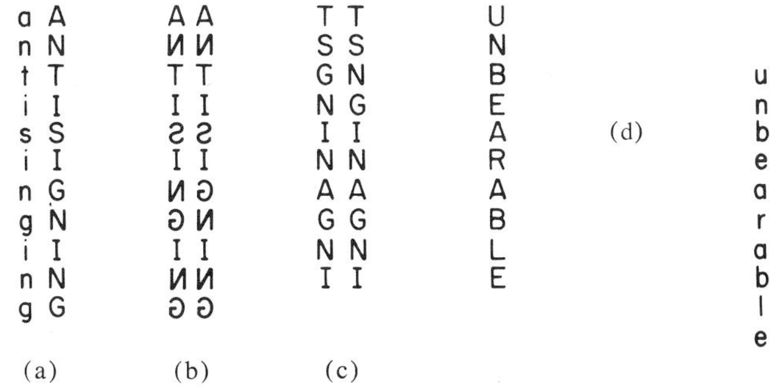

FIGURE 16 Simultaneous and successive comparison of legible and illegible words. A: Meaningful, legible, simultaneous. B: Meaningful, illegible, simultaneous. C: Meaningless, legible, simultaneous. D: Successive.

by about 20°. Both words could not now be seen foveally with one fixation, so the subject had to consult his memory of at least one of them. Otherwise, procedures were as before. Now, however, the effects of familiarity were evident: when the words were illegible or unfamiliar and unpronounceable they took more time to judge. With familiar words, one or two fixations suffice to decide whether the words are same or different; with illegible or unpronounceable stimuli, subjects must compare the two words piece by piece. As we would predict, it makes no difference whether the words are of the same shape (both capitals) or of different shape (capitals and lower case); comparison times remain essentially unchanged.

These two sets of experiments, simultaneous and successive comparison, thus have diametrically opposite results. This is what we would expect if the learned ability to recognize letter-groups as chunks, and to recognize legible letters better than illegible ones, is due to the formation of appropriate units in encoding and storing momentary glimpses, and not to changes in the immediate processing of form.

If this is true—if the components of visual form picked up in the momentary glance remains unchanged by perceptual learning—then we should be able to demonstrate that some appropriate phenomenon which depends on form pick-up, other than the same-difference judgment, also remains unchanged. The results obtained in the following pilot study on apparent motion are fully consistent with the above conclusions; subjects are still too few in these experiments for appropriate significance tests, but this now seems to me almost an armchair issue. I cannot believe, after seeing how it looks, that when the following experiments have more trustworthy data, they will turn out otherwise.

(c) and (d) *Successive Comparison with Variable ISI*. In these experiments, the two 12–letter words were projected, in repeated succession, for 1 sec each, on the same spot on the projection screen, separated temporally by a variable inter stimulus interval (ISI). Subjects had to say whether the two words were the same or different. At a short ISI (say, 40 msec), spelling (and shape) differences produced apparent motion, detected in one or two cycles, regardless of whether the words were familiar or unfamiliar, upright or inverted. However, with one word in upper case and one in lower, apparent motion occurred even when the two words had the same spelling (since the words' forms were now different, regardless of spelling), so from three to twelve cycles were required to make a judgment. With increased ISI (say, to 1000 msec), it made no difference whether the words were in the same type face or not, but their familiarity and their legibility became crucial: subjects needed one or two cycles to make the same-difference judgments for familiar words, while for a meaningless or illegible word-pair they required as high as a dozen cycles, as they observed, stored and compared the first word, piece by piece, with the second. Increasing the ISI past the point at which form-differences produce apparent motion has made the task dependent on memory, and now the effects of having learned to read are clearly manifested.

The results of all of these experiments with word recognition are consistent with the idea that perceptual learning produces changes in the way in which momentary glimpses are stored, not changes in the form as registered in those glimpses.

What is stored? Here, unlike the schematic maps we probed earlier, the results show no compelling evidence of visual storage (and in this sense, experiments in reading may be very poor tools for the study of visual perception). With words (or displays easily encoded in words), a simple means of storage is, of course, at tongue's tip—repeated auditory rehearsal (Glanzer and Clark, 1963; Levin, 1965; Sperling, 1963). The superiority of pronounceable material in our successive

comparison conditions is certainly consistent with this storage mechanism (cf.
also Conrad, 1964). If purely auditory
rehearsal storage mechanisms were all we
had, however, then the difference between
homonyms (words that are spelled differently but sound alike, as in Figure 16D)
should be indetectible under successive
comparison conditions, yet we have found
no differences in the same-difference judgments of homonymic and nonhomonymic
pairs.

Perhaps it is not an auditory storage but
one of *articulatory intentions,* or of the
programs to initiate the visual-vocal behaviors, that translate graphemes into
speech.

One would expect such programs to be
somewhat different for homonyms, since
the grapheme-phoneme correspondence,
and hence the translation rule, would be
different. I cannot develop this point here,
but I urge anyone interested in this question to obtain George Sperling's 1966 International Congress paper, in which a similar
proposal, independently developed and
more completely thought through, is very
clearly presented and defended (Sperling,
1967).

This is not the time, however, to pursue
this intriguing question. I would like instead to examine one more experiment
in recognition, and then summarize what
I have discussed.

There is one other easy demonstration
of perceptual learning: if we rotate human
faces, and transform them from positives
to photographic negatives, their expressions
become unreadable. This certainly would
seem to be the result of perceptual learning. Unlike the effects of learning to read,
however, expressions might be learned very
early. Therefore we might find changes in
sensory processing demonstrable in recognizing different facial expressions, where
we didn't do so with text recognition.

This hypothesis once seemed plausible
to me, but no longer. The successive comparison procedure using drawn faces instead of words (Figure 17), seems to give

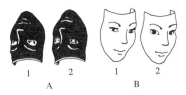

FIGURE 17   Immediate and delayed succession, faces. A: Inverted negatives. B: Upright
positives. In both (A) and (B), pattern 2 is
projected after a variable interstimulus interval
on the place previously occupied by pattern 1.

the same pattern of results as with
words: with short ISIs, it doesn't matter
whether the faces are inverted negatives
or upright positives, since even small differences in disposition of the facial features
produce apparent motion that is easy to
detect within a couple of presentation
cycles. With increased delay times, however—ca. 1000 msec—it takes many cycles
to detect differences between the inverted
negative faces; upright and positive faces
are still discriminated, when different, in
one or two cycles, even when separated
by the long ISIs.

As in printed text, learning to perceive
facial expressions apparently means acquiring ways of storing the expressions, not
changes in the reception process. And
here, it seems to me, there is *finally an area
of perception from which it is reasonable
for the social and clinical psychologist to
borrow: an area at which the New Look
should have been looking, instead of at
tachistoscopic word-recognition and psychophysical size-matching.* Something like the
way in which schematic maps seemed to
bring the otherwise meaningless sequences
of Figure 15 into manageable chunks, or
in which linguistic meaning codes phonemes into phrases, must surely be found
in the perception of social movements and
events. In *Potemkin,* Eisenstein cut from
face to face, building up *across* their diverse physiognomies a single expressive
sequence; drawn facial expressions can be
set in sequences (cf. Figure 18) that are
distinguishable from each other by their
timing differences when viewed as upright positives, and that are very difficult

FIGURE 18   Elements of an expressive sequence.

to distinguish as sequences of inverted negatives. Upright, they express a single familiar facial event but, inverted, the sequence of successive patters is meaningless and beyond span.

Until now I have talked about how successive glimpses are organized into perceived stationary forms, or *schematic maps,* and about techniques for studying such stored structures. But these last remarks are to a different point: that successive glimpses can also be organized into and stored as perceived temporal events, or *schematic sequences;* that these schematic sequences can, as a start, be studied by similar techniques; and that they suggest similar but more socially interesting questions. How are such sequences stored—as programs for arranging one's own features in some well-encoded order? How do set, experience, stress, motivation effect expressive schematic sequences? How standard are such sequences? What are the dimensions of individual differences?

These questions run far afield, and I do not have preliminary observations with which to guide speculation. Let me summarize what I've covered today.

Summary

(1) There is a sense in which it is meaningful and useful to ask whether a subject "really" perceives the structure he is naming, and to use the appropriate form-dependent phenomena both to define and to test the point.

(2) Analyses of the perceived forms of reversible-perspective figures and of "impossible pictures" suggest the operation of local depth cues of limited effect which determine apparent local spatial arrangement, more than they suggest effects of an over-all perceptual organization dependent on the total configuration of the stimulus pattern. Indirect methods intended to reveal the action of such local depth cues seem to do so.

(3) The perceived structure of an object may consist of two separable components: (a) the features glimpsed in momentary glances, and (b) the integrative *schematic map* into which those features are fitted. I have offered a technique for studying the structure of such schematic maps, at least for certain kinds of scenes and objects, and it may be applicable to other kinds of perceived structure as well.

(4) The contents of the momentary glance may be relatively immune to the effects of set and learning, and it is in the storage structure—the schematic map, in the case of form perception—that the effects of learning are to be found. Form-dependent phenomena in the areas of recognizing text and recognizing facial expression are consistent with this proposal. Recent data by Posner (1966) is very much to this point, and those of Anne Pick can be similarly interpreted (1965).

If you try translating the above terms into the old words: momentary glance into "sensation," schematic map into "image," and perceptual structure into "perception," the fit is very good indeed. The units and measures have changed, but the main features are surprisingly close to those outlined by Helmholtz, Wundt, and Titchener.

References

ATTNEAVE, F. *Applications of information theory to psychology.* New York: Holt, Rinehart and Winston, Inc., 1959.

AVERBACH, E., and A. CORIELL. Short-term memory in vision. *Bell Systems Tech. J.*, 1961, *40*, 309–328.

CONRAD, R. Acoustic confusions in immediate memory. *Brit. J. Psychol.*, 1964, *55*, 75–83.

GARNER, W., H. HAKE, and C. ERIKSEN. Operationism and the concept of perception. *Psychol. Rev.*, 1956, *63*, 317–329.

GLANZER, M., and W. CLARK. Accuracy of perceptual recall: An analysis of organization. *J. verb. Learn. verb. Behav.*, 1963, *1*, 289–299.

GLANZER, M., and W. CLARK. The verbal loop hypothesis: Conventional figures. *Amer. J. Psychol.*, 1964, *77*, 621–626.

HABER, R. N. The effects of coding strategy on perceptual memory. *J. exp. Psychol.*, 1964, *68*, 257–362.

HABER, R. N. Nature of the effect of set on perception. *Psychol. Rev.*, 1966, *73*, 335–351.

HABER, R. N., and R. B. HABER. Eidetic imagery: I. Frequency. *Percept. mot. Skills*, 1964, *19*, 131–138.

HARRIS, C., and R. N. HABER. Selective attention and coding in visual perception. *J. exp. Psychol.*, 1963, *65*, 328–333.

HAYES, W., J. ROBINSON, and L. BROWN. An effect of past experience on perception: An artifact. *Amer. Psychologist*, 1961, *16*, 420 (Abstract).

HEBB, D. *The organization of behavior.* New York: Wiley, 1949.

HENLE, M. The experimental investigation of past experiences as a determinant of visual form perception. *J. exp. Psychol.*, 1942, *30*, 1–22.

HOCHBERG, J. Perception: Toward the recovery of a definition. *Psychol. Rev.*, 1956, *63*, 400–405.

HOCHBERG, J. Psychophysics and stereotype in social perception. In Sherif, M., and M. Wilson (Eds.), *Emerging problems in social psychology.* University of Oklahoma Press, 1957.

HOCHBERG, J. Nativism and empiricism in perception. In Postman, L. (Ed.), *Psychology in the making.* New York: Knopf, 1962.

HOCHBERG, J. Reading pictures and text: What is learned in perceptual development? *Proc. 18th Int. Congr. Psychol.*, 1966, Sympos. 30, 18–26.

HOCHBERG, J. Components of literacy: Speculations and exploratory research. In press.

HOCHBERG, J., and V. BROOKS. Effects of previously associated annoying stimuli (auditory) on visual recognition thresholds. *J. exp. Psychol.*, 1958, *55*, 490–491.

HOCHBERG, J., and V. BROOKS. The psychophysics of form: Reversible-perspective drawings of spatial objects. *Amer. J. Psychol.*, 1960, *73*, 337–354.

HOCHBERG, J., and V. BROOKS. "Edges" as fundamental components of the visual field. Paper read at the 1962 meetings of the Psychon. Soc.

HOCHBERG, J., S. HABER, and T. RYAN. "Perceptual defense" as an interference phenomenon. *Percept. mot. Skills*, 1955, *5*, 15–17.

HUBEL, D., and T. WIESEL. Receptive fields, binocular interaction and functional architecture in the cat's visual cortex. *J. Physiol.*, 1962, *160*, 106–154.

JULESZ, B. Binocular depth perception of computer-generated patterns. *The Bell System Tech. J.*, 1960, *39*, 1125–1162.

KOPFERMANN, H. Psychologische Untersuchungen über die Wirkung zweidimensionaler Darstellungen körperlicher Gebilde. *Psychol. Forsch.*, 1930, *13*, 293–364.

LEVIN, H. Studies of various aspects of reading. *Project Literacy Reports*, 1965, no. 5, 13–25.

McFARLAND, J. The effect of different sequences of part presentation on perception of a form's parts as simultaneous. *Proc. 73rd Annual Conv. Amer. Psychol. Assoc.*, Wash., D.C.: A.P.A., 1965.

MILLER, G. The magic number seven, plus or minus two. *Psychol. Rev.*, 1956, *63*, 81–97.

PARKS, T. Post-retinal visual storage. *Amer. J. Psychol.*, 1965, *78*, 145–147.

PICK, A. Improvement of visual and tactual form discrimination. *J. exp. Psychol.*, 1965, *69*, 331–339.

POSNER, M., and R. MITCHELL. A chronometric analysis of classification. Mimeo. publ., University of Oregon, 1966.

POSTMAN, L. Experimental analysis of motivational factors in perception. In *Current theory and research in motivation.* Lincoln, Nebr.: University of Nebraska Press, 1952.

SPERLING, G. The information available in brief visual presentations. *Psychol. Monogr.*, 1960, *74* (11, Whole No. 498).

SPERLING, G. A model for visual memory tasks. *Human Factors*, 1963, *5*, 19–31.

SPERLING, G. Successive approximations to a model for short-term memory. *Acta Psychologica*, 1967, *27*, 285–292.

TAYLOR, J. *Design and expression in the visual arts.* New York: Dover, 1964.

WOODWORTH, R. *Experimental psychology.* New York: Holt, Rinehart and Winston, Inc., 1938.

A Threshold Difference Produced by a Figure-Ground Dichotomy[*]

BERNARD WEITZMAN

The New School for Social Research, New York

A previous finding (Weitzman, 1963) suggested the possibility that division of the perceptual field into figure and ground regions results in a threshold difference between figure and ground contours. To examine this possibility discrimination thresholds for 2 lines were determined, in tachistoscopic presentation, for 29 college student and student nurse Ss. Fixation was central between the lines, one of which was contained in a figural region, and the other in a ground region. Retinal equivalence of the 2 lines was indexed by an interpolated task. The prediction that the figural contour would have a lower discrimination threshold than the ground contour was supported, at the .05 level, by the results. The finding was interpreted as requiring that the possibility of modification of stimulus input, as a result of the dichotomizing of stimuli into figure and ground regions, be included in any complete description of contour perception.

In a previous paper Weitzman (1963) demonstrated that the contour of a figural region produces an aftereffect of greater magnitude than that produced by the contour of a ground region. The aftereffect of a stimulus contour is modified in that paradigm by its position in a figure-ground dichotomy. The modification, as a

* *Journal of Experimental Psychology,* 1963, vol. 63, pp. 201–205. This paper is based upon a portion of a dissertation submitted to the Psychology Department of the Graduate Faculty of Political and Social Sciences of the New School for Social Research, in partial fulfillment of the requirements for the PhD degree. The author wishes to express his gratitude to his committee member, Gustav Levine, for his inestimably valuable concern and criticism at every stage of the research, and in the preparation of this paper. The author also wishes to thank J. R. Whittier, Director of Psychiatric Research at the Creedmoor Institute of Psychobiologic Studies, for the patience and support which made the undertaking and completion of this study possible. The tachistoscope employed in this experiment was designed and built by the Scientific Prototype Corporation of New York City.

correlate of a phenomenal event, implies the necessity of investigating the role of central processes in contour perception. An adequate theoretical model must, therefore, include not only the modification of psychological processes by stimulus input, but the converse as well.

In attempting to explain the obtained differential effect of the previous experiment it may be hypothesized that there exists a threshold difference between the figural and the ground contour. That is, (assuming either the Köhler-Wallach, 1944, or the Osgood-Heyer, 1952, model as a frame of reference) a threshold difference seen as a functional increase in stimulus intensity for the figural contour, should result in differential intensity in the CNS processes. A threshold differential favoring the figural contour would result in a relatively more intense process in the CNS region corresponding to the figural contour. By comparison in the central region corresponding to the ground contour there would be a less intense process. This difference in intensity of central processes, it may be reasoned, would be reflected in the obtained figural aftereffect of greater magnitude on the side of the figural contour. While it remains an empirical question, whether or not greater stimulus intensity will always produce a greater figural aftereffect, there is sufficient basis in the literature for using the assumption for hypothesis generation. Köhler and Wallach (1944, p. 330) present the theoretical postulate that greater intensity of CNS processes will result in larger figural aftereffects, and report a verifying experiment. The finding of Hochberg and Triebel (1955) that brightness differences are necessary for the production of figural aftereffects implies the correctness of Köhler and Wallach's speculation. The findings of Marquart (1954) and of Freeburne and Hamilton (1949) contain the same suggestions. Finding a threshold difference to obtain would not only contribute to understanding of the previous finding, but would also provide a psychophysical description of one effect of the organization of the visual field into a figure-ground dichotomy.

The present paper reports the results of an investigation designed to answer the following question: When figure and ground contours are positioned symmetrically with reference to the retina, does division of the perceptual field into figure and ground regions result in a lowering of the threshold for accurate discrimination of the figural contour, as compared with the ground contour? It is hypothesized that there is such a resulting difference in thresholds.

Method

MATERIALS

Three figures were constructed. Figure A consisted of a black outline square, 2 in. on a side, vertically bisected by an outline profile of a human face. The profile faced to the viewer's right, i.e., the face occupied the left side of the figure. An eye was drawn in an appropriate position on the face. The profile of a human face was used in this design in order to bias strongly the direction of figural organization. Pilot investigations had indicated that the use of a nonsense contour with instructions to S to organize one side as figural was inappropriate in a test of the present hypothesis because of the high rate of spontaneous reversals reported by Ss. The bottom contour of the square was a straight line containing two gaps. Each gap was equidistant from one side of the square, and each was equidistant from the center of the bottom contour. The gaps were each $\frac{3}{16}$ in. long. An eye was drawn on the face further to enforce the desired direction of organization, and to lower the threshold of figure-ground dichotomizing. This was deemed necessary because pilot work had indicated that, without the eye, the particular profile employed sometimes had a higher threshold than the gaps, whereas, in order to test the hypothesis, a lower threshold was needed. Figure B was a duplicate of Figure A with the bottom contour deleted. Figure B was introduced, both as a device to further lower the figure-ground threshold, and to increase the accuracy of scoring of correct responses. The necessity for the use of this device became apparent in the course of pilot investigations. Figure C was a rectangle, $\frac{1}{2}$ in. high and $\frac{1}{4}$ in. wide. Drawn within the borders of this rectangle were seven letters and numbers in three rows. Row No. 1 contained the number 7 and the capital letter A. The second row contained the number 1 and the letters B and X. The third row contained the number 4 and the letter W. A pre- and postexposure field was prepared consisting of a black dot on a buff field. The dot, serving as a fixation point, was so positioned that it coincided, spatially, with the geometrical center of Figure A and C. Figures and fixation field were drawn on a buff colored mat board.

Figures A and C were presented in a three-channel, Dodge-type tachistoscope, electronically controlled. Figure A, when presented in the first field of the tachistoscope, delivered a direct view of the drawing to S. When presented in field 3, Figure A appeared as a mirror image, its profile facing to the left. In this case Figure C was presented in field 1, giving S a direct view of its contents. When Figure A was presented in its direct view, a mirror drawing of Figure C was presented in the third field of the tachistoscope, delivering, from this position, a noninverted image of Figure C and its contents. The second field of the tachistoscope was always used for exposure of the fixation dot as a pre- and postexposure field. All three fields of the tachistoscope were matched in intensity with a Photovolt electronic photometer, Model 501-M, at the viewing aperture. Each field yielded an illumination of approximately .075 ft-c.

PROCEDURE

The Ss were presented, tachistoscopically, with the drawing consisting of a black outline square vertically bisected by an outline profile of a human face. The bottom contour of the square contained two gaps, one to the right of the profile and the other to the left. Exposure time was gradually increased until Ss saw both gaps. Because a test of the hypothesis required that neither gap be favored by its retinal position, a task orientation was introduced into the experimental design which, along with instructions for the experimental task, would help to maintain central fixation. Figure C, the small rectangle, appearing in the center of the field, was randomly interspersed in the presentation series. The Ss were instructed to discriminate the contents of this rectangle. The central placement of the rectangle and its relatively small dimensions required central fixation for maximum efficiency in reading its contents. In addition, Ss' discriminations within this figure could be taken as a gross index of

the degree to which fixation actually was central.

The experiment was run in two conditions: Condition I used Figure A in the first field of the tachistoscope, i.e., profile seen as facing to the viewer's right. Condition II used Figure A in the third field of the tachistoscope, i.e., with the profile seen as facing to the viewer's left. In each condition S was given Figure B to inspect before looking into the tachistoscope. He was instructed that he would be shown on a screen (E's way of referring to the tachistoscope) a picture exactly like the one he was examining (Figure B) except in one respect. The picture he would be shown on the screen would have the bottom finished in some way. The S's job would be to try to describe in what way the picture was finished at the bottom. The S was then asked to look at the screen and asked if he saw the black dot. He was told that it was very important that he keep strongly focused on the dot whenever he was looking at the screen. He was further instructed to keep his head pressed against the rubber eyepiece so that his head would not move. He was informed that the picture would be shown very quickly at first, probably too quickly for him to see it clearly, but that it would be shown again and again, more and more slowly, until he could see it clearly. He was reminded that it was very important to keep focused on the dot.

The S was then informed that some of the time he would be shown, on the screen, a small rectangle with letters and numbers written inside it. When this rectangle appeared his job would be to try to read the letters and numbers. He was told that the rectangle would be presented very quickly at first but that it would be shown again and again, more and more slowly, until he could read the letters and numbers. He was told that, in this case also, it was crucial that he remain focused on the dot. He was reminded that his job was to describe how the bottom of the picture was completed when the picture was shown on the screen, and to read the letters and numbers in the rectangle when that was shown on the screen. He was reminded of the importance of keeping focused on the dot and was informed that E would say "ready" before each presentation in order to permit him to renew his focus.

The initial exposures of Figures A and C were always .005 sec. The exposure time was increased, independently for each figure, in .001-sec steps to .01 sec, then increased in steps of .01 sec to .1 sec, and then in steps of .1 sec to 1 sec. The order of presentation of Figures A and C was determined by a table of random numbers. After each exposure S was asked to describe what he had seen, until he began to offer such descriptions spontaneously. When an S experienced difficulty in describing what he had seen E offered him Figure B and asked him to describe, with reference to this drawing, what he had seen. In pilot studies in which the mirror image of the profile was randomly interspersed in the presentation series, Ss who had discriminated the profile in one direction were unable (within the exposure intervals employed) to discriminate the mirror image. They reported this mirror image as a nonsense figure. Since, in the present procedure, S described what he had seen after each exposure, E felt certain of the phenomenal status of his stimulus material. In no case did an S report a reversal of the figure once it had been discriminated. The procedure was continued until S reported seeing a straight line across the bottom of the picture containing two symmetrically placed gaps; one to the right of center and one to the left. At this point the figure was removed from the tachistoscope, handed to S, and he was asked if this was the picture he was describing.

SUBJECTS

Five male graduate students and 24 student nurses were volunteers for this experiment. The five males and ten of the females participated in one condition, and the remaining fourteen females were Ss in the second condition.

Results

The requirement of the hypothesis is that accurate discrimination of the figural side of Figure A should take place earlier than accurate discrimination of the ground side. Discrimination was scored as accurate when S reported that one side contained a gap in the bottom contour, centered on that one side. Twenty-four of the 29 Ss discriminated the figural side accurately before the nonfigural side; 12 in Condition I and 12 in Condition II. Of the remaining 5 Ss, 2 discriminated the nonfigural side first, both in Condition I. One S in Condition I and 2 Ss in Condition II discriminated both sides simultaneously.

The probability of such a finding occurring by chance is, for each condition independently, .05 as determined by the two-tailed sign test.

Of the 29 first discriminations of the letters and numbers in Figure C, the number 7, $\frac{1}{8}$ in. to the left and above the fixation point at a 45° angle, was discriminated first six times in Condition I and five times in Condition II. The letter A, $\frac{1}{8}$ in. to the right and above the fixation point at a 45° angle, was discriminated first eight times in Condition I and eight times in Condition II. The remaining first discriminations were the letters X and B. The letter X lay $\frac{1}{8}$ in. to the left of the fixation point and B $\frac{1}{8}$ in. to the right. Each of these letters was discriminated first by 1 S. In all cases the first letter discrimination took place some time after discrimination of the figure had been established but before discrimination of the gap. There is, then, by inspection, no indication of a lateral bias in visual focus, i.e., toward or away from the figural side.

Discussion

The lack of any bias in the direction of the figural side in the responses given by Ss to Figure C gives support to the assumption that the task and instructions were sufficient to maintain centrality of fixation.

The results indicate that accurate discrimination occurs earlier within the contours of the figure than within the contours of the ground, when figure and ground contours are given equal retinal privilege. It is concluded that lowered threshold for accurate discrimination of figural contours, as compared with ground contours, is a consequence of a figure-ground dichotomy. It is not, however, possible from the present findings to state whether this modification of thresholds is best described as figural facilitation, ground inhibition, or a combination of both types of process.

One may conceive of the present paradigm as involving the examination of a single contour in two different contexts: as part of a figure, and as part of a ground. In this instance the two contexts were presented simultaneously in order to permit a comparison of their thresholds. In analyses of the nature of contour perception, typically, only one contour is presented on a homogeneous background. This one contour may be said to be equivalent to the figural side of the present paradigm. Statements which are made as to the conditions of perception, from the results of single contour paradigms, although presenting important information as to the nature of the formation of contour percepts (e.g., analyses in terms of "on-off" mechanisms), have not been able to include the variable, here shown to be relevant, of figure-ground status.

For some psychologists, notably those with a gestalt orientation, the possibility of organizing the stimulus field into figure and ground regions has been taken as the precondition for form perception as such.

Since even an isolated contour may not be said to be either without form, or unrelated to a ground, the concept of figure-ground is necessary, within the gestalt frame of reference, even in the case of the "isolated" contour. The reversibility of many figure-ground relationships has been assumed, by them, to indicate that at least partial control of perceived stimulus qualities in such situations resides in the processes of the CNS. For other psychologists (Osgood and Heyer, 1952) analyses and explanations of experimental results involving contour perception have seemed possible by invoking processes, such as "on-off" firings, which are observable by presently available physiological techniques. The present finding of a direct psychophysical correlate of figure-ground dichotomizing makes clear the importance of utilizing and further exploring the concept of figure-ground in relation to contour perception. The present paradigm also makes available a psychophysical indicator (and perhaps upon further exploration, a definition) of a figure-ground dichotomy.

References

FREEBURNE, C. M., and C. E. HAMILTON. The effect of brightness on figural after-effect. *Amer. J. Psychol.,* 1949, 62, 567–569.

HOCHBERG, J. E., and W. TRIEBEL. Figural after-effects with colored stimuli. *Amer. J. Psychol.,* 1955, 68, 133–135.

KÖHLER, W., and H. WALLACH. Figural after-effects: An investigation of visual processes. *Proc. Amer. Phil. Soc.,* 1944, 88, 269–357.

MARQUART, D. I. The satiational theory of figural after-effects. *J. gen. Psychol.,* 1954, 51, 83–91.

OSGOOD, C. E., and A. W. HEYER, JR. A new interpretation of figural after-effects. *Psychol. Rev.,* 1952, 59, 98–118.

WEITZMAN, B. A figural aftereffect produced by a phenomenal dichotomy in a uniform contour. *J. exp. Psychol.,* 1963, 66, 195–200.

Summation and Learning in Perception[*]

D. O. HEBB
McGill University

This chapter begins a revision of perceptual theory. The immediate objective is to show that "simple" perceptions are in fact complex: that they are additive, that they depend partly on motor activity, and that their apparent simplicity is only the end result of a long learning process.

The preceding pages have tried to show that the crucial problem of perception must be dealt with explicitly at the very beginning of a psychological theory; and that one has the choice of two approaches to this problem. One must decide whether perception is to depend (1) on the excitation of *specific cells* or (2) on a *pattern of excitation* whose locus is unimportant. Current opinion seems tacitly to have accepted the Gestalt argument (and Lashley's argument) that the only tenable assumption is the second of these possibilities.

The theory to be presented here is diametrically opposed to this aspect of Gestalt theory, and is based on assumption 1, that a particular perception depends on the excitation of particular cells at *some* point in the central nervous system. Now the Gestalt argument depends, I believe, on another assumption: that when one perceives a simple figure (such as square or circle) one perceives it directly as a distinc-

* Hebb, D. O., *The Organization of Behavior*, New York: John Wiley and Sons, 1949, ch. 2, pp. 17–37.

tive whole, without need of any learning process and not through a prior recognition of the several parts of the figure. If one makes this assumption—if the perception of a square is as simple and immediate as it seems to us as adults—I believe that the Gestalt argument is unanswerable. But if on the other hand the perception is additive, a serial reconstruction (though very rapid and "unconscious" for the normal adult), the theoretical problem would be very much changed.

In this chapter, accordingly, an attempt is made to show that quite simple diagrams are not perceived directly as *distinctive* wholes—that, though the stimulus has a unitary action in the figure-ground relationship, the perception of identity depends on a series of excitations from the parts of the stimulating diagram. If this can be established, it will remove the *necessity* of accepting field theory; and the following chapter will then attempt to show that field theory actually is not consistent with some of the facts of perception.

The work of Senden (1932) and of Riesen (1947) is fundamental to my argument here. Senden's monograph is a compilation of all published reports on the vision of the congenitally blind given sight by a surgical operation after the patient was old enough to talk to the examiner and describe what he saw. In some respects the data are incomplete, but the report is repeatedly referred to here because it contains the only existent evidence concerning the course taken by the early development of human perception. At first sight, some of the reported facts are literally almost incredible, since they differ so much from what would be predicted by current theory (either of perception or of learning). There is, however, a considerable unanimity among the writers reviewed by Senden, some of whom evidently were not aware of the reports made by others; and the work of Riesen (1947), who reared chimpanzees in darkness to an age when the normal chimpanzee makes an effective use of vision, fully confirms Senden's clinical evidence.

The two reports, by Senden and Riesen, are complementary; and, though many details are not clear, the human and chimpanzee data taken together seem to require radical changes in the theory of perception and of learning.

Distinction of "Primitive Unity" from Other Properties of the Perceived Figure

As a preliminary, certain terms must be defined. I want to show that simple figures do not always act as wholes, innately. But it is undoubtedly true that they sometimes do so in one respect—in the figure-ground relationship: so this property of a perceived figure is to be distinguished from others, in which summation and learning are important. Accordingly, the following are distinguished: the conceptions of (1) a primitive, sensorily determined unity, (2) a nonsensory unity, affected by experience, and (3) the identity (also affected by experience), of a perceived figure.

The *primitive unity* of a figure is defined here as referring to that unity and segregation from the background which seems to be a direct product of the pattern of sensory excitation and the inherited characteristics of the nervous system on which it acts.

Rubin (1921) elaborated the conception of the figure-ground relationship, in a study of visual perception of patterns with clearly marked boundaries. In order to elucidate the relation of figure to ground (the relation of the perceived object or surface to other objects and surfaces which make up the background) he put particular stress on "ambiguous" figures (Figure 1). This is the special case in which either of two parts of a diagram may be seen as figure, each alternating as part of the ground when the other is figure. The principles he established, however, are most fully operative in the unambiguous figure, made up of a homogeneous zone of color surrounded by another color and having a sharply defined boundary—an abrupt transition in brightness from one zone to the other at all points. Such a figure may or may not be regular. It is as well illustrated

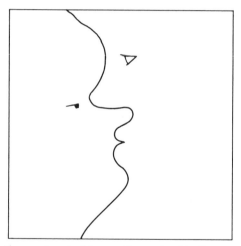

FIGURE 1   Ambiguous figure. In this diagram it is possible to see either of two profiles, but only rarely can the two be seen simultaneously; they alternate instead. When a figure appears on the left, the profile of a rather chubby man, the white area on the left appears as a more solid surface and one that is nearer to the observer. This relationship is reversed when a figure appears on the right—the profile of one suffering from gigantic tumors of the neck and of the frontal bone. The theoretical importance of such reversals of figure-ground relationships has been stressed by Gestalt psychologists, though there is considerable difficulty in subsuming the instability under perceptual theory.

by a splash of ink or by a silhouette of an animal as by a white circle on a black stimulus card.

An area thus sensorily delimited is seen as *one*, unified and distinct from its surroundings, by any normal person, by the congenitally blind on the first occurrence of vision following operation for cataract (Senden, 1932), by the normal rat (Lashley, 1938*b*), and apparently also at first vision by the rat that has been reared in darkness (Hebb, 1937*a*). The unity and distinctiveness of such figures from their background, then, is independent of experience, or "primitive."

It is not possible to specify exactly the stimulating conditions which determine the primitive figure-ground organization. I do not exclude as nonprimitive the perception of groupings; nor the segregation of a patch of color which has ill-defined boundaries. There are suggestions in Senden's (1932) monograph and in rat behavior that the perception of such units in the visual field may also be independent of experience. Senden's monograph is of the first importance for understanding the perceptual process, but in several respects the evidence is far from clear. The earlier writers whose reports are summarized did not recognize some of the psychological problems to which their observations are relevant. What Senden does show, in the fact that patients always responded to certain objects as wholes and could on occasion detect differences between objects even in spite of nystagmus, is that there is a primitive or innate figure-ground mechanism. He does not make it possible to state its limiting conditions.

The "Nonsensory" Figure

The *nonsensory figure-ground organization* is defined as one in which the boundaries of the figure are not fixed by gradients of luminosity in the visual field. It is affected by experience and other nonsensory factors, and is not inevitable in any

perception. In contrasting the primitive and the nonsensory figure, however, one need not imply that a perceived figure must be either of one or the other kind. They are rather two extremes, and in most perceptions both sensory and nonsensory factors affect figure-ground organization.

The one of these extremes, in which exactly the same figural boundaries are recognized by anyone, has already been illustrated. The other is quite common in ordinary experience, although I have not found any discussion that makes its meaning explicit. It is implied, for example, by Gibson and Crooks (1938) in their discussion of the perceptual field of the automobile driver, and the shrinking or expanding of a perceived zone of safety from *potential* collision. In general terms, the nonsensory figure occurs in perception whenever the subject responds selectively to a limited part of a homogeneous area in the visual field. One may look at the "middle part" of a rope as distinct from the rest, in knot-tying, or perceive the "foreground" of an unbroken landscape. It is a commonplace that in human perception many entities exist, like the place in a continuous expanse of lawn where a flowerbed is to be put in, such that no sensory delimitation of figure from ground can even be suggested. The "corner" of a room certainly does not always refer to a geometrical point; it is extended, and yet does not comprise all of the two (or three) rectangular surfaces which determine it. Its locus is sensorily fixed, but not its boundaries, and language is full of terms with a similar implication for the theory of perception.

Even commoner in everyday perception is the perceived entity in which both sensory and nonsensory factors cooperate. Here the figural boundary may follow one of a number of possible luminosity gradients in the field, the particular one that is effective being usually determined by experience in one form or another. This is illustrated by Leeper's (1935) experiment, which demonstrated a lasting control, *by earlier experience,* of the particular perception that is made with Boring's ambiguous figure, "My wife and my mother-in-law" (Boring, 1930). Another illustration is the process of slow learning to see a configuration in a particular way, as in the gradual decrease of the difficulty a novice has in following the boundaries of a thalamic nucleus that are obvious to the expert.

There is reason to believe that the rat, as well as man, finds some figure-ground relations obvious and inescapable, and detects others only after prolonged experience. That is, the distinction of primitive and nonsensory figures applies also to the rodent's perception. Lashley (1938*b*, pp. 156, 185) points out that success in discrimination and generalization evidently depends on the rat's finding a differentiating characteristic between two figures, or one that is common to a pattern already known and the new one which is presented in the testing situation. It is equally clear that the distinctive part of the test pattern is not obvious to the rat at once; this part, whatever it is, is what determines the response and becomes the true figure (as contrasted with what the experimenter meant to be the figure), the rest merging into ground.

In general, Gestalt writers on the organization of the figure have been concerned to show that it cannot be reduced to experience and learning, and have thus selected cases for discussion in which sensory dynamics alone is enough to produce an effective figure-ground organization. They have, that is, concentrated attention on the primitive figure, and they give the impression that the spontaneity of its organization is a property of any figure. True, one can find many passages in the literature on Gestalten that refer to figures not sensorily delimited, but no stress on the fact that this implies some role of learning in the delimitation.

Köhler (1929), for example, has written: "Since 'real form' presupposes a segregated whole, the existence of 'form' de-

pends upon factors *of stimulation* similar to those upon which the segregation and organization of wholes depend. Again, definite relations in the total constellation *of retinal stimuli* are found to be decisive for the existence of real form" (p. 202; my italics draw attention to the stress put on sensory factors). Again, after referring to Gottschaldt's experiments, Köhler says: "After these results, whoever defends the automatic influence of past experience upon our seeing definite forms, will have incumbent upon him the task of supporting his theory by other experiments. *If such an influence exists, it must be restricted to rather special cases*" (p. 208; italics mine).

Attention is drawn to this aspect of Gestalt theory because it helps one to define the point at which one can diverge from the theory without failing to recognize the great contribution it has made to modern psychology, which has been shaped to a great extent by the impact of Gestalt ideas on behaviorism. There are few psychologists who would not own a debt of this kind to Gestalttheorie, and few who do not also feel the need of qualifying the theory in some way, though it is not easy to see just how this is to be done without losing the values that have been obtained with its help.

In the pages from which the passage above is taken, Professor Köhler, I believe, provides the necessary clue. His argument appears to depend on a complete antithesis of experience and innate sensory dynamics, and it is this antithesis that we may avoid. The question that is asked by Köhler is whether sensory organization is wholly innate, or wholly experiential.[1] If these are

---

[1] In the monograph of Köhler and Wallach (1944, pp. 316, 323) there are also passages that seem not intelligible unless one is thinking in terms of such an extreme dichotomy between completely organized sensory processes (innately) and completely unorganized ones. This does not do justice, either to current learning theory, or to the effectiveness of the earlier Gestalt arguments in favor of an innate sensory organization.

the only two alternatives, the argument is unanswerable. Köhler and Koffka and Lashley have unquestionably slain the dragon of pure learning theory, in the field of perception, and no one today would argue that perceptual organization is wholly acquired; there is some innate organization. But this of course does not show that the organization is entirely innate. There is always a possibility that perception has a partly innate, partly learned organization; and that besides the figure that has a "primitive unity" there are "nonsensory figures" in which experience has an important role.

I propose, then, that Gestalt theory made an essential contribution when it showed that there are innate factors in perception, but that it has tended to carry the argument too far in denying that learning and experience have any important role in the perception of simple configurations (apart, of course, from learning the *meaning* of the configurations). This, as we have seen, has led to emphasis on a dominant role of sensory dynamics; important as sensory processes are, however, they do not completely dominate either behavior or perception.

It is also important to see that the argument against an effect of experience on perception often requires the assumption that *any* perceived figure is perceived as a whole, in all respects. Thus the upper diagram of Figure 3 has been regarded as quite unfamiliar to the observer (Köhler, 1929). Subjects shown this diagram for the first time failed to find another which is concealed in it, and which they had been shown before. The conclusion was drawn that an unfamiliar configuration obscured a familiar, smaller one—that sensory dynamics dominates experience and the effects of learning. But the experimental diagram, actually, was unfamiliar only as a whole: its parts, two parallelograms and a set of parallel lines forming a Z, were certainly not unfamiliar to the experimental subjects. Consequently, the

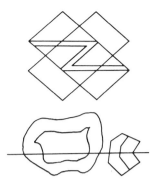

FIGURE 2   Diagram from Köhler, *Gestalt psychology,* 1929 (figure 10 and 12). Courtesy of Liveright Publishing Corporation and the author.

conclusion is valid only if the total figure is an unanalyzable whole, which it surely is not.

In the lower· diagram of Figure 2, a "4" is concealed. That it may not be recognized is evidence that sensory dynamics on occasion may override experience, in the delimitation of a figure. This is a valid point. But when one looks for it, the 4 can be seen, and this is not explained by Gestalt theory. A "special vector" (Köhler, 1929) is operating, but this special vector seems to be the factor of attention and experience that is involved in the nonsensory figure. Our problem is to find out how to modify Gestalt theory so that it can comprise this factor of attention and not have to deny the importance of learning in perception.

Furthermore, Gestalt emphasis on the primitive figure, which has a marked stability, obscures the fact that in ordinary perception any figure-ground relationship is a highly unstable one, with a practically constant fluctuation from one organization to another. Even when one perceives the compact, clearly delimited figure which is such that any observer at once sees it, one finds that the stability of the figure-ground relation is not great; or, better, that its stability consists of a continual *recurrence*, instead of a constancy, of the figure. It is notorious that attention wanders, and this is another way of saying that in perception any figure is unstable; one looks at this part of the configuration and that, and notices its corners or smooth contour, in the intervals between seeing the figure as a whole. In ordinary perception, moreover, the instability is far greater (Boring, 1933; Pillsbury, 1913).

An adequate account of perception cannot be given in terms of a figure-ground organization that has any great duration in time, even when gaze is fixated at a single point in a configuration. The fluctuations of attention which occur point directly to a fundamental importance, in any perception, of nonsensory factors. This of course has already been demonstrated for complex indeterminate figures by Carmichael, Hogan, and Walter (1932) and by Zangwill (1937); I propose that the same factors must be taken into account in the perception of square or circle as well.

"Identity" in Perception

Identity is defined here as referring to the properties of association inherent in a perception. The reference has two aspects: first, a figure is perceived as having identity when it is seen immediately as similar to some figures and dissimilar to others— that is, when it falls at once into certain categories and not into others. This similarity can be summed up as spontaneous association, since it may occur on the first exposure to the stimulus object. Secondly, the object that is perceived as having identity is capable of being associated readily with other objects or with some action, whereas the one that does not have identity is recalled with great difficulty or not at all, and is not recognized or named easily. Identity of course is a matter of degree and, as I shall try to show, depends on a considerable degree of experience; it is not innately given.

Thorndike (1931, p. 87) has presented an approach to this conception, using the term "identifiability," and has proposed that identifiability promotes the formation of associations. If one carries the analysis a little further, it appears that the proposition is circular. Identifiability is not merely a perceptible difference of one figure from another when the two are side by side, but implies a remembered difference —identifiability is clearly, in the instances Thorndike gives, recognizability; and recognition is one form of association. Thus Thorndike's proposition is that associability affects the occurrence of associations.

The real point at which he is driving seems to be that there are genuine differences of associability in different patterns. Also, more is involved in these differences than the number of trials necessary to establish recognition; there are also the spontaneous associations referred to in speaking of similarity. Recognizability goes with selective similarity, or generalization: the figure that is readily remembered is also perceived as belonging to a particular class of figures, and remembered so.

An irregular mass of color or a pattern of intersecting lines drawn at random has some coherence and unity, but one such figure is not readily recognized and distinguished from others when it is seen a second time, and generalization (or similarity) is not selective among a number of such stimuli. There is not a total lack of distinctiveness and of generalization, however. Two of Thorndike's figures which lack identity are not indistinguishable when seen together; and mistaking one figure for another can be called generalization. Lashley and Wade (1946) distinguish between the "so-called generalization" which means only a failure to observe differences and the generalization which involves perception of both similarities and differences. The amorphous figure, lacking in identity, is generalized in the first sense only.

A further illustration of these points is found in the development of identity in the perception of chimpanzee faces by one who has seen no chimpanzees before. Two animals seen side by side are obviously different in details, but the inexperienced observer is not able easily to remember one selectively. Also, all chimpanzees at this stage look alike; the "so-called generalization" occurs. With experience the perception of identity increases. Similarity is still perceived between animals, and confusion between some animals is still possible; but there is a marked change in the perception, as shown in a much more selective similarity of one animal to others, and in the radical increase of the observer's capacity to associate even a new chimpanzee with a specific name. Thus identity is a matter of degree: readiness of recognition, and the extent to which generalization is selective.

This discussion has been meant to establish the conception of "identity" as an important property of perception which should be kept carefully distinct from the "unity" of the perceived figure (as well as from its "meaning"). Unity may be innately determined, an immediate property of sensory dynamics, whereas identity is dependent on a prolonged experience. Because these two things have not been separated in the past, it has appeared that perceptual organization is innate. Some aspects of the organization *are* present, apparently, at the first experience; but others are not.

Independence of Unity and Identity in Simple Figures

The examples of the preceding section dealt with complex perceptions. I wish next to review the evidence that shows that unity and identity have separate determinants even in quite simple perceptions. Seeing a circle as a single coherent object is not the same as seeing it as a distinctive object, selectively recognizable.

First, the evidence for man. It has already been said that the figure-ground segregation is good at the initial occurrence of human vision, as shown by Senden's

(1932) reports, at the very time when perception of identity appears to be practically nil. Unity then can be perceived without identity. Investigators (of vision following operation for congenital cataract) are unanimous in reporting that the perception of a square, circle, or triangle, or of sphere or cube, is very poor. To see one of these as a whole object, with distinctive characteristics immediately evident, is not possible for a long period. The most intelligent and best-motivated patient has to seek corners painstakingly even to distinguish a triangle from a circle. The newly seeing patient can frequently find a difference between two such figures shown together, just as the normal adult can readily detect differences between two of Thorndike's figures lacking "identifiability," but the differences are not remembered. There is for weeks a practically zero capacity to learn names for such figures, even when tactual recognition is prompt and complete.

Another facet of the same lack of capacity is the failure to generalize as normal persons do. When the patient first gets to the point of being able to name a simple object promptly, recognition is completely destroyed if the object is slightly changed or put into a new setting. The patient who had learned to name a ring showed no recognition of a slightly different ring; having learned to name a square, made of white cardboard, could not name it when its color was changed to yellow by turning the cardboard over; and so on. These reports consistently indicate that the perceived whole at first vision is *simultaneously unified and amorphous*. There is not a single instance given in which the congenitally blind after operation had trouble in learning color names; but a great number in which the perception of identity in a simple figure was poor indeed (Senden, 1932, pp. 135–141).

A second evidence comes from species differences in the perception of identity. For coherent patterns and simple groupings the figure-ground relationship appears to be the same from rat to man, so the significant differences of perceptual generalization (one aspect of identity) argue strongly that figural unity and identity have separate bases. (*a*) The discrimination of simple geometrical figures by man and chimpanzee is unaffected by reversal of brightness relations between figure and ground (Gellerman, 1933); a white triangle on a black ground is generalized by these anthropoids to include a black triangle on a white ground. For the rat, such a reversal completely disrupts discrimination, and no amount of training with the white triangle alone will produce "recognition" of a black one. There is some uncertainty about the phylogenetic level at which the capacity for this generalization appears; see Lashley (1938*b*, p. 144), Smith (1936), and Neet (1933); but between the rat, and chimpanzee or man, the difference in this respect seems complete (although for simple figures only; human perception of more complex figures in reversed brightness is definitely defective, as in recognition of photographic negatives). (*b*) The perception of a triangle or square by the rat is not generalized, without specific training, to include a similar rotated figure (Fields, 1932) but is generalized so by chimpanzee and by two-year-old children, although a corresponding head rotation also occurs (Gellerman, 1933). (*c*) Perception of a triangle is not generalized either by rat or chimpanzee to include a triangle made up of small circles, but the generalization is made by two-year-old children (Gellerman, 1933; Lashley, 1938*b*).

Thus the perception of identity is different in different mammals; the perception of primitive unity is practically the same.

Further evidence of the independence of unity and identity is found in the peculiar "equivalences" or generalizations often observed in rat behavior, and in the anomalies to be found in the relative

difficulty with which the rat learns to discriminate between certain patterns. Two discriminations that are equally easy, from the human point of view, present very unequal difficulty for the rat. For normal man a square and a circle are no less obviously distinct than erect and inverted triangles; yet the rat readily learns to discriminate between the triangles and consistently has trouble with circle versus square (Lashley, 1938*b*, pp. 155–156). Some animals that have learned other patterns (thus showing that their acuity is sufficient for the task) show no sign of discriminating circle and square at all. A five-pointed star and an *H* are for man clearly, inevitably distinct, while the rat distinguishes them with difficulty and no faster learning occurs than with quite irregular figures (Lashley, 1938*b*, p. 157). Such facts mean a great difference of rat from man in perceiving the identity of simple, regular figures.

The same is evident in the patterns which may be "equivalent" for individual rats, and in some failures of equivalence. One animal may transfer his response from an erect triangle (versus an inverted one) to a single horizontal line low on the stimulus card (versus another higher on the card), while another animal fails to discriminate the complete triangles with which he was trained, when a slight change is made of their positions on the respective stimulus cards. It is very doubtful in such cases that the rat has perceived the pattern as a distinctive whole, and it seems that a response is frequently determined by only a part of a figure as simple as a triangle.

Lashley (1938*b*, p. 182) has recognized this, but interpreted it by comparing the rat to a ski-jumper who does not pay attention in his jump to nonessentials such as the shape of a spectator's hat. The general interpretation was made that there is little significant difference in the perception of simple figures by rat and man, but this conclusion is not supported by the evidence.

When identity is distinguished from unity, we find great species differences in the perception of identity and not in what is seen as a primitive unity. The analogy between the rat's perceiving all the detail of a triangle in the jumping apparatus, and the ski-jumper's perception of a hat, is valid—except that it sets the human subject a much more difficult task. It is inconceivable that a ski-jumper would not perceive a large triangle as such, fully structured, if it lay close to and marked the point of safe landing in an otherwise plain field, as it does for the rat in the jumping apparatus. The rat, however, may respond selectively to only the part of the figure which lies nearest the point to which he jumps, although his field of vision is wide and although (as Lashley has demonstrated) he perceives much more than he has to in making a discrimination.

These considerations are the more convincing because the evidence of the rat's frequent failure to see the triangle as a distinctive whole figure coincides with Senden's description of the congenitally blind after acquiring vision—the normally reared rat, and a man seeing for the first time, both have precisely the same kind of difficulty.

It is reasonable to conclude that the perception of identity (as defined) follows the same principles in rat and man but is much more highly developed in normal man. Since there is no evidence of any clear difference of the primitive figure-ground organization perceived by these two species, but strong suggestions that it is the same for both, the evidence is consistent with the idea that identity and figural unity have separate physiological bases. They are, that is, psychologically independent. This makes it possible to suppose that additive processes may occur in the development of identity without denying that the figure has a primitive unity.

Learning to Perceive Simple Figures

The facts already adduced in the last section have indicated a role of learning in the perception of triangle or square as distinctive wholes. The idea that one has to learn to see a triangle must sound extremely improbable, and so I shall now present the evidence to this effect more systematically.

We have seen that the perceptions of the congenitally blind after operation are almost completely lacking in identity. Senden (1932, pp. 155–157) reports cases in which there was an immediate perception of differences in two figures seen together, but also one definite instance in which even this was not possible. Thus the patient sometimes saw differences between a sphere and cube, sometimes not (p. 90). Color has been found to dominate form persistently in the first vision of these patients. Eleven months after operation the color names learned by a patient in hospital were retained, but the little that had been learned of form was forgotten (p. 135). An egg, potato, and cube of sugar were seen by a patient repeatedly, until naming was prompt, but then were not recognized when put into colored light; the cube of sugar was well named when it was seen on the table or in the investigator's hand but not recognized when suspended by a thread with a change of background (p. 138).

Such patients, when learning has proceeded far enough, manifest the characteristic generalizations of the normal person, so the initial difficulties are not to be put down to structural defects of the sensory apparatus (Senden, pp. 173–175).

Riesen (1947) has fully confirmed the conclusion that ordinary visual perception in higher mammals presupposes a long learning period. His observations concerning the almost complete visual incapacity of chimpanzees reared in darkness, and the slowness of learning, are of the greatest importance. They show that Senden's similar results with man are not due to some inadequacy of the clinical tests, nor peculiarly human.

The course of perceptual learning in man is gradual, proceeding from a dominance of color, through a period of separate attention to each part of a figure, to a gradually arrived at identification of the whole as a whole: an apparently simultaneous instead of a serial apprehension. A patient was trained to discriminate square from triangle over a period of 13 days, and had learned so little in this time "that he could not report their form without counting corners one after another. . . . And yet it seems that the recognition process was beginning already to be automatic, so that some day the judgment 'square' would be given with simple vision, which would then easily lead to the belief that form was always simultaneously given" (Senden, 1932, p. 160). The shortest time in which a patient approximated to normal perception, even when learning was confined to a small number of objects, seems to have been about a month.

It is possible then that the normal human infant goes through the same process, and that we are able to see a square as such in a single glance only as the result of complex learning. The notion seems unlikely, because of the utter simplicity of such a perception to the normal adult. But no such argument can be valid, since Lashley (1937) has shown that subjective simplicity and immediacy may be very deceptive as an index of physiological simplicity. There are moreover residual traces of learning in normal perception, and hints of its complexity.

Gellerman (1933) reports that chimpanzees and two-year-old children recognized a triangle that had been rotated through 120° from the training position, but (in the one protocol that is given) responded selectively only *after* a head rotation; and persistent head rotation con-

tinued in the later discriminations. Older human subjects do not need to make the same receptor adjustment to recognize the figure in two positions, and so this generalization may be a learned capacity, simple as it seems to us.

Consider also the following evidence, which is suggestive though perhaps not conclusive. When a simple figure such as square, circle, or triangle, subtending a retinal angle of from 2° to 10°, is fixated at one point, it tends in a second or so to become almost amorphous except near the point of fixation. The effect is not due to fatigue alone, nor to poor acuity outside the macular zone: since (1) a single straight line does not suffer nearly as much, (2) shifting fixation back and forth between two corners of a triangle does not restore the clarity with which the third is seen, and (3) an 8° circle drawn with a line 2 mm wide, and a 4° circle drawn with a line 1 mm wide, seem to give approximately the same effect.

The factors involved are evidently complicated; it will be found, for example, that with a large figure merely *imagining* eyemovements (of following the contours) will restore definition of the figure. Also, these "imaginary" eyemovements, or subliminal activations of the motor system, occur more frequently and are less easy to control in looking at a smaller than at a larger figure, and it is hard to be sure that the size of the figure is unimportant. But this at least seems definite, that a stable, clear, and effective perception of circle or square is more possible with eyemovement than without. Once the question is asked, anyone can verify for himself the falsity of the implicit assumption (usually made in the study of perception) that the figure acts always as one, without a reinforcing perception of its parts as distinct from the whole.

My point is not that eyemovements are essential to perception by a sophisticated observer (nor, in the following paragraph, that they are completely necessary for an image); but that the perception is definitely clearer, more effective, with them than without. This is really an evident fact. It is to be interpreted in the light of all evidence, cited above, showing that the perception of square or circle is slowly learned *and depends originally on multiple visual fixations.*

Directly in line with such phenomenological observations are the following introspections. I find it very difficult to have a clear image of a triangle, square, or circle without imagining or actually making a series of eyemovements. Several others, asked to make observation on this point, have reported the same thing. It is hard or impossible, that is, to have a clear image of a triangle as fixated at one point. Eyemovements definitely improve the "image." They do not take the form, necessarily, of following the figure's contours, but are apt to jump from point to point, perhaps three to four points in all. Thus the distinctiveness of the image is not merely in the eyemovement pattern, for approximately the same series of eyemovements may contribute to a good image either of circle or square. Activation of the motor system, overt or implicit (even possibly within the cerebrum alone, with no activity of the final common paths), *contributes essentially to the development of visual integration without being sufficient to it.* As I have said, such evidence is hard to evaluate, but it points to the same conclusion as Senden's evidence, already cited, and is supported by it.

Clark and Lashley (1947) have confirmed the observations of Kennard and Ectors (1938) and Kennard (1939), and have provided what appears to be an independent confirmation of the argument above. Kennard found a one-sided loss of vision by monkeys on extirpation of the opposite frontal eyefield, a cortical motor area for head-and-eye movement. Clark and Lashley have demonstrated this phenomenon convincingly, with an adequate method of testing. The most significant

and striking observation was startle by the monkey when an object was passed from the blind side into the seeing side, at the moment of passing the midline. One might have argued that the animal could "see" an object in his apparently hemianopic field but was not able to move his eyes toward it. The observation referred to rules that interpretation out, and other observations showed that the hemianopia is a genuine failure to see (though it is transient, disappearing in a week or two).

Now the question is what the motor cortex can have to do with visual perception—unless perception intimately involves a motor activity, liminal or subliminal. There is no reason to think that the frontal cortex has anything to do with the reception of visual sensation, and the alternative seems to be that it must have something to do with the elaboration of sensation into visual perceptions. In Chapter 5 will be found a treatment of perception which supposes that perception of even a simple object involves a "phase sequence." This is a chain of central cortical events with motor links. Although the motor activations may be subliminal and do not always produce overt response, their role is essential in any perception. This would account for the observations of Kennard and Ectors, and Clark and Lashley, which therefore can be considered to be a confirmation of the argument of Chapter 5 as well as the argument of the preceding paragraphs.

Conclusions

Animal experiments and the human clinical data alike indicate that the perception of simple diagrams as distinctive wholes is not immediately given but slowly acquired through learning. Introspective observations which would not carry much weight in themselves appear to agree fully with other evidence, showing vestiges of a summative process involved in perceiving the identity of circle or triangle; although such a figure is seen by the adult clearly and is effectively discriminated at a single glance, there are still traces left of complexities such as the learning process described by Senden would produce, which for normal persons must have occurred in early infancy and which makes the unified perception possible.

The subjective experience of an irreducible simplicity in the perception of square or circle may then be fully analogous to the illusion of the image of the letter-square (Woodworth, 1938, p. 42), where the subject thinks he has an actual image of the square but can be shown not to have. The experiment is as follows:

The subject is shown a diagram such as

x	e	a	q
r	l	i	s
o	f	z	g
d	y	u	p

and studies it until he has, apparently, an image of the whole square and can "look at" it and read the letters off, one by one. If he really has such an image, it will not matter in what direction he is asked to "read." Actually, it is found that the subject cannot reproduce the letters as fast from right to left as from left to right, or promptly give the four letters, *p, z, l, x,* that make up the diagonal from lower right to upper left. So what seems a simple, immediately given image of the whole is actually a serial reconstruction of parts of the figure. An "image" of triangle or square is simpler, longer practiced, but may be fundamentally the same. The perception of such figures, also, may involve a temporal sequence.

Although the perception of identity is good at a glance, it is improved by several glances at different parts of the figure. This process of "successive part reinforcement," as an *aid* to perception, exists at the same time as an essential unity of the whole; and theory must provide for the additive process, with its motor elements, as well as for the primitive unity.

This argument is not in any way a return to the old idea that sensory integration occurs solely through motor activity, or that the distinctiveness of a perception is solely or mainly due to distinctive eyemovement. We know that this is not true. But there are three theoretical possibilities, not two: (1) perceptual integration is wholly the result of motor activity; (2) it is wholly independent of motor activity; and (3) the motor activity is important but not all-important—the position that is taken here.

Grant fully that visual integration cannot be reduced to a synthesis of unrelated elements through effector activity, and the question remains, how much significance the motor factor may still have. Receptor adjustment (head-and-eyemovement) is the most prominent feature of visual perception whether in rat, chimpanzee, or man— *except* in long-practiced habits. The assumption has been tacitly made that the adjustments are unimportant for theory (once it was shown that they were not the whole answer). The fact of eyemovement has been treated only as a further (negative) evidence that the locus of excitation in the retina is unimportant, since the changing retinal projection does not disturb perception. But obviously another point of view is possible. The thesis of this chapter is that eyemovements in perception are not adventitious. They contribute, constantly and essentially, to perceptual integration, even though they are not the whole origin of it.

References

BORING, E. G. 1930. A new ambiguous figure. *Amer. J. Psychol.,* 42, 444–445.

BORING, E. G. 1933. *The physical dimensions of consciousness.* New York: Century.

CARMICHAEL, L., H. P. HOGAN, and A. A. WALTER. 1932. An experimental study of the effect of language on the reproduction of visually perceived form. *J. Exp. Psychol.,* 15, 73–86.

CLARK, G., and K. S. LASHLEY. 1947. Visual disturbances following frontal ablations in the monkey. *Anat. Rec.,* 97, 326.

FIELDS, P. E. 1932. Studies in concept formation. I. *Comp. Psychol. Monog.*, 9, No. 2.

GELLERMAN, L. W. 1933. Form discrimination in chimpanzees and two-year-old children: I. Form (triangularity) *per se. J. Genet. Psychol.*, 42, 3–27.

GIBSON, J. J., and L. E. CROOKS. 1938. A theoretical field-analysis of automobile driving. *Amer. J. Psychol.*, 51, 453–471.

HEBB, D. O. 1937. The innate organization of visual activity: I. Perception of figures by rats reared in total darkness. *J. Genet. Psychol.*, 51, 101–126.

KENNARD, M. A. 1939. Alterations in response to visual stimuli following lesions of frontal lobe in monkeys. *Arch. Neurol. Psychiat.*, 41, 1153–1165

KENNARD, M. A., and L. ECTORS. 1938. Forced circling in monkeys following lesions of the frontal lobes. *Arch. Neurol. Psychiat.*, 1, 45–54.

KOHLER, W. 1929. *Gestalt psychology.* New York: Liveright.

KOHLER, W., and H. WALLACH. 1944. Figural after-effects: An investigation of visual processes. *Proc. Amer. Phil. Soc.*, 88, 269–357.

LASHLEY, K. S. 1937. Functional determinants of cerebral localization. *Arch. Neurol. Psychiat.*, 38, 371–387.

LASHLEY, K. S. 1938. The mechanism of vision: XV. Preliminary studies of the rat's capacity for detail vision. *J. Gen. Psychol.*, 18, 123–193.

LASHLEY, K. S., and M. WADE. 1946. The Pavlovian theory of generalization. *Psychol. Rev.*, 53, 72–87.

LEEPER, R. W. 1935. A study of a neglected portion of the field of learning—the development of sensory organization. *J. Genet. Psychol.*, 46, 41–75.

NEET, C. C. 1933. Visual pattern discrimination in the *Maccacus rhesus* monkey. *J. Genet. Psychol.*, 43, 727–757.

PILLSBURY, W. B. 1913. "Fluctuations of attention" and the refractory period. *J. Phil. Psychol. Sci. Meth.*, 10, 181–185.

RIESEN, A. H. 1947. The development of visual perception in man and chimpanzee. *Science*, 106, 107–108.

RUBIN, E. 1921. *Visuell wahrgenommene Figuren: Studien in psychologischer Analyse.* Teil I. Berlin: Gyldendalske Boghandel.

SENDEN, M. v. 1932. *Raum- und Gestaltauffassung bei operierten Blindgeborenen vor und nach der Operation.* Leipzig: Barth.

SMITH, K. U. 1936. Visual discrimination in the cat: III. The relative effect of paired and unpaired stimuli in the discriminative behavior of the cat. *J. Genet. Psychol.*, 48, 29–57.

THORNDIKE, E. L. 1931. *Human learning.* New York: Century.

WOODWORTH, R. S. 1938. *Experimental psychology.* New York: Holt.

ZANGWILL, O. L. 1937. A study of the significance of attitude in recognition. *Brit. J. Psychol.*, 28, 12–17.

Eidetic Imagery: I. Frequency*

RALPH NORMAN HABER   RUTH B. HABER

University of Rochester

Summary. *Eidetic imagery, defined as a visual image persisting after stimulation, relatively accurate in detail, colored positively, and capable of being scanned, was measured in nearly all children in an elementary school in New Haven, Conn. Care was taken to specify and follow precise methods for the measurement, and strict criteria were used for the discrimination of eidetic images from after images and from memory. Discontinuous distributions of scores were found on all of the measures used to define eidetic images, with 12 Ss (8%) falling into this qualitatively different eidetic category on each measure. Their images lasted as long as 4 min., during which nearly all of the details of the stimulus could be reproduced. However, their memory of the stimulus was not much better after their imagery had faded than that of Ss who did not have eidetic imagery. These results were discussed in terms of models of translation of stimulation into memory, and further research was outlined.*

Some children (and a very few adults) are able to maintain a complete visual image of a stimulus from which they can describe the stimulus in detail. This eidetic imagery is notably different from most adult perception, in which the visual image of a stimulus fades almost immediately and any description of the stimulus must be based on a normally incomplete memory. These two characteristics of eidetic imagery —long-term visual imagery and accurate reports without memory—should have given it great theoretical interest. However, current theories of perception have not considered visual imagery to be very important. Sperling (1963), in perhaps the most comprehensive model of the translation of stimulation into memory, does not mention visual imagery, with the exception of after images. For him, the offset of the stimulus energy is the end of the stimulus, and all further processing of that stimulation uses different aspects of encoded memory. While he shows (Sperling, 1960) that a dark pre-exposure field increases the duration of what he calls short-term memory (presumably because of the long after images produced), in other places both he (Sperling, 1963) and Averbach (Averbach and Coriell, 1961) talk of short-term memory as already having undergone some encoding.

* *Perceptual and Motor Skills*, 1964, vol. 19, pp. 131–138. Copyright © 1964 Southern Universities Press. This research was supported in part by Grant MH-03244 from the National Institute of Mental Health to Yale University, under the direction of the first author. We would like to thank Miss May White, the Superintendent of Schools for Elementary Education of the City of New Haven, Miss Margaret R. Fitzsimons, Principal, and each of the teachers of the Roger Sherman Elementary School of New Haven, for their permission to test the children, and for their kind support throughout the project.

Eidetic imagery is important in this connection because it is sufficiently long and accurate to allow extensive and complete reports of the stimulus to be made without benefit of the intervening processes described in Sperling's model. Indeed, if eidetic imagery is as prevalent as the literature indicates, then perhaps initially in the life of the child, all translations from stimulation to reports may be through eidetic images, and not until later are the elaborate encoding and rehearsal processes necessary. Of course, any report in words of a visual stimulus requires encoding into words, but if the image of the stimulus is long, this encoding does not have to be accomplished from an imperfect memory.

With these issues in mind, this research was designed first to ascertain whether eidetic imagery occurs, and then to examine the nature of the imagery, specifically how it is used by the perceiver in reporting what he sees. This report presents data relevant primarily to the first question.

Eidetic images have been distinguished from memory by the preservation of fine detail (which is usually lost in memory), by S's report that a visual image still persists after the stimulus has been removed, and by behavior which indicates that S is indeed attending to such an image. Eidetic images have been distinguished from after images by their persistence (after images fade rather rapidly), by their reliability of evocation from even low-contrast stimuli (after images are usually difficult to arouse from such stimuli), by their positive representation of color (after images, especially long ones, are usually negative), by their independence of visual fixation (after images usually require fixation to form, while eidetic images do not), and by the lack of effects of eye-movements during report (after images move with the eye, while eidetic images can be scanned visually).

Perhaps 200 empirical, semi-empirical, and clinical studies, mostly German, have been made of this phenomenon, although by 1925 as many were being done in this country as abroad. Kluever has been the major reviewer of this work, with extensive reviews in 1928, 1931, and 1932, while Jaensch has been the primary systematizer, as a representative of the Marburg School, with a major book in 1925 and another in 1930. By 1937, however, interest and research, as judged by publications, had nearly ended, with only 12 papers listed in *Psychological Abstracts* during the past 25 years. The reasons for so sharp a change probably included the lack of a sound theoretical base, the behavioristic climate against this introspective subject, and the strangeness and unusualness of the behavior, at least as viewed by adult psychologists. No serious doubts were raised about the validity of eidetic imagery as a phenomenon, even though the methodology of assessment has been both poorly described and poorly executed. Eidetic imagery just ceased to excite scientists. The majority of the dozen references since 1937 are clinical reports of individual eidetic persons, usually patients.

A review of all of the research findings of eidetic imagery would be out of place here, in view of able earlier reviews of Kluever, and because of the many serious methodological deficiencies of the early work. Percentages of children said to possess some form of eidetic imagery ranged from 30 to 90, depending upon the age and population sampled, with a rough average of all studies around 50%. Nearly every investigator has reported that eidetic imagery was common, and that eidetic Ss could easily be found among any population of children. Different investigators have reported different peak ages; some have indicated a negative correlation with age, while others have pointed to puberty or shortly before as the age of greatest prevalence. All investigators have reported zero or near-zero frequencies among adults, although, as far as is known, no longitudinal studies have been reported.

Method

SUBJECTS

All Ss were students in the Roger Sherman Elementary School of New Haven, Conn., during the academic year 1961–1962. The school had 245 children registered, of whom 179 were tested. Those missed were either consistently absent ($N = 14$) or because of time pressures were not included in the random samples drawn from the lower grades. Of the 179 Ss tested, 28 were not scorable, due to malfunctions of the tape recorder, leaving 151 in the sample.

TESTING SITUATION

S was brought into a small room which contained a table with an easel on it. The easel (30 in. wide by 24 in. high, in a neutral grey finish) was tilted away from S slightly, and had a narrow ledge along the bottom on which the pictures were rested. S was seated 20 in. away from the easel, his eyes level with the middle of it. Room illumination was normal, with strong sunlight blocked by curtains when necessary. A tape recorder transcribed both S's and E's voices.

PROCEDURE

The sequence of events was the same for each S. He first was shown a 4-in. red square, mounted on a board 10 in. by 12 in., of the same material as the easel. E placed the stimulus on the easel, left it there for 10 sec., and then removed it rapidly. S reported what he still saw on the easel. Three other colored squares (blue, black, and yellow), always in this order, were presented in a similar fashion. After the fourth square was shown, four pictures were presented for 30 sec each, in the same manner.

The following instructions were given to S at the beginning.

We are going to play a game with colors and with pictures. Here on this easel I am going to show you some colors and some pictures, and then we are going to talk about them. When I put a colored square here (pointing), I want you to stare at the center of it as hard as you can, and try not to move your eyes at all as long as I leave the square there. When I take the square away, I want you to continue to stare as hard as you can where the square was. If you stare hard enough, you will still be able to see something there. It is very much like when you stare hard at a light bulb, and then look away—you can still see something out there in front of your eyes. (If any child acted as if he was unfamiliar with this demonstration, he was instructed to try it then with one of the overhead lights in the room.) The important thing is to stare hard at the colored square when I put it on the easel—do not take your eyes away or move them around. When I remove the square, do not look at me, or follow the color as I take it away, but keep staring at the place where it was on the easel. As soon as I take the color away, I want you to tell me what you still see there, if you see anything. You do not have to wait until I ask you—you can begin telling me right away. OK, here is the first colored square.

E was watching carefully during the exposure to be sure S did not move his eyes. If S reported that he saw nothing at all after the square was removed, he was encouraged by being assured that it was all right to see things after the color was removed. If he still said he saw nothing, he was reminded to stare hard, and not to move his eyes at all, and he was questioned again as to whether he knew what these instructions meant. Then E presented the next square, increasing the duration by 10 sec over the previous exposure.

If S said he saw something, he was allowed to report spontaneously. When he stopped, he was questioned on whichever of the following items he had not reported: Was the image still visible? What was its color and shape? Did color and shape change, and if so, how? In what direction did the image move? How did it disappear? Did it move when the eyes moved (S was instructed to try to move his eyes to the top of the easel)? After these points had been covered, and the image had faded completely, E gave the initial instructions again, and showed another square. The same procedure was followed for the four squares.

After the last square was shown and S had finished his response, the instructions for the pictures were given.

Now, I am going to show you some pictures. For these, however, I do not want you to stare in one place, but to move your eyes around so that you can be sure you can see all of the details. When I take the picture away, I want you to continue to look hard at the easel where the picture was, and tell me what you can still see after I take it away. After I take it away, you also can move your eyes all over where it was on the easel. And be sure, while the picture is on the easel that you move your eyes around it to see all of the parts.

All four pictures were presented for 30 sec each. E watched closely to be sure the pictures were scanned and not fixated. The first picture was of a family scene, black pictures pasted on a grey board to form a silhouette. The second, constructed in the same way, was of an Indian hunting, with a deer, other animals, and some birds. The third, in full color, showed an Indian fishing in a canoe, with many fish in the water. The fourth, also in color, from *Alice in Wonderland*, depicted Alice standing at the base of a large tree staring up at the Cheshire cat. A number of other similar pictures had been used in pretesting and in extra testing with some of the same Ss.

After the first picture was removed, S was told to continue to look at the easel, and to tell E whatever he could still see. S was reminded that he could move his eyes. If S reported seeing something, E asked if he was actually seeing it then or remembering it from when the picture was

still on the easel. E asked frequently if he was still seeing it, since Ss often would not report the fading of the image but would continue reporting it from memory. If S stopped his report, E asked if he could see anything else. If S said no, but said he was still seeing an image, E asked if he could describe anything else about that image. E probed for further description and attributes of all objects still visible in the image. S also was asked to move his eyes if he had not done so spontaneously. E noted the relation between direction of gaze and details of report. Whenever S said the entire image had faded, E asked him to describe the picture from memory, with as many details as possible. The same kind of probing questions were asked.

If, after the picture was removed, S said that he saw nothing, E asked him to describe the picture from memory with as many details as possible. The probing questions described above were asked.

This process was repeated for all four pictures. The average time for testing varied from 10 min. with a young S having no visual imagery to more than 30 min. for an older S with extensive imagery.

At the beginning of the next academic year, 34 Ss were retested using the same procedures and the same pictures and colors. The 34 were selected so as to include most Ss who had earlier produced long-term and accurate images, some Ss with partial images, and a few Ss who never had reported an image to any of the pictures.

SCORING

The tape recordings were encoded onto specially prepared data sheets, which indicated the content of all responses (images and memory). The reliability of this condensation of the data was nearly perfect, since the coding sheets had categories for every object and most of their attributes for each stimulus; the coder rarely had to make any scoring decision. All further scoring was done from these data sheets except the durations of responses, which were taken directly from the tape recordings.

For the results to be reported here, 8 scores were assigned to each S by the first author. His scoring reliability was checked by a second judge who also scored each S on the same 8 indices. In each case, the reliability exceeded $r = +0.81$ for the continuous ratings, and 99% agreement for the dichotomous ratings. Two scores indicated whether or not the images for the squares and the pictures were colored positively. Two scores indicated the durations of the images for the pictures and for the squares. Two scores, on a 5-point scale, indicated the accuracy of the coloring of the images for the pictures and for the memory of the pictures. Finally, two scores, on a 9-point scale, indicated the accuracy of the details of the images for the pictures and the memories for the pictures. The four scores assigned to rating scales were summary ratings made of the completeness of the images and memories.

Results

Eighty-four of the 151 Ss (55%) reported images of at least one of the pictures. As might be expected, a positive relationship between accuracy and duration was found, although the only Ss who had both very high accuracy and duration scores were those who saw images of all four pictures. The 12 most extreme Ss in that group were discontinuous from the remaining 72 Ss on several measures. They were the only Ss who saw four images, all 48 of which lasted over 40 sec., all of which had an accuracy of 6 or greater (the majority were 8 or 9), 90% of which were positively colored (as compared to 34% for the remaining Ss), and 100% of which could be scanned with the eyes (as compared to 2%). Since these latter two scores had been proposed as criteria to distinguish eidetic images from after images, and be-

cause of their far superior accuracy and duration, these 12 Ss seemed to be reporting eidetic images of the pictures, while the remaining 72 Ss seemed to be reporting after images or weak visual images of some other kind. Given this discontinuity on nearly every measure relevant to a definition of eidetic imagery, these 12 Ss appeared to possess an imagery which was qualitatively different from that of all of the other Ss in the sample.

The most striking aspect of the eidetic child's report was the vividness and completeness of an image that was "out there" in front of him. There was no qualification in his speech, such as "I think I see," nor did he ever use the past tense as he might have if he were combining imagery and memory. He was able to report very fine detail, such as the number of feathers worn by each of the 10 Indians in one pretest picture, the different colors in a multi-colored Indian blanket, the expressions on the faces, and the various poses of the persons, and all from the same image. Even if these reports were based on memory, which they did not seem to be, it would be quite unusual. One of the clearest examples of eidetic imagery occurred when E showed the next picture, mistakenly thinking that S had indicated that the image to the previous one had faded. After the second picture had been removed, S described her eidetic image, which was clearly a fusion of the images of the two stimuli. She said that she knew this was happening, but was still seeing it.

In addition to the differences in accuracy and duration between the 12 eidetic Ss and the 72 other Ss who produced some kind of imagery (non-eidetic image), the eidetic Ss also had more positive (i.e., black) images to the two silhouette pictures (92% vs 28%, $t = 6.53$, $p < .001$), and greater accuracy of color in their images of the two remaining pictures than the non-eidetic-image Ss ($t = 4.30$, $p < .001$). For the responses to the colored squares, and for the memory of the pictures, the eidetic Ss were compared with the 72 non-eidetic-image Ss who produced some images to the pictures, and with the other 67 Ss who never reported an image of any of the pictures (no-image Ss). The differences between the eidetic Ss and the other two groups were not quite so striking, but they were still highly significant (all t tests exceeded 3.00, $p < .01$). In no instance did the non-eidetic-image Ss and the no-image Ss differ significantly. The eidetic Ss saw more after images to the colored squares (3.8 as compared with 3.2 and 3.0), more of which were positively colored (43% as compared to 19% and 14%), and which lasted more than twice as long as those of either of the non-eidetic groups (35 sec as compared with 14 and 13 sec). The differences in memory among the three groups were much smaller than expected, although for both the accuracy of detail and of color, the eidetic Ss were significantly superior to both of the other groups (all $ts > 2.10$, $p < .05$).

The eidetic Ss did not differ from the school population in their sex or race. Their ages varied from 8 to 12 yr. Since no children older than these were tested, no indication was available of the upper age limit. No eidetic children were found below the second grade. However, since there were so few eidetic children at all, conclusions regarding their distribution throughout the population must be very cautious. Further, clear evidence of difficulty was found in the younger children (ages 4 through 6 or 7) in understanding what was expected of them and in their communication of what they were seeing and remembering. On the basis of these observations and results in this age range, previous positive results of eidetic imagery in children this young or younger should be viewed with extreme caution.

Nine of the 12 eidetic Ss were retested 8 mo. later, along with 25 other Ss. None of the non-eidetic Ss, based on the original classification, produced any images in the retest to any of the pictures that were as long or as accurate as the poorest image of the eidetic Ss. Of the original 9 who were retested, all but one showed the same type of imagery. While the relationships between original and retest scores for these 9 Ss were generally low, they were all off the distributions on both testing. One S failed to produce any eidetic images on the retest, even though she had an average of nearly 3 min. of imagery originally, with very fine accuracy. E reported that this S seemed extremely anxious on the retest, and was very concerned as to the reason she was being tested again. With this one exception, the retesting further supported the classification of Ss into eidetic and non-eidetic.

Implications

Contrary to a voluminous literature, the prevalence of eidetic imagery in an elementary school in New Haven was quite low—about 8%. However, the 12 Ss who were classified as eidetic were not merely the end of a continuous distribution, but rather were children who showed qualitatively different behavior on this simple perceptual task. Therefore, eidetic imagery does exist as a verifiable, identifiable characteristic in children. This first study has not attempted to explore further how these children were different from the 92% of children without this ability. That is to be followed up.

The most likely explanation of the discrepancy from previously reported frequencies is in terms of the methodological differences in the techniques used to assess the presence of eidetic imagery. This study used very strict criteria and very careful observation of the behavior of Ss' eyes, as well as their verbalizations. Many experiments in the literature classified Ss as eidetic if they produced *any* images of pictures. Following this criterion, 55% of the children would be eidetic in this study. However, it seems apparent that most of these images were after images—they persisted for very short periods of time, they were usually negative in color, they could not be scanned with the eye, and they included very little detail of the stimulus. Therefore, it is assumed that these results represent a closer approximation to the prevalence of eidetic imagery in the general population of children than does the previous literature.

It has not been possible to differentiate after images from other kinds of weak imagery in this study, if in fact they can be differentiated at all. To be able to have done so would have required that the imagery last long enough so that the effects of eye-movements and the accuracy of representation could have been assessed. While neither of these would have been conclusive, it might have been possible to offer a better distinction than we can now.

Evidence has been presented, however, that 55% of the children had some kind of imagery to the pictures, with 8% having eidetic imagery. These 8% could use their imagery to report details of the stimulus, very much as if they had a nearly perfect memory lasting for the duration of the imagery. It was somewhat surprising that their actual memory for the stimulus, after the imagery had faded, was not also strikingly better than that of the non-eidetic Ss. Apparently, the eidetic Ss were not using the time during which the image was present to encode the stimulus for later recall, nor were they taking advantage of their practice in reporting the stimulus from their imagery.

The presence of imagery of this fidelity and duration certainly requires inclusion in any kind of theory or model of the translation of stimulation into memory. Originally, it had been hoped we could carry out extensive experiments with large groups of eidetic Ss, so as to provide data for the construction of such a model. However, because of the small percentage found, this has not been feasible. Therefore, work is proceeding with detailed examination of these 12 Ss. This effort will provide a short-term longitudinal study, in which a number of different aspects of the relationship between perception, imagery, encoding, and memory can be analyzed.

References

AVERBACH, E., and A. S. CORIELL. Short-term memory in vision. *Bell System tech. J.*, 1961, *40*, 1–20.

JAENSCH, E. R. *Die Eidetik.* Leipzig: Quell and Meyer, 1925.

JAENSCH, E. R. *Eidetic imagery and typological methods of investigation.* New York: Harcourt Brace, 1930.

KLUEVER, H. Studies on the eidetic type and eidetic imagery. *Psychol. Bull.*, 1928, *25*, 69–104.

KLUEVER, H. The eidetic child. In C. Murchison (Ed.), *A handbook of child psychology.* Worcester, Mass.: Clark Univer. Press, 1931. pp. 643–668.

KLUEVER, H. Eidetic phenomena. *Psychol. Bull.*, 1932, *29*, 181–203.

SPERLING, G. The information available in brief visual presentations. *Psychol. Monogr.*, 1960, *74*, no. 11 (Whole No. 498).

SPERLING, G. A model for visual memory tasks. *Human Factors*, 1963, *5*, 19–31.

Previous and Concurrent Visual Experience as Determinants of Phenomenal Shape[*]

DOROTHY DINNERSTEIN

Rutgers University, Newark

The experiments to be described here illustrate an alternative to the generally accepted dichotomy between perception and memory, or between the intrinsic structure of the field and the effects of previous experience. When antecedent and concurrent determinants of visual shape are compared, it becomes clear that certain effects of past experience on present experience correspond so closely with effects of concurrent influences as to make unnecessary the use of separate terms in thinking about them. The matter can instead be formulated as follows: A visual area, like any other stimulus-item, is part of more than one functionally relevant larger unit. Phenomenal shape is governed by, and can be altered by change in any one of, a number of larger structures, some spatially and some temporally extended. When—as often happens—the influence of one such larger structure competes with the influence of another, the outcome depends on their relative strength. This is as true when one of the competing structures is temporal and the other spatial as when both are spatial. The differences between temporal and spatial structures, while of the utmost importance and interest, can be adequately conceived of only after this similarity between them has been appreciated.

[*] *American Journal of Psychology*, 1965, vol. 78, pp. 235–242.

Experiment I, The Interaction of Spatial and Temporal Structures in Determining the Shape of a Flat Area

Shown in Figure 1 is Area X, the visual entity whose context is manipulated in this experiment. In Figure 2, the presence of an adjoining area changes Area X from an *el* to a partly hidden member of a pair of squares. An earlier study has shown that while in Figure 2 Area X is described as square by virtually all Ss, in Figure 3 it is *el*-shaped for over half of them.[1] In that study, which dealt with a number of cases of phenemenal overlapping, configurational factors such as similarity, simplicity, and symmetry were stressed. Other writers have pointed to familiarity as an additional factor.[2] Indeed, since such natural forces as gravity and surface-tension guarantee that structurally stable and economical shapes will have been encountered frequently in the past,

[1] Dorothy Dinnerstein and Michael Wertheimer, Some determinants of phenomenal overlapping, *Amer. J. Psychol.*, 1957, 70, 21–37. There it was shown that whether one of two contiguous areas will appear to continue behind the other depends not only on the individual shapes of both these areas, and on the relation between them, but also on the nature of outlying, noncontiguous areas.

[2] Alphonse Chapanis and R. A. McCleary, Interposition as a cue for the perception of relative distance, *J. gen. Psychol.*, 1953, 48, 113–133.

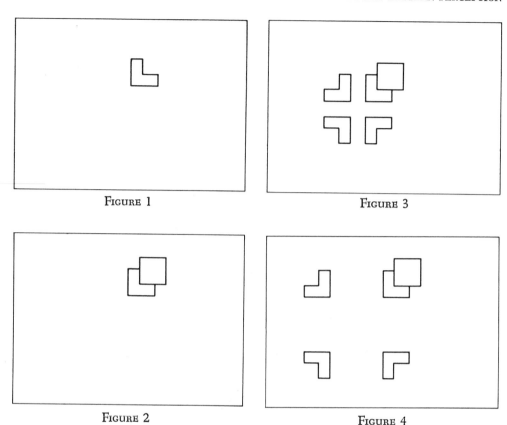

FIGURE 1

FIGURE 3

FIGURE 2

FIGURE 4

prior experience even may be regarded as an *alternative* explanatory principle,[3] with learning perhaps underlying the importance of configurational factors.[4] One can, on the other hand, take the contrary view that it is configurational factors, operating across time, which underlie the interaction between earlier and later experience and make learning possible.[5] Thus, one can think of successive experiences (the interaction among which constitutes learning) as temporally extended groups in some

ways comparable to spatially extended groups such as the square-pair and *el*-constellation of Figure 3. It then becomes possible to study the roles of prior and concurrent experience in parallel terms, by comparing the effects of variations in two of the larger structures of which Area X is part, one spatial and the other temporal.

Experiment IA: Effect of Varying a Spatial Structure. Presumably the reason why Area X looks more like an *el* in Figure 3 than in Figure 2 is that in Figure 3 the dense nearby group of similar areas can be seen as a symmetrical constellation only if Area X is *el*-shaped. If this is true—that is, if the change from Figure 2 to Figure 3 does reflect competition between two structures and not, say, the mere presence of additional visual items—then weakening one of these structures should increase the influence of the other. For this

[3] C. B. Zuckerman and Irvin Rock, A reappraisal of the roles of past experience and innate organizing processes in visual perception, *Psychol. Bull.*, 1957,54, 269–296. Irvin Rock, The present status of Gestalt psychology, in J. G. Peatman, and E. L. Hartley (eds.), *Festschrift for Gardner Murphy*, 1960, pp. 127–128.

[4] J. J. Gibson, *The Perception of the Visual World*, 1950, pp. 142–143.

[5] Wolfgang Köhler, *Gestalt Psychology*, 1947, Chs. 8, 9, e.g., 277–278, 318.

first experiment, the *el*-constellation was weakened—see Figure 4—by moving its members further apart.[6]

As in all the experiments to be described, black line-drawings on 8 × 11-in. white cards were displayed to classroom groups of students in undergraduate psychology. In the present case, Figures 2, 3, and 4 were shown to three separate groups of Brooklyn College Ss, preceded in each case by a neutral series (Series N, consisting of Figures 5, 6, and 7), whose function becomes clear below. Each group saw, in succession, the three members of Series N, followed by *one* of the other figures. Each figure was displayed for 10–12 sec, after which the Ss replied in writing (the reply took 60–90 sec) to the request "Describe briefly what this is. State what surfaces, if any, appear to go behind other surfaces." The next drawing then was shown.

RESULTS

Descriptions of the Series-N figures were examined only to confirm that these drawings were, as expected, seen in a generally uniform way by all the Ss. The first three rows of Table I show how Area X was characterized.[7] In Figure 2, X was described as one of a pair of squares ("two overlapping squares," "two squares, one covering the other in part") by nearly all the Ss. In Figure 3, it was so described by less than one-third of the Ss ($P < 0.001$),[8] while more than half described it

---

[6] Another experiment, not reported here, gave the same results when the symmetry of the constellation, rather than its density, was reduced.

[7] As the quoted protocols indicate, such categorization generally was a fairly simple matter. Subsequent tests showed inter-judge disagreement in fewer than 5% of cases.

[8] The P-values quoted in this paper are based on Fisher's exact test of the raw frequencies of the two main types of description. They were calculated with the coöperation of Professor F. Lehman, of the Newark College of Engineering, on an IBM-computer already programmed, in connection with another project, to perform this operation.

SERIES N

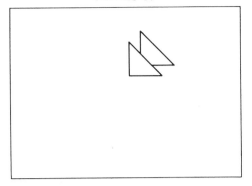

FIGURE 5

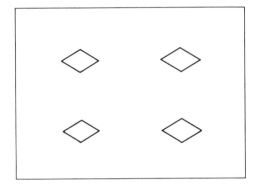

FIGURE 6

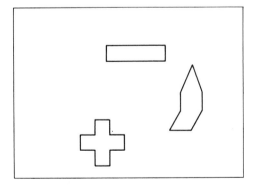

FIGURE 7

as one of a set of *els* ("four L-shaped figures with one square next to one of the L-figures," "four L-shaped figures in box-formation with the upper-right L partly covered by a square").[9] In Figure 4, however, Area X again was described as a square ("three Ls," and "one square overlapping another square") by most Ss; it appeared as an *el* less than one quarter as often as in Figure 3 ($P < 0.001$).

Experiment IB: Effect of Varying a Temporal Structure. Could the ineffectual constellation-quality of the *el*s of Figure 4 now be supported by embedding them in turn in some strong larger group of constellations, just as the ineffectual *el*-quality of Area X in Figure 2 was supported by embedding it in the strong constellation of *el*s in Figure 3? If structures across time do have functional resemblances to those in space, it should be possible to accomplish this with a temporally extended group of constellations.

In Experiment IA, one of the local *spatial* structures embracing Area X was altered, while the immediate temporal context was kept constant. In the present experiment, a local *temporal* structure—the pre-series—was altered, while the spatial context was kept constant. A new group was shown Figure 4 preceded by Series *El*, which consisted of Figures 5, 8, and 9.[10]

RESULTS

As the last two rows of Table 1 show, membership in a series of *el*-constellations (*El*) instead of in a neutral series (*N*) dramatically strengthens the effect of Figure 4's weak *el*-constellation. It triples the percentage of Ss describing Area X

---

[9] These results replicate those of Dinnerstein and Wertheimer (*op. cit.*, 26–27). As before, seeing Area X as *el*-shaped apparently did not preclude seeing it continue behind its neighbor. This fact is interesting in connection with the problem of phenomenal overlapping *per se*.

[10] Note that the first member of Series *El* was the same as in Series *N*. It was intended to fulfill the expectation, created by the instructions, that some overlapping areas would appear, leaving S freer afterward to describe Area X either as *el*-shaped or as square.

SERIES *El*

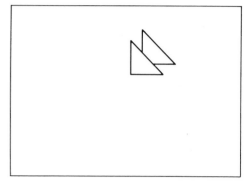

FIGURE 5

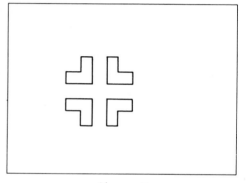

FIGURE 8

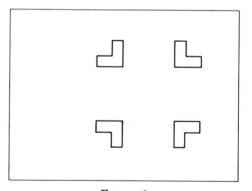

FIGURE 9

as an *el*, and halves the percentage describing it as a square ($P = 0.002$). Table 1, then, makes the broad point that certain effects of earlier on later experiences correspond functionally with effects of concurrent experiences on each other. A

TABLE 1

Effects of Spatial and Temporal Context: Experiments IA and IB

PRECEDING SERIES	DRAWING DESCRIBED	N	PERCENTAGE OF SS DESCRIBING AREA X AS		
			SQUARE	EL	AMBIGUOUS
N	2	23	96	4	0
N	3	32	28	53	19
N	4	56	79	12	9
EL	4	31	42	42	16

temporal structure (Series *El*) like a spatial one (Figure 3's *el*-constellation) can, if it is strong enough in relevant respects, fortify one of its members against the requirements of a competing structure.

Experiment II.: The Interaction of Spatial and Temporal Structures in Determining Depth in an Ambiguous Figure

It should be noted that of the two structures compared in the preceding experiment, one (the drawing) was a sub-unit of the other (the series). Thus, the two differed not only as to spatial vs temporal extension but also as to content and internal organization. In the experiment now to be described, the spatial and temporal structures compared were identical in content: as a result, a special characteristic of temporal effects *per se* could be considered.

The same pattern in two different positions is shown in Figures 10 and 11. Earlier work has established that virtually all Ss describe Figure 11 as a cube, while most describe Figure 10 as a flat hexagonal line-pattern.[11] Is this effect of the orientation of the drawing due to (a) forces of visual organization *per se*, which determine whether a two- or a three-dimensional organization of the figure will place it in a more stable relation to the larger spatial structure provided by the

[11] Dinnerstein and Wertheimer, *op. cit.*, 30.

edges of the card and the main horizontal-vertical dimensions of the visual field? or is it due to (b) the greater empirical frequency with which rectangular solids in S's past have appeared as resting flat rather than standing on their edges? Stated thus, the question, like the question of the role of familiarity in overlapping, is insoluble. The present study was conceived in the

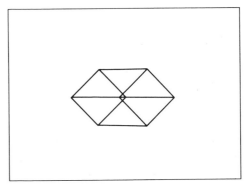

FIGURE 10

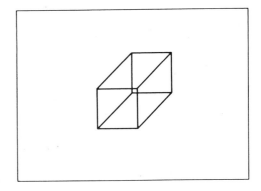

FIGURE 11

view that (a) and (b) do not differ enough to be regarded as true alternatives: the experiential structures in which Figures 10 and 11 appear can be so varied as to make it clear not only that past experience does indeed influence the phenomenal depth of each of these figures, but also that this influence may closely resemble that of corresponding concurrent experience.

Experiment IIA: Effect of Varying Spatial Context.   For the current purpose, the unequivocally cubic Figure 11 needed to be replaced with a slightly weaker version of itself which would be described as flat by a minority of Ss roughly as large as the minority describing Figure 10 as cubic. In an exploratory study, Figure 12 was selected to meet this requirement.[12]

Three separate groups of students at Rutgers University were presented, respectively, either with Figure 10 alone, with Figure 12 alone, or with the two figures side-by-side.[13] In the third condition, position-effects were controlled by placing each figure to the left for half of the Ss and to the right for the other half and, since no significant differences appeared, the results for the two subgroups were combined. Exposure- and writing-times were 10 and 90 sec, respectively, when a figure appeared alone; 15 and 150 sec when the two appeared together. The instructions were to "Describe briefly what

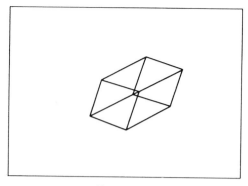

FIGURE 12

this is." Those Ss who saw both figures together were asked to describe them on two opposite pages of a booklet in order that the descriptions could be scored independently. Protocols were classified in terms of the presence or absence of depth.

RESULTS

The middle row of Table 2 shows that Figure 10, viewed alone, was described as flat ("a hexagon with lines coming together at center to form a diamond," "a group of triangles that combine to form a six-sided figure," "stop-sign divided into sections") rather than cubical ("rectangle showed in perspective on a white background," "rectangular box—three dimensional picture") by more than a 3 : 1 ratio, while Figure 12 yielded the opposite results ($P < 0.001$). The importance for depth of the spatial relation of a figure to the main axes of the visual surround thus is confirmed. The influence of these main axes may, however, be counteracted by that of a conflicting spatial structure. As the top row of Table 2 shows, Figure 12, predominantly cubical alone, is described as flat by half of the Ss when accompanied by Figure 10 ($P = 0.010$). Thus, membership in the pair, whose influence is opposed to that of the spatial framework, proves an effective competing determinant. The predominantly flat Figure 10, it should be noted, yields only insignificantly to the presence of Figure 12, an asymmetry of

[12] The writer is indebted to Anthony Fazio, James DeChesare, and Robert Schoen, who made drawings, served as Es, and scored protocols, both for the exploratory study and for an early version of the Experiment IIA. These preliminary studies revealed effects on phenomenal depth not only of the drawing's position, but also of its size relative to line-thickness and perhaps also to the size of the background-card.

[13] Each experimental group consisted of two small classroom-groups whose data are combined to give the totals of Table 2. Differences between the separate groups in no case approached significance.

influence that will be referred to again below.

The main result to be noted here is that descriptions of Figure 12 can be affected drastically by the presence (concurrent) of Figure 10. Experiment IIB will show that a corresponding, though not identical, effect occurs when the pair-structure competing with the influence of the main axes of the visual field is temporally rather than spatially extended.

Experiment IIB: Effect of Varying Temporal Context. The two groups of Ss who had, for the purposes of Experiment IIA, seen and described Figure 10 or Figure 12 alone immediately afterward were shown and asked to describe the other figure; the interval between the two figures was the 90-sec period allowed for describing the first. The Ss turned to a new page in their answer-booklets before seeing and describing the second figure.

RESULTS

The bottom two rows of Table 2 show for each of these figures the influence of previous experience of the other. Figure 12, prevailingly cubical in isolation, was described as flat by more than half the Ss for whom it followed Figure 10 ($P <$ 0.001). Thus, the previous experience of Figure 10 seems to have had about the same effect as its concurrent presence. In turn, Figure 10, prevailingly flat in isolation, was described as cubical by more than half the Ss for whom it followed Figure 12 ($P < 0.001$). Thus, Figure 12, which exerted an insignificant influence across space, proved more effective across time.[14] This finding points to an important peculiarity of temporally extended structures; namely, that later sub-units, upon arrival, interact with earlier ones as current percepts with memory-traces. Under circumstances which now require experimental definition, an item (such as Figure 12) may be more resistant to reorganiza-

tion by neighboring items, and more prone to impose its organization on them instead, when it is present only as a trace than when it is visible.[15] Note, however, that such explorations of the differences between spatial and temporal structures become conceptually possible only after their similarity has been appreciated.

Summary

Two studies of phenomenal shape show that interaction between a spatial and a temporal structure can closely resemble

[14] In a pilot version of this experiment, with the drawings larger in relation to card-size and to line-thickness, it was Figure 10 (alone usually flat) which proved more labile (i.e., became usually cubic) when the two figures appeared together, and which proved more influential across time (coming first) than across space (coming concurrently). It is not at all clear why line-thickness, etc. should effect the relative lability of these two figures, nor does the question seem relevant for the concerns of this study. What does seem clear is that with the present procedure the more labile of two figures, flat or cubical, profits more by temporal priority. The limits of the conditions under which this holds true remain to be explored.

[15] Ongoing explorations of this feature of temporal structures have involved two procedures the results of which have some methodological relevance to the data reported above. The question can be asked whether, when successive figures are presented and each described before the next is shown, results indicating influence of an earlier on a later part of the sequence reflect the effect of one visual unit on another or merely the effect of the writing of one description on the writing of the next. When Experiment IIB is repeated, with Ss being asked to describe only the second of the two figures they have seen, the results are substantially the same as those of Table II, making it clear that the reported effect does not depend on the writing of descriptions of the earlier figure. Another question is whether an account in words perhaps reflects some purely verbal emphasis on a fleeting aspect of a complex visual percept rather than an expression of its stable and central character. When Ss are asked to provide reproductions instead of descriptions, the original findings again are confirmed. Drawings of Figure 12 which are two-dimensional and bilaterally symmetrical occur significantly more often, and three-dimensional drawings lacking bilateral symmetry occur significantly less often, when this figure has been preceded by Figure 10 than when it has not been so preceded.

TABLE 2

Effects of Spatial and Temporal Context: Experiments IIA and IIB

CONDITION	PERCENTAGE OF SS DESCRIBING FIGURE 10 AS				PERCENTAGE OF SS DESCRIBING FIGURE 12 AS			
	N	FLAT	CUBICAL	BOTH	N	FLAT	CUBICAL	BOTH*
Simultaneous	44	64	25	11	44	48	43	9
Alone	43	79	21	0	47	26	72	2
Successive	47	38	53	9	43	58	40	2

* Since protocols describing alternative organizations of the figure were more common than in Experiment I, their frequency is noted.

interaction between two spatial structures. In the light of this resemblance, unique characteristics of temporal organizations invite examination. The main point to be made is that certain phenomena usually conceived of as effects of past experience on perception are subject to the same principles which govern perception itself.

Distortion of Visual Space as Inappropriate Constancy Scaling*

RICHARD L. GREGORY
Cambridge University

Distortions of visual space associated with certain simple patterns have been investigated since the beginning of experimental psychology (1), and many theories have been proposed (2) but so far none, in my opinion, has been satisfactory in explaining these so-called "geometrical" illusions. Figures 1, 2 and 3 show representative illusions of the kind we are considering.

The traditional theories fall into three

* Nature, 1963, vol. 199, pp. 678–680. This work was supported by the U.S. Air Force under Grant No. AF-EOAR 63–93 and monitored by the European Office, Office of Aerospace Research and also by the Medical Research Council.

classes: (A) That certain shapes produce, or tend to produce, abnormal eye movements. (B) That some kind of central "confusion" is produced by certain shapes, particularly non-parallel lines and corners. (C) That the figures suggest depth by perspective, and that this "suggestion" in some way distorts visual space.

The eye movement theories are difficult to support because the illusions occur undiminished when the retinal image is optically stabilized on the retina (3) or when the figures are viewed as after-images following illumination by a bright flash of light. Further, since distortions can occur

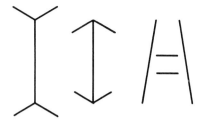

FIGURE 1   (a) The Müller-Lyer; (b) The Ponzo illusion

in opposed directions at the same time (as with the Müller–Lyer figure (4) (Figure 1a) it is difficult to see how either overt or incipient eye movements could be involved. The various "confusion" theories all suffer from vagueness, and they give us no idea as to why the distortions should occur in the observed directions, or only in certain kinds of figures. The perspective theory (2) is inadequate because it does not suggest why or how perspective should

produce distortions in flat figures, but it does imply a generalization which seems to hold true of all the known illusion figures, and this gives a clue vital to understanding the origin of the illusions.

The illusion figures may be thought of as flat projections of typical views of objects lying in three-dimensional space. For example, the outward-going Müller–Lyer arrow figure is a typical projection of, say, the corner of a room—the fins representing

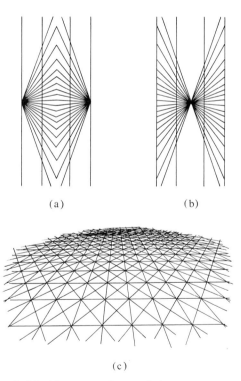

FIGURE 2   (a) and (b) Alternative forms of the Hering illusion. The vertical lines are bowed inwards and outwards, respectively. (c) An illusion showing how parallel lines indicating distance seem to diverge when presented on a texture gradient. (The texture taken from Gibson, *The Perception of the Visual World,* 1951.)

the intersections of the walls with the ceiling and floor—while the in-going arrow is a typical projection of an outside corner of a house or a box, the converging lines receding into the distance. The following generalization seems to hold for all the illusion figures thought of in this way: The parts of the figures corresponding to distant objects are expanded and the parts corresponding to nearer objects are reduced. Thus in the Müller–Lyer figure the vertical line would be further away in the diverging case, and is expanded in the illusion, and vice versa, while in the Ponzo figure the upper horizontal line would be farther away and it also is expanded in the flat illusion figure.

Given that this generalization holds for all the illusions, why should these distortions occur?

Do we know of any other perceptual phenomena involving systematic perceptual modification of the retinal image? There is a well-known set of phenomena which certainly does involve perceptual modification of retinal images—size constancy (5) (6). This is the tendency for objects to appear much the same size over a wide range of distance in spite of the changes of the retinal images associated with distance of the object. We may refer to the processes involved as constancy scaling. Now in constancy scaling we find known processes which not only could but also must produce distortion of visual space if the scaling were set inappropriately to the distance of

an observed object. It is strange that apparently only one writer, Tausch, has considered constancy in connection with the geometrical illusion (7).

We can see our own scaling system at work in the following demonstration of Emmert's law (8). The after-image of a bright light is "projected" on to a series of screens lying at various distances, or a single screen moved away or towards the observer. Although the effective retinal image is constant, the after-image perceived as lying on a screen looks larger the farther the screen is from the observer. Complete constancy would give a doubling in size for each doubling of distance, and the amount of scaling can be quantified under various conditions for stationary or moving screens (9) (10).

Clearly inappropriate constancy scaling would produce distortion of visual space, but why should this occur with the illusion figures which are in fact flat and are generally seen to be flat? It is generally assumed that constancy scaling depends simply on apparent distance (as Emmert's law might suggest); but if we are to suppose that constancy scaling can operate for figures clearly lying on a flat surface we must challenge this assumption, and suggest that visual features associated with distance can modify constancy scaling even when no depth is seen. If we are to suppose that the illusions are due to misplaced constancy scaling, we must suppose that the scaling can be set directly by depth

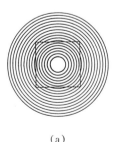 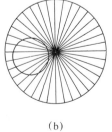

(a)   (b)

FIGURE 3   Further distortions to be expected on the distance hypothesis; the concentric circles and spokes set the constancy scaling by indicating depth. (Figures, though not interpretation, from Orbison, *American Journal of Psychology,* 1939, vol. 52, p. 39.)

features of flat figures, and that the scaling is not set simply as a function of apparent distance as is generally thought to be the case.

Perspective drawings and photographs are seen to depict objects as if they lay in three dimensions, and yet at the same time they appear flat, lying on the plane of the paper, and so they are perceptually paradoxical. The surface texture of the paper evidently prevents the perspective from making the objects appear truly three dimensional, for if we remove all texture and view with one eye, then perspective drawings can look as impressively in depth as the real world viewed with one eye.

We have presented the well-known illusion figures with no background texture —by making wire models coated in luminous paint so that they glow in the dark, or using back illuminated transparencies— and we find that, viewed with one eye, they look three dimensional, provided the angles are not marked exaggerations of perspective. The Müller–Lyer arrows, for example, look like corners and not like flat projections when presented as luminous figures in the dark, and those parts which appear most distant are the parts which are expanded in the illusions as normally presented on textured paper. What happens to the distortions when we remove the background texture is complex, and will be discussed more fully elsewhere; but, in general, distortions are reduced or disappear.

Emmert's law may suggest that constancy scaling arises directly from apparent distance; but there is retinal information indicating the distance of each position of the screen, and possibly this might serve directly to set the scaling. However, the following demonstration shows conclusively that scaling can occur simply as a function of apparent depth and independently of retinal or other sensory information.

Figure 4a shows the well-known Necker cube figure—a skeleton cube which reverses spontaneously in depth so that sometimes one face, sometimes another, appears the nearer. As shown on textured paper, it is paradoxical in the manner described here —it looks as if it were in depth and yet it is seen to be flat on the paper. By making a luminous model of this figure, and viewing it in the dark, we find that it still reverses but now it looks like a true three-dimensional figure, and it undergoes size changes—the apparently farther face looking somewhat larger than the nearer, showing that constancy scaling is now operating. Since the retinal image remains unchanged it follows that the scaling is set under these conditions as a simple function of apparent distance. This is shown most dramatically with a three-dimensional luminous cube. This looks like a true cube when seen correctly, but when perceptually reversed in depth it looks like a truncated pyramid, the apparently front face being the smaller (11).

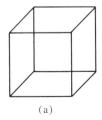 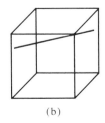

(a) (b)

FIGURE 4   (a) The Necker cube. This reverses in depth. When viewed as a self-luminous figure, the apparent front looks smaller, the back larger. (b) Humphrey's figure. The oblique line is seen as slightly bent; the direction of bending being determined by the angle against which it is placed, and not by the way the cube appears to lie in depth.

It thus appears that there are two ways in which constancy scaling can be set. We may name these:

(1) *Primary constancy scaling.* This is set by perspective or other features normally associated with distance. These features can be at variance with apparent distance in special cases, such as the illusion figures. (We call it "primary" because it seems to be primitive, and to be mediated by neural systems situated early in the perceptual system.)

(2) *Secondary constancy scaling* is set simply by apparent distance, and this may be a function of previous knowledge and is not necessarily tied directly to visual information. Its existence is suggested but not proved by Emmert's law; but it is conclusively demonstrated with the ambiguous self-luminous objects which change their shape systematically according to which faces appear nearer or farther though there is no change in the retinal image. Errors in apparent distance should produce distortion of visual space via this secondary scaling system and the well-known moon illusion may be an example.

Although the self-luminous figures do clearly demonstrate what we have called the secondary constancy scaling system, what clear evidence have we for the primary system, supposed to be set by typical depth cues even in the absence of depth perception. For our present purpose it is much more important to demonstrate the existence of primary than secondary scaling. To get evidence for primary scaling entirely independent of the illusions is very difficult, but the following is at least suggestive.

(1) It has been noticed by Humphrey (12) that a straight line drawn across a corner of a Necker cube (Figure 4b) appears bent. Now this is particularly interesting because the direction of bending is the same which ever way the cube appears to lie in depth. It is bent in the direction to be expected if constancy scaling is operating from the typical perspective interpretation of the angle against which the line lies.

(2) In primitive races living in houses without corners the geometrical illusions are reduced (13) (14). If learning is important, this would be expected.

(3) In a case of a man blind from the first few months of life, but gaining his sight after operation fifty years later, we have found that the illusions were largely absent, and his constancy appeared abnormal or absent although he could at that time, some weeks after the corneal graft operation, recognize common objects (15). This has been noted in other cases. (In fact, it was this observation which suggested to me this kind of theory of the illusions.)

We should expect the different scaling systems to have somewhat different time-constants, and we are attempting to measure these to establish their separate existence quite apart from considerations of distortions of visual space.

It further may be suggested that figural after-effect—distortions similar to the geometrical illusions, but produced as a result of prolonged viewing of a suitable stimulus pattern and transferring to a second test pattern—may be due to the primary scaling being set by depth features present in the stimulus pattern, this scaling taking some time after lengthy fixation to become appropriate to the second test pattern, so the second pattern is distorted by scaling carried over from the earlier pattern. Preliminary experiments are providing strong evidence that figural aftereffects can be thought of in this way, and such a theory would have advantages over present theories of the figural after-effects which are ad hoc, involve dubious physiological speculation and fail to make useful predictions (16) (17).

In attempting to give a general account of all illusions involving systematic distortions of visual space, either while viewing a figure or following on prolonged viewing and relating the distortions to a known perceptual phenomenon—size constancy—we have not attempted to specify the neural processes involved, and we believe this to be impossible at this time. Recent work on recording from the visual regions of the cat's brain while presenting the eyes with moving or fixed patterns (18) gives promise that the underlying neural mechanisms may soon be revealed.

References

1. BORING, E. G., *Sensation and Perception in the History of Experimental Psychology* (New York, 1942).
2. WOODWORTH, R. S., *Experimental Psychology* (Holt, New York, 1938).
3. PRITCHARD, R. M., *Quart. J. Exp. Psychol.*, 10, 2, 77 (1958).
4. MÜLLER-LYER, F. C., *Z. Psychol.*, 9, 1; 10, 421 (1896).
5. THOULESS, R. H., *Brit. J. Psychol.*, 21, 339 (1931); 22, 1 (1931); 22, 216 (1932).
6. VERNON, M. D., *A Further Study of Visual Perception* (Camb. Univ. Press, 1954).
7. TAUSCH, R., *Psychologische Forschung*, 24, 299 (1954).
8. EMMERT, E., *Klin. Mbl. Augenheilk.*, 19, 443 (1881).
9. GREGORY, R. L., J. G. WALLACE, and F. W. CAMPBELL, *Quart. J. Exp. Psychol.*, 11, 1, 54 (1959).
10. ANSTIS, S. M., C. D. SHOPLAND, and R. L. GREGORY, *Nature*, 191, 416 (1961).
11. SHOPLAND, C. D., and R. L. GREGORY, *Quart. J. Exp. Psychol.* (in press).
12. HUMPHREY, G. (personal communication).
13. SEGALL, M. H., and D. T. CAMPBELL, *Cultural Differences in the Perception of Geometric Illusions* (unpublished monograph, State Univ. of Iowa and Northwestern Univ., 1962).
14. SEGALL, M. H., D. T. CAMPBELL, and M. J. HERSKOVITZ, *Science*, 139, 769 (1963).
15. GREGORY, R. L., and J. G. WALLACE, *Recovery from Early Blindness. Exp. Psychol. Soc. Mon.* 2 (Heffer, Cambridge, 1963).
16. KOHLER, W., and H. WALLACH, *Proc. Amer. Phil. Soc.*, 88, 269 (1944).
17. OSGOOD, C. E., and A. W. HEYER, *Psychol. Rev.*, 59, 98 (1951).
18. HUBEL, D. H., and T. N. WIESEL, *J. Physiol.*, 160, 106 (1962).

Binocular and Stereoscopic Viewing of Geometric Illusions*

PETER SCHILLER

Massachusetts Institute of Technology

MORTON WIENER

Clark University

In two recent experiments Ohwaki (1960) and Springbett (1961), extending the earlier work of Witasek (1899) and Lau (1922, 1925), showed that the illusory effect of geometric illusions is greatly reduced when they are shown stereoscopically, with the "test" element of the illusion shown to one eye and the "inducing" element shown to the other. Both Ohwaki and Springbett conclude from the results of their experiments that illusory effects can be attributed primarily to retinal rather than central processes.

Boring (1961) and Day (1961) question the conclusions drawn by Ohwaki and Springbett. Boring notes that when two disparate stimuli are shown, one to each eye, resolution of such disparity often results in depth perception. It is likely that reduction of illusory effects under stereoscopic viewing can be attributed to the resolutions in depth rather than to retinal processes.

Day considers an additional factor. He notes that binocular rivalry occurs when certain illusions are presented stereoscopically. In his study, repeating and extending Ohwaki's, Day found that the reduction of illusions under stereoscopic conditions can be attributed to both binocular rivalry and depth perception of the stimuli. However, since these two factors only reduce but generally do not eliminate the illusory effect, it is reasonable to assume that central processes must be operative in the perception of illusions. Day concluded that the interpretations of Ohwaki and Springbett regarding the retinal origin of geometric illusions thus seem unjustified.

In light of the available evidence and reasoning, the relative contributions of retinal and central processes can more directly be evaluated by two means: (1) the elimination or reduction of retinal rivalry and depth effects, and (2) a psychophysical measurement of the magnitude of the illusions. As long as rivalry and depth effects are present in stereoscopic presentation of illusions, there is a confounding of variables, i.e., possible retinal processes in the illusory effect are confounded with binocular rivalry and depth effects. Furthermore, unless psychophysical methods are used, a precise evaluation of the magnitude of illusory effects is not possible.

If a viewing situation could be established which would minimize binocular rivalry and depth effects under stereoscopic presentation, a better evaluation could be made of the processes underly-

* *Perceptual and Motor Skills*, 1962, vol. 15, pp. 739–747. Copyright © 1962 Southern Universities Press. This research is part of a research program supported by U.S.P.H.S. Grant M–3860 awarded to the second author. The authors are indebted to Drs. Hans-Lukas Teuber, Joachim Wohlwill, and Joseph McFarland for their helpful suggestions.

ing illusions. If under such viewing conditions the magnitude of the illusions approached that of binocular viewing, it would be reasonable to assume that central processes are of prime importance in the perception of illusions. If, on the other hand, under such viewing conditions the magnitude of the illusions does not increase beyond that reported by Day, Ohwaki, or Springbett, the hypothesis that retinal processes are critical in the perception of illusions would become tenable.

A viewing situation which approximates the required conditions is one in which stimuli are presented stereoscopically for very short durations, allowing for only one fixation. Pilot studies carried out by these investigators showed that binocular rivalry and depth effects under such conditions of single fixation are markedly reduced when disparate stimuli are presented stereoscopically.

Reduction of binocular rivalry under short exposure conditions involves two considerations. First of all, binocular rivalry of figures generally occurs only when the stereoscopically presented disparate stimuli overlap, or are in close proximity. When the stimuli presented are *not* in close proximity (as the test and inducing elements of the Ebbinghaus illusions), little rivalry occurs, unless, as the eyes resolve the images, the test and inducing elements begin to overlap. Under short exposure conditions, such "swimming" of the stimuli is minimized; the figures remain fixed in position and little, if any, retinal rivalry occurs. Secondly, our pilot studies showed that there is a reduction in binocular rivalry even for overlapping stimuli under short exposure conditions. Stereoscopic presentation, of even such stimuli as an overlapping circle and rectangle, results in little rivalry under short exposure conditions, in contrast to the much greater degree of rivalry under long exposure conditions.[1]

[1] Further research is now investigating this parameter.

The aim of this experiment was (1) to employ stereoscopic viewing conditions which minimize depth effects and binocular rivalry, (2) to employ the psychophysical measure of constant stimuli to assess the magnitude of the illusory effects, and (3) to select illusions which vary in the degree of overlap of inducing and test elements to control for the possibility that decrease in the illusory effect is some function of the probable degree of binocular rivalry.

Method

SUBJECTS

Five paid volunteer Ss were selected on the basis of equal visual acuity for both eyes.

APPARATUS

A stereoscopic tachistoscope was employed (see Figure 1) in which stimuli could be exposed both binocularly and stereoscopically. The illusions were presented in this apparatus for all conditions. The tachistoscope was driven by an electronic timing unit (Scientific Prototype Mfg. Co., modified Model 1 B).

MATERIAL

Five illusions were tested (see Figure 2). For each illusion two sets were drawn,

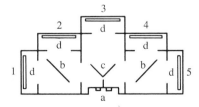

FIGURE 1 Viewing apparatus. Top view of stereoscopic viewer, showing the five fields: (a) eyepiece; (b) two-way mirrors with 50 percent transmitting and 50 percent reflecting characteristics; (c) two-way mirrors with 33 percent transmitting and 67 percent reflecting characteristics; (d) Scientific Prototype tachistoscopic tubes, two per field.

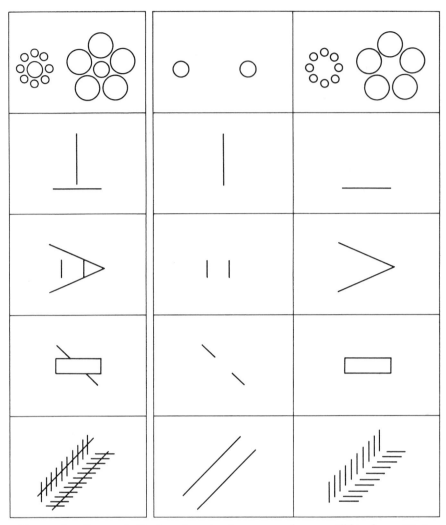

FIGURE 2   Geometric illusions in order from top to bottom: Ebbinghaus, Horizontal-Vertical, Ponzo, Poggendorff, Modified Zoellner. The left column shows binocular viewing and the right columns, stereoscopic viewing. Test stimuli are on the left, and inducing stimuli, on the right.

one for binocular presentation and one for stereoscopic presentation. The stereoscopic sets had the test and inducing elements drawn on separate cards. For each illusion seven test cards (or pairs of cards for the stereoscopic conditions) were made. The test figures varied in seven steps for each of the illusions as follows: (1) *Ebbinghaus Illusion*—The size of the test circle was varied from 8 mm to 14 mm in diameter in 1-mm steps. The standard circle was 13 mm. The distance from the inner tangent of the inducing circles to the outer tangent of the test circle was constant for all seven comparison figures. (2) *Horizontal-Vertical Illusion*—The length of the vertical line was varied from 25 to 43 mm in 3-mm steps. The horizontal standard line was 40 mm. (3) *Poggendorff Illusion* —The relation of the two diagonal lines was displaced from a true diagonal over a range of 9 mm in 1.5-mm steps. (4) *Ponzo Illusion*—The length of the left line varied from 9 to 18 mm in 1.5-mm steps. The standard line was 12 mm. (5) *Modified Zoellner Illusion*—The parallel lines were displaced from each other in 2° steps from a true parallel. The length of the lines was 90 mm. The angular relationship of the cross hatches to the parallel lines was held constant.

The size of the figures and the magnitude of the steps between the test stimuli were determined on the basis of a pilot investigation.

DESIGN

Each S was tested under five conditions, two of which were binocular and three stereoscopic.

The two binocular presentations were: (1) "long exposure" (each stimulus card was exposed for a period of 1.5 sec for each judgment) and (2) "short exposure" (each stimulus was exposed for .11 sec). Two successive exposures were made for each judgment, with approximately a 1-sec interval between the two presentations.

The three stereoscopic presentations were: (1) "long exposure" (stimuli were exposed for 1.5 sec as in the binocular viewing condition), (2) "short exposure" (stimuli were exposed twice for .11 sec as in the binocular condition), (3) "short-successive exposure" (the test and inducing elements were presented in rapid succession, each for .055 sec duration). For each judgment, two presentations of this successive exposure of test and inducing elements were made. The inducing element was always presented first. In a pilot investigation, this order of presentation was shown to have minimal masking effects. In a successive presentation condition, that is, where the inducing and testing elements are not present simultaneously, it was expected that there would be a further reduction of rivalry effects.[2]

---

[2] This condition is somewhat similar to procedures used in investigating figural after-effects. Typically the figural after-effect is opposite to that of the illusion effect. However, because of the very brief durations and the relatively low intensities of illumination little if any figural after-effect would be expected.

PROCEDURE

There were 10 testing sessions for each S. During each session five responses were obtained for each of the 35 stimuli. There were two testing sessions for each of the viewing conditions making a total of 10 exposures per S for each stimulus. The presentation order of the viewing conditions was balanced among Ss.

A method of paired comparisons was used. For each stimulus presented Ss had to make one of two choices as follows: (1) Ebbinghaus Illusion: to state whether the left test circle appeared smaller or larger than the right test circle (see Figure 2), (2) Horizontal-Vertical Illusion: to state whether the vertical line appeared longer or shorter than the horizontal line, (3) Poggendorff Illusion: to state whether the top half of the diagonal line appeared to the left or to the right of the true diagonal, (4) Ponzo Illusion: to state whether the left line appeared shorter or longer than the right line, (5) Modified Zoellner Illusion: to state whether the parallel lines appeared to be converging or diverging at the right top corner.

For each illusion the test cards were presented in a random order. Prior to presenting the stimuli Ss were asked to keep their eyes on a little red cross which was placed in the center of the blank field. Ss were instructed to make their choices solely on the basis of their perceptual experience. Throughout, an attempt was made to keep Ss naive about the conditions of presentation. Ss were also told that they might, at times, have difficulty in seeing the stimuli or parts of them. They were asked to report when these changes occurred as well as to report when the stimulus or part of the stimulus appeared to move.

Results

S was given a score of 1 for each trial on which he reported the illusory effect for the particular stimulus pattern. Inspection of the data showed no significant Ss by conditions interaction. Therefore, the combined data for all five Ss were analyzed. These data are shown in Table 1.

For each of the illusions, italicized figures in the table represent the point at which the test stimuli were objectively equal. A score of 50 in Table 1 indicates that all Ss reported the presence of the illusory effect for that given test figure. Thus, each entry reports the over-all number of times Ss reported seeing the illusion.

The results for the Ebbinghaus circles show that the illusion is seen under all viewing conditions when the sizes of the two test stimuli are identical. As the sizes of the test stimuli diverge, the illusory effects decrease, but the differences between binocular and stereoscopic presentation conditions are minimal. The illusory effect is greater for the short exposure than for the long exposure under both the binocular and stereoscopic viewing conditions. The smallest effect appears with the stereoscopic long exposure.

Almost no change over viewing conditions is found for the Horizontal-Vertical lines. Again, however, the illusory effect is the smallest with the stereoscopic long exposure.

The results with the Poggendorff figure show only a slight reduction in the illusory effect under short stereoscopic presentation. In contrast, the illusory effect is markedly reduced with both stereoscopic successive and stereoscopic long exposure viewing. Again, stereoscopic long exposure viewing shows the greatest reduction in the illusory effects. The illusion is seen most of the time under all viewing conditions when the test stimuli are equivalent.

For the Ponzo figure there is a reduction in the illusory effect under stereoscopic conditions, with the stereoscopic long exposure showing the greatest reduction. Although the over-all illusory effect decreases with stereoscopic presentation, when the test figures are equal in size, only a minimal decrease in the illusory effect occurs.

The greatest reduction in the illusory effect under stereoscopic presentation conditions occurs for the Modified Zoellner figure. The illusory effect is reduced even when the test stimuli are parallel to each other. This is the only figure which shows such reduction in the illusory effect under stereoscopic viewing when the test stimuli are equivalent to each other.

Ss' verbal reports indicated that binocular rivalry and depth effects played a greater role under stereoscopic long viewing conditions than under other conditions. These reports of binocular rivalry and depth effects were most marked for the Modified Zoellner figure.

Discussion

The findings of this study are consistent with the views of Day and Boring. The results suggest that illusory effects can be attributed primarily to central factors. When binocular rivalry and depth effects are reduced in the stereoscopic viewing by making the exposures brief, the illusory effect approaches that of the binocular presentation for most of the illusions used in this study. On the other hand, stereoscopic long exposure viewing considerably reduces the illusory effect in most instances.

The results also show that the extent to which the illusory effect is diminished under stereoscopic viewing conditions depends not only on the length of the exposure time, but also on the proximity or overlap of the inducing and test figures. The closer the proximity and the greater the overlap, the more the illusory effect is decreased under stereoscopic viewing. Thus the Ebbinghaus circles and the Horizontal-Vertical lines show little or no decrement with short stereoscopic presentation; the Ponzo and Poggendorff figures, which have a closer proximity of inducing and test figures, show a greater decrease with stereoscopic presentation; the Modified Zoellner figure, which has almost a complete overlap of test and inducing figures, shows the greatest decrement with

TABLE 1

Number of Instances for all Ss Indicating Presence of Illusory
Effect for 5 Illusions and 5 Viewing Conditions

COMPARISON FIGURES	BINOCULAR		STEREOSCOPIC		
	LONG EXPOSURE	SHORT EXPOSURE	LONG EXPOSURE	SHORT EXPOSURE	SUCCESSIVE SHORT
Ebbinghaus					
8 mm.		3		5	
9		5		7	3
10	1	7		8	5
11	6	13	6	18	11
12	36	42	30	39	35
13*	50	50	49	47	47
14	50	50	50	50	50
Total	143	170	135	174	151
Horizontal-Vertical					
25 mm.					
28		1		1	
31		1	3	3	3
34	23	29	14	21	23
37	48	46	45	47	41
40	50	50	50	50	50
43	50	50	50	50	50
Total	171	177	162	172	167
Poggendorff					
− 7.5 mm.					
− 6.0		1			
− 4.5	1	5	1	4	7
− 3.0	30	32	13	30	20
− 1.5	45	45	39	41	31
0	50	50	46	50	48
+ 1.5	50	50	47	49	48
Total	176	183	146	174	154
Ponzo					
9.0 mm.	50	50	50	50	50
10.5	50	50	50	50	50
12.0	49	49	48	46	40
13.5	41	42	11	26	22
15.		12		1	2
16.5					
18					
Total	190	203	159	173	164
Modified Zoellner					
+ 4°	50	50	50	49	50
+ 2°	50	50	50	50	47
0°	48	50	37	41	30
− 2°	31	40	4	19	7
− 4°	1	7	1		2
− 6°					
− 8°					
Total	180	197	142	159	136

* Italic figure is the value where the test figure is the same as the standard stimulus.

stereoscopic presentation. These findings suggest that the stereoscopic short exposure is most effective in reducing binocular rivalry and/or depth effects when the stimuli overlap the least.

For all of the illusions used, with the exception of the Modified Zoellner figure, the illusory effect was found to be the least under the stereoscopic long exposure condition. It is also under this latter condition that depth effects and binocular rivalry effects were most likely to be reported. Shortening the exposure time, while not completely eliminating depth effects and binocular rivalry, did decrease them, with a concomitant increase in the illusory effect.

Contrary to expectation, the successive exposure condition (in contrast to simultaneous exposures) did not result in an increase in the illusory effect under stereoscopic viewing. It is possible that under this condition depth effects were more prevalent because of the temporal separation of the stimuli presented. Unfortunately qualitative data are not available in this study to assess this latter hypothesis. Even though the explanation offered seems plausible, there were no clear indications by Ss of this effect: no S reported that the test and inducing elements of any of the figures appeared in succession under this viewing condition.

An interesting additional finding is that the illusory effect was greater for all figures under the binocular short exposure than under the binocular long exposure condition. Such increase in the illusory effect under short exposure conditions is reported by Piaget (1961) who systematically varied the exposure time in presenting the Mueller-Lyer illusion to both adults and children. Another, though perhaps unlikely possibility (see Footnote 2) is that the figural after-effects in a successive presentation procedure may have operated in the direction opposite to that of the illusory effects and may account for these findings.

In conclusion, the results of this experiment support the views of Boring and Day and are inconsistent with those drawn by Springbett and Ohwaki. Day's study as well as our findings clearly indicates that central mechanisms are important determinants in the perception of geometric illusions.

Summary

Boring and Day point out that the noted reduction in geometric illusions under stereoscopic viewing can be attributed to binocular rivalry and depth effects, rather than to retinal processes as suggested by Ohwaki and Springbett. This study investigates this question further by: (1) employing short tachistoscopic exposures to minimize depth effects and binocular rivalry, (2) employing a psychophysical measure to assess more accurately the extent of the illusory effect, (3) exploring the illusory effects over a range of illusions varied in the degree of probable retinal rivalry. The findings support the theoretical view that illusory effects can be attributed primarily to central factors.

References

Boring, E. G. Letter to the editors. *Scientific American*, 1961, 204, 18–19.

Day, R. H. On the stereoscopic observation of geometric illusions. *Percept. mot. Skills*, 1961, *13*, 247–258.

Lau, E. Versuche ueber das stereoskopische Sehen. *Psychol. Forsch.*, 1922, 2, 1–4.

Lau, E. Ueber das stereoskopische Sehen. *Psychol. Forsch.*, 1925, 6, 121–126.

Ohwaki, S. On the destruction of geometrical illusions in stereoscopic observation. *Tohoku Psychol. Folia*, 1960, 29, 24–36.

Piaget, J. *Les mechanismes perceptifs*. Paris: Presses Universitaires de France, 1961.

Springbett, B. M. Some stereoscopic phenomena and their implications. *Brit. J. Psychol.*, 1961, 52, 105–109.

Witasek, S. Ueber die Natur der geometrisch-optischen Taeuschungen. *Z. Psychol. Physiol. Sinn.*, 1899, *19*, 81–174.

Some Effects of Contour
on Simultaneous Brightness Contrast*

PHYLLIS W. BERMAN
University of Wisconsin

H. W. LEIBOWITZ
Pennsylvania State University

Simultaneous brightness contrast was measured as a function of: (a) the orientation of a test object, shaped as a figure 8, on a half light, half black surround, (b) type and width of a contour separating the figure halves on the divided background. 48) adult Ss matched the brightness of the figure half on the dark background with that on the light surround. Subjective contrast was significantly greater: (a) when the figure 8 was presented with its rings on backgrounds of different brightness than when each ring lay on both backgrounds, (b) when figure halves were moved apart, each into its own surround, rather than when a dividing line separated the halves, (c) as width of the contour between halves was increased. The results are discussed in terms of the contribution of the border to subjective contrast obtained with complex stimulus configurations.

A gray stimulus viewed against a white background will appear darker than when viewed against a black background. This is an example of simultaneous brightness contrast, a phenomenon which can be interpreted in terms of neural inhibition at the retinal level following the implications of a number of recent electrophysiological experiments (Ratliff, Hartline, and Miller, 1963). Differences in excitation are exaggerated by interaction, the magnitude of the difference depending in a systematic manner on the luminance difference, size of background and test-fields, and the separation between the fields (Diamond, 1960, 1962; Heinemann, 1955).

* *Journal of Experimental Psychology,* 1965, vol. 69, pp. 251–256. Supported in part by Research Grant M–1090 from the National Institute of Mental Health of the National Institutes of Health, United States Public Health Service. The authors wish to express their appreciation to R. B. Freeman, Jr. for assistance in the preparation of the manuscript.

There are, however, some aspects of the subjective contrast effect, such as its relation to contour, which do not fit readily into a theoretical approach based simply on neural inhibition. In a classical demonstration, Wundt showed that a gray paper placed over the border between a black and white area will tend to appear uniformly gray despite the expected effects of simultaneous contrast (Osgood, 1953). If however, a contour is added to the gray stimulus, so as to separate the portion viewed against the black from that viewed against the white background, the expected contrast effect is manifested. Helson (1943) discussed this phenomenon in terms of the "assimilation" of the contrast effect within a common border. Koffka (1935) theorized that shape acts as a "force of cohesion" which plays a role in the appearance of contrast. He suggested that if a gray object is used which has two clear subdivisions, degree of contrast will vary with its orientation on the contrast-inducing background. These phenomena suggest that subjective contrast depends, not only on luminance differences, but also on the presence of an identifiable contour or shape with respect to the stimulus.

The present experiments were designed to determine quantitatively the magnitude of the subjective contrast effect as a function of the width of the contour separating the two halves of a figure 8 test object, and as a function of the orientation of the test object on the black and white background. Such data should be of value in evaluating the importance of contour as a contributing variable to the phenomenon of simultaneous brightness contrast.

Apparatus

The stimulus consisted of a figure 8 cut from neutral density film $(D = 0.7)$ and mounted flush against a piece of vertically positioned milk glass. Illlminance was provided by a 300-w., 110-v. ac projector system focused on the opposite side of the milk glass. The right half of the stimulus (see Figure 1) was positioned within a clear rectangle and appeared less luminous than its background. The left half of the figure was surrounded by opaque black paper and appeared more luminous than its background. Except for the figure 8 and the light background surrounding the right half of the figure, there were no other stimuli in the visual field. The remaining portions of the milk glass were covered with opaque black paper.

The S was able to match the two halves of the figure 8 by means of a pair of polaroid filters. The polarizer, made from sheet polaroid, was placed over the figure half lying on the background. The analyzer, a similar piece of polaroid mounted in glass, was placed in the eyepiece through which S observed monocularly with the natural pupil. The S rotated the analyzer until the two figure halves appeared equal. The matched luminance value of the left half of the figure could be calculated from the angular position of the analyzer and the calibration data of the polaroid system.

The figure 8 stimulus was symmetrical horizontally and vertically with an outside diameter of each ring of $2\frac{1}{4}$ in. The rings were $\frac{3}{8}$ in. width. The viewing distance was 34.5 in. at which the maximum dimensions of the figure 8 were $3.72 \times 7.44°$ of arc. The bright background against which the right half of the figure was viewed subtended a visual angle of $13.7 \times 5.8°$ of arc.

TABLE 1

Average Log Matched Luminance in Millilamberts of Groups A, B, C, and D as a Function of Width Divider or Separation between Figure Halves

GROUP	WIDTH DIVIDER IN MINUTES OF ARC								
	0	0.5	1.0	2.0	4.0	8.0	15.9	31.9	63.7
A	1.13	0.97	0.95	0.78	0.80	0.65	0.31	0.13	−0.15
B	0.08	−0.20	−0.15	−0.10	−0.22	−0.24	−0.39	−0.51	−0.71
C with separation	0.92						−0.15	−0.25	−0.43
C with divider	0.92						0.49	0.12	−0.08
D with separation	0.12						−0.45	−0.62	−0.64
D with divider	0.12						−0.43	−0.51	−0.80

Note.—Groups A and B are from Exp. I. Groups C and D are from Exp. II.

The magnitude of the contour was varied by presenting the stimulus with no inserts between the two halves of the figure, and by placing vertical wires or strips of the following widths symmetrically over the center of the figure: .005, .01, .02, .04, .08, .16, .32, and .64 in. These dividers corresponded to visual angles of 0.5, 1.0, 2.0, 4.0, 8.0, 15.9, 31.9, and 63.7′ of arc. The luminance of the right half of the test figure was constant at log 2.0 mL. and the background luminance was constant at log 2.7 mL.

Experiment I

METHOD

Two groups of 12 Ss each, volunteers with normal vision from the elementary psychology classes at the university, first made four practice matches using a square test object and a dividing strip subtending 63.7′ of arc. Group A was then presented the figure in the vertical position, and Group B in the horizontal position (see Figure 1). The nine experimental conditions for each group, i.e., eight dividers and no divider, were counterbalanced by a 9×9 Latin-square design. Subjects 10, 11, and 12 were presented with the same sequence as Ss 1, 2, and 3 since ordinal position, as indicated by analysis of variance, was not a significant variable. The S made four matches at each of the experimental conditions.

Each S was given a period of preliminary dark adaptation after which instructions were given regarding the nature of the task and the method of rotating the polaroid in the eye-piece so as to produce a match between the two halves of the test object. The Ss were instructed not to try to match any one section of the figure with any other section, but to make the best overall match possible.

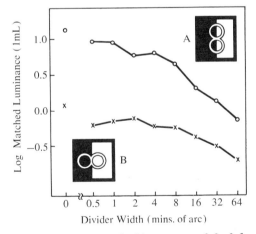

FIGURE 1   Log matched luminance of the left half of a figure 8 test object viewed against a black background matched with the right half viewed against a light background. (The background luminance was constant at log 2.7 mL. The luminance of the right half of the figure was constant at log 2.0 mL. The data in the upper curve, indicated by circles, were obtained with vertical orientation of the configuration [Insert A; no divider present]. The data for the lower curve, indicated by crosses, were obtained with a horizontal orientation [Insert B].)

RESULTS

The data are presented in Table 1 and plotted in Figure 1 as the log matched luminance as a function of width of the divider for the two orientations used. Table 2 is a summary of an analysis of the variance associated with these data. All terms tested in this analysis are significant at the .001 level.

Even in the absence of any divider between the two halves of the test field, indicated by the zero position on the abscissa axis of Figure 1, considerable contrast existed. Whereas the luminance of the portion of the figure viewed against the white background was log 2.0 mL., it was matched by the portion viewed against the black background at an average value of log 1.1 mL. for the vertical, and log 0.1 mL. for the horizontal orientation.

The effect of introducing the divider is considerable, amounting to factors of approximately 16 to 1 for the vertical, and 5 to 1 for the horizontal orientation. As

TABLE 2

Analysis of Variance of Maching Scores of Groups A and B Using Nine Width Dividers

SOURCE	DF	MS	F
Between Ss			
Figure position (FP)	1	427,645.0	19.44***
Error (b)	22	22,339.1	37.34***
Within Ss			
Width divider (WD)	8	25,994.8	43.46***
WD × FP	8	2,827.4	4.73***
Error (w)	176	598.2	
Total	215		

*** p < .001.

dividers of greater width were introduced the amount of contrast was systematically increased, indicated by the increasingly lower luminance values of the left half of the figure required to produce a match between the two halves of the test figure. This effect was exhibited with the test object in both orientations, but there was significantly more contrast for all divider widths with the test figure oriented horizontally than with the vertical orientation.

Increasing the width of the divider had a greater effect with the test figure in a vertical position. This can be seen in Figure 1 and is reflected by the significant interaction between Width Divider and Figure Position in the analysis of variance presented in Table 2. An extended Alexander trend test was used to determine whether the increase in contrast was significantly more linear with the test figure in the vertical position than with it in the

TABLE 3

Analysis of Variance of Matching Scores of Groups C and D with .160-, .320-, and .640-In. Dividers and Separation between Halves

SOURCE	DF	MS	F
Figure position (FP)	1	99,487.6	15.93***
Ss/FP	22	6,244.6	33.97***
Width between halves (W)	2	15,071.7	32.76***
Between divider and separation (D-S)	1	17,844.5	16.35***
FP × D-S	1	19,716.9	18.07***
W × FP	2	745.9	1.62
W × D-S	2	1,683.5	9.16***
W × FP × D-S	2	5,968.4	32.47***
Ss/FP × W	44	460.1	2.50**
Ss/FP × D-S	22	1,091.1	5.94***
Ss/FP × W × D-S	44	183.8	
Total	143		

Note.—Ss/FP is the error term for FP. Ss/FP × W is the error term for W and for W × FP. Ss/FP × D-S is the error term for D-S and for FP × D-S. Ss/FP × W × D-S is the error term for all other terms.
** p < .01.
*** p < .001.

horizontal position (Grant, 1956). The interaction term was broken into the component terms, Between Group Slopes, Quadratics, Cubics, and Deviations from the Expected. Of these, only Between Group Slopes is significant, $F(1, 22) = 8.86, p < .01$.

Experiment II

METHOD

In Experiment I the dividing strip covered part of the test object so that an increase in the width of the divider decreased the effective area of the test object as well as the background. Since area is an important variable in contrast (Diamond, 1960, 1962), a control experiment was conducted in which the two halves of the test object were physically separated so that, while the width of the "contour" between them increased as in Experiment I, their areas, as well as the area of the light background, remained constant. Two additional groups of 12 Ss each were tested under conditions of no divider, and with dividers as well as separations of .16, 3.2, and .64 in. Group C was presented with the test object in the vertical position, and Group D with it in the horizontal position.

The order of presentation of the seven treatment conditions was determined by a 7×7 Latin-square design with the same design being repeated for both groups. The results of a t test between the most divergent scores indicated that ordinal position was not significant, so that the five additional Ss in each group were presented with the same order of treatment conditions as Ss 1, 2, 3, 4, and 5.

RESULTS

The data are presented in Table 1 and Table 3 presents an analysis of the variance of these data. Since only one measurement per S represents the zero level of both the Divider and Separation conditions, only the scores for the .16, .32, and .64 widths were included in this analysis.

As in Experiment I, both Width and Figure Position are significant sources of variability.

The overall effect of separation of the halves of the test figure was to produce significantly more contrast than was perceived when a dividing strip was used to create a contour between the figure halves. The significance of the interaction term, Figure Position $\times$ Divider Separation, reflects the fact that this effect differed for the two orientations of the test figure used. Separation produced more contrast when the test figure was in the vertical position. For the horizontal orientation, either procedure produced similar results.

In the analysis summarized in Table 3 Width $\times$ Figure Position is insignificant but the second-order interaction, Width $\times$ Figure Position $\times$ Divider Separation, is significant. Analyses of variance were computed separately for the Separation condition and for the Divider condition and data for the zero level of each was included. Width $\times$ Figure Position was significant only for the Separation condition, $F(3, 66) = 4.60, p < .01$. This finding differs from the result in Experiment I, that Width Divider $\times$ Figure Position is significant, but with nine instead of three widths dividing strips used.

Width is a significant variable in both the Separation condition, $F(3, 66) = 62.83, p < .001$, and the Divider condition, $F(3, 66) = 36.39, p < .001$. However, the increase in contrast perceived with increasing widths between figure halves differed in the Separation and Divider conditions. This is indicated by the significant interaction, Width $\times$ Divider Separation, in Table 3.

Discussion

The results of the present experiments provide quantitative confirmation of the phenomenal impressions derived from early demonstrations. The contribution of border to the subjective contrast effect is clearly demonstrated by the marked change in the magnitude of contrast resulting from the introduction of thin dividing strips between the halves of the test object. Of particular interest is the influence of the smallest divider used in Experiment I, which subtended only 30″ of arc. This value corresponds to the angle subtended by individual cones in the center of the human fovea, and is approximately the same order of magnitude as the threshold for grating acuity (Leibowitz, 1953). This fine line is seen here to be adequate to increase contrast or both orientations of the figure. It is highly unlikely that the effect of a line of this width, which represents approximately 0.2% of the total width of the test object in the vertical orientation and 0.1% of the total width in the horizontal orientation, can be ascribed to changes in luminance or area relationships. The finding that there is not less but more difference in brightness between figure halves in the Separation condition indicates that the findings cannot be attributed to changes in area resulting from introduction of dividing strips. A more plausible explanation would be in terms of an "equalizing mechanism" such as that described by Fry (1948; Fry and Bartley, 1935), which is assumed to be responsible for the assimilation of differential contrast effects throughout the whole figure or, when the divider is introduced, within the figure halves.

When there is no divider introduced, the shape of the figure itself may have an influence similar to the effect of such a contour. The extent to which this is manifested depends on the position of the test object on the divided background. Because the figure 8 test object is of such a shape that two component parts are identifiable, the position of these two parts on the divided background is important. More contrast is observed between the figure

halves viewed against different backgrounds than when the rings of the figure each lie on both the black and white backgrounds, as in the vertical orientation.

Of interest is the observation that considerable subjective contrast exists in the absence of any dividing line between the two halves of the figure on backgrounds of different brightness. The effect is probably not noticeable in the more familiar demonstrations of this phenomenon using paper stimuli. With such stimuli contrast appears to be reduced by the presence of the visible microstructure of the paper surface, and it may be increased by observing test objects through a diffuser such as tissue paper (Woodworth and Schlosberg, 1955). In the present stimulus arrangement transmitted light was utilized and no microstructure was visible. In addition the luminance differences among the test object and the light and dark backgrounds with transmitted light are far in excess of that available with paper stimuli. Thus, the present arrangement results in far more favorable conditions for contrast than ordinarily exist. The familiar observation that a divider is necessary for contrast to be manifested seems to be a special case resulting from the use of paper stimuli.

In the present experiments the role of the shape of the test object and of fine dividing lines has been demonstrated. It follows that simultaneous contrast is not a simple function of luminance and spatial variables. This does not imply that these variables are not fundamental to contrast, but rather that additional concepts are needed to fully explain subjective contrast with more complex stimulus configurations.

References

DIAMOND, A. L. A theory of depression and enhancement in the brightness response. *Psychol. Rev.*, 1960, 67, 168–198.

DIAMOND, A. L. Simultaneous contrast as a function of test-field area. *J. exp. Psychol.*, 1962, 64, 336–345.

FRY, G. A. Mechanisms subserving simultaneous brightness contrast. *Amer. J. Optom.*, 1948, *45*, 1–17.

FRY, G. A., and S. H. BARTLEY. The effect of one border in the visual field upon the threshold of another. *Amer. J. Physiol.*, 1935, *112*, 414–421.

GRANT, D. A. Analysis of variance tests in the analysis and comparison of curves. *Psychol. Bull.*, 1956, *53*, 141–154.

HEINEMANN, E. G. Simultaneous brightness induction as a function of inducing- and test-field luminances. *J. exp. Psychol.*, 1955, *50*, 89–96.

HELSON, H. Some factors and implications of color constancy. *J. Opt. Soc. Amer.*, 1943, *33*, 555–567.

KOFFKA, K. *Principles of gestalt psychology.* New York: Harcourt, Brace, 1935.

LEIBOWITZ, H. Some observations and theory on the variation of visual acuity with the orientation of the test object. *J. Opt. Soc. Amer.*, 1953, *43*, 902–905.

OSGOOD, C. E. *Method and theory in experimental psychology.* New York: Oxford Univer. Press, 1953.

RATLIFF, F., H. K. HARTLINE, and W. H. MILLER. Spatial and temporal aspects of retinal inhibitory interaction. *J. Opt. Soc. Amer.*, 1963, *53*, 110–120.

WOODWORTH, R. S., and H. SCHLOSBERG. *Experimental psychology.* New York: Holt, Rinehart and Winston, Inc., 1955.

*Perceptual Grouping Produced by Line Figures**

JACOB BECK

University of Oregon

2 experiments, one with 2- and one with 3-line figures, studied the relative effectiveness of differences in orientation and shape in producing grouping by similarity. The results showed that changes in shape or orientation which leave the component lines of the figures vertical and horizontal do not facilitate grouping as readily as changes which alter the direction of the component lines to 45° and 135°. These results corroborate and extend the findings of Beck (1966a, 1966b) and are discussed in relation to the problem of specifying the properties of line figures that produce grouping by similarity.

In an earlier study Beck (1966a) used a method based upon threshold measurements to test the effectiveness of changes in the orientation and shape of line figures in producing grouping by similarity. Two sets of figures, for example, a pattern of upright *T*s (A in Figure 1) and a pattern of *T*s tilted at 45° (B in Figure 1), were combined so that a single equally spaced field was given. When the brightness of

the two patterns was equal, there was no separation of the field into two groups of upright and tilter *T*s. However, when the brightness of the pattern of upright *T*s was reduced, the perceptual field separated into two groups—the less bright upright *T*s and the brighter tilted *T*s. Measurements of the amount by which the luminance of the upright *T*s had to be reduced in order for the figures to segregate into two perceptual groups permitted an evaluation of the relative effectiveness of changes in shape and orientation in producing perceptual grouping. The results showed that changes in shape or orientation which leave the

* *Perception and Psychophysics*, 1967, vol. 2, pp. 491–495. This research was supported by National Science Foundation Grant GB–2901. The preparation of this paper was supported by National Science Foundation Grant GB–5285.

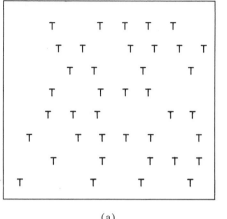
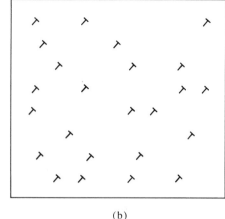

(a)　　　　　　　　　　　　　　　　　　　　　　(b)

FIGURE 1　Sample displays used in experiments. (A illustrates the pattern of upright *T*s employed as the standard in Exps. I and II. B illustrates a pattern of *T*s
tilted at 45°, one of a larger number of comparison patterns used. The two patterns were combined so that a single equally spaced field of upright and tilted *T*s
was obtained. In the experiment, the patterns consisted of red luminous figures
against a black background.)

component lines of the figures vertical and
horizontal do not facilitate grouping as
readily as changes which alter the direction
of the component lines to 45° and 135°.

When the brightness of the upright *T*s
was reduced, separation of the field into
two groups of figures, however, did not occur suddenly but gradually. Since the experiments required that Os maintain a
stable criterion for the point at which the
field was judged to separate into two
groups, six highly practiced Os served in
the experiments. The present study examines the generality of the earlier results.
Two separate groups of naive Os served
under changed experimental procedures.
Instead of asking Os to reduce the brightness of the upright *T*s to the point where
perceptual grouping occurred, the Os were
now shown the combined field with the
upright *T*s set at three lower luminance
levels. The Os task was to scale the clarity
with which the combined field separated
into two groups when the upright *T*s were
set at each of these three luminance levels.
Two independent experiments, one with 2-
and one with 3-line figures, examined the
relative effectiveness of changes in shape

and orientation in producing perceptual
grouping.

Method

APPARATUS

The stimulus display in Experiments I
and II consisted of an equally spaced field,
9.9 × 10.4 in, projected onto a smooth black
wall 37 in from the O. Each field was composed of two patterns of figures, a standard
pattern and a comparison pattern. Two
matched projectors were used, a slide of
the standard pattern was placed in one
projector and slides of the comparison patterns were placed in the other. The standard pattern, which was always present,
consisted of 40 upright *T*s and is shown as
A in Figure 1. The comparison patterns
consisted of 24 figures and were varied. B
in Figure 1 shows a pattern of *T*s tilted
at 45°, one of a larger number of comparison patterns used in this study. When
the patterns were of equal brightness, an
O saw a single field made up of 2 kinds of
luminous figures against a black background. When the standard pattern was set

at luminances lower than that of the comparison pattern, the field tended to segregate into two groups of figures. The brightness of the standard pattern was set at 3 lower levels by means of a variac. A red Wratten filter, number 29, was placed in each projector to minimize color temperature changes.

Luminance measures were taken with a Spectra-Pritchard photometer, employing a 30-minute arc field. The meter was placed at 90 in. from the targets and subtended a circular field of approximately .8 in. in diameter. The luminance of each figure averaged over this aperture was measured. All luminance measures refer to the mean luminance of the figures making up a pattern.

Stimuli for Experiment I. In Experiment I, 9 comparison patterns composed of 2-line figures were used. The lines of each figure were .3 in long and .031 in wide; they were always at right angles to each other. The figures making up each pattern were first made by affixing a self-sticking black tape to matte white cardboard. Reversal film was used to prepare slides in which the white background became opaque and the black lines became transparent. In the photographic process great care was taken to insure that the lines composing the different figures would be equal in brightness. The 9 comparison patterns were: (*a*) an upright *T*, (*b*) a *T* on its side, (*c*) an inverted *T*, (*d*) an upright *T* rotated 45°, (*f*) a ±, (*g*) a ± rotated 45° to form an *X*, (*h*) a backward *L*, and (*i*) the *L* shape rotated 45° to form a *V*. The 2 lines making up each figure, when projected, were .3 in. and the separation between adjacent figures when the standard and comparison patterns were combined was approximately .85 in. The luminance of the comparison patterns was always set at .07 ft-L. The luminance of the standard pattern was set at .039, .032 and .025 ft-L. The 9 comparison patterns, when combined with the standard pattern and presented at each of

these 3 luminance levels, made a total of 27 stimulus displays. The 27 stimulus displays were presented to each *O* in a different random order, with the constraint that each of the patterns appear once in every block of 9 trials.

Stimuli for Experiment II. In Experiment II, 4 comparison patterns composed of 3-line figures were used. All lines were again .3 in. in length and at right angles to one another. The patterns were prepared and projected as in Experiment I. They were: (*a*) an upright *F*, (*b*) an *F* on its side, (*c*) an *F* rotated 45° and (*d*) an upright *H*. The brightness of the individual lines composing the figures was visually matched to the brightness of the lines in Experiment I. Since this experiment used 3-line instead of 2-line figures, the average luminance within the aperture was now .1 ft-L. The standard pattern again consisted of upright *T*s, this time set at .057 ft-L., .047 ft-L. and .039 ft-L. The 4 comparison patterns, when combined with the standard and presented at each of these 3 luminance levels, made a total of 12 stimulus displays. The 12 stimulus displays were again presented in a different random order to each *O*, subject to the constraint that each of the patterns appear once in every block of 4 trials.

PROCEDURE

There was no light in the room in which the experiments were conducted, other than that coming from the projectors. The Os viewed the stimuli binocularly. No chin rest was employed. The general procedure is best described by the instructions given. The instructions (slightly abridged to eliminate some of the examples given) in Experiment I were: "I will show you a series of displays all composed of red figures. Each of the displays you will see is composed of 2 separate patterns; this one (the *O* was shown the pattern of upright *T*s) will be present in all displays; this one (the *O* was shown the pattern of *T*s on their side) will change from trial to trial.

I am interested in finding out how much these patterns stand out relative to each other when they are presented together (the O was shown the standard pattern of upright Ts together with the comparison pattern of Ts on their side). As the shapes are different, it is easy to pick out the figures that are different. This, however, is not the judgment I wish you to make. Rather, I would like you to indicate how clearly one of the patterns as a whole group stands out relative to the other. An exaggerated example of what I mean is this. (The pattern of upright Ts was set at .015 ft-L; the pattern of Ts on their side at .07 ft-L.) In the experiment, you will never see this extreme an example, but as you see, all the Ts on their side stand out as a complete pattern, separate from the upright Ts. In this case this does not happen. (The O was shown the pattern of upright Ts and Ts on their side at .07 ft-L.) I would like you to indicate the degree to which the two patterns are seen as separate groups, by means of a 6-point rating scale, where 0 indicates that the two patterns cannot be seen as separate, but are seen as one display with differences in shape; and 5 indicates that they are very clearly seen as 2 separate groups. During the experiment a given pattern will be repeated a number of times, but no pattern will be shown more than once under the same conditions. This means there will be no inconsistency involved in assigning a value of 1 to a pattern in one trial and later assigning a value of 5, for example, to the same pattern in another trial." In order to familiarize Os with the stimuli, the entire set was shown before the experiment began.

The instructions in Experiment II were the same as in Experiment I except that the examples presented were now chosen from the comparison patterns used in Experiment II.

OBSERVERS

The Os were summer school students at Harvard University who were paid to participate. Two separate groups of Os made judgments. Nineteen Os served in Experiment I and 14 Os served in Experiment II.

Results

Figures 2 and 3 summarize the data obtained in Experiments I and II. In these figures the luminance of the standard pattern is indicated above each row. The first figure in each pair of figures shown illustrates the figures composing the standard pattern and the second one the figures composing the comparison pattern. The number below each pair of figures is the mean rating of the degree to which the standard and comparison patterns were perceived to group. The comparison patterns have been arranged so that they go from the least to the greatest amount of grouping. The grouping produced by the comparison patterns, disregarding the luminance of the standard, can be obtained by totaling the mean ratings at each of the three luminance levels. They are shown in the bottom rows in Figures 2 and 3. These numbers represent the scores obtained when the ratings given a comparison pattern at each luminance level are summed for each O and the total of the sums divided by the number of Os.

The over-all effects of Figure Shape and Luminance in producing grouping are obtained from a 3 x 3 analysis of variance. Tables 1 and 2 show that the factors of Figure Shape and Luminance are significant at beyond the .001 level in both Experiments I and II. The Figure x Luminance interaction is significant at the .005 level in Experiment I and the .05 level in Experiment II. Even though the interaction was significant, examination of Figures 2 and 3 shows that the treatment factors have the same rank or approximately the same rank for each level. As the luminance of the standard pattern is decreased, rated grouping increases for each comparison pattern. At each luminance level, the rank order of the grouping produced by the dif-

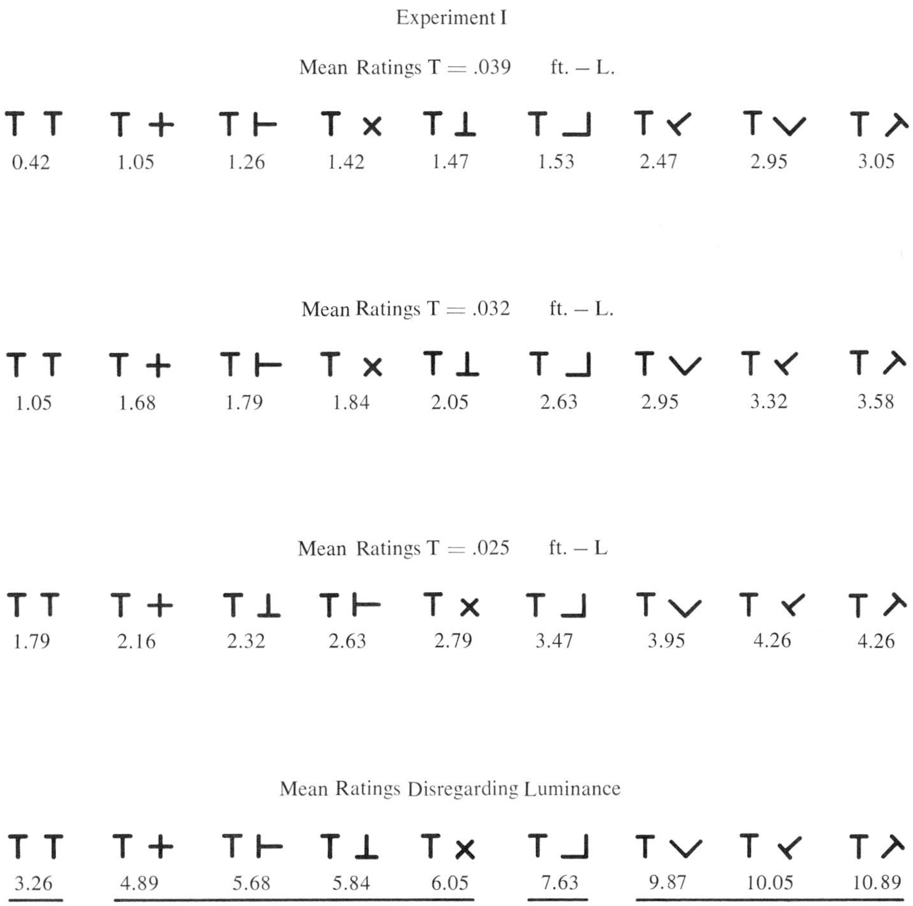

Experiment I

Mean Ratings T = .039   ft. – L.

T T	T +	T ⊢	T ×	T ⊥	T ⌐	T ⋎	T ⋁	T ⋏
0.42	1.05	1.26	1.42	1.47	1.53	2.47	2.95	3.05

Mean Ratings T = .032   ft. – L.

T T	T +	T ⊢	T ×	T ⊥	T ⌐	T ⋁	T ⋎	T ⋏
1.05	1.68	1.79	1.84	2.05	2.63	2.95	3.32	3.58

Mean Ratings T = .025   ft. – L

T T	T +	T ⊥	T ⊢	T ×	T ⌐	T ⋁	T ⋎	T ⋏
1.79	2.16	2.32	2.63	2.79	3.47	3.95	4.26	4.26

Mean Ratings Disregarding Luminance

T T	T +	T ⊢	T ⊥	T ×	T ⌐	T ⋁	T ⋎	T ⋏
3.26	4.89	5.68	5.84	6.05	7.63	9.87	10.05	10.89

FIGURE 2   The mean ratings of the degree to which the standard and comparison patterns were perceived to group in Exp. I. (The first figure in each pair of figures shown illustrates the shape of the figures composing the standard pattern; the second one, the shape of the figures composing the comparison pattern. The luminance of the standard pattern is indicated above each row. The rated grouping disregarding luminance and averaged over Os is shown in the bottom row. A Tukey test of multiple comparisons was used to compare the means. Those means which do not differ significantly from each other at the .01 level are underscored by the same line.)

ferent figures is approximately the same. This homogeneity reflects the fact seen in Tables 1 and 2 that the mean squares for Luminance and Figure Shape are very much larger than the mean squares for their interaction (Lindquist, 1953, p. 143).

In order to compare the degree to which different figures produce grouping, a Tukey test of multiple comparisons was applied to the over-all mean ratings. The means that do not differ significantly from each other at the .01 level are underscored by the same line in Figures 2 and 3. The re-

sults show that in both Experiments I and II changes in the orientation or shape of the figures without changes in the orientation of the component lines do not as readily facilitate the separation of the field into distinct perceptual groups. In Experiment I, the comparison patterns, T on its side and inverted T, involved differences in the orientation of the figures and the comparison pattern backward L involved a difference in the shape of the figures, but in both cases the component lines remained vertical and horizontal; the comparison

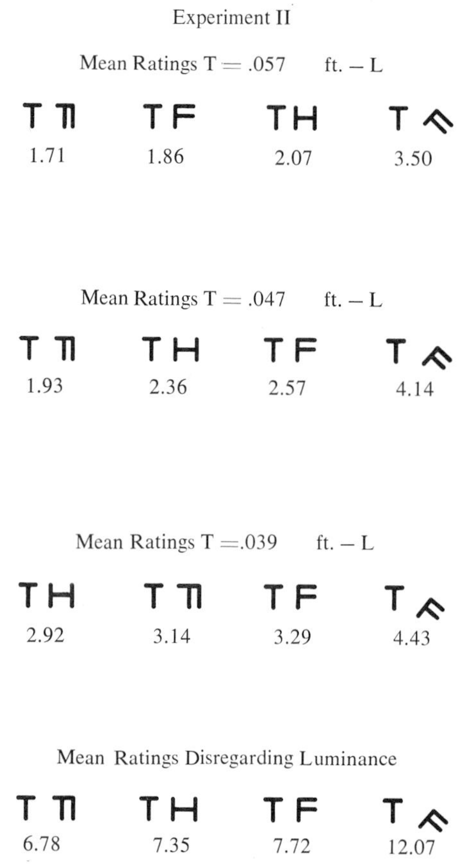

Experiment II

Mean Ratings T = .057   ft. − L

T ⊓   T F   T H   T ⌃
1.71   1.86   2.07   3.50

Mean Ratings T = .047   ft. − L

T ⊓   T H   T F   T ⌃
1.93   2.36   2.57   4.14

Mean Ratings T = .039   ft. − L

T H   T ⊓   T F   T ⌃
2.92   3.14   3.29   4.43

Mean Ratings Disregarding Luminance

T ⊓   T H   T F   T ⌃
6.78   7.35   7.72   12.07

FIGURE 3   The mean ratings of the degree to which the standard and comparison patterns were perceived to group in Experiment II. (The first figure in each pair of figures shown illustrates the shape of the figures composing the standard pattern; the second one, the shape of the figures composing the comparison pattern. The luminance of the standard pattern is indicated above each row. The rated grouping disregarding luminance and averaged over Os is shown in the bottom row. T Tukey test of multiple comparisons was used to compare the means. Those means which do not differ significantly from each other at the .01 level are underscored by the same line.)

patterns T rotated 45°, inverted T rotated 45°, and V, involved changes in orientation and shape in which the component lines are tilted rather than vertical and horizontal. Figure 2 shows that the tilted figures differ significantly at the .01 level from the vertical-horizontal figures but not between themselves. In Experiment II Figure 3 shows that an F tilted at 45° grouped

TABLE 1

Summary of the Analysis of Variance of Os Judgments of Grouping in Exp. I

SOURCE OF VARIATION	DF	MS	F
Figures (F)	8	43.7	23.00***
Luminances (L)	2	76.4	58.77***
Observers (O)	18	18.6	
F × L	16	.87	2.81**
F × O	144	1.9	
L × O	36	1.3	
F × L × O	288	.31	
Total	512		

*** $p < .001$
** $p < .005$

TABLE 2

Summary of the Analysis of Variance of Os Judgments of Grouping in Exp. II

SOURCE OF VARIATION	DF	MS	F
Figures (F)	3	27.4	28.25***
Luminances (L)	2	19.1	32.93***
Observers (O)	13	4.23	
F × L	6	.74	2.31*
F × O	39	.97	
L × O	26	.58	
F × L × O	78	.32	
Total	167		

*** $p < .001$
* $p < .05$

significantly better than either an upright F, an F on its side, or an upright H.

As in the earlier study of Beck (1966a), not all 45° rotations facilitated grouping. A ± rotated 45° to form an X has the same tilt as the lines of a tilted T and V, yet it groups less readily. It should also be noted that not all vertical and horizontal arrangements of lines produce the same grouping. The backward L grouped better than the other figures with vertical and horizontal lines at each of the three luminance levels. The Tukey test shows that it differed significantly from both the upright figures and from the rotated figures. The results also indicate that the addition of a line to both the upright and the tilted figures facilitates perceptual grouping. When the luminance of the standard pattern was set at .039 ft-L, the rated groupings of the comparison patterns are consistently higher in Experiment II than in Experiment I (P = .021, Fisher exact probability test).

Discussion

Since Wertheimer (1923), psychologists have pointed out that similarity serves as a basis for perceptual grouping. An examination of similarity relationships, however, reveals that not all kinds of similarity produce grouping equally well. The present results corroborate the findings of Beck (1966a, 1966b) that line orientation is an important variable. If the orientation of a figure's lines are changed to 45° and 135°, perceptual grouping relative to figures with vertical and horizontal lines will be improved. Changes in figure orientation or shape, however, which maintain a vertical and horizontal orientation of the component lines do not as readily facilitate grouping. Beck (1966b) has shown that the decisive variable is the tilt of the lines and not changes in the vertical and horizontal dimensions which accompany changes in figure orientation. Beck (1966a, 1966b) also showed that the rated similarity of the figures is not a good predictor of the degree to which figures will cohere to form perceptual groups.

Though going beyond the scope of the data, a brief discussion of two questions pertaining to the results is useful. Though an individual is sensitive to many pattern differences, not all differences that an individual can discriminate seem capable of producing perceptual grouping. The two pairs of figures *T* and *T* on its side and *T* and *T* tilted 45° viewed individually are equally discriminable. Yet, when one is presented with a large number of figures the field *T* and *T* tilted 45° groups readily while the field *T* and *T* on its side fails to group. A characterization of the variables that facilitate grouping is important. If one assumes that different properties of figures are responded to at different neural levels in the visual system, it is then possible that the processes involved in grouping are most sensitive to those properties that are selectively responded to at an early stage in the visual system. What is suggested is that the processes in grouping are based on a spontaneous direct response to relatively simple properties such as brightness, size, and line direction. Perhaps the reason that differences in figural orientation and figural similarity do not produce strong grouping is that these are observed through the mediation of a higher less spontaneous inspection process. The greater grouping produced by a backward *L* in Experiment I suggests that the presence of a right angle facilitates grouping. This property, however, did not appear in an earlier study (1966a). The basic importance of line orientation is consistent with Gibson (1950) who has suggested that the direction of a line is a basic element in the perception of a figure and Hubel and Wiesel (1962) who found specific receptors for line orientation when studying the cortical neurons in area 17. This interpretation of the results is of course speculative and provisional until verified by further experiments.

A second question concerns why the figure *X*, in which the component lines of a ± have been tilted at 45° and 135° does not group as well as a tilted *T* or *V*. One explanation is that the visual system is sensitive to the orientation of the over-all distribution of brightness of the total figure. If we assume that the visual system "averages" brightness over the whole area of a figure (such as the distribution of brightness obtained when the figure is out of focus) the orientation of this brightness distribution as well as the orientation of the component lines of a figure may be important. An upright T and a tilted T differ not only in the direction of their lines but also in the direction of the distribution of brightness. The distributions of brightness for a $\pm$ and an X because of their symmetry are much more similar to each other and to an upright T. It should be pointed out that the improved grouping produced by the addition of a line in Experiment II may be the result of an increased difference in the over-all brightness of a figure as well as due to a difference in the number of lines composing a figure. Independent variation of the average brightness of a figure and the number and arrangement of lines in a figure is especially difficult and caution is, therefore, required in assessing the relative importance of these variables.

References

BECK, J. Perceptual grouping produced by changes in orientation and shape. *Science,* 1966a, *154,* 538–540.

BECK, J. Effect of orientation and of shape similarity on perceptual grouping. *Perception and Psychophysics,* 1966b, *1,* 300–302.

GIBSON, J. J. *The perception of the visual world.* Cambridge: Riverside Press, 1950.

HUBEL, D. H. and T. N. WIESEL. Receptive fields, binocular interaction, and functional architecture in the cat's visual cortex. *J. Physiol.,* 1962, *160,* 106–123.

LINDQUIST, E. F. *Design and analysis of experiments in psychology and education.* Cambridge: Riverside Press, 1953.

WERTHEIMER, M. Untersuchungen zur lehre von der gestalt, II. *Psychol. Forsch.,* 1923, *4,* 301–350.

Sequential Part Presentation: A Method of Studying Visual Form Perception*

JOSEPH H. McFARLAND

Antioch College

Everyday perception of a form's parts as simultaneous and joined is viewed as a perceptual achievement dependent on the central operations of analysis and integration. Experiments have been conducted which employ a method of stimulus presentation which assures that neural response simulates the hypothesized analysis operation, viz. sequential part presentation. Perceptual measures are employed which are assumed to reflect the hypothesized integration. In one experiment, interpart intervals between the sequentially presented sides of a line triangle were varied and 50% points determined for judgments of simultaneity and joining between the lines. In a second experiment, these thresholds were also determined, but for side part versus angle part presentation of the line triangle. With side part presentation, thresholds for both judgments of simultaneity and joining were found to be higher. It is concluded that normal perception of form, i.e., perception of parts as simultaneous and joined, can take place at larger intervals when sequential response is to side parts.

In studying visual form perception, it is customary to present the parts of a stimulus

* *British Journal of Psychology,* 1965, vol. 56, pp. 439–446. This work was supported at Clark University by National Institutes of Health, Grant R–6403 (A), U.S. Public Health Service.

form simultaneously. Although this method is in common laboratory use, a theoretical rationale for the method is seldom, if ever, provided in current theoretical treatments of form perception.

While searching for such a rationale, it

has become clear that the Gestalt treatment of form perception, though subject to diverse criticisms (cf. Hebb, 1949; Helson, 1926; Lashley, Chow and Semmes, 1951; Nagel, 1963; Piaget, 1952) does provide an argument for employing this method. In brief, the argument can be developed as follows. Forms in our everyday experience appear with their parts simultaneous in time and joined in space. Thus, in terms of the principle of isomorphism, the central nervous system processes simultaneously all portions of retinal stimulation arising from a form (cf. Koffka, 1935). Accordingly, in studying visual form perception, it is appropriate to present all parts of the form simultaneously.

If this is the rationale tacitly employed by many investigators, then a paradoxical situation has indeed been created. While in theory progress has been made beyond the Gestalt heritage (cf. Gibson, 1950; Hebb, 1949; Lashley, 1951; Piaget, 1963; Uhr, 1963), a Gestalt rationale is still employed in choosing a method of stimulus presentation for the study of form perception.

In view of this situation, two objectives are indicated: (1) the development of a rationale, in terms of present theory, for the method of simultaneous part presentation; and (2) the development of new theoretical models and theoretically appropriate methods of stimulus presentation.

In pursuance of the latter objective, three steps have been taken which are reported here. First, an approach has been developed which treats form perception as dependent on central operations of analysis and integration. Secondly, a method of stimulus presentation has been devised which is appropriate to this approach. Finally, experiments have been conducted which indicate the heuristic value of this approach and method for providing information on the process of visual form perception.

As to the approach, visual form perception is conceptualized as dependent on a central mechanism that performs operations of analysis and integration. Analysis entails the production of sequences of responses to line and to angle portions of retinal stimulation; integration entails the production of a response to the products of analysis.

In terms of this theoretical model, everyday perception of a form's parts as simultaneous in time and joined in space is considered the perceptual achievement of these operations of analysis and integration. While a form's parts may be simultaneous and joined in terms of retinal stimulation, the perception of simultaneity and joining is viewed as dependent on the postulated central mechanism which produces a sequence of responses to parts—analysis; and which then produces a unitary response to the sequence of responses—integration.

The method of stimulus presentation that has been devised consists of presenting the parts of a form sequentially. This is considered an appropriate method for two reasons. First, it can be assumed that the response of the visual system to a form presented by this method simulates, in part, the hypothesized analysis entailed in everyday form perception when the form is presented with its parts simultaneous. Secondly, it is assumed that perception of the stimulus form presented by this method is the achievement of the hypothesized operation of integration. Thus, with this method of stimulus presentation, appropriate variation of stimulus parameters permits variation of the analysis operation and the consequences for integration, as manifested in perception, can be studied.

Two experiments employing this method are reported. In the first experiment, the intervals between the sequentially presented sides of a form are varied from 0 to 300 msec and thresholds for non-simultaneity and non-joining of parts are determined. These threshold intervals are assumed to define the limiting intervals at which normal form perception can occur for a sequence of responses to side parts.

In the second experiment, two conditions are employed. In one condition, as in the first experiment, a form's side parts are presented sequentially; in the second condition, the same form's angle parts are presented sequentially. Here also the intervals between the sequentially presented parts of the form are varied. The aim of this experiment is to provide information on the limiting intervals at which normal form perception can take place for a sequence of responses to side versus angle parts.

Experiment 1

METHOD

Stimulus. The stimulus was a luminous (0.44 ft.-lamberts) equilateral line triangle. Sides were 1 degree in length by 4 min in width at 17 in. The form was presented on a dark background, straight ahead at eye level, with one side in a horizontal orientation. Sides were flashed in sequence for 10 msec each. The sequence employed was base, then right side, and then left side. Interpart intervals (1) between the base and right side, and (2) between the right and left sides, were maintained equal and varied from 0 to 300 msec in 25 msec steps. This method, it may be noted, is similar to one employed by Brown and Voth (1937) and, more recently, by Müller (1963).

Apparatus. The sides of the stimulus form were prepared as three 35 mm slides. These slides were independently projected on to a ground-glass rear projection screen by means of three Sylvania R 1131 C bulbs. (These bulbs were originally designed for use in photographic transmission and have fast rise and decay times.)

For each stimulus presentation there were five time periods to be controlled and/or varied: the duration of flash for each of the three bulbs and the two intervals between the sequential flashing of the bulbs. These time periods were controlled by five solid state electronic timers per-

mitting variation from 1 to 1000 msec. (Reliability was ± 5% and repeatability was ± 1% over the entire range.) Flashing of the bulbs in the appropriate sequence with appropriate intervals was achieved by an electronic logic circuit. (This equipment is now a standard item by the Polymetrics Division, Pennsylvania Optical Co., Reading, Pa.)

Design. The stimulus was presented by a method of limits with ten trials at each of the thirteen interpart intervals: five in an ascending, and five in a descending series. Thus, there were 130 trials for each subject. Four males and four females were employed in each of two series sequences, ascending-descending and descending-ascending, making a total of sixteen subjects. Two males and two females in each of the series sequences were retested 24 hr later.

Procedure. All testing was carried out in a dark room and subjects were dark-adapted for 10 min prior to testing. During the dark adaptation period, subjects were instructed as follows: "In a few minutes I will ask you to open your eyes and look straight ahead. I will give you a 'ready' signal and then flash a line triangle on the screen in front of you. As soon as you have seen the form, close your eyes. When your eyes are closed, I want you to report on certain temporal and spatial relations between the parts of the form you have seen. First, tell me whether the sides are simultaneous, overlapping, or successive in time.—When the sides come on and go off together, they are simultaneous; when they come on or go off in succession, but at some time more than one is on, they are overlapping; when they come on one at a time and no two are on at the same time, they are successive.—Then tell me whether all the sides are or are not joined to make a perfect triangle. If some do not join, tell me which pair or pairs of sides do not join to make a perfect angle.—Always make this judgment as if the sides were simultaneous."

After 10 min of dark adaptation, testing commenced and was usually complete within 45–60 min. During the testing period, subjects' heads were supported by a chin rest and lateral head movements were partially restrained.

RESULTS

The judgments of temporal relations show the typical functions for three category judgments (Figure 1A). In contrast to the judgments of temporal relations however, the judgments of spatial relations show a complex, non-linear decline with increase in interpart intervals (Figure 1B). These judgments initially decline, parallel with judgments of simultaneity, reach a plateau at 75–100 msec, and then slowly decline further. Examination of individual functions shows that this plateau is attributable in part to the fact that between

50 and 125 msec, twelve subjects show a paradoxical increase in judgments.

For the eight subjects retested 24 hr later, the overall forms of the functions are comparable for both test days. Product-moment correlation coefficients for the 50% points are +0.696 for simultaneity, +0.328 for succession, and +0.913 for all ends joined. Only the correlations for simultaneity and all ends joined are significantly different from zero ($P < 0.05$). While all day 2 thresholds are elevated, this difference is not significant at the 0.05 level as determined by variance analysis.

The limiting intervals for simultaneity and joining, viz. from onset of the first until offset of the last part, were obtained by adding the three 10 msec part durations with the two interpart intervals at the respective thresholds, 41 and 52 msec. Thus, the mean limiting interval is 112 msec for simultaneous judgments which is significantly different from the limiting interval

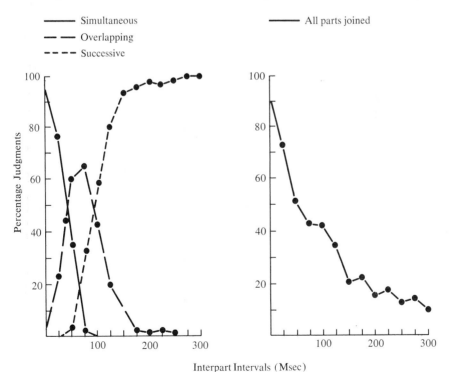

FIGURE 1 Experiment I: Mean percentage judgments of simultaneous, overlapping, and successive (A), and of sides joined to make a perfect triangle (B) as a function of interpart intervals (msec).

of 134 msec for judgments of all ends joined (Table 1). (Owing to the non-linear change in judgments for all ends joined, it was impossible to determine a 50% point for four of the sixteen subjects in the conventional manner. For these subjects, another measure was employed: the interpart interval at which judgments had declined to a minimum prior to showing the paradoxical increase referred to above.)

Experiment II

This experiment was basically the same as Experiment I with one main exception. Two conditions of presenting the triangle were employed: (1) sequential side part presentation, and (2) sequential angle part presentation. Accordingly, minor details of

method, design, and procedure were changed.

For the angle part presentation, the three angles, formed by bisecting the sides of the triangle, were flashed sequentially, each for 10 msec. The sequence was right angle, then top angle, and finally, left angle. For both side and angle part presentation, the stimulus form was identical in all respects and the same as that employed in Experiment I. Two males and two females in each of the two series sequences employed in Experiment I were tested in each of two conditions sequences: side-angle part presentation and angle-side part presentation. Thus, there were sixteen subjects. Half of the subjects were tested at interpart intervals from 0 to 100 msec, with both conditions presented in the same test-

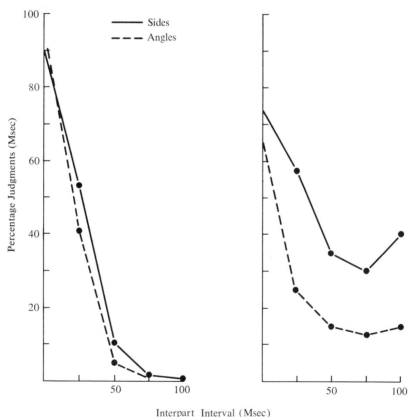

FIGURE 2 Experiment II: Mean percentage judgments of 'simultaneity' (A), and of 'parts joined' to make a perfect triangle (B), as a function of interpart intervals (msec) for side and angle part presentation.

TABLE 1

Mean Limiting Intervals (msec) for Judgments of Simultaneity and of Parts Joined to Make a Perfect Triangle, Exp. I and II

(Limiting intervals, from onset of the first until offset of the last part, were obtained by adding the three 10 msec part durations to the two interpart intervals at the respective 50% points.)

EXPERIMENT	PARTS	SIMULTANEOUS	ALL PARTS JOINED
1	Sides	112	134
2	Sides	84	102
2	Angles	71	52

ing session; the remaining half were tested at interpart intervals from 0 to 300 msec, with conditions separated by 24 hr.

RESULTS

Examination of the data for the subjects who provided judgments for three categories of time relations at interpart intervals from 0 to 300 msec shows that all functions are basically similar to those obtained in Experiment I. Functions for simultaneity and all parts joined for subjects tested from 0 to 100 msec are similar to the corresponding functions obtained for subjects tested from 0 to 300 msec.

Comparison of the "simultaneity" and "parts joined" functions for the two conditions (Fig. 2A, B) shows that angle-part presentation significantly decreases both 50% points. It is also clear, from examining the limiting intervals (Table 1), that the direction of the difference between intervals for simultaneity and side parts joined is comparable to the difference obtained in Experiment I, but opposite to the direction of the difference between intervals for simultaneity and angle parts joined. This interaction is significant ($P < 0.05$).

Discussion

It will be recalled that everyday perception of form is viewed as the perceptual achievement of the central operations of analysis and integration. The operation of analysis produces sequences of responses and the operation of integration produces a response to this sequence of responses. Normally, a form's parts are perceived as simultaneous and joined. The thresholds employed here are assumed to define the limiting intervals at which normal perception can be achieved to the hypothesized sequences of responses.

Viewed in these terms, the findings show: (a) as time between sequential responses increases, both perception of simultaneity and joining show an initial rapid and linear decrease; (b) when sequential response is to side parts, joining can be perceived over a larger interval than simultaneity; when sequential response is to angle parts, simultaneity can be perceived over a larger interval than joining; (c) when sequential response is to side parts, both joining and simultaneity can be perceived over larger intervals than when sequential response is to angle parts (see Table 1).

The fact that both perception of simultaneity and joining show a parallel decrease, as time between response increases, suggests that these two features of normal form perception depend on a common mechanism as proposed here. However, it is clear from the overall pattern of limiting intervals, that the operations of integration hypothesized to underlie these two features of form perception are not identical; they differ depending on whether responses to side or angle parts are integrated. Moreover, it is also evident that there is a differential integration underlying perception of line parts as simultaneous and joined versus perception of angle parts as simultaneous and joined.

Clearly the interpretation offered for these findings is subject to the reservation that, since eye movements are not monitored during stimulus presentation, eye movements between presentation of stimulus parts may be contributing to the definition of limiting intervals for simultaneity and joining. When, however, the limiting intervals for simultaneity (71, 84, 112 msec) and joining (52, 102, 134 msec) are compared with the smallest reported latency for a saccade (120 msec) (cf. Bartz, 1962; Ditchburn and Ginsborg, 1953; Ginsborg, 1953; Nachmias, 1959; Ratliff and Riggs, 1950; Tinker, 1958; Wertheimer, 1954), it is clear that saccadic eye movements are probable at only one (134 msec) of the limiting intervals. Furthermore, if saccadic eye movements were contributing to the perception of nonsimultaneity and non-joining of all parts, one might expect to see a sharp decrease in responses of simultaneity and joining at or immediately after an interpart interval (45 msec) when the period from onset of the first until offset of the last part coincides with the period of latency for a saccade (120 msec) When Figures 1 and 2 are examined, however, this expectation is not supported. It may be added, however, that there is no evidence at present which excludes the possibility that eye movements contribute to the findings reported here via generation of peripheral and/or central extra-ocular feedback.

In order to facilitate comparison with the related findings of others, it may be noted that the findings reported here shed some light on two questions of current interest, viz. what are the characteristics of the neural mechanism determining (a) temporal relations, and (b) figural relations between visual stimuli?

With respect to temporal relations, it has been proposed that the period of the EEG alpha rhythm is a manifestation of the central mechanism determining apparent simultaneity between stimuli (McCulloch, 1951; Murphree, 1954; Stroud, 1955). The findings here show that only when response is to line parts in sequence does the limiting interval for simultaneity fall within the range of alpha periods; when response is to angle parts the limiting interval for simultaneity is smaller than the smallest alpha period. This feature of the findings suggests that apparent simultaneity between stimuli is not a simple function of their occurrence within a centrally determined and fixed interval, but depends upon the mode of integrating different stimuli.

In regard to the problem of figural relations, Lashley's (1942) suggestion that a line is the simplest visual element is still pertinent. Recent electrophysiological work has indicated that certain cells in the visual cortex of cats respond optimally to line stimuli in different orientations (Hubel and Wiesel, 1959; Hubel, 1963). Thus, it may well be that form perception in humans depends on the output of such figural specific cells. Accordingly, one might speculate that perception of form entails a response to line parts of the form —analysis, and then a response to this response—integration (Hebb, 1963). The findings here might then be interpreted as supporting this speculation since perception of simultaneity and joining can be achieved at larger intervals when line parts are presented than when angle parts are presented. However, an alternative interpretation for these findings may be offered from the vantage point of the view proposed here. Simply that human form perception depends on both a differential response to line and angle parts of a form

—analysis, and a differential integration of line and angle part responses.

At present the operations of analysis and integration described here are hypothetical. There is little support for their usage in terms of present knowledge of the human nervous system's functioning. Nevertheless, formulation of these hypothetical operations has led to a method and to experiments which have provided new information concerning visual form perception.

References

BARTZ, A. (1962). Eye-movement latency, duration, and response time as a function of angular displacement. *J. exp. Psychol.* 64, 318–24.

BROWN, J. F. and A. C. VOTH. (1937). The path of seen movement as a function of the vector-field. *Amer. J. Psychol.* 49, 543–63.

DITCHBURN, R. W. and B. L. GINSBORG. (1952). Vision with a stablized retinal image. *Nature, Lond.,* 170, 36–7.

GIBSON, J. J. (1950). *The Perception of the Visual World.* Cambridge, Mass.: Riverside.

GINSBORG, B. L. (1953). Small involuntary movements of the eye. *Brit. J. Ophthal.* 37, 746–54.

HEBB, D. O. (1949). *The Organization of Behavior.* New York: Wiley.

HEBB, D. O. (1963). The semiautonomous process: its nature and nurture. *Amer. Psychologist,* 18, 16–27.

HELSON, H. (1926). The Psychology of Gestalt. *Amer. J. Psychol.* 37, 25–62.

HUBEL, D. H. (1963). Integrative processes in central visual pathways of the cat. *J. opt. Soc. Amer.* 53, 58–66.

HUBEL, D. H. and T. N. WIESEL. (1959). Receptive fields of single neurones in the cat's striate cortex. *J. Physiol.* 148, 574–91.

KOFFKA, K. (1935). *Principles of Gestalt Psychology.* New York: Harcourt Brace.

LASHLEY, K. S. (1942). The problem of cerebral organization. In *Biological Symposia,* vol. VII, ed. H. Kluver, Lancaster, Pa.: Catell.

LASHLEY, K. S. (1951). The problem of serial order in behavior. In *Cerebral Mechanism in Behavior,* ed. L. A. Jeffress, New York: Wiley.

LASHLEY, K. S., L. K. CHOW, and J. SEMMES. (1951). An examination of the electrical field theory of cerebral integration. *Psychol. Rev.* 58, 123–36.

McCULLOCH, W. S. (1951). Why the mind is in the head. In *Cerebral Mechanisms in Behavior,* ed. L. A. Jeffress, New York: Wiley.

MÜLLER, K. (1963). Der Aufbau figural-optisher Phänomene bei sukzessiver Reizung. *Psychol. Arb.,* no. 7.

MURPHREE, O. D. (1954). Maximum rates of form perception and the alpha rhythm: An examination and test of current nerve net theory. *J. exp. Psychol.* 43, 57–61.

NACHMIAS, J. (1959). Two dimensional motions of the retinal image during monocular fixation. *J. opt. Soc. Amer.* 49, 901–8.

NAGEL, E. (1963). Wholes, sums, and organic unities. In *Parts and Wholes,* ed. D. Lerner, New York: Free Press of Glencoe.

PIAGET, J. (1952). *The Origins of Intelligence in Children.* New York: International Universities.

PIAGET, J. (1963). Le développement des perceptions en fonction de l'âge. In *Traité de Psychologie Expérimentale,* vol. VI, ed. P. Fraisse, and J. Piaget, Paris: Universitaires de France.

RATLIFF, F. and L. A. RIGGS. (1950). Involuntary motions of the eye during monocular fixation. *J. exp. Psychol.* 40, 687–701.

STROUD, J. (1955). The fine structure of psychological time. In *Information Theory in Psychology,* ed. H. Quastler, New York: Free Press of Glencoe.

TINKER, M. A. (1958). Recent studies of eye movements in reading. *Psychol. Bull.* 55, 215–31.

UHR, L. (1963). "Pattern Recognition" computers as models for form perception. *Psychol. Bull.* 60, 40–73.

WERTHEIMER, G. (1954). Mechanisms of saccadic eye movements. *AMA. Arch. Ophthal.* 52, 710–24.

Two Operations in Character Recognition: Some Evidence from Reaction-time Measurements[*]

SAUL STERNBERG

Bell Telephone Laboratories

Theories of the recognition of a visual character may be divided into three sets, defined by the way in which the stimulus is encoded before being compared to a memorized target character. A character-classification experiment was performed in which the test stimuli were characters that were either intact or degraded by a superimposed pattern. Analyses of reaction-times in the experiment lead to the rejection of two of the three sets of theories. There appear to be at least two separate operations in the recognition or classification of a character. The first encodes the visual stimulus as an abstracted representation of its physical properties. The second, which may occur more than once, compares such a stimulus representation to a memory representation, producing either a match or a mismatch. A theory of high-speed exhaustive scanning in memory underlies the experiment and is given new support. The method of reaction-time analysis that is introduced, an elaboration of the Helmholtz-Donders subtraction method, may be applicable to the general problem of the invariance of perceived form under certain transformations of the stimulus.

Consider this simple task of recognition: a person is presented with a stimulus and is asked to judge whether or not it is a particular character. At some point between stimulus and response, a representation of the stimulus encounters a memory representation of the monitored character, and the two are compared. What is the nature of the encoded stimulus? In the formation of this representation, how much analysis of the stimulus is carried out?

At least two lines of approach to the problem of character recognition lead one to expect that the stimulus is processed to a considerable extent as its representation is formed. First, in some character-recognizing machines the stimulus is normalized, or subjected to filtering operations such as "thinning" and "smoothing," before being tested (Doyle, 1960; Minsky, 1963; Selfridge and Neisser, 1963; Stevens, 1961; Unger, 1959). Other artificial recognizers carry the preprocessing further, incorporating a stage in which features are extracted from the stimulus; these features are tested in the subsequent decision process (Bomba, 1959; Fischler et al. 1962; Stevens, 1961). Indeed, it has been argued that if characters are subject to noise or distortion then such a high degree of stimulus preprocessing is necessary in a workable recognition scheme (Uhr, 1963). A second line of approach is found in neuro-

[*] Perception and Psychophysics, 1967, vol. 2, pp. 43–53. The experiment on which this report is based was performed at The University of Pennsylvania with the support of Grant GB-1172 from the National Science Foundation. Part of the work was described at the A.F.C.R.L. Symposium on Models for the Perception of Speech and Visual Form (Boston, November 1964; Proceedings in preparation, M.I.T. Press.) I thank C. L. Mallows, P. Mermelstein, G. Sperling, N. S. Sutherland, and A. Treisman for helpful suggestions.

physiology. Recent animal studies show that the information available at the higher visual centers is not simply a mapping of the retinal image, but that abstracted features of the stimulus can be represented as well (Hubel, 1963).

Also relevant to the preprocessing of visual stimuli are recent developments in the study of "short-term" or "operating" memory. If characters were retained in memory as visual images, there would be no reason to expect a high degree of stimulus preprocessing before stimulus- and memory-representations were compared. A *raw image* ("direct copy") of the stimulus would be sufficient for comparison to the image of a monitored character. But Conrad (1964), Sperling (1960), and others have concluded that a visual character is often retained in memory in the form of a representation of its spoken name. The existence of such a representation would introduce the possibility that in the recognition task the stimulus is preprocessed to the point of naming and, a fortiori, identification.[1]

But whereas (a) there seems to be a theoretical need for a highly processed stimulus representation, (b) evidence of the neural machinery is becoming available, and (c) its existence is plausible in the light of our knowledge of memory, the behavioral evidence is sparse. This is not surprising. In a certain sense, the stimulus is lost until the response occurs. More specifically, the behavioral effects of most experimental manipulations can be attributed as easily to the operation of comparing stimulus- and memory-representations as to the encoding operation by which the stimulus representation is formed. What is needed are tools that allow the dissection of the behavioral effects into those attributable to the comparison operation, and those attributable to the encoding

operation. Such analysis would provide information about the nature of the operations, and therefore about the stimulus representation.

CHARACTER CLASSIFICATION

A tool of the required kind is provided by a recently discovered phenomenon in what may be described as a *character-classification task*. This is a generalization of the simple recognition task first mentioned. On each of a sequence of trials a character is presented as a test stimulus. The subject makes a *positive response* if the character is a member of a small memorized set of characters, called the *positive set,* and makes a *negative response* otherwise. For example, the subject may be told to operate the right-hand lever if the test stimulus is a "3" or a "7" and to operate the left-hand lever otherwise. In this example the positive set is of size two. The ensemble of possible test stimuli may consist of all the ten digits. The subject is encouraged to respond as rapidly as he can, while maintaining a low error-rate.

Results of several experiments on character-classification support a theory of high-speed scanning in memory (Sternberg, 1966). According to this theory, the time between stimulus and response is occupied, in part, by an exhaustive serial-comparison process. A representation of the test stimulus is compared successively to a sequence of memory representations, one for each member of the positive set, successive comparisons having the same mean duration. Each comparison results in either a match or a mis-match. After the search is completed, a positive response is initiated if there has been a match, and a negative response otherwise.

A few of the findings that support the exhaustive-scanning theory are as follows: first, mean latencies of both positive and negative responses increase linearly with the number of characters in the memorized set. This has been found for sets of up to six characters, with ensembles of digits or

---

[1] Nonvisual storage would *require* such a high degree of preprocessing only if a stored item could not be converted into visual form, for comparison with visual stimulus-representations.

letters.[2] Second, the mean increase in latency per character is approximately the same for positive responses as for negative responses. This equality suggests that the search is exhaustive, rather than being terminated when a match occurs. The magnitude of the latency increase indicates an average scanning rate between 25 and 30 characters per second. Third, although the size of the positive set affects the reaction time, the size of the full ensemble does not.

Although these findings provide no direct evidence about the nature of the representations that are successively compared, the rate of scanning, which is about four times the maximum rate of "internal speech" (Landauer, 1962), is suggestive. If the rate at which acoustic (or articulatory) memory representations can be scanned is limited by the rate of internal speech, then the use of such representations in the comparison operation is precluded.

Figure 1 is an idealization of the data obtained in a character-classification experiment. Mean reaction-time is plotted as a function of the size of the positive set. This *reaction-time function* is linear:

$$\overline{\text{RT}} = a + \beta s. \qquad (1)$$

Assuming the validity of the scanning theory, one is led to the following interpretation of such data. The slope, β, of the function is a measure of the mean time taken by the comparison of the stimulus representation to the memory representation of one character (comparison time). This comparison process will be called

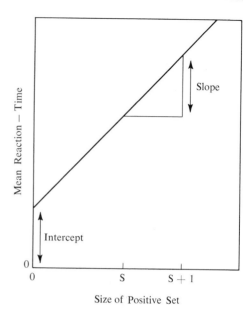

FIGURE 1 Idealized data from a character-classification experiment. The slope is a measure of the mean time taken by the comparison of the stimulus representation to the memory representation of one character (Operation 2). The zero-intercept is a measure of the mean time taken by the events before and/or after the series of comparisons, which include the formation of the stimulus representation (Operation 1).

Operation 2. The zero-intercept, a, is a measure of the mean time taken by events before and/or after the series of comparisons. These include the formation of the stimulus representation, which will be called *Operation 1*. Whereas Operation 1 is carried out only once, Operation 2 may occur several times, once for each character in the positive set.

THEORIES OF CHARACTER RECOGNITION

Theories of the character-recognition process fall into three broad classes, depending on the kind of stimulus representation postulated. Two or three examples from each class are described in Table 1. In theories of Class A, Operation 1 is inconsequential, and Operation 2 is carried out directly on a raw image of the stimulus. In theories of Classes B and C the

---

[2] For sets that consist of more than half of the ensemble this finding probably holds only if the subject is kept from making use of the *complement* of the positive set. Such large sets have therefore been studied only in experiments in which a new series of digits defining the positive set is presented on each trial, and (a) the time interval between series and test stimulus is too short to allow the subject to find the complement and/or (b) the subject is required to recall the series after his binary response.

stimulus representation is a processed version of the stimulus. In B1 and B2 it is a refined image; Operation 1 involves filtering and/or normalizing processes. In B3 the representation is a list of relevant features of the stimulus; Operation 1 involves the extraction of features. In theories of Classes A and B, Operation 1 produces a representation based on physical properties of the stimulus that can be specified without identification of the stimulus; the memory representation then used in Operation 2 is a character prototype, of either the template or feature-list variety. According to theories of Class C, on the other hand, Operation 1 identifies the stimulus, producing a representation based on its meaning or name, which encounters a memory representation of similar kind in Operation 2. In C1 the representation produced by Operation 1 incorporates neither sensory nor motor components (see e.g., Humphrey, 1951). In C2 it is an acoustic or articulatory image of the spoken name of the character.

TWO POSSIBLE EFFECTS OF STIMULUS DEGRADATION

It will now be evident how a character-classification experiment might provide a dissection tool. In the present study the experimental manipulation was the degrading of the test stimulus by superimposition of a checkerboard pattern. When the positive set contains just one member we have the simple recognition task in which the subject must decide whether the test stimulus is or is not a particular character. Suppose that his decision takes longer if the test stimulus is degraded. This fact alone does not allow us to determine whether the increase in reaction time is due to Operation 1, or Operation 2, or both. One can make this determination, however, by varying the size of the positive set and evaluating separately the effects of degradation on slope and intercept.

Let us consider how the reaction-time function (Equation 1) might change when the test stimuli are degraded. Two ex-

TABLE 1

Some Alternative Theories of Character Recognition

THEORY	OPERATION 1	STIMULUS REPRESENTATION	MEMORY REPRESENTATION	OPERATION 2
A1		raw image	template	template-matching
A2		raw image	feature list	feature-testing
B1	image-refining	refined image	template	template-matching
B2	image-refining	refined image	feature list	feature-testing
B3	feature-extracting	feature list	feature list	feature-list-matching
C1	identifying	imageless concept	imageless concept	concept-matching
C2	identifying and naming	image of spoken name	image of spoken name	acoustic or articulatory matching

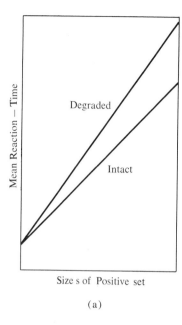
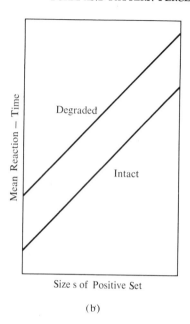

(a)   (b)

FIGURE 2   Two possibilities of the effect of test-stimulus degradation on the reaction-time function. The left-hand panel (a) corresponds to theories of Class A
and Equation 2. The right-hand panel (b) corresponds to theories of Class C
and Equation 3.

treme possibilities are shown in Figure 2. Suppose first that Operation 1 is inconsequential, and the stimulus representation is a replica of the stimulus, as in theories of Class A. The duration of Operation 1 would then be unaffected by degradation, and the increase in reaction time would have to arise from an increase, $\Delta \beta$, in the mean duration, β, of the comparison process. One would expect the slope of the function to increase, but not its zero-intercept (Figure 2a):

$$\overline{RH} = a + (\beta + \Delta\beta)s. \qquad (2)$$

At the other extreme, the stimulus representation might be a sufficiently processed version of the stimulus so that it incorporated none of the degradation. One example of such a representation is an image of the spoken name of the character, as in Theory C2. In this case there would be no reason for an increase in the duration, β, of the comparison process. The increase in reaction time would have to

reflect an increase, Δa, in the time to form the stimulus representation. One would expect an increase in the intercept, a, of the reaction-time function, but not in its slope (Figure 2b):

$$\overline{RT} = (a + \Delta a) + \beta s. \qquad (3)$$

Analyses such as these depend, of course, on the validity of the exhaustive-scanning theory and, more generally, on the existence of additive reaction-time components and the validity of using the Helmholtz-Donders subtraction method for their measurement. On the other hand, the present study provides as byproducts several new tests of the theory, as well as additional information about the scanning process.

Method

Apparatus. Test stimuli were digits (about 0.6 in. high) produced by a Burroughs "Nixie" tube (Type 6844A). A beam-splitter caused a checkerboard pattern (about 7 cycles/in.) that was illuminated by an array of neon lamps (Type NE2H) to be superimposed on the digits. The degradation thus produced had previously been found to cause an increase in reaction time without substantially increasing the low error-rate. A warning signal and fixation aid was provided by an annulus that surrounded the digits and could be illuminated by a second set of neon lamps. On either side of the Nixie display was a translucent panel that could be illuminated to provide feedback signals. The subject viewed the display binocularly from a distance of about 29 in. while seated in a dimly lit booth, his head supported by a chin-rest. He rested his elbows on the table in front of him, positioning the fingers of each hand lightly on the table and immediately behind a lever which he could operate by flexing his fingers, thereby pulling it toward him. Near the beginning of its stroke the lever produced a contact-closure. The lever that was operated by the subject's dominant hand represented the positive response. The subject wore headphones through which white noise was steadily delivered at a comfortable level, in order to mask apparatus and other sounds.

Trial Events. A trial consisted of the following events: (a) intertrial interval of 2.0 sec, (b) warning signal (illumination of annulus) for 1.25 sec, (c) display of test stimulus or 44 msec, either intact or degraded, (d) subject's response (operation of one of the two levers), (e) feedback light displayed for 0.75 sec. from occurrence of response. (The panel on the side of the lever that had been operated was illuminated in green if the response was correct, in red if incorrect.) The time from onset of test stimulus to lever displacement was recorded with an accuracy of ± 1 msec.

Test-stimulus Sequences. The purpose of the experiment was to determine the difference between reaction times to intact and degraded test stimuli for positive sets of size s = 1, 2, and 4. It was important to avoid confounding the variation in s with three other factors that might affect performance in this situation (Garner, 1962, ch. 2), namely (a) response entropy, (b) stimulus entropy, and (c) systematic differences from digit to digit. This was accomplished by means of the arrangement shown in Figure 3. For a given subject, each of the ten subscripted letters represents a particular digit, and the

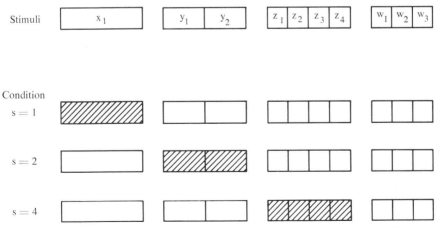

FIGURE 3 Arrangement for varying size of positive set while stimulus population and response frequencies remain fixed. Letters represent test stimuli and cell widths represent their relative frequencies. Those cells in a row that are hatched represent stimuli in the positive set in that condition.

width of its cell represents the relative frequency with which it occurred in the population of test stimuli. The relative frequencies were x_1, $\frac{4}{15}$; each y, $\frac{2}{15}$; each z, $\frac{1}{15}$; and each w, $\frac{1}{15}$. For a given subject the stimulus population was the same in all three conditions; the important difference among conditions was in the assignment of stimuli to responses. In the row of cells associated with a condition, a hatched cell represents a digit assigned to the positive set of that condition. In each condition the test stimuli in the population were presented in a different random order.

With this arrangement, the size of the positive set could be varied without altering the relative frequency ($\frac{4}{15}$) of positive responses. Furthermore, for a given subject the relative frequency with which a particular digit occurred as a test stimulus and, a fortiori, the stimulus entropy and the sequential properties of the test-stimulus sequence, were the same from condition to condition. It should be noted that in order to exploit the invariance of the test-stimulus population so as to balance the effects of individual digits over conditions, data from the positive and negative responses in a condition had to be pooled rather than examined separately; this was done in the main analysis.

A fourth condition, with s = 3, was used for practice. For a given subject, the positive set was composed of the digits represented by w_1, w_2, and w_3. In order that the relative frequency of positive re-

sponses be $\frac{4}{15}$, as in the other conditions, the test stimulus population had to be altered slightly.

Design. Each of twelve subjects was run for two sessions lasting about 1 hr. and separated by about a week. Each session had four parts, one for each value of s, and each part had two subparts, one with intact and one with degraded test stimuli. Part 1 was always the s = 3 condition. In the remaining parts a pair of subjects was assigned to each of the six possible orders of the s = 1, 2, and 4 conditions. One member of each pair had subparts in the order intact, degraded; the other member had the reverse order. For each subject the order of degraded and intact subparts and of conditions s = 1, 2, and 4 were reversed from Session 1 to Session 2. Trials were grouped in blocks of 18; there were three blocks per subpart except for condition s = 3, in which there were two.

In each session, three different identifications of digits with the letters of Figure 3 were used, with two pairs of subjects assigned to each. The composition of the resulting positive sets is given in Table 2. For each subject the sets in the two sessions were "orthogonal": any two digits in the same set in Session 1 were in two different sets in Session 2.

Subjects. Subjects, students at The University of Pennsylvania, were paid for

TABLE 2

Composition of Positive Sets of Sizes s = 1, 2, and 4

SUBJECTS	SESSION 1			SESSION 2		
	s = 1	s = 2	s = 4	s = 1	s = 2	s = 4
1–4	5	4,9	0,1,3,7	7	3,8	1,5,6,9
5–8	8	2,7	3,5,6,9	9	0,6	2,4,5,8
9–12	7	0,9	2,3,5,6	2	1,5	0,3,4,7

their services. The twelve subjects were selected from a group of twenty on the basis
of the accuracy of their performance in
Session 1. Any subject who made more
than three errors in the last 36 trials in
any of the last six subparts in that session
was eliminated.

Payoffs and Other Aspects of Procedure.
For each block of 18 trials a subject received a score of one point per 0.01 sec.
in his mean reaction-time and 10 points
per error. In each session the lowest-scoring
half of the subjects were each paid a $1.00
bonus. In both sessions a subject was told
his mean reaction-time, number of errors,
and score, after each block in part 1. After
this he was told only his overall errors,
mean time, and score, for each part at the
end of that part. He was able to rest after
each block.

At the beginning of Session 1 the 10
digits were displayed serially several times,
both intact and degraded. Before each part
the subject was told the composition of the
positive set. A right-handed subject, for
example, would be told: "In the next part
of the experiment, the digits for which the
right-hand lever is correct are . . . The
other lever is correct for all other digits."

Results

Excluded from the analyses were the
data from part 1, the first block of each
subpart, and the first three trials of each
block. Also excluded were the occasional
trials (2.2% in Session 1 and 2.5% in Session 2) on which the response was incorrect. There remained about 29 latencies
per subpart for each subject, which included latencies of both positive and negative responses. To avoid possible effects
on mean reaction-times of individual differences among digits (see section on test-
stimulus sequences), the latencies of positive and negative responses were pooled
and their arithmetic mean obtained. Means
over subjects of the resulting values are

displayed in Figure 4. Also shown are four
lines that were fitted by least squares, and
their equations.

BASIC FEATURES OF THE
REACTION-TIME FUNCTION

Although the experiment was not designed as a test of the exhaustive-scanning
theory, two features of the data are of
particular relevance to its validity, and
merit examination. The first is the linearity
of the reaction-time function. The data are
well described by the linear functions
shown in Figure 4, which account for
99.6% of the variance within the four sets
of means.

The second feature is the relation between the slopes of the latency functions
for positive and negative responses. Lines
fitted separately to the overall mean latencies of positive and of negative responses
differ in slope by 5.4 ± 2.8 msec/charac-
ter (SE [standard error of the mean] based
on 11 df), with the negative function the
steeper. This difference was not affected
systematically by either test-stimulus
degradation or session. The p-value derived
from a t-test for slope equality is 0.08. A
small slope difference in the opposite direction (-1.6 ± 3.0 msec/character) was
observed in a previous experiment of similar design.[3] Taken together with the
present results, that finding reduces, but
does not eliminate, one's suspicion that
there may be a small but systematic difference. On the other hand, the difference is
small enough clearly to favor an exhaustive
process (for which slopes are expected to
be equal) over one that terminates when
a match occurs (for which the positive
slope is expected to be half the negative).

The zero-intercept of the estimated
latency-function for positive responses,
which were required on about 27% of the
trials, exceeds the corresponding value for
negative responses by 22.4 ± 9.5 msec.
(SE based on 11 df); this intercept differ-

[3] Experiment 2 in Sternberg, 1966.

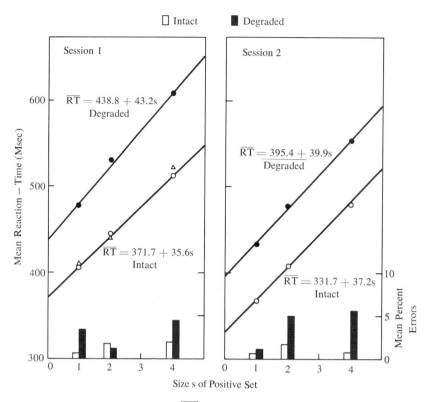

☐ Intact   ■ Degraded

FIGURE 4   Mean reaction-time ($\overline{\text{RT}}$) and error percentage as functions of size of positive set for intact and degraded test stimuli. Left-hand and right-hand panels show data from Sessions 1 and 2, respectively. Each point (circles) represents about 29 observations from each of 12 subjects. Lines were fitted by least squares; their equations are displayed. Triangles represent data from a previous experiment.[4]

ence was not affected systematically by either test-stimulus degradation or session.

In the previous experiment, (3) which took place in a single session, test stimuli were intact, but instead of being flashed for 44 msec. they were exposed until the response occurred. Nevertheless the pooled means (triangular points in Figure 4, least squares line being RT = 369.4 + 38.3s msec) are almost identical to the values for intact stimuli in Session 1 of the present experiment (RT = 371.7 + 35.6s msec).

EFFECTS OF TEST-STIMULUS
DEGRADATION ON THE REACTION-
TIME FUNCTION

The increases that degradation produced in the slope and zero-intercept of the

reaction-time function are shown in Table 3 for the two sessions. Degradation affected the intercept markedly in both sessions. The difference between the effects in the two sessions is small, amounting to 3.4 ± 7.4 msec. (SE based on 5 df.)[4] The effect of degradation on the slope is substantially smaller in absolute value than its effect on the zero-intercept and is sig-

[4] The experimental unit in these analyses was the pair of subjects having the same order of conditions s = 1, 2, and 4 but opposite orders of intact and degraded subparts. The data for each pair were averaged and then corrected for the mean part-of-session effect. Lines were fitted by least squares to the corrected values. For each of the six pairs of subjects, and for each session, the increases produced by degradation in slope and zero-intercept were determined. SEs were based on these values for each of the two sessions, or on the appropriate differences between them.

TABLE 3

Effects of Test-Stimulus Degradation on Estimated Parameters of the Reaction-Time Function (SEs are based on 5 df.)

EFFECT OF DEGRADATION	SESSION 1	SESSION 2
Increase in mean zero-intercept (msec)	67. ± 5.7	63.7 ± 10.4
Increase in mean slope (msec/character)	7.6 ± 2.4	2.7 ± 3.8

nificant in Session 1 only. (In Session 1 the value of t for the slope effect is 3.22 with 5 df; the p-value for the positive tail is 0.013. The corresponding p-value for Session 2 is 0.25.) The difference between the slope effects in the two sessions is 4.9 ± 3.3 msec/character (SE based on 5 df; t is 1.49, and the p-value for one tail is 0.10).[5]

The reaction-time functions changed in two respects from session to session. First, as already indicated, the functions for intact and degraded test stimuli are more nearly parallel in Session 2 than in Session 1. Second, there was a general increase in speed, with the mean zero-intercept reduced by 41.7 ± 13.8 msec from first to second session (SE based on 5 df). The increase in speed occurred gradually within both sessions; the overall mean reaction-time was 521.6, 490.0, and 480.1 msec in parts 2–4 of Session 1, and 458.5, 451.6, and 450.5 msec in parts 2–4 of Session 2. On the other hand, there appears to have been no general reduction in slope.

[5] For the six experimental units (pairs of subjects) the differences between estimated slopes for degraded and intact test stimuli in Session 1 were 14.7, 12.0 9.8, 6.5, 3.9, and −1.2 msec/character. In Session 2 these differences became 16.2, 1.3, −2.0, −5.0, 11.8, and −6.3 msec/character respectively. The estimates of slope- and intercept-effects in Session 1 appear not to have been biased by the rejection of subjects who exceeded the error-rate criterion in that session (see section on design). For the rejected subjects both of the mean effects fell within one SE of the values for accepted subjects.

COMPARISON OF EFFECTS OF
TEST-STIMULUS DEGRADATION
ON LATENCIES OF POSITIVE AND
NEGATIVE RESPONSES

The magnitudes of the effects of degradation on latencies of positive and negative responses were determined from the combined data for conditions in which s = 1, 2, and 4. Combining these data produced considerable overlap of the populations of test stimuli that contributed to positive and negative means, although these populations were not identical (see Figure 3). The results are displayed in Table 4. Evidently, the extent to which the response to a test stimulus is slowed by degradation does not depend on whether the stimulus is a member of the positive set.

Discussion

NATURE OF THE STIMULUS
REPRESENTATION

On the basis of these findings and the exhaustive-scanning theory, what can be said about the nature of Operation 1 and the stimulus representation it produces? Although the reaction-time functions of Session 2 closely resemble the hypothetical functions shown in the right-hand panel of Figure 2, the data from Session 1 depart significantly from both of the extreme

TABLE 4

Comparison of Effects of Degradation on Latencies of Positive and Negative Responses
(Data from conditions with s = 1, 2, and 4 have been combined. SEs are based on 10 df.)

EFFECT OF DEGRADATION	SESSION 1	SESSION 2
Mean increase in positive-response latency (msec)	84.8	68.6
Mean increase in negative-response latency (msec)	84.2	70.6
Difference (msec)	$+0.6 \pm 6.3$	-2.0 ± 8.6

possibilities shown in that figure. The representation is apparently very far from a raw image of the stimulus, contrary to theories of Class A. It is sufficiently abstracted so that, in Session 2, the degradation of the test stimulus does not prolong the comparison operation. This conclusion follows from the virtual equality of the slopes of the two reaction-time functions in that session. The marked effect of degradation on reaction time is due, in both sessions, primarily to a change in some part of the process other than the comparison operation. It is plausible to assume that the affected part of the process occurs *before* the comparison stage and is, in fact, Operation 1. (The magnitude of the effect of degradation on the zero-intercept, about 65 msec, then provides a lower bound for the duration of Operation 1 with degraded test stimuli.)

The major effect of test-stimulus degradation then, is on Operation 1. But degradation can influence the comparison operation as well. This is shown by the 21% difference that was observed in Session 1 between the slopes of the reaction-time functions for intact and degraded stimuli. Visual degradation could influence Operation 2 only if there were residual degradation in the stimulus representation. It follows that, contrary to theories of Class C, what is represented are physical properties of the stimulus, rather than the identity or the name of the character. The

observed reaction-time functions appear to be consistent only with theories of Class B.

According to these findings, then, identification need not be functionally prior to classification. This suggests (without implying) that it might not have temporal priority either, and that it could therefore be absent altogether in a classification task. Neisser (1963, 1964) has drawn this conclusion from subjects' reports of failure to "see" characters that are rejected in the course of visual search.

The existence of evidence showing that visual memory-representations are used in Operation 2 does not imply that they are also used in the retention of the positive set. Retained acoustic representations, for example, might be converted into the appropriate form when required. (By the same token, the occurrence of "acoustic confusions" in the recall of visually presented characters does not per se imply acoustic storage, but only an acoustic representation at some stage.)

The effect of degradation on slope was less in the second session than in the first, suggesting that some sort of learning occurred. This would not be surprising, since the degradation was produced by superimposition of a fixed pattern, and the ensemble of test stimuli was the same from session to session. The improvement cannot be attributed to familiarity with particular positive sets, since their composition was changed from session to session (see section on design). Nor can it be attributed to a general increase in efficiency of the comparison operation, since the slope of the reaction-time function for intact stimuli did not change from session to session. This invariance of slope, together with the equality of the intercept effects from session to session, also makes unlikely the possibility of the fundamental change, with practice, from a visual to a nonvisual stimulus representation. One cannot decide on the basis of these data, however, whether the improvement resulted from Operation 1 becoming more effective at eliminating degradation from the representation, or from Operation 2 becoming less sensitive to the degradation that remained.[6]

ALTERNATIVE MECHANISMS
FOR THE SLOPE EFFECT

Among the assumptions about the scanning process that were made in the previous section is that the number of comparisons on a trial equals the size, s, of the positive set. Given this assumption, any increase that stimulus degradation produces in the slope of the reaction-time function must reflect a corresponding increase in the mean comparison-time. An alternative is that there is an increase in the mean *number* of comparisons. This could result from at least two mechanisms that merit consideration.

Multiple Memory-Representations. The first is the generation of multiple memory-representations (variants) for some or all of the characters in the positive set. Such a technique is used in some artificial recognizers (e.g., Mermelstein and Eden, 1964). It would provide a means of counteracting potential defects in a visual stimulus-representation produced by Opera-

tion 1. For example, if degradation might alter or obliterate certain stimulus features then, for some of the characters in the positive set, Operation 2 would involve the comparison of the stimulus-representation to more than one feature list, thus increasing the effective size of the set. The number of variants per character, and hence the number of comparisons per trial, would be increased when the subject expected the test-stimulus to be degraded. This would lead to an increase in the mean comparison-time *per character,* and hence in the slope, with no change in the mean comparison-time *per variant.* Unless we make additional assumptions, the results of the present experiment do not permit us to discriminate between an increase in the number of memory representations and an increase in the mean comparison-time per representation.

Multiple Stimulus-Representations. The second possible mechanism in which degradation would influence the number of comparisons made rather than the comparison time, is the generation of multiple stimulus-representations, which might be proposed in an attempt to salvage theories of Class C. A degraded test stimulus might occasionally be ambiguous, producing representations of more than one character; a serial-comparison process would then be carried out for each. Suppose that two representations, rather than one, were generated by Operation 1 on a proportion, p, of the trials. Then the mean number of comparisons would be $(1 + p)s$ rather than s:

$$\overline{RT} = (a + \Delta a) + \beta (1 + p)s. \quad (4)$$

The result would be a slope increase of 100p% with no change in the mean time per comparison. This explanation would reconcile the observed slope effect with theories of Class C, thereby weakening

---

[6] This argument is one of several in the present paper that depend on the assumption that any effect of degradation on an operation will be revealed by a change in the duration of that operation.

our conclusions. Multiple stimulus-representations would also give rise to false-positive responses. The proposed mechanism must be rejected because it leads to several predictions about such errors that are inconsistent with the data, given the magnitude of the observed slope-effect. (For example, even if stimulus ambiguity were the only source of false positives, the mean proportion of positive responses on negative trials would be ps/9, or 0.095 for s = 4 in Session 1; the observed value is only 0.045 for the 20 subjects run in that session, and 0.023 for the subset of subjects who met the error-rate criterion.)

IMPLICATIONS FOR THE
EXHAUSTIVE-SCANNING THEORY
AND SOME COMPETITORS

It has been assumed that an increase in response latency caused by stimulus degradation might arise from one or both of two possible sources: (a) an effect on Operation 1. This operation precedes the classification decision; any change (Δa) in its duration should therefore affect positive and negative responses equally. (b) An effect on Operation 2. Since scanning is exhaustive, this operation occurs the same number of times (s) whichever decision is required; any change $(\Delta \beta)$ in its duration should likewise affect positive and negative responses equally. The observed equality of the increases in positive- and negative-response latencies therefore supports the above assumption.

On the other hand, this equality of effects is hard to reconcile with a theory in which the amount of processing of the stimulus depends on whether or not it is a member of the positive set. Such a theory, involving the operation of a hierarchy of feature recognizers, has been put forward by Neisser (1963, 1964) for monitoring in visual search. He proposes that a stimulus is tested first for gross features, is processed further only if it passes the first test, and so on. More tests are therefore carried out for targets than for non-

targets. If degradation increased the duration of such tests, its effect on response latency would increase with the number of tests. If this kind of theory were valid for the present experiment one might therefore expect stimulus degradation to have a greater effect on positive- than on negative-response latencies. (An alternative possibility is that by obliterating some features, degradation would increase the number of tests required before a nontarget was rejected, thereby increasing the latency of negative responses. A positive response would entail the testing of all pertinent features, whether the stimulus was degraded or not; its latency would therefore be unaffected. Again, the effects of degradation would be unequal, but in the opposite direction.)

The exhaustive-scanning theory describes a process of comparison of stimulus- and memory-representations. Many of the previously available findings (Sternberg, 1966) were consistent with an alternative theory in which scanning consists, instead, of the search for a "marker" associated with one of the memory representations of the positive set. Each possible test stimulus is represented in memory before the trial begins. When a test stimulus is presented it is identified and the corresponding memory representation is "marked." The duration of this operation is independent of the size of the positive set. The representations of members of the positive set are then serially and exhaustively scanned for the presence of a marker. This theory may now be rejected because, like theories of Class C, it cannot be reconciled with an effect of stimulus degradation on the scanning rate.

The effects on reaction time of experimental variations have occasionally been explained in terms of changes in the amount of time occupied by the sampling of information from the stimulus (e.g., Fitts et al. 1963; Stone, 1960). That this kind of explanation may be of limited usefulness for simple-reaction time has been shown, for example, by Raab and Fehrer (1962), who found that differences in the luminance of a 2-msec flash could produce differences of 120 msec in reaction time. The present experiment provides similar evidence for choice-reaction time. First, the effects on reaction time of both degradation (65 msec) and set size (as much as 130 msec) were greater than the duration of the test stimulus (44 msec). Second, the reaction-time function for intact stimuli appears to be unaffected by whether the test-stimulus exposure is brief or long (response-terminated).

FURTHER APPLICATION OF
THE METHOD

It may be possible to apply the experimental technique described here to the general problem of explaining "form constancy," the invariance of object identification with respect to certain transformations of the stimulus (Attneave, 1962). There are many ways of transforming a stimulus without necessarily altering a classification or identification response. The addition of a checkerboard is one example; others are rotation, reflection, magnification, blurring, and distortion. But whereas a response may be the same despite a stimulus transformation, its latency may not be. In such cases, investigating the locus of changes in latency may reveal something of the mechanism that underlies the response invariance.

References

ATTNEAVE, F. Perception and related areas. In S. Koch (Ed.), *Psychology: A study of a Science.* New York: McGraw Hill, vol. 4, 1962. pp. 619–659.

BOMBA, J. S. Alpha-numeric character recognition using local operations. *Proc. east. joint Comput. Conf.,* 1959, 16, 218–224.

CONRAD, R. Acoustic confusions in immediate memory. *Brit. J. Psychol.,* 1964, 55, 75–84.

DOYLE, W. Recognition of sloppy, hand-printed characters. *Proc. west. joint Comput Conf.,* 1960, 17, 133–142.

FISCHLER, M., R. L. MATTSON, O. FIRSCHEIN, and L. D. HEALY. An approach to general pattern recognition. *IRE Trans. inform. Theory,* 1962, 8, 64–73.

FITTS, P. M., J. R. PETERSON, and G. WOLPE. Cognitive aspects of information processing: II. Adjustments to stimulus redundancy. *J. exp. Psychol.,* 1963, 65, 423–432.

GARNER, W. R. *Uncertainty and structure as psychological concepts.* New York: Wiley, 1962.

HUBEL, D. H. Integrative processes in central visual pathways of the cat. *J. Opt. Soc. Amer.,* 1963, 53, 58–66.

HUMPHREY, G. *Thinking.* London: Methuen, 1951.

LANDAUER, T. K. Rate of implicit speech. *Percept. mot. Skills,* 1962, 15, 646.

MERMELSTEIN, P., and M. EDEN. Experiments on computer recognition of connected handwritten words. *Inf. Cont.,* 1964, 7, 255–270.

MINSKY, M. Steps toward artificial intelligence. In E. A. Feigenbaum and J. Feldman (Eds.), *Computers and thought.* New York: McGraw Hill, 1963. pp. 406–450.

NEISSER, U. Decision-time without reaction-time: Experiments in visual scanning. *Amer. J. Psychol.,* 1963, 76, 376–385.

NEISSER, U. Visual search. *Scient. American,* 1964, 210, 94–102.

RAAB, D., and E. FEHRER. Supplementary report: The effect of stimulus duration and luminance on visual reaction time. *J. exp. Psychol.,* 1962, 64, 326–327.

SELFRIDGE, O. G., and U. NEISSER. Pattern recognition by machine. In E. A. Feigenbaum and J. Feldman (Eds.), *Computers and thought.* New York: McGraw Hill, 1963. pp. 237–250.

SPERLING, G. The information available in brief visual presentations. *Psychol. Monogr.,* 1960, 75, No. 11 (Whole No. 498).

STERNBERG, S. High-speed scanning in human memory. *Science,* 1966, 153, 652–654.

STEVENS, MARY E. *Automatic character recognition: A state-of-the-art report.* NBS Tech. Note 112. Washington, D. C.: U. S. Department of Commerce, 1961.

STONE, M. Models for choice-reaction time. *Psychometrika,* 1960, 25, 251–260.

UHR, L. "Pattern recognition" computers as models for form perception. *Psychol. Bull.,* 1963, 60, 40–73.

UNGER, S. H. Pattern detection and recognition. *Proc. IRE,* 1959, 47, 1737–1752.

Mechanism of the Figural Aftereffects*

LEO GANZ

New York University

It is suggested that the figural aftereffects are actually a species of simultaneous illusion in which the afterimage of the inspection object acts as an inducing figure. The afterimage displaces the test contour in phenomenological space because the inducing contour exerts inhibition on the test contour. A simple mathematical theory is described which accounts for the spatial distribution of displacements.

When contours of visual objects are close together, they often induce shifts in their respective *apparent* locations. Since the objects are not, in fact, changed in their positions in the visual field, it must be the neural correlates of these edges or lines which somehow interact, shifting each other's positions in their topographic pro-

* *Psychological Review,* 1966, vol. 73, pp. 128–150.

jection in the visual system. The phenomenological result is a deviation in perception from verdicality, an illusion. In Figure 1 the lines of the square on the left traversing the concentric circles are so affected by each intersecting arc as to increase slightly the angle of each intersection, especially if the angle of intersection is somewhere midway between zero and 90°. This gives the square a slightly concave appearance. Many illusions—such as

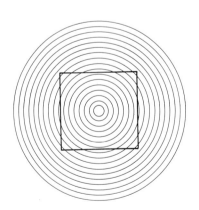 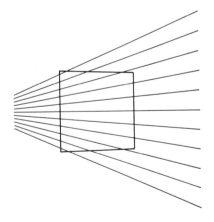

FIGURE 1   Two geometrical illusions. (In the left figure, the lines of the square traversing the concentric circles are seen by many observers to turn toward the center of the circles. In the right figure, the square is seen as a trapezoid, the side closer to the intersection of the converging lines looking larger. (Note that in both cases the phenomenon involves a growth in the angles formed by lines intersecting at 10°–40°.)

those of Hering, Wundt, Müller-Lyer, Zöllner, and Poggendorff—seem to involve such a common principle.

There is another class of contour shifts—the figural aftereffects—in which the inducing contour[1] seems to act proactively. The experimenter (E) presents an inducing figure in the observer's (O's) visual field, then removes it, and then presents a test figure. Even with this temporal separation between the two figures, the first still continues to act on the second so as to shift the second's apparent position.

Figure 2 illustrates an experiment involving such a procedure (Köhler and Wallach, 1944). O is first shown the two black rectangles (marked I in the figure), which are the inducing figures. He fixates the X mark. Then, usually after about 60 seconds of inspection, these rectangles are removed. Now the two outline squares (each a test figure) are shown, and O again fixates the X mark. Frequently O will report that the square on the left looks higher than that on the right (in fact they are equally high). This is a typical *displacement effect*; contours are repulsed away from the edge of the previously shown inspection figure. The displacement effect is typically maximal not when the inducing and test lines abut, but when they are actually separated. Köhler and Wallach have called this the paradoxical distance effect.

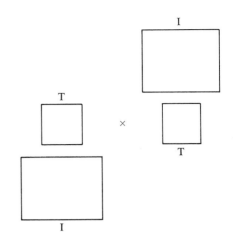

FIGURE 2 A stimulus configuration used by Köhler and Wallach (1944) to study figural aftereffects. (O fixates the X mark, and the I figure is presented. Then the I figure is removed, and the T figures are presented. The T figures are then seen more dimly, and repelled away from the former locus of the I figures. The repulsion is reported by many Os when I and T are presented together.)

[1] Using commonly accepted terminology, we call the *inducing figure* a line, edge, object, etc., introduced as an independent variable into O's sensory field, visual or other. The test figure is a dependent variable, a type of probe stimulus, upon which the effect is exerted. In this paper we will be concerned mostly with a dimming or displacement in appearance. The *comparison figure* is any figure which is placed far enough away from the inducing figure so as to be only mildly affected by the independent variable. Thus, any change in appearance or position of the test figure is gauged by contrasting it with the less affected comparison figure. The *interfigural distance* (S) is always the distance between the inducing and the test figure (in minutes of visual angle unless otherwise noted).

In the experiment illustrated in Figure 3, we first presented O with a circle as an inducing figure, and O fixates the X mark on the right edge of the circle. This figure is then removed, and an outline rectangle, T, is presented, with the same fixation mark, X, as shown. O reports that the left part of the rectangle looks as though it has shrunk (a *size effect*, often equivalent to the displacement effect and again involving a repulsion away from the inspection-figure contour). Subjects also report that the test contours left of the fixation mark (inside the former inspection circle) look dimmer, or washed out, with less contrast (the so-called *color effect*). Lastly, the left half of the rectangle is often seen further back in space (the *depth effect*).

It is not necessary to present the inducing and test figures in succession to see the displacement effects. Many Os looking at Figures 2 or 3 from about 3 meters distance, with the inducing and test figures shown simultaneously, still report the dis-

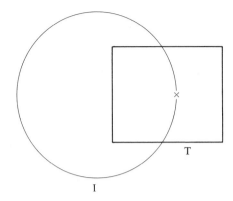

FIGURE 3   Same as in Figure 2.

their earlier experiments and has recently been reiterated (Logan, 1960). Do the two sets of displacement effects have identical mechanisms? This constitutes the point of departure of the present theory.

The initial theory of the "Figural After-Effects" (Köhler and Wallach, 1944) used simple physical principles involving current flow in a volume conductor such as the visual cortex to derive the distortions in perceptual appearance. The theory attracted considerable attention, some of it critical (Day, Pollack, and Seagrim, 1959; Hebb, 1949; McEwen, 1958; Spitz, 1958). The main criticisms have been that:

placement effects we have described. This similarity in results between the simultaneous and successive presentations was already apparent to Köhler and Wallach in

1. Lateral direct-current flow can be disrupted without noticeable

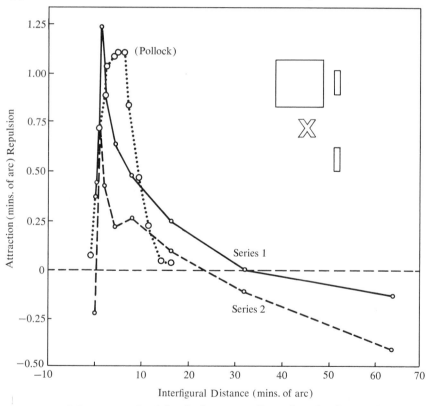

FIGURE 4   The magnitude of the displacement effect when the distance between the inducing and the test figure is varied. (The inducing figure is a white square, and the test figure is a white vertical line. *They are presented together,* as depicted in the insert, in the manner of a simultaneous illusion. The curves on the left represent two successive series of measurements with *I* and *T* figures presented together, N = 60. The rightward curve, Pollock, 1958, represents data, adjusted in height, from *a successive presentation: I* and then *T*.)

changes in perceptual function (Lashley, Chow and Semmes, 1951; Sperry and Miner, 1955; Sperry, Miner, and Myers, 1955).

2. The theory assumes that a topologically faithful "picture" is transmitted to the cortex (Hebb, 1949), but in fact each synaptic stage is the site of radical information processing (Hubel and Wiesel, 1959, 1962; Kuffler, 1953; Lettvin, Maturana, McCulloch, and Pitts, 1959).

3. The theory is basically a fatigue theory, yet the effects build up almost instantaneously (Ikeda and Obonai, 1953; Köhler and Wallach, 1944, p. 355; Oyama, 1953, 1956). In fact, as we have seen, one often obtains quite comparable results by presenting the inducing and test figures simultaneously. In a recent experiment, 60 subjects were shown a simultaneous pres-

entation of the inducing and test figures originally used by Köhler and Wallach. The contour repulsions obtained are given in Figure 4. A comparison with an experiment in which the figures were presented successively (Pollack, 1958) suggests a close correspondence of the two sets of results (see also Ikeda and Obonai, 1955; Ikuta, 1956; Logan, 1960; Nozawa, 1953).

4. Displacements sometimes occur *toward* satiated areas, as in the experimental results shown in Figure 5 (see also Ganz, 1964; Ganz and Day, in press; Nozawa, 1953a, 1953b; Smith, 1954).

5. Independent indexes of the hypothetical construct "satiation"—for example the color effects and the displacement effects—can be shown to be independent (Ganz and Day, in

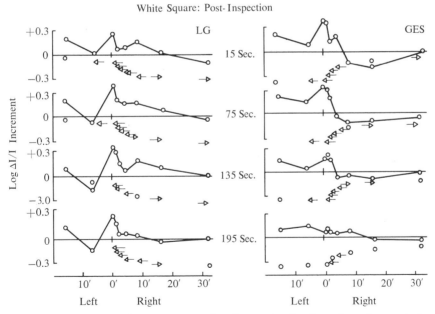

FIGURE 5   The solid lines represent the *changes* in the detection of a vertical white line at various distances from the edge of a previously presented white square *after* a 2-minute inspection of the square. (Positive values represent a loss in sensitivity. The arrowheads point in the direction of contour displacements at those same distances. Measurements are depicted for 1-minute intervals—15, 75 seconds, and so in. Left of the origin, the vertical white line was *inside* the locus of the previously presented square, N=2. Arrows pointing toward the origin, O', represent attraction effects.)

press). It is likely that they can occur at different neural loci.

The Osgood-Heyer (1952) theory is also a fatigue theory and so cannot be reconciled with Criticisms 2–5 above. As a hypothetical construct, it has not accorded well with some facts of visual physiology (Deutsch, 1956).

A New Theory of Figural Aftereffects

To provide a satisfactory mechanism of the figural aftereffects, two phenomena must be accounted for *independently*: (a) How do contours displace one another? and (b) How do contours interact when they are temporally separated? We will first provide a somewhat general and qualitative description of a theory. This will be followed by a more detailed exposition.

It appears that most of the difficulties inherent in the earlier theories evolved from their attempt to deal with both the displacement effect and the time-binding (proaction) effect with a single mechanism. Since the two effects display a rich variety of independent behavior, there is no recourse but to consider two separate mechanisms: The two chosen in the present study are lateral inhibition (I) and light adaptation. We want to explore the possibility that all *contour displacements* which are induced by neighboring figures and are restricted to about 10 or 20 minutes of arc in human perception are due to the operation of such inhibition. This is considered to apply to geometrical illusions (such as in Figure 1) and to many figural aftereffects (such as Figure 2 or 3). In this, our theory owes something to the ideas of Day (1962) and Deutsch (1964) in which similar approaches were suggested. As we will show below, the inhibition typically diminishes as the distance between the contours is increased. This descending function is actually steepest at very small distances, just a few minutes

of arc. It is easy to understand that when a contour is being inhibited by such a steep function, the portion of the contour near the inhibiting figure will be inhibited more than the portion at a greater distance. This must shift the mean of the contour's distribution *away* from the inhibiting figure. This is the repulsion effect.

Now such a theory, by itself, would lead one to think that the greatest repulsions occur when the two contours are *least* separated, which is when they touch. Yet the distance paradox tells us that empirically it has been found that repulsions are small or nil when the two contours touch. There are at least two plausible reasons why this should be so. One is that at very small interfigural distances, the two contours summate their excitations. In such a situation, it is likely that O actually confuses the inducing-figure and the test-figure contours (Taylor, 1962). Secondly, it is known that eye movements are present during the presentation of the test figure. Such movements must sometimes cause the test figure to be placed on one side of the inducing figure's edge and sometimes on the other. This is increasingly the case as the interfigural separation is made smaller. The displacement effect, a repulsion, is opposite in direction on the two sides of the inducing figure. Thus, when such cross-overs are frequent, we will be adding judgments made now with one displacement, now with an opposite one, with the net result close to zero. Thus, net displacement (which is what the grouped experimental results give us) will approach zero as interfigural distance approaches zero. Although we are in general agreement with Taylor that contour confusion must play a part, the evidence below suggests that this is not sufficient. The present model explores the second alternative.

We next consider the temporal problem: How does the inducing figure act proactively, crossing a time gap to displace the test figure? When O views a dark figure, there is a corresponding retinal area which dark adapts more than its surround; the portion of the retina of a subject where a bright figure is imaged will be a site of greater light adaptation in comparison with the surround. When the inducing figure is then removed, O will view stimuli with a heterogeneously adapted retina: a retina with some regions that are more dark adapted and regions that are more light adapted than the remainder. The result is that under normal levels of illumination, the subject will, in fact, continue to perceive the inducing figure. It will be seen as a light-dark reversal of the original, and it will decay in time. But while it is present, its edges will interact with the test figure as they do in simultaneous illusions. This is because the stimuli which are created by a heterogeneously light-adapted retina are stimuli which in many respects *are identical,* from a neural point of view, to those created by a distal stimulus onto a homogeneously adapted retina. In many situations the subject cannot actually discriminate between the two inducing figures, an ordinary stimulus originating in the distal environment and an afterimage (Barlow and Sparrock, 1964; Brindley, 1963). We suppose that the contours interact, even when interocularly produced, at the visual cortex to produce simultaneous illusions. The afterimage exists beyond the preservation of the distal figure and decays in time. This is the mechanism which bridges the time gap in the figural aftereffect situation; or, more properly, the processes of light and dark adaptation bridge that time gap.

Below we first examine the evidence on lateral inhibition, and we then present the theory in a quantitative form. We next examine the spatial distribution of displacement effects as they follow from the theory. In a subsequent paper we will compare the growth and decay of light and dark adaptation on the one hand and the growth and decay of figural aftereffects on

the other. The similarities in temporal properties, which are quite striking, will be used to substantiate our argument.

LATERAL INHIBITION

Psychophysical Evidence. Because of diffraction at the edge of the pupil and because light is scattered within the eye (Bartley, 1951, pp. 924–926; Boynton and Riggs, 1951), slit-shaped stimuli of high contrast are projected on the retina as broad, diffuse distributions (Flamant, 1955) considerably degraded in contrast. The anatomy and physiology of the retina suggest considerable spatial integration, even in the fovea, extending minimally to many minutes of arc and maximally (as in the periphery) to 1 or 2 degrees of arc, perhaps more. These facts might seem difficult to reconcile with the finding that in many vertebrate species visual resolution (the smallest consistently detected gap between two thin bars) is of the order of a single minute of arc. In fact, it is well known that the effects of spatial integration are held in check by a counterforce: lateral inhibition. Psychophysically, lateral inhibition is manifested by the appearance of contrast: Black solid figures appear blackest at their edges with white; white surfaces appear brightest at their edges with dark figures. Phenomenological contrast was known to Aristotle, was utilized technically by Leonardo da Vinci to enhance light values (Boring, 1942), and was first examined quantitatively by Lehmann (1886) and Hess and Pretori (1894).

Of the aspects of simultaneous contrast which are of interest to us, it should be noted that brighter stimuli inhibit dim ones more readily the greater the brightness difference of the two patches. This can be seen in Figure 6, taken from Heinemann (1955). In the figure the more intense inducing stimulus produces more inhibition. And for a range of values, it appears that the log matching luminance is a linear

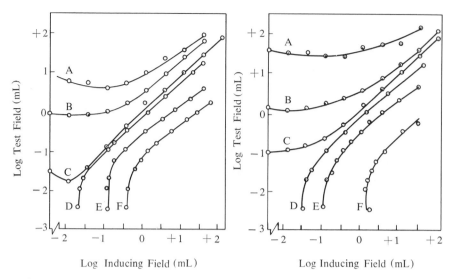

FIGURE 6   The test-field luminance needed to match a constant comparison field.
(When the inducing field, which surrounds the test field, is made more intense,
it inhibits the action of the test field. The test field must then be increased in
luminance to obtain a match with the comparison field. A, B, C, and so on, indicate decreasing intensities of the comparison field—Heinemann, 1955.)

function of the log inducing luminance.
One study (Leibowitz, Mote, and Thurlow, 1953) reports the dimming of the test
field by the inducing field to be proportional to the log inducing field luminance.

Lateral inhibition is quite sensitive to

the distance between two stimuli. For example, Beitel (1936) found that the empirical curve relating the amount of inhibition of the inducing stimulus on the
test stimulus, as a function of luminance,
was steeper when the two stimuli were

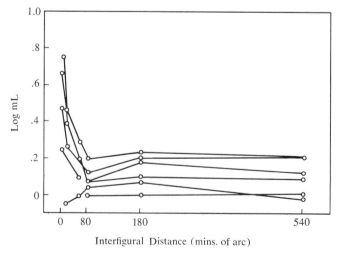

Interfigural Distance (mins. of arc)

FIGURE 7   The amount of inhibition exerted by a figure on another when their
separation is varied. (The various functions depict effects of inducing figures of
different intensities. An ordinate value of 1.00 log mL represents a 10-fold dimming of the test figure; zero mL represents no effect. Adapted from Leibowitz
et al., 1953.)

adjoined more closely. In Figure 7, adapted from the data of Leibowitz et al. (1953), we see that inhibition diminishes when the distance between two stimuli is increased. *Most of the inhibition occurs within the initial 10 minutes of arc, whether the inducing stimulus is strong or weak.* Thus, when the inducing stimulus is more intense, the distance function is steeper. This property will be utilized in the theory below.

Contour Inhibition. Thus far we have described only inhibition that is a function of luminance levels. There is, however, an inhibitory effect which is more properly described as that of one contour edge on another, and this effect will be of particular interest to us. It has been observed that the resolution of two bright parallel bars is improved by increasing their intensity (Fry and Cobb, 1935). For wide bars (33 minutes of arc) acuity was continuously increased at higher luminance levels. However, with thinner bars (3 minutes of arc) acuity sharply declined with luminance levels above about .5 log trolands. The interpretation was made that acuity declines in the case of the thin bars, at higher luminance levels, because the two edges of each thin bar, 3 minutes of arc apart, were inhibiting one another. The effectiveness of this variable was confirmed by Fry and

Bartley (1935) using a test situation depicted in Figure 8. The threshold of a difference in brightness between areas B and A is determined. The introduction of a dark ring at the outer border of B with C and concentric with A is found to raise that threshold. The threshold rise is greater the closer the dark ring is to the AB border. It appears that the B-C *edge* is exerting an inhibition on the A-B *edge,* thus making its detection more difficult. A very similar type of contour inhibition seems to play a predominant role in one type of metacontrast (Alpern, 1952; Kolers and Rosner, 1960; Werner, 1935) where one edge interferes with an adjoining one presented somewhat earlier in time (usually on the order of 100 milliseconds). Metacontrast contour interference is more powerful when the two contours are closer (Kolers and Rosner, 1960).

There is an additional difference between simultaneous contrast and contour inhibition which is pertinent. Brightness contrast is an asymmetrical phenomenon: Bright areas inhibit dimmer ones, but dim areas have little effect on brighter ones (Graham and Granit, 1931; Heinemann, 1955). Contour inhibition, however, is much more symmetrical: A white edge on a gray background exerts about as much inhibition on the detection of a dark line as does a black edge on a gray background.

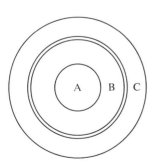

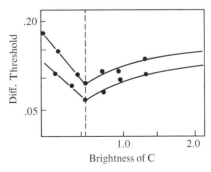

FIGURE 8 By either increasing or decreasing the luminance of Annulus C, we can introduce a contour at the B-C junction. (This appears to interfere with the differential brightness threshold at the A-B junction. The lowest threshold is obtained when the B and C luminances are equal, that is, when there is no contour between B and C. The results are shown in the figure on the right—from Dittmers, 1920.)

In an experiment by Dittmers (1920) a stimulus situation very similar to that in Figure 8 was used. The effect of varying the brightness of C upon the differential threshold for A was investigated. The results are also shown in Figure 8 (right). The threshold is lowest when the luminance of B and C are equal, that is, when no edge is present between B and C. Making C either brighter or darker interferes with the establishment of an edge contour between A and B. This must mean that it is the luminance discontinuity per se at the B-C edge which interferes, partly independent of the direction of the gradient. Fry and Bartley (1935) have obtained the same symmetry with a basically similar stimulus. Since figural aftereffects also show such a symmetry—approximately equal displacement effects are obtained with white-on-black or black-on-white inspection figures—inhibition must have a similar symmetry if it is to be invoked as the mechanism of displacement. Simpler simultaneous contrast does not have this symmetry: White inhibits dim regions, but darker areas do not inhibit the brighter ones (Heinemann, 1955). For example, Graham and Granit (1931) found that two adjoining semidiscs of unequal brightness affected each other's critical flicker fusion (CFF) asymmetrically. The CFF of the less bright areas diminished slightly (about 1.5%) while that of the brighter area increased (about 5.4%).

Physiological Evidence. The physiological analysis of inhibition has paralleled the psychophysical data so clearly, although it trails the latter in precision, that it seems worthwhile to present some of that evidence. For one of the advantages of an inhibitory model of contour displacement is precisely that the mechanism is well documented physiologically, and in some detail. The physiological analysis of inhibitory mechanisms in the visual system begins with the work of Hartline (1940)

who measured the receptive fields of single optic fibers of the frog, and therefore of single ganglion cells, using very small spots of light. Small areas of stimulation were shown to follow Ricco's law of areal summation. But increasing the area beyond a certain point actually increased the threshold. This was one of the earliest neurophysiological indications of the operation of a visual inhibitory mechanism. Kuffler (1953) demonstrated the existence of an antagonistic (inhibitory) annulus surrounding the receptive field in the retina of the cat. A small spot of light in the center of a receptive field might give an on response, but if the spot was moved to the periphery, the same cell showed an off response. The two spots together gave a much weaker response, the stronger spot luminance determining whether the response would take on the characteristic of the center or the periphery. Thus, a true antagonistic mechanism was at play. Barlow (1953) has shown, on the frog's retina, a similar mechanism at work. First, the response of a spot of light is measured when placed in the center of the receptive field. Next, a second spot is introduced which, although it registers no response itself, inhibits the response to the centrally placed spot. Furthermore, *this inhibitory action is proportional to the intensity of the second spot.* Because we are interested in the proactive inhibitory effects of a stimulus, it is interesting to cite one of Kuffler's (1953) observations. He noted that the suppression of an off response, by stimulation of an on area of a receptive field, could be seen for some time after the on area's stimulus had been turned off. "It was found that beam (A) to an on area could suppress (B) stimulation of an off area for varying periods after the (A) had been turned off. *The time course of the inhibitory after effect depended on the duration and the intensity of (A)* [p. 53; italics mine]." Conversely, a ganglion cell which gave an off effect was often found not to respond to a small spot of light directed to the on area during the period of the off discharge. Thus, the antagonistic action of a receptive field has been found to outlive the duration of the stimulus.

Hubel and Wiesel (1959, 1962) have extended this analysis, examining the receptive fields of cortical neurons. These receptive fields take on complicated shapes and are frequently elongated. Whatever the shape, the cortical neuron gives its strongest response (for so-called "simple" fields) only when numerous light spots are used to summate the activity within the field. (For example, a narrow, slit-shaped stimulus oriented vertically within a vertical receptive field gives a maximal response.) As with retinal cells, and also lateral geniculate cells, these cortical cells have receptive fields with flanks of an inhibitory character. But what makes the response of cortical cells distinct is that line stimuli or edges are the more powerful

stimulators, and closely adjoining or parallel lines and edges are the more powerful inhibitors. Diffuse light gives a minimal response. This clearly appears to provide a mechanism for edge inhibition per se, such as has been described above.

Binocular summation is another distinctive property of the cortical cells. Summation occurs between similarly oriented stimuli, such as two horizontal lines presented to corresponding retinal areas of the two eyes; inhibition occurs when a stimulus is presented to the inhibitory flank of the other eye. This is shown in Figure 9, taken from Hubel and Wiesel (1959). The mutual suppression of closely adjoining parallel contours has long been known in psychological literature. (For the binocular suppression of contours, see Asher, 1953; Day, 1961.) But this is the first evidence we have of a neurophysiological mechanism. It provides a clear physiolo-

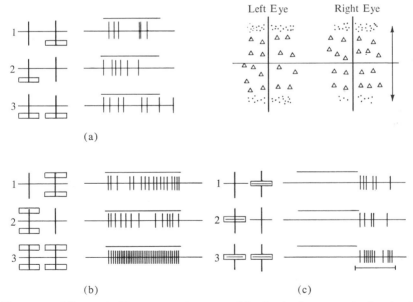

(a)

(b)   (c)

FIGURE 9   The vertical lines are action potentials of a single neuron in the visual cortex of the cat. (A horizontal white bar when it first enters the top of the receptive field gives an on response, then an off response at the center of the field, and an on response again at the bottom of the receptive field. This can be obtained from stimulation of either or both eyes, if corresponding retinal points are used. When both eyes are stimulated together, Record 3 in the illustration, an even stronger response is obtained. In Records A and B, the on response is seen to be activated by either eye and to summate binocularly; in C, this is shown to apply to the off response.)

logical basis for a theory in which a contour process originating in one eye and a second contour process originating in the other eye are both projected cortically and inhibit each other at the cortical site.

Hartline, Ratliff, and Wagner (1956) and Ratliff and Hartline (1959) have made a quantitative analysis of lateral inhibition among single ommatidia of the limulus eye. Although there are many apparent differences between arthropod and vertebrate visual systems, contrast-enhancing mechanisms seem to be present in both (including the Mach bands), and this suggests that we can gain something from a comparison of the two systems, proceeding with due caution.

In the limulus eye, interaction among ommatidia is inhibitory; there is no neural spatial summation. If we measure the response of a single ommatidium and then illuminate neighboring ommatidia, the threshold of the receptor unit being measured is raised, the number of impulses it discharges in response to a suprathreshold flash is diminished, and the frequency with which it discharges impulses during steady illumination is reduced. The following factors affect the magnitude of inhibition:

1. Intensity—the more intense the inhibitory illumination, the deeper and longer is the initial depression in frequency of discharge. *The steady level is linearly related to log intensity of inhibition.*

2. Area—the larger the size of the neighboring area that is illuminated, the greater the slowing down in rate.

3. Distance—the effectiveness of the inhibition diminishes with distance. If inducing and test stimulus are further apart on the surface of the compound eye of the limulus, then the slope relating the intensity of the inducing figure to the amount of inhibition of the test figure is flattened. This also must mean that the slope of in-

hibition (I) as a function of distance between I and T is steeper when I is more intense.

The effect of induction and test is mutual. The inducing figure's inhibition of the test figure depends on the illumination of the test figure, since the test figure in turn inhibits the inducing figure. Thus, the rate of discharge, r_p, in the receptor "p," set among a population of n interacting receptors, is given by the set of n simultaneous equations of which one is:

$$r_p = e_p - \sum_{j=1}^{n} k_{pj}(r_j - r^o_{pj})$$
$$1 \leqslant p \leqslant n, \quad [1]$$

where e_p is the discharge from receptor p when it is illuminated alone, r_j is the discharge from a neighboring receptor, j ($j = $ 1, 2, etc.), *after* interaction with all the other n receptors in its neighborhood, k_{pj} is the coefficient of inhibition of receptor j on receptor p, and r^o_{pj} is the threshold amount of discharge in j just needed to inhibit I. This equation has been found to fit the limulus data with great precision and has successfully accounted for additional phenomena such as disinhibition and the Mach-band phenomenon. For our purposes the following properties of the equation should be noted. Inhibition is a quantity which is simply subtracted from single-unit discharge; each receptor after being itself inhibited contributes its own inhibition in a simple, additive way. Inhibition is a linear function of receptor discharge, and this is a linear function of log intensity (Hartline, 1940). As distances increase, it is empirically found that the proportionality constant k_{pj} is smaller. Thus, with a smaller distance, the function of inhibition and intensity has a steeper slope. Also, at high intensity, inhibition as a function of distance is steeper. This, in turn, must mean that inhibition as a function of distance has a negative slope and, moreover, is not linear, but is exponential or possibly a polynomial of higher order.

To summarize the neurophysiological contribution, separate inhibitory mechanisms have been discovered which seem to underlie both brightness contrast and contour inhibition (including binocular effects). Both types of inhibition diminish with distance. Inhibition is proportional to the log intensity of the inducing stimulus, and the spatial function is steeper for more intense inducing stimuli. Inhibition can sometimes operate as an aftereffect. And, at least in limulus, *the effect is additive*. A certain amount of discharge frequency, a result of neighboring activity, is subtracted, and the resultant is expressed by a simple sum of simultaneous equations.

AN INHIBITORY MECHANISM OF CONTOUR DISPLACEMENT

We suppose first that the neural correlate of a contour can be represented by a ridge of activity with a cross section which, for illustration, is depicted by T in Figure 10. We will assume that the mean of the distribution will determine the apparent position of the contour as it is measured in an alignment task. The variance of the distribution will determine part of the variance of the alignment judgments. We suppose further that I, the inducing figure, exerts inhibition. The effect of inhibition is to subtract excitation from the test figure's distribution. In other words, the apparent position of the test figure in the presence of some other figure, I, is given simply by the net distribution. Net T is shown by the dashed line in Figure 10.

Köhler and Wallach (1944) found equivalent repulsion displacements occurred whether white-on-black or black-on-white inspection figures were used. Although attempts have been made to demonstrate that these are not equivalent (Ganz and Day, in press), the evidence is equivocal. Assuming, in the absence of clear

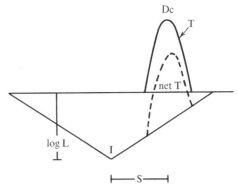

FIGURE 10 T represents a theoretical spatial distribution of a cross section of neural excitatory ridge to which a test-figure contour gives rise in the visual system. (The edge of an inducing figure is placed by E at a distance, S. This I figure is thought to generate lateral inhibition equally on both sides. The inhibition diminishes rectilinearly with distance. The amount of inhibition is proportional to the log contrast of the inducing figure, log L. In this model, the inhibition is subtracted at each point from the T distribution to give a residual excitation, net T. Displacement, D, occurs because the mean of the net-T distribution is shifted away from T.)

evidence to the contrary, that they are equivalent, it appears that the type of inhibition which is exerted by I on T which causes it to be displaced is the type restricted to the action of contours on contours, which has been described above.

As a first approximation, it seems plausible (Leibowitz et al., 1953; Ratliff and Hartline, 1959) to assume that for a white line on a grey surround the amount of inhibition is a linear function of the log luminance (log L) of the inhibiting contour. This contour inhibition appears to decay exponentially over a distance of some 120 minutes of arc, with the greatest drop occurring in the first few minutes of arc. For simplicity, we explore a linear model in which the inhibition simply drops linearly to zero at a point m away on both sides of the inhibiting edge. This is shown in Figure 10. If the middle of the test figure is at the center of a coordinate system and the inspection figure at −S on the abscissa, then it can be shown that the amount of inhibition, I, at a point, x, is given by:

$$I_x = 1 - \log L \left(1 - \frac{S}{m}\right) + \frac{\log L}{m} x, \quad [2]$$

where L is the luminance of the inducing figure, S is the distance between the inducing and test figures, and m is one-half the width of the total region over which inhibition is exerted by the inducing figure. Log L/m gives the slope of the inhibitory function.

First we would like to show that the actual shape of the test-figure distribution is not a critical variable. In Figure 10 we illustrate the cross section of a straight contour, T, which has a width $-i$ to $+i$. Let the function which relates this cross section to the variable x on the abscissa be $f(x)$. In a control test in which the inducing figure is not presented, the mean of the test-figure distribution is given by:

$$\bar{x} = \int_{-i}^{i} xf(x)dx.$$

Then the net distribution will be:

$$\text{net } \bar{x} = \int_{-i}^{i} x[f(x) - I_x]dx.$$

Substituting Equation 2 into this expression, integrating, and collecting terms, and letting $b = \log L/m$, we get:

$$\text{net } \bar{x} = \bar{x} - \tfrac{2}{3}bi^3.$$

By definition, contour displacement, D, is given by the mean of the net distribution less the mean of the control distribution, hence:

$$D = -\tfrac{2}{3}bi^3. \quad [3]$$

Since $f(x)$ is not in the equation, it can be seen that the displacement is independent of the particulars of the test

figure's distribution, although it is sensitive to the width of the test figure. Moreover, the amount of displacement, D, is proportional to the slope of the inhibition function, b. And since b equals log L/m, we see that contour displacement is (a) proportional to the log of the inducing contour luminance, and (b) inversely proportional to the spread of in the inhibition, m.

In the treatment below, we use the convention that the inducing figure is placed at the origin and that the test figure is placed a distance, S, away. If that is the case, and using a test figure of unit width, we get the following distribution:

Test-figure position	Displacement
$S \leqslant -m$	0
$-m < S \leqslant 0$	$-b$
$0 \leqslant S < m$	b
$m \leqslant S$	0

Remembering that the inhibition's slope is negative on the left of the inducing figure edge and positive on the right side of the inducing edge, this means that a repulsion displacement occurs on both sides of the inducing figure, and that it is always equal to the slope of the inhibitory function of the same strength, if only the test figure is presented within the region from $-m$ to $+m$.

ROLE OF EYE MOVEMENTS

A subject's eyes move even though a fixation point is provided, and he makes his best effort to fixate steadily (Ratliff and Riggs, 1950). The subject's eyes move during the inspection-to-test-figure interval, drifting away in all directions from the subject's own mean fixation position. These eye movements have the effect of changing the true interfigural distance at any moment. This must mean that when the results of a block of trials are combined for any one interfigural distance value, set by E, the results actually represent the pooling of a whole distribution of interfigural distance values. This distribution will be very broad if the subject drifts a lot from the fixation point and will be quite narrow if the subject has more precise fixation. What then can we expect the subject's eye-movement drifts to be?

Barlow (1952) has taken a measure of the error involved in O's successive fixational pauses. The scatter of eye-movement positions when the subject indicated that he was satisfied with his fixation was 6.5 minutes of arc (5.2 minutes of arc after correction for changes in head position). Two other direct-measurement techniques yielded values ranging from 6.5–5.7 minutes before correction. A subjective method, in which O estimates the vertical distance between his fixation point and the after-image of a previous fixation point, yielded a standard-deviation value of 6.3 minutes of arc.

We are now in a position to examine the figural aftereffect situation. Let σ be the standard deviation of the subject's fixation position in the horizontal plane. From Barlow's data, σ equals about 5 or 6 minutes of arc. We consider the situation in which E sets the average interfigural distance at some value less than σ. If the inducing figure has been presented left of the test figure, then, during postinspection, the test figure will be displaced an amount b to the *right* (repulsed) whenever the eye movements bring the test figure momentarily right of the edge of the afterimage of the inducing figure (but not more than m away from I). A definite probability can be attached to the event that an eye movement momentarily brings the test figure left of the afterimage edge (but not more than m away from that edge), and then the displacement will be a repulsion an amount b, but in a leftward direction. Thus, the momentary displacement is not determined, as in previous theories, but is probabilistic, depending on the errorlike vagaries of fixation scatter. For an alignment response, which normally requires multiple fixations, the expected displace-

ment would be the sum of the products of displacements at various t-figure positions each multiplied by the probability of the t figure assuming such a position. Assuming the distribution of fixation positions to be normal, with a standard deviation defined as σ, we get as the equation of expected displacement[2], D_S:

$$D_S = \frac{b}{\sigma\sqrt{2\pi}}\left[\int_0^m e^{-\frac{(x-S)^2}{2\sigma^2}}\,dx - \int_{-m}^0 e^{-\frac{(x-S)^2}{2\sigma^2}}\,dx\right]. \quad [4]$$

We have plotted the expected displacement when $m = 4$ minutes of arc, and $\sigma = 5$ minutes of arc (after Barlow's re-

[2] For computation, it is convenient to use the following transformation:

$$D_S = \frac{b}{\pi}\left[2\int_0^{\frac{S}{\sqrt{2}\sigma}} e^{-\gamma^2}d\gamma + i\int_0^{\frac{m-S}{\sqrt{2}\sigma}} e^{-\gamma^2}d\gamma - \int_0^{\frac{m+S}{\sqrt{2}\sigma}} e^{-\gamma^2}d\gamma\right],$$

where $i = 1$ if $o < S < m$, and $i - = 1$ if $m < S$. The bracketed functions are the integrals of the error function:

$$\int_0^x e^{-\gamma^2}d\gamma,$$

which has been tabled (United States National Bureau of Standards Computation Laboratory, 1954).

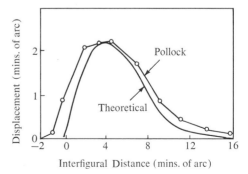

FIGURE 11   A comparison of the distribution of figural aftereffects, as they are predicted by the inhibitory model ($\sigma = 5$; $m = 4$) with the results of an experiment (Pollack, 1958).

sults) in Figure 11. It compares favorably with Pollack's (1958) data on figural aftereffects which are also shown in the same figure. It can be seen that the course of the displacements as we vary the interfigural distance is predicted to a first approximation by the theory. The prediction is made on the basis of only one completely free parameter, the constant L which relates the contrast of the inducing figure to its inhibitory potential, the parameter m being undetermined but bounded by empirical data, and the parameter σ being completely determined, and

$$b = \frac{\log L}{m}.$$

Furthermore, the free parameter L is a vertical scale factor and does not otherwise affect the curve.

It might be of interest to note, with regard to the parameter m, that Mach bands, the band of black near a border with white and a band of white near a border with black, have their maximum at about 2–6 minutes of arc (Fiorentini and Radici, 1958) which is about the same location as the point of maximum displacement. The Mach bands are almost certainly an inhibition-disinhibition phenomenon (Ratliff and Hartline, 1959). A recent theory by von Békésy (1960) of the Mach bands, from a schematized summation-inhibition neural unit, used a value of r (roughly equivalent to m in our theory) of 10 minutes of arc. The Leibowitz et al. (1953) data would indicate that the greater proportion of inhibition is dissipated in the first 10 minutes of arc. The discrepancy between the suggested values of 10 minutes of arc from the Leibowitz et al. and von Békésy studies and the 4 minutes of arc which is optimal in the present model probably means that a linear model is to that extent inadequate. Although an exponential decay function of inhibition fits the empirical data on inhibition and figural aftereffect better, the

linear model has the advantage of simplicity. However, in the absence of more extensive data on the displacement-distance function, more precision does not seem warranted at present. Moreover, it is our primary interest to show how much of the variance can be accounted for by the simplest model.

EFFECT OF AN INDUCING FIGURE ON THE VARIANCE OF ALIGNMENT JUDGMENTS

The inhibition model can generate an independent and new prediction which is at variance with the expectations based on prevalent theories of aftereffects. The inhibition model specified that eye movements sometimes place the retinal projection of a test-figure contour on one side of the inducing-figure contour, sometimes on the other. This will occur a significant proportion of the time when the interfigural distance is less than two or three times the standard deviation of the eye-movement distribution, σ. The displacement of the test-figure contour occurs in opposite direction on the two sides of the inducing-figure contour. Thus, the apparent positions of the test line will be more variable when the interfigural distance is small. This is because, at a small interfigural distance, the test figure is successively placed on both sides of the inducing-figure contour and thus becomes prone to displacements in opposite directions. This in turn will give rise to a bimodal distribution of apparent contour positions, a distribution that has a higher variance than a unimodal distribution. At large interfigural distances, the test figure will cross the inducing-figure boundary only rarely. Thus, it will be exposed to displacements predominantly in one direction. This, in turn, will produce a unimodal distribution which would result in a smaller variance of alignment judgments.

We can derive an explicit expression for the variance of O's contour alignments solely attributable to the effects of the inducing figure. In a control run when no inducing figure is shown, O's alignments are some direct function of the mean of the excitation distribution which the test figure arouses, $\bar{x}$. If E places an inducing figure at a particular interfigural distance, S, then the expected displacement would be D_S (see Equation 4). Thus, O's *average* alignment would be a direct function of $\bar{x} + D_S$. If the test figure is presented briefly (.1 second or less; a brief enough presentation so that eye movements would not cause significant displacements during the time interval) and happens to fall right of the inducing figure's afterimage (but not more than m minutes away), it would be displaced an amount b. Then the apparent position on that trial would be given by $\bar{x} + b$. Thus, the deviation from O's average judgment, attributable solely to the displacement, would on that trial be given by $(\bar{x} + b) - (\bar{x} + D_S)$, or $(b - D_S)$. Depending on where the test figure falls, during that brief presentation, we have the following deviations:

Test-figure position	Deviation
$x < -m$	$0 - D_S$
$-m \leqslant x < 0$	$-b - D_S$
$0 < x \leqslant m$	$b - D_S$
$m < x$	$0 - D_S$

The expected variance, for a specific interfigural distance, S, is then given by the product of each of these deviations squared and their probabilities:

$$V_S = (b + D_S)^2 \frac{1}{\sigma\sqrt{2\pi}} \int_{-m}^{0} e^{-\frac{(x-S)^2}{2\sigma^2}} dx$$

$$+ (b - D_S)^2 \frac{1}{\sigma\sqrt{2\pi}} \int_{0}^{m} e^{-\frac{(x-S)^2}{2\sigma^2}} dx. \quad [5]$$

If we let

$$P_a^b = \int_{a}^{b} e^{-\frac{(x-S)^2}{2\sigma^2}} dx,$$

then Equation 4 becomes

$$D_S = b(P_o^m - P_m^o).$$

Substituting into Equation 5 and collecting terms, we get

$$V_S = (b^2 + D_S^2)P_m^m. \quad [6]$$

Substituting the constants we used above to compute D_S into Equation 6, we obtain a function which is plotted in Figure 12. The figure shows a theoretical function which peaks somewhere at a very small interfigural distance, the value at an interfigural distance of 0 being indeterminate, and then drops exponentially reaching a value which is approximately equal to 0 at about 30 minutes of arc. There are, of course, other sources of variance in O's judgments. These other sources can be estimated from alignment judgments performed in the absence of inducing figures. The different variance sources will then simply add in the figural aftereffect situation.

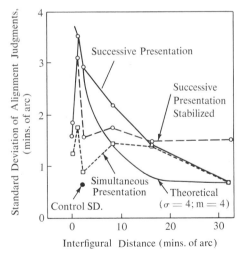

FIGURE 12 The standard deviation of vernier alignment judgments (control value) and of vernier alignments when one of the lines is in the vicinity of an inducing figure. (As the distance separating inducing from test figure is made smaller, the standard deviation is seen to increase, especially in the successive presentation. Predicted values, derived from the inhibitory model, using the same parameter values as in Figure 11, are also shown.)

Since we are interested in the varia-bility due to the scatter of momentary test-figure placements, we want to compare our theoretical function to data obtained in ex-periments in which the test figure has been presented very briefly. If the test figure is presented for a longer time, then O can sample a number of eye-movement posi-tions, and thus the variability of test-figure positions due to eye movements will be reduced as the square root of the number of samples. This follows since a judgment would then be based effectively on the mean number of positions. Thus, the mean would represent the standard devi-ation of a sample mean, that is, the stand-ard error. The results of an experiment (Ganz, 1964) in which the test figure was presented for .12 second is shown in Figure 12. The descending character of the stand-ard deviation in the successive presenta-tions as S is increased is quite evident. A second study by Ganz and Day (in press) utilized a method of limits in which each stimulus presentation lasted .3 second. The results are shown in Figure 13. The stand-ard deviation again is seen to fall as S is increased. In absolute level, the standard deviation is much smaller, but if we re-member that each exposure was about 3 times as long and that each threshold was determined by 4 runs (ABBA in order), then it would appear that we should multi-ply these values by the square root of 12 to obtain a comparable estimate of the standard deviation on single brief ex-posures. When this is done, the height of the theoretical curve and of the curve from the study by Ganz and Day become quite comparable (the results depicted have *not* been so adjusted). Finally, the data of Pollack (1958) and of Ganz and Day (in press), both studies using a method of adjustments, are shown in the same figure. Here the method of adjustment was used, and in these cases it is not possi-ble to estimate the duration of the test-figure exposure period. Notice, however, that both studies yielded descending func-

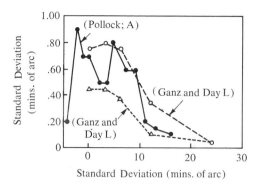

FIGURE 13   The standard deviation of vernier alignment judgments at various distances from the location of a previously presented inducing figure. (*A* signifies vernier judgments obtained with a method of average error where the test figure is presented for an undetermined dura-tion; *L* signifies the use of a method of limits, with a .3-second test-figure exposure. Com-pare with Figure 12, where shorter exposures were used.)

tions as the parameter S increased. Also, both functions are slightly lower in mag-nitude than the function obtained with the method of limits. This is understand-able when it is realized that the method of adjustment probably gives the subject the longest stimulus exposure of all these conditions.

It is felt that the prediction of increased standard deviation of alignment near the inducing-figure contour border is specific to an inhibitory model such as the one presented here. It does not follow from the other theories of the figural aftereffect (Köhler and Wallach, 1944; Osgood and Heyer, 1955) where displacements are held to be very small near the inducing-figure border. Thus, the oscillations of the test figure on both sides of the contour of the inducing figure when the interfigural distance is very small would not lead to greater variations in alignment. These theories predict greater variability of align-ment where the slope of the displacement function is steepest. This occurs at least at two points, each the same distance from the inducing figure's edge on either side, and at the point of maximum displace-ment. Put differently, at 0 interfigural distance, the standard deviation of the displacement should be about the same as at a very large interfigural distance since in both cases there is very little displacement. But as Figures 12 and 13 show, this is in fact not the case. Only a theory in which there is strong displacement near the interfigural distance of zero, as in the present model, could predict the type of descending standard-deviation function we have found.

Notice that our equation for D_8 implies that the paradoxical distance effect is not inherent in the displacement phenomenon. It evolves from intrinsic errors that arise from the oscillation in the actual momentary test-figure position. These are caused by eye movements and other errors of fixation, or even possibly from errors in E's positioning of the test figure from trial to trial. The latter seems a reasonable possibility since 1 or 2 minutes of arc are frequently close to the limits of error of the apparatus employed (Ganz, 1964; Köhler and Wallach, 1944; Pollack, 1958).

In Taylor's (1962) theory the displacements occur because the subject's alignment judgments are *better* in the presence of the inducing figure. Taylor feels that the inducing figure acts as an anchor, and this effect is stronger when the interfigural distance is small. It is unlikely, however, that more accurate judgments should come to be associated with greater variance.

An observation was often made, especially under conditions of very careful fixation (Ganz, 1964), that during the post-exposure period the apparent position of the test figure changed *while O observed it*, often from one side of the inducing figure's edge to the other side. This is not accounted for except in a model that includes the effects of sudden corrective eye movement saccades which might bring the test figure to the other side of the inspection contour during the observation period.

If our theory is correct, the distribution of displacements should change if the scatter of eye movements is altered. One

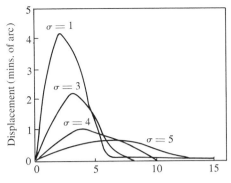

FIGURE 14   The effect of varying the scatter of horizontal eye movements (σ) on the distribution of figural aftereffects, as derived from the inhibitory model.

experimental way of accomplishing this is to stabilize the retinal image. The result of such stabilization should be to restrict the variance increases of the alignment judgments largely to the region in the immediate vicinity of the inducing-figure edge. This would be the result predicted from Equation 6 if the parameter σ is reduced in value. This is shown in Figure 14. An experiment on image stabilization (Ganz, 1964) confirmed this expectation. The results of this experiment are given in Figure 12: successive presentation, stabilized.

We should also consider the case where, although eye movements are not reduced, the test figure does not vary in its position with respect to the inducing figure. This would be the case when the inducing and test figure are presented together. In such a situation, the increase in alignment variability at small interfigural distances should be absent. In Figure 12 the data obtained under the simultaneous presentation show only very small variance increments. To this extent our expectations appear to be confirmed.

FIGURAL AFTEREFFECTS AS SIMULTANEOUS ILLUSIONS

The theoretical model presented here considers the displacements which occur in the figural aftereffect situation to be a consequence of a simultaneous illusion—mutual contour inhibition—brought about by the decaying trace of the afterimage upon the test contour. We have shown that a theoretical model of mutual contour inhibition does predict displacements of appropriate location and variability. One would like to know whether such displacements occur when an actual inducing-stimulus object is substituted for the postulated afterimage. In other words, do simultaneous illusions occur which are similar in direction and magnitude to the figural aftereffect?

Presenting an inducing and test figure together (unlike the afterimage situation) effectively reduces the magnitude of the eye-movement component. During the simultaneous illusion, any eye movement would move both inducing and test figure together across the retina. Thus, the inducing figure would retain its distance and direction with respect to the test figure. It is unlikely that the effective eye movements would be completely nullified, since contour inhibition appears to act with a definite latency (Kolers and Rosner, 1960). In Figure 14 we have depicted the figural aftereffect distributions which the theory predicts when the parameter σ, the standard deviation of the eye position during fixation, is reduced. We see that as the peak of the point of maximal displacement approaches the edge of the inducing figure the peak is steeper, and its magnitude is greater. In Figure 4 we see the results of an experiment with 30 subjects in which the inducing and test figures were presented simultaneously (Ganz, 1964). Two successive series of measurements are shown. Pollack's (1958) experiment in which similar figures were presented in the aftereffect paradigm is also included in the same figure for comparison. We see that the simultaneous experiment did yield a point of maximum displacement nearer to the inducing-figure edge (1 minute of arc) than the value obtained from Pollack's data (about 4.5 minutes of arc) or to any

figural aftereffect experiment known to the author.

It should be noted, finally, that the Inhibition Model predicts that contour displacements will occur with or without fixation tremor. It is only the magnitude of the displacements and the point of maximal displacement which change with such errors of fixation. Thus, the theory is not inconsistent with the fact that figural aftereffects are found under conditions of retinal image stabilization (Ganz, 1964; Hochberg and Hay, 1956; Krauskopf, 1960).

Summary

The edges of objects in the visual field appear to repulse one another when they are brought close together. These mutual shifts have long been known to us in the case of the classical geometrical illusions. Such effects can be obtained even when a pair of neighboring contours is presented successively. These are known as the figural aftereffects.

A quantitative theory is proposed to account for these perceptual aberrations. The two aspects of the aftereffect—the shifts in contour position and the temporal separation which can be introduced between inducing and test contour—are treated separately. According to the theory, the displacement arises because the neural correlates of visual contour inhibit one another. The inhibition is proportional to the log of the contour intensity (more exactly to its contrast above or below background level). The inhibition is a decreasing linear function of the separation between the contours. These two assumptions, both documented psychologically and physiologically, are sufficient to generate a predicted contour displacement. Eye-movements during fixation, also documented, are shown to produce a statistical distribution of repulsions at various intercontour distances. By introducing empirically derived values for the equation parameters, a distribution of figural aftereffects is generated which agrees well with experimental values.

Two independent sets of predictions are generated by the model. First, the model predicts a very steep rise in response variability as the test contour is brought closer to the inducing contour (particularly when the two are presented successively). Second, certain changes in the mode of presentation—retinally stabilized, simultaneous presentation, short test-figure presentation—are predicted to yield different distributions of figural aftereffects. The data available to date corroborate the predictions.

The mechanism which bridges the time gap is described only briefly. We hope to consider it in more detail in a subsequent communication. The figural aftereffects are, it is believed, simultaneous illusions which are in many ways no different from the classical geometrical illusions. When the inducing figure is removed, an afterimage of the inducing figure remains in O's visual field. The neural correlates of that afterimage then repulse the test figure's neural correlate, in accordance with the displacement mechanism just described. The lines of evidence which support an afterimage explanation are strongly suggestive, though perhaps not conclusive. That is, it is found that the onset, the initial intensity, and the decay of figural aftereffects and afterimages are strikingly similar, often involving the same parameter values. They, in turn, both appear to reflect the operation of light- and dark-adaptation mechanisms.

Thus, it appears possible that most of the quantitative properties of the figural aftereffects will be reduced to the operation of a number of basic visual mechanisms: adaptation, inhibition, and ocular tremor.

References

ALPERN, M. Metacontrast: Historical introduction. *American Journal of Optometry,* 1952, *29,* 631–646.

ASHER, H. The suppression theory. *British Orthoptic Journal,* 1953, *10,* 1–9.

BARLOW, H. B. Eye movements during fixation. *Journal of Physiology,* 1952, *116,* 290–306.

BARLOW, H. B. Summation and inhibition in the frog's retina. *Journal of Physiology,* 1953, *119,* 69–88.

BARLOW, H. B., and J. M. B. SPARROCK. The role of after-images in dark adaptation. *Science,* 1964, *144,* 1309–1314.

BARTLEY, S. H. The psychology of vision. In S. S. Stevens (Ed.), *Handbook of experimental psychology.* New York: Wiley, 1951. pp. 924–926.

BEITEL, R. J. Inhibition of threshold excitation in the human eye. *Journal of General Psychology,* 1936, *14,* 31–61.

BÉKÉSY, G. VON. Neural inhibitory units of the eye and skin: Quantitative description of contrast phenomena. *Journal of the Optical Society of America,* 1960, *50,* 1060–1070.

BORING, E. G. *Sensation and perception in the history of experimental psychology.* New York: Appleton-Century, 1942.

BOYNTON, R. M., and L. A. RIGGS. The effect of stimulus area and intensity upon the human retinal response. *Journal of Experimental Psychology,* 1951, *42,* 217–226.

BRINDLEY, G. S. After-images. *Scientific American,* 1963, *209,* 84–93.

DAY, R. H. On the stereoscopic observation of geometrical illusions. *Perceptual and Motor Skills,* 1961, *13,* 247–258.

DAY, R. H. Excitory and inhibitory processes as the basis of contour shift and negative after-effect. *Psychologia,* 1962, *5,* 185–193.

DAY, R. H., R. H. POLLACK, and G. N. SEAGRIM. Figural after-effects: A critical review. *Australian Journal of Psychology,* 1959, *11,* 15–45.

DEUTSCH, J. A. The statistical theory of figural after-effects and acuity. *British Journal of Psychology,* 1956, *47,* 208–215.

DEUTSCH, J. A. Neurophysiological contrast phenomena and figural after-effects. *Psychological Review,* 1964, *71,* 19–26.

DITTMERS, F. Über die abhängigkeit der unterschiedesschwelle für Helligkeiten von der antagonistischen Induktion. *Zeitschrift für Sinnesphysiologie,* 1920, *51,* 214–232.

FIORENTINI, ADRIANA, and TILDE RADICI. Brightness, width and position of Mach bands as a function of the rate of variation of the luminance gradient. *Atti della Fondazione Giorgio Ronchi,* 1958, *13,* 145–155.

FLAMANT, FRANCOISE. Étude de la repartition de lumière dans l'image retinienne d'une fente. *Revue Optique,* 1955, *34,* 433–459.

Fry, G. A., and S. H. Bartley. The effect of one border in the visual field upon the threshold of another. *American Journal of Physiology*, 1935, *112*, 414–421.

Fry, G. A., and P. W. Cobb. A new method for determining the blurredness of the retinal image. *Transactions of the American Academy of Ophthalmology and Otolaryngology*, 1935, *40*, 423–428.

Ganz, L. Lateral inhibition and the location of visual contours: An analysis of figural after-effects. *Visual Research*, 1964, *4*, 465–481.

Ganz, L., and R. H. Day. An analysis of the satiation-adaptation mechanism of figural after-effects. *American Journal of Psychology*, 1966, in press.

Graham, C. H., and R. Granit. Comparative studies on the peripheral and central retina: VI. Inhibition, summation, and synchronization of impulses in the retina. *American Journal of Physiology*, 1931, *98*, 664–673.

Hartline, H. K. The effects of spatial summation in the retina on the excitation of the fibers of the optic nerve. *American Journal of Physiology*, 1940, *130*, 700–711.

Hartline, H. K., F. Ratliff, and H. G. Wagner. Inhibition in the eye of the limulus. *Journal of General Physiology*, 1956, *39*, 651–673.

Hebb, D. O. *The organization of behavior*. New York: Wiley, 1949.

Heinemann, E. G. Simultaneous brightness induction as a function of inducing and test-field luminances. *Journal of Experimental Psychology*, 1955, *50*, 89–96.

Hess, C., and H. Pretori. Messende Untersuchungen über die Gesetzmässigkeit der simultanen Helligkeitscontrastes. *Albrecht von Graefe's Archiv für Ophthalmologie*, 1894, *40*, 1–24.

Hochberg, J. E., and J. Hay. Figural after-effect, after-image, and physiological nystagmus. *American Journal of Psychology*, 1956, *69*, 480–482.

Hubel, D. H., and T. N. Wiesel. Receptive fields of single neurones in the cat's striate cortex. *Journal of Physiology*, 1959, *148*, 574–591.

Hubel, D. H., and T. N. Wiesel. Receptive fields, binocular interaction and functional architecture in the cat's visual cortex. *Journal of Physiology*, 1962, *160*, 106–154.

Ikeda, H., and T. Obonai. The quantitative analysis of figural after-effect: I. The process of growth and decay of figural after-effect. *Japanese Journal of Psychology*, 1953, *24*, 59–68.

Ikeda, H., and T. Obonai. Studies in figural

after-effects: IV. The contrast-confluence illusion of concentric circles and the figural after-effect. *Japanese Psychological Research*, 1955, *2*, 17–23.

Ikuta, H. Displacement in figural after-effect and simultaneous illusions. *Japanese Journal of Psychology*, 1956, *27*, 218–226.

Köhler, W., and H. Wallach. Figural after-effects: An investigation of visual processes. *Proceedings of the American Philosophical Society*, 1944, *88*, 269–357.

Kolers, P. A., and B. S. Rosner. On visual masking (metacontrast): Dichoptic observation. *American Journal of Psychology*, 1962, *73*, 2–21.

Krauskopf, J. Figural after-effects with a stabilized retinal image. *American Journal of Psychology*, 1960, *73*, 294–297.

Kuffler, S. W. Discharge patterns and functional organization of mammalian retina. *Journal of Neurophysiology*, 1953, *16*, 37–68.

Lashley, K. S., K. L. Chow, and J. Semmes. An examination of the electrical field theory of cerebral integration. *Psychological Review*, 1951, *58*, 123–136.

Lehmann, A. Über die Anwendung der Methode der mittleren Abstufungen auf den Lichtsinn. *Philosophische Studien*, 1886, *3*, 497–533.

Leibowitz, H., F. A. Mote, and W. R. Thurlow. Simultaneous contrast as a function of separation between test and inducing fields. *Journal of Experimental Psychology*, 1953, *46*, 453–456.

Lettvin, J. Y., H. R. Maturana, W. S. McCulloch, and W. H. Pitts. What the frog's eye tells the frog's brain. *Proceedings of the Institute of Radio Engineers*, 1959, *47*, 1940–1951.

Logan, J. A. A general approach to the study of visual illusions and figural after-effects. *Australian Journal of Psychology*, 1960, *12*, 235–236. (Abstract)

McEwen, P. Figural after-effects. *British Journal of Psychology Monograph Supplement*, 1958, no. 31.

Nozawa, S. Prolonged inspection of a figure and the after-effect thereof. *Japanese Journal of Psychology*, 1953, *23*, 217–234. (a)

Nozawa, S. Prolonged inspection of a figure and the after-effect thereof. *Japanese Journal of Psychology*, 1953, *24*, 47–58. (English summary, 84–85) (b)

Osgood, C. E., and A. W. Heyer. A new interpretation of the figural after-effect. *Psychological Review*, 1952, *59*, 98–118.

Oyama, T. Experimental studies of figural

after-effects: I. Temporal factors. *Japanese Journal of Psychology*, 1953, 23, 239–245.

Oyama, T. Temporal and spatial factors in figural after-effects. *Japanese Psychological Research*, 1956, 3, 25–36.

Pollack, R. H. Figural after-effects: Quantitative studies of displacement. *Australian Journal of Psychology*, 1958, 10, 269–277.

Ratliff, F., and H. K. Hartline. The responses of *Limulus* optic nerve fibers to patterns of illumination on the receptor mosaic. *Journal of General Physiology*, 1959, 42, 1241–1255.

Ratliff, F., and L. A. Riggs. Involuntary motions of the eye during monocular fixation. *Journal of Experimental Psychology*, 1950, 40, 687–701.

Smith, K. "Attraction" in figural after-effects. *American Journal of Psychology*, 1954, 67, 174–176.

Sperry, R. W., and Nancy Miner. Pattern perception following insertion of mica plates into visual cortex. *Journal of Comparative and Physiological Psychology*, 1955, 48, 463–469.

Sperry, R. W., Nancy Miner, and R. E. Meyers. Visual pattern perception following subpial slicing and tantalum wire implantations in the visual cortex. *Journal of Comparative and Physiological Psychology*, 1955, 48, 50–58.

Spitz, H. H. The present status of the Köhler-Wallach theory of satiation. *Psychological Bulletin*, 1958, 55, 1–28.

Taylor, M. M. Figural after-effects: A psychophysical theory of the displacement effect. *Canadian Journal of Psychology*, 1962, 16, 247–277.

United States National Bureau of Standards, Computation Laboratory. Tables of the error function and its derivative. Washington, D. C.: United States Government Printing Office, 1954.

Werner, H. Studies on contour: I. Qualitative analyses. *American Journal of Psychology*, 1935, 47, 40–64.

Visual Noise Causes Tunnel Vision[*]

NORMAN H. MACKWORTH
Harvard University

Abstract—Ss had quickly to detect similarities between two uppercase letters presented peripherally and one other central letter falling on the fovea. These three characters were so legible that this task was very easy when the three letters were flashed on by themselves. But the addition of extra letters to this display seriously impaired performance. The periphery of the retina could no longer accurately detect at a glance whether items were similar. Foveal performance was also affected to some extent by extra items in the periphery of the retina.

Introduction

People usually select the information they want from a general background of unwanted material. Pattern recognition often involves peripheral matching in the sense that comparisons are made between one foveal item and many others placed in the differences are noted between two or more entirely peripheral items. This process of "peripheral matching" also guides eye movements which are by no means random walks, as Boynton (1960) and others have recently made clear. Selective visual attention usually involves direct movements of the fovea from one rich source of data to another. The most frequent choice ever made is where to look next. The fovea is such a busy sensor that it has to sample only essential data almost continuously. To reduce random search, eye movements must often be planned from data acquired by the peripheral retina. The main contention is that the addition of visual noise in the form of unwanted signals can destroy this vital peripheral matching. Pattern recognition is impaired because similarities can no longer be recognized quickly between wanted foveal and peripheral items—and the fovea must therefore be used more often.

Method

Twenty Harvard and Radcliffe undergraduates were tested individually and all had normal vision or corrected normal vision. After dark adapting for 10 min, the S was instructed to fixate the small dot in the center of the screen and to attend to

[*] *Psychonomic Science*, 1965, vol. 3, pp. 67–68. This research was supported in part through the Cooperative Research Program of the Office of Education, U. S. Department of Health, Education, and Welfare, Contract No. OE–4–10–136, Project No. E–020 to the Harvard University Center for Cognitive Studies; and in part by the National Aeronautic and Space Administration Research Grant NsG718, to the Guggenheim Center for Aerospace Health and Safety. I am also grateful to Dr. Donald A. Norman for advice as well as to Joyce Hiebert, Jack Sansolo, and Susan Tevlin for excellent assistance.

the entire width of the screen. He inspected successive patterns of upper-case letters briefly flashed on for 100 msec at 2.5 ft-L. and centered on his fixation point. Between displays the field was less than 0.1 ft-L. He was asked to report "Yes" when the center also occurred on both sides.

In order to vary the amount of visual noise, three kinds of *displays* were prepared. In all displays the three matched letters were always halfway up the screen and occupied the same positions relative to the fixation point. The *Three Letter* displays showed only three letters for recognition and this was the No Noise condition in Figure 1. Both of the Noise conditions in Figure 1 presented extra unwanted letters in addition to the matched letters. The *Line* displays showed one line of 17 letters, and the *Page* displays showed 22 lines of letters consisting of altogether 374 letters covering the whole display area. The second main variable was *the width subtended by the row of recognition stimuli*. In the Three Letter displays, the three recognition letters were close together, slightly spread or widely scattered. In both Noise displays, these matched letters were

similarly distributed. With viewing distances of 28 and 56 in, the three recognition widths subtended 1, 3 and 5 degrees, or 2, 6 and 10 degrees respectively. Only the 1 or 2 degree presentations were entirely foveal; the other widths required peripheral and foveal discrimination. The letters were 0.25 in high and 0.5 in between centers: they were of high contrast on 8.5 × 11 in white backgrounds. Each of the nine arrangements of displays and widths was prepared in two different versions—with the three recognition letters as N or C. The resulting 18 cards were randomly mixed with an equal number of catch displays which had either no matching letters at all or only one matching letter to one side of the central letter.

Results and Discussion

Figure 1 shows that the extra unwanted letters or visual noise gave the main effect. Virtually perfect scores were made with the Three Letter (No Noise) at all widths of recognition display. But the addition of unwanted letters to these identical patterns of three wanted letters gave a catastrophic reduction in recognition scores. These Noise conditions were harmful either as Line or as Page displays. The worst impairment was found when the recognition letters stretched into the peripheral retina. These noise displays subtending 3 to 10 degrees averaged only 10 per cent correct. Foveal recognition was also, however, definitely impaired by peripheral visual noise, even when the three matching letters were adjacent to each other. Recognition scores for material in the fovea fell to three-quarters or two-thirds of achievement at the noise-free level when extra unwanted letters fell on the periphery of the retina. The displays, the widths, and also the interaction between these variables were all significant ($p < 0.01$) by analysis of variance, but individual differences, viewing distances, and the nature of the recognition letter had no effect. Bringing the matching

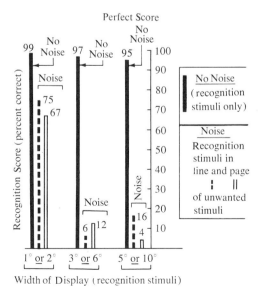

Width of Display (recognition stimuli)

FIGURE 1

TABLE 1

Percentage Correct Recognition of Matched Trios

Display Type			Recognition Display Width	
			3° – 6°	5° – 10°
RN	N	NS	43	41
NT	N	ZN	79	81

letters near the end of the line of letters was established as a second-order benefit in the Line display in which the widest recognition patterns were the least accurately read.

This end-of-the-line effect was followed up in another study with 20 further Harvard and Radcliffe Ss. The tachistoscopic conditions were identical except that now only five letters were presented in 100 msec. Even two extra noise letters can drastically reduce recognition scores for three wanted letters—provided the two noise letters are added just outside the wanted letters. They have much less effect when they are placed just inside the wanted letters; the recognition score doubles when the wanted letters are outside the unwanted. This suggests that the scanning of the visual image once it has been formed may be undertaken from the outside inward towards the fovea (see also the results of Haselrud and Clark, 1957).

Both investigations show that visual noise impairs peripheral matching. These considerable changes in performance partly depend on retinal confusions, but they also appear to involve non-retinal factors since even doubling the viewing distance did not alter recognition scores. The possible disadvantages of moving back, such as smaller visual angles between the visually smaller letters, might conceivably have been balanced by benefits from these being read by less peripheral parts of the retina, but the No Noise evidence in Figure 1 makes this rather unlikely.

The concept of the useful field of view helps to understand the results. The useful field of view is the area around the fixation point from which information is being briefly stored and read out during a visual task. When there is too much information, the useful field contracts to prevent over-loading of the visual system, just as the pupil constricts with too much light. The useful field of view is therefore varying in width from moment to moment according to the amount of information on the display. The useful field cannot exceed the normal physiological limits set by the ordinary visual acuity fields. But these experiments show that information overload from too many unwanted signals can prevent the useful field from reaching the size of the normal plotted fields, as Teuber et al. (1960) and Sanders (1963) have also mentioned. The Page displays here are believed to resemble the massive overload conditions used by Volkmann (1964), as well as by Chaikin et al. (1962). There was not enough time to form the visual image. These investigators have demonstrated that allowing more time broadened the effective tachistoscopic fields. This suggests that with considerable overloading the visual image is formed from the center outwards; visual noise would therefore produce a temporary tunnel vision. The Line displays only slightly overload the visual systems so that here the visual image was fairly well-formed according to the evidence of Sperling (1963); the difficulty was now in scanning the visual image because this recognition of items such as letters is the slowest part of the process. This kind of scanning appeared to be inwards towards the center.

In both circumstances, extraneous visual stimuli destroyed peripheral recognition because the whole stimulus pattern was so complex; as Hake (1957) comments, the limited exposure times were no longer sufficient to process the main signals in addition to this extra information. Mackworth and Mackworth (1959) had noted this visual overload effect as also have Kaplan and Carvellas (1965), unlike Neisser (1963). Tunnel vision occurred because priority was given to foveal items. Even foveal performance was, however, definitely impaired by the addition of unwanted peripheral stimuli.

References

BOYNTON, R. M. In *Visual search techniques*. Nat. Acad. Sci.—Nat. Res. Council Publ. No. 712, 1960, 232.

CHAIKIN, JOYCE D., H. H. CORBIN, and J. VOLKMANN. Mapping a field of short-time visual search. *Science*, 1962, *138*, 1327–1328.

HAKE, H. W. *Contributions of psychology to the study of pattern vision*. WADC Technical Document 57–621, ASTIA Document No. AD142035, 1957, 50.

HASLERUD, G. M., and R. E. CLARK. On the redintegrative perception of words. *Amer. J. Psychol.*, 1957, 70, 97–101.

KAPLAN, I. T., and T. CARVELLAS. Scanning for multiple targets. *Percept. mot. Skills*, 1965, in press.

MACKWORTH, JANE F. Interference and decay in very short-term memory. *J. verbal Learn. verbal Behav.*, 1964, 3, 300–308.

MACKWORTH, N. H., and JANE F. MACKWORTH. Remembering advance cues during searching. *Brit. J. Psychol.*, 1959, 50, 207–222.

NEISSER, U. Decision time without reaction time: experiments in visual scanning. *Amer. J. Psychol.*, 1963, 76, 376–385.

SANDERS, A. F. *The selective process in the functional visual field*. From Inst. for Perception RVO-TNO. Nat. Def. Res. Organization TNO. Soesterberg, The Netherlands, 1963, 33.

SPERLING, G. A model for visual memory tasks. *Hum. Factors*, 1963, 5, 19–31.

TEUBER, H. L., W. S. BATTERSBY, and M. B. BENDER. *Visual field defects after penetrating missile wounds of the brain*. Harvard University Press, Cambridge, 1960, 83.

VOLKMANN, J. H. H. CORBIN, NANCY B. EDDY, and CAROL COONLEY. *The range of visual search*. Electronic Sys. Div. Tech. Document. Rep. No. ESD-TDR-64-535, 1964.

CHAPTER 5

Perception
of Objects
in Space

Nonrelational Judgments of Size and Distance*

WILLIAM EPSTEIN
University of Kansas

Experiments which purport to demonstrate the influence of specified variables on the perception of *absolute* size or distance[1] are frequently reinterpreted as dealing with relational effects.[2] It also has been asserted that any experiment employing a visual comparison-object deals, of necessity, with relational effects.[3] These arguments create uncertainty about a recent demonstration that "assumed size" can determine absolute perceived distance.[4] It was decided, therefore, to repeat the original assumed-size experiment employing nonvisual (tactual) measures of the size and distance of individual "coins" pre-

sented usually without any accompanying visual stimuli. If visual relationships were responsible for the original results, then the elimination of these relationships should give different results.

APPARATUS

Each standard was mounted on a thin black rod and placed on a black table-top at approximately eye-level. Provisions were made to restrict O to stationary, monocular, aperture-vision when desired. It was also possible to present the standard in isolation in surrounding darkness, illuminated by a spot of light which corresponded exactly to the dimensions of the standard.

MATERIALS

Two sets of standards were used. The training set consisted of three copper disks with diameters of 1.75, 2.38, and 2.86 cm., respectively. The test-standards were the mounted photographs of the dime, quarter and half-dollar which were used in the earlier study. Each of these standards had a diameter of 2.38 cm.—the normal size of a quarter.

The size-comparison series was a set of seven disks cut from one sheet of copper. The disks varied in diameter from 1.43-3.33 cm. in steps of 0.125 cm. They were glued to the surface of a wooden panel, arranged horizontally in order of size. The distance-comparison object was a coiled

* *American Journal of Psychology,* 1966, vol. 79, pp. 120–123. This study was supported by Grant MH 4153–04 from the National Institute of Health.

[1] W. H. Ittelson, Size as a cue to distance: Static localization, *Amer. J. Psychol.,* 1951, *64,* 54–67; A. H. Hastorf, The influence of suggestion on the relation between stimulus size and perceived distance, *Amer. J. Psychol.,* 1950, *29,* 195–217.

[2] William Epstein, The known-size-apparent-distance hypothesis, *Amer. J. Psychol.,* 1961, *74,* 333–346; W. C. Gogel, B. O. Hartman, and G. S. Harker, The retinal size of a familiar object as a determiner of apparent distance, *Psychol. Monogr.,* 1957, *71,* 1–16.

[3] J. C. Baird, Retinal and assumed size cues as as determinants of size and distance perception, *J. exp. Psychol.,* 1963, *66,* 155–162; Gogel, The size cue to visually perceived distance, *Psychol. Bull.,* 62, 1964, 217–225.

[4] Epstein, The influence of assumed size on apparent distance, *Amer. J. Psychol.,* 1963, *76,* 257–265.

rope which could be pulled by E through O's hand. The length of the rope which was drawn could be read on a cm.-scale. Neither the rope nor the size-comparison series was visible to O.

OBSERVERS

The Os were 45 students in an introductory psychology course. None of them required corrective lenses.

PROCEDURE

Each O was assigned to one of the three standard-coin conditions in the order of his appearance in the laboratory. The procedure was divided into two parts. (a) *Training stage:* Each O made distance- and size-judgments of nine size-distance combinations; the three training disks placed at three distances: 100, 135, and 170 cm. The nine combinations were presented in random order under full-cue conditions. O matched his visual impressions of size by selecting the raised comparison-disk which was subjectively equal to the standard. For the distance-judgments, E pulled the rope through O's hand until O tightened his grip and said "stop." No effort was made to control the rate with which the rope was drawn. For both types

of judgment, O was corrected after each trial. (b) *Testing stage:* The standard coin was presented at a distance of 135 cm. and O made judgments of distance and size, first under totally reduced conditions of observation, then under unrestricted conditions. The procedure for obtaining judgments was the same as in the training stage except that no corrections were made.

Results

The reason for introducing the training stage was to insure that Os could accurately match tactual and visual impressions of size and distance prior to the critical test. The results showed that the Os were able to perform at a high level of accuracy. The mean distance-judgments were 89.47 ($SD = 15.32$), 126.79 ($SD = 21.39$), and 163.21 ($SD = 25.43$) for the 100-, 135-, and 170-cm. standard distances, respectively. The mean size-judgments were 1.89 ($SD = 0.10$), 2.37 ($SD = 0.12$) and 2.69 ($SD = 0.14$) for the 1.75-, 2.38-, and 2.86-cm. standard disks, respectively.

The results for the testing stage are presented in Table 1. Under conditions of monocular observation, the half-dollar (H) was localized most distantly, and the dime (D) was judged to be nearest. The

TABLE 1

Apparent Distance and Size of Standard Coins with Monocular and Binocular Vision
(Physical distance = 135 cm.; physical size = 2.38 cm. All entries in cm.)

	APPARENT DISTANCE				APPARENT SIZE			
	MONOCULAR VISION		BINOCULAR VISION		MONOCULAR VISION		BINOCULAR VISION	
STANDARD	MEAN	SD	MEAN	SD	MEAN	SD	MEAN	SD
Dime	103.56	20.14	117.03	14.45	2.08	0.30	2.36	0.14
Quarter	128.10	27.65	123.73	12.27	2.26	0.31	2.47	0.18
Half-dollar	151.30	31.62	123.07	16.11	2.60	0.43	2.45	0.28

perceived distance of the quarter (Q) was between that of D and H. Analysis of variance yielded an F of 11.22 ($df = 2/42$, $p < 0.001$). Duncan's multiple-range test showed that all the differences between the means are significant (Q-D, $p < 0.05$; H-Q, $p < 0.05$; H-D, $p < 0.01$). An analysis of the binocular data for distance yielded a nonsignificant F (< 1).

Table I also shows that, under the reduced conditions, H was judged to be largest, D smallest, and Q was intermediate. An analysis of variance yielded an F of 19.10 ($df = 2/42$, $p < 0.001$). Duncan's test showed that all the differences between the means were significant ($p < 0.05$). An analysis of the binocular data for size did not reveal any significant variations.

Next the size-distance relationship was assessed by means of the Spearman rank-correlation coefficient (corrected for ties). The size-distance invariance hypothesis requires a significant positive correlation between perceived size and perceived distance. The coefficients were -0.024, 0.015, and 0.66 ($p < 0.01$) for D, Q, and H, respectively.

A final analysis involved the comparison of three values for each standard: objective distance, obtained apparent distance, and theoretically required apparent distance. The latter is the value required by the known-size-apparent-distance hypothesis, and is determined by the formula: theoretical distance = (apparent size/physical size) (physical distance).[5] The predictions of apparent distance based on the known-size hypothesis are closely approximated by the data for Q and H. The mean apparent distance for D falls short of the theoretically required distance by 12 percent.

---

[5] Epstein, *op. cit.*, *Amer. J. Psychol.*, 1963, 76, 260.

Discussion

The judgments of distance obtained in the present experiment conform to those of the original study. The size-judgments are also similar to those obtained previously. Since the present procedure did not involve visual comparisons, it is reasonable to conclude that the findings are not methodological artifacts of the sort described in the introductory section.

Judgments of size and distance were not always positively correlated for the Os under each condition. Although the expected positive correlations *were* obtained in the original study, evidence that the size-distance link was not to be interpreted too rigidly was also present in that study. Evidently, knowledge of the perceived size for a given O does not permit an exact prediction of the distance at which the O will perceive the standard. It cannot be ascertained from the data whether this failure is due to the unreliability of the measures of size and distance, or to some procedural flaw, *e.g.* availability of conflicting distance-cues, or whether these repeated failures imply an inherent limitation of the hypothesis.

Summary

Nonvisual measures of the perceived size and distance of coins were obtained. The purpose was to determine whether earlier results indicating a relationship between assumed size and perceived absolute distance were artifacts of the visual relationships introduced by the use of visual comparison-objects. The results of the present study were generally in agreement with those of the earlier study, leading to the conclusion that the assumed-size-perceived-distance relationship was not a methodological artifact.

Perceived Shape and Its Dependency on Perceived Slant[*]

PETER K. KAISER

University of Rochester

Koffka's suggestions that perceived shape and perceived slant "will be coupled together so that if 1 changes, the other changes also" and that errors in perceived shape vary as some function of errors in perceived slant were examined. Ss described, by means of appropriate response mechanisms, the shapes and slants of trapezoids. Shape and slant responses were made both monocularly and binocularly. The changes in reported shape varied as a function of changes in reported slant. Also, shape response errors varied as a function of slant response errors under monocular viewing when Ss had no prior binocular experience with the trapezoid. The functions relating perceived shape to perceived slant were comparable to the function predicted by the Beck and Gibson shape-slant invariance hypothesis.

As one moves about, his visual surroundings appear stable and objects maintain their apparent shapes regardless of their orientation with respect to O. Since visual information is mediated through the retina, how is it that one tends to report the object shape of things and not the shape projected on the retina? One explanation postulates that the slant of the object is taken into account. Descartes (1638) noted that ". . . the shape is judged by our knowledge or opinion of the disposition of the diverse parts of the objects. . . ." More recently, William James (1890) noted,

that "it is not the cross and ring pure and simple which we perceive, but the cross so held, the ring so held [p. 259]."

The first formal statements of this shape-slant relationship were presented by Koffka (1935, pp. 229–233). He proposed "invariant" relationships between perceived shape and perceived slant. From his statements, these relationships are interpreted by the present writer, as being monotonic and the precise functions are dependent on the "total sets of conditions." Beck and Gibson (1955) restated Koffka in a more restricted form, proposing the shape-slant invariance hypothesis. This hypothesis states that "a retinal projection of a given form determines a unique relation of apparent[1] slant to apparent shape [p. 126]." This unique relation is described by the family of shape-slant combinations that project identical retinal images. Koffka

[*] *Journal of Experimental Psychology*, 1967, vol. 75, pp. 345–353. This research was supported by the University of California Patent Income Fund and by United States Public Health Service Grant NB–05185 held by J. P. Thomas. The paper is based upon a PhD dissertation submitted to the University of California, Los Angeles. The author is indebted to G. E. Mount and J. P. Thomas for their generously given guidance and support. Portions of this paper were presented at the American Psychological Association Convention 1966.

[1] No distinction is made among the terms apparent, perceived, and reported.

proposed multiple invariant relations, while Beck and Gibson proposed one.

Several studies (Beck and Gibson, 1955; Bower, 1966; Wallach and Moore, 1962) have shown that perceived shape depends on cues for slant. Limited support for a general shape-slant correspondence has been found by Stavrianos (1945), Beck and Gibson (1955), Epstein, Bontrager, and Park (1962), and Winnick and Rogoff (1965). However, their data do not demonstrate the function or functions relating perceived shape to perceived slant, and cannot be considered sufficient support to verify a shape-slant invariance hypothesis. At least two investigators, Nixon (1958) and Flock (1964), were unable to find any systematic relationship between perceived shape and perceived slant.

The research reported in this paper examines Koffka's (1935) general suggestions that "the two aspects of the percept (shape and slant) will be coupled together so that if one changes the other changes also [p. 229]"; and that "it . . . is probable that the amount by which the figure appears turned from normal decreases as the constancy of shape decreases [p. 232]." More specifically these suggestions are examined in the context of the Beck and Gibson shape-slant invariance hypothesis.

Koffka's second suggestion implies that as errors in perceived slant increase (decrease), errors in perceived shape will also increase (decrease). Error refers to the discrepancy between the physical shape (slant) and S's report of shape (slant) on different observations. If Beck and Gibson (1955) are correct, the function relating shape errors to slant errors and the function relating reported shape change to reported slant change should correspond to the function (unique relation) of the invariance hypothesis.

Changes in reported slant were obtained by varying the cues for depth, i.e., binocular disparity. The Ss viewed the stimuli monocularly and binocularly. The difference between stimulation produced by monocular and binocular viewing is manifested mainly in the perception of depth (i.e., in this case, slant). Without binocular disparity as a depth cue, S has less information with which to make judgements of slant. Therefore, one can expect that S will report slant differently under binocular viewing. If this is the case, will he also report shape differently? In utilizing this technique, it is assumed that no distinction is necessary in the interpretation of the invariance hypothesis for monocular and binocular viewing. If this assumption is valid, we may conclude that obtained changes in reported shape are primarily due to the effect of changes in perceived slant.

Method

Apparatus. All stimulus displays were housed in a common box (Figure 1). The shape response apparatus (a), standard stimulus (b), and slant response apparatus (c) were placed 30° apart, tangent to an arc of radius 105 cm. They were viewed through a viewing slot (d) placed at the center of the arc. The box was illuminated by four 20-w. cool white fluorescent tubes (e) placed on the floor, ceiling, and two walls at the front of the box. Light baffles (f) were placed in front of each tube so that the displays would not receive direct illumination. The inside front wall and a 7-in. border on the walls, floor, and ceiling adjacent to the inside front wall were painted flat white. Illuminating the inside of the box in this manner produced homogeneous illumination with no visible shadows about the standard stimulus. The remainder of the box was painted flat gray. Mounted on the front of the viewing box was a combination head-holder chinrest.

The standard stimuli were three trapezoids cut from tempered aluminum, .0020 in. thick. The sizes and shapes of the trapezoids were designed so that when placed at 15°, 45°, and 65° away from the frontal-parallel plane top receding away, they pro-

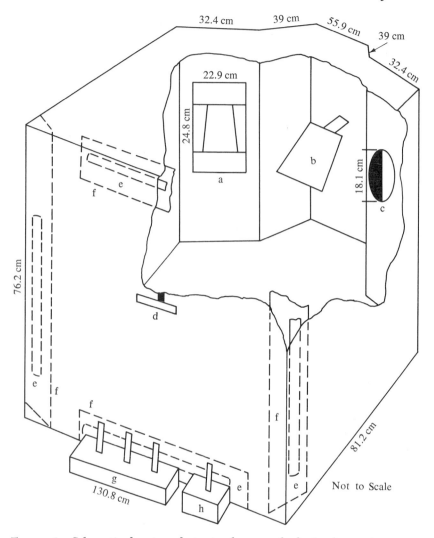

FIGURE 1   Schematic drawing of viewing box, standard stimulus, and response mechanisms. (Letters identify components in text.)

jected identical retinal images. Each trapezoid at its respective slant subtended the following visual angles: top = 8°, height = 5°, and base = 10°. The formulas used to determine these shapes are reported by Kaiser (1966). The surfaces of the trapezoids were painted flat white. The base edge of each stimulus was filed to a knife edge so that when slanted the thickness of the metal would be minimally visible. The luminance of the stimuli were 12 ft-L for the 15° stimulus, 8.5 ft-L for the 45° stimulus and 6.5 ft-L for the 65° stimulus. The luminance of the gray background about the stimuli was approximately 3 ftL.

These measurements were made with a Spectra brightness spot meter. The stimuli were mounted on a plate whose angle of slant was controlled by turning a crank attached to a worm gear and nut arrangement. The stimuli were slanted about a horizontal axis placed at eye level, i.e., directly opposite the viewing slot at a distance of 105 cm. Access to the mounting plate was through a side door.

The shape-response apparatus permitted S to report shapes ranging from isosceles triangles with the apex at the top to isosceles triangles with the apex at the bottom. These shapes included triangles, trapezoids, and rectangles. The equipment imposed the restriction that the maximum size of the shape response could not be more than 24 cm. high and 22 cm. wide. This restriction is more than 2 cm. larger than the maximum height and width of any of the standard stimuli. Only a few Ss were affected by this restriction. They attempted to report the base of the 15° stimulus as being wider than 22 cm. and were asked to scale down the size of the shape response. The shape response was made by adjusting four masks surrounding a flat white background. The top and bottom masks moved vertically; the vertical masks moved horizontally. Also, the vertical masks could be rotated to vary the slant of the sides of the shape response. A more detailed description of this apparatus is given by Kaiser (1966). The fronts of these masks were painted the same color as the inside of the box. The background behind these masks presented a homogeneous white surface regardless of the position of the masks. The Ss were given three controls (Figure 1g) to make the shape responses: one varied the height, a second the width, and the third the angles of the sides.

The Ss made slant responses by rotating a half-black half-white disc (Flock, 1964) by means of a control switch (Figure 1h). When the division between the black and white halves was vertical this indicated that the standard stimulus was vertical; when it was horizontal, the standard was parallel to the line of sight. Rotation clockwise indicated that the top of the standard was slanted toward S and vice versa.

Subjects. The Ss were 30 undergraduates fulfilling a requirement of the introductory psychology course at UCLA. They were naive with respect to the purpose of the experiment. On their last eye examination, all Ss had normal acuity without corrective lenses.

Procedure. Each S was assigned to one of three stimulus-slant conditions and one

of two viewing conditions (monocular or binocular first). The assignment was made in an irregular order. There were five Ss in each of the six conditions. Thus, each S viewed only one stimulus shape at its respective slant. The S was instructed in the use of the response mechanisms and given a short practice period with a stimulus that was not one of the standards. Practice was conducted monocularly when monocular was the first condition and binocularly when binocular viewing was the first condition. The right eye was used under the monocular condition; the left eye being occluded by an eye patch. Each S was given the following instructions:

I will place various shaped objects at various slants into the box. Your task is to answer two questions. 1. What is the shape of the object placed in the box by E? 2. At what slant did E place the object in the box? When you make the shape response, the figure you make in the shape response apparatus should be the same size and shape as the object placed in the box. There might possibly be one difference between the object I placed in the box and your shape response. Your reproduction of the object should look as if the object is in a vertical position, i.e., perpendicular to your line of sight. The object in front of you, however, may be slanted to your line of sight. For example, suppose you look at the object in the box, and you wish to say that it is a circular disc and it is slanted away from you. You would make a circular disc[2] on the shape apparatus that is the same size and shape as the disc in front of you. However, the disc that you make on the re-response mechanism will be vertical while the disc placed in the box will be slanted. If you make a perfect response, you, theoretically, should be able to reach into the box, take the circular disc and place it directly over your response and it would fit perfectly.

At this point S was asked if he had any questions and E explained any portion of

---

[2] This is only an example. A circular disk could not be constructed with this shape-response apparatus.

the instructions that were unclear. The S was told, further, that he would always make the slant response first. After completing the slant response, he would make the shape response. Then he could look iteratively among the standard stimulus, his slant response and shape response as often as he liked, making any adjustments to his responses that he felt were required. A trial was ended when S said that the shape and slant responses indicated exactly what he wanted to tell E about the shape and slant of the standard stimulus.

At the end of each trial E closed the viewing slot and measured the slant response from the rear of the slant response apparatus. This measure was taken from a protractor-pointer arrangement attached to the rear of the black-and-white disc. The E also measured the height, width of the top, and width of the base of the shape response directly from the rear of the masks. The slant responses were measured to the nearest degree and the shape responses to the nearest millimeter.

The E then went through the motions of changing the standard stimulus. However, the standard was not changed. The purpose of this procedure was to discourage Ss from responding from trial to trial under the assumption that they were always looking at the same stimulus. Finally, E changed the setting of the shape and slant response mechanisms to new positions.

Each S made three sets of responses under each viewing condition, e.g., three shape and three slant responses monocularly and three shape and three slant responses binocularly.

Results

The shape response measures were reduced to height to base (h/b) ratios and to top to base (t/b) ratios. Analyses of the change scores and error scores were not performed on the raw h/b and t/b measures. These measures for stimuli that project identical retinal images are not linear functions of slant, but curvilinear. There-

fore, it was not meaningful to combine the data in this form for the different stimuli at their respective slants. This difficulty was overcome by transforming h/b and t/b scores so that, under the Beck and Gibson hypothesis, they are linear functions of slant. These transformations[3] and the rationale for them are reported by Kaiser (1966). The *nontransformed* shape scores will be written as h/b and t/b while the *transformed* values will be written as h'/b' and t'/b'. In addition to combining the transformed shape response data for different slant conditions, linear regression analyses may now be used to evaluate the agreement between obtained and predicted results.

Table 1 shows the mean slant responses, mean h/b (untransformed) and mean t/b (untransformed). Each mean is the average of three responses. In previous experiments (Kaiser, 1966, Experiment A and I) Ss were given 10 trials. These investigations showed that the intra-S reliability was very high. Therefore, the use of three trials per S, per condition was considered justified. As expected, slant judgments were more accurate binocularly than monocularly.

Change scores were computed as follows. The slant response, h'/b' and t'/b' (transformed scores) obtained under monocular viewing were subtracted from the slant response, h'/b' and t'/b' under binocular viewing for each S.

Figure 2a shows the change in h'/b'

---

[3] Briefly, the transformations were obtained as follows. The curvilinear function relating h/b to slant was derived for the stimuli subtending visual angles described above. An arbitrary straight line (h'/b') was drawn through this function and an equal interval scale assigned to the associate ordinate. To determine the value of h'/b' corresponding to a particular h/b, the slant value associated with that h/b is obtained. The h'/b' associated with this same slant is the transformed value. An analytical derivation proved this graphical technique accurate. Transformation of the t/b was obtained by a similar graphical technique.

The following expression describes the transformations:

'h/b' $= k[f^{-1} (h/b)] + a$. Where: $k =$ slope of linear function; $a =$ intercept of linear function; $f =$ curvilinear function of slant.

TABLE 1

Summary of Shape and Slant Responses

	MONOCULAR FIRST					
STIMULUS	MONOCULAR MEAN			BINOCULAR MEAN		
SUBJECT	SLANT	h/b	t/b	SLANT	h/b	t/b
15						
YD	27	.83	.90	15	.65	.85
MF	20	.63	.86	24	.62	.91
JB	28	.60	.82	16	.52	.81
GT	11	.62	.88	13	.54	.88
KV	−1	.50	.77	15	.58	.80
M	17.0	.64	.85	16.5	.58	.85
45						
LF	59	1.24	.94	40	.83	.85
ED	11	.55	.83	26	.76	.94
AB	38	.78	.91	36	.93	.98
JR	12	.52	.82	32	.57	.83
SW	27	.76	.85	27	.76	.85
M	29.4	.77	.87	32.2	.77	.89
65						
RB	−21	.49	.81	58	1.15	.95
DT	20	.83	.88	38	1.38	.98
PT	10	.62	.86	55	1.27	.98
SC	43	.91	.98	58	1.31	1.00
ED	21	.54	.75	64	1.09	.97
M	14.6	.68	.86	54.6	1.24	.98

	BINOCULAR FIRST					
STIMULUS	MONOCULAR MEAN			BINOCULAR MEAN		
SUBJECT	SLANT	h/b	t/b	SLANT	h/b	t/b
15						
AS	2	.54	.77	15	.53	.80
FW	35	.84	.96	9	.53	.77
RP	18	.71	.86	10	.58	.87
NB	26	.51	.82	22	.51	.81
RB	17	.65	.89	3	.54	.83
M	19.6	.65	.86	11.8	.54	.82
45						
MK	25	.68	.77	25	.77	.80
DJ	14	.62	.86	37	.70	.83
ME	17	.72	.87	24	.76	.89
GB	38	.68	.87	44	.75	.86
KH	24	.62	.84	44	.72	.87
M	23.6	.66	.84	34.8	.74	.85
65						
GS	46	1.19	.98	51	1.29	.97
NS	56	1.04	.98	58	1.18	.98
JC	59	1.13	.99	68	1.23	1.01
MT	46	.55	.81	61	.99	.93
JW	60	1.21	.99	63	1.33	.99
M	53.4	1.02	.95	60.0	1.20	.98

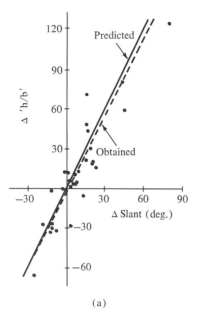

(a)

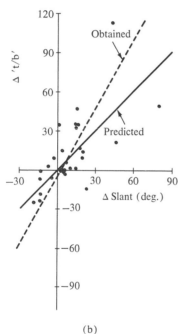

(b)

FIGURE 2   Change in h'/b' and t'/b' as a function of change in slant responses when going between monocular and binocular viewing.

as a function of the change in reported slant when going between monocular and binocular viewing. The change in reported h'/b' (Δ[h'/b']) is significantly correlated

with the change in reported slant (Δ slant), r (30) = .90 p < .01. A regression line was computed by the method suggested by Worthing and Geffner (1943) for the case when "liability of error occurs" in both variables. The slope of this regression is 1.89. The predicted line, if Ss responded in terms of the Beck and Gibson hypothesis, for this experiment, is 2.00. The change in t'/b' (Figure 2B) is significantly correlated with the change in slant responses, r (30) = .68, p < .01. The slope of the obtained regression line is 1.80; however, the predicted slope for this experiment is 1.00.

Figure 3 shows the results of the error analyses for monocular viewing conditions as the first condition and as the second condition. Error was computed by subtracting Ss' responses from the physical measures. For example, if S reported a slant of 60° when the physical slant was 45°, he made a slant response error of 15°. When monocular viewing is the first condition, the shape errors are significantly correlated with slant errors. The correlation between h'/b' error and slant response error is .95 (df = 15; p < .01). The obtained regression line for the h'/b' is 1.87; the predicted line is 2.00. For t'/b' it is 1.25 and the predicted line is 1.00. Under the monocular condition, when binocular viewing was first, the shape response errors were not significantly correlated with the slant response errors.

Table 2 presents a summary of the error analyses and the change analyses.

For binocular viewing, both as the first and second viewing condition the correlations between shape error and slant error did not reach significance. However, the binocular response errors fell within the range of the monocular response errors. Most of the binocular responses fell near the point of zero-slant error and zero h'/b' and t'/b' error. The failure to obtain significant results under binocular viewing is probably due to the small range of response errors relative to the interS variability;

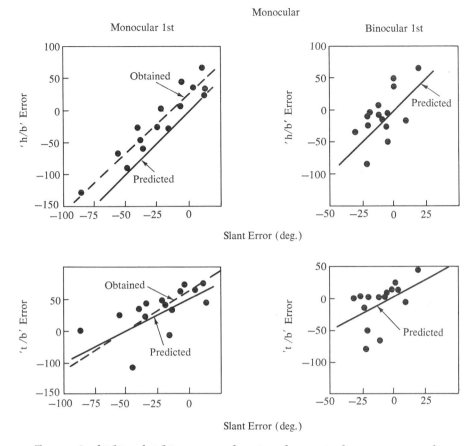

FIGURE 3   h'/b' and t'/b' errors as a function of errors in slant responses under monocular viewing when used as first and second viewing conditions.

therefore, these results do not detract from the importance of the monocular results.

Discussion

The error analyses in this experiment are in accord with the error analyses of two previous investigations (Kaiser, 1966, Experiment A and I). In agreement with Koffka's (1935) suggestion, a close correspondence was obtained between errors in perceived shape and errors in perceived slant. The relationship between errors in h'/b' and errors in slant is a fair approximation of the function predicted by the Beck and Gibson (1955) shape-slant invariance hypothesis. While t'/b' errors as a function of slant errors show a similar relationship, the correspondence to the

Beck and Gibson hypothesis is not as good as that provided by h'/b'. Agreement with the predicted function is found only under monocular viewing when Ss had no prior binocular experience with the stimuli. The relationship was not found under binocular viewing primarily due to the small range of response errors compared with the interS variability. These results lend support to Epstein's et al. (1962) findings that under objective instructions Ss made accurate shape responses. While the instructions in the experiment reported in the present paper can be considered objective, they differ from Epstein's et al. in one significant way. Their Ss were instructed to report the "actual physical dimensions of the target even if the match you make doesn't look

TABLE 2

Summary of the Analyses

ERROR ANALYSIS	r	df	REGRESSION COEFFICIENT	
			PRE-DICTED	OB-TAINED
h'/b' monocular-monocular 1st	.95*	15	2.00	1.87
t'/b' monocular-monocular 1st	.65*	15	1.00	1.25
h'/b' monocular-binocular 1st	.63	15	2.00	
t'/b' monocular-binocular 1st	.46	15	1.00	
h'/b' binocular-monocular 1st	.38	15	2.00	
t'/b' binocular-monocular 1st	.13	15	1.00	
h'/b' binocular-binocular 1st	—.36	15	2.00	
t'/b' binocular-binocular 1st	.35	15	1.00	
Change Analyses[a]				
h'/b'	.90*	30	2.00	1.89
t'/b'	.65*	30	1.00	1.80

*p < .01.
[a] In the analysis of response changes, monocular first and binocular first data are combined.

equal in shape to you." The Ss in my experiment did not receive the latter part of this instruction. It would seem that the important question is how the actual physical dimensions appear to Ss.

The results of the change analyses lend support to Koffka's proposal concerning the covariance of changes. Furthermore, this relationship can be described by the function proposed by the invariance hypothesis. The h'/b' changes demonstrate this function considerably better than the t'/b' changes do.

In the error and the change analyses, the relationship between h'/b' and slant adheres more closely to the predicted relationship than does the relationship between t'/b' and slant. This difference can, in some measure, be accounted for by the smaller range of t'/b' responses. If Ss had responded precisely as predicted by the invariance hypothesis, the range of h/b (not transformed) scores would have been .81 while the range of t/b scores would have been only .16. This difference in ranges may account for the smaller correlation coefficients obtained for t'/b' data than for the h'/b' data. However, one would expect that if the correlations were smaller, then the slope of the regression lines should also be smaller than predicted. The regression lines for the t'/b' data in all analyses were greater than the predicted 1.00. No interpretation is made for this paradoxical finding.

The failure of previous investigators to find particular relationships or to provide strong support for a given shape-slant relationship probably can be attributed to the experimental methodology and the analyses to which the data were subjected. The following methods employed in the present research seem to have contributed to obtaining the "invariant" (Koffka, 1935) relationships reported in this paper. (a) Since both conceptions, (Koffka's and Beck and Gibson's) of the invariant relations state that the shape-slant relationship should be obtained for a retinal image of a given form, all the standard stimuli projected identical retinal images. Thus, if the invariance hypothesis were tenable, the relationships between reported shape and reported slant should yield a single function. However, this function has to be evident over the interS variability. Therefore, several stimuli projecting identical retinal images, instead of one stimulus, were used in order to obtain a larger range of slant response changes and errors. Extending the range of these slant responses should not affect the relationship between reported shape and reported slant if an invariance hypothesis is valid. (b) For a given retinal image object shape (h/b, t/b) is a curvilinear function of object slant. If S responds in terms of the invariance hypothesis, the reported shape should also be a curvilinear function of reported slant. Demonstrating this function can be difficult, unless S variability is small. Also, when using differently shaped stimuli at different slants, untransformed error and change scores cannot be meaningfully combined in one analysis. There-

fore, h/b and t/b scores were transformed to permit straight line analyses of the data from different stimuli, facilitating the comparison of obtained data with predicted functions. It was thus possible to test the Beck and Gibson hypothesis in a manner less obscured by S variability.

The following methodological improvements may have contributed to obtaining data in accord with the function predicted by the invariance hypothesis. (a) The shape and slant response mechanisms were viewed under the same conditions as the standard stimulus by housing them in a common viewing box. (b) Simultaneous shape and slant responses were approximated by allowing Ss to make adjustments to their initial responses in an iterative fashion until satisfied that *both* responses represented their perception of the shape and slant of the stimulus. (c) The shape-response mechanism had sufficient degrees of freedom so Ss could report all aspects of their perception of the shape of the stimulus. The Ss could report the shape as they perceived it. They were not constrained to construct the shape response about any single fixed dimension (e.g., fixed width of response apparatus).

References

BECK, J., and J. J. GIBSON. The relation of apparent shape to apparent slant in the perception of objects. *J. exp. Psychol.*, 1955, 50, 125–133.

BOWER, T. G. R. Slant perception and shape constancy in infants. *Science*, 1966, 151, 832–834.

DESCARTES, R. On the visual perception of size, shape, and distance. In *La Dioptrique*, Leiden: 1638. Cited by R. J. Herrnstein and E. G. Boring (Eds.), *A source book in the history of psychology*. Cambridge: Harvard Univer. Press, 1965. pp. 113–124.

EPSTEIN, W., H. BONTRAGER, and J. PARK. The induction of nonveridical slant and the perception of shape. *J. exp. Psychol.*, 1962, 63, 472–479.

FLOCK, H. R. Come conditions sufficient for accurate monocular perceptions of moving surface slants. *J. exp. Psychol.*, 1964, 67, 560–572.

JAMES, W. *The principles of psychology.* Holt, 1890.

KAISER, P. K. An investigation of shape at a slant. Unpublished doctoral dissertation, University of California, Los Angeles, 1966.

KOFFKA, K. *Principles of gestalt psychology.* New York: Harcourt Brace, 1935.

NIXON, M. C. Perceived shape and slant. Unpublished masters thesis, University of Sydney, 1958.

STAVRIANOS, B. Relation of shape perception to explicit judgements of inclination. *Arch. Psychol.*, 1945, 41, 296.

WALLACH, H., and M. E. MOORE. The role of slant in the perception of shape. *Amer. J. Psychol.*, 1962, 75, 285–293.

WINNICK, W. A., and I. ROGOFF. Role of apparent slant in shape judgements. *J. exp. Psychol.*, 1965, 69, 554–563.

WORTHING, W. A., and J. GEFFNER. *Treatment of experimental data.* New York: Wiley, 1943.

On Homogeneous Retinal Stimulation and the Perception of Depth[*]

THOMAS NATSOULAS

University of Wisconsin

A review of recent experiments showing that where the perception of voluminous fog does not occur consistently under conditions attempting homogeneity of visual stimulation, there are sources of inhomogeneity which can produce the impression of a surface. As homogeneity is approached, the volume experience becomes more reliable. A view of this phenomenon, other than Gibson's—which does not deal with it on the grounds of poor reliability—or Koffka's—which attributes it to the fundamental nature of the perceptual system is presented. It is based on kinesthetic stimulation as a likely source of visual space anisotropy with respect to perceived distance.

Recently Gibson (1959) argued persuasively for a theory of "perception as a function of stimulation." A key assertion in the theory was that "The stimulus variables for vision must exclusively be found in a textured optical array, supplemented by the transformation relating a simultaneous pair of them, and by the transformations relating a continuous sequence of momentary arrays" (p. 474). As applied to the visual perception of depth, the theory requires that such ex-

periences be produced by certain attributes of the textured optical array, especially variations in "density, disparity, and motility" (p. 475). It seems reasonable to conclude from the theory that the perception of visual depth should not occur under conditions of homogeneous retinal stimulation.

Yet there is evidence, discussed below, that visual depth is experienced when visual stimulation is not patterned. This fact leaves the theorist two alternatives: to state the theory in a way more consistent with experimental data; or to argue, on some grounds, that this type of visual

[*] *Psychological Bulletin*, 1963, vol. 60, pp. 385–390.

experience, depth under homogeneous conditions, does not fall within the present bounds of the theory.

Gibson (1959; Gibson and Waddell, 1952) has taken the latter course: There exist perceptual phenomena which take place in response to "impoverished, ambiguous, or equivocal pattern stimulation" (Gibson, 1959, p. 466). These experiences are unreliable, varying across observers and from time to time in the observer. They are not considered immediately because they are a function of something other than stimulation; only perceptions for which a correspondence can be demonstrated with attributes of optical arrays serve initially as subject matter. Corollaries will be stated eventually encompassing the excluded events. Among these events is the perception of visual depth under homogeneous retinal stimulation.

To omit from consideration certain classes of data is a useful and unobjectionable strategy for the early stages of theoretical development, especially when criteria are specified. It is another matter to ask whether the particular omission meets the explicit standard. The standard in the present instance seems to be variability, both within and between observers. The following examination of the findings of recent experiments attempts to determine whether one such omission is justified.

Gibson, Purdy, and Lawrence (1955) eliminated all inhomogeneities in stimulation beyond the circular first aperture of an optical tunnel. The results from 10 practiced observers were summarized in a few sentences:

Words like filmy, translucent, soft, milky, hazy, or misty were generally applied to the luminous circular area. Sometimes this looked flat or two-dimensional, sometimes it looked deep, like "3-dimensional light," and for two Os it looked like a homogeneous convex sphere or disk which later became concave. Faint rings or circles were sometimes (but not always) apparent, and an

impression of depth usually accompanied this. Something tunnel-like was often seen, but the reports were variable as between Os and from one moment to the next" (Gibson et al., 1955, p. 9).

That an impression of depth can occur under homogeneous conditions, but that it is very variable is indicated by this experiment. By virtue of the lack of a demonstrated correspondence with a particular perception or response, the presented stimulus pattern falls nicely into the category of conditions temporarily to be neglected (Gibson, 1959). On the other hand, the conditions of stimulation were only partially homogeneous; there was, of course, the gross inhomogeneity between the optical tunnel and the visible piece of Vinylite plastic which bears the aperture.

Gibson and Waddell (1952) referred to Katz's (1935, p. 89) observation that distant objects whose microstructure is not visible are experienced, nevertheless, as having a solid surface character because of the "framing contours . . . and meaningful setting." Cohen (1957) demonstrated that the introduction of a small, homogeneous, circular spot (8 centimeters in diameter at 1 meter distance) into a homogeneous field of different intensity or wave length yields an experienced recession of the previously present, pervading fog. A gross inhomogeneity between two areas, therefore, affects the way the homogeneous one is perceived. The two- and three-dimensional impressions of the tunnel area in the experiment of Gibson, Purdy, and Lawrence might have alternated depending on where the observer looked, a soft surface quality occurring when a point on the plastic sheet was fixated, and an experience of depth when the tunnel area was looked at directly.

Using a hemispherical lighting fixture in which the observer placed his face and was stimulated by light shining through from the outside, Gibson and Dibble (1952) and Gibson and Waddell (1952) found that what is experienced is a "luminous fog" or "sea of light." However, they pointed out that the descriptions were not consistent; at times "something vaguely surface-like" was experienced. They ascribed the inconsistency to facial temperature and auditory stimulation from breathing. Cohen (1957) suggested that facial shadows may have been responsible.

In further work Gibson and Waddell used two translucent hemispheres made from a table tennis ball and fitted to each eye. Under high intensity of light stimulation the retinal images were "approximately homogeneous." Hochberg, Triebel, and Seaman (1951), employing the same method, fastened eyelashes to eyelids to remove a conceivable remaining source of inhomogeneity. The grain of the translucent surfaces might have contributed further inhomogeneities, but neither article suggested this, although the mention of "approximate" homogeneity may intend this factor.

With regard to the question of whether perception of depth occurs reliably under homogeneous retinal stimulation, the study of Gibson and Waddell (1952) leaves some doubt. Several, practiced observers "tended to agree that the experience had some kind of voluminous or space-like quality and . . . the reports also agreed that the experience was indefinite, indeterminate, or ambiguous" (p. 267). This is a result to be expected when conditions approximate homogeneity; what is experienced will depend on where one is looking and whether the momentary and successive arrays are homogeneous.

Because the practiced observers might have been prejudiced in their reports by knowledge of earlier findings, 13 relatively naive observers served in the experiment proper. Three representative reports were given by Gibson and Waddell. All of these, although not explicitly referring to depth, implied the perception of something with volume. "Fog coming up to my eyes," "a white that you could see into," "same penetrability" as fog, and "might wander in it

for hours" are phrases taken from each report. Terms such as curtain, wall, and screen were used but "less frequently." The impressions varied between observers and within some observers from moment to moment.

The variability in this experiment might be a result of two factors.

1. The presence of gross inhomogeneities in stimulation can lead to extended effects such as the perception of a homogeneous area as surface rather than deep fog. Argument for this assertion is given above, in the discussion of the findings of Gibson, Purdy, and Lawrence (1955). One can add that Gibson and Dibble (1952) also have suggested this effect in another context. They wrote, "However, it is possible that the steep intensity gradient at the *contour* may have been the effective stimulus for the impression in this case rather than the texture within the contour." In addition to the already mentioned possible inhomogeneities in this experiment, 6 of 13 observers reported an impression of a closed boundary, suggesting an additional source, perhaps a change in intensity of illumination at those parts of the eyecups which constituted the periphery of the field of vision.

2. Another source of variable reports, suggested by Cohen (1957), may have been a consequence of the preliminary training session during which the observers practiced and were given instruction in the description of perceived object qualities. As Cohen put it, the observer then may "seek something other than fog." Thus the observer was placed in an approximately homogeneous situation set to respond to any inhomogeneity. That reports of "fog, mist, haze, and cloud" exceeded those of "curtain, wall, and screen" is evidence for the tendency to have a volume experi-

ence even under conditions departing from optimal homogeneity.

Hochberg, Triebel, and Seaman (1951), using a similar method of stimulation, took an additional precaution in attempting to equate intensity over the entire field. They mounted on each side of the headrest, reflectors of white cardboard. (This may not have been necessary or useful in the Gibson and Waddell experiment, because the method of illumination involved reflected light from an entire wall and floor; Hochberg, Triebel, and Seaman sent light through the eyecups by means of a slide projector.) The results show that only 1 of 12 observers reported seeing a surface. The rest experienced a fog or cloud.

Most recently Cohen (1957) used an apparatus comprised of intersecting spheres, each 1 meter in diameter. The internal surfaces of these hollow spheres were diffuse reflectors; they produced indirect uniform illumination over the entire internal surface when a small part was illuminated directly. Even at high intensities, no texture was visible. When the two spheres were equally illuminated, the circular aperture (8 centimeters in diameter) between them, the circle of their intersection, was not visible as such. To eliminate inhomogeneities from face shadows, Cohen prepared for each observer a mask which served as part of the wall of one sphere. An appropriate hole in the mask permitted monocular viewing from a point directly opposite the aperture between spheres. The spheres were illuminated by means of two beams of light passed into the farther sphere through two openings out of the observer's area of vision. One beam passed through the aperture between spheres and was directed to a point 20 centimeters above the observer's eye.

Sixteen relatively naive observers responded to a condition of homogeneous visual stimulation. The most characteristic report was of a foglike experience.

Cohen contrasted the consistency of these reports with the variability shown by Gibson and Waddell (1952). Here the fog was seen "to extend an indefinite distance." Distance judgments were indeterminate. The introduction of a difference in intensity or wave length between the nearer sphere and the farther sphere as seen through the aperture resulted in reduced fog density and increased fog distance from the observer. Even when the intensity gradient was greatest (aperture area 2.3 times as bright), fog was reported in more than half the cases.

One can conclude from this discussion of recent experiments as follows.

1. In experiments where the perception of voluminous fog does not occur consistently, there are sources of inhomogeneity which can produce the impression of a surface.

2. As homogeneity is approached, the volume experience becomes more reliable.

3. If more intensive experimentation bears out the above conclusions, it will be necessary to revise Gibson's theory (1959) so that the reliable phenomenon of depth under conditions of homogeneous retinal stimulation can be handled.

Another theorist, Koffka (1935), has accepted depth experience under homogeneous conditions as facts on the basis of Metzger's (1930) early experiments. To produce a homogeneous field, Metzger used as reflector surface a white-washed wall with wings at the four sides. The observer sat before the wall at a distance and in an orientation such that his entire visual field was comprised of stimulation from the wall and wings. Only under conditions of relatively low illumination was Metzger successful in producing a homogeneous retinal field. At brighter levels the space filling fog receded and was transformed into a surface at a distance. This change with intensity was said to result from inhomogeneities of stimulation produced by the microstructure of the wall. That an increase in the inhomogeneity of effective stimulation was responsible is made credible by Cohen's results (1957). They showed a recession of fog as the degree of inhomogeneity between circular aperture and internal surface of the sphere increased.

From Metzger's results, Koffka (1935), drew a "fundamental principle of psychophysical organization" which states: "Under the simplest possible conditions of stimulation our perception is three-dimensional; we see space filled with neutral colour stretching into a more or less indeterminate distance" (p. 115). This effect is attributed by Koffka to the nature of the perceptual system.

A view of the phenomenon, other than Koffka's and Gibson's interpretations, is suggested by the presence in experience of inhomogeneity under visual stimulus-conditions which are homogeneous. Two types of experienced inhomogeneity can be distinguished under the following headings.

1. Relatively localized: Close scrutiny by the observer of the visual field under homogeneous conditions of stimulation, it is claimed (Koffka, 1935), results in "points of light and cloudlike structures shifting through his field" (p. 120). Cohen (1957) observed, under presumably homogeneous conditions, possibly related phenomena: a "cracked ice effect" and a "weblike structure." These could be eliminated through minute adjustments of the brightness of the circular aperture. Cohen tentatively ascribed the effect to minimal intensity differences between sphere and aperture, insufficient to produce more localized articulations in experience. Hochberg, Triebel, and Seaman (1951) reported that some observers experienced "hallucinatory objects and patterns." Gibson and Waddell (1952) reported inhomogeneous experiences which they

attributed to shadows on the retina from sources in or on the eye. These seemed to move with the eye.

2. Pervasive: The pervasive effect of tridimensionality is an instance of inhomogeneity in experience present under conditions of homogeneous stimulation. An analysis of what is meant by perceiving depth leads to statements such as (a) under conditions of fixated, monocular viewing, parts of the optical array are experienced as more distant than other parts; or (b) under conditions of free viewing, looking in one direction results in an experience of an optical array which seems less distant than the one experienced when looking in another direction. Ordinarily such effects are attributed primarily to differential stimulation provided within or between optical arrays (Gibson, 1959). However, when differential stimulation is absent, such spatial anisotropies must be ascribed to differential functioning of the perceptual system.

In discussing the presence of directional gradients in visual space, i.e., visual space's having an up and a down, a right and a left, Köhler (1940) traced the development of this structure to extravisual or kinesthetic sources to the "structure of motor space" (p. 17). A result of this structuring of visual space, according to Köhler, is that a figure can be experienced as different depending on its locus and orientation. In considering the changes in perception which result from reversing the position of objects in pictures, Gaffron (1956) speculated in a similar way:

> Thus the phenomena on right-left reversal need not be caused by any laterality in primary visual sensory processes but rather by their integration with visual motor and proprioceptive processes for which a primary laterality appears to exist (p. 286).

Studies of the anisotropy of visual space with respect to depth have been conducted with well differentiated figures (Adair & Bartley, 1958; Gaffron, 1950). These studies have demonstrated that objects are experienced as closer to the observer when they are at the left in a picture than at the right. The reversal in position is accomplished by presenting the mirror-image of the picture. Adair and Bartley (1958) have used an indirect method for showing the effect. The observer was required to adjust the distance of a drawing which was twice the size of the standard until it was experienced as being an equal distance away. On some trials the variable was identical to the standard; on other trials it was the standard's mirror-image. Gaffron (1950, 1956) appears to have presented the observer with paintings and their mirror-images and asked about the apparent nearness of objects within the paintings. A number of convincing demonstrations that the reader is asked to look at himself are provided as well (Gaffron, 1950). To what extent these results will be generalized to less structured, optical arrays remains to be seen. (Fisher 1961) used the direction of autokinetic movement as a measure of right-left anistropy on the grounds that "the autokinetic situation is so completely unstructured and therefore maximizes the possibilities for a person to impose his own biases upon the stimulus" (p. 64).

The proposed view for the perception of depth under homogeneous retinal stimulation can be summarized as follows. The perception of depth must involve differential reactions of perceived distance to aspects of a single optical array or to successive optical arrays. When stimulating conditions cannot be responsible for such differential reactions, it is necessary to attribute the effect to differential functioning of the perceptual system brought on by other factors. A likely source of space anisotropy with respect to visual distance is kinesthetic stimulation. The latter results in the visual impression that stimulation coming from one part of the visual field has a nearer source than equivalent stimulation coming from another part.

References

ADAIR, H., and S. H. BARTLEY. Nearness as a function of lateral orientation in pictures. *Percept. mot. Skills*, 1958, 8, 135–141.

COHEN, W. Spatial and textural characteristics of the *Ganzfeld*. *Amer. J. Psychol.*, 1957, 70, 403–410.

FISHER, S. Achievement themes and directionality of autokinetic movement. *J. abnorm. soc. Psychol.*, 1961, 63, 64–68.

GAFFRON, M. Right and left in pictures. *Art Quart.*, 1950, 13, 312–331.

GAFFRON, M. Some new dimensions in the phenomenal analysis of visual experience. *J. Pers.*, 1956, 24, 285–307.

GIBSON, J. J. Perception as a function of stimulation. In S. Koch (Ed.), *Psychology: A study of a science*. Vol. I. *Sensory, perceptual*, and *physiological formulations*. New York: McGraw-Hill, 1959. Pp. 456–501.

GIBSON, J. J., and F. N. DIBBLE. Exploratory experiments on the stimulus conditions for the perception of a visual surface. *J. exp. Psychol.*, 1952, 43, 414–419.

GIBSON, J. J., J. PURDY, and L. LAWRENCE. A method of controlling stimulation for the study of space perception: The optical tunnel. *J. exp. Psychol.*, 1955, 50, 1–14.

GIBSON, J. J., and D. WADDELL. Homogeneous retinal stimulation and visual perception. *Amer. J. Psychol.*, 1952, 65, 263–270.

HOCHBERG, J. E., W. TRIEBEL, and G. SEAMAN. Color adaptation under conditions of homogeneous visual stimulation (*Ganzfeld*). *J. exp. Psychol.*, 1951, 41, 153–159.

KATZ, D. *The world of colour*. London: Kegan Paul, Trench, Trubner, 1955.

KOFFKA, K. *Principles of Gestalt psychology*. New York: Harcourt, Brace, 1935.

KÖHLER, W. *Dynamics in psychology*. New York: Liveright, 1940.

METZGER, W. Optische Untereuchungen am Ganzfeld: II. Zur Phänomenologie des homogenen Ganzfelds. *Psychol. Forsch.*, 1930, 13, 6–29.

An Experimental Analysis
of Subject-Object Relationships in Perception*

JOSEPH GLICK
Yale University

It is difficult to do adequate honor to a man who has honored us so much by being with us. It is more difficult still to define the relationship between my work and Heinz Werner's monumental work, since in its most basic sense his work does not stand as a corpus of concepts made static by history which can be ritually invoked or ignored. True to his own love for the dynamics of thought and the centrality of development, his system was at all points developing; and is developing still.

It was my privilege to be a student at Clark during a period of great developmental spurts; a point at which two of the major themes of Werner's approach to psychology which seemed at first to be disjunctive, and in tension with one another, were beginning to become integrated in an hierarchical and organic structure. The two systems in tension were sensori-tonic theory and developmental theory. It is the story of this tension; and the attempts at its resolution that I would speak of today.

The tension between sensori-tonic and developmental theory might be simply and probably misleadingly, expressed by saying that while developmental theory provides a picture of the organism functioning by

use of a variety of hierarchically organized processes; it appears that sensori-tonic theory pictures the organism functioning with only one.

For example, in his work on developmental theory Werner postulated that the organism, in the course of development progresses from a state of sensori-motor contact with the world, in terms of action, to a level at which behavior is governed by perceptual, concrete structures, (what Bruner now calls the Iconic level) to a state at which behavior is governed by conceptual and abstract processes. The relationship between these levels was conceived of as being one of progressive subordination of developmentally earlier processes, in the service of developmentally more advanced processes.

In the work on sensori-tonic theory, however, it appeared that the experimental attempt was to reduce higher level functioning; viz. perceptual activity to sensori-motor structures which were conceived of as equilibrial states of the organism.

My own research was originally in the field of sensori-tonic theory; our experimental attempt was to demonstrate that underlying perception of spatial localization of objects there were organismic processes that might best be expressed in terms of equilibrial mechanisms. I should like to present some of this evidence and to show where certain inconsistencies in it, led to

* Seymour Wapner and Bernard Kaplan (Eds.) *Heinz Werner: 1890–1966* (Worcester: Clark University Press, 1966.)

the realization that developmental theorizing could help to put our hourse in order, by treating the problem of the relationship between equilibrial structures and higher level conceptual factors.

There is a good deal of evidence to show that if one stimulates a subject asymmetrically in a dark room there are measureable shifts in various aspects of apparent object location. For example, if we present a tone through earphones, to either the right or left ear, the position of a luminous rod experienced as being vertical shifts to the side opposite that of stimulation; e. g. if the left ear is stimulated, the luminous rod must be tilted to the right in order to be experienced as being vertical. It is shifts like these (obtained in a variety of experimental settings; with a variety of different types of asymmetrical stimulation) which have been taken as evidence for the operation of an equilibrial mechanism. This mechanism is interpreted as reflecting a tendency of the organism to restore a state of stable bi-lateral organization in the face of stimulation which uni-laterally affects it. Simply put: asymmetrical stimulation leads to a tendency to fall toward the side of stimulation which is counteracted by an increase of tonus on the side opposite stimulation (so that we will not fall) and that this counteraction is reflected in the perceptual shift of the object.

There is other evidence, however, which suggests that an equilibrial interpretation is alone insufficient to account for the range of phenomena encountered. For example, asymmetrical auditory stimulation has been shown to lead to no main effect on perception of another dimension of left-right spatial organization—the apparent straight-ahead. Instead of neat shifts of localization we encounter individual variation. If there is an equilibrial mechanism involved here, and it is the only factor operative, we should certainly expect its effects to be manifest across a variety of coordinates of left-right spatial organization.

The contrasting cases of the uniform effects of asymmetrical stimulation on apparent verticality and the individual variation in apparent straight-ahead led us to seek for other factors which might be involved in spatial localization.

One clue to this puzzle was an old observation of Koffka's, that apparent straight-ahead has two meanings; or rather two definitions. On the one hand apparent straight-ahead reflects an "egocentric" localization—that is objects are seen as straight-ahead when they intersect a projection of the median sagittal plane of the body. If we draw a line down the center of the body, so that this line bisects the body into two symmetrical halves; and then project that line out into space perpendicular to the body—this would be the median sagittal plane. It may be readily seen that this plane is dependent upon our own spatial perspective—it moves with us as we move in space. Contrastingly, straight-ahead could be conceived of as some point in space external to our own perspective—for example, if it was defined as the center of the frontal wall of this room. This definition of straight-ahead defines this coordinate in terms which are external to our own perspective—that is, the same point would be straight-ahead no matter where we were turned. It requires the conception of space as a container defined by coordinates external to ourselves, within which both our body and objects are located.

It is clear from this analysis that the two differing definitions of straight-ahead may be made to define different spatial points—as is the case, for example, when the subject faces a corner of this room—his median sagittal plane projects to a corner of the room, while the center of the room is distant from this projection. They may also be made to define the same point—as is the case when your median sagittal plane projects directly to the center of the room. Although, in this latter case, the physical definition of straight-ahead overlaps the cognitive differences between these two definitions are still maintained. In one case, a point at the center of the room is seen as having direct relationship to one's own body, a relationship which has been termed, "non-polarized"; while in the other it is seen as utterly independent of ourselves and our vicissitudes, a "polarized" relationship between subject and object.

On the basis of this analysis of the dual meanings of straight-ahead it was expected that the wide individual variation, which had previously been observed in the attempt to assess the effects of asymmetrical sound on apparent straight-ahead, might have been due to subjects spontaneously adopting differing definitions of this spatial coordinate. This expectation was born out in experimentation. Subjects were presented with asymmetrical auditory stimulation; sound to the right or left ear, and were required to adjust a luminous line until it was straight-ahead of them, in an otherwise dark room. After their judgments were made, a protocol was administered to elicit the kind of spatial conceptualization that they had utilized.

If the results of this experiment are looked at without benefit of these protocols then we have a total bust—there is no effect of asymmetrical sound. If, however, subjects are divided into different groups on the basis of their protocols—in other words if you attempt to relate their performance to what they tell you they tried to do—then there are highly significant results. Those subjects who adopted an egocentric definition of straight-ahead, and accordingly a "non-polarized" relationship, shifted their perception of the line as straight-ahead toward the side of stimulation; while those who adopted a more "objective" definition, a "polarized" relationship, shifted opposite to the side of stimulation.

In a similar line of experimentation we have attempted to go beyond the mere noting of individual differences—we wanted to produce some of our own. Not only that, we wanted to produce them within the same individual. If the differential effects of asymmetrical stimulation are really attributable to the different definitions of straight-ahead adopted by our Ss, and not to some other factor that might have co-varied with these different definitions—it should be possible to produce results like those obtained above by providing subjects with different definitions of straight-ahead.

This was done; and the results provided striking confirmation of expectations.

Subjects were presented with asymmetrical auditory stimulation; and were given two differing cognitive sets. One set instructed them to regard a luminous visual object to be localized as being in line with the center of their bodies—that is to use the object as an indicator of where the center of their body was felt to be. In the other set, the subject was directed to regard the "object-to be localized" as independent of his own egocentric perspective, and to attempt to localize the object with respect to a spatial perspective defined by the experimental room. All subjects were given each set—the separate testing sessions were separated by a week. These subjects, when they had been given a cognitive set directing them toward egocentric localization performed as did those subjects who spontaneously adopted this attitude: straight-ahead shifted toward the side of stimulation. Contrastingly when these same subjects were given the opposing set, they performed as did those subjects who had spontaneously adopted this set—straight-ahead shifted opposite the side of stimulation.

This same experiment, utilizing two other types of asymmetrical or directional stimulation, in combination with different cognitive sets, has been performed, with results essentially comparable to those reported above.

What these studies have shown, is that perception is indeed organismic, as Heinz Werner claimed; that factors from diverse sensory systems (such as sound and sight) interact; and lead to perceptual shifts. The studies have also shown that perceptual shifts attendant upon such stimulus factors and their organismic effects, are governed by the cognitive state of the organism.

This generalization has provided a powerful tool for both the looking backward to order old data that may have been in disarray; but in also looking forward to new data. The look backward reveals that in all previous studies where we were talking about perceptual shifts as if they were a direct function of the presentation of asymmetrical stimulation; there can be shown to be some cognitive factor operative. A brief example may illustrate this point. Remember that our original problem was the attempt to reconcile the invariant effects of asymmetrical auditory stimulation on apparent verticality; with the highly variable effects of this same stimulation on apparent straight-ahead. If we have now shown cognitive factors to be operative for straight-ahead; which produced variability; may there not be some cognitive factor operative in the apparent vertical situation to preclude the appearance of variability? That this is the case may be readily shown: the spatial coordinate of verticality is defined in life, and certainly in our experimental instructions, in terms of the external spatial field. We tell the subject: "adjust the rod until it is straight up and down, like a flag pole, parallel to the walls of the room." Here we are introducing a cognitive attitude without realizing it— we have directed the subject to conceive of the object with respect to the external spatial field. Under these conditions subjects perform as did those who defined straight-ahead in external or "polarized" terms—a shift of perception of apparent verticality opposite to the side of stimulation. It may be shown that if the same task is given, but defined now in egocentric terms, as for example when you tell a vertical subject to align the rod with his body position—(which is really still vertical) there is a shift characteristic of those subjects who adopt an egocentric definition of straight-ahead—the rod must be shifted to the side of stimulation to be seen as in line with body position. Finally, many of the supposed cases of failure to replicate Werner's and Wapner's findings, have confused the matter utterly by introducing instructions which direct S to think of vertical in both terms, e. g. "adjust the rod until it is straight up and down, like a flagpole, or your own erect body."

While the look backward is a tidying operation, the look forward to new data is exciting. A more recent study undertaken in cooperation with Drs. Werner and Wapner draws out the developmental implications of this position.

In the course of development we should expect that spatial definition progresses from a body-related egocentric perspective to one in which objects are seen as distinct from the subject and conceptualization of space is in terms of more abstract and external coordinates. If this is the case, then it might be expected that the pattern of shifts attendant upon the presentation of asymmetrical stimulation to adults who adopt an egocentric attitude should characterize the spontaneous performance of children; and that as children themselves become more adult there should be a shift toward a non-egocentric pattern. This study was performed as part of a larger cross-sectional and longitudinal project. The cross-sectional data are in—and strongly support this expectation. Children perform in an egocentric fashion until approximately the age of 11; at which point there is a cross over to a more objective manner of performance.

I believe that evidence like this bears witness to the power and scope of Heinz Werner's approach to psychology. To his view the performance of anything, anywhere, by anybody was a developmental problem. It is a powerful contribution, and a mighty task, to take developmental theory into a room filled with tilting chairs, median planes, a cacophony of asymmetrical sounds and to make that dark room ablaze with meaning.

References

BAUERMEISTER, M. 1962, The relationship between subjective body space and objective external space under conditions of body tilt. Microfilmed Ph.D. dissertation, Clark University, Worcester, Mass.

GLICK, J. 1964, An experimental analysis of subject-object relationships in perception. Microfilmed Ph.D. dissertation, Clark University, Worcester, Mass.

McFARLAND, J., S. WAPNER, and H. WERNER. 1962, The relation between perceived location of objects and perceived location of one's own body. Percept. Mot. Skills, *15*, 331–341.

WAPNER, S. 1964, Some aspects of a research program based on an organismic-developmental approach to cognition: Experiments and theory. J. Amer. Acad. Child Psychiat. *3*, 193–230.

WAPNER, S. and H. WERNER. 1957, *Perceptual Development,* Worcester, Mass. Clark Univ. Press.

WERNER, H. 1957, *Comparative Psychology of Mental Development,* New York International Universities Press.

WERNER, H. 1937, Process and achievement. Harvard Educational Review. *7,* 353–368.

WERNER, H. and B. KAPLAN. 1963, *Symbol Formation,* New York, Wiley.

WERNER, H. and S. WAPNER. 1949, Sensory-tonic field theory of perception. J. Personal. *18,* 324–338.

WERNER, H. and S. WAPNER. 1956, Sensory-tonic field theory of perception: basic concepts and experiments. Revista di Piscologia, *50,* 315–337.

Binocular Depth Perception without Familiarity Cues*

BELA JULESZ
Bell Telephone Laboratories

Random-dot Stereo Images with Controlled Spatial and Temporal Properties Clarify Problems in Stereopsis

Research in stereopsis (*1*) is traditionally devoted to quantifying the relationship between disparity (*2*) and perceived depth. Problems of the horopter, perceptual limits of disparity, the metric of the perceived space, and so on, are all examples of this classical problem-posing and have been thoroughly investigated (*3*). Strangely enough, the related problem of how disparty is derived—that is, how the corresponding left and right retinal projections of an object are found—has been ignored. This lack of interest is the more remarkable since the matching of the horizontally shifted corresponding point domains in the left and right fields is accomplished almost without deliberation, although these point domains generally differ in brightness and shape (owing to reflections and perspective). Perhaps the inherent limitations of the stimuli used may have caused researchers to shy away from studying binocular depth perception as a pattern-matching process. Indeed, simple

* *Science,* 1964, vol. 145, pp. 356–362. Copyright © 1964 by the American Association for the Advancement of Science.

line drawing were too limited for the exploration of pattern matching, while real-life pictures were unsatisfactory because of the many complex familiarity cues which interacted in uncontrollable ways.

Four years ago I posed two intimately related questions along these lines, which constituted a new paradigm. They were: (i) Would it be possible to create an artificial sensory environment devoid of all depth and familiarity cues except disparity? (ii) Could depth still be perceived under these conditions of "familiarity deprivation" (4, 5)? This paradigm was never systematically raised before, and yet it is so familiar. It is a long-known fact, exploited in aerial reconnaissance, that objects camouflaged by a complex background are very difficult to detect monocularly but jump out if viewed stereoscopically. Nevertheless, despite the difficulty, the hidden objects can be monocularly detected. Even if every surface of the three-dimensional environment were covered with a homogeneous random texture, the closer surfaces would seem to have coarser granularity than the ones farther away. [This retinal gradient of textures which is attributable to perspective yields a strong monocular depth cue (6).] Therefore the questions of whether an environment can be *ideally* camouflaged and of whether objects that are hidden when viewed monocularly can be perceived in depth still remained to be answered.

In order to obtain such an answer a novel technique of random-dot stereo images was devised. Such a stereo pair is shown in Figure 1. When viewed monocularly, both fields of Figure 1 give a homogeneous random impression without any recognizable features. But when viewed stereoscopically, this image pair is vividly perceived in depth, with a center square in front of its surround. [A prism in front of one eye greatly facilitates fusion of the stereo pairs. A satisfactory prism can be made of gelatin, as described in (7).]

The emphasis, in this brief article, is on demonstrating this and similar recently observed perceptual phenomena, with comments on certain implications of these findings for stereopsis.

Stereopsis without Familiarity Cues

Figure 2 illustrates how Figure 1 and similar random-dot stereo images (particularly Figure 3) are generated. It represents a small stereo pair composed of a matrix of 9×10 picture elements. The equally probable randomly selected black and white picture elements which are contained in corresponding areas in the left and right fields are labeled in three categories. (i) Those contained in corresponding areas with zero disparity (which when viewed stereoscopically are perceived as the surround) are labeled 0 or 1. (ii) Those contained in corresponding areas with non-

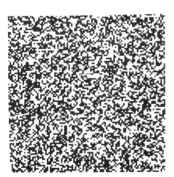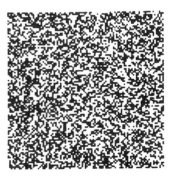

FIGURE 1   Basic random stereo pair. When the two fields are viewed stereoscopically, the center square appears in front of the background. [See (7) for a description of an aid useful in stereoscopic viewing.]

1	0	1	0	1	0	0	1	0
1	0	X	A	A	B	B	0	0
0	0	Y	B	A	B	A	1	1
0	1	0	0	1	1	1	0	1
1	1	A	B	A	B	A	0	0
0	0	B	A	B	A	B	1	0
1	1	0	1	0	1	1	0	0
1	0	A	A	B	A	X	0	1
1	1	B	B	A	B	X	1	0
0	1	0	0	0	1	1	1	1

1	0	1	0	1	0	0	1	0
1	0	A	A	B	B	Y	0	0
0	0	B	A	B	A	X	1	1
0	1	0	0	1	1	1	0	1
1	1	B	A	B	A	B	0	0
0	0	A	B	A	B	A	1	0
1	1	0	1	0	1	1	0	0
1	0	Y	A	A	B	A	0	1
1	1	Y	B	B	A	B	1	0
0	1	0	0	0	1	1	1	1

FIGURE 2   Illustration of the method by which the stereo pair of Figure 3 was generated.

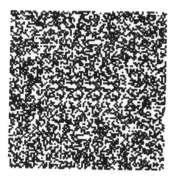

FIGURE 3   Stereo pair which, when viewed stereoscopically, contains an upper rectangle perceived in front of the surround, a lower rectangle perceived behind the surround, and an ambiguous middle rectangle perceived either in front of or behind the surround.

zero disparity (which when viewed stereoscopically are perceived in front of or behind the surround) are labeled A or B. (ii) Those contained in areas which have no corresponding areas in the other field (that is, project on only one retina and thus have no disparity) are labeled X and Y. The 0 and 1 picture elements are identical in corresponding positions of the two fields. The positions of the A and B picture elements belonging to corresponding areas in the two fields are also identical, but are shifted horizontally as if they were a solid sheet. Because of this shift some of the picture elements of the surround are uncovered and must be assigned new brightness values (X and Y). Since these areas lack disparity, they can be regarded as undetermined in depth. Figure 2 contains three rectangles in the left and right fields,

composed of A and B picture elements. Each field contains an upper, middle, and lower rectangle which can be regarded as corresponding left and right "projections" of a rectangular planar surface located in depth when viewed from different angles. The projections of the upper rectangle (that is, the corresponding upper rectangles in the left and right fields) are horizontally shifted relative to each other in the nasal direction by one picture element, the corresponding lower rectangles are shifted in the temporal direction to the same extent, while the corresponding middle rectangles have a one-picture-element periodicity and may be regarded as being shifted in either direction. The low density of picture elements and the large disparities would prevent stereopsis in a pattern corresponding to Figure 2. In order to achieve stereopsis, the number of picture elements would have to be increased considerably. For this reason a computer is used.

It would be impractical to generate without a computer adequately complex stimuli of several thousand brightness elements and given constraints for each experiment. Figure 3 is a computer-generated version of Figure 2; it has 100×100 picture elements, and for each of its three rectangles the disparity is six picture elements. The disparity is always chosen to be an integral multiple of the width of the picture element; therefore, when viewed monocularly, each of the two fields gives an impression of homogeneous randomness, without gaps or boundaries (4, 5). The upper rectangle, when the images are fused, is seen in front of the surround (as in Figure 1). The lower rectangle is perceived behind the surround, while the middle rectangle can be seen in front or behind at will.

Of course, instead of two brightness levels, any number of levels can be introduced, and instead of rectangular surfaces, any complex surface can be portrayed by this technique and give rise to stereopsis (8). Minimum area size, dot intensity, disparity, perception time, number of brightness levels, and other factors show strong interdependencies, which can be explained by statistical analysis. But before considering such interdependencies, I discuss some interesting observations which can be readily made when Figures 1 and 3 are viewed stereoscopically.

The main result of these observations is that the paradigm mentioned above is answered in the affirmative: Stereopsis can be obtained in the absence of monocularly recognizable objects or patterns. As a consequence, the many depth cues for monocular vision—cues such as the apparent size of familiar objects, interposition (the superimposing of near objects on far objects), and linear perspective—which in a familiar environment strongly influence the final percept, do not operate here. In this case the complex pattern-recognition processes (which themselves are based on involved learning and memory processes) can be overcome, and this greatly simplifies the study of binocular depth perception. The problem is reduced to that of finding how similar patterns are matched.

It is important to note that in these observations the quality of stereopsis (that is, the time required for stereopsis, the stability of the fused image, the amount of binocular rivalry, and so on) is excellent in spite of the absence of all other depth cues. As a matter of fact, since every picture element has disparity (in contrast to ordinary pictures, which contain large homogeneous areas without depth information) the random-dot stereo images are usually *easier* to perceive in depth. For these effective stimuli, several quantitative limits of various parameters which were determined as borderline values for stereopsis can be extended.

It should also be mentioned that the statistical, topological, and heuristic properties of the random-dot stereo images are controlled by the experimenter; thus the observations are more amenable to analysis.

The basis of stereopsis is disparity, as was demonstrated by Wheatstone with his stereoscope (9). Nevertheless, there are special instances when depth can be perceived in the absence of disparity. An example is the Panum phenomenon (10), where one image of a stereo pair consists of two parallel vertical lines in a homogeneous surround while the other image contains a single vertical line. When one of the vertical lines in the two images is fused (when the images are viewed stereoscopically), the other line, for which there is no corresponding representation in the other member of the pair, is also perceived in depth; it has a somewhat "floating" look but appears clearly behind the fused line. Such stimuli are particularly unsuitable for getting better insight into this phenomenon since they are "simple" only from a most irrelevant point of view—they are simple to draw. In fact, line drawings are *degenerate* forms of real-life images (which are composed of objects with textured surfaces) and as a result the perceptual performance to be studied becomes needlessly complicated and disguised. Indeed, the areas in Figures 2 and 3 which are without disparity (the areas represented in Figure 2 by X and Y and in Figure 3 by the corresponding dots) are a generalization of Panum's unpaired line, and their perception (which is quite stable) can be simply described and explained: Undetermined areas (areas without disparity) are perceived at the depth of the most distant adjacent determined area (area with disparity) (4, 5). This rule is illustrated in Figure 3, where undetermined areas at the left and right edges of the rectangle that is seen in front when the images are viewed stereoscopically are perceived as continuations of the background, while, for the rectangle seen behind the surround, the undetermined areas are perceived as belonging to the rectangle. (This is the reason why the lower rectangle looks wider than the upper one.)

This perceptual phenomenon is in agreement with the common experience that the image of each point of a closest surface is projected on both retinas, whereas a surface behind it has points which are totally or partly hidden. Thus, an area which is partly hidden and represented only on one retina is perceived as a continuation of the exposed parts of the surface behind the superimposed one. This effect is even more apparent for random-dot patterns, since the undetermined and the determined areas which are perceived as being at the same depth have identical textures.

The Panum phenomenon can be approached also in the context of binocular rivalry. In this interpretation, the determined area exerts an additional stabilizing effect, namely the prevention of binocular rivalry in the proximate undetermined areas. A remark on the implica-

tions of those findings for Gestalt psychology is given in (11).

Stereopsis under Brief Exposures

Besides disparity, there are two secondary depth cues for binocular vision: convergence and correlative accommodation (differential focusing). Both depend on muscle action. Since Dove in 1841 (12) demonstrated stereopsis under very brief exposures (much too short for any muscle activity), the importance of focusing and convergence is regarded as negligible. (In addition, the fact that, in a stereo image, areas in front and behind can be simultaneously perceived is hard to explain in terms of convergence.) Therefore, contrary to naive belief, stereopsis is the result of central nervous system processing, and the main purpose of convergence is the coarse alignment of corresponding retinal areas. This coarse alignment insures that the corresponding retinal areas are within the region of patent stereopsis. This does not mean that, for longer exposures, convergence motions and proprioceptive influences might not affect stereopsis. Dove's result, and many similar findings since (13), have conclusively demonstrated that stereopsis can occur as a result of central nervous system processing alone, and this view is generally accepted by workers in this field (3). However, von Karpinska (14) believed that these tachistoscopic experiments were successful only when the subject knew beforehand what he was expected to see. This and similar arguments are still voiced, and therefore the finding (15) that random stereo images (such as that of Figure 1) can also be perceived in depth under conditions of tachistoscopic presentation is not without interest. Since, in such experiments, the subjects have no familiarity with the stimulus at all and nevertheless, in a 1-millisecond exposure, correctly perceive the middle square in front or behind (when the two cases are presented in a randomly mixed order), the most plausible objection to Dove's finding is removed.

Perhaps an even more important consequence of the finding that random stereo pairs are perceived in depth in brief exposures is that Hering's theory on the role of double images is disproved. According to this theory, images not fused are seen double and are crossed or uncrossed depending on whether they lie in front of or behind the point of convergence. The extent to which this cue is utilized could not be previously determined, since double images were inseparable from the applied stimuli. The forms in random stereo pairs, on the other hand, are not recognizable until the forms are perceived in depth, and thus it is impossible to perceive double images either before or after fusion (15).

It is surprising that, without secondary depth cues, space sense can develop so rapidly (the effective presentation time is longer than the flashes, due to the persistent afterimages, but is, nevertheless, very brief). The time required for stereopsis increases with larger parallax shifts, smaller area size, and more complex (that is, nonplanar) surfaces.

Perception and Attention Time

These tachistoscopic experiments were useful only for studying perceptual performance in the absence of eye motions. In order to get better insight into the temporal aspects of perception, particularly into the perception time required, the afterimages have to be "erased." A new "stereo erasing" technique was developed, in which the erasing stimulus is a random-dot stereo pair.

This new technique also utilizes the ambiguous depth phenomenon (random wallpaper effect) which is demonstrated in Figure 3 (16). If the upper rectangle perceived in front of the surround is viewed first, then the ambiguous middle rectangle is also seen in front of the surround. On the other hand, if the lower rectangle perceived behind the surround is viewed first, then the ambiguous middle rectangle is seen behind the surround. This finding holds for tachistoscopic exposures too, and thus is not the result of the subjects maintaining the same convergence but is, rather, the result of his maintaining attention for the same perceptual organization (depth plane).

In these tachistoscopic experiments, brief presentation of an unambiguous stereo pair (a pair having a center square with either a temporal or a nasal disparity) was followed by presentation of an ambiguous stereo pair (a pair having the same disparity but in both directions). The picture elements in the second stimulus differed from those in the first. Thus, the second stimulus erased the afterimages of the first stimulus, and therefore the real presentation time for the first stimulus was known. It was found that, when presentation time was adequate, the second, or ambiguous, stimulus was consistently perceived at the same depth as the first, or unambiguous, stimulus. (The unambiguous stereo pair was presented with temporal or nasal disparity, in mixed order.) Perception of the ambiguous stimulus was influenced by perception of the unambiguous stimulus even when the first stimulus was not consciously perceived. When the first stimulus was presented for a time shorter than this "perception time for stereopsis," or when the second stimulus was delayed by an interval longer than the "attention time," the second stimulus became independent of the first and could be perceived as having depth opposite to that of the first. This finding and the fact that perception and attention times were typically under 50 milliseconds (17) make it appear most unlikely that convergence motions might have been initiated. The subjects were unaware that the second stimulus was ambiguous. These facts imply that the first stimulus serves as a "depth marker" and determines which of the possible depth organizations should be attended to. Such an internal attention mechanism was nicely demonstrated by Pritchard when viewing the reversal of a Necker-cube under conditions of retinal stabilization (18). [The problem of whether this mechanism is a parallel or a sequential process is discussed in (19).]

Binocular Similarity

In the experiments summarized above, pattern-matching consisted of the relatively simple task of finding identical patterns in the two fields, differing only in their horizontal positions. In the experiments reported next the congruency of the corresponding patterns was perturbed to various extents by several manipulations. There are many ways to introduce such distortions. One way is to simulate real-life situations under more controlled conditions. In ordinary binocular vision the two retinal projections are generally quite different in brightness and shape, owing to reflections and perspective. Distortions which simulated such vision were introduced by blurring one of the fields, adding uncorrelated random noise, expanding one field uniformly, complementing certain points (by changing black to white and white to black), and so on. One of the many possible perturbations (4, 5), the uniform expansion of one field, is illustrated in Figure 4. Differences in the size of the retinal images for the two eyes (aniseikonia) are never as great as the size

differences of Figure 4; nevertheless, depth is easily perceived in Figure 4, which is derived from Figure 1 by uniform expansion of one of the fields (by 10 percent in both dimensions). Since in these computer-generated stimuli every point contributes to stereopsis, depth can be perceived even under tachistoscopic conditions if the centers of Figure 4 are aligned. This means that, in addition to the horizontal disparity, some vertical shift can be tolerated. When random-dot stereo images are used, most quantitative findings on the limits of disparity as determined with simple line drawings (3) seem to be very conservative and can be extended.

In addition to expansions, rotations of one of the computer-generated stereo fields by 7 degrees of arc can give rise to stereopsis during brief exposures, a finding which is the more remarkable since the time of exposure is too brief to permit cyclotorsional eye movements. All these experiments show that the central nervous system has processing powers far beyond the requirements of common usage.

In the experiments described next I tried perturbations of a complexity which never occurs under ordinary conditions, in order to study the limits of pattern matching. Two corresponding patterns are called "binocularly similar" if they can be fused and perceived in depth. The quality of the percept may be regarded as an indicator of the similarity of the patterns.

One surprising finding was that the

 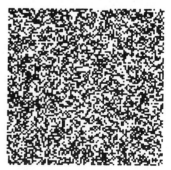

FIGURE 4   Stereo pair identical to that of Figure 1 except for the fact that one field is expanded uniformly in both dimensions by 10 percent. Stereopsis is easy to obtain.

FIGURE 5   Stereo pair identical to that of Figure 1 except for the fact that in the left field the diagonal connectivity is broken; 75 percent of the picture elements of the stereo pair are identical. Stereopsis is easy to obtain.

monocular similarity of two patterns can be quite different from the binocular similarity. This is illustrated in Figure 5, which is derived from the basic stereo pair of Figure 1 by breaking of the connectivity along the diagonals in the left field. If, along the + 45-degree and − 45-degree diagonals, three adjacent picture elements had identical brightness values, the middle one was complemented (that is, was removed from fusion). As a result of this procedure in Figure 5 only 25 percent of the picture elements became complemented while 75 percent were kept identical in the two images. Although the two patterns appear exceedingly dissimilar when viewed monocularly, the binocular similarity is very high, inasmuch as stereopsis is easily obtained. This observation has another implication. It has already been proved that monocularly recognizable objects are not necessary for stereopsis. Nevertheless, one might object that, in Figure 1, similar micropatterns can be perceived in the two fields, as viewed monocularly, and that these might serve as the basis for fusion. The fact that the patterns of Figure 5 look so different on both a micro and a macro level, when viewed monocularly, and that the images can nevertheless be perceived in depth is strong evidence that the pattern processing occurs *after* the binocular combination of the stereo images has occurred. This pattern processing reveals that 75 percent of the picture elements of the two fields are identical, a fact disguised by

the dissimilarity of the fields when viewed monocularly (5). This observation—that the processing has to occur after the binocular combination of the images—is in agreement with recent neurophysiological findings by Hubel and Wiesel (20).

It is interesting to note that binocular similarity cannot be described solely in terms of quantitative point-by-point identity between a pair of patterns. There are several ways of removing the same percentage of picture elements from fusion, and for these various ways the quality of depth perception may differ greatly. Thus, binocular similarity depends greatly on the topology of the perturbing configurations. One crucial factor in visual perception is the connectivity of adjacent elements. The perturbing configurations which destroy this connectivity to the greatest extent in the combined field produce the greatest perceptual degradation (4, 5).

With such techniques many inherent pattern organizations can be studied; one interesting class, involving contour dependencies, is discussed in the next section.

Role of Contours in Stereopsis

One of the most common beliefs concerning stereopsis is that contours are important (3). The usual definition of contours as boundaries between configurations that represent recognizable objects when viewed monocularly has to be modified, since the experiments described above illustrated that stereopsis can be achieved in the absence of such configurations. A contour may be alternatively defined as a boundary between white and black clusters. For real-life situations the two definitions coincide. Belief in the importance of contours is based on a classical experiment by Helmholtz (21). It is a belief which has never been questioned since his day. Helmholtz used a black line drawing of a simple object in a white surround as one stereo image and its complement (negative) as the other. In spite of some binocular rivalry the stereo pair could be fused. Because the two fields were everywhere different except for the location of the contours, it was inferred that contours are crucial for stereopsis. On the other hand, if one field of Figure 1 is complemented, stereopsis is destroyed (4). Moreover, it is possible to perceive depth, without any binocular rivalry, for random stereo pairs which are identical everywhere *except* at the contours (15).

These findings seemingly contradict the results of Helmholtz's experiment. This apparent contradiction arises from the spatial complexity of the stimulus. This is illustrated by Figure 6. To generate Figure 6, the outline of the pattern of Figure 1 was generated at the boundaries between black and white clusters, and one of the fields was complemented. These stereo fields have a great spatial density of outline, and stereopsis is very difficult. If one

reduces this density by expanding a small area in each field, stereopsis is greatly facilitated, approximating that in Helmholtz's case.

Discussion

The techniques mentioned above make it possible to study stereopsis in its purest form. Nevertheless, the study is limited to problems concerning the sensation of relative depth in a small region around the convergence point (22). (How the entire visual space is built up from such regions by successive convergence motions and how these space samples are integrated in a unique percept are problems far beyond the scope of this research.)

Under these ideal conditions several of the observed phenomena can be explained by relatively simple statistical arguments. As an example, let us analyze the following finding: For a given disparity the corresponding point domains in the two fields (for example, the center square of Figure 1) must possess a minimum number of picture elements (and thus be of a certain size) to be perceived in depth. This critical point-domain size increases with increased disparity and decreases with increased number of brightness levels in the stimuli. These experimental findings can be easily explained, as follows. Any two *uncorrelated* random images of black and white picture elements have 50 percent

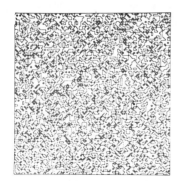 

FIGURE 6   Stereo pair generated by outlining the fields of Figure 1 and complementing one of them. Stereopsis is very difficult to obtain.

identical elements, by chance alone. With three or more brightness levels in the stimulus this chance identity is reduced to 33 percent or less. Thus, corresponding point domains in the left and right fields have to contain more correlated points than the cluster formed by chance correlation. Since with a smaller number of brightness levels the probability increases that non-corresponding *adjacent* dots will form correlated clusters (false clusters) of considerable size, the critical size of corresponding clusters has to be increased. Only then is the probability negligible that a false cluster will occur that is similar in size to a critical area. If the corresponding areas are above the critical size, then they need not be identical, only similar. But, to achieve stereopsis, this similarity has to be more than the chance correlation (see Figure 5). The probability of finding large false clusters increases as the fields (which contain them) get larger. This corresponds to the observation that with increased disparity (that is, with increased image area to be searched for corresponding patterns) the size of the critical area has to be increased to obtain stereopsis.

In this analysis, clusters formed by *proximate* points of *similar* (correlated) brightness played a dominant role. This cluster formation (or connectivity detection) is basic for monocular texture discrimination too (23) and reminds one of figure and ground discrimination.

One can explain many of the observed phenomena by regarding them as a search for connected clusters in the combined binocular field (4). In order to test the validity and power of these notions, a computer program was written (called AUTOMAP-1) which complies a three-dimensional contour map from high-resolution stereo images (24). This computer simulation is a sort of active description, a model whose form reflects something of the structure of the phenomena represented, but which also has the character of a working machine (25). The results were

satisfactory (the essentials of this heuristic model are given in 4, 23 and 24). Some assumptions in the model were experimentally confirmed by White (26).

Random-dot stereo images are now used in fields other than that of stereopsis, for studying optical illusions (27), binocular rivalry (28), and perceptual learning (16); some findings might bear on subliminal perception. Possible applications range from automatic map compilation (24) to clinical uses [for example, x-ray stereofluoroscopy (29)].

The paradigm itself can be generalized, and analogue techniques might be used for studying apparent motion and skin localization (30). Such a generalization was recently applied in a study of auditory memory (31). These refined techniques may have some implications for auditory localization too, where work with correlated auditory noise was begun as early as 1948 and produced some interesting phenomena (32).

Summary

The reported phenomena were obtained through the use of special techniques. (i) All monocular depth and familiarity cues were removed from the stimuli (through the use of random-dot stereo patterns). (ii) The statistical and topological properties of the stimuli were precisely known (since they were generated according to a specific computer program). (iii) Convergence motions of the eye and proprioceptive cues were eliminated (through the use of tachistoscopic illumination). (iv) The time of presentation was under control (through erasure of the persistent afterimages). Under these conditions stereopsis could be studied in its purest form. It was shown that depth can be perceived in the absence of monocular depth and familiarity cues and of all binocular depth cues except for disparity. These findings have important implications for some existing theories of stereopsis and open up areas for further research. Some phenomena based on stereo erasure are reported here for the first time. It has been demonstrated that the perception of ambiguous depth organizations can be influenced, even subliminally, by a preceding unambiguous stimulus. Perhaps the most interesting result is the finding that the correspondence of objects and patterns in the two retinal projections can be established without actual recognition of the objects and patterns. This pattern matching is based on some relatively simple processes of finding connected clusters formed by adjacent points of similar brightness, and the processes seem to be amenable to rigorous analysis.

References and Notes

1. Stereopsis is the sense of relative depth in a limited region around the point of convergence, attributable to disparity of corresponding points on the two retinas. Stereopsis is more general than fusion, since with increased disparity (above the fusion threshold but within the limit of patent stereopsis) corresponding points can be seen as double (often with one image suppressed) but still perceived in depth.
2. In this article the term *disparity* is used in a generic sense for similar terms such as retinal disparity, binocular disparity, geometrical disparity, binocular parallax (shift), and so on.
3. For an up-to-date review on the traditional aspects of research in depth perception see K. N. Ogle, in *The Eye*, H. Davson, Ed. (Academic Press, New York, 1962), vol. 4, p. 209 [abstracted in *Science 135*, 763 (1962)].
4. JULESZ, B. *Bell System Tech. J. 39*, 1125 (1960).
5. JULESZ, B. in *Information Theory, 4th London Symposium*, C. Cherry, Ed. (Butterworths, London, 1961), p. 212.
6. GIBSON, J. J. *Am. J. Psychol. 63*, 367 (1950).
7. A concentrated solution of gelatin is prepared by dissolving the gelatin in hot water. It is then poured into a glass or plastic container which has at least one optically transparent and flat surface.

The container is tilted by 15 to 20 degrees and is kept in this position until the gelatin sets. (The process can be speeded up by refrigeration.) The flat surface of the container and the hardened top surface of the gelatin form an optical wedge which can be used as a viewing prism.
8. JULESZ, B. and J. E. MILLER, *Bell System Tech. J. 41*, 663 (1962).
9. WHEATSTONE, C. *Phil. Trans. Roy. Soc. London 371* (1838).
10. PANUM, P. L. *Untersuchungen über das Sehen mit Zwei Augen* (Kiel, 1858).
11. The observed phenomena have important implications bearing on Gestalt psychology. According to a typical view of this school [E. Lau, *Psychol. orsch. 2*, 1 (1922)] stereopsis is not a result of disparity, but each eye works up its stimulus complex into a Gestalt, and it is the difference between these Gestalten which gives rise to an impression of depth. This argument is still debated, since some of the experiments (involving optical illusions) which were designed to illustrate Gestalt factors have given controversial results. The fact that stereopsis can be obtained with the random-dot images without any monocular cues decisively settles this question, since no Gestalten can be "worked up."
    It might still be argued that Gestalt factors may operate after the left and right images are fused. In this context it is important to observe what happens at the vertical boundaries of the center square of Figure 1. The probabilities that the black-and-white picture elements will be perceived as belonging to the rectangle or perceived as belonging to the surround are equal. Indeed, when viewed stereoscopically, the vertical boundaries of the center square of Figure 1 look fuzzy instead of being perceived as straight lines, as one would expect if some Gestalt organization had taken place (since a square has a "good Gestalt"). If the stimulus contains black, white, and gray picture elements of equal frequency of occurrence, then the probability that a dot at the boundary belongs only to the square increases to 2/3. This statistical argument is in agreement with the observed fact that a square looks less fuzzy at the boundaries when it is com-

posed of random dots having three or more brightness levels. This comment is by no means to be interpreted as a critique on Gestalt psychology but merely as an implication that stereopsis operates on a primitive level where Gestalt considerations do not enter.

That some of the more complex Gestalt factors—such as goodness of form, symmetry, and closure—are not a prerequisite for stereopsis does not mean that some more basic factors, particularly proximity and similarity can be omitted. Their importance in perception was first stressed by Gestalt psychologists, especially by Koffka and Wertheimer. Similarly, throughout this article I stress the notion of connectivity, into clusters, of adjacent dots of similar brightness. But there is a difference between my approach and that of Gestalt psychologists. They developed these powerful notions to show that perception of form was a more involved process than had been previously believed, while I am using these same notions, restricted to random-dot patterns, to show that certain processes in stereopsis (and in visual discrimination of texture) are simpler than had been expected and amenable to rigorous analysis.

12. Dove, H. W. *Ber. Preuss. Akad. Wiss. 1841,* 251 (1841); *Ann. Physik. 110,* 494 (1860).
13. Langlands, N. M. S. *Trans. Opt. Soc. London 28,* 45 (1926).
14. Von Karpinska, L. *Z. Psychol. Physiol. Sinnesorg.* 57, 1 (1910).
15. Julesz, B. *J. Opt. Soc. Am.* 53, 994 (1963).
16. Julesz, B. *ibid.* 54, 576 (1964).
17. These findings were for a picture size of 6 degrees of arc (image size, 100×100 picture elements; size of center squares 48×48 picture elements); disparity, 7 minutes of arc; stimulus brightness, 5 footlamberts (55 lumens/m^2).
18. Pritchard, P. M. *Quart. J. Exptl. Psychol.* 10, 77 (1958).
19. The ambiguous stereo pairs, when presented by themselves for a brief period, were usually perceived in only one way. When a slight (10 percent) bias was introduced (to counteract the subject's natural bias), it proved to be excessive and reversed the perceived depth. If the preferred depth level were the first level given attention and the other depth levels were searched sequentially only afterward, then a 90-percent match at the preferred depth level would be more than adequate for stopping the search. That, instead, the 100-percent match is perceived at the unpreferred depth level is strong evidence for the parallel process. Recently Dodwell and Engel came to the same conclusion, utilizing Efron's technique of presenting alternate stereo images with various time delays [see P. C. Dodwell and G. R. Engel, *Nature 198,* 39 (1963); R. Efront, *Brit. J. Ophthalmol. 41* 709 (1963)].
20. Recent neurophysiological findings revealed binocular neural units in the striate cortex of the cat. These units were activated by simultaneous stimulation of corresponding regions in the left and right retinas. Both summation and antagonism between receptor fields of the two eyes were demonstrated [see D. H. Hubel and T. N. Wiesel, *J. Physiol. 160,* 106 (1962)].
21. Von Helmholtz, *Physiological Optics,* J. P. C. Southall, Ed. (Dover, New York, rev. ed., 1962), vol. 3, p. 512 and plate IV.
22. For details on this region of patent stereopsis and on the problem of the horopter, see K. N. Ogle, in *The Eye,* H. Davson, Ed. (Academic Press, New York, 1962), vol. 4.
23. Julesz, B. "Special Issue on Sensory Information Processing," *IRE PGIT* [Professional Group on Information Theory] *Publ. IT-8* (1962), p. 84.
24. Julesz, B. in *Proceedings IFIP* [International Federation of Information Processing] *Congress 1862,* M. Popklewell, Ed. (North-Holland, Amsterdam, 1963), p. 439. This computer program takes the point-by-point differences between the left and right fields with all possible shifts prior to subtraction. This produces an ordered set of "analog depth planes" in which adjacent points of minimum value are connected into clusters. The search for these clusters of points with the same disparity immediately gives the cross sections (contour lines) of objects in a natural way.
25. Minsky, M., in *Computers and Thought,* E. A. Feigenbaum and J. Feldman, Eds. (McGraw-Hill, New York, 1963), p. 413.

26. WHITE, B., *Am. J. Psychol.* 75, 411 (1962).

27. PAPERT, S., *Nature 191,* 733 (1961); J. Hochberg, "Illusions and figural reversal without lines," address presented at the 4th annual meeting of the Psychonomic Society, Byrn Mawr, Pa., 1963.

28. KAUFMAN, L. "Form and depth perception in Julesz patterns," address presented at the 35th meeting of the Eastern Psychological Association, Philadelphia, 1964.

29. STAUFFER, H. M., *The Reduction of Patient Dose,* R. D. Moseley, Jr., and J. H. Rust, Eds. (Thomas, Springfield, Ill., 1963), p. 193.

30. For phenomena in skin localization see G. von Békésy, *Experiments in Hearing* (McGraw-Hill, New York, 1960), p. 567.

31. GUTTMAN, N. and B. JULESZ, *J. Acoust. Soc. Am.* 35, 63 (1963); B. Julesz and N. Guttman, *ibid., p.* 1895

32. LICKLIDER, J. C. R., *ibid.* 20, 150 (1948); E. M. Cramer and W. H. Huggins, *ibid.* 30, 413 (1958).

The Formation and Transformation of the Visual World*

IVO KOHLER

Innsbruck University

Summary of the Long-Term Studies

The following summary includes only those studies in which the subject was required to wear spectacles continuously for five days or longer. Shorter studies were also undertaken, but mainly in the early phases of experimentation. Some experiments had to be interrupted prematurely; this occurred when some subjects complained of dizziness or nausea, became depressed, or could not stand the pressure of the spectacles against the nose or ears.

I want to extend my warmest thanks to all subjects for their cooperation; they all gave their very best, regardless of the duration of the experiment. The demands made on some of them were almost in-

tolerably hard. Even before the spectacles were put on, they all had to undergo exhausting tests: the apparatus had to be fitted and measurements had to be taken during normal vision; then the spectacles were put on, subjecting the subject to a host of novel and confusing experiences. To avoid collisions, stumbling, or false moves, the subject had to maintain extreme caution and constant vigilance. To help the subject overcome this first critical stage and to assist him in adapting to this new set of circumstances, the services of a solicitous and protecting companion were often required. The subject was required to keep a daily record of his experiences. Every day, for hours on end, he was given tests to assess the progress of his adaptation. On the last day the subject's private life ceased altogether and became completely subordinated to the

* *Psychological Issues,* 1964, vol. 3, pp. 28–46, 116–133.

science of measurement. All this would have been enough in itself, but there was more to come. Once the spectacles were removed, the subject had to cope with all sorts of aftereffects. These were so strong at times (causing dizziness and nausea) that the assistance of a companion was again necessary. And naturally, the experimenter did not want to miss the opportunity to measure the gradual cessation of the aftereffects. This often required the subject to be available for weeks after termination of the experiment proper.

In the interest of clarity, the following experiments have been subdivided into three groups: (a) inversion[1] experiments; these are essentially replications of Stratton's experiments; (b) studies involving the use of prismatic and half-prism spectacles; and (c) studies with special colored spectacles.

A. Inversion Experiments

A thoroughgoing inversion experiment has not been attemped since Stratton's day (1896, 1897). His results and conclusions appeared so flawless to his contemporaries that no one even bothered to replicate them. Consequently, there followed a hiatus of more than twenty-five years.

The first to break it was Ewert (1930). Ewert also went a step further. Stratton had been concerned only with monocular vision; Ewert experimented with binocular vision, using spectacles especially prepared by the Spencer Lens Company. Although operating with narrow fields of vision and double images arising from nearby objects,

Ewert did succeed in completing several long-term studies. However, he showed surprisingly little concern for what appears to be the major problem: the genesis of veridical perception. Since he contented himself with merely observing overt behavior, he must have assumed a one-to-one relationship between adaptive behavior, such as correct prehension, and veridical perception. However, we know that behavior can be adaptive in spite of inverted visual impressions. Thus, the assumption that adaptive behavior depends solely on an approximately correct view of the world cannot be made without further qualifications.

In 1927, W. Stern investigated veridical perception with right-angle prisms which inverted visual images. Unfortunately, his method caused the field of vision to narrow even more, and gave rise to intrusive peripheral reflections. It began to look as if the technical difficulties encountered in this kind of experimentation were of such magnitude as to foredoom any hopes for further progress.

In 1928, however, a major breakthrough occurred with Erismann's discovery that visual images could be inverted with the use of mirrors. The effect was the same as that created by any puddle of water in the street. By using a mirror instead of lenses or prisms, Erismann was able to produce inversions without left-right reversal. The mirror was made of metal and attached below the eyes in a horizontal position. In this way the field of vision could be increased by increasing the size of the mirror, without exposing the eye to unreflected light. Of course, beyond a certain optimal size, the device became cumbersome; furthermore, this arrangement also had the disadvantage of obstructing the subject's view of his feet and the ground below him. Nevertheless, the arrangement did enable the experimenter to conduct experiments of several hours' duration in the laboratory.

Krüger (1939) also used mirrors to in-

---

[1] Kohler calls the effect of his optical devices "inversion," as did Stratton. But it might better be called "reversal," since the effect is to reverse either right-left or up-down, *but not both*. A lens or lens system such as Stratton used reverses *both* meridians of an image. Kohler reversed only one of the meridians, using not lenses but mirrors or prisms. It should be noted that the phrase "upside down" is ambiguous; it may mean either Stratton's (and Ewert's) inversion or Kohler's up-down reversal—Ed., *Psychological Issues*.

vert visual images. However, his apparatus —consisting of several mirrors—does not seem to lend itself readily to continuous long-term experiments. Although his study contains noteworthy observations (we shall refer to them again), Krüger, like Ewert, overlooked the essential problem.

In 1947, Erismann's apparatus was adapted for use outside of the laboratory, a step made possible by means of a relatively minor but nevertheless significant technical modification. Upon the suggestion of one of our subjects, Dr. W. von Kundratitz, the mirror was attached to the forehead, that is, above the eyes instead of below the eyes. This suggestion turned out to be extremely valuable. It was now possible to double the size of the mirror. The mirror could easily be attached to the forehead by means of a frame mounted on the head, and this made it possible for the subject to view his own feet as well as objects near his body. The entire device could be covered by a cap and, when worn outdoors, was no more conspicuous than some oversized visor. The visual field measured approximately 40° by 80° from side to side.

Snyder and Pronko (1952), of the University of Wichita, reported an investigation in the course of which a subject continuously wore spectacles similar to Ewert's for no less than thirty days. However, here too it seems that the experimenter was primarily concerned with overt behavior rather than with a possible correction of vision. Another relevant and very interesting investigation, this one by a Russian, has been reported in *Universum* (1950, No. 2). According to this article, patients suffering from cataracts regained their sight when their corneas were used as focusing screens for projecting real images. By the time these images reached the retina they were right side up. This, however, did not disturb the patients, who, so the author maintains, soon began to perceive objects as right side up. Appar-

ently, inversion of the retinal image is not a necessary prerequisite for veridical perception.

Now for our own experiments:

1. FEBRUARY, 1947.
DURATION: 6 DAYS

The spectacles used in this study had been designed by the subject himself, Dr. von Kundratitz. At first, this subject saw everything inverted, could not grasp objects without making errors, was extremely unsure of himself, and had to be escorted at all times. After three days, marked improvement was noted in all respects. On the fourth day, the subject went on a bicycle trip; on the last day he went on a skiing excursion (see Plate 2). During all this time, however, his perceptions were only sporadically right side up; things appeared right side up only when they were simultaneously touched, when a plumb line was used, or when they happened to be in the subject's immediate vicinity. During a simulated fencing match, the subject parried all blows correctly, even though the opponent was seen upside down. Immediately after removal of the spectacles, in favorable conditions —i.e., when the visual field was narrowed down and the background was uniform without containing reference points for up and down—the subject occasionally saw upright objects as inverted, but only for the first few minutes. For the next two days, the subject reported having apparent movement experiences and slight spells of dizziness.

2. FEBRUARY, 1947.
DURATION: 9 DAYS

Correct veridical vision was achieved by subject M. after wearing the experimental spectacles for nine days. After an initial period of disruption, the subject's behavior became adaptive in a remarkably short time, even though the visual impressions continued to be inverted for a while. After four or five days, however, his vision also underwent a remarkable change: it seemed as if the verticality dimension had "gotten lost." To illustrate: two adjacent heads, one upright, the other inverted, were *both* perceived as upright. Gradually, more and more objects appeared right side up. After the spectacles were removed, however, objects appeared to revert to their previous upside-down position —this without any apparatus covering the eyes or in any way obstructing the visual field: for a few minutes people and furniture seemed suspended from the "ceiling," head downward. Even half an hour later, while taking a walk outside, the subject reported that the reflection of a house and tree seen in a puddle appeared considerably more upright than the house and tree itself. Short periods of disorientation and inverted vision occurred for several days after the experiment proper, particularly soon after awakening in the morning. As before, the adjustment of overt behavior preceded the correction of vision.[2]

Erismann, in collaboration with Rohracher, carried out a series of shorter experiments from 1928 to 1933. Although

[2] Incidentally, the wearing of the spectacles also brought about disturbances in the position of eyes and head. While wearing the spectacles, it was necessary to raise the head and eyes somewhat. As time went on, however, the corresponding kinesthetic sensations ceased and the subject no longer experienced the position of his head and eyes as unusual. All the more surprising, therefore, were his sensations after removal of the spectacles. Now that the subject was forced really to look straight ahead, in order to take in the entire scene, it seemed to him that he was looking down, or that the floor was giving way under him. This caused him to maintain for a while a peculiarly crooked position (since it was easier for him to assume the previously "normal" position of his eyes, thereby lowering his head by about 30°). Such alterations in kinesthetic sensitivity are not infrequent; where they determine a person's *sense of orientation,* their role is of crucial importance. This becomes evident when a subject, who has just taken off his prismatic spectacles, reports a certain fixation point as being straight ahead when it is actually located at his side, precisely because he experiences looking to the side as looking straight ahead.

they used less suitable devices, their observations were of great value to the present study (see Rohracher, 1932, unpublished Ms. a, b).

3. AUGUST, 1950. DURATION: 10 DAYS (123 HOURS)

This study focused on the period of transition during which up-right vision first begins to emerge. What are the causes of this process, and how does it unfold? We made the following observation: when the subject (M. in this case) was permitted to reach for and touch an object in his immediate vicinity, a new integration immediately took place; the object, first seen as inverted, now suddenly appeared to be right side up. (The experience of this "reinversion" was somewhat similar to Schröder's [1858] well-known stair illusion.) The same result was obtained when the subject touched the object with a stick. In both cases, the subject's hands were the first objects reported seen in an upright position. Simultaneous sensations of touch thus appear to be one of the determining factors of the phenomenon. Another factor seems to be the experience of gravitational pull. When the subject was presented with a weight attached to the end of a line, he correctly perceived the relative position of the weight (to the line) as soon as he took the end of the line in his hand; and once the pendulum was seen correctly, the perception of more distant objects also became veridical. When the subject experienced a strong gravitational force by driving uphill in a car, the landscape righted itself perceptually. Familiarity with objects proved to be a third determining factor involved in veridical vision. A candle, at first seen in an inverted position, wick downward, was seen right side up as soon as it was lit. The same effect was observed when the object was a burning cigarette: in this instance, it was the direction of the smoke that indicated to the subject which part of the visual world was "up" and caused the percept to correct itself.

Another line of approach we used was one in which the subject was deprived of all clues that could serve as reference points for veridical perception. For example, the subject was seated in front of a uniformly illuminated white screen. We then introduced various objects into this neutral field. These were held in place by means of wires or sticks, so that the experimenter's hand was not exposed. The subject now had to rely solely on his immediate impression when judging whether, for example, a bottle was right side up or upside down, or the apex or the base of a triangle was "up." A simpler procedure was just to let the subject read; if he read an M as a W, then we knew at once that his vision was inverted, etc.

In this investigation we found that after five days the subject's adaptation had progressed to a point where perceptual errors hardly ever occurred. Two or three days were enough for overt behavior to become normal. (The entire experiment has been recorded on film.)[3]

B. Experiments Involving the Use of Prismatic Spectacles [Wedge Prisms]

1. JANUARY, 1933.
DURATION: 10 DAYS

The subject (S.) wore binocular prismatic spectacles whose angle at the apex was 15°, the bases arranged to the left. All signs of behavioral difficulty (e.g., errors in prehension) disappeared after only one day. A day later apparent visual

[3] A research film about the last experiment is available, entitled "Upright Vision through Inverting Glasses," made in Austria by Pacher and Peithner, Vienna, 1950. Delivery for the United States: E. J. Mauthner, P. O. B. 132, Cathedral Station, New York 25, New York.

Recently, Kottenhoff (1961) summarized all inversion experiments since Stratton.

motions disappeared, curves began to flatten out, and figures became less distorted. Six days after the subject had begun to wear the spectacles, he went on an extended skiing trip in the course of which he rescued a fellow skier who had had an accident. After ten days of continuously wearing the spectacles, all objects had straightened out and were no longer distorted. The subject then removed the spectacles. Immediately, impressions of curvature, distortions, and apparent movement set in. The subject complained: "What I experienced after I took off the spectacles was much worse than what I experienced when I first started wearing them. I felt as if I were drunk." Aftereffects continued for four days.

2. FEBRUARY, 1933.
DURATION: 12 DAYS

Upon the suggestion of Professor Erismann, the same subject now wore a pair of spectacles of which only the bottom halves were prisms, the top halves being ordinary glass. The strength of the prisms was 10°. The object of this study was to develop perceptual integration in the presence of disconnected and displaced images. After twelve days, such integration occurred sporadically. Following removal of the spectacles, a vertical luminous line was variously seen as two lines (monocularly!), in fragmented form, or in an oblique position. Unfortunately, the subject paid too little attention to his eye movements and to the position of his head. These factors, as we found out later, have an important bearing on this phenomenon.

3. APRIL, 1933.
DURATION: 22 DAYS

This time, the subject (S.) wore a monocular prismatic spectacle with a 15° angle. It was noted that the perceptual aftereffects *were transferred to some degree to the other eye, which had been covered during the entire experiment.* Otherwise, the same effects were observed as before (in January). Concerning curvature, the aftereffect was noticeable for a few weeks.

4. SEPTEMBER, 1933.
DURATION: 18 DAYS

Professor Erismann was the subject in this experiment. He wore a pair of binocular prismatic spectacles with a 15° angle. Although his adaptation was somewhat slower and not as complete as that of subject S., the results were of great value to us because *this was the first time that the origin of variable aftereffects was observed.* Some aftereffects were noted even after weeks: for example, curvatures were still noticeable for as long as twenty-three days of post-experimental vision.

5. JUNE, 1936.
DURATION: 5 DAYS

Binocular prismatic spectacles with an angle of 15° were used in this study. This time, however, the procedure was modified in the following manner: when, after two days, an aftereffect was clearly present, the subject put on a pair of *compensatory* spectacles, which he wore for another three days. (These were somewhat weaker prismatic spectacles which served the purpose of correcting for the aftereffect.) The question which we wanted to answer was whether the aftereffect would remain constant, although corrected. It was expected that if the corrected aftereffect decreased only a slight amount, all straight lines would immediately become curved again. Unfortunately, the study was never completed, because the subject (M.) was not present during the last two days and the necessary tests could not be performed to confirm his impressions.

6. JANUARY, 1941.
DURATION: 36 DAYS

The subject (the author himself) wore a monocular prismatic spectacle with a 15° angle for a period of twenty-three days. During this period, vision became almost completely adapted to the spectacle, especially for objects seen straight ahead and in the center of the field. Apparent movements, distortions of angles, and disorientation disappeared almost completely; on the other hand, straight lines continued to be seen as more or less curved. For ten days after this initial period, the author then wore prisms with a 4° angle which compensated for the aftereffect of curvature. As a consequence, objects appeared completely straightened out. Other aftereffects, however, such as apparent movements, distortions, and anomalies of orientation, were not fully corrected since they were stronger than the compensating prism. Somewhat later the bending resumed, while the other aftereffects, for which the prism had been too weak, were now increasingly corrected until the 4° prism became too strong for them also. We therefore concluded that aftereffects persist in a constant way only when they are kept over-corrected, that is, when a remnant of "overstimulation" in the form of curvatures, distortion, obliquity, asymmetry, etc., remains. Following removal of the corrective spectacles, what little remained of the curvature aftereffect persisted most tenaciously for several months. A similar, though not as pronounced, effect was noted in the other eye, which had been covered while the spectacles were being worn.

7. JANUARY, 1941.
DURATION: 6 DAYS

The subject (K.) wore a 20° monocular prismatic spectacle. The right eye remained uncovered because of poor vision. The procedure was essentially the same as that of the other studies which have been described. The curvature aftereffect lasted three to four days.

8. JANUARY, 1941.
DURATION: 5 DAYS

This study was undertaken to investigate the possibility of creating adaptation when the bases of the prisms were rotated 90° from the left side to the bottom of the frames. In these conditions horizontal lines became curved: the ceiling and floor appeared arched, and did so in the stage of the aftereffects. In the former experiments when the prism bases were arranged to the left, the bending and the aftereffect of curvature were restricted to the vertical dimension, that is, to lines parallel to the cephalocaudal axis. Since oncoming objects appeared farther away than they actually were, this subject was particularly endangered; it was therefore necessary to provide especially careful guidance, a responsibility which was alternately assumed by two other subjects wearing spectacles. However, even in this case, such close supervision was necessary only during the first day. The subject became adapted after only a few errors. Once the spectacles had been removed, however, errors in locomotion and prehension recurred. The direction of these errors was the opposite of that manifested during the first day of wearing the spectacles. The same was true of the direction in which horizontal lines now appeared to be curved. Slight aftereffects remained for several days.

9. FEBRUARY, 1941.
DURATION: 9 DAYS

The subject (G.) wore a monocular prismatic spectacle. Initially, the angle was 20°, but it was increased to 30° for the last fifteen hours of the experiment. This subject reacted in a special way: while there was very little adaptation to curvature, apparent movements and errors in prehension disappeared almost entirely. Nevertheless, there was a distinct bending aftereffect once the spectacle was removed. This lasted for only a few seconds, but reappeared with increased intensity whenever she closed her eyes.[4] As a result of

---

[4] There are, of course, individual differences in the degree and rate of adaptation. Jaensch and Mandowsky's investigations (1932) are relevant to this issue. They demonstrate that adaptation to perceived curvatures proceeds more slowly with "disintegrated" than with "integrated" subjects. The latter are also more likely to experience strong aftereffects, which, however, are more short-lived.

this peculiarly unstable aftereffect, the visual images of this subject had an extremely variable quality: straight objects —for example, long and heavy steel pipes —curved and straightened out while the amazed subject was in the very act of looking at them. It took several days for her vision to stabilize.

10. SEPTEMBER, 1946.
DURATION: 8 DAYS

The subject (N.) wore a monocular prismatic spectacle with a 20° angle. The other eye was covered. Again, all the usual phenomena occurred. The emphasis in this study, however, was on *the effects of prismatic deviation on perceptual orientation.* For this reason we were primarily interested in studying errors of prehension, alterations in the optical median, and asymmetry of eye-head-body posture. When wearing prisms, the subject is always forced to move his eyes and head in a direction different from that in which he is reaching, so that there is a marked discrepancy between the position of head and torso of which the subject is completely unaware. This subject was no exception. He thought he was looking straight ahead when actually his head was turned 6° to 9° to the right of the body median. When this posture was corrected, the subject experienced a distortion to the left of his head versus body. The errors in visual direction disappeared to the same degree that this "torsion" developed during the first days of the experiment. After removal of the prism the head posture quickly returned to normal. The bending aftereffect, however, was still occasionally present for five days.

An interesting feature of monocular studies is that once normal vision has been restored, the sensitivity of the eye which had been covered is drastically altered: for several days thereafter, there is an increase in sensations of brightness, contrast, and color as compared to the uncovered eye; in binocular vision, perceptions of depth are enormously heightened.

11. NOVEMBER, 1946 TO MARCH, 1947. DURATION: 124 DAYS

This was a binocular study in which the author served as the subject. Starting with 15° spherical prisms, further distortions were induced by reversing the prisms and thereby turning the convex side of the prisms toward the eyes. This was followed by a ten-day study of aftereffects, using compensatory prisms. During the final month of the study, the angle was increased once more, to 20°.

This experiment, the first of such long duration, was significant for other reasons too. In the first place, the aftereffects obtained were of optimal strength. In the second place, it gave rise to a number of peculiar aftereffects which I have already referred to as "situational." Not only curvatures, distortions, deviations, apparent movements, etc., were found to leave traces in the sensorium, but also the variations in intensity of these disturbances. It is known that the deflection of rays by a prism is minimum when the subject is looking through the center of the prism. As soon as the subject deviates from this line of vision, either horizontally or vertically, the distortions increase: angles become even more acute or obtuse, and lines which were close to being perpendicular or horizontal now appear markedly slanted. Furthermore, the quality of the perceptual alteration depends on the direction in which the subject's line of vision deviates. Thus, the same object appears thin when viewed through one side of the prism, and broadened when viewed through the other side, objectively horizontal or vertical lines are displaced one way when seen from below and another way when seen from above. And all this takes place for the same retinal area, the center of normal, accurate vision. The question therefore arises: what are the aftereffects of so many different and contrasting sensory influences?

The situational aftereffect provides the answer; it is an aftereffect whose characteristics depend on particular conditions, in this case on the direction of the line of vision. Thus, the separation between two poles was decreased when looked at from the left, and increased when looked at from the right. Earlier, during the wearing of the spectacles, the reverse had occurred. In other words, what we have here is a special kind of negative aftereffect: it occurs only when the total situation is the same as the one in which the prism-induced alterations originally occurred. This principle is applicable to all other aftereffects as well: those involving deformations, obliquities, apparent movements, etc. Whenever head and eyes are turned after removal of the spectacles, additional perceptual anomalies occur; these are exactly opposite to the ones which occurred in the same conditions of eye-head posture while the prisms were being worn. The experience is most uncanny; it is as if phantom prisms with a refraction exactly opposite to that of the experimental spectacles were before the eyes.

The most impressive, but also the most puzzling, phenomenon which I observed was a particular aftereffect which entered the domain of color theory.[5] Since prisms are known to deflect shortwave rays more than longwave rays, they are capable of breaking up white light into its chromatic components. It is for this reason that our subjects were exposed to a rich array of rainbow fringes which, in accordance with well-known principles, appeared to be adjacent to all contrasting contours: depending on the direction in which a dark area changed into a brighter one, the colors of these rainbows were sometimes yellowish-red (comprising the long-wave sector of the spectrum), at other times blueish-green (comprising the short-wave sector of the spectrum). However, as time went on, this phenomenon gradually became weaker, and after several months of wearing the spectacles it disappeared altogether (pro-

[5] Gibson (1933) was the first to mention this phenomenon. Using prisms, he obtained it after only a few days, but added that Hering's theory of afterimages cannot account for it.

vided the illumination was not excessively bright). Apparently, the so-called *chromatic aberration of the ordinary (uncorrected) prisms had been exactly compensated for* by some physiological or psychological factor. Equally strange was the aftereffect: now, *in conditions of normal vision, a reversed chromatic deviation* appeared; it seemed as if the subject himself had acquired the ability to split white light into its chromatic components. Careful examination (using yellow sodium light), however, revealed that this was a special kind of afterimage phenomenon: we found that this splitting also occurred when the light was monochromatic. Whenever a brightness difference was discriminated, the complementary part of the half-spectrum appeared at the region of transition. Whenever the short-wave part of the spectrum appeared while the spectacles were being worn, the long-wave part of the spectrum was now subjectively present, and vice versa.

The other results of this study, including those of the interpolated compensation experiment, agreed with the previous ones. Aftereffects continued to interfere with normal vision for weeks following removal of the spectacles. It was further noted that those aftereffects which had taken longest to build up were the ones which persisted longest.

12. APRIL TO JUNE, 1947.
DURATION: 50 DAYS

This was a binocular half-prism study in which the author again served as the subject. Details of the procedure are contained in Chapter 3. The following is only a brief summary.

The spectacles were constructed so that upward vision had to pass through a prism with a 10° angle of refraction (base left). Downward vision was normal. In other words, the upper half of the spectacles distorted vision in the manner which has already been described, while the lower half permitted normal vision. The question

we sought to answer was whether adaptation would be possible in these conditions.

The initial results gave a negative answer to the question. The instant the subject looked down (through the clear part of the spectacles), whatever progress he had made in adapting to the half-prism was immediately undone by the appearance of the aftereffect and the consequent contrary visual experience. Since obviously little is gained by exchanging one illusion for another, one can hardly speak of a purposeful adaptation in this part of the experiment.

After approximately ten days the subject noted a slight differential increase in the intensity of the aftereffects (curvatures, distortions, errors in prehension, and especially apparent movements) when looking up as compared with looking down, *when he was not wearing the spectacles.* Gradually, this difference was also noted when the subject *wore* the spectacles; there was an increase in adaptation to the prism but without concomitant disturbances of normal vision, that is, the initial aftereffects when the subject looked down ceased. In other words, *the subject's vision had become differentially adapted to both conditions.*

The subject's experiences after removal of the spectacles were consistent with those preceding it: depending on the direction of the subject's gaze, the same stimuli, that is, stimulus patterns, gave rise to different sensations of spatial forms, even of colors (namely, effect of color dispersion through prisms). What had first been an "unconditioned" aftereffect ("unconditioned" because it followed only a certain kind of impingement on the retina) was now a "conditioned" aftereffect, depending on the facilitating or inhibiting action of the subject's eye-head position as a new contributing factor. This "semi" aftereffect was especially noticeable in relation to visual orientation and the perception of movement when adaptation to the half-prisms was complete.

I observed still another form of adaptation. Since rays passing through the prism are deflected sideways in relation to the clear portion of the glass, objects occupying the entire visual field appeared bisected, and the two parts were out of line with each other. The subject adapted to this illusion by developing a special kind of eye movement: while the subject had the experience of looking up and down, he was actually looking diagonally. By doing this, he was able to perceive the object as continuous, whereas actually the half-prism spectacles divided the image and displaced its component parts. As soon as the subject stopped moving his eyes, however, the discontinuity of the image immediately became apparent. The acquired eye movements persisted even after removal of the spectacles and gave rise to opposite illusions.

It should be mentioned, however, that these illusions were not as enduring as the ones described earlier, some of which lasted for as long as two months. After a while, however, they lost their conditioned character.

C. Experiments with Colored Spectacles

1. JANUARY, 1947.
DURATION: 20 DAYS

The subject (A.) wore a pair of spectacles of which the left halves were colored blue and the right halves were colored yellow. Thus whenever the subject looked to his left, everything appeared blue, and whenever he looked to his right, the world appeared yellow. The lines dividing the two fields were in the center of the spectacles and coincided in binocular vision. In the course of the experiment, it was noted that *both colors* subjectively faded away. This suggests that the same retinal areas became simultaneously adapted to complementary color stimuli. This fact was confirmed when the spectacles were removed; now the fovea clearly was selectively sensitive to color, the sensitivity being determined by the direction in which the subject happened to be looking. Looking to the right resulted in increased sensitivity to blue (a "situation" in which yellow had previously been the predominant color); looking to the left, on the other hand, was followed by increased sensitivity to yellow. Although this situational aftereffect was weak, it nevertheless lasted for eleven days.

2. FEBRUARY, 1947.
DURATION: 22 DAYS

The subject in this study (A.'s brother), who was nearsighted, wore his own spectacles, each lens of which he agreed to have marked with a black dot. The dot had a diameter of one centimeter and was located slightly below the center of each lens. During binocular distance vision, the two dots coincided. Since this artificial scotoma forced the subject to keep his head in an unaccustomed position while reading, it irritated him a great deal at first. The black spot in his visual field was annoying at other times also. After a while, however, the subject became quite used to it, even though no perceptual changes occurred: the black spot continued to be present. Nevertheless, a *positive,* that is, an even darker, aftereffect was noticed several times before and after removal of the spectacles, for example, in a dark room just before the subject fell asleep. However, the aftereffect was not strong enough to be investigated further.

This observation, the only one of importance in this particular study, appeared to have a parallel in an illusion which several of our subjects reported after the removal of whatever experimental spectacles they had been wearing: it seemed to them that their visual fields contained dark rims and temples, as if they were still wearing the spectacles. The illusion occurred independently of eye movements, so that any part of the frame—rims or temples—was directly visible.

3. MARCH TO APRIL, 1947.
DURATION: $8 + 19$ DAYS (WITH A TWO-WEEK INTERRUPTION)

The spectacles used in this study were ordinary spectacle glasses (0 diopter), covered with a red, transparent diagonal stripe made of celluloid, one centimeter wide. The two colored stripes coincided binocularly and created the plastic illusion of a red beam diagonally cutting across the visual field. With time, however, this colored stripe began to fade away. When the spectacles were removed, a peculiar aftereffect appeared: whenever the subject happened to look at an achromatic stimulus object located in that part of the visual field formerly occupied by the red "beam," he faintly saw a *green-colored* afterimage. This phenomenon persisted for three to four days.

4. JUNE, 1947.
DURATION: 19 DAYS

The author wore two different sets of spectacles in this study: a pair of completely blue-colored spectacles in the morning, and a pair of completely yellow-colored spectacles in the afternoon. The spectacles were exchanged every day at 1 P.M. As a consequence of wearing these spectacles, the world appeared at first unusually and unpleasantly discolored. By the time the spectacles were exchanged, however, the color had become barely visible. In fact, there were moments when the subject saw everything as yellow when looking through the blue spectacles, and vice versa. This always happened when he entered a dark place after having spent some time in a bright one. Gradually, the rate of adaptation increased, and the color of the spectacles began to fade away as soon as they were put on. But *a situational aftereffect never occurred.* All that remained after removal of the spectacles was an increased sensitivity to yellow, which persisted for a few days. Nor did this sensitivity in any way depend on the time of day.

Apparently, variations in the timing of stimulation (especially when the time intervals are long) do not serve as a condition for the production of situational aftereffects.

5. AUGUST, 1947.
DURATION: 27 DAYS

This time, red-green spectacles, modeled after the yellow-blue spectacles, were used. The colored sections were arranged in such a way that the subject saw everything as green when looking down, and red when looking up. Again, the colors gradually faded away; but only after an initial stage of mutual enhancement of complementarities, in keeping with Hering's theory. When the spectacles were turned upside down, on the other hand, both the red lower and the green upper visual fields seemed much more saturated. The remainder of the experiment yielded results consistent with expectations. A slight situational aftereffect occurred for a long as twelve days following removal of the spectacles: colors as well as grays appeared to be "warmer" in the lower than in the upper half of the visual field. The aftereffect was even more pronounced when the field of vision was reduced, for example, when the subject looked through a tube or was asked to discriminate surface colors. At times, the effect was so accurate that, depending on the position of head and eyes, the subject could see the line dividing the two colored afterimages.

6. MAY TO JUNE, 1948.
DURATION: 60 DAYS

The author wore a pair of yellow-blue spectacles, as described above. The results not only confirmed the earlier ones, but, because of the longer duration of this study, also yielded a number of refinements which threw additional light on the genesis of the situational aftereffect. For details of the procedure, see Chapter 4. What follows is merely a brief summary.

Initially, the aftereffects of the two filters canceled each other when the subject shifted his fixation from one field to the other. The complementary color then appeared abnormally intense. This successive contrast gradually disappeared; color intensity became constant and no longer increased with shifts from field to field. The afterimages for each color remained, so to speak, in each field and were no longer carried over.

Another observation was that changes in eye movements facilitated adaptation to the two-toned spectacles to a greater extent than changes in head movements (the eyes being fixated). This observation is of interest because the retinal effects of both types of movement should be the same. The subject, who spent a good portion of his waking time reading and writing, was in the "habit" of preferring eye movements to head movements, and this apparently enhanced the aftereffect for this particular situation.

Both colors had become equally faint by the time this experiment neared the end. Quantitative tests with the spectacles on indicated a 50 percent adaptation. For free vision, however, the deviation in color perception was considerably less, which is probably due to the very close connection between the aftereffect and the situation eliciting it. Simply wearing the empty frames with a fine thread halving each field was capable of facilitating the aftereffect. Be that as it may, when the subject took off his spectacles, he had the impression that objects to his left were bathed in warm, yellowish candlelight, while objects to his right tended to take on colder colors. This illusion *moved with the subject's head movements* (as formerly the spectacles had), but *not with eye movements*. The gradual disappearance of this aftereffect could be observed for weeks.

Theoretical Considerations

I now wish to keep my earlier promise to take up where we left off in the introductory chapter and to consider the implications of the experimental results in greater depth.

I shall first discuss the theoretical difficulties confronting us. Then I shall propose a possible solution of these difficulties, make some criticisms of Hering's theory, and suggest some ways of supplementing it. I shall conclude this work by indicating ways in which the results may be applied to other fields of interest.

A. The Theoretical Problem

As we have seen, there are all kinds of aftereffects. Some always depend on stimulation of certain retinal areas, in Hering's sense. Others are peculiarly autonomous: sometimes they occur, sometimes they do not, and sometimes it is only their complements that we observe; yet—as can easily be verified—we find that it is always the same stimulus which impinges on the same retinal area.

As long as we focus our attention exclusively on isolated retinal areas and their functions, these "variable" or "intermittent" sensory reactions to one and the same stimulus make no sense at all. This limited point of view gives rise to obstacles which can be surmounted only with a great deal of difficulty.

Only if we broaden our horizon and consider the *total stimulus situation* (which, after all, is the setting for every sensation) will we be able to discover that these fluctuations in sensory experiences and in the subjective spatial standards are not random. Only then do we find that *their occurrence or nonoccurrence is governed by very specific environmental factors.* To repeat: only by considering the total (including the nonoptical) stimulus situation is it possible to conceive of these varying sensory reactions to constant stimuli impinging on the same retinal area as being not random but lawful.

Even if we accept this position, however, we may still find ourselves on the wrong track. I am referring here to the common mistake of attributing a cause-and-effect relationship to events which have been found to corelate, for example, kinesthetic and color sensations.

The paradox of different afterimages arising from one retinal area, which we have mentioned so many times, is a case in point. We have repeatedly stated that opposite aftereffects are kept from "clashing" on a retinal area by "situational" factors. But this is only a descriptive, not an explanatory, statement. We are still faced with the enigma of how these situational factors succeed in altering visual experiences instantly. What needs to be concretely demonstrated is the relationship between the total situation and the individual sensation. Not until this has been done will it be possible to understand the peculiar sensory fluctuations accompanying changes in situational factors.

Gestalt psychology, which never tires of emphasizing this relationship, can never provide us with an answer to the question: "How does the contraction of a neck muscle influence retinal sensitivity to color?" To keep asserting that every reaction of an organism to a stimulus is a "total response" is not answering the question at all. On the contrary, it is misleading. As our findings have shown, a total response is not a given; *it gradually evolves*. Concomitant conditions, which at first have nothing to do with optical sensations, end up being "conditioned stimuli." Since it is only in the end that the sensations "take into account" previously unrelated aspects of the environment, it obviously must have taken them some time to develop into total responses. The solution must therefore take a different form.

To put this problem in proper perspective, let us, for the sake of argument, hand over our experimental subject to a hypothetical naïve or neutral examiner, and let us do this at the very moment the subject takes off his experimental spectacles. Let us pretend that this subject has just removed yellow-blue spectacles, after having worn them for a long time, and that he is now being examined by an ophthalmologist or a psychophysicist. After examining the subject, the examiner is forced to come to the astonishing conclusion that certain head and eye positions exert an apparently direct influence on sensations of color. Empirically, however, he knows that retinal sensitivity to color depends on the condition of the underlying sensory substances (in this case yellow and blue substances), and that these, in turn, can only be activated or modified by corresponding color stimuli. How then account for the additional variations induced by contractions of neck or eye muscles? Traditional color theory does not tell him a word about this. The same may be said about the dispersion aftereffect. How explain the fact that the different color experiences resulting from brightness contrasts vary systematically according to whether a dark shade is to the left of a light shade or to the right of it?

Our hypothetical examiner would find himself just as confused if we now presented him with a subject who had been wearing *distorting spectacles* for months and had just taken them off. True, it would be easier for him to conceive of kinesthetic influences in a situation such as this one which involves spatial localization. This does not mean, however, that it would now be any easier for him to attribute optical phenomena to nonoptical variables.

Problems such as that of "absolute" or "egocentric" localization will never be solved as long as positions of the body are excluded from consideration. The exact location in space of a perceived object cannot be determined on the basis of retinal conditions alone. How could we tell whether it was seen medially or laterally? The same holds true for movements of the entire visual image. As far as the retina is concerned, the effect is the same regardless of whether it is the observer or his surroundings that move. The fact that we are able to distinguish perceptually between these two types of movement clearly indicates that nonoptical variables, for example, kinesthetic sensations while walking, influence perception.

Yet, somehow, even this answer is not entirely satisfactory. Why make this careful distinction between optical and kinesthetic sensations (belonging to two different sensory modalities and therefore not comparable) if, as in the above case, they are only going to become "fused" again in the end? In these circumstances it is easy to understand why one would feel reluctant to formulate coworking hypotheses and would stubbornly continue to search for optical explanations.

This does not mean, however, that such illusions as tilted visual images or apparent movements of objects accompanying changes in head and body position cannot be explained at all. It only means that the explanation must be based on the recognition that *the relationship between the two sets of sensory data is variable and not static.* This much we can safely infer from the observation that kinesthetic factors are always involved in the perception of directionality and impressions of movement of the entire visual field relative to the observer's body. Somehow we must revise the so-called "compensatory equation" between certain movements of the image and of the head (which were formerly thought to "neutralize" each other, so that the resulting percept was motionless). Otherwise we will never be able to account for the apparent movements after removal of the spectacles. The same holds true for the other anomalies of the total visual field.

An even more difficult problem is posed by the peculiar *alterations in position within the visual field.* The problem is similar to that involved in color perception. How can we explain the rubbery transformations of the internal proportions of the visual image that accompany changes in the position of head and eyes?

As far as the retina is concerned, the stimulation is the same whether the head moves in a horizontal or in a vertical direction, as long as the eyes keep focusing on the object in question. Nevertheless, distances will subjectively increase and decrease in these circumstances, angles will contract and expand, parallel lines will converge and diverge, and so on.

If we ascribe size and form perception to the reactiveness of retinal elements, and their spatial values to light and color stimuli, then the results of the prism experiments suggest that *the coordination between these retinal elements and their spatial values is a variable and not a static one.* There is the possibility that in certain circumstances spatial values may be transferred from one retinal element to one adjacent to it. In this case, the realignment has to be such that stimulation of the same retinal element can variously give rise to percepts of acute and obtuse angles, of lines converging left, right, up, and down, of squares, rectangles, rhombuses, and rhomboids, and of straight and diversely curved lines.

These seemingly farfetched assumptions can be supported by clinical observation of certain cases in which the relative position of retinal elements is altered by a disease. Such patients report corresponding distortions in certain parts of the visual field, for example, the parts of a network which fall within the diseased portion of the retina will appear no longer symmetrical and square but enlarged, reduced, or somehow twisted out of shape. We know this phenomenon by the name of "metamorphopsia." It is one which has frequently been studied. Wundt, for example, investigated the process in one of his eyes.

Let us assume that every retinal element is endowed with a certain spatial value and that, as a consequence, every stimulus maintains its place in the visual field.[6] If we assume this, it follows that shifting retinal elements must take their spatial values along with them and that, consequently, a mix-up in subjective standards must ensue in the diseased area. The process would be analogous to taking measurements with a yardstick of which a portion is wrongly calibrated. Measurements taken with this portion of the yardstick would obviously be incongruent with measurements taken with the accurate part of the yardstick.

So far, everything is clear. But now comes a complication. It has been observed that the vision of patients cured of metamorphopsia gradually becomes normal again, even though no concomitant realignment of retinal elements has taken place. This clearly suggests that spatial values need not necessarily be tied to particular retinal elements. They can be *relocated* in their relationship to one another. Whether such a relocation is interpreted on an empirical or a nativistic basis is irrelevant.

We could probably approach the problem of relocation of spatial values with even greater flexibility if we applied Hering's theory to space perception. We do not apprehend the dimensions of objects any

more directly than we do wavelengths. We must bear in mind that the physiology of the visual apparatus always intervenes between a wavelength and the corresponding color sensation. In other words, the light rays must first interact with some nervous substance before any sensation can be experienced. The effect of the rays— the intensity and quality of the sensation experienced—is always dependent on the condition of this nervous substance.[7] The same stimulus can give rise to a new sensation if the condition of the nervous substance has changed. The traditional experiments on visual afterimages demonstrate this point in the simplest and most elementary manner.

This state of affairs prevails not only in the case of color vision but also in the case of space perception. Again a physiological element intervenes between the patterning of stimuli on the retina—the actual spatial stimulus—and the perceptual experiences of size and shape. Only now this element is the momentary distribution of spatial values. We may also call it the "subjective standard." Although it cannot be as rapidly transformed as color sensitivity, it can be transformed just as thoroughly. The transformation takes place whenever a certain area of the retina is continuously subjected to certain biases of stimulation; for example, a preponderance of curvatures, distorted angles, unsymmetrical lines, etc. To put it in Hering's words, the perception of space is a product of the visual "substance" just as much as is the perception of color. . . .

The possibility that spatial values may be transformed without necessitating corresponding changes in the position of

---

[6] This in no way contradicts the equally plausible assumption that spatial values may change as a result of experience. "Native endowments" are not immutable and incompatible with further development. Conversely, the mere fact that spatial values *are* influenced by experience does not establish experience as the sole determinant. A valid formulation must take into account both the nativists' *and* the empiricists' point of view.

It is entirely possible for spatial values to change in accordance with definite principles, even though they are constitutionally determined. They may change either because of the action of some other constitutional factor, or because of the effects of external stimuli. No one is going to have any doubt that the ability to perceive colors is inborn just because of adaptational phenomena. Similarly, it would appear unreasonable to doubt that we are born with spatial values, even a particular distribution of spatial values, just because they change as a result of prolonged stimulation of a certain sort.

[7] By "substance" I mean neither some kind of chemical substance nor some kind of retinal structure. What I am talking about is the *total* nervous process which underlies sensations and which extends from the retina all the way to the visual brain center. Changes in the visual substance therefore include peripheral as well as central aftereffects. Lack of clarity on this point may easily lead to misinterpretations.

retinal elements serves us well in interpreting the visual disturbances experienced by the subjects in our prism experiments. Our hypothetical ophthalmologist or psychophysicist can now assert that the distribution of spatial values on the examined parts of these subjects' retinas was *abnormal*; that it was of such a nature as to cause straight vertical lines to be seen as curved, right angles as acute or obtuse, regular intervals as irregular, etc.

This conceptualization, however, covers only a fraction of the experimental results. For as soon as the subject changes the position of his head or of his eyes in relation to his head, the arrangement of spatial values, which we have just now so laboriously analyzed, is immediately altered: it may become either more or less abnormal; it may even reverse itself altogether. Thus we find that the spatial values of the individual retinal areas (that is, the relations among them) not only vary but, more than that, *the variations themselves vary*. At certain times, the observed retinal area reacts perfectly normally; a fraction of a second later, however, it reacts completely abnormally: the same object changes in size and shape whenever the head or the eyes move. As we have already shown, these subjective experiences are completely verifiable by means of objective procedures in which the subject is not conscious of his deviant sensory experiences.

This brings us to the point where we left off when we were discussing the disturbances in color sensitivity resulting from the wearing of yellow-blue spectacles. In both cases, incidental conditions, which "should" not have had any effect on the internal proportions of visual images, directly influenced the perceptual process. Again and again, standards of size, angulation, and movement within a single retinal area were found to vary, even though the stimulus remained the same. The same phenomenon manifested itself in different ways in adjacent areas. Hence the "rubbery" world, which always impressed the subject so much after removal of the prismatic spectacles.

The peculiarity of the findings which our studies have brought to light may be underscored by extending their implications to the sense of touch. Suppose we asked someone to hold a small metal die in his closed hand. We would then expect certain sensations of pressure, texture, and temperature to occur at the points of contact between the die (its corners and edges) and the palm of the hand. It should make no difference at all whether the arm were flexed, extended, raised, or lowered; the sensations emanating from the die should be the same in all cases. But suppose our subject were to insist that this was not so; suppose he were to report that the die became bigger when he raised his arm, felt colder when he extended his arm, or was shaped like a square and not like a cube when he lowered his arm. We would say nonsense! It would be inconceivable to us that the position of the arm should have any influence whatever on sensations of touch and temperature on the palm of the hand.[8] And yet this is exactly what we observed in the visual modality. There we found that the contraction of an eye or neck muscle influenced the inner proportions of a perceived object. How is this possible?

B. The Solution: A Glance at Hering's Theory of Sensations

Let us now see how an examiner who is familiar with the subject's past experiences would find a way out of this seemingly hopeless dilemma. He would first of all

---

[8] Köhler and Dinnerstein (1947) reported just such a phenomenon. They too did a long-term study and found that, after their subjects had been practicing for weeks (an hour or more a day) on tapered wooden bars, a constant interval between thumb and index finger [subjectively] varied in size as soon as the arms moved. Subjectively, the edges of a control bar did not feel parallel but appeared to taper off in the wrong direction. As in our study, the aftereffect was extraordinarily persistent.

note that certain special conditions "enhance" or "suppress" afterimages[9] (colored as well as spatial) which are the natural result of certain stimuli impinging on certain retinal areas. The longer the period of stimulation, the more differentiated become the stimulus traces which accumulate in the retinal area. The retinal area becomes the isomorphic equivalent of mnemonic details by "sorting" all excitations according to the circumstances governing their recurrence, and not by merely summating them unselectively. If it did that, adaptation to alternating complementary stimuli (opposite distortions) would be completely impossible, as I have repeatedly pointed out.

To recapitulate: the link between the original optical data and the situational factors is established not directly but in a roundabout way, via afterimages which are sometimes enhanced, sometimes suppressed. Not that this solves the problem; it only puts the problem in a different perspective. The question still remains: how do the eye muscles manage to interfere with the afterimages?

A partial answer may be found in the distinction between *peripheral* (superficial) and *central* (far-reaching) aftereffects.

As long as stimuli are of short duration, their effects can only be peripheral, or, at best, restricted to a limited area. No real differentiation is possible between regularly recurring and "accidental" aspects of the total situation coincident with these stimuli, and the traces which are formed in the sensorium remain equivocal. Only prolonged stimulation can bring about such a distinction.[10] That is why, after short periods of stimulation, some deviations of retinal reactivity still remain localized; that is, each retinal area still functions in accordance with its own average past and "disregards" other aspects of the situation. After prolonged stimulation, on the other hand, the reverse takes place: now the situational factors are excluded from consideration only in special cases, that is, when they lack uniqueness.

Thus, in the case of fully prismatic spectacles, curvatures were present regardless of what other factors were present in the situation; consequently, the aftereffect remained localized. But in the case of half-prism spectacles, curvatures appeared with regularity only in very specific conditions (position of head and eyes); as a result, the aftereffects freed themselves from the affected retinal area and thus became dependent on other situational factors. In the light of Hering's theory, those findings indicate not only that the underlying sensory substance had become altered by the end of the experiment, but that the degree of alteration must have been determined by concomitant recurrent features of the total situation. This means that we can no longer speak of the condition of the nervous substratum in static terms. Instead, we must speak of it in terms of a "profile" which varies in accordance with the characteristics of the total given stimulus situation.

Stated more precisely, in the *full-prism*

---

[9] In the strict sense of the word, these are no longer ordinary afterimages but more far-reaching effects, in other words, "aftereffects" affecting central visual areas. As we have seen in experiments with monocular prisms, visual disturbances spread over the entire optical apparatus after only a few days (even the covered eye reacts abnormally). That the seat of the disturbance is clearly *central* is further evidenced by the stability and duration of these aftereffects, and, in particular, by the "situational" aftereffect itself, which certainly cannot originate in the periphery. We may rightly assume, therefore, that "afterimages" which are influenced by situational factors no longer represent peripheral physiological changes of the sensory substance.

[10] This fact, if given its proper place in a theory of sensations, would amply cover the results of all our experiments. It is imperative that we distinguish between *accidental* and *regular* conditions. The former cannot exert a differential influence on sensory processes because they are equally distributed; the latter, however, can do so. What is applicable to sensations and sensory processes in general is also applicable to particular cases, specifically to all those sensations which occur most frequently in certain situations.

case, the situation did not have a chance to make itself felt; it was too indistinct, because the sensation was just as frequently present in other situations. Only a *differentiated* effect makes it possible for a connection to appear between the sensation and the total situation. Where no such differentiation has developed, no need exists to go beyond classical theories of sensation. The aftereffects in such a case are completely autonomous. The curvature aftereffect (in the fully prismatic study) is an instance of this; its connection with certain stimuli impinging on the retina remains invariant—it is not affected by different movements of the head. Thus, it appears to be a local phenomenon.

Only for this reason was Gibson (1937) able to generalize from color vision to the perception of straight lines on the basis of simple principles of adaptation.

Let me clarify this analysis by applying it to *motor behavior*. A muscle can react in many different ways. The specific way in which it reacts is always determined by the demands of a particular situation. This does not necessarily have to be accompanied by awareness. Thus, a "situational" reaction gradually becomes differentiated from a "general" reaction.

The following may serve as an illustration. Someone who is used to a certain typewriter will make typing errors as soon as he begins to use another typewriter with a different arrangement of keys. The earlier machine always exerts a disrupting effect on the later one, at least for some time. On the other hand, someone who has been forced to use many different typewriters for a long time will eventually be able to use them all with equal proficiency. His typing habits have become differentiated, that is, machine-specific, with a characteristic "set" for each machine being used. In other words, the situational factor has become interwoven with the state of the muscles at any given time. What were at first generalized aftereffects of typing have become specific to certain situ-

ations. To put it differently, the reactions have become "conditioned."

Similarly, the reactions of the *sensorium* to external stimuli can become conditioned once the state of the sensory apparatus has become differentiated with respect to *different situations*.

Just as a long period of practice is necessary for any intricate chain of motor reactions to become automatized, so a long period of stimulation is necessary before sensory reactions become associated with situational factors. In order for a connection to become established between a sensation and a particular situation, afterimages must first become *central* aftereffects. The physiologically plausible solution which I propose for the problem of how muscular contractions are related to color sensations may thus be based on the assumption of *mutually facilitating and inhibiting central aftereffects*.[11]

The hypothetical naïve examiner was quite accurate when he noticed *variable* abnormalities of sensitivity in examining our experimental subject; and he was quite correct in attributing these abnormalities to very specific conditions pertaining to the total stimulus situation rather than calling them hallucinatory phenomena. He could not help thinking in terms of "conditioned" sensations. He erred, however, in inferring a direct causal relationship between these conditions and the observed sensory abnormalities. The reason for his mistake is that Hering's theory, on which he based his thinking, offered no possibility for conceiving of differentiated aftereffects of previous stimulation. Consequently, it did not occur to him to ascribe the fluctuating phenomena to aftereffects. He was confined in a theoretical straitjacket.

---

[11] The experiments with the yellow-blue spectacles are a case in point. Not only did changes in the position of head and eyes lead to corresponding afterimages, the reverse also took place: yellow and blue surfaces in the visual field induced the subject to assume an "appropriate eye position."

If he had realized that Hering's theory was applicable only to special cases, the right answer would immediately have presented itself. When I say *special cases* I am talking about stimuli of short duration whose occurrence does *not* invariably depend on the presence of certain concomitant conditions in the total situation. Only in these unlifelike conditions do the individual "nerve keys"—to use Tschermak's term—react in isolation from the rest of the situation. We get entirely different results if, *coincident with certain optical stimuli, a particular aspect of the total situation has been consistently emphasized.* Then the aftereffects become situational aftereffects, and we are suddenly faced with the enigma of an external factor whose influence cannot be explained in purely sensory terms.

Any attempt to generalize to *all stimuli* and to *all stimulus durations* is doomed to failure if it is based on isolated theories of sensation which ignore conditioning processes and which have been derived from the observed effects of short-term or nontypical stimulation.

Although Hering's law of assimilation and dissimilation may be valuable in explaining *individual* stimulus effects on the sensory substance, it is absolutely useless when applied to *complex* stimulus effects, such as different or opposite stimuli influencing a single sensory area. In the latter case, assimilation and dissimilation cancel each other out, and what remains is some watered-down average stimulus effect on the sensory substance.

That is why Hering's theory of sensations never reckons on the kind of *long-lasting* alterations of the sensory substance which we observed at the conclusion of our experiments and which took weeks and months, not just a few minutes, to become extinguished. An exponent of Hering's theory would dismiss long-term investigations such as ours as lacking ecological validity. He would say they have no practical value, because they are so far removed from the conditions which normally prevail. Ordinarily, the stimuli which impinge on our retinas are in fact varied and not prolonged. They are not biased and do not eventually give rise to aftereffects. A straight line, for example, no matter how long it is observed, can never cause the subjective standard to change.

It is time that we give extra thought to this whole phenomenon of *increasingly veridical perception* which always occurs when experimental spectacles of any kind have been worn for some time. What is the *advantage* when a taut string, for example, begins to look straight to us no matter how curved the corresponding retinal image may be? Or when a rigid substance keeps its rigidity no matter how elastic it has been made to appear with the spectacles?

We are confronted here with a peculiar relationship between optical and physical facts. We always find that it is the physical dimensions of things which have a tendency to become visually correct. This is due to the fact that physical dimensions are among the most frequent and symmetrically distributed stimuli. Consequently, it is with these stimulus qualities that unique perceptual experiences of straightness, right-angularity, and good form tend to become associated. It is always the physically unique stimuli which gradually become the reference standards for our percepts. This is the reason why, in the process of adaptation, it is always the world with which we are familiar which wins out in the end. It does so in the interest of simplicity and economy.

It follows that the classical theory of sensations is applicable only to very simple adaptational phenomena, and not to those which, as in the case of the half-prism spectacles, involve multiple alterations of sensory reactiveness within a single retinal area. Otherwise, biased alterations of the sensory apparatus would increase the error, not reduce it; sensory adaptation to the total situation could never take place.[12]

What good is a theory of sensation which is not applicable to complex situations and which necessitates our formulating *ad hoc* hypotheses every time some incidental condition is found to be present? Yet this is precisely the state that the study of perception has been in.

C. Possible Applications of the Results

As a general principle, we may expect aftereffects to occur whenever *sensory data have become transformed through the action of some special added condition.* The aftereffects may be related to specific stimuli in the past history of the current total situation (the one transformed by the special condition) or in the history of the one preceding it. Keeping the possibility of situational aftereffects in mind, it would behoove us to look for *"unusual stimulus configurations"* operative in the past. This could be done by means of conventional statistical methods.

These configurations should not be hard to find. They may be the product of a particular *life style* or of some *natural law operative in the environment.* Even a superficial record of ordinary stimulus patterns and sequences should convince us that they are lawful phenomena and not mere chance occurrences.

Such a record would evidence an *unmistakable correspondence* between changes in retinal images and *certain positions and movements of the body, head, and eyes.* Furthermore, this correspondence would be highly systematic, and not random. Even the optical data themselves would appear in a new light in this sample of everyday conditions. We take too much for granted that objects remain motionless while we voluntarily move our eyes (when the eye movements are involuntary, the "specific past" is not a determining factor), that object size remains constant while the observer's distance from the object varies (as in approaching an object). I have a hunch that our perceptual experiences would be quite different if the situational factor were removed, that is, if we were in a state of anesthesia upon approaching an object. It is even possible that those factors which are supposed to have a "direct effect" on optical sensations, such as "limits of the visual field," "limits of subjective clearness," "gradients of subjective clearness," and "attention," may turn out to have an indirect effect brought about by *aftereffects* (in the sensory substance).

The same applies if we compare "habitual" with "nonhabitual" ways of looking at things. Although there are, for example, many ways in which we can hold our heads while inspecting a painting, we usually maintain a standard stance when we do so, that is, we stand up straight, move our eyes with moderate frequency, etc. Without realizing it, we thereby insure that the distribution of excitations on the retina of the observing eye remains approximately the same each time we look at the picture. If the picture is in color, the effect will be that certain colors will always stimulate the fovea when we look upwards, and certain other colors will always stimulate it when we look downwards. The same regularities will prevail when we look to the right or to the left. Our selective perception of geometric shapes in various

[12] A theory of sensations can have heuristic value only if it is able to explain the aftereffects which are produced by complex stimuli. Such a theory must place the emphasis not on stimuli in general but on *situation-specific* stimuli. Distinct aftereffects may occur even though the sum total of all the stimuli impinging on a retinal area average out to nothing. This happens whenever there is a preponderance of stimuli whose occurrence is limited exclusively to specific situations. *The existence of such specific "invariances" within the variability of stimulation, and their sensorial aftereffects, makes it possible to predict far-reaching aftereffects even in real life situations.*

parts of the picture will similarly vary systematically, depending, in each case, on how we hold our head. The "stability" of the areas surrounding each part of the picture will further contribute to the constancy of our percepts. But suppose we looked at the picture under less habitual conditions. Then we would immediately observe that the colors and shapes look quite different: the hues would appear more intense, the shapes less symmetrical, and slight "errors," which ordinarily we would never "see," would now be distinctly noticeable. That is why some painters use a mirror while working on a painting. The mirror serves to accentuate incongruities which otherwise would go unnoticed. Without realizing it, they are protecting themselves against "situational adaptation." Another illustration: while riding a bicycle one is completely insensitive to the effects of acceleration in normal conditions of body posture; however, as soon as one takes on an unusual posture (for example, bending the head backwards or looking at the rear axle), one immediately becomes aware of the acceleration.

Our daily lives offer countless instances where the absence of *seemingly "irrelevant" concomitant conditions* is found to alter a situation profoundly. In these circumstances, we somehow feel that things are not the way they should be; whether we know what is missing or not, we cannot rationalize this peculiar feeling away. This strongly suggests that some connection must have been formed in the deeper layers of the nervous system between isolated aspects of experience and the "familiar" situation.

Professor Erismann tells us of a peculiarly irritating feeling he once had while he was taking a walk. He traces it to the fact that he had left his cane at home that day. Not that he ever used it for locomotion. But he was in the habit of carrying it on his arm. Therefore, the missing cane was hardly an "insignificant"

object. It was so "significant," in fact, that, according to him, it spoiled his whole walk for him. Even the beautiful scenery lost its appeal that day. And all this because he did not carry a cane on his arm!

We are told that Michelangelo, after completing his work on the ceiling of the Sistine Chapel, had gotten so used to lying on his back while painting that he was unable to read a book in any other position. This too shows that *more* must have been involved than a mere change in the position of his head. The related fact that we all have difficulty reading upside-down print is again not due to any change in the geometric properties of the letters— these remain the same—but to a change in the "customary relationship" between the letters and corresponding retinal spatial values. Changes in the usual pattern of the letters further contribute to our difficulty. Just compare the upper and lower halves of a "normal" figure 8 with one that is upside down. In *normal conditions,* both parts of the figure look approximately the same, even though they actually are not. (The experience is like the one reported by subjects wearing our experimental prisms: to the left, everything looks contracted; to the right, everything looks expanded.) In *abnormal conditions,* however, the difference in size between the two parts will look surprisingly large.

I have often wondered why each half of the retina has *different standards of size.* Our prism experiments have shown that these standards are not invariant. All one needs to do in order to increase or decrease the standards is to subject one part of the retina to prolonged stimuli of increased size and another part of the retina to prolonged stimuli of reduced size. As far as I know, only one investigator, T. Lipps, has come up with an answer to that. According to Lipps, the disparity in retinal size standards is due to the fact that most of us are right-handed and tend to give precedence to objects in the right region of the visual field. Consequently, one half of the retina is usually exposed to slightly larger images. So far, little attention has been given to this fact.

A question which has not yet been answered concerns the *difference between empirical and mathematical horopters*. The difference is presumably due to an "unsymmetrical" distribution of "experiences." Since the floor and objects on it are closer than the ceiling, the distribution of stimulation on the upper half of the retina is different from that on the lower half: those on the lower half tend to be smaller, more distant.

The so-called "moon illusion" is a problem which has occupied many investigators for thousands of years. Although it has been known for some time that the perceived size of an object is little affected by whether it is seen "above" or "straight ahead," it is still not clear what the "immediate" interaction is like between these two sensations. In an extremely revealing investigation, von Allesch (1931)[13] attributes differences in size standards to the *life style* which characterizes a human being. This is undoubtedly an important step in the direction of "situational" aftereffects.

There are other factors, too, which are relevant to the moon illusion. They are usually referred to as *empirical localization motives*. But are not these exactly the kinds of "incidental conditions" which, if present, have been shown to have such profound effects on our visual experiences?

[13] Von Allesch demonstrated that lack of homogeneity in space perception is closely related to species-typical behavior. While man's orientation is horizontal, that of the lemur, with which von Allesch experimented, is vertical. Consequently, the latter experiences a different kind of size illusion. Now it seems to me that biologically determined behavior tendencies might well create their own "preferred situations," in our sense of the term. It does not seem too farfetched, therefore, to explain lack of homogeneity in terms of the situational aftereffect.

There is no end to the examples which can be given[14] to show that the presence or absence of such "conditions" is a major determinant of sensory experiences. And even if we considered all of them, there would still remain those stimulus "characteristics" which are contained in the very nature of things and thereby insure that the incidence of stimuli is *not* a random one. Consider gravity, for example; gravity not only affects our tactile sense, it also influences specific patterns and sequences of optical stimuli. Thus, since the direction of gravitational pull is downwards, it is "low" stimuli which show the highest probability of occurrence. Horizontally, on

[14] The results of our experiments have not only theoretical but also practical implications. One of these pertains to the practice of *ophthalmology*. The physician sometimes worries whether his patient will be able to get used to the disagreeable side effects of powerful spectacles. He need worry no more. In cases of strabismus, for example, where prisms are used to correct the condition, he may find it perfectly safe to prescribe much more powerful spectacles than he has ever prescribed before.

Optometry and the *manufacture of optical instruments* are further practical areas to which our results may be applied. Those engaged in these fields will want to know about the enormous capacity of the visual organ to compensate for spherical and chromatic aberrations in lenses. They may no longer find it necessary to make exact corrections on the lenses when these are being consistently worn.

Finally, *psychologists working in courts* and physicians interested in *forensic medicine* will want to know about the persistent and far-reaching traces which "ordinary" stimuli can leave in the sensorium of the individual. It may well prove to be possible to reconstruct peculiarities of the delinquent's past environment on the basis of minor abnormalities in his current sensory experiences. It should be possible, for example, to prove that someone used to wear spectacles, even though he is currently not wearing them for the purpose of disguising himself. His own eyes will give him away, because he will not be able to perceive "straight lines" when he holds his head in a certain position. The kinds of errors he makes should even make it possible to determine the kind of spectacles he used to wear. Furthermore, since aftereffects result from other peculiarities of past optical situations as well as from certain habits of long duration, all sorts of other secrets of his hidden past may be uncovered.

the other hand, the distribution is much less skewed. The same applies to movement stimuli. Every object, particularly every animate object, moves in a "characteristic" way. The fact that we have become thoroughly adapted to all this is evident as soon as we look through inverting lenses. The effect is the same as if a dog, for example, suddenly were seen to move like a horse. Only then would we become aware of how "peculiarly" horses really move. Before, we would have thought there was nothing strange about the horse.

An entirely new world has been opened to us, a world of complex stimuli interacting with a sensitive organism. We have seen that a sensory reaction is a product not only of its predecessors, its neighbors, and of residues in its own region, but of any and all the influences affecting the organism. We have discovered *one* of the laws by which at first *separated, unrelated parts are organized into a whole*, and we have done so, not in opposition to, but with the aid of, scientific methods. And this gives us a special feeling of satisfaction.

Concluding Remarks

This presentation should be regarded primarily as a factual report. It is hoped, however, that it will stimulate further work in an area which, since Stratton's pioneering days, has been largely neglected, and that it will thereby generate further knowledge of basic perceptual processes. The effort, exacting though it may be, should be well worth while. Of all the areas of psychology, this one seems most likely to shed light on our assumptions regarding our experiences and is most closely in line with contemporary natural philosophy.

In conclusion, I wish to extend my sincere thanks to Professor Rohracher for his unfailing efforts to make publication of this manuscript possible and for his many helpful editorial suggestions. I am further grateful to Professor Mayer-Hillebrand for the stimulation she and her

writings gave me, particularly her still unpublished article, "Die Tendenz zum Gleichgewicht als psychologisches Grundgesetz." I am particularly indebted to my esteemed teacher, Professor Erismann. It was through his lectures and later through working with him that I gained the background necessary for this work. Let me not neglect to add that he was generous enough to let me have my own way even when he did not completely agree with my particular approach to the experimental task.

References

ERISMANN, T. Das Werden der Wahrnehmung. *Proc. Congr. German Psychol. Assn.* Bonn, 1947, p. 54.

EWERT, P. H. A Study of the Effect of Inverted Retinal Stimulation upon Spatially Coordinated Behavior. *Genet. Psychol. Monogr.* 1930, vol. 7, no. 3/4.

GIBSON, J. J. Adaptation, After-Effect and Contrast in the Perception of Curved Lines. *J. Exp. Psychol.*, 1933, *16*, 1–31.

GIBSON, J. J. Adaptation with Negative After-Effect. *Psychol. Rev.*, 1937, *44*, 222–244.

JAENSCH, W. and C. MANDOWSKI, Die klinische Bedeutung psychischer Labilität bei optischen Wahrnehmungsvorgängen. *Med. Welt*, 1932, *6*, 1162.

KÖHLER, W. and D. DINNERSTEIN. Figural After-Effects in Kinesthesis. 1947.

KRÜGER, U. *Über die Art der Wahrnehmung eines künstlich verkehrt gemachten Gesichtfeldes.* Dissertation, 1939, Breslau Institute of Physiology. Printed by Eugen Jakubik.

ROHRACHER, H. Das "Sehen mit dem Hinterkopf" und die Orientierung in der so gesehenen Welt. *Ber. Kongr. dtsch. Ges. Psychol.*, Hamburg, 1932, *12*, 413–415.

ROHRACHER, H. Das Problem des Aufrechtsehens und die Lokalisation von oben und unten. (Unpublished ms. *a*)

ROHRACHER, H. Experimentelle Beiträge zur Lokalisation von vorn und hinten. (Unpublished ms. *b*)

SCHRÖDER, H. Über eine optische Inversion bei Betrachtung verkehrter, durch optische Vorrichtung entworfener, physischer Bilder. *Ann. Phys. Chem.*, 1958, *181*, 298–311.

SNYDER, F. W. and N. H. PRONKO, Vision with Spatial Inversion. Wichita, 1952. University of Wichita Press.

STRATTON, G. M. Some Preliminary Experiments on Vision without Inversion of the Retinal Image. *Psychol. Rev.*, 1896, 3, 611–617.

STRATTON, G. M. Vision without Inversion of the Retinal Image. *Psychol. Rev.*, 1897, 4, 341–360, 463–481.

VON ALLESCH, J. Zur nicht-euklidischen Struktur des phänomenalen Raumes. 1931.

Relations between the Central Nervous System and the Peripheral Organs*

E. VON HOLST

Max-Planck-Institut, Wilhelmshaven

The relation of the Central Nervous System (CNS) to the peripheral senses and muscular movement is an old and much discussed problem. Here we are at the heart of the physiology of behaviour, and in comparison to that which is not known, our present knowledge is very meagre and vague! Under these circumstances, our knowledge and conceptions are dependent upon the method which happens to be popular at the moment. In this field, the method which has played the greatest role consists of, first, artificially inactivating the CNS and then, through peripheral stimulation, evoking a particular response. On this basis, the CNS is often held to be only a reflex-mechanism, yet we know today that this view is one-sided. In order to be in co-ordinated activity, the CNS often needs a minimum of stimulation or loading by afferent impulses; the conception of chain-reflex-co-ordination has been recognised almost everywhere as being incorrect. Isolated, that is de-afferented, parts of the nervous system show continued electrical activity. One can therefore say that, as a rule, deafferented ganglion cells,

* *British Journal of Animal Behaviour*, 1954, vol. 2, pp. 89–94.

under otherwise normal conditions, possess "automaticity."

These facts allow us to regard the function of the peripheral senses from a new viewpoint. The classical reflex-concept assumes that the peripheral stimulus initiates the central nervous activity. Since we now know that this supposed cause is often unnecessary, it is possible to start from the CNS. We can ask the question, what effect is produced on the sensory-receptors by the motor impulses which initiate a muscular movement? Thus, we look from the opposite direction, not from the outside inward, but from the centre to periphery. You will quickly see that in this manner we shall come upon new problems and experimentally verifiable hypotheses.

In order to make myself clear, I should like first to explain a few terms. The whole of the impulses which are produced by whatever stimuli in whatever receptors I shall term *afference,* and in contradistinction to this I shall call the whole of the motor impulses *efference.* Efference can only be present when ganglion cells are active; afference, on the contrary, can have two quite different sources: first, stimuli produced by muscular activity, which I shall call *re*-afference; second, stimuli produced by external factors, which I shall call *ex*-afference. Re-afference is the necessary afferent reflexion caused by every motor impulse; ex-afference is independent of motor impulses.

Here are some examples: when I turn my eyes, the image present on the retina moves over the retina. The stimuli so produced in the optic nerve constitute a re-afference, for this is the necessary result of my eye movement. If I shake my head, a re-afference necessarily is produced by the labyrinth. If, on the other hand, I stand on a railway platform looking straight at a train when it starts to move, the moving image on the retina of my unmoving eye produces an ex-afference; likewise, when I lie in a tossing ship, the impulses of my labyrinth will constitute an ex-afference. If I shake the branch of a tree, various receptors of my skin and joints produce a re-afference, but if I place my hand on a branch shaken by the wind, the stimuli of the same receptors produce an ex-afference. We can see that this distinction has nothing to do with the difference between the so called proprio- and extero-receptors. The *same* receptor can serve both the re- and the ex-afference. The CNS, must, however, possess the ability to distinguish one from the other. This distinction is indispensable for every organism, since it must correctly perceive its environment at rest and in movement, and stimuli resulting from its own movements must not be interpreted as movements of the environment. I want to describe experiments which show how the CNS distinguishes between ex-afference and re-afference.

When one rotates a striped cylinder around a quietly sitting insect, for instance the fly Eristalis, the animal turns itself in the same sense (Figure 1a). This is a well-known optomotor-"reflex." As soon as the animal moves itself, for instance, "spontaneously" (or stimulated by a smell), one observes that it turns itself unhindered by the stripes of the stationary cylinder. We must ask ourselves why the animal at every

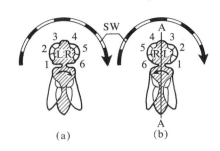

FIGURE 1   Insect (Eristalis) in striped cylinder (SW), L, R = left, right eyes; a = head in normal position, b = head in turned position.

turn is not turned back by his optomotor-"reflex," since the movement of the image on the retina is the same as in the first case, when the cylinder moved and the animal was stationary. A possible answer according to the reflex - theory is that in locomotion the optomotor-"reflex" is inhibited or "blocked." But we shall see that this answer is incorrect. It is possible, as has been shown by my colleague Mittelstaedt, to turn the head of the insect through 180° about the long axis (Figure 1b A-A); then the head is fixed to the thorax, so that the two eyes are effectively interchanged and the order of the visual elements is reversed. The unmoving animal now responds, when the cylinder turns to the right, by turning itself to the left, as is to be expected from the reversed position of the eyes. If it is indeed the case that in spontaneous (or otherwise caused) locomotion the optomotor-reflex is "blocked," the animal should move *un*hindered in the stationary cylinder. But the opposite is the case; once the insect begins to move, it spins rapidly to right or left in small circles until it is exhausted. We have observed the same behaviour with fishes, whose eyes have been turned 180° about the optic axis. But we have found this behaviour only in patterned optical surroundings; in optically homogeneous surroundings the animal moves normally. This indicates that the optomotor-"reflex" is not "blocked" in locomotion, but on the contrary, the associated re-afference plays an important role. Exactly what that role is will be made clearer by the next example.

If a vertebrate is turned over on its side by external forces, the well-known righting "reflexes" are initiated by the ex-afference of the labyrinth. But, just as in my first example, every animal is able to take up any position without righting reflexes being produced by the re-afference of the labyrinth. Again, it has been believed that the reflexes were "blocked" during position changing; and, again, we can show that this is not the case.

The righting reflexes, as is well-known, are released by the statoliths in the labyrinths, which, when the head is tilted, produce a shearing force on the underlying sensory organ, as we have found in fishes. One can increase this mechanical force which the statoliths exert on the sense organs, through the addition of a constant centrifugal force. We have built for this purpose a small revolving laboratory, capable of more than doubling the gravitational force. In this manner the statolith is made heavier, and the corresponding shearing stimuli produced by every tilting of the head are quantitatively increased. If one records the tilting of free swimming fish under these conditions, one finds that the degree of tilting becomes proportionally less, the heavier the statoliths are made. (For the method of measurement see Von Holst and Mittelstaedt, 1950). If the statoliths are removed, then the behaviour of the fish is the same under normal and centrifugal conditions. We see, therefore, that the re-afference of the labyrinth is not "blocked", but has a quantitative effect upon the *degree* of tilting, and, indeed, the greater the re-afference, the smaller the degree of the movement. One can say that the CNS "measures" the degree of movement by the magnitude of the re-afference thereby released.

Thus we have learned two facts: if the form of the re-afference is reversed, as in the first example, then the initiated movement is increased progressively. Secondly, if the re-afference keeps its normal form but is increased, as in the second example, the initiated movement is correspondingly decreased. These facts allow us to formulate a hypothesis about the mechanism here involved. We shall propose that the efference leaves an "image" of itself somewhere in the CNS, to which the re-afference of this movement compares as the negative of a photograph compares to its print; so that, when superimposed, the image disappears. Figure 2 illustrates this in a number of subsequent steps. A motor impulse, a "command" C (Figure 2a), from a higher centre HC causes a specific activation in a lower centre LC (Figure 2b), which is the stimulus-situation giving rise to a specific efference E (Figure 2c) to the effector EF (i.e. a muscle, a joint, or the whole organism). This central simulus situation, the "image" of the efference, may

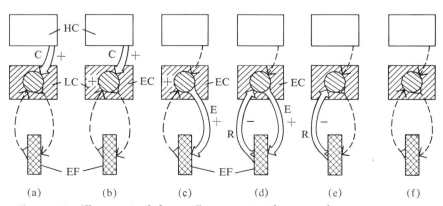

FIGURE 2   Illustration of the re-afference principle; see explanation in text.

be called "efference copy," EC. The effector, activated by the efference, produces a re-afference R, which returns to the lower centre, nullifying the efference copy by superposition (Figure 2d–f). Because of the complementary action of these two components we can arbitrarily designate the whole efferent part of this process as plus (+, dark coloured) and the afferent part as minus (—, white coloured). When the efference copy and the re-afference exactly compensate one another, nothing further happens. When, however, the afference is too small or lacking, then a + difference will remain or when the re-afference is too great, a — difference will remain. This difference will have definite effects, according to the particular organisation of the system. The difference can either influence the movement itself, or for instance, ascend to a higher centre and produce a perception.

Let us first consider the simple situation of Figure 2. The initiated movement will continue, until the re-afference exactly nullifies the efference copy. Then we must predict the following: first, if through external influence the re-afference is increased, then the initiated movement will end prematurely. We have already seen that this is the case in the fish labyrinth experiment with the centrifuge. Secondly (Figure 3a), if the re-afference is inverted, that is changed from — to +, there will be

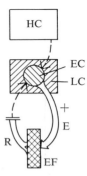

FIGURE 4   Illustration of the experiment with interrupted afference; see explanation in text.

no nullification, but summation (Figure 3b) and the movement will progressively increase, as we have already seen in the experiment with the inverted eyes[1]. Thirdly (Figure 4), in the case where the re-afference is lacking (for instance, due to the destruction of the afferent pathways) the initiated movement will not be increased, as in the second case, but will continue until something else limits it. This behaviour occurs widely and can be seen particularly well in fish without labyrinths in optically homogeneous surroundings. Every turning or tilt leads to circling or summersaulting. Also, in the human disease Tabes dorsalis, where the dorsal roots are destroyed, the well known exaggerated, ataxic movements of the limbs indicate that the same mechanism is involved. Therefore, contrary to the chain-reflex theory, the stimulus, originating with every movement, that is the re-afference, produces not an augmenting, excitatory, but a *limiting*, effect on the movement. Only those forms of locomotion, such as the swimming of fish, which do not require a constant adjustment to the surrounding medium, proceed just as before after de-afferentation. These movements are automatically co-ordinated in the CNS and therefore require no limiting re-afference (Von Holst, Lissmann).

With this simple scheme we are able to understand a number of previously un-

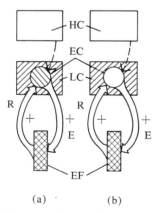

(a)   (b)

FIGURE 3   Illustration of the experiment with the eyes in turned position (Figure 1); see explanation in text.

---

[1] This is the so-called "positive feed-back."

explained types of behaviour. The most hypothetical part of this theory is the postulated efference copy: this "image" in the CNS, produced by the "command" and matched by the re-afference. I am going to present direct proof of the existence of this phenomenon. For this purpose I choose two human examples in which the difference between the efference copy and re-afference is transmitted to a higher centre and produces a perception. My first example is concerned with the already mentioned human eye movement.

A re-afference from the actively moving eye can have two sources: firstly, movement of the image across the retina and secondly, impulses from the sensory cells of the eye muscles. The former results in a conscious perception; the latter is of no importance for the following consideration. Consider my eye mechanically fixed and the muscle receptors narcotised (Figure 5a). When I want to turn my eye to the right, an efference E and, according to the theory, an efference-copy EC is produced, but the immovable eye does not produce any reafference. The efference-copy will not be nullified, but transmitted to higher centres and could produce a perception. It is possible to predict the exact form of this perception (Von Holst und Mittelstaedt, 1950). The perception, if I want to turn my eye to the right, must be that "the sur-

roundings have jumped to the right." This is indeed the case! It has been known for many years from people with paralysed eye muscles and it has been established exactly from the experiments of Kornmuller on himself that every intended but unfulfilled eye movement results in the perception of a quantitative movement of the surroundings in the same direction. Since here *nothing* happens on the afferent pathways, this false perception *can* only result from the activity, originated by the intention of the eye movement, being returned to higher centres. This is another way of saying that the unmatched efference-copy causes the perception.

Now, we make a simple experiment and turn the paralysed eye mechanically to the right (Figure 5b). In this case both the motor intention and also the efference-copy are lacking, but the image moves across the retina and afference A is transmitted, unmatched by an efference-copy, to higher centres and produces, as is known, the perception that "the surroundings move to the left." This is also a false perception. If now we combine the first case with the second, that is, if my eye is moved mechanically at the same time I intend this movement—which is the same as *voluntarily* moving a *normal* eye—then in fact these two complementary effects just mentioned are produced: firstly, the perception of the

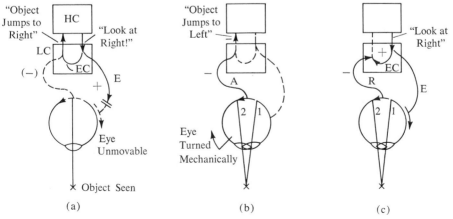

FIGURE 5   Illustration of the experiments with human eye; see explanation in text (for the letters compare the text of Figure 2).

returning "command" causing a jump of the surroundings to the right and, secondly, an image-motion on the retina producing a jump of the surroundings in the opposite direction. These two phenomena, the efference-copy and the re-afference, now compensate each other (Figure 5c); and as a result *no moving* of the surroundings is perceived. The surroundings appear stationary during this normal eye movement, and *this* perception is *physically correct*. As we have already seen, the correct perception results from two opposite and false perceptions which cancel each other. Thus, we understand a phenomenon with which Psychology has been concerned for many years, that is, the perception of the surroundings as nearly stationary during eye movements ("Raumkonstanz").

Now we come to the second example, visual accommodation. The eye is focussed for distant vision when at rest, since the elastic lens is flattened by its zonal fibres. For near-accommodation a circular muscle, working against these fibres, allows the lens to round up. We should also like to apply our theory to this system. If the accommodation apparatus is narcotised, (for instance by atropine), that is, the eye is permanently accommodated for distant vision, than an intention for near-accommodation will start a motor-impulse, which cannot be nullified by any re-afference and, therefore, must return to a higher centre, where it can produce a perception. This is indeed the case. All objects in the visual field become small, and this false perception is called "micropsia." The same phenomenon must exist with a normal eye, if we imprint an after-image of a distant cross on the retina and then look upon a near surface. Since the after-image remains the same size and sharpness on the retina, it must appear very small on the near surface, because again only the "command" for accommodation returns to the centre of perception. This is also the case, as one can easily convince oneself. These false perceptions appear, although the *peripheral stimulus-situation* is *un*altered. If, on the contrary, the *accommodation* of a normal eye is *un*altered, that is, if we look first at a small and then at a large cross at the *same* distance, then naturally the changed afference will be transmitted to the centre of perception and we see the second cross to be larger. Now we combine this last case with the first, that is, we observe with a *normal* eye a cross, moving from a distant point nearer to the eye. This initiates the accommodation-impulse, which returning, tells us "the cross is becoming smaller"; but at the same time the enlargement of the retinal image states, "the cross is becoming larger." The two cancel one another out, with the result that we perceive the cross to be of *constant* size. Again, the correct perception is the result of two opposite false perceptions; and, further, we come to an understanding of a phenomenon, long discussed in Psychology, the "Grössen Konstanz der Seh-Dinge" (Hering), which means that we see the objects to be nearly the same size irrespective of their distance from us.

I could present still further examples from man and from lower and higher animals which would show what role the re-afference plays in general in behaviour. It serves either to limit the magnitude of movement or to insure the constancy of the perceived surroundings during movement, and so makes possible the distinction between real and apparent motion of objects. The first step in both of these functional mechanisms is the comparison of the re-afference with the efference-copy.

In conclusion, permit me a few general considerations. I have attempted to show through the example of this central nervous mechanism, that it is possible in the field of the Physiology of Behaviour to avoid formulating "theories," which are only generalised descriptions of observations; rather should we follow the example of the exact sciences, namely, that a theory must exactly predict what will happen under defined conditions, so that one can by experiment verify or disprove it. Thus one avoids the error of false generalisation, which often occurs in central nervous physiology. For this reason I would like to emphasize that the principle of re-afference is only *one* of *many* central nervous mechanisms. There exists a large number of other mechanisms with other modes of function, and of these we know as yet very little. We recognise fragments of some of them and call them "reflexes"; but this term denotes fragments of very different mechanisms. I believe the whole Central-Nervous System is a "hierarchical system" of such different functional parts, a concept which you find also in Tinbergen's book "The Study of Instinct."

One final point. I have spoken of neither electrical spikes, nor nerve pathways, nor anatomical centres, in which particular functions might be localised. In the realm of behavioural analysis these things are indeed of secondary interest. The functional schemata, constructed in order to illustrate definite causal relationships, are quite abstract, although the consequences they predict are concrete and experimentally verifiable. The physiologist who fully understands such a causal system is still unable to deduce where the cell elements which perform this function are located, or how they operate. Such questions are dealt with at another level of investigation, where the electrophysiologist works and develops his own terminology. It is useful and justifiable for every level of investigation to have its own language, but we must expect, that, with a greater advancement of our knowledge, it will be easy to translate one such language into another. Until such a time, each field must develop along its own lines, unhindered by the many possibilities for misinterpretation.

References

VON HOLST, E., and E. MITTELSTAEDT (1950). *Naturwissenchaften*, 464–476.

Perceptual Adaptation to Inverted, Reversed, and Displaced Vision*

CHARLES SAMUEL HARRIS

Bell Telephone Laboratories

Recent research has shown that a simple form of adaptation to prism-produced displacement of the visual field consists primarily of a proprioceptive change—a change in the felt position of the arm seen through prisms—rather than a visual, motor, or visuomotor change. More complex sorts of adaptation (to inversion, reversal, and other optical transformations) can also be understood as resulting from changes in the felt locations of parts of the body relative to other parts. Contrary to the usual empiricist assumption, vision seems to be very stable, whereas the position sense is remarkably flexible. When the two senses provide discrepant information, it is the position sense that changes.

For over a century, psychologists have been experimenting with optical devices that displace, reverse, or invert the retinal image. When a person first puts on such a device, he misses things he reaches for and bumps into things he is trying to walk around. But after a while he adapts. He ends up behaving normally despite the optical distortion.

Typically, experimenters have accepted this adaptation as evidence for or against various theories about the origin of visual space perception in the infant. But even if one hesitates to generalize from adult behavior to infant development, adaptation to optical distortions is of interest in revealing how perceptual-motor systems work and how they can be modified.

Recently there has been much concern with the mechanisms for adapting to optical distortions and with the conditions that are necessary for such adaptation to take place. Less attention has been given to the *end product* of adaptation. What change does the adaptation procedure produce in the subject? How does the adapted subject differ from one who has not adapted?

Previous investigators have offered diverse answers to this question. For example, Kohler (1964) and Taylor (1962) believe that adaptation results in a change in visual perception. Smith and Smith (1962), on the other hand, claim that it consists mainly of learning specific motor responses. Held and Freedman (1963) say that adaptation "represents a change in state of the relevant sensorimotor control system" based on the storage of "newly correlated information" derived from "the one-to-one relation between movement and its sensory feedback."

* *Psychological Review*, 1965, vol. 72, pp. 419–444. Based in part on a doctoral dissertation submitted to the Department of Psychology, Harvard University. Preparation of this paper was supported by NIMH Grant MH-10,711 and NSF Grant GB-3546. Some of the research cited was supported by NSF and NIMH predoctral fellowships and by an NSF postdoctoral fellowship. I am grateful to Charles R. Hamilton, Judith R. Harris, Richard Held, Alice Isen, R. Duncan Luce, Jacob Nachmias, Fred Stollnitz, and Benjamin W. White for their helpful criticisms and suggestions.

This paper proposes another interpretation of adaptation: that it consists of changes in the position sense for various parts of the body. A change in position sense has been clearly demonstrated in one form of adaptation to displaced vision. The extension of this interpretation to other forms of adaptation is more speculative but seems to make sense out of a mass of otherwise perplexing data. (For summaries of earlier experimental work on adaptation see Held and Freedman, 1963; Kohler, 1964; Smith and Smith, 1962; Taylor, 1962.)

THE POSITION SENSE

Even in the dark we can perceive the relative locations of the various parts of our bodies. The sense that enables us to do this will be referred to as the *position sense*, and the perception of the position will be called a *felt position*. Changes in the position sense will be called, for want of a better adjective, *proprioceptive* changes. (The term *kinesthesis* will be restricted to the perception of movements of parts of the body.)

The position sense is a psychological phenomenon; its physiological basis has not yet been conclusively established. Receptors in the joints seem to play the major role (Rose and Mountcastle, 1960); however, efferent activity may enhance the responses of these receptors, making the position sense more accurate during active movement (Lloyd and Caldwell, 1965). The fact that monkeys can perform acts with a deafferented limb (Taub, Elman, and Berman, 1964) suggests that a "sense of innervation," registering the motor outflow to the limb, may be able to take over the functions of sensory inflow. Indeed, motor outflow seems to be the sole basis for registering the position of the eyes (Brindley and Merton, 1960; Helmholtz, 1962b; Ludvigh, 1962). If motor signals do play this role, though, the nervous system must somehow register the *positions* called for, not the *movements;* otherwise we would lose track of body parts whenever they

were moved (or kept from moving) by an outside force.

Although information registered by the position sense is usually available to introspection, we are not constantly aware of the locations of all of our body parts. And sometimes a subject's conscious perception of the positions of some body parts (especially his eyes) is vague and variable, even though there is abundant behavioral evidence that these positions are being "taken into acount" accurately. In general, the hypotheses presented in this paper apply whether the position information is conscious, potentially conscious, or not available to consciousness.

Adaptation to Displaced Retinal Images

ARM ADAPTATION

Adaptation to inversion or reversal of the visual field may take many days or even weeks. However, as Helmholtz reported in 1866, a person can adapt to sideways displacement of the visual field in just a few minutes (Helmholtz, 1962b, p. 246).

If you look through prisms that displace the apparent locations of seen objects to the right, for example, and try to reach quickly for something, you will miss it by reaching too far to the right. But after just a few more attempts, your aim will improve considerably. When the prisms are then removed, however, you will reach too far to the left. For convenience, both the improved reaching while wearing prisms and the aftereffect when they are removed will be referred to as *adaptation* (i.e., adjustment to new conditions), since they are presumably manifestations of a single underlying change. The amount of adaptation (the *adaptive shift*) is indicated by the difference between a subject's responses on pre- and postadaptation tests. (During these tests the subject must not be allowed to see his hand; otherwise, by moving it slowly and guiding it visually, he would always be able to point correctly.)

Proprioceptive Changes. If a person's eyes are closed when he first puts on displacing prisms, he is surprised when he opens his eyes and looks at his hand. Because the prisms shift its visual image, his hand does not appear to be where he felt it was. If the discrepancy between the seen and felt locations of the hand is to be eliminated, either the person's visual perception or his position sense (or both) must shift.

According to the proprioceptive-change hypothesis, the subject comes to feel that his arm is where he saw it through prisms—even though this makes that arm's position sense erroneous (nonveridical). That is, after such a change, the subject's judgment of that arm's position relative to any other part of the body will be incorrect. If the prisms are removed and the subject tries (without seeing his hand) to reach for a target that he sees in a certain place, he will move his hand until he feels that it is in that place—but it will actually be off to one side of it. The same thing will happen if he tries to point at a sound or simply to point straight ahead. Only when judging the whereabouts of his hand relative to objects seen through prisms will he be accurate.

It is not clear a priori whether a proprioceptive shift would make a subject misperceive arm positions other than those he saw while adapting. Since neurons in the proprioceptive system have rather large receptive angles (Mountcastle, Poggio, and Werner, 1963), a change in the operating level of proprioceptive neurons in the central nervous system might exert an effect over a wide range of arm positions. At any rate, the presence or absence of such a shift should depend mainly on the actual position of the arm, not on the movements by which the position was reached.

Other Interpretations. Five other simple, plausible conceptions of the nature of adaptation can also account for the rapid improvement in reaching for objects seen

through prisms. Each, however, suggests a different set of predictions about other behavior. These five conceptions, which are often implicit rather than explicit in previous investigators' writings, have been presented in greater detail elsewhere (Harris, 1963a). They are described briefly below, together with some of their predictions about a subject who adapts by pointing with one arm, using a stereotyped arm movement, at a single target seen through prisms.

1. *Conscious correction of one's aim.* When the subject misses the target, he realizes that the prisms are deceiving him about the target's location and so deliberately aims to one side of visual targets; when the prisms are removed, he goes back to pointing normally.

2. *Altered visual perception.* A changed translation from retinal image to perception makes a target which at first looked off to the side appear to be straight ahead. This new perception can be demonstrated by any appropriate judgment of, or response to, a visual target seen with or without prisms.

3. *Reorientation of the perceptual frame of reference.* Perception of all external stimuli, visual or auditory, is shifted to one side; perception of the arms, however, is unaffected (if perception of the arm shifted too, the subject would show no adaptive shift in pointing at targets).

4. *Visuomotor recorrelation.* Visual perception does not change, but a given visual input is paired with a different motor output. Since only the visuomotor system used during adaptation is altered, the unexposed arm and all nonvisual targets are unaffected.

5. *Motor-response learning.* The practiced arm acquires a new motor response to stimuli from a given

spatial location regardless of their modality. There is a generalization decrement when the subject uses arm movements that differ from the practiced one.

Table 1 summarizes the predictions of the proprioceptive-change hypothesis and the other five conceptions. Several other, more sophisticated theories are discussed briefly at the end of this paper. Unfor-

TABLE 1

Test Performance Predicted by Six Interpretations of Adaptation to Displaced Vision

TEST TASK	PROPRIOCEPTIVE CHANGE IN THE ARM	CONSCIOUS CORRECTION	VISUAL PERCEPTION	FRAME OF REFERENCE	VISUOMOTOR RECORRELATION	MOTOR LEARNING
Same as during adaptation[a]	+	+	+	+	+	+
Pointing at visual target without prisms	+		+	+	+	+
Pointing at visual target with unexposed hand		+	+	+		?
Verbal judgment of location of visual target		?	+	+		
Pointing at auditory target[b]	+			+		+
Verbal judgment of location of auditory target[b]				+		
Pointing straight ahead[b]	+					+
Pointing at visual target with different arm movements	+	+	+	+	?	
Pointing at visual targets in different locations	?	+	+	+	?	
Judgment of distance between hands[b]	+					
Judgment of location of passively moved adapted arm relative to visual target	+	+	+	+		
Pointing with adapted hand at unexposed hand[b]	+					+
Pointing with unexposed hand at adapted hand[b]	+					

Note.—The subject adapts by pointing with one arm, using a stereotyped arm movement, at a single target seen through prisms. A + indicates the prediction of an adaptive shift as large as that obtained with the task used during adaptation.

a Except that (as with all the other tests) the subject cannot see his hand and receives no information about his accuracy.

b While blindfolded.

tunately, these theories often make equivocal predictions, or none whatever, about many of the tests listed in Table 1.

Experimental Findings. Harris (1963a, 1963b) carried out six of the tests listed in Table 1. The subjects, whose heads were held stationary by a bite board, adapted by pointing for 3 minutes at a visual target seen through prisms that displaced its image 11° to the right or left. Adaptation was found to produce sizable and significant adaptive shifts, which were virtually identical whether measured by pointing at visual targets, at auditory targets, or "straight ahead." The shift was no smaller when subjects pointed at targets several inches from the one they had practiced on, even though the arm movements used then differed from the practiced one. However, adaptation had little or no effect on pointing with the unexposed hand. Nor did it affect judgments of whether a given auditory target sounded straight ahead. (Hein and Held, 1960, had previously reported that, with a similar adaptation procedure, there was no change in judged location of visual targets.) Others have independently demonstrated the adaptive shifts with auditory test targets and with pointing straight ahead (Pick, Hay and Pabst, 1963) and the absence of any shift in pointing with the unexposed hand (H. B. Cohen, 1963; Hamilton, 1964a; Mikaelian, 1963; Scholl, 1926). Subsequent studies have also confirmed these three findings (Goldstein[1]; Hay and Pick, in press; McLaughlin and Bower, 1965; McLaughlin and Rifkin, 1965).

On the basis of these results, five of the notions listed in Table 1 may be ruled out. The data can be accounted for only by the first interpretation: that adaptation consists of a change in the felt position of the adapted arm relative to the rest of the body.

Further Tests. The proprioceptive-change interpretation implies that a subject should make errors in judging how far his adapted hand is from other parts of his body—for example, his other hand. This prediction was tested by having subjects (who had adapted their right arms by pointing at a target seen through prisms) move their unexposed hands to specified subjective distances from their adapted hands while blindfolded (Harris, 1963a). After seeing their right hands shifted to the right by base-left prisms, subjects felt their hands to be farther apart, at a given physical distance, than when their hands were not adapted. Subjects who wore base-right prisms felt their hands to be closer together. These results demonstrate that there is in fact a change in the felt location of the adapted hand relative to the other hand.

During these tests, the subject was not allowed to make any active movements motor-learning or conditioned-response with his adapted arm. Thus, a simple theory of adaptation is inadequate: Although self-produced movements may be an essential precondition for adaptation, they are not a necessary part of the end product. The adaptive shift is evident whether the subject actively points at a target during the test or a luminous target is moved until he says it is right over his stationary hand (Hamilton and Hillyard[2]). A change in the position sense will indeed *affect* motor responses of the adapted arm, but the change does not itself *consist* of newly acquired motor habits. On the contrary, it is a *perceptual change* (in the felt position of the adapted arm).

The most direct evidence for the hypothesized change in position sense is obtained when the subject points with his unexposed arm (which points correctly at all other targets) at his stationary adapted arm. Harris' (1964) results fell just short of significance, but more recently Efsta-

---

[1] Donald Goldstein, personal communication, June 1964.

[2] Charles R. Hamilton and S. A. Hillyard, personal communication, August 1964.

thiou and Held (1964) and Goldstein[3] have found large and significant shifts on this test, as well as on pointing with the adapted hand at the unexposed hand. Both findings were anticipated by Scholl (1926).

Related Findings. Several other recent studies fit in well with the proprioceptive-change hypothesis. Bossom and Hamilton (1963) and Hamilton (1964b) found that adaptation to displaced vision—in contrast to visual discrimination learning—shows complete interocular transfer and no intermanual transfer in split-brain monkeys; the adaptation is specific to the arm, not the eye. Nielsen (1963), Hay, Pick, and Ikeda (1965), Rock and Victor (1964), and Wertheimer and Arena (1959) have demonstrated that vision may immediately and completely dominate the position sense when the two disagree, a finding analogous to the smaller but longer lasting adaptive shifts discussed above.

All in all, it seems reasonable to conclude that, when a person watches one hand through prisms with little head movement, the adaptation is mainly a change in the felt position of that arm relative to the rest of his body. Although their own data did not rule out all alternative hypotheses, other investigators have independently, at about the same time, reached similar conclusions: that such adaptation takes place in the "kinesthetic spatial system" (Hochberg, 1963; Pick et al., 1963) or, more specifically, in the adapted arm's position sense (Hamilton, 1964a, 1964b). A similar hypothesis was proposed earlier by Scholl (1926).

HEAD-BODY ADAPTATION

Another way to adapt to displaced vi-

[3] It is convenient to think of arm adaptation as a change in the felt position of the adapted arm, with that of the rest of the body remaining unchanged. However, the same phenomena would be observed if the perception of the arm stayed the same and that of all of the rest of the body changed. Strictly speaking, we can detect only a changed relationship between the two. This is even clearer in the case of head-body adaptation.

sion is simply to walk around while wearing prisms (Hay and Pick, in press; Held and Bossom, 1961; Kohler, 1951, 1964; Taylor, 1962). The results are quite different from those of arm adaptation. When presented with a visual target after the prisms are removed, the subject points incorrectly with *both* arms, even if he saw neither one through prisms (Bossom and Held, 1957), and says the target *looks* straight ahead of him when it is actually somewhat off to one side (Held and Bossom, 1961; Kohler, 1964).

Is this type of adaptation, then, completely unlike arm adaptation? Probably not. Just as the felt relationship between arm and body is altered by moving the arm while wearing prisms, so perhaps the felt relationship between head and body is altered by moving the head while wearing prisms.[4] The three investigators who independently proposed this hypothesis—Hamilton (1964a), Harris (1963a, 1963c), and Mittelstaedt (1964)—were unaware that Kohler (1951, p. 23) had already observed just such a phenomenon: A subject who wore prisms developed the "habit" of holding his head turned 6°–9° to the right of his body midline but was "completely unaware of the deviation.[4] He felt that his head was pointing straight ahead.

It is the unawareness, not the turning, that is crucial. Contrary to Smith and

[4] "*Als Prismenträger ist man ständig gezwungen, Auge und Kopf gegenüber der Greifrichtung etwas verdreht zu halten. Und in der Tat liess sich als Nachwirkung dieser aufgezwungenen 'Lebensgewohnheit' eine merkbare Verdrehung zwischen Kopf und Rumpf nachweisen, welche aber der Aufmerksamkeit der Vp. vollkommen entging. Sie meinte gerade und unverdreht zu stehen, während sie in Wirklichkeit den Kopf nach rechts gedreht hielt (6–9 Grad von der Köpermediane abweichend). Korrigierte man aber die Rechtslage des Kopfes, so entstand im Erleben der Vp. der Eindruck einer Linksverdrehung [cf. Kohler, 1964, p. 38].*"

The Fiss and Gleitman translation (Kohler, 1964) differs, in many places, from the German papers on which it is based (Kohler, 1951, 1953). Though usually slight, the discrepancies are sometimes misleading at crucial points. Therefore, the present writer's translations are occasionally given instead.

Smith's claim (1962, pp. 92, 116–117), a "compensatory reaction" of turning the head cannot in itself counteract the prism-produced visual displacement: The perceived location of an object (relative to one's body) does not normally change when one turns one's head, because the new position of the head is taken into account. Perception of the object changes only if a subject misperceives the orientation of his head.

Whereas misperception of just one arm affects only tests that involve that arm, virtually any test will show the effects of misperceived head orientation. If a subject feels his head to be pointing straight ahead of his body when it is really somewhat turned, then when he sees an object directly in front of his nose he will incorrectly (if he is not wearing prisms) perceive that object to be straight ahead of his body. If he tries to point at it with either hand, he will point straight ahead of his body and thus point incorrectly. (Such misperception of head position would, of course, lead to improved accuracy of performance while the prisms are on.) Similar results will occur even if the test apparatus constrains the subject to hold his head straight relative to his body, as in Held and Bossom's (1961) procedure. When Kohler forced his subject to point his head straight ahead, the subject felt that it was turned several degrees to the left (1951, pp. 23–24).

A change in the felt relationship between head and body necessarily entails a change in the perceived direction of visual targets relative to the body. But it would be inaccurate to describe such adaptation as solely a change in visual perception, since, for example, altered perception of head orientation would also result in altered auditory localization.

Intermanual Transfer. A number of investigators have found that if a subject watches one hand through prisms, with little head movement, the adaptation is completely or almost completely confined

to the exposed hand. Helmholtz (1962a, p. 157), however, reported considerable adaptation of the unexposed hand as well. How can these findings be reconciled?

A plausible answer was suggested independently by Hamilton (1964b) and Harris (1963a, 1963c). They both noted (as did H. B. Cohen, 1963) that subjects whose heads were immobilized while they adapted showed little intermanual transfer, whereas those who were free to move their heads, as Helmholtz was, exhibited considerable transfer to the unexposed hand. Hamilton and Harris concluded that moving the head while wearing prisms leads to a change in the felt position of the head relative to the body, which would make the subject mispoint with both hands even if he never saw them through prisms. If he did see one arm through prisms, he would show a larger aftereffect with that arm than with the unexposed arm (since, in addition to the error caused by misperceiving the orientation of his head, there would also be a misperception of the exposed arm's orientation), thus manifesting "partial intermanual transfer."

If this analysis is correct, the term intermanual transfer is, in this context, something of a misnomer. Transfer implies that the adaptive change in one arm (or relevant parts of the nervous system) somehow spreads to or induces a similar change in the other arm (or contralateral part of the nervous system). Although this possibility has not been definitely ruled out (as Hamilton, 1964b, noted), it is simpler to assume that the measured adaptation in the unexposed arm results wholly from head-body adaptation, which affects both arms equally, and that there is in addition some arm adaptation of the exposed arm.

Wooster's Experiment. The concept of altered position sense of the head removes much of the mystery from a phenomenon reported by Wooster (1923). Her subjects reached beneath an opaque board to point at targets that were visible, through prisms, above the board. Surprisingly, even subjects who never saw their hands through prisms and so had no "knowledge of error" gradually became more accurate. Wooster considered a number of possible reasons for the improvement, tested them in further experiments, and found that none fitted all of her data.

Although Wooster's subjects did not walk around while wearing prisms, they were free to move their heads and so could have undergone head-body adaptation. Had Wooster tested the unpracticed arm, she might have been even more surprised to find that it had improved just as much as the practiced one.

A change in the proprioceptively perceived relationship between head and body could also account for many of the findings reported by Wallach, Kravitz, and Lindauer (1963), by Bossom (1964), and by McLaughlin and Rifkin (1965), as well as for the aftereffects of the incidental vertical displacements produced by Stratton's (1897, p. 471) and Kohler's (1964, p. 32) inverting goggles.

EYE-HEAD ADAPTATION

All of the phenomena ascribed above to head-body adaptation (except for Kohler's direct observation of a change in felt head position) might equally well be due to a change in the registered relationship between the eyes and the head (Harris, 1963a)—a modification of the "judgment of the direction of the gaze," as Helmholtz (1962b, p. 246) put it. Indeed, Kohler (1964, p. 32) says that in his experiments alterations in "kinesthetic sensations" from the eyes were often encountered.

Unlike head-body adaptation, eye-head adaptation would not affect auditory localization. Thus, a subject who misperceived the orientation of his eyes should misperceive the location of a visual target relative to that of a sound from an unseen source (Harris, 1963a). Recent studies have demonstrated just such an auditory-visual mismatch. After certain adaptation procedures, a subject errs in judging where

on a luminous visual scale a sound is coming from (Hay and Pick, in press; Wallach and Bernheim[5]). He points in one direction at a light and in another at a sound which is actually in the same place (Hay and Pick, in press; McLaughlin and Bower, 1965).

These and other findings reported by Hay and Pick (in press), McLaughlin and Rifkin (1965), and McLaughlin and Bower (1965), as they acknowledge in their later papers, are all attributable to a change in registered eye position plus a change in the exposed arm's position sense, with the amounts of the two changes varying during the course of adaptation.[6]

Because incorrect registration of eye position would entail incorrect localization of all seen objects, one can say that eye-head adaptation alters visual perception. But this alteration is fundamentally different from purely visual modifications such as dark adaptation and localized figural aftereffects. It is more akin to altered position sense in the arm or head. Thus it seems inadvisable to make a sharp distinction between "proprioceptive adaptation" (of the arm) and "visual adaptation." Such a distinction might, for example, lead to a fruitless search for modifications in the pathways connecting the retina to the visual cortex.

Half Prisms. Prisms that cover only the upper half of the eye displace the upper half of the visual field relative to the lower half, making a straight vertical line look discontinuous. Kohler (1964) reported that subjects who adapt to half prisms say that the line eventually looks straight and unbroken most of the time despite the discontinuous retinal image.

Although this adaptation sounds like a purely visual change—a change in perceived relationships *within* the visual field

[5] Hans Wallach and Joseph Bernheim, personal communication, December 1963.

[6] Part of the shift that Hay and Pick (in press) attributed to arm adaptation may actually be due to head-body adaptation; Hay and Pick's tests do not distinguish between the two.

—Kohler's other observations indicate otherwise. When an adapted subject was asked to move his eyes straight up and down in the dark, Kohler says, the subject actually moved them in a jagged line, with a sideways jump approximately in the middle of the movement (*"einen seitlichen Sprung ungefähr in der Mitte der Bewegung"*— Kohler, 1951, p. 73; cf. 1964, p. 93). With more rapid eye movements, the path became diagonal. But the subject "always thought that his eyes moved vertically and without sudden deflections [1964, p. 94]." Apparently, the subject perceived a broken line as straight only because he felt that the jagged eye movement he made in scanning it was straight. What happened when the subject *fixated* the dividing line between the prism and nonprism areas? Kohler (1964, p. 83) says explicitly that, when fixated, vertical lines looked just as discontinuous after many days of adaptation as they had at first. Clearly, there was no change in the purely "pictorial" aspect of visual perception, but only in those perceptions of visual location that depend on the registration of positions and movements of the eyes. Note that the adaptation did not entail any change in scanning *behavior:* When scanning the discontinuous line, the subject made essentially the same eye movements after adapting as he had before. The only change was that a jagged eye movement was interpreted as straight. This is a perceptual change, not the acquisition of new motor responses.

Curvature. Straight vertical lines look curved when viewed through a sideways-displacing prism because the prism displaces the top and bottom of the visual field more than the middle. The curvature is a set of relative displacements of the same sort as produced by a half prism. So perhaps adaptation to curvature also involves altered registration of eye movements without any change in scanning behavior. After adapting, the subject may feel that his eyes are moving in a straight

line when they are actually tracing out a curve.[7] Perhaps the "unstable aftereffect" experienced by one of Kohler's subjects ("straight objects—for example, long and heavy steel pipes—curved and straightened out while the amazed subject was in the very act of looking at them"—1964, pp. 37–38) was due to alternate scanning and fixation.

An analogous case of curvature adaptation, resulting from altered kinesthetic perception of movements of the arm, was recently studied in collaboration with Judith R. Harris (Harris, 1964). Subjects moved one hand back and forth along a horizontal straight line while looking through prisms that made the line look curved upwards or downwards. Before this practice and again afterwards, they were asked to draw straight horizontal lines while blindfolded. The prediction was that if a subject ran his hand along a straight line that looked curved upward, for example, a straight horizontal arm movement would come to *feel* curved upward, so the subject would compensate and draw a *downward* curve in order to feel that his arm was moving in a straight line. A significant shift, in the predicted direction, was found. Note that this shift cannot be due to an intermodal figural aftereffect, because the shift is in the wrong direction; it cannot be motor learning, because the arm movements made during practice were actually straight.

Adaptation to Inverted Retinal Images

Is a proprioceptive-change interpretation appropriate when subjects adapt to optical transformations more drastic than displacement? Stratton's (1896, 1897) re-

[7] This idea was developed in conversations with Julian Hochberg. Experiments by M. M. Cohen (1963) and Held and Rekosh (1963) suggest that there are at least two kinds of curve adaptation; the registered eye-movement explanation applies to only one kind.

ports on his adaptation to "reinversion" of the retinal image indicate that the answer is yes.

STRATTON'S EXPERIMENTS

Proprioceptive Changes. Stratton's reports are indeed difficult to comprehend—at times they sound bizarre, at times, self-contradictory. But it is clear that Stratton experienced proprioceptive changes similar to those considered above, though far more extensive and less stable.

When he first looked through inverting lenses, Stratton (1896) says,

> . . . the parts of my body were *felt* to lie where they would have appeared had the instrument been removed; they were *seen* to be in another position. But the older tactual . . . localization was still the *real* localization [p. 614].

Soon, however,

> . . . the limbs began actually to feel in the place where the new visual perception reported them to be. . . . The seen images thus became *real things* just as in normal sight. I could at length *feel* my feet strike against the *seen* floor, although the floor was seen on the opposite side of the field of vision from that to which at the beginning of the experiment I had referred these tactual sensations. I could likewise at times feel that my arms lay between my head and this new position of the feet; shoulders and head, however, which under the circumstances could never be directly seen, kept the old localization they had had in normal vision, in spite of the logical difficulty that the shape of the body and the localization of hands and feet just mentioned made such a localization of the shoulders absurd [p. 615].

Proprioceptive changes such as these account for the behavioral aspects of Stratton's adjustment to inverted vision.[8] If the felt locations and movements of his hands and feet came to agree with their seen lo-

cations and movements, he would have no trouble reaching for or kicking things, whereas before adapting he had to move the limb in a direction that felt wrong. When the new proprioceptive perceptions became stable enough to persist even when the limb was out of sight, responses with that limb would be completely normal with no need for conscious deliberation.

These proprioceptive changes also explain Stratton's feeling that he had achieved a "reharmonization" of touch and sight: Whenever he touched an object with an adapted limb, he felt it to be where he saw it, because he felt the limb to be in a new location that agreed with its visual location.

Upright Vision. Stratton was not primarily interested in behavioral adjustments nor in proprioceptive or intersensory alterations. He wanted to find out whether the usual (inverted) orientation of the retinal image is necessary for seeing things as upright. If so, Stratton (1896) said, "It is certainly difficult to understand how the scene as a whole could even temporarily have appeared upright when the retinal image was *not* inverted [p. 616]." Yet, he claimed, this was precisely what happened. After several days of adaptation, the world seen through inverting lenses sometimes appeared to be "in normal position" (1896, p. 616), "right side up" (1897, pp. 358, 469), "rather upright than inverted" (1897, p. 354). Some psychologists have taken these statements as conclusive evidence of a change in Stratton's visual system. Others have maintained that Stratton's assertions mean nothing at all. Walls (1951), for example, insisted that Stratton's descriptions of the scene as "upright" were "entirely metaphorical" (p. 191) and that actually all that Stratton achieved was a harmony between current perceptions and inverted eidetic imagery of objects outside the field of view (p. 200).

Stratton himself, on the other hand, thought it was quite natural for things to

---

[8] Since Stratton's lens system rotated the retinal image through 180°, he actually adapted both to inversion and to reversal. Kohler's (1951, 1964) experiments, using mirrors that inverted the retinal image without reversing it, generally support Stratton's observations.

come to look upright again since he believed that "harmony between touch and sight, . . . in the final analysis, is the real meaning of upright vision [1897, p. 457]." But although "harmony between touch and sight" might indeed make the perceived orientation of the body and of the seen world agree, both body and world might still be perceived as *inverted* rather than upright. Perceived uprightness must depend on some other factor. That factor, as many investigators have pointed out, is the sensations of pressure and tension in the feet, legs, and body produced by the pull of gravity. Recently, experiments on subjects with labyrinthine defects led Clark and Graybiel (1963) to suggest that such pressure cues, rather than labyrinthine cues, may in fact be the major determinants of the perceived direction of gravity. Under zero-gravity conditions, for instance, subjects perceive the direction of the surface that their feet are touching as downward (Simons, 1959).

When Stratton first put on inverting lenses, he felt gravity pulling *away* from the seen location of the floor; "the general feeling was that the seen room was upside down; the body of the observer . . . was felt as standard and as having an upright position [1897, p. 348]." But gradually he began to feel that his feet, then his legs and arms, then most of his body were all in "the place where the new visual perception reported them to be [1896, p. 615]." The new proprioceptive localization was not stable—sometimes he even seemed to feel his limbs in both the normal and the new locations at once (1897, pp. 345–346, 465)—but when his legs and body were clearly felt to be in the new place, so, of necessity, were the gravitational pulls. Because the direction of the pull of gravity is, by definition, *down,* objects seen to lie in the same direction from the head as the legs were felt to be were perceived as down. So the floor looked "down," making the room look "right side up."

Since Stratton's head and shoulders "kept the old localization they had had in normal vision," he should then have felt that his legs and body were not on the same sides of his eyes as his chin and shoulders. In other words, his head should have felt inverted! This is evidently just what happened:

> Outer objects . . . frequently seemed to be in normal position, and whatever there was of abnormality seemed to lie in myself, as if head and shoulders were inverted and I were viewing objects from that position, as boys sometimes do from between their legs [1896, p. 616].[9]

Stratton's simile conveys exactly the sense in which things seen through inverting lenses looked upright. They did *not* look the same as they did before the goggles were put on. Rather, they looked upright relative to the felt direction of gravity, the way things look when seen from between the legs. If you set a book upright on the floor and look at it from between your legs, you will see the bottom of the book as "down" and the top as "up." You will see the pointed part of a capital A above the open part. In this sense, everything will look upright. And yet, you will have trouble reading the book —the letters will look rather like upsidedown print.

KOHLER'S EXPERIMENTS

Kohler's accounts (1951, 1964) of adaptation to inversion help clarify the role of gravitational pulls on proprioceptively adapted body parts. When a partly adapted subject, who still saw the world as inverted, took hold of a string with a weight attached to the other end, he suddenly *saw* the weight as hanging from the the string instead of floating upward like a balloon. The explanation may be that the hands and arms are often the first parts

---

[9] "At other times," Stratton (1896) noted, "the inversion seemed confined to the face or eyes alone [p. 616]."

of the body to adapt (Taylor, 1962). So, when the weight pulled on the subject's arm and attracted his attention to it, he felt it pulling toward where he saw the floor and therefore perceived that direction as "down."

Several writers (e.g., Klein, 1960, p. 103) have assumed that gravitational cues provide a direct access to reality—a veridical standard to which visual perception, when shown the error of its ways, conforms. According to the present interpretation, however, gravitational cues will make the inverted scene look upright only if they are felt by some proprioceptively adapted body part. Prominent gravitational cues in an *unadapted* area (produced, for instance, by a weight hanging from the subject's chin) might make the scene look even more clearly inverted.

If we assume that the adaptive change is in the felt direction of gravity, not in the visual system, we can make sense of Kohler's (1964) report that one subject, who had been wearing inverting goggles for several days, said that "two adjacent heads, one upright, the other inverted, were *both* perceived as upright [p. 32]." Apparently, one head (the physically erect one) looked upright in that its chin was seen below its forehead; the other one (normally oriented on the retina) looked more natural, more recognizable as a normal face.

ILLUSORY MOVEMENTS OF THE VISUAL FIELD

Ordinarily, when you move your head downward, objects enter your field of view from below and travel to the top. If you perceive the external world as stationary. If you move your head downward while wearing inverting goggles, though, objects enter the visual field from the top and travel downward. As a result, the world appears to be moving rapidly downward. (With reversing goggles, sideways movements produce a similar illusion.) After a few days the

illusory swinging diminishes, until eventually the world appears stationary during head movements (Kohler, 1964; Stratton, 1897; Taylor, 1962).

This sort of adaptation may also be more closely related to proprioceptive arm adaptation than to purely intravisual phenomena. Stratton (1897, p. 58) noted that he saw the world as stationary only when he misperceived the direction in which *he* was moving: "Movements of the head or of the body . . . seemed to be toward that side on which objects entered the visual field, and not toward the opposite side," as they had felt when he first put on inverting lenses. This sounds like a kinesthetic change, which would stabilize visual perception without any change in the neural mechanism that normally takes head movements into account to yield a stationary visual world; only the felt movement of the head, the input to this mechanism, changes.

Adaptation to Reversed Retinal Images

Kohler (1953, 1964) has described in detail how subjects who wear right-angle prisms, which reverse their retinal images right for left, eventually achieve normal behavior and what he calls "correct seeing" (1964, p. 140). At first reading, his account is as bewildering as Stratton's.

"PIECEMEAL" ADAPTATION

When a person puts on reversing prisms, Kohler says, he initially reaches in the wrong direction for things, makes wrong turns, and sees all writing as mirror writing. In attempting to cope with reversed vision, the subject tries out various tactics, such as deliberately heading left when his goal appears to be on his right. As the subject adapts behaviorally, during the course of several weeks, he becomes able to walk, reach, and turn correctly without resorting to such "tricks." Concurrently, Kohler claims, his visual perception changes in a peculiar piecemeal fashion: Some parts of the visual field are perceived correctly while other parts remain reversed. For example, after 18 days:

> Inscriptions on buildings, or advertisements, were still seen in mirror writing, but the objects containing them were seen in the correct location. Vehicles driving on the "right" . . . carried license numbers in mirror writing . . . the subject is capable of localizing both sides of, say, a "3" correctly (open to the left, the curves to the right) and still see it mirrorwise [1964, p. 155]!

At this stage, even though the subject's spontaneous behavior is usually correct, he often becomes confused and makes "errors" when asked to attend to his "immediate visual experience."

After many weeks, Kohler says, the subject's behavior and vision are both reoriented. He achieves "almost completely correct impressions, even where letters and numbers were involved [1964, p. 160]."

When one thinks of adaptation as a change in visual perception, these observations are incomprehensible. How can vision ever be partly right way round, partly reversed?

DETERMINANTS OF JUDGMENTS

In attempting to make sense of Kohler's puzzling observations, it is helpful to bear in mind four different determinants of what a subject says when the experimenter tries to find out whether he sees things right way round. The first two determinants are distinguishable aspects of perception, whereas the other two are essentially irrelevant to spatial perception. Doubtless, people differ in which of these factors enter into their judgments in a given situation, and a given person may judge differently at different times. But it is often possible to find out operationally which factors the subject's report is based on and to design experiments that avoid the ambiguities of previous reports.

1. *Directional perception.* When asked "Does that object appear to be on your right or on your left?," many people probably make a directional judgment relative to their dominant hand. If the object is seen to lie on the same side of the body as the right hand, the subject says: "It's on my right" or "on my right-hand side." The same kind of judgment can be elicited whether or not the words right and left are used, whether or not the subject has a dominant hand, and whether or not he refers the judgment to his hand: The experimenter can simply touch any spot on the subject's body and ask whether an object appears to be on the same side of his body as the touched spot.

Such a judgment is based on one aspect of spatial perception—perception of the location of an object relative to some part of the body. This is the sort of perception that usually guides motor behavior such as reaching for an object or walking toward it (cf. the concept of "manipulable regions," Kohler, 1964, p. 163).

2. *Pictorial perception.* Most of the debate on adaptation to distorted vision has concerned this aspect of visual perception, though it has not been clearly differentiated from other determinants of subject's judgments. Pictorial perception consists of "looking at" the "picture" received by the visual system (cf. Gibson's, 1950, concept of "the visual field"). It is most obvious in successive comparisons: For example, we can ask a subject whether an arrow he is looking at is pointing the same way as the locomotive in a painting he saw before the experiment began.

The perception of "clockwise" or "counterclockwise" motion and "east" or "west" on a map are probably pictorial perceptions for most people, based on purely visual memories.

Thus, to test for changes in pictorial perception, we can keep a subject from seeing any clocks or maps during the experiment and then ask him whether something appears to be moving clockwise or counterclockwise, or whether it is on the same side as the 9 on a clock or the east coast on a map. As long as the subject has a visual image of a clock or a map, he need not even think about the labels "right" and "left," nor about any part of his body, when making his judgment. (Occasionally a subject may make a directional judgment when asked to make a pictorial one—for example, if he remembers that the locomotive in the painting was "going toward my right"—that is, toward his right hand. But such exceptions have no theoretical importance once recognized for what they are.) Even when he uses the terms right and left, which are often characteristic of directional judgments, the subject may be making a pictorial judgment: Some people habitually think of a certain part of the visual field as "the lower left corner" without referring at all to any part of the body.

3. *Familiarity.* A subject often describes his first perceptions through reversing goggles as "strange," "unusual," "unfamiliar," "new," or "mirror imaged." Later he describes them as "normal," "natural," "all right," "usual," "familiar," "right way round" (see Kohler, 1964, p. 142). Such descriptions are based almost entirely on past experience with particular stimuli or classes of stimuli and can be changed through repeated visual observation, even without distorting spectacles. For example, a person (perhaps an apprentice typesetter) who practices reading mirror writing may soon say that it is beginning to look "natural" or "all right." But neither his directional nor his pictorial

perception has changed. If asked to judge the location of part of a letter (relative to part of the body or to visual memories), a person gives the same answer whether the letter looks "familiar" or "strange."

4. *Labels.* It is risky to let a subject use the words right and left. First, the same word may be used to label two quite different sorts of perception, pictorial and directional. Second, a subject wearing reversing prisms could decide to start calling everything right that he formerly called left, even if he had not adapted at all. And third, he may be inconsistent or hesitant about which word to use even when his perception is completely determinate, stable, and clearcut; as Kohler (1964) put it, "there are people who always have trouble when asked to tell quickly where right or left is, but who never have difficulty in reaching for seen objects [p. 153]." Labels like right and left do not affect perception; it is irrelevant that the subject has learned to call a certain direction left and another direction right.[10]

PROPRIOCEPTIVE CHANGES

With these distinctions in mind, it is possible to reexamine Kohler's observations and conclude that adaptation to reversed vision can be ascribed to a radical change in the felt location of the arms, legs, and body relative to the head and eyes, without any change in pictorial visual perception.

Kohler (1953, p. 110; cf. 1964, p. 153),

[10] Terms like "upright" and "inverted" are even more ambiguous. Saying that an object looks upright may mean that it appears to be in its usual position, that it looks the same as it did before inverting goggles were put on, that it looks the same as it feels, that its top is perceived to be pointing away from the direction of gravitational pulls, that its bottom appears to be near where one's feet are, or that it is oriented appropriately to the rest of the visual scene.

in fact, did observe some proprioceptive and kinesthetic changes during the course of adaptation to reversal. After several days of wearing the goggles, he reported, there was:

> . . . a weakening of the right-left orientation of the body image, which becomes uncertain, especially in connection with movements that have been deliberately practiced in reverse. The subject may even turn left, with full confidence, when he does a "right face" with his eyes closed. When he moves his head and hands, the kinesthetic position- and movement-sensations are completely in accord with the (reversed) visual field. Yet ultimately this leads to a "dead end" (two errors that cancel each other!).[11]

In a footnote, Kohler added:

> . . . by touch, doors, for example, seem to open in a reversed direction (as compared with earlier), as if they had been turned around in the meantime. However, the pre-experimental "right-left" of the body image remains unchanged in the shoulder and upper-arm region, and from there it undertakes its new conquest. When the attention is concentrated on this region, there is almost never any error.[12]

Clearly, Kohler regarded these kinesthetic and proprioceptive changes as

temporary aberrations of no theoretical importance, leading only to a "dead end." Since proprioception and vision were *both* reversed, Kohler thought that both must proceed to a further, "correct" stage before adaptation could be complete. Stratton's reports, however, suggest that proprioceptive and kinesthetic changes, far from being temporary and trivial, become more and more extensive as adaptation progresses and are directly responsible for the "correct" perceptual judgments that ultimately emerge.

In order to clarify this interpretation of adaptation to reversal, let us consider a hypothetical experiment in which we test the subject's perception by having him look at a blackboard bearing an L on his left and an R on his right (Figure 1A). Immediately after putting on reversing spectacles, the subject says that he feels that his right hand (the one he writes with) and the right side of his body are near the same end of the blackboard—namely (since he is looking at it through reversing prisms), the end with a backwards L on it (Figure 1B). But when he holds up his writing hand and looks at it, he sees it nearer to the backwards R.

Now he starts adapting. If the proprioceptive-change hypothesis is correct, there is a change in the felt locations of his hands relative to his body. That is, his writing hand not only *looks* as if it is nearer to the backwards R, it now *feels* nearer as well (Figure 1C). Thus the subject feels his right hand to be near the (physically) left side of his body.

Suppose we ask the subject to turn right. He most likely assumes we mean toward the hand he writes with. Accordingly, he turns toward where he feels that hand to be, and the experimenter writes down that the subject turned left when told to turn right. The error is not due to uncertainty or "weakening of the right-left orientation of the body image"; if, instead of asking the subject to turn right, we touched his right hand and asked him to turn toward it, he would make the same

---

[11] "*Aber auch umgekehrt schwächt sich das Rechts-Links der Körperfühlsphäre und wird unsicher, besonders im Zusammenhang mit jenen Bewegungen, die man absichtlich verkehrt eingeübt hat. Die Vp. kann mit voller Evidenz sogar bei geschlossenen Augen 'rechts um' machen und dreht sich dabei in Wirklichkeit nach links. Sie macht Kopfwendungen und Handbewegungen, deren kinästhetische Lage- und Bewegungsempfindung ganz mit der (verdrehten) visuellen Welt übereinstimmt. Was dabei letzten Endes herauskommt, führt aber in eine 'Sackgasse' (zwei Fehler, die sich gegenseitig aufheben!).*"

[12] "*Das führt so weit, dass sogar im Tasten z. B. Türen (gegenüber früher) verkehrt aufzugehen scheinen, als wären sie inzwischen versetzt worden. Worauf sich das vorexperimentelle 'Rechts-Links' im Körpergefühl aber versteift und von wo es dann seinen neuen Vorstoss unternimmt, ist die Schulter und Oberarmpartie. Wenn man darauf die Aufmerksamkeit konzentriert, gibt es kaum jemals eine Verwechslung.*"

(This footnote refers to the sentence that ends with "*übereinstimmt*.")

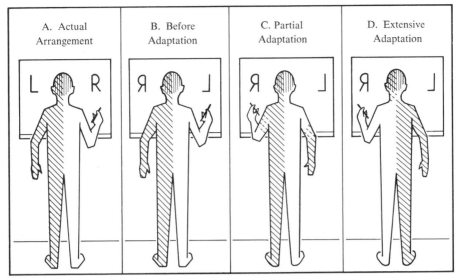

FIGURE 1   A subject's perceptions during the course of adaptation to reversed vision, according to the proprioceptive-change hypothesis. (In all cases perception of letters is visual; perception of the subject's head and body is proprioceptive. A: The actual physical arrangement. B: The subject's perceptions when he first puts on reversing goggles. C: The subject's perceptions at an intermediate stage of adaptation, with only his arms adapted. D: The subject's perceptions at an advanced stage of adaptation.)

error. If we touched his (unadapted) right shoulder, however, or if the subject focused his attention there, he would turn correctly to the right.

When we now ask the subject which end of the blackboard appears to be on his right, he may fall into the state of indecision that is so characteristic of Kohler's partly adapted subjects. His right hand feels closer to the letter R, whereas his right shoulder feels closer to the L. Depending on which region of his body he concentrates on, he can consider either the L or the R as being on his right. Thus he may switch his judgment back and forth from "right" to "left" without the slightest change in visual perception. Moreover, Stratton's reports indicate that the partly adapted subject sometimes feels his hand to be in two different places at once, with fluctuations in which of the localizations seems most "real." So even if the subject keeps judging relative to his hand, his judgments may waver. And, of course, he may switch back and forth from directional to pictorial judgments.

With further adaptation, according to the proprioceptive-change hypothesis, the felt locations of the subject's legs, torso, and perhaps even his shoulders and most of his head, change. He again feels, as he felt before the experiment started, that the (physically) right half of his body is near the hand he writes with. Now he can reach accurately for objects seen through the reversing goggles, turn correctly, and correctly judge the directions of objects relative to his body.

PICTORIAL PERCEPTION

But still his pictorial visual perception remains unchanged. The letters on the blackboard and the license plates on cars look just the same as they did when he first put on reversing goggles. The only difference is that he now feels the right side of his body to be on the same side as the curve of the backwards R that he sees (Figure 1D), so he says the curve is "on my right."

Why, then, does writing eventually come to look "normal" through reversing goggles? Because, with practice, mirror writing becomes familiar and easy to read, whether the letters are actually printed in reverse or simply look reversed because one is wearing special goggles. Indeed, Kohler's (1964, p. 160) subject reported that "the first words to rectify themselves were the common ones," which were seen most often through the reversing goggles. But it is a mistake to conclude that pictorial perception reversed and "mirrorwise seeing" ("*spiegelbildliche Sehen*"—Kohler, 1953, p. 113) became established. We would not say that about someone who learned to read mirror writing without wearing reversing spectacles.

Given this interpretation of adaptation, it is not surprising to hear that one stubborn subject (Taylor, 1962, p. 180) "achieved satisfactory behavioral adjustment" but "denied that he ever perceived the world the right way round through his spectacles," even after 71 days of wearing them. When questioned closely, this subject said that all of his "incorrect" judgments were made by deciding whether his right temple or his left temple was closer to the part of the visual field he was judging. Stratton's reports suggest that even after the felt location of the rest of the body has changed, the area around the eyes does not, so judgments made relative to the temples would remain unchanged. Or, the subject may have been trying to tell the experimenter that he was making a pictorial judgment, based on an unaltered visual memory of right and left. In either case, this subject's perceptions—visual and proprioceptive—were probably just the same as those of subjects who, according to Taylor, managed to "perceive the world the right way round."

AFTEREFFECTS

The "peculiar experiences" (Kohler, 1964, p. 158) that the adapted subject encounters when he takes off the experimental spectacles are just what one would expect if the subject has undergone proprioceptive changes, has become accustomed to the reversed appearance of particular stimuli, but has experienced no change in pictorial perception.

When Kohler (1964, p. 158) removed his reversing goggles, after weeks of adaptation, and looked at a picture which he had seen before but not during the experiment, the picture immediately looked familiar. The person in it appeared (pictorially) to be running, as before, from left to right. Nevertheless, the person was seen as running toward the *left* edge of the page, that is (as Kohler makes clear), toward where Kohler felt his (adapted) left shoulder to be.

Kohler (1964, p. 160) does report that another subject, the one who "achieved almost completely correct impressions" while wearing reversing goggles, *saw* the whole room mirrorwise when the spectacles were removed. But the evidence for this statement is that the subject read p's as q's, b's as d's, and 10:30 on a clock as 1:30—which is just what would happen, without any perceptual change, if one read nothing but mirror writing and saw nothing but backwards clocks for 37 days.

Limitations of the Proprioceptive-Change Hypothesis

Although changes in the position sense may underlie most of the phenomena of adaptation to optical distortions, there are some kinds of adaptation that cannot be so interpreted. For example, adaptation to the chromatic dispersion produced by prisms ("color fringes"—Kohler, 1964) seems to depend on changes in "contour detectors" within the visual system (Hay, Pick and Rosser, 1963; McCollough, 1965a). Adaptation to bicolored spectacles (Kohler, 1964) has been shown to depend on retinal color adaptation and simultaneous contrast (McCollough, 1965b). There appear to be several forms of adaptation to tilting, curvature, and other optical distortions (see, e.g., M. M. Cohen, 1963; Held and Rekosh, 1963; Kohler, 1964; Mikaelian and Held, 1964; Morant and Harris, 1965; Ohwaki, 1961). Some of these appear to be purely visual changes; others may be based on changed registration of head or eye positions and movements.

Many adaptation situations probably include some motor-skill learning. This component may sometimes be even larger than that due to proprioceptive changes (as, perhaps, in Smith and Smith's, 1962, studies) or it may be much smaller but still considerable. For example, Hall (1964) and Harris (unpublished data) both found that when the arm movement used during adaptation differed grossly from that used in the tests, there was some decrement in the measured adaptive shift. (Hall's data have been published by Freedman, Hall, and Rekosh, 1965.)

In some cases, a proprioceptive-change interpretation requires additional assumptions similar to those made by other theories. For instance, the increased variability of responses that follows watching one's hand through a variable prism whose amount of displacement keeps changing (Cohen and Held, 1960; summarized by Held and Freedman, 1963) could be due to increased uncertainty about arm position. Many of the "conditional aftereffects," which others ascribe to the conditioning of visual perceptions to nonvisual cues (Kohler, 1964; Taylor, 1962) can be attributed to the conditioning of altered position sense to these same cues.

Recently, several experimental findings have been cited as directly ruling out a proprioceptive change in adaptation to displacement. Efstathiou and Held (1964) reported that adapting one hand to displacing prisms had no effect on blindfolded subjects' reaching for the remembered locations of targets they had previously felt. They also found that the measured adaptive shift was smaller when the unexposed hand served as test target than when the target was a visually perceived object. Bauer and Efstathiou (1965) found

an adaptive shift in pointing "straight ahead" only if subjects were first tested on pointing at visual targets; if tested on straight ahead first, the shift was sizable, but in the wrong direction. And H. B. Cohen (1963) reported that adaptation with the target in the retinal periphery does not transfer completely to test targets on the fovea. It is difficult to assess these findings since each is contradicted, directly or indirectly, by other findings (e.g., Goldstein[13]; Hamilton and Hillyard[14]; Harris, 1963a). The reasons for the empirical disagreements have not been satisfactorily worked out.

In the reports of Stratton (1897), Kohler (1964), and Taylor (1962), several passages seem to describe perceptual changes that cannot be attributed to altered position sense. Further work is needed to determine whether these statements are based on confusions about the various determinants of subjects' verbal reports or result from some complicated alterations in position sense or do in fact represent other sorts of adaptive change.

Other Theories of Adaptation

STRATTON

After reading Stratton's striking descriptions of the proprioceptive changes he underwent, one is surprised to find him saying in his theoretical discussion that "the tactual perceptions, as such, never changed their place," and "the restoration of harmony between the perceptions of sight and those of touch was in no wise a process of changing the absolute position of tactual objects so as to make it identical with the place of the visual objects [1897, p. 476]." He seems to be ignoring his own introspections when he claims that there is neither a change in proprioceptive localization nor

[13] Donald Goldstein, personal communication, June 1964, May 1965.
[14] Charles R. Hamilton and S. A. Hillyard, personal communication, July 1964, August 1964.

a change in visual localization, but only a change in the relationship between the two. This noncommittal idea has proven quite appealing to many present-day psychologists.

Clearly a change either in vision or in the position sense would result in a changed relationship between the two. But saying that only the relationship between the two modalities changes is ignoring information about the changes *within* one (and only one) of the modalities.

Stratton's own reports make it clear that the first step in his adapting to inverted vision was to feel that his feet were in a new location relative to the rest of his body—a change within the position sense. Gradually, the felt locations of more and more of his body swung into line with that of his feet, that is, into line with the inverted visual scene. True, the final result was a new relationship between the position sense and visual perception, but this new relationship was brought about entirely by changes in the position sense, with no changes in vision.

In 1897, Stratton (pp. 472–475) theorized that adaptation is the attachment of new visual imagery to tactual sensations and, concurrently, the attachment of new tactual imagery to visual sensations. If we ignore the second half of this formulation and just postulate that adaptation consists of associating new visual imagery of parts of the body with proprioceptive stimuli from those parts, we can deal with much of the relevant data, provided we make one additional assumption: that the felt position of a limb is not directly connected with proprioceptive stimuli, but is a byproduct of where the limb is mentally pictured. The visual imagery notion, then, would make the same predictions as the proprioceptive-change hypothesis, but requires an extra step—a step that some subjects' introspections deny.[15]

---

[15] In a later paper, Stratton (1899) did state, contradicting his earlier theoretical views, that

TAYLOR

Taylor (1962, 1964) attempts to explain all perception, from depth perception to color vision, with a single hypothetico-deductive theory. According to this theory, visual perception of an object is determined by the "activation" of stimulus-response engrams—neural traces of the responses (especially walking, reaching, and verbal responses) that have been conditioned to similar stimuli. Taylor apparently believes that adaptation to displacement, inversion, or reversal of the retinal images leads to changes in directional perception and perhaps to pictorial changes as well (1964, p. 73). However, he thinks that these perceptual changes, though genuine, are largely the result of changes in verbal labeling (1962, pp. 179–181, 185). He expects adaptation to progress in piecemeal fashion with visual perception becoming more and more veridical as the subject acquires a larger number of appropriate responses (1962, pp. 188, 197, 207).

Beyond this, it is difficult to derive unequivocal predictions. For example, Taylor's theory could predict either way about transfer to most of the tasks in Table 1, depending on what assumptions are made about steepness of generalization gradients, breadth of "equivalence classes," degree of "interpenetration" of sensory modalities, and relative importance of motor behavior and implicit verbal responses.

KOHLER

Kohler's (1964) studies of adaptation to

"the place in which any part of the body is persistently seen influences the localisation of the dermal and kindred sensations arising in that part. If one were to see his feet, for instance, in some direction different from their present visual position, he would in the end refer thither their kinaesthetic impressions also [p. 463]." But only a few subsequent writers (notably Walls, 1951; Smith and Smith, 1962) have paid much attention to Stratton's later interpretation or even to his original detailed descriptions of proprioceptive changes.

a wide variety of visual distortions have provided the inspiration, directly or indirectly, for much of the research in this field. He has concentrated on setting down his observations rather than on providing a detailed theory. It is clear that he agrees with Taylor that adaptation involves changes in directional perception, based on the acquisition of new behavioral responses to transformed retinal images (see, e.g., pp. 163–164). With prolonged exposure to reversing spectacles, Kohler says, there are eventually pictorial changes, with more and more stimuli "seen correctly" (pp. 140, 163–164). Unlike Taylor, however, Kohler thinks that verbal labeling is of no great significance in adaptation.

Although Kohler did mention (in a footnote) that "alterations in kinesthetic sensitivity" may be "of crucial importance" (p. 32) in adapting to displacement, he did not make much use of these alterations in explaining other aspects of adaptation. In fact, in his discussions of reversed vision, he regards such alterations as transitory—normal proprioception and kinesthesis are soon reinstated, and form the basis for the "correct" visual perception that ultimately emerges. In his theoretical discussions, Kohler did not attempt to explain the simpler phenomena of adaptation to displacement, inversion, and reversal of retinal images, but rather dealt with the complex "situational aftereffects."

HELD

In an extensive series of carefully controlled experiments, Held and his co-workers have demonstrated the importance of active movement and movement-produced visual feedback ("re-afference") in producing adaptation. These experiments set the pattern for most of the recent work in the area: brief adaptation periods with quantitative before-after measurements.

Held has been primarily concerned with the necessary preconditions for adaptation; he has said little about the nature of the adaptive change (see, e.g., Held, 1961).

It is not clear whether Held believes that adaptation involves any perceptual changes, visual or proprioceptive. For instance, Held and Freedman (1963) say that adaptation "represents a change in state of the relevant sensorimotor control system, such that [after complete adaptation] the input-output or stimulus-response relation becomes identical to that which existed prior to rearrangement [p. 457]." Recently Efstathiou and Held (1964) proposed a tentative theory of arm adaptation to displacement, according to which "the change responsible for the shifts occurs in a representation, within the nervous system, of the spatial relation between the exposed arm and directions that are defined independently of that arm." Further elaboration of this model is necessary to determine how it differs from the proprioceptive-change interpretation.

SMITH AND SMITH

Smith and Smith (1962) claim that adaptation consists of acquiring highly specific perceptual-motor skills. They seem to deny that there is any general reorientation of perception, whether directional or pictorial (1962, pp. 83, 311). Their research and theory supplement the proprioceptive-change interpretation by dealing with situations in which proprioceptive changes probably are minimized because there is a large spatial separation between the felt location of the hand and its televised visual feedback. The acquisition of highly specific perceptual-motor skills is facilitated by Smith and Smith's tasks, which permit continuous visual feedback and stress speed of execution. Indeed, their usual measure (speed of performance) is sensitive only to the development of highly practiced motor skills. However, it is possible that adaptation of Smith and Smith's three movement systems—locomotion, transport, and manipulation—may in part represent, respectively, proprioceptive head or eye adaptation, arm adaptation, and acquisition of manipulatory skills.

Werner and Wapner (1955) have discussed some of Kohler's findings in terms of their organismic sensory-tonic field theory, attributing adaptation to changes in the subject's "organismic state (sensory-tonic distribution)." Basically, though, their account simply restates Kohler's observations. Some of their statements would match the present author's if the words "felt position" of certain body parts were substituted for such abstract terms as "organismic state" or "equilibrial axis." But Werner and Wapner consider the organismic state to be only one part of the process that determines body perception, not the perception itself. Moreover, the organismic state is assumed to include "not only postural, but emotive, motivational factors, etc. [p. 133]," which are clearly beyond the scope of the present formulation.

Preconditions and Mechanism for Adaptation

VISUAL PROPRIOCEPTIVE DISCREPANCY

Although the proprioceptive-change interpretation of adaptation does not specify any particular process or precondition for the change, it is tempting to assume that adaptation results from a discrepancy between proprioceptive and visual information. One effective way to produce such a discrepancy is to look at some part of one's body through distorting goggles, but it is not the only way. For instance, when a subject walks while wearing displacing prisms, his position sense may indicate that his head is turned to one side of the direction of movement, whereas the retinal flow pattern (Gibson, 1950; Held and Freedman, 1963) may indicate that the head is pointing right along the axis of movement.

On the other hand, there is no logical necessity that proprioceptive inputs be

used at all by the mechanism that recalibrates the position sense. It could be, as Helmholtz (1962b) suggested, that adaptation is based on the changes in the retinal image that result from a given "effort of the will," or, in Held and Freedman's (1963) terminology, on motor corollary discharges and visual reafference contingent upon active movement. Or the proprioceptive change could be due to the laying down of engrams of conditioned responses, like those postulated by Taylor (1962).

Some proprioceptive changes may arise from something like "sensory fatigue," without any direct participation by vision. Hein (1965) has found that after simply holding their heads turned to one side for 10 minutes, even with their eyes closed, subjects point incorrectly at visual targets. This "postural after-effect," as Hein called it, probably was due to a change in felt head orientation. Similarly, Kohler (1951, p. 18) reports that subjects who wear displacing prisms tend to hold their eyes in an abnormal position that eventually comes to feel normal once more. Such a "fatigue" effect could indeed produce some of the phenomena of adaptation to displacement, but it can underlie neither adaptation to inversion or reversal nor arm adaptation to displacement.

ACTIVE MOVEMENT

A number of experiments by Held and his colleagues have shown that active movements by the subject play an important role in adaptation to several optical distortions (Held and Freedman, 1963). Although some recent investigators have claimed to find extensive adaptation with passive exposure (e.g., Wallach et al., 1963; Weinstein, Sersen, Fisher, and Weisinger, 1964), active movement does seem greatly to facilitate adaptation.

Theories that consider the end product of adaptation to consist of new motor responses or new visuomotor correlations (e.g., Held, 1961; Smith and Smith, 1962; Taylor, 1962) also assume that active movement is a crucial precondition for adaptation. On the other hand, Hamilton (1964a) has listed several ways to account for the importance of active movement without postulating any motoric component in the end product. For example, the position sense during active movement may differ from (and be more precise than) that during passive movement. Or motor discharges may act as a "catalyst" that permits a joint's position sense to change.

Implications for Perceptual Development

Psychologists have traditionally looked to studies of adaptation to distorted vision for clues about the development of visual perception in the infant. The usual, empiricist assumption (outlined by Berkeley in 1709 in his *New Theory of Vision;* see Berkeley, 1910) is that visual space perception is "secondary": It is based on the spatial sensations given by touch, kinesthesis, and position sense. As Dewey (1898) put it: "Ultimately visual perception rests on tactual. . . . Spatial relations are not originally perceived by the eye, but are the result of the association of visual sensations with previous muscular and tactual experiences [p. 165]."

This belief in the primacy of touch is so ingrained that experimental results are sometimes flagrantly misinterpreted in order to support it. Carr (1925), for instance, concluded: "It is thus obvious that the Stratton experiment involves no reconstruction or alteration of tactual . . . space. It is the visual system that is disrupted and then reorganized so as to conform to touch . . . [p. 141]." Stratton's, Kohler's, and Held's findings have beeen cited over and over as evidence that visual space perception is flexible and therefore must have been acquired through tactile-proprioceptive and motor experience. The reinterpretation of these findings that has been presented here suggests the opposite conclusion. Vision seems to be largely inflexible, whereas the position sense is remarkably labile.

The implication, if one dare draw any, is that the Berkeleyan notion should be turned around. It seems more plausible to assume that proprioceptive perception of parts of the body (and therefore of the locations of touched objects) develops with the help of innate visual perception rather than vice versa.[16] A growing number of recent studies support the view that many aspects of visual perception are not influenced by experience and are largely innate (e.g., Bower, 1964; Fantz, 1965; Gibson and Walk, 1960; Hubel and Wiesel, 1963; Robinson, Brown, and Hayes, 1964). Furthermore, if the position sense were innate—if each spot on the skin were proprioceptively "preaddressed"—the local sign lodged in a baby's fingertip might go on forever signaling that his arm is 10 inches long.

So, when a baby stares raptly at his outstretched hand, he is probably finding out where his hand is, not what his visual sensations mean. He is making use of an adaptive mechanism that keeps his position sense accurate despite extensive and uneven growth of his body. This mechanism enables us to use the precise, detailed information that vision provides, as a means of continually readjusting our vaguer and more variable position sense.

References

BAUER, J., JR., and AGLAIA EFSTATHIOU. Effects of adaptation to visual displacement on pointing "straight ahead." Paper read at Eastern Psychological Association, Atlantic City, April 1965.

[16] Clearly vision is not the *only* basis for acquiring and maintaining the position sense or blind people would have no idea where their arms and legs were. Vision may, however, provide the quickest and most exact recalibration.

BERKELEY, G. *An essay towards a new theory of vision*. New York: Dutton, 1910.

BOSSOM, J. Mechanisms of prism adaptation in normal monkeys. *Psychonomic Science,* 1964, *1,* 377–378.

BOSSOM, J., and C. R. HAMILTON. Interocular transfer of prism-altered coordinations in split-brain monkeys. *Journal of Comparative and Physiological Psychology,* 1963, *56,* 769–774.

BOSSOM, J., and R. HELD. Shifts in egocentric localization following prolonged displacement of the retinal image. *American Psychologist,* 1957, *12,* 454. (Abstract)

BOWER, T. G. R. Discrimination of depth in premotor infants. *Psychonomic Science,* 1964, *1,* 368.

BRINDLEY, G. S., and P. A. MERTON. The absence of position sense in the human eye. *Journal of Physiology,* 1960, *153,* 127–130.

CARR, H. A. *Psychology: A study of mental activity*. New York: Longmans, Green, 1925.

CLARK, B., and A. GRAYBIEL. Perception of the postural vertical in normals and subjects with labyrinthine defects. *Journal of Experimental Psychology,* 1963, *65,* 490–494.

COHEN, H. B. Transfer and dissipation of aftereffects due to displacement of the visual field. *American Psychologist,* 1963, *18,* 411. (Abstract)

COHEN, M. M. Visual curvature and feedback factors in the production of prismatically induced curved line aftereffects. Paper read at Eastern Psychological Association, New York, April 1963.

COHEN, M., and R. HELD. Degrading visual-motor coordination by exposure to disordered re-afferent stimulation. Paper read at Eastern Psychological Association, New York, April 1960.

DEWEY, J. *Psychology*. (3rd ed.) New York: American, 1898.

EFSTATHIOU, AGLAIA, and R. HELD. Cross-modal transfer of adaptation to eye-hand rearrangement. Paper read at Eastern Psychological Association, Philadelphia, April 1964.

FANTZ, R. L. Ontogeny of perception. In A. M. Schrier, H. F. Harlow, and F. Stollnitz (Eds.), *Behavior of nonhuman primates*. New York: Academic Press, 1965. Pp. 365–403.

FREEDMAN, S. J., SARAH B. HALL, and J. H. REKOSH. Effects on hand-eye coordination of two different arm motions during compensation for displaced vision. *Perceptual and Motor Skills,* 1965, *20,* 1054–1056.

GIBSON, ELEANOR J., and R. D. WALK. The "visual cliff." *Scientific American,* 1960, *202*(4), 64–71.

GIBSON, J. J. *The perception of the visual world*. Boston: Houghton Mifflin, 1950.

HALL, SARAH B. Transfer of adaptation within the arm. Unpublished senior honors thesis, Harvard University, 1964.

HAMILTON, C. R. Interm.anual transfer of adaptation to prisms. *American Journal of Psychology,* 1964, *77,* 457–462. (a)

HAMILTON, C. R. *Studies on adaptation to deflection of the visual field in split-brain monkeys and man*. (Doctoral dissertation, California Institute of Technology) Ann Arbor, Mich.: University Microfilms, 1964, No. 64–11,398. (b)

HARRIS, C. S. *Adaptation to displaced vision: A proprioceptive change*. (Doctoral dissertation, Harvard University) Ann Arbor, Mich.: University Microfilms, 1963, No. 63–8162. (a)

HARRIS, C. S. Adaptation to displaced vision: Visual, motor or proprioceptive change? *Science,* 1963, *140,* 812–813. (b)

HARRIS, C. S. The nature of adaptation to displaced vision. Paper read at Eastern Psychological Association, New York, April 1963. (c)

HARRIS, C. S. Proprioceptive changes underlying adaptation to visual distortions. *American Psychologist,* 1964, *19,* 562. (Abstract)

HAY, J. C. and H. L. PICK, JR. Visual and proprioceptive adaptation to optical displacement of the visual stimulus. *Journal of Experimental Psychology,* 1966, *71,* in press.

HAY, J. C., H. L. PICK, JR., and KARREN IKEDA. Visual capture produced by prism spectacles. *Psychonomic Science,* 1965, *2,* 215–216.

HAY, J. C., H. L. PICK, JR., and EDWENNA ROSSER. Adaptation to chromatic aberration by the human visual system. *Science,* 1963, *141,* 167–169.

HEIN, A. Postural after-effects and visual-motor adaptation to prisms. Paper read at Eastern Psychological Association, Atlantic City, April 1965.

HEIN, A. V., and R. H. HELD. Transfer between visual-motor systems of adaptation to prismatic displacement of vision. Paper read at Eastern Psychological Association, New York, April 1960.

HELD, R. Exposure-history as a factor in maintaining stability of perception and coordination. *Journal of Nervous and Mental Disease,* 1961, *132,* 26–32.

HELD, R., and J. BOSSOM. Neonatal deprivation and adult rearrangement: Complementary techniques for analyzing plastic sensory-motor coordinations. *Journal of Comparative and Physiological Psychology*, 1961, 54, 33–37.

HELD, R., and S. J. FREEDMAN. Plasticity in human sensorimotor control. *Science*, 1963, 142, 455–462.

HELD, R., and J. REKOSH. Motor-sensory feedback and the geometry of visual space. *Science*, 1963, 141, 722–723.

HELMHOLTZ, H. VON. *Popular scientific lectures*. (Ed. by M. Kline) New York: Dover, 1962. (a)

HELMHOLTZ, H. VON. *Treatise on physiological optics*. (Trans. and Ed. by J. P. C. Southall) Vol. 3. New York: Dover, 1962. (b)

HOCHBERG, J. On the importance of movement-produced stimulation in prism-induced after-effects| *Perceptual and Motor Skills*, 1963, 16, 544.

HUBEL, D. H., and T. N. WIESEL. Receptive fields of cells in striate cortex of very young, visually inexperienced kittens. *Journal of Neurophysiology*, 1963, 26, 994–1002.

KLEIN, G. S. Cognitive control and motivation. In G. Lindzey (Ed.), *Assessment of human motives*. New York: Grove Press, 1960. Pp. 87–118.

KOHLER, I. Über Aufbau und Wandlungen der Wahrnehmungswelt. *Österreichische Akademie der Wissenschaften Sitzungberichte, Philosophisch-historische Klasse*, 1951, 227, 1–118.

KOHLER, I. Umgewöhnung im Wahrnehmungsbereich. *Die Pyramide*, 1953, 3, 92–96, 109–113, 132–133.

KOHLER, I. The formation and transformation of the perceptual world. (Trans. by H. Fiss) *Psychological Issues*, 1964, 3(4).

LLOYD, ANDREE J., and L. S. CALDWELL. Accuracy of active and passive positioning of the leg on the basis of kinesthetic cues. *Journal of Comparative and Physiological Psychology*, 1965, 60, 102–106.

LUDVIGH, E. Possible role of proprioception in the extraocular muscles. *Archives of Ophthalmology*, 1952, 48, 436–441.

McCOLLOUGH, CELESTE. Color adaptation of edge-detectors in the human visual system. *Science*, 1965, 149, 1115–1116. (a)

McCOLLOUGH, CELESTE. The conditioning of color perception. *American Journal of Psychology*, 1965, 78, in press. (b)

McLAUGHLIN, S. C., and J. L. BOWER. Auditory localization and judgments of straight ahead during adaptation to prism. *Psychonomic Science*, 1965, 2, 283–284.

McLAUGHLIN, S. C., and K. I. RIFKIN. Change in straight ahead during adaptation to prism. *Psychonomic Science*, 1965, 2, 107–108.

MIKAELIAN, H. Failure of bilateral transfer in modified eye-hand coordination. Paper read at Eastern Psychological Association, New York, April 1963.

MIKAELIAN, H., and R. HELD. Two types of adaptation to an optically-rotated visual field. *American Journal of Psychology*, 1964, 77, 257–263.

MITTELSTAEDT, H. The role of movement in the origin and maintenance of visual perception: Discussion. In, *Proceedings of the Seventeenth International Congress of Psychology*. Amsterdam: North-Holland, 1964. P. 310. (Abstract)

MORANT, R. B., and JUDITH R. HARRIS. Two different after-effects of exposure to visual tilts. *American Journal of Psychology*, 1965, 78, 218–226.

MOUNTCASTLE, V. B., G. F. POGGIO, and G. WERNER. The relation of thalamic cell response to peripheral stimuli varied over an intensive continuum. *Journal of Neurophysiology*, 1963, 26, 870–834.

NIELSEN, T. I. Volition: A new experimental approach. *Scandinavian Journal of Psychology*, 1963, 4, 225–230.

OHWAKI, SONOKO. An investigation of figural adaptation: A study within the framework of sensory-tonic field-theory. *American Journal of Psychology*, 1961, 74, 3–16.

PICK, H. L., JR., J. C. HAY, and JOAN PABST. Kinesthetic adaptation to visual distortion. Paper read at Midwestern Psychological Association, Chicago, May 1963.

ROBINSON, J. S., L. T. BROWN, and W. H. HAYES. Test of effects of past experience on perception. *Perceptual and Motor Skills*, 1964, 18, 953–956.

ROCK, I., and J. VICTOR. Vision and touch: An experimentally created conflict between the two senses. *Science*, 1964, 143, 594–596.

ROSE, J. E., and V. B. MOUNTCASTLE. Touch and kinesthesis. In J. Field (Ed.), *Handbook of physiology*. Section 1. *Neurophysiology*. Vol. 1. Washington, D. C.: American Physiological Society, 1960. Pp. 387–429.

SCHOLL, K. Das räumliche Zusammenarbeiten von Auge und Hand. *Deutsch Zeitschrift für Nervenheilkunde*, 1926, 92, 280–303.

SIMONS, J. C. Walking under zero-gravity conditions. United States Air Force, Wright Air Development Center, Technical Note No. 59–327, 1959. Cited by J. P. Loftus, Jr., and Lois R. Hammer. Weightlessness.

In N. M. Burns, R. M. Chambers, and E. Hendler (Eds.), *Unusual environments and human behavior*. New York: Free Press, 1963. Pp. 353–377.

SMITH, K. U., and W. K. SMITH. *Perception and motion*. Philadelphia: Saunders, 1962.

STRATTON, G. M. Some preliminary experiments on vision without inversion of the retinal image. *Psychological Review*, 1896, 3, 611–617.

STRATTON, G. M. Vision without inversion of the retinal image. *Psychological Review*, 1897, 4, 341–360, 463–481.

STRATTON, G. M. The spatial harmony of touch and sight. *Mind*, 1899, 8, 492–505.

TAUB, E., S. J. ELLMAN, and A. J. BERMAN. Conditioned grasp response in a deafferented primate limb. *American Psychologist*, 1964, 19, 510. (Abstract)

TAYLOR, J. G. *The behavioral basis of perception*. New Haven: Yale Univer. Press, 1962.

TAYLOR, J. G. What is consciousness? *British Journal of Statistical Psychology*, 1964, 17, 71–76.

WALLACH, H., J. H. KRAVITZ, and JUDITH LINDAUER. A passive condition for rapid adaptation to displaced visual direction. *American Journal of Psychology*, 1963, 76, 568–578.

WALLS, G. L. The problem of visual direction. *American Journal of Optometry*, 1951, 28, 55–83, 115–146, 173–212.

WEINSTEIN, S., E. A. SERSEN, L. FISHER, and M. WEISINGER. Is reafference necessary for visual adaptation? *Perceptual and Motor Skills*, 1964, 18, 641–648.

WERNER, H., and S. WAPNER. The Innsbruck studies on distorted visual fields in relation to an organismic theory of perception. *Psychological Review*, 1955, 62, 130–138.

WERTHEIMER, M., and A. J. ARENA. Effect of exposure time on adaptation to disarranged hand-eye coordination. *Perceptual and Motor Skills*, 1959, 9, 159–164.

WOOSTER, MARGARET. Certain factors in the development of a new spatial coordination. *Psychological Monographs*, 1923, 32(4, Whole No. 146).

Vision and Touch: An Experimentally Created Conflict between the Two Senses[*]

IRVIN ROCK   JACK VICTOR

Yeshiva University

Abstract. Observers were presented with an object whose visual shape, because of optical distortion, differed considerably from its tactual shape. After simultaneously grasping and viewing the object, the observers were required to indicate their impression of it by drawing it or by matching another object to it. The results reveal that vision is strongly dominant, often without the observer's being aware of a conflict.

The experiments in this report are designed to answer the question: If contradictory information is given to two senses of an

* *Science*, 1964, vol. 143, pp. 594–596. Copyright © 1964 by the American Association for the Advancement of Science.

observer about the properties of an object, what will be his experience? By means of optical distortion, an observer can be given a visual impression of an object which is at odds with his tactual impression of that same object. Will the observer be aware of this contradiction or will one unified impression be experienced? If a unified impression is experienced, will it be a compromise between the visual and tactile sensations or will one sense dominate? Although analogous experiments have been carried out on the problem of localization and on the perceived upright, the conflict between vision and touch concerning properties such as shape or size has not been investigated.

Several experimental procedures were used. In all experiments, the subject viewed a standard object through a transparent plastic optical element which compressed the image along its horizontal axis only, thus changing the object's visual shape. While the subject was looking at the object, he was also instructed to reach behind and to grasp it through a black silk cloth, which prevented the subject from seeing his hand, since any distortion in the visual appearance of his hand could lead to a loss of experimental naivete. The subject viewed the object through an eye piece set into the front of a box. He saw it within the small field provided by a circular opening in front of the optical element. The subject placed his right arm around to the rear of the box which was 40.6 cm deep and, through a large opening (and through the cloth hanging directly behind) grasped the object, a 25 mm white square, 1 mm thick, made of a hard plastic material, attached to a thin black metal stem set vertically in a hole in the bottom of the box. The image of the width was optically reduced by a transparent piece of plastic, 0.6 cm thick, with parallel sides, which served as an optical lens element. The element could be bent around a vertical axis only, by turning a dial to the desired degree of reduction; thus it formed a portion of a thick-walled cylinder. Rays striking the plastic at an angle of incidence other than 90° were displaced. This effectively compressed the image of the object along one axis only. In these experiments the plastic was bent to reduce

the width of the image by approximately one half. The plastic was placed 15.2 cm in front of the standard square and 25.4 cm from the observer's eye.

The question of how to measure what the subject experienced was an interesting one. After viewing and grasping the standard, the subject could be asked to select a comparison object which he judged to match the standard. But how should the comparison object be presented, visually or tactually? Eventually we decided on three different experiments: (i) visual comparison only, (ii) tactual comparison only, and (iii) a quite different method in which the subject was asked to draw a picture the same shape as the standard. In this last method, the subject utilized both visual and tactual senses in making his reproduction. Different subjects were used for each experiment. In all experiments, the subject was instructed either to draw or to match in accordance with his "impression" of the standard. In this way no bias was introduced for vision or touch, as would be the case if we asked him to match what he had "seen," or what he had "felt."

In each experiment there were three conditions. In the experimental condition, the subject viewed the standard and at the same time grasped it manually. Pains were taken to insure that he viewed and grasped the standard simultaneously and that he never performed one maneuver without the other. He then selected or drew a rectangle which seemed to correspond in shape to the standard. This was the main condition in which vision and touch yielded conflicting information. The subject was not told what his task was to be afterward until after he had been exposed to the standard. This was to prevent him from using his fingers to measure or otherwise engage in judgmental efforts at accuracy. Such efforts, in the preliminary experiments, had often led to awareness of the experimental conflict situation. In the vision-control condition, the subject only viewed the standard. This afforded an empirical check on the distortion produced by the optical element. It was also an indication of what was expected in the drawing or matching task when the standard was perceived only visually. In the touch-control condition, the subject only grasped the standard. This gave a measure of the central tendency and accuracy of shape discrimination by touch alone and, also, indicated what was expected when the standard was experienced by touch only. In all conditions, 5 seconds were allowed in which to perform the experiment. Only one judgment was obtained from each subject because additional judgments could not have been made with the desired naivete. Separate subjects served in each of the two control conditions so that they too would be naive as to what the task would entail until the object had been experienced.

In the first experiment the subjects made drawings of their impression of the shape of the standard. The drawings were carefully measured at the top and bottom for width and the two values were averaged. The two sides were then measured in the same way for the length. The proportion of the length to the width was the measure used to represent the perceived shape. The mean proportion of length to width for the ten subjects in this experiment was 1.85; the vision-control subjects yielded a mean of 1.9, and for the touch control subjects, the mean proportion was 0.98. In this experiment, the same subjects served as controls for both touch and vision after the conflict condition, the order of the two being counterbalanced among the ten subjects. The order did not seem to make any difference. Since the objectively correct drawing should have been a square, the fact that the experimental subjects were drawing a rectangle of almost a 2 : 1 ratio (which was exactly what they did, on the average, in the vision-control condition) indicates that vision was completely dominant. The ab-

solute length and width were both considerably underestimated, but they were not asked to attend to the absolute size of the standard, only to its shape.

In the second experiment the method of selecting a comparison match by vision alone, under one experimental and two control conditions, was utilized. Selection was made from a rack which had a series of rectangles on stems set in holes in its base, with dimensions ranging from 8.6 to 31.8 mm in width; the height was constant at 25 mm. The rectangles were varied in steps representing a constant fraction of approximately 12.5 percent of the width. In the experimental condition, the subject selected a comparison stimulus which he considered to be the same width as his impression of the width of the standard. He only looked at the comparison object; he looked at and grasped the standard but he only viewed the comparison. This procedure may be thought to be biased in favor of a visual resolution since the subject selected by using vision alone. However, he was not aware that he would have to make a match from vision, and therefore he could not be said to be concentrating more on vision in his perception of the standard because of the comparison task. It could also be argued that it should not make any difference what comparison technique was used, since the subject received a unitary impression and would communicate this impression by whatever type of comparison he made. That is, once he "decided" what he had experienced, it should not be crucial which method or modality he employed to tell us what he had experienced. The mean ($N = 10$) for the experimental condition was a width of 14.1 mm; for vision alone the mean width obtained was 13.4 mm; and for touch alone the mean width was 23.1 mm. The results clearly show a favoring of a visual resolution. There is not too much difference between the average vision-control match and the experimental (or conflict) match. Two subjects who gave experimental matches in the direction of touch account for the slight difference obtained.

A word should be said about the method of computing the means in this and the following experiment. Since the absolute magnitude of steps increases in size as the series increases, computing a mean directly from the variable selected by each subject would bias the results in an upward direction. Hence the mean of the step-ranks was used in the actual computation. This was then converted back to a metric value by interpolation so that it would be more meaningful.

In the final experiment, comparison with the standard was made by touch alone. One experimental and two control conditions were used. The rack used in the second experiment was also used for this one. The subject could grasp the first rectangle and then move his hand along the rack, feeling each rectangle in turn. The rack was so placed that selections were made in an ascending order for half of the subjects and in a descending order for the other half of the subjects. If the previous experiment can be considered biased toward a vision resolution then this experiment should, if anything, be biased toward a touch resolution. Again, however, it could be argued that matching by touch or vision should give the same results.

For ten subjects the means for the conflict condition was a width of 14.5 mm, for vision alone the mean width was 14.1 mm, and for touch alone the mean width was 20.5 mm. It will be noted that in all of our experiments the vision-control outcome indicates that the phenomenal effect of the optical compression was not fully one-half. Also, in the second and third experiments the touch-control outcome was, on the average, less than the objective size of the standard. Hence, predictions based on dominance of touch or vision are not quite as far apart as originally desired.

The results of all three experiments show that, with few exceptions, the visual impression is completely dominant. Analogous experiments were conducted in which the visual "size" of an object is altered by means of a lens. The conflict between visual and tactual size is also resolved more or less completely in favor of visual size. An experimental procedure added at the end of some of the experiments on size will serve to illustrate another important point about the dominance of vision. The subject was asked to look at and grasp the standard. While still grasping it, he was then told to close his eyes and open them again. He was then asked if the standard felt any different when his eyes were open or closed; 23 out of 38 subjects tested in this way reported that the object "felt" larger when their eyes were closed. The remainder did not report any definite impression.

In other words vision is so powerful in relation to touch that the very touch experience itself undergoes a change. The object actually feels the way it looks and this is why we believe that most subjects were unaware of a conflict in these experiments.

Although about one subject in five did become aware of the conflict, it is remarkable that there were so few. There was a tendency for these subjects to resolve the conflict more in the direction of touch than naive subjects do. Reporting a conflict does not necessarily indicate a spontaneous registration of contradictory perceptions. The subject may have been suspicious of the apparatus or (and this occasionally did occur despite efforts to prevent it) looked away or up, giving him an uncontaminated tactual impression so that he became aware of the conflict. In any event, the answer to our starting question as to whether a unified impression would be experienced in the conflict condition is a qualified "yes." Generally the subject is unaware of the conflict, which means he does have a unified impression. Further, that impression is dominated by what he sees. It seems clear that it is possible to study this type of sensory conflict experimentally and this is an important first step.

At this stage of the work no attempt has been made to differentiate the various aspects of touch perception, that is, whether based on tactile or kinesthetic sensations, passive or active components, simultaneous or temporal integration, and the like. We are using the term "touch" in the broadest possible way to stand for any and all aspects of sensory experience based on the mechanical contact of the observer with objects which can yield information as to the properties of such objects (1).

The results have implications for theories of the genesis of visual perception (for example, that visual shape derives from tactual shape) and for theories concerning spatiality in general. Bishop Berkeley had said, "Visible figures are the marks of tangible figures; and . . . it is plain that in themselves they are little regarded or upon any score than for their connection with tangible figures, which by nature they are ordained to signify" (2). Our results point in a very different direction.

References

1. Gibson, J. J. Psychol. Rev. 1962, 69, 477.
2. Berkeley, G. An Essay Towards a New Theory of Vision (Scribners, New York, rev. ed. 1929).

Visual and Proprioceptive Adaptation to Optical Displacement of the Visual Stimulus*

JOHN C. HAY
Smith College

HERBERT L. PICK, Jr.
University of Minnesota

The effects of long-term optical displacement of the visual stimulus were measured in a wide variety of sensory coordinations. The pattern of changes observed indicated that a transient adaptation in the proprioceptive system is succeeded by a stable adaptation in the visual system. It was found that viewing the whole body during optical displacement, rather than just a part of it, serves to induce the visual adaptation.

When the environment's optical direction from the eye is displaced to one side of

* Journal of Experimental Psychology, 1966, vol. 71, pp. 150–158. This research was supported by Research Grant MH 07588-02 from the National Institutes of Health to the University of Minnesota. Special thanks are due to Karren Ikeda and Carol Ovitz for their assistance in several of the experiments, and to the Department of Psychology of Cornell University which provided research facilities.

its objective direction, as by a wedge prism in front of the eye, the normal coordination of vision with the other spatial senses is correspondingly altered. There have been several studies of adaptation to optical displacement, and of the kind of experience needed to induce it (Held and Hein, 1958; Helmholtz, 1925). These studies have usually employed eye-hand coordination as the dependent variable. If S points to a visible target, while looking through a prism, his error is initially comparable to the optical displacement imposed by the prism, so long as he does not see his hand. If, however, he is allowed to look at his moving hand through the prism for a few minutes, his eye-hand coordination shows a compensatory change even when the hand is again concealed. This phenomenon shows that the visual and proprioceptive systems have been recoordinated: A new hand position gives S the feel of coinciding with the visual direction of the target. But eye-hand recoordination does not, by itself, tell us whether the adaptive change occurred in the seen location of the target, in the felt location of the hand, or in some central system that relates the two (Walls, 1951).

Recent studies have indicated that the adaptation induced by looking at one's hand through a prism is proprioceptive in nature (Harris, 1963; Pick, Hay, and Pabst, 1963). The evidence comes from testing other hand coordinations along with eye-hand coordination. At the same time that S is found to reduce his error in pointing at visible targets, he starts to show errors in pointing at sounds or "straight ahead." The changes in pointing at visual and nonvisual targets are similar in size and direction. This uniform change in hand positioning, irrespective of the sense modality of the target, seems most reasonably explained by supposing that the proprioceptive system of the hand, during the prismatic view, was "recalibrated" to match the externally imposed visual error.

The present study concerns the question of whether the optically displaced visual system always draws other systems into alignment with itself, or whether some kinds of prism exposure can induce an adaptation within the visual system itself. Our method involves studying the pattern of changes in several different sensory coordinations, and then inferring the locus of the adaptation.

In Exp. I, Ss engaged in their normal activities during 6 weeks of continuous exposure to spectacle prisms. This exposure condition would seem to give the best opportunity for all possible adaptive mechanisms to operate. Changes in eye-hand and ear-hand coordination were measured throughout. In Exp. II, the battery of coordination tests was enlarged to isolate possible changes in the visual or auditory systems. Finally, Exp. III sought to identify the factors which determine the kind of adaptation that takes place.

Experiment I

Eye-hand and ear-hand coordination were measured in a group of eight Ss who wore prism spectacles continuously for 6 weeks (The general results for this group, including adaptation to various prismatic distortions, are summarized in Pick and Hay, 1964.) So long as a shift in the proprioceptive "feel" of the hand is the only adaptation, these two coordinations should show identical changes during exposure.

METHOD

Prism-exposure conditions. Six women and two men, between the ages of 18 and 36, carried out their normal activities as college students while wearing 20 diopter prisms, mounted base left or base right in 40-mm. round spectacle frames. The optical displacement was approximately 11°, to the left for half the group, to the right for the others. The combined prismatic fields of the two eyes spanned about 60° vertically and 90° horizontally; side shields prevented any nonprismatic view. One S dropped out of the experiment after 33 days.

Coordination tests. Eye-hand coordination was measured with an apparatus based on Held and Gottlieb's (1958) design. The S saw a set of six targets reflected in an oblique mirror, and he reached under the mirror to mark their apparent locations on a concealed surface at the same distance as the targets. Ear-hand coordination was measured with a form of the apparatus used by Pick et al. (1963): While blindfolded, S heard a clicker sound from each of five positions, and he marked its apparent direction on a pad of newsprint mounted below the clicker. These two coordination tests were given before, during, and after the prism-exposure period.

RESULTS

Figure 1 shows the group's mean errors on both eye-hand and ear-hand coordination over the course of the experiment. The error is expressed in terms of its angular extent relative to the right eye. Positive errors are in the direction of the optical displacement; thus adaptation is indicated by a declining error. Ninety-five percent confidence limits given in parentheses beside each test's record are based on the mean daily standard error of the test.

Eye-hand coordination changes. For 12

days prior to prism exposure, the eye-hand record shows close to zero constant error. When the spectacles are first put on, on Day 0, the discontinuity in the record shows that an error of about 8° is produced. (The discrepancy from the optical displacement of 11° may be due to some rapid adaptation before this test was administered.) An adaptive change is found by Day 1, compensating for 70% of the initial error. Further exposure leads to essentially complete compensation, although the last 12 tests continue to show a slight but significant ($p \leqslant .05$) difference from the preexposure tests. When the prisms are removed, on Day 42, the adaptation state is manifested by an aftereffect error opposite to the initial prism effect. This negative aftereffect shows a readaptation which approximately mirrors the prism adaptation curve.

Ear-hand coordination changes. The ear-hand record before exposure shows no consistent bias, but manifests less precision

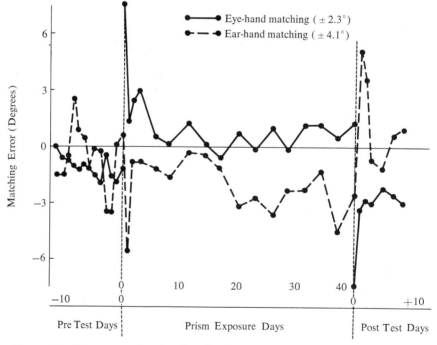

FIGURE 1   Errors in eye-hand and ear-hand coordination during 42 days exposure to optical displacement. (Ninety-five percent confidence limits given in parentheses.)

than the eye-hand record. No change is registered, of course, when the prisms are first put on. Concurrent with the compensatory eye-hand change on Day 1, the ear-hand record shows a parallel change, as if both were due to a shift in felt hand position, in accord with the short-term exposure findings of Harris (1963) and Pick et al. (1963). The ear-hand error is transitory, however, being succeeded by a reverse shift on Day 2. During the following 15 days of exposure, no evidence of a chronic ear-hand error is found, as would be expected if there were a purely proprioceptive adaptation to the prisms. On Day 20 and thereafter, a negative drift develops which is not readily explained by any theory.

During the first day without the spectacles, a transitory ear-hand error again appears, opposite to the first, as if the beginning of readaptation induced an opposite constant error of hand localization.

DISCUSSION

The first stages of adaptation during the "naturalistic" prism exposure conditions of the present experiment appear to induce the same pattern of coordination changes that Harris (1963) and Pick et al. (1963) found in short-term exposure to the hand alone. The ear-hand error disappears quickly, however, while the eye-hand compensation remains. A second process of adaptation is therefore indicated, one which develops at a slower rate.

Assuming that a proprioceptive alteration occurs in the first stages of prism exposure, slower acting changes in either vision or audition could explain the subsequent coordination pattern. A visual system change might take place, stabilizing the eye-hand compensation, while allowing the quick acting proprioceptive adaptation to dissipate. Alternatively, the binaural localization system could be drawn along with proprioception into alignment with vision, cancelling the ear-hand error. The same interpretations apply to the events during readaptation.

Experiment II

Four new coordination tests were added to the eye-hand and ear-hand tests in a replication of the first stages of Exp. I. These tests were designed to confirm the occurrence of a non-proprioceptive adaptation; to show more clearly whether this adaptation is in one of the other sensory systems; and, if so, whether the new adaptation occurs in vision or in audition.

An *ear-eye coordination* test required S to identify the visual direction of a concealed sound source. Changes in this test should confirm the existence of adaptation elsewhere than in body proprioception.

An *eye-head coordination* test required S to turn his head until he was directly facing a visible target. The S's setting of his head identifies what combination of ocular posture and retinal image position evokes in him the visual impression of straight ahead. Changes in this test therefore suggest an alteration within the visual system.

An *ear-head coordination* test required S to turn his head so that he was directly facing a concealed sound source. His head setting identifies what binaural stimulation evokes in him the auditory impression of straight ahead. Changes here would therefore suggest an alteration in the auditory system.

Finally, a *head-hand coordination* test required S to point straight ahead of his nose, with his eyes shut. Changes in this test should identify alterations in the felt position of the hand relative to the head.

METHOD

Prism-exposure conditions. The prism exposure of the first 6 days of Exp. I was repeated on seven new S's, four women and three men, from the same population. Four wore base-left, three base-right prisms.

Coordination tests. A new apparatus was used in order to administer all coordination tests, except the head-hand coordination, on the same measurement scale, and to improve the precision of auditory localization. A horizontal scale of numerals, 2 cm apart at 50 cm from the eye, provided visible targets, and identifying markers for reporting the visual directions of sounds. Three loud-speakers, 5 cm in diameter, were mounted just below the visual scale, one straight ahead and the others 5 cm. to the right and left. They were concealed from view by a cloth screen running the length of the visual scale. Half-second pulses of white noise could be delivered to them from a tape recorder to provide audible targets. The surrounding walls were lined with sound-absorbent tile. Beneath the speakers and the visual scale, there was a row of 30 push buttons, 2 cm apart on centers, which registered S's manual judgments of target position. The buttons, along with S's hands and body, were concealed from view by a shelf that projected from below the speakers to S's chin. The S's head rested on a chin piece, and was rigidly located by a bite board molded in dental impression compound. The bite piece and chin rest were mounted on a Bausch and Lomb head support which permitted rotation. The S could thus turn his head, aiding himself with his left hand on the support post, and his head position could be measured by means of a pointer at the base of the support post.

Three test procedures were administered with this apparatus, and they provided measures of eye-hand, ear-hand, ear-eye, eye-head, and ear-head coordination. In one procedure, S was told a number on the visual scale, turned his head so that he was facing it (eye-head coordination), and then pushed the button which he felt to be directly under the number (eye-hand coordination). In the second procedure, S was presented with a train of white noise pulses from one of the speakers, turned his head so that he was facing it (ear-head coordination), and then pushed the button directly under the sound (ear-hand

coordination). In the third procedure, S was again given the audible target, again turned his head towards it (ear-head coordination again), and then reported the visual scale number closest to the direction of the sound (ear-eye coordination). These tests were given in a mixed order, 10 measures on each (doubled for the ear-head test), and they took about 20 min in all. They were given before, during, and after prism exposure. In this experiment, S did not wear the prisms during testing, but he did wear a pair of empty spectacle frames to match the visual framework of exposure.

The head-hand test was given in another apparatus which held S's head in a fixed position, giving a stable direction for hand pointing. His head fixed by a bite board, and his eyes blindfolded, S reached out and put his right index finger on a glass pane 57 cm from his head, locating it so that it felt to be directly in front of his nose. Ten measures were taken on this test on each testing occasion.

RESULTS

Figure 2 shows the changes in coordination on the six tests over the course of the experiment, using the preexposure measures as the base line. Positive changes are compensatory for the optical displacement (or error producing for nonvisual tests in the direction opposite the optical displacement). An analysis of variance shows a significant variation between coordination tests, $F(4, 24) = 5.84$, $p \leqslant .01$; but does not show a reliable interaction among their records over time, $F(16, 96) = 1.21$, $p \leqslant .20$.

Eye-Hand Coordination Changes. A stable compensation is again found, almost reaching its maximum in the first 12 hours of exposure.

Ear-Hand Coordination Changes. A transient change is found here as in Exp.

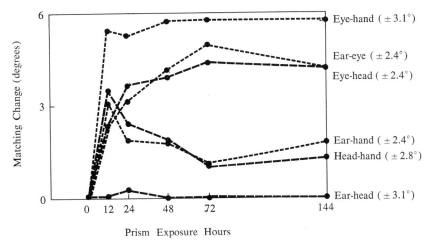

FIGURE 2   Changes in six coordination tests during six days exposure to optical displacement. (Ninety-five percent confidence limits given in parentheses.)

I, showing a gradual decline after a rapid initial rise. The error does not return to zero as in Fig. 1; the improved precision of the present apparatus may be a factor in this difference.

Ear-Eye Coordination Changes. A compensatory change is found in this new test, showing a gradual rise, and thus confirming the hypothesis of a nonproprioceptive adaptation developing more slowly than the proprioceptive adaptation.

Eye-Head Coordination Changes. The compensatory change in this test matches that of the preceding test throughout, suggesting that the two coordinations reflect in common an adjustment in the visual system.

Ear-Head Coordination Changes. No reliable change is found in this coordination, indicating that no alteration occurred in the binaural localization system.

Head-Hand Coordination Changes. This test shows the same transient change as the ear-hand test, confirming a brief adjustment to the proprioceptive system.

Relationships Between the Coordination

Changes. The ear-eye and ear-hand changes taken together seem to equal the eye-hand change over the course of the prism exposure. This suggests that processes acting in the first two coordinations are having a combined influence on eye-hand coordination. It is reasonable to suppose that these processes are adaptations in the visual and proprioceptive systems.

DISCUSSION

The pattern of coordination changes shown in Figure 2 is exactly that to be expected if a gradual adaptation in the visual system accompanies a rapid, largely transitory one in the proprioceptive system. The visual adaptation by itself accounts for the ear-eye and eye-head records; the transient proprioceptive adaptation by itself accounts for the ear-hand and head-hand records; and the two together account for the eye-hand record.

Supplementary Study. A similar experiment, using 3 days of prism exposure, was summarized in Pick and Hay (1964). This study measured ear-eye coordination along with eye-hand and ear-hand coordination, in nine Ss not used in any of the present experiments. The records for this group are congruent with Figure 2, showing a large eye-hand adaptation, a somewhat smaller ear-eye change, and a transient ear-hand error.

Experiment III

What conditions of prism exposure induce an adaptation of the visual system? In the two foregoing experiments, where a visual adaptation was found, an indefinite variety of prismatic views was experienced by S as he carried out his normal life activities, and a long period was allowed for those experiences to have an effect. These exposure conditions contrast with those of the studies by Harris (1963) and Pick et al. (1963), in which prism exposure was limited to a view of one hand, and lasted 5 min or less. The latter studies appear to have produced a purely proprioceptive adaptation. Does the difference in things viewed through the prism, or the difference in exposure time, account for the difference in adaptations? The present experiment varied the kind of visual experience during prism exposure, to see if this factor could account for differences in the nature of adaptation.

An *expansion pattern-exposure* condition (Cond. A) was tested, during which S walked towards a visible target and experienced the optical displacement of the center of expansion in the visual field (cf. Held and Freedman, 1963). It was hypothesized that the purely visual discrepancy between the normal and the prismatic expansion pattern might induce adaptive adjustments within the visual system. To keep the effects of this visual discrepancy distinct from those of intersensory conflict (see below), all parts of S's body were concealed from his view during this exposure conditions.

The *hand-exposure condition* (Cond. B) used by Harris (1963) and by Pick et al. (1963) was repeated, using an ear-eye coordination test to check the absence of a visual adaptation in this condition.

A *body-exposure condition* (Cond. C)

was tested, during which S viewed the greater part of his own body, and saw and heard his own movements and their consequences. In this condition, a great many nonvisual stimuli were placed in conflict with vision, and might reasonably be expected to induce a change in it.

METHOD

Prism-exposure Conditions. Fifteen minutes of prism exposure was given to 54 under-graduate girls divided into three treatment groups of 18 each. The exposure conditions, ordered in terms of the amount of his body which S was allowed to see through the prism, were as follows:

Condition A: Expansion Pattern Exposure. The S walked back and forth between two eye-level targets, which he was instructed to fixate during approach. The targets were at opposite ends of a 20-ft track; the pace was uncontrolled, and varied between 30 and 120 sec for each 40-ft circuit. A cardboard box was fitted over S's shoulders to conceal his body from view.

Condition B: Hand Exposure. The S's head was on a chin rest, his body concealed by a curtain suspended from the chin rest. He reached under the curtain with his right hand to sort playing cards.

Condition C: Body Exposure. The S walked the same track as in Cond. A, but this time he controlled his course by watching two guidlines on the floor 1 ft apart. Each footstep was required to just touch the edge of a floorboard, and to be preceded by dropping and catching a small ball on an elastic cord. These requirements effectively forced S continually to watch his moving body.

In order to maximize the adaptation effects to be compared, the prism strength used was 26 diopters, giving a displacement of approximately 15°. A Risley variable prism, mounted in a modified skin diver's mask, was used: The right eye had a 60° round field, the left eye was covered. The mask was worn throughout the experiment, providing a uniform visual framework during exposure and testing. The rotary prism was set to zero power for pre- and post-tests; during exposure, it was set to produce left displacement for half the Ss in each condition, right displacement for the others.

Coordination Tests. The three co-ordinations between eye, ear, and hand were tested, using the same apparatus as in Exp. II. The S's head was not free to turn in this experiment. Twenty measures on each coordination were taken in mixed order, before and after prism exposure; this took about 5 min. each time.

RESULTS

The coordination changes produced by the three exposure conditions are shown in Figure 3. An analysis of variance shows significant variation between exposure conditions, $F(2, 51) = 26.3$, $p \leqslant .001$; be-

tween coordination tests, $F(2, 102) = 32.5$, $p \leqslant .001$; and an interaction between them, $F(4, 102) = 3.90$, $p \leqslant .01$.

As the amount of the body seen through the prism increases, the eye-hand and ear-hand changes show a common pattern, with a maximum change produced by hand exposure. This is consistent with the theory that a proprioceptive adaptation underlies them both, during short-term exposure. It also suggests that the change imposed on proprioception by optical displacement is reduced when the "feel" of the whole body is put into conflict with vision.

In contrast, ear-eye coordination shows a different dependence on exposure conditions: The only reliable change was produced by body exposure, $p \leqslant .001$. A visual adaptation is thus indicated, and this interpretation is supported by the fact that the eye-hand change reliably exceeds the ear-hand change only in this condition, $p \leqslant .05$.

DISCUSSION

Prism exposure to the moving body ap-

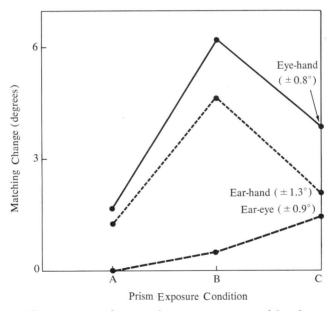

FIGURE 3 Changes in coordinations between eye, ear, and hand as a result of different visual exposures during optical displacement. (Exposure conditions ordered in terms of increasing S's exposure to his own body. Ninety-five percent confidence limits given in parentheses.)

peared to induce a visual adaptation. At the same time, body exposure reduced the proprioceptive adaptation from that produced by hand-only exposure. Exposure to the prismatic displacement of the optical expansion pattern induced no visual adaptation.

The body-exposure condition involves a high degree of discrepancy between vision and the other sensory systems. The S saw and felt his body moving, and he saw, heard, and felt contacts of his body with the floor and the ball. The expansion pattern-exposure condition, instead of an intersensory conflict, provided a discrepancy from the usual optical results of walking. We may infer that visual adaptation to optical displacement is induced by a sufficiently strong conflict with other sensory systems. The hand-exposure condition, inducing no visual adaptation, may be supposed to provide insufficient intersensory conflict.

Supplementary Study. The body-exposure condition was repeated on 12 new Ss, and eye-hand coordination was tested with both hands. The results were in agreement with those of Figure 3: $4.2 \pm 0.9°$ change in the coordination of the right hand with the eye, $4.2 \pm 1.3°$ for the same with the left hand; $3.1 \pm 1.8°$ change in ear-hand coordination; and $1.5 \pm 1.1°$ change in ear-eye coordination (95% confidence limits).

General Discussion

Adaptations appear to occur in both the visual and the proprioceptive systems to optical displacement. The visual adaptation occurs less readily than the proprioceptive one, but is more enduring when prism exposure is long extended. Proprioceptive adaptation can be induced, as has been previously reported (Harris, 1963; Pick et al., 1963), by viewing one's hand through a prism for a few minutes. Visual adaptation requires putting a greater

variety of nonvisual stimuli into conflict with the optical displacement, by viewing most of one's body through a prism. The visual adaptation appears to replace an initial, quick acting proprioceptive adaptation during long-term prism exposure.

To what part of the visual system might this adaptation be due? Helmholtz (1925) originally suggested that optical displacement is compensated for by a change in "sensed" eye position: An oblique position of the eyes comes to evoke the impression of straight ahead. Such an eye-position adaptation may seem attractively consistent with the proprioceptive adaptation in "felt" hand position, but this parallel may be misleading: Neurological theory does not attribute the registration of eye posture to a proprioceptive system (Whitteridge, 1960). Some neurological evidence does make it reasonable to attribute changes in eye-hand coordination to modifications in eye posture, whatever the basis for its registration: Patients with a newly paralyzed eye muscle tend to point to one side of visual targets (Alpern, 1962). As a further argument for assigning any visual adaptation to eye posture or its sensing, the anatomical structure of the rest of the visual system appears unsuited for adaptive changes in visual directions (Walls, 1951).

References

ALPERN, M. Physiological characteristics of the extra-ocular muscles. In H. Davson (Ed.), *The eye*, vol. 3. N. Y.: Academic Press, 1962, pp. 153–176.

HARRIS, C. S. Adaptation to displaced vision: Visual, motor or proprioceptive change? *Science*, 1963, *140*, 812–813.

HELD, R., and N. GOTTLIEB. Technique for studying adaptation to disarranged hand-eye coordination. *Percept. mot. Skills*, 1958, *8*, 83–86.

HELD, R., and S. J. FREEDMAN. Plasticity in human sensorimotor control. *Science*, 1963, *142*, 455–462.

HELD, R., and A. V. HEIN. Adaptation of disarranged hand-eye coordination contingent upon reafferent stimulation. *Percept. mot. Skills*, 1958, 8, 87–90.

HELMHOLTZ, H. v. *Treatise on physiological optics*. Vol. 3. Rochester, N. Y.: Optical Society of America, 1925. Pp. 246–247.

PICK, H. L., JR., J. C. HAY, and J. PABST. Adaptation to prismatic distortion. *Psychon. Sci.*, 1964, 1, 199–200.

PICK, H. L., JR., J. C. HAY, and J. PABST. Kinesthetic adaptation to visual distortion. Paper presented at Midwestern Psychological Association, Chicago, May 1963.

WALLS, G. L. The problem of visual direction. *Amer. J. Optom.*, 1951, 28, 55–83, 115–146, 173–212.

WHITTERIDGE, D. Central control of eye movements. In J. Field, H. W. Hagoun, and V. E. Hall (Ed.), *Handbook of physiology*. Vol. 2. Washington, D. C.: American Physiological Society, 1960. pp. 1089–1109.

CHAPTER *6*

Perceptual Learning and Development

Perceptual Behavior: The Necessity for a Developmental Approach to Its Study[*]

ROBERT H. POLLACK

Institute for Juvenile Research, Chicago

MARY ROSE CHAPLIN

University of Sydney

In psychological theorizing, "development" usually refers to investigations in which the changes that accompany increasing age are studied in systematic fashion. This is not the meaning intended here. An approach that is more general and, at the same time, applicable to much shorter periods of time will be suggested. Developmental studies using the traditional approach will, of course, be referred to wherever applicable in connection with their specific contributions to a theory of perceptual behavior.

Let us first consider two sets of experimental investigations that have a single member in common, and one study that bridges the gap between these two sets of investigations. The common study is Werner's work on contour building as a function of time (13), now recognized as being part of the more complex topic of metacontrast (Kolers and Rosner, 7). Werner presented his subjects with a disk for an interval of 12 to 25 msec; followed by a blank field for 120 to 240 msec; followed by a concentric ring, the inner diameter of which equalled that of the disk, for 12 to 25 msec. Characteristically, subjects reported only the ring, sometimes with a very bright inner field. Further investigation showed that the contours of ring and disk need not coincide, and that a shortening of the inter-stimulus interval could compensate to a point for increasing non-coincidence. Here is a phenomenon in which the second of two successively viewed figures assimilates the contour of the first and, when non-coincidence obtains, probably involves either a displacement or attraction of the disk's contour. The results just described were obtained with successive viewing of the stimuli. Other studies, in which the total stimulus configurations were similar but where the fixation of the stimuli was simultaneous, showed related results. Ogasawara (8), in his study of the Delboeuf illusion, showed that the inner circle of a concentric pair appeared to increase in size while the outer one appeared to decrease, thus showing an apparent and rather immediate attraction of parallel contours without, however, the disappearance of any part of the configuration. A recent study by George (4), in which pairs of close parallel lines mutually approached and sometimes became a single line, demonstrated how prolonged fixation affected such stimuli. Pollack (11), employing a Delboeuf figure made up of squares, also showed attraction effects after prolonged fixation.

Although these studies dealt with apparently discrete phenomena such as meta-

[*] *Acta Psychologica*, 1963, vol. 21, pp. 371–376. Copyright © North-Holland Publishing Co.

contrast, geometric illusions, and fixation aftereffects, they appeared to employ similar stimuli in similar configurations and demonstrated similar results. Perhaps their difference lies in the different stimulus durations.

Another set of studies (Piaget and Lambercier, 9) employed stimuli similar to those described by Werner, but presented them in succession. Two circles, one 20 mm in diameter and one 28 mm in diameter, to the left and right respectively of a central fixation point, were fixated for 100 msec. This was followed by two 24 mm circles, placed concentrically with respect to the first two circles. Here there was no phenomenal attraction-quite the opposite. The left 24 mm circle was judged distinctly larger than the right one. This phenomenon is known as the Usnadze effect. Köhler and Wallach (6) and George (3) presented sequences of similar figures. In their experiments, the first set of figures was fixated for a longer period of time; the results obtained, however, were identical. Thus studies concerned with immediate geometrical illusions, and those with figural after-effects of displacement, provide similar results. Again, the outstanding difference between these experiments is the duration of stimulus presentation.

The two groups of studies are bridged in the work of Ikeda and Obonai (5) where a transition between simultaneous and successive presentation of concentric circles was effected. The result was a change from Delboeuf illusion to Usnadze effect when the interval between presentation increased to between 200 and 300 msec. It is interesting to note that the effect of succession manifests itself only when presentation of stimulus elements is longer than momentary, and the interval between their presentation is increased beyond 200–300 msec. It may also be surmised that prolonged fixation makes both simultaneous and successive effects more clearly manifest.

Ontogenetic studies with the metacon-

trast effect have yet to be performed, but work with the Delboeuf illusion (Piaget et al., 10) and with the Usnadze effect (Piaget and Lambercier, 9) demonstrated a decline with chronological age of the former and an increase of the latter, thus raising the probability of two distinct developmental trends. Pollack (12), using the figural after-effect version of the Usnadze figure, demonstrated a fall in frequency of after-effect from ages four to ten and then a rise to adulthood. This perhaps indicates that fixation in young children might substitute for the process underlying succession, which emerges slowly during childhood. Thus, a simultaneous contrast between the after-effect of a previously fixated stimulus and a stimulus now present could be taking place rather than the temporal integration of two events discrete in time so characteristic of adult successive comparison. The results produced are the same: a repulsion displacement effect. In the Werner study (13), on the contrary, the short duration of the stimulus elements, coupled with the short interval between them, simulates prolonged simultaneous fixation while obliterating the element presented first.

Time, therefore, seems to be a crucial dimension for study. The passage of time, however brief, appears to result in a change in perceptual behavior. Is not, then, change in behavior through time a most useful definition of development? Such a definition prejudges no issues as to whether development is to be considered progressive, regressive, or both; or whether the dimension "simple-complex" is involved. Nor does it, in itself, prejudge the purported determinants of behavior working through time. In our opinion, to define development as a change in behavior through time seems to be indicated.

Perception itself, however, is another matter. It will be defined here as a pattern of behavioral changes resulting from some external or internal physical energy change which impinges upon and activates a receptor system. The system can be described as an anatomical network made up of the particular receptor impinged upon and all the interaction and feedback mechanisms pertaining thereto, including all brain areas involved. Thus, physiologically, receptor activation sets in motion a series of peripheral and central neurochemical events and they, in turn, facilitate, dampen, or maintain the initial receptor activity (Duke-Elder, 2).

The process—and in this interpretation perception *is* a process—could conceivably go on interminably unless the pattern becomes repetitive (thus giving the appearance of behavioral stability), the tissue involved adapts and becomes less able to respond (Adrian, 1), or external events occur to change the quality of receptor activity. Since perception treated in this way requires time, it is a developmental process.

Each bit of perceptual behavior is the termination of a sequence of events which began at the moment of impingement of the correlated stimulus. Such sequences are usually of very short duration, so that the term most apt to characterize them is Werner's (14) term *microgenesis.* Microgenesis is used in contrast with such terms as *ontogenesis* (i.e., changes with chronological age), and *phylogenesis* (i.e., evolutionary change). The link between microgenesis and ontogenesis lies in the latter being the sequence of change in microgenetic patterns in individuals of the same species, while phylogenesis deals with changes in ontogenetic patterns between species. If perception is accepted as a developmental process, then it becomes of prime importance to locate any sample of perceptual behavior within some developmental sequence.

The provision of developmental sequences in perception can serve as a descriptive framework within which to classify and at least temporally order groups of phenomena. Furthermore, knowledge of the developmental sequences can distinguish among phenomena with phenotypical similarity. Once a sequence is known, the manipulation of relevant determining variables at different points in the time sequence can be undertaken, and their relative potencies and interactions noted. For most experimental psychologists, investigation would take place within microgenesis, while tradition conscious developmental and comparative psychologists might be more likely to organize these data within their own larger frameworks.

For a summary view of the viewpoint presented here, it would be helpful to return to the groups of experimental studies discussed above. They represent for the most part—in the view of their authors—investigations of discrete, sometimes offbeat phenomena, employed to promote various theories or partial theories of perception. Yet there appears to be evidence that these phenomena fall into two groups, each member of which occurs at a different point in the temporal sequence for each specific kind of behavior. At the same time, a look at the illusion studies, for example, shows that they are opposite in character and tend to differ ontogenetically, despite the classification of these phenomena under the rubric illusion. This would imply that the Köhler size effect is more like the Usnadze effect, instead of being like the attraction effects observed by George (4) and by Pollack (11) which are, in turn, similar to the Delboeuf illusion. Recognition of these similarities and differences must drive investigators to search for determinants active in any given microgenetic sequence as against those active in another microgenetic sequence. At the same time it must be recognized that any observed bit of behavior is only a time sample, not a total phenomenon in itself.

Viewing the behavioral world as here suggested has its difficulties as well as its advantages. Chief among the former is the dilemma of whether to use cross-sectional or longitudinal modes of observation. Cross-sectional data reveal relatively little about the individual. Longitudinal data, on the other hand, are perforce contaminated by those stimuli that are introduced to obtain observations at various points in the time sequence, as well as by the stimulus effects of the responses elicited. This is a conflict, however, that is common to all scientific disciplines.

The authors prefer to end their discussion on this cautious note: It appears that development, i.e., behavioral change over time, must be considered in any theory of perceptual behavior; the mechanics of its consideration, however, offer stumbling blocks that are not inconsiderable.

References

1. ADRIAN, E. D. The Basis of Sensation. London: Christophers, 1928.
2. DUKE-ELDER, W. STEWART. Textbook of Ophthalmology, vol. 1. London: Kimpton, 2nd ed., 1958.
3. GEORGE, F. H. On the figural after-effect. Quart. J. exp. Psychol., 1953, 5, 128–135.
4. GEORGE, F. H. Acuity and the statistical theory of figural after-effects. J. exp. Psychol., 1962, 63, 423–425.
5. IKEDA, H., and T. OBONAI. Studies in figural after-effects: IV. The contrast confluence illusion of concentric circles and the figural after-effect. Jap. Psychol. Res., 1955, 2, 17–23.
6. KÖHLER, W., and H. WALLACH. Figural after-effects: an investigation of visual processes. Proc. Amer. phil. Soc., 1944, 88, 269–357.
7. KOLERS, P. A., and B. S. ROSNER. On visual masking (metacontrast). Dichoptic observation. Amer. J. Psychol., 1960, 73, 2–21.
8. OGASAWARA, J. Displacement-effect of concentric circles. Jap. J. Psychol., 1952, 22, 16–25.
9. PIAGET, J., and M. LAMBERCIER. Recherches sur le développement des perceptions: V. Essai sur un effet d' "Einstellung" survenant au cours de perceptions visuelles successives (effet Usnadze). Arch. Psychol., Genève, 1944, 30, 139–196.
10. PIAGET, J., E. BOESCH, and B. VON ALBERTINI. Recherches sur le développement des perceptions: I. Introduction à l'étude des perceptions chez l'enfant et analyse d'une illusion relative à la perception visuelle de cercles concentrique (Delboeuf). Arch. Psychol., Genève, 1942, 29, 1–107.
11. POLLACK, R. H. Displacement after-effects: Succession vs. simultaneity in the presentation of parallel contours. Paper read at the 15th annual conference of the British Psychological Society, Australia Branch, Melbourne, 1959.
12. POLLACK, R. H. Figural after-effects as a function of age. Acta Psychologica, 1960, 17, 417–423.
13. WERNER, H. Studies on contour: I. Qualitative analyses. Amer. J. Psychol., 1935, 47, 40–64.
14. WERNER, H. Microgenesis and aphasia. J. abnorm. soc. Psychol., 1956, 52, 347–353.

Developmental Changes in the Location of Form Discrimination Cues*

LARRY C. KERPELMAN

University of Massachusetts

ROBERT H. POLLACK

Institute for Juvenile Research, Chicago

Summary.—Two experiments are reported on age changes in form discrimination cues. In the first, a pilot study for another investigation, a drop was noted between ages 5 and 6 yr. in children's ability to discriminate among five irregular pentagons. In an attempt to clarify this unexpected finding, a dimensional analysis of the stimulus attributes of the pentagons was undertaken. This led to several hypotheses, tested in the second experiment. The results of that experiment with children aged 3½ to 7½ yr. suggested that the bottom attributes of the stimuli were the most salient features for all ages. As the children became older, however, a top-to-bottom scanning process appeared to increase in importance. Suggestions for further research were made.

The present report describes a preliminary analysis of some of the cues that are used in discriminating forms and the changes in their use that occur over a relatively short developmental span. An unexpected finding in a pilot experiment for another investigation led to a further experiment in an attempt to clarify the pilot findings. Both experiments are reported here.

Experiment I

In connection with another investigation, the pilot study reported here was undertaken. The purpose was to find three or four geometric forms that were mutually equally discriminable within each of three age groups.

METHOD

Subjects. Ss were 30 nursery school children (15 of each sex) between the ages of 3½ and 6½ yr[1] There were 10 aged 4 yr, 12 aged 5 yr, and 8 aged 6 yr, a year group being defined as ½ yr before to ½ yr after the year birthday.

Stimuli. Five irregular pentagons, selected from Boynton and Bush (1956), were enlarged by means of a pantograph to cover an area of approximately 4.55 in¹ (range, 4.00 to 4.96 in¹), drawn on black construction paper, and cut out. The pentagons used and the orientation in which they were presented are illustrated in the top row of Figure 1. Five practice stimuli were also made from black construction paper: circle, equilateral triangle, square, rectangle, and parallelogram. The sets of stimuli were constructed in duplicate. A

* *Perceptual and Motor Skills*, 1964, 19, pp. 375–382. © Southern Universities Press 1964. Portions of this paper were presented at the 1964 American Psychological Association Convention in Los Angeles. Grateful acknowledgement is made to Mrs. Elizabeth Sarris, Director of Jack and Jill Day Nursery, La Grange Park, Illinois for her cooperation in providing Ss and facilities.

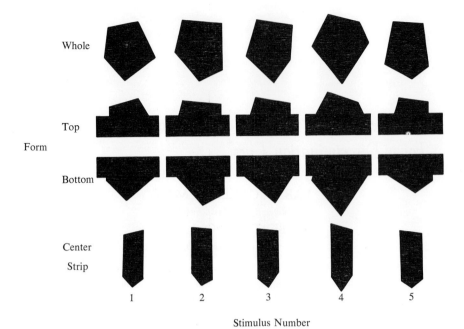

FIGURE 1   Stimulus forms used in investigation. (Orientation shown is orientation in which stimuli were always presented.)

circular grey cardboard field 11 in. in diameter was used for stimulus presentation.

Procedure.   Ss were tested individually. Each S was seated at a table opposite E. On the table was the circular field covered by a cardboard screen. First the practice forms were presented. They were placed around the edge of the field with one identical to one of the perimeter stimuli placed in the same orientation in the middle. When the screen was lifted E said: "This is a game we are going to play. Here is a circle in the middle. I want you to find the one around it that is just the same as the one in the middle. Put your finger on the one that is just like the one in the middle." Each practice stimulus was alternately used as the standard (St) on succeeding trials, the St being changed behind the cover screen after each trial. The comparison (Co) stimuli were randomly rearranged around the periphery after two or three trials.

When it was clear that S could per-

form the practice discriminations (usually only five trials were necessary), the discrimination task proper was begun. The procedure was the same as for the practice task. Ss were told after the practice task: "Now we're going to play the same game, only this time it will be harder, so look carefully at every one before you make your choice." The stimuli were set out behind the cover screen, and when it was removed E said: "Now here are some other things. I want you to find the one around the sides that is just the same as the one in the middle. You show me which one is the same."

Each S was given 30 trials, each of the 5 stimuli serving as St on 6 trials according to a prearranged random order. All St and Co stimuli were presented in the same orientation shown in Figure 1. No reinforcement was given, but Ss were encouraged in a general manner throughout. All trials were timed. Due to practical limitations, each age group was run on a separate day.

Results

The data were analyzed in terms of number of correct responses, as there were enough errors to render response latency meaningless as a measure. Scores were in terms of number of correct discriminations out of 6 trials per stimulus for each S.

The results are graphically illustrated in Figure 2. Simple randomized design analyses of variance for each stimulus yielded significant age trends for Stimulus 1 ($F = 3.89$, $df = 2/27$, $p < .05$) and Stimulus 4 ($F = 5.28$, $df = 2/27$, $p < .025$), the .05 level being the significance level used throughout this paper. Completely unexpected, however, was the distinct drop in discrimination performance between ages 5 and 6 yr. on 4 of the 5 stimuli. Although t tests indicated that the drop in performance was not statistically significant for any of the 4 stimuli, it was consistent enough to provoke an inquiry into the possible causes. It simply may have been due to the fact that each age group was run on a different day. Still, other directions were explored in an at-tempt to elucidate this curious and unex-pected finding.

Experiment II

A crude analysis of the results of the above study was undertaken which yielded several hypotheses concerning the per-ceptual mechanisms that Ss of various age groups might have used in their discrimina-tions. The analysis consisted of measure-ment of each of the stimuli on seven di-mensions: (a) horizontal width at lower angle, (b) length of longest bottom side, (c) extent of bottom angle, (d) length of longest top side, (e) extent of topmost angle, (f) vertical length from bottom angle, and (g) area. The first three di-mensions suggested bottom features, the middle two, top features, and the last two suggested features of the entire pentagon. Each stimulus was compared on these seven features with the stimulus it was most confused with by Ss of each age group and the one it was least confused with. If the former differed on a dimen-sion by less than a predetermined amount, or the latter differed by more than that same amount, a tally mark was given on that dimensional attribute. By so doing, a rough determination of the attributes which each age group seemed to be using in making their discriminations was ob-tained.

Several hypotheses concerning the discriminative mechanisms that might have been operative resulted. The analysis sug-gested that discriminations were made by the 4- and 5-yr.-olds mainly on the basis of differences in the bottoms of the stimuli. The 6-yr.-olds seemed to use a combination of top attributes-vertical extent-bottom at-tributes in making their judgments. The possibility occurs that, while bottom dif-ferences may have been the predominant cue for the younger children, the other children were beginning to switch to a top-to-bottom scanning determination of

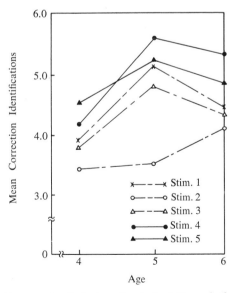

FIGURE 2 Relative discriminability of the pentagons as a function of age. (Experi-ment 1)

stimulus differences.[1] This transition may have interfered with discrimination of the stimuli, i.e., the developmentally older method was being replaced by a new method of form perception, and performance may have dropped as a result of the disruption due to the transition of methods. If this speculation were true, then the performance curve might be expected to rise again once the transition period was weathered, perhaps at Age 7.

Exp. II was undertaken to confirm the findings of Exp. I and to investigate further the dimensions of the stimuli that Ss of various ages might have used in making their discriminations. Ss aged 7 yr. were included to extend the developmental curves. The replication aspect was undertaken by presenting Ss aged 4, 5, 6, and 7 yr. with the same task used in Exp. I. Three other sub-groups of Ss were used to investigate the possible effects on their discrimination of the hypothesized stimulus attributes. These sub-groups were presented with just parts (top, bottom, or center vertical strip) of the pentagons which had been used previously.

If it were true that the bottoms of the stimuli provided the main cues for discrimination for the 4- and 5-yr.-old Ss, then a rising developmental curve was expected between 4 and 5 yr. as occurred with the wholes in the previous experiment. If it were further true that the 6-yr.-olds were in a transition phase of using vertical extent as well as top and bottom cues, and if the introduction of a new cue were responsible for the performance decrement found at this age in Exp. I, then

this decrement was not expected to occur if bottoms only were presented. Since the tops of the stimuli did not show a change in emphasis with age in the above analysis and were apparently less used than the bottoms, a gradual linear developmental increase was expected for Ss shown tops only. Since 4- and 5-yr.-old Ss appeared to use mainly the bottoms, they were not expected to show a performance facilitation for the center strip. If the hypotheses about the process used by the 6-yr.-olds were correct, however, then a performance rise was expected with the 6-yr.-old Ss given the center strip only. The magnitude of this rise, further, was not expected to go above the level of performance of Ss presented the wholes. Ss presented the whole stimuli were expected to perform as in the previous experiment.

METHOD

Subjects. Ss were 80 children (40 of each sex), ranging in age from $3\frac{1}{2}$ to $7\frac{1}{2}$ yr., obtained from nursery schools and playgrounds.[2] They were divided into 4 age groups: 4, 5, 6, and 7 yr., a year group being defined as previously.

Stimuli. In addition to the whole (W) pentagon stimuli and the practice forms used in Exp. I, 3 sets of part-forms were constructed from black paper for this experiment. The orientation of the whole pentagons was such that the bottom half contained 3 angles and the top half 2. The 5 bottom (B) stimuli were formed by drawing a line horizontally across the respective W-stimuli from the highest of the 3 bottom vertices, thereby leaving two angles. Onto this area was attached a

---

[1] It is just as likely that a bottom-to-top scanning occurred. Work by Ghent (1963, 1964), however, points to scanning as beginning at the top of a stimulus and going downward, and that is the mechanism assumed here. In any case, some kind of scanning must have occurred if both top and bottom attributes contributed to the discrimination of the older children, for the mean vertical extent of the stimuli (14° 10′) was so large that it precluded clear viewing of the stimuli in a single glance.

[2] The cooperation of the following in providing Ss is gratefully acknowledged: Mrs. L. Pitelka, Director of Mother Goose Nursery School, Hillside, Illinois; Mrs. H. York, Director of Neighborhood Playhouse Kindergarten, Bellwood, Illinois; and Mrs. Kent Brandon, Activity Supervisor of Glenview, Illinois Park District. The authors also wish to thank Dr. Dorothy Nelson for her assistance in running Ss.

rectangular area 1×3 in. This was done to give all 5 stimuli a similar configuration with only the bottoms differing. Mean area of the B-stimuli was 4.67 in² (range, 3.90 to 6.00 in².

The 5 top (T) stimuli were constructed by drawing a horizontal line ½ in below the lowest of the 2 top vertices of the respective W stimuli, also leaving two angles. Again a rectangular area was attached for the reason indicated above. Mean area of the T-stimuli was 4.14 in² (range, 3.91 to 4.40 in²).

The center strip (C) stimuli were constructed by drawing two parallel vertical lines ½ in on either side of the bottom center vertex of the W-stimuli. A rectangular area was not incorporated into these forms because it was felt that this would interfere with the scanning process hypothesized. Mean area of C-stimuli was 2.58 in² (range, 2.45 to 2.80 in²). While the rank order of area of these 5 stimuli did not correspond exactly to that of their corresponding W-, B-, and T-stimuli, it differed only slightly. All forms are pictured in Figure 1. Mean vertical visual angle subtended by the five stimuli within each form group, assuming a 12-in viewing distance was 14° 10′, 5° 50′, 3° 38′ and 13° 5′ for the W-, B-, T-, and C-forms, respectively. Mean horizontal visual angle was 10° 30′, 14° 15′, 14° 15′, and 3° 25′ for the same forms.

Procedure. The procedure was the same as in Exp. I. The 20 Ss within each age group were randomly assigned to 1 of 4 sub-groups, each sub-group being given the task of discriminating among either W-, B-, T-, or C-forms. Thus each S worked only with the whole-form or with one of the part-forms. The N in each cell was 5, with sex divided 3 and 2 within each cell. Ss of different ages were run on the same day.

RESULTS

The data again were analyzed in terms of number of correct responses. Sex of Ss was ignored since it had no significant effect on performance in Exp. I.

A two-way analysis of variance of the W-forms in both experiments revealed a significant Ages effect ($F = 4.22$, $df = 2/33$, $p < .025$), a significant Replications effect ($F = 5.15$, $df = 1/33$, $p < .05$), and a non-significant interaction. The findings of Exp. I were not repeated: the groups in this experiment exhibited a *rise* in performance between 5 and 6 yr. on 4 of the 5 W-stimuli.

Although a replication of results for the W-stimuli did not occur, it was felt that it would still be of value to analyze the component-forms (T, B, and C) data of this experiment in an attempt to shed light on the developmental course of the perceptual process. A two-factor analysis of variance, summarized in Table 1, showed significant main effects of Ages and Forms, as well as significant interaction between Ages and Forms.

In order to pinpoint the source of the

TABLE 1

Analysis of Variance of Part-forms

SOURCE	df	MS	F	p
Age	3	203.24	14.33	<.001
Forms	2	238.65	16.83	<.001
Age × Forms	6	32.83	2.32	<.05
Within	48	14.18		
Total	59			

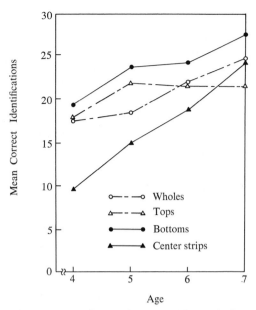

FIGURE 3 Relative discriminability of the whole-forms and part-forms as a function of age. (Experiment II)

Ages × Forms interaction, separate simple randomized design analyses of variance at each age level were computed. The results indicated significant Forms effects at Age 4 ($F = 6.97$, $df = 2/12$, $p < .01$), Age 5 ($F = 11.17$, $df = 2/12$, $p < .005$), and Age 7 ($F = 5.19$, $df = 2/12$, $p < .025$), but not at Age 6. Further analysis of the means of the form sub-groups within each age group using Scheffe's S-method (McNemar, 1962, p. 286) indicated that the significant Forms effect was due mainly to significantly poorer discrimination of the C-forms at Ages 4 and 5. At Age 7 the Forms effect was due to significantly poorer discrimination of the T-forms. The foregoing discussion may be clarified by reference to Figure 3. Trend analyses of the performance curves of each form with age indicated a significant increasing linear trend of the Bottoms ($F = 16.89$, $df = 1/16$, $p < .001$) and of the Center Strips ($F = 38.71$, $df = 1/16$, $p < .001$), but no significant trend—linear or curvilinear—for the Tops. A simple randomized design analysis of variance across ages within the T-forms revealed no significant

Age effect either, whereas there were significant Age effects for B- and C-forms.

Discussion

The results of Exp. I were not replicated in Exp. II. The drop in performance between Ages 5 and 6 in the former study may have reflected the confounding effect of day of running, as suggested previously. Another plausible alternative explanation is that since the drop was not a statistically significant one, the fact that it occurred on 4 out of 5 pentagons may merely have been a chance occurrence. Whatever the cause, the break in the increasing developmental trend apparently was not a replicable effect.

Yet the unexpected finding did lead to a more searching look at the data. The dimensional analysis of the discrimination performance of the pilot Ss led to hypotheses concerning the perceptual mechanisms of children in a discrimination task of this kind that were, for the most part, borne out in Exp. II. The B-forms were most easily discriminated at all age levels. Discriminability of these forms increased gradually with age in a linear fashion, again suggesting that the bottoms were the most salient features of the figures. Discrimination performance on the tops did not exhibit a significant age trend: the contribution of the tops, whatever it might have been at Ages 4 and 5, leveled off markedly after that. The center strips, however, were discriminated poorly at Age 4, but proficiency increased in steeply linear fashion up to Age 7. At that point, discrimination of the center strips was almost equal to that of the wholes, as predicted.

In general, then, the dimensional analysis of the data of Exp. I and the empirical results of Exp. II tend to support each other. The picture that emerges is one in which—with full opportunity to examine the stimuli—younger children tend to use the bottoms of the pentagonal stimuli as cues to discriminate among them, but with age a top-to-bottom scanning of the stimuli plays a progressively greater role. This is in line with the finding of Ghent (1963) that the tendency of children to scan a form from top to bottom increases with age. A subsequent study by Ghent (1964) showed the beginning of a tendency to scan to occur between 4 and 5 yr. The difference between this finding and that of the present investigation may be due to differences in stimulus presentation: Ghent's Ss were shown the discriminanda at tachistoscopic exposure speeds.

An informational analysis of the forms used and the results obtained might also be applied, although cautiously, because the forms used in the present experiment were not randomly generated. Focusing on only one dimension of the forms, sidedness, it can be seen that the Wholes and Center Strips are 5-sided, while the Tops and Bottoms are 8-sided. Findings using adult human Ss (Brown, Hitchcock, and Michels, 1962) and tree squirrel Ss (Michels, Pittman, Hitchcock, and Brown, 1962) indicated that discrimination of 4- and 5-sided forms is more difficult than for 7- and 8-sided ones. While greater difficulty of discrimination holds for the 5-sided C-forms for Ages 4 and 5 yr., it does not hold for these forms at 6 and 7 yr. or for the 5-sided W-forms at any age. Of course, this analysis focuses on only one defining dimension, albeit one which has received most attention in the literature. The interaction of other dimensions (see Attneave, 1957), not considered here, may better account for the results within an information theory framework. For example, the nature of construction of the Center Strips made them appear more bilaterally symmetrical than the Wholes from which they were derived. It may be speculated that discrimination is more difficult among stimuli which are more bilaterally symmetrical than among those which are not, although this is in direct contrast to the empirical findings of Rapaport (1957). This speculation holds only for the younger ages, where Center Strip performance was significantly poorer. It suggests the possible advisability of adding another variable in informational analysis of form discrimination performance, i.e., developmental parameters.

The generality of the conclusions reported here is based on the particular stimuli, irregular pentagons, since these were not randomly generated shapes (Attneave and Arnoult, 1956). It is also based on the assumption that discrimination of the part-forms is equivalent to the perceptual mechanisms which those part-forms were designed to tap, especially the assumption that the center strips evoke a top-to-bottom scanning, rather than the reverse. Further research is needed using other shapes, larger samples, and more refined partialling of the various discrimination mechanisms which were presumably operative in the present investigations. If account is taken of the above factors, future experimentation might shed further light on the issues raised and the tentative conclusions drawn in the present work.

References

ATTNEAVE, F. Physical determinants of the judged complexity of shapes. *J. exp. Psychol.*, 1957, 52, 221–227.

ATTNEAVE, F., and M. D. ARNOULT. The quantitative study of shape and pattern perception. *Psychol. Bull.*, 1956, 53, 452–471.

BOYNTON, R. M., and W. R. BUSH. Recognition of forms against a complex background. *J. Opt. Soc. Amer.*, 1956, 46, 758–764.

BROWN, D. R., L. HITCHCOCK, JR., and K. M. MICHELS. Quantitative studies in form perception: an evaluation of the role of selected stimulus parameters in the visual discrimination performance of human subjects. *Percept. mot. Skills*, 1962,,14, 519–529.

GHENT, L. Stimulus orientation as a factor in recognition of form. Paper read at Eastern Psychol. Assn, New York, April, 1963.

GHENT, L. Age changes in the mode of perceiving geometric forms. Paper read at Eastern Psychol. Assn., Philadelphia, April, 1964.

McNEMAR, Q. *Psychological statistics.* (3rd ed.) New York: Wiley, 1962.

MICHELS, K. M., G. G. PITTMAN, L. HITCH-COCK, JR., and D. R. BROWN. Visual discrimination: tree squirrels and quantified stimulus dimensions. *Percept. mot. Skills,* 1962, *15,* 443–450.

RAPPAPORT, M. The role of redundancy in the discrimination of visual forms. *J. exp. Psychol.,* 1957, 53, 3–10.

Some Aspects of a Research Program Based on an Organismic-developmental Approach to Cognition: Experiments and Theory*

SEYMOUR WAPNER
Clark University

This paper is restricted to a description of the research program on perception and other cognitive operations which Heinz Werner and I initiated at Clark University some fifteen years ago. Our research program is embedded in an experimental-theoretical approach which we now refer to as organismic-developmental. The organismic aspects of this view were specified for perception in sensory-tonic field theory (Werner and Wapner, 1949, 1952b, 1956b; Wapner and Werner, 1957); the developmental aspects derive from Heinz Werner's comparative-developmental point of view (Werner, 1940, 1957).

In characterizing the research program: (1) I shall outline our general aims; (2) I shall very briefly describe some general features of the organismic-developmental approach; (3) I shall briefly describe the research program in the course of elaborating some specific features of the theoretical approach; and (4) I shall summarize some research findings on selected problem areas which will both concretize the theoretical-experimental features alluded to, and, hopefully, suggest areas of clinical application.

The most general aim of our research program is to understand perception and other cognitive operations in broad enough terms to encompass the general mechanisms underlying these features of behavior as well as their occurrence under a variety of conditions and in a variety of groups and individuals.

We make two basic assumptions: (1) that perception and certain other aspects of cognition have to be conceived in terms of an interrelationship between sensory input and intra-organismic factors, and (2) that this interrelationship exists at an elementary level as well as on the level of complex personality reaction. Given these two assumptions, the research program currently deals with a number of general

* *Journal of The American Academy of Child Psychiatry,* 1964, vol. 3, pp. 193–212, 226–230.

This research program is supported by PHS Grant MH-00348 from the National Institute of Mental Health; recent studies utilizing pharmacological agents have been largely supported by PHS Grant MH-02262 from the National Institute of Mental Health.

This paper, in slightly altered form, was presented as the Academic Lecture at the 1963 meeting of the American Academy of Child Psychiatry in Hershey, Pennsylvania.

areas approached from the *organismic-developmental* point of view.

First, from the *organismic perspective* we study general mechanisms underlying sensory-intra-organismic interdependence. Second, from the *developmental perspective* the general mechanisms underlying behavior are studied in terms of: the changes that occur from childhood to adulthood, from adulthood to old age; their occurrence in psychopathology including such groups as schizophrenics, brain-injured, mentally retarded, emotionally disturbed, etc.; the changes that occur under certain drugs like Lysergic Acid Diethylamide (LSD-25); the changes that occur in the formation of these behaviors; and, finally, the occurrence of these behaviors as individual differences in normal adults.

Programmatic research of this kind is necessarily an endeavor which is the work of many individuals.[1] The broad scope of the program provides the advantage that each problem area approached can contribute to over-all conceptualization when treated generally and yet be of wide enough significance to warrant systematic treatment for its own sake. Over the years, despite the extensive efforts of many colleagues and students, only small beginnings have been made in actualizing the general objective of our research program. We may look at its current status by considering some general features of the approach.

Some General Features of the Organismic-Developmental Approach

The organismic perspective features *cross-sectional* analysis of organismic systems in the attempt to characterize mechanisms that underlie perception and other

cognitive processes; the developmental perspective considers *change* in a system undergoing transition. Change is described in terms of a systematic principle which defines developmental progression in formal, structural, or organizational terms. This is the orthogenetic principle which states: with development there is increasing differentiation and hierarchic integration (Werner, 1940, 1957). Though for purposes of exposition the two perspectives may be described and treated separately, they are interrelated in so far as both focus on formal, structural, or organizational aspects of behavior and assume an organism actively directed toward goals. This commonness of focus is manifest: (1) in the forms of analysis common to both (viz., part-whole and means-end relations) (Werner, 1940, 1957; Wapner, 1963; Werner and Kaplan, 1963); (2) in the categories of behavioral operations common to both (viz., biologic-organismic, sensori-motor, perceptual, conceptual); (3) in the classification of the ends (viz., objects or events) toward which the various cognitive operations are directed; (4) in the stress on interrelationship (i.e., between levels of operation, between classes of objects or events, between conditions); (5) in the stress on field-theoretical analysis with respect to reciprocal relations between organism and environment, e.g., interactive as well as polar relations between self and world (Wapner and Werner, 1963); (6) in the insistence upon dynamic rather than static conceptualization (Werner, 1959); (7) in the differentiation of means vs. ends and the analysis of process rather than achievement (Werner, 1937; Werner and Kaplan, 1963); and (8) in an orientation toward probing rather than proving (Werner, 1959).

Despite the common features of the two perspectives, there are differences. The similarities and differences may be seen by reviewing a schematic outline of the research program, and considering how the program is shaped first by the organismic

[1] Our collaborators are too numerous to list here. Some will be mentioned in the course of the presentation; the names of others can be gleaned from the publications, Ph.D. theses, M.A. theses, and papers listed.

perspective and then by the developmental perspective.

Schematic Representation of Research Program and Some Additional Features of the Organismic-Developmental Approach

The research program can be briefly described by the schema presented in Figure 1. The figure is four-dimensional in design, each dimension representing one category of analysis, but with the total plan of research representing interaction of all four dimensions. Consider first the three dimensions within a cube:

Within the up-down dimension of the cube four levels of cognitive operations are represented. These may be concretized by describing them in terms of differences between self and world: operations on the *biologic-organismic level,* where the separation of self and object is minimal, are exemplified by physiological intra-organismic mechanisms which play a role in cognition, and include such operations as physiological adaptation of the retina to light and dark, postural mechanisms, etc.; operations on the *sensorimotor level* represent little advance in the separation between self and world since these operations are dependent on direct, motoric, concrete manipulation of objects; for *perceptual operations* there is greater differentiation between self and world in so far as these operations require the organism to be contemplatively directed toward the properties of objects in external space; and, finally, the greatest differentiation of self and world holds for *conceptual operations* since they involve manipulation of symbols which are differentiated from and representative of objects. From the organismic perspective these cognitive operations are viewed as alternative means of achieving a given end or goal. The developmental perspective stresses analysis in terms of means-end relations and is concerned with the problem of emergence of the operations and of the relations between them. Considering the progression from early to late stages of development, biologic-organismic operations are assumed to emerge first, these are followed by sensorimotor operations, then by perceptual operations, and, finally, by conceptual operations. They are related in terms of the general principle of development: An operation that emerges at a later stage in development does not take the place of the operations already present, but is hierarchically related to it;

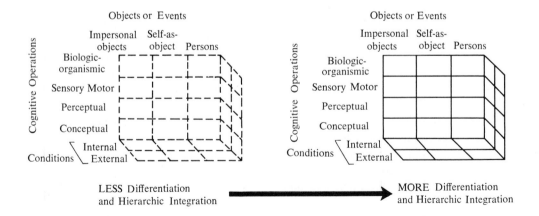

Comparison of developmentally ordered groups, conditions, stages of emergence, etc.

FIGURE 1   Schematic representation of research program.

the mature individual is assumed to have at his disposal the early as well as the late appearing functions.

Considering the left-right dimension of each cube, three basic classes of objects or events are specified: (1) *impersonal objects,* or events which deal with temporal changes in properties or relations between properties of impersonal objects; (2) *body-as-object,* or events which involve temporal changes in properties of body-as-object; (3) *person-as-object,* or events which deal with temporal changes in properties of persons or relations between persons.

Considering the near-far dimension of the cube, two classes of conditions are delineated, viz., (a) internal conditions or states of the organism (alterable by such factors as changes in posture, drugs, etc.), and (b) external conditions (e.g., physical, social, etc.).

The fourth dimension, linking the two cubes, represents the developmental aspect which stresses *change* in the organismic system. This dimension, as represented by a shift from a dotted-line cube to a solid-line cube, is characterized by a developmental progression in terms of a shift from a state of relative dedifferentiation to a state of greater differentiation and hierarchic integration, and has reference to comparisons between individuals, groups, conditions, stages of emergence, etc., as long as they represent a series which can be ordered developmentally.

The actual investigations conducted may be restricted to the combinations of categories defining a cell within the cube, e.g., effect of changes in internal postural state on the perceptual properties of an object, or it may be more complicated in so far as it involves relations between cells constituting the four dimensions already specified (object or event; operations; conditions; developmental status), e.g., the changing relations between perception of object position and perception of one's own body position under body tilt, depending upon developmental status of the subject.

The choice of problems, the nature of the experimental designs, and the mode of theoretical interpretation are dependent upon certain theoretical considerations underlying the two aspects of the approach. Some representative aspects of theory and their consequences for experiment will be considered, first for the organismic, then for the developmental aspect of the approach.

Organismic Aspects

Let us consider three features of the organismic perspective that have shaped our experiments. The first is that *behavior must be considered in relation to the context of total organismic activity.* This proposition is in keeping with the central postulate of sensory-tonic field theory which states that perception is a reflection of a relation between sensory input (proximal stimulation) and ongoing organismic states. "Proximal stimulation" is defined as stimulation of sensory surfaces which issues from a physical object; "organismic state" represents the total ongoing state of the organism as it is affected by past history, present internal stimulation, and by stimulation from sources other than those of the object attended (Werner and Wapner, 1949, 1952b, 1956b; Wapner and Werner, 1957).

This means that perception is, so to speak, a reflection of a part, "proximal stimulation," in relation to the context of organismic activity, "organismic state." This relationship is defined symbolically by sRo, where "s" represents proximal stimulus, "o" represents organismic state, and "R" represents relationship. Given this formulation, it follows that changes in perception can occur as a function of changes in either aspect of the polarity "organism: object," i.e., there are changes in perception with changes in the organismic context, on the one hand, or with changes in the part, i.e., proximal stimulus, on the other. This leads to experimentation where the consequences for perception are studied by variation of proximal stimulation and by variation of the state of the organism, whether transient in the laboratory or as an ongoing state that exists in nature (e.g., Blane, 1962; Comalli, 1963). Studies of this kind will be elaborated later on.

Consider another aspect of the organismic perspective, viz., the proposition that in the organism *subsystems do not operate in isolation, but rather that organismic subsystems interact.* This leads to the proposition that a change in organismic state pertains not to one but to all sense modalities. This general assumption of organismic functioning led to experimentation on intermodal effects of various kinds of stimulation and on figural adaptation (Werner and Wapner, 1955b). We may single out the studies by Alvin Goldstein (1955) which showed that following *visual adaptation* to a tilted visual field there were significant changes in *tactual-kinesthetic* perception of verticality (see also Ohwaki, 1959, 1961; Giannitrapani, 1958; Mayer, 1961). Another example pertinent here is a study by Gorrell (1953) which demonstrated that *auditory* stimulation had a significant effect on *visual* critical flicker frequency. In normal adults, tone lowered critical flicker frequency: and high tone (2400 cycles) lowered it to a greater degree than low tone (270 cycles).

The third proposition is that the *organism is a system which exhibits directedness toward goals and furthers its goals by a multiplicity of means.* It is in the context of this assumption that we deal with analysis of behavior in terms of means-end relationships, and focus on the distinction between process and achievement (Werner, 1937). This distinction implies that there is no one-to-one relationship between process and achievement or between means and ends, but rather that the organism can further its goals or ends by a multiplicity of means. In our work conducted within the research program described here, the notion of functional equivalence

represents one specification in perception of the principle of multiplicity of means for achieving a given end (Werner and Wapner, 1952b, 1956b). Werner (1940) treats this problem in terms of "analogous functions" and provides extensive evidence in support of this principle, e.g., he shows how object constancy may be achieved by perceptual as well as by physiological and conceptual processes. Given a variety of cognitive operations (means) for approaching a given goal, there emerges the problem of the relations among cognitive operations. One approach to the problem of relations among sensorimotor, perceptual, and conceptual operations has been to inquire whether these operations are related in a *cooperative* or *supportive* fashion, on the one hand, or, on the other, whether they are related in a *vicarious* or *antagonistic* fashion. The problem has been formulated as one of determining experimentally the conditions and factors making for cooperative vs. vicarious relationships between operations. The experimental treatment of this problem will be concretized later on when research findings are presented. Before doing so we may examine some aspects concerning the developmental perspective to see how it shapes experimentation.

Developmental Aspects

The developmental point of view[2] focuses on analysis of *change* in a living, growing system. Development is defined in terms of the progressive changes in a system undergoing transition. As already noted, comparisons are made in terms of the orthogenetic principle which states that with development there is increasing differentiation and hierarchic integration. This principle of comparison can be ap-

---

[2] The point of view described is based upon Werner's (1940, 1957) systematic treatment; see also a recent statement and elaboration with respect to symbolization and language by Werner and Kaplan (1963).

plied to any series which can be ordered developmentally, and thereby is not restricted to ontogenesis. Because it concerns analysis of the stages of a system in transition, it can be applied to the analysis of problems of general psychology, psychopathology, retarded development, aging, and individuality, as well as to problems of ontogenesis.

For example, such *general problems* as the formation of behavioral acts can be studied. For this purpose we make the assumption that the emergence of behavior is characterized in terms of progressive stages which parallel in structure the changes of the developmental sequence. Hence, the establishment of a sensorimotor pattern, a percept, or a concept is expected to change progressively in keeping with the law of development, e.g., there should be greater differentiation and hierarchic integration of parts in the course of establishing the final product, and this should be the case, independent of whether we are dealing with sensorimotor behavior, perceptual or conceptual behavior.

Problems of *psychopathology* may be approached through utilization of the developmental perspective by relating variation due to growth with variation due to psychopathology. Two assumptions are made here, viz., (1) that any organism operates on a multiplicity of levels (progression-regression hypothesis); and (2) that psychopathological groups operate at levels in certain areas which are formally similar to earlier levels of development (regression hypothesis). In parallel fashion *psychopharmacological agents, like LSD-25,* have been of interest on the assumption that they induce "regressed" states of behavior. Moreover, *aging* is studied on the grounds that through the entire life span there is "developmental progression" followed by "developmental regression" with respect to formal, organizational features of behavior.

Thus, the child, the aged, the schizophrenic, the individual under LSD-25 are expected to show less differentiation and hierarchic integration in behavioral processes as compared with a normal adult. We do not have data available with respect to all of these comparisons. Such data are being accumulated slowly and are available only for selected problem areas.

Before describing some of the empirical findings one precaution pertinent to the expectation of similarity in formal features of behavior among groups having a common developmental standing requires special emphasis. *Such similarity does not imply identity.* If similarity is uncovered, further probing in terms of process analysis is appropriate and is expected to reveal differences. From the patterns of empirically uncovered similarities and differences the organismic-developmental concepts are sharpened and their realm of applicability defined.

Some Research Findings in Selected Problem Areas

In illustrating our work, two general classes of studies on selected problems will be presented: (1) those studies which attempt to delineate general mechanisms in terms of cross-sectional analysis from the organismic perspective; and (2) those studies which focus on change from the developmental perspective. Thus, data will be presented on general mechanisms, and on differences among developmentally ordered groups; the latter will include experimental findings concerning behavioral changes from childhood to adulthood, changes from adulthood to old age, differences between schizophrenics and normals, and changes under conditions of LSD-25.

The experimental findings to be presented are concerned with the following problems: object localization; physiognomic perception; relations between perceived object position and body position; body perception; relations among cognitive operations; and maintenance of directed activity.

Object Localization

The earliest work in our research program dealt with general perceptual mechanisms involved in space localization. Among other reasons, this problem area was chosen for study because of its fundamental importance for man in adapting to the world in which he lives, and more specifically because it appeared to us to be the simplest problem area where organismic factors could be demonstrated, through controlled experiment, to play a role in perception.

Earlier approaches to space perception, as in classical psychophysics, characteristically employed sensory theory which made the assumption that sensory factors alone contribute to perception, and also ruled out the study of individual differences. Later these sensory theories were replaced by motor theories which have the virtue of recognizing that factors other than sensory factors also contribute to perception. Such motor theories fail, however, because they have difficulty in handling the problem of interaction of sensory and motor factors, which, in our view, is the key to adequate handling of the problem of projective perception. During the last fifteen years, experimental psychology in this country (cf., the "New Look" in perception, e.g., Bruner and Krech, 1950) caught up with the generally acknowledged proposition that perception may be influenced by emotions or the individual's motivation. Through this work, projective perception which focuses on the contribution of subjective factors within the individual—previously the domain of the clinical psychologist—became a generally respectable experimental research area.

Our own organismic approach—as specified in sensory-tonic theory—assumes that any perception is essentially projective. By this we mean that the organismic state has to be considered as an integral part of perception, whether we deal with Rorschach responses or responses in any

perceptual situation, for example, with judgments of size, form, location of objects, etc. (Werner and Wapner, 1956a). This general formulation served as the basis for a systematic series of studies on space localization investigating such dimensions of space as verticality (upright), the median plane (left-right), and apparent eye-line (up-down), and distance (near-far) relationships. Working with all of these aspects of space localization a large number of studies were undertaken where there was systematic variation of both aspects of the polarity, "organismic state: proximal stimulus." These systematic studies led to the formulation of three general mechanisms, one dealing with the role of stimuli to the organism coming from sources other than the object—termed by us extraneous stimulation—and the other two dealing with stimulation from the object itself—termed by us static and dynamic object stimulation.

VERTICALITY

General mechanisms. In our studies on perception of verticality, the subject had the task of adjusting a luminous rod, in a dark room, to a physical position which appeared straight-up-and-down. This task was carried out with adults under a variety of stimulus conditions presumed to change the state of the organism. In all of these cases, there was unilateral stimulation to one side of the body, e.g., head tilt, body tilt,[3] auditory stimulation, electrical stimulation to the neck muscle, rotary acceleration around the vertical axis of the body, and emotional stimulation (danger to one side) (e.g., Werner and Wapner, 1949; Wapner, Werner, Chandler, 1951; Werner, Wapner, Chandler, 1951; Wapner, Werner, Morant, 1951). In adults, it was found that all of these forms of unilaterally applied stimulation operated in a functionally equivalent manner with respect to the end product, position of apparent vertical:

---

[3] Restricted to small body tilts (less that 45°).

the apparent vertical rotates relatively opposite the side to which the stimulation is applied. These findings on perception of verticality were not treated as isolated bits of data, but were considered together with findings from neuropathology, such as Kurt Goldstein's (1939) observations that cerebellar patients fall to the side of the lesion, and thereby provided the basis for a hypothetical mechanism to account for our findings in organismic terms (for details see Werner and Wapner, 1952b, 1956b; Wapner and Werner, 1957). The variety of these forms of stimulation were presumed to change neuromuscular state, which in turn made for systematic changes in perception of verticality.

In parallel fashion, systematic studies were undertaken of the effect of variation of the other aspect of the polarity, viz., "proximal stimulus," on perception of verticality. Variation of "object stimulation" —e.g., position of the rod at the beginning of a trial—like "extraneous stimulation," had systematic effects on perception of verticality. The findings were as follows: the physical position of the apparent vertical is relatively closer to the position in which the stimulus object is located at the beginning of the trial. The mechanism formulated for operation of object stimulation may be briefly summarized as follows. A biological tendency is assumed which operates toward maintaining or re-establishing stable relationships between "proximal stimulus" and "state of the organism," such that the organismic state changes in keeping with the stimulus input (for details see Werner and Wapner, 1952a, 1952b, 1956b; and Wapner and Werner, 1957).

Age changes from childhood to maturity and in older people. Following the general principle that developmental studies could profitably be undertaken utilizing situations where general mechanisms had been studied first, a few years ago we conducted a developmental study on perception of verticality (Wapner and Werner, 1957) with subjects between the ages of six and nineteen years; this was followed more recently by a study which included subjects from twenty to eighty years of age. Perception of verticality was tested under three body positions (30° left tilt; erect; 30° right tilt) representing variation of extraneous stimulation, and under four starting positions of the rod (30° and 10° CCW, 30° and 10° CW rotation) representing variation in object stimulation.

Striking changes were found with age. The whole picture on changes in effect of body tilt on perception of verticality that occur from six to eighty years of age is as follows. For young boys from six to fifteen, the apparent vertical (physical position in which a rod must be placed to appear vertical) is located to the *same* side as body tilt; between sixteen and fifty years, however, the opposite effect occurs, namely, apparent vertical is located *opposite* the *side* of body tilt; and finally in older men from sixty-five to eighty years of age the apparent vertical is again located to the *same* side as body tilt (Comalli, Wapner, Werner, 1959).

Developmental changes in effect of starting position were found to occur only within the younger age range: the starting position effect is greatest at the youngest age level, decreases markedly until the nineteen-year level, and following this there are no consistent developmental changes throughout the age levels studied, including the sixty-five- to eighty-year group.

Both of these effects occurring during the period of growth through adolescence are interpreted by us as an expression of the orthogenetic principle which states that the development proceeds from a state of globality and lack of differentiation—in this case between self and object—to a state of increased differentiation. We interpret our results in accordance with this principle by assuming that at early stages of development lack of differentiation of self and object manifests itself in two ways: (1) by *egocentricity* where proximal stimuli are interpreted in terms of one's own body position—as evidenced by apparent vertical located to side of body tilt; and (2) by *stimulus boundedness* where the organism readily changes in keeping with stimulus— as evidenced by greater starting position effects.

Similarly, during aging, there occurs, again, a reversal in the relation between tilt of body and position of apparent vertical. This indicates that in older people once again there is a more egocentric organization of space parallel to that characteristic of children in so far as the object world is determined through body as referent. Hence, in old age, as in childhood, there is decreased differentiation in the "self: world" polarity as manifested by greater egocentricity.

Psychopathology. Based on the regression hypothesis, a number of studies were conducted dealing with perception of verticality in schizophrenics (Carini, 1955; Liebert, Wapner, Werner, 1957; Wapner and Krus, 1960a). Consider Carini's findings for catatonic-hebephrenic and paranoid schizophrenics as compared with normals. As obtained in earlier studies, Carini found that the position of the apparent vertical was located relatively *opposite* the side of body tilt in normal adults; in contrast, for the catatonic-hebephrenic group, the position of the apparent vertical was located to the *same* side as body tilt, and for the paranoids it fell in between these extremes. No significant differences between groups were found in regard to effect of starting position on the apparent vertical. Other studies replicated the body tilt effect and provided some limited evidence for greater starting position effects in schizophrenics.

Drugs. Studies were also conducted of the effects of LSD-25 on perception of verticality (Liebert, Wapner, Werner, 1957;

Wapner and Krus, 1960a). Suffice it to say that the expected effects were found in general for starting position but not for body tilt and that the latter is being investigated further.

These studies on perception of verticality with developmentally ordered groups may be summarized as follows. The apparent vertical is located to the *same* side as body tilt (30°) in children, older people (sixty-five to eighty years), and catatonic-hebephrenic schizophrenics, whereas apparent vertical is located to the side *opposite* body tilt in normal adults (twenty to fifty years); the findings under LSD-25 are opposite expectation. Significantly greater starting position effects occur in younger children as compared with normal adults and in normals under LSD-25 compared with placebo conditions whereas there is only a tendency for greater starting position effects in schizophrenics; in contrast, there are no significant differences in starting position effects in older people compared with middle-aged adults.

EYE LEVEL

The second aspect of localization of objects to be reviewed concerns the up-down dimension of space. Apparent eye level is defined as a line in space, *perceived* as being in the horizontal plane which bisects both eyes (under the normal forward gaze) into symmetrical upper and lower hemispheres. The experimental situation for studying the up-down dimension of space is a very simple one. In a dark room the subject has the task of adjusting a luminous line to a position in space which appears to be at eye level, i.e., neither below nor above.

General mechanisms. Parallel to the studies on apparent verticality, apparent eye level has been investigated with respect to changes in such variables as neuromuscular state and object stimulation. These studies yield analogous findings to those obtained with perception of verticality both for extraneous stimulation (Glick, 1959; Sziklai, 1961; Sziklai, Wapner, McFarland, Werner, 1963) and for object stimulation (Kaden, Wapner, Werner, 1955; Wapner and Werner, 1955a; Jaffee, 1952; Comalli, Werner, Wapner, 1957).

Age changes from childhood to old age. In the developmental study mentioned earlier (Wapner and Werner, 1957) it was found that the apparent eye level is located above objective eye level in six-year-old children and shifts systematically to a position below objective eye level in twenty-year-old adults. In mature adults, twenty to fifty-five years of age, the apparent eye level remains consistently below objective eye level. In older age groups (sixty-five to eighty years of age) the apparent eye level once again tends to move upward with increase in age but this difference is not significant.

Psychopathology and Drugs. Analogous results for apparent eye level have been obtained with psychopathological groups (Carini, 1955; Wapner and Krus, 1960a). The apparent eye level is located highest in catatonic-hebephrenic schizophrenics, lowest in normal adults, with paranoids falling in between. These data served as the basis for the expectation that the apparent eye level would shift upward under LSD-25 as compared to placebo conditions (Wapner and Krus, 1960a). Various studies with normals support this expectation: in normal adults the apparent eye level is located significantly higher under LSD-25 than under placebo conditions; the same relation obtains for schizophrenics under LSD-25 but is less potent.

The interpretation of these findings on apparent eye level for psychopathological groups in terms of comparative-developmental conceptualization is complicated by findings from other studies which show that changes in affective state significantly affect position of apparent eye level. Three related studies are pertinent here. In one

study there is evidence that apparent eye level shifts upward under success as compared with psychologically induced failure (Wapner, Werner, Krus, 1957b); a second study of manic-depressive psychotics shows that the apparent eye level is located relatively upward for those in the manic phase vs. relatively downward for those in the depressed phase (Rosenblatt, 1956); and a third study shows that apparent eye level shifts relatively upward under energizing as contrasted with tranquilizing drugs (Krus, Wapner, Freeman, 1958). The findings of these three studies have led to the following interpretation: changes in mood are presumed to be accompanied by changes of organismic state in terms of up-down vectorial qualities which are reflected in changes in the up-down dimension of space. The findings of the mood studies, together with the findings of the studies of ontogenesis, psychopathology, and the LSD-25 studies, pose a question of a possible multidetermination of the up-down dimension of spatial organization. The systematic changes in position of apparent eye level from childhood to adulthood have been conceived to reflect changes dependent upon maturity functions (e.g., wishful striving, postural strain upward, etc.). The specific mechanisms have not yet been worked out but seemingly involve variables not related to mood changes. If this is the case, then one would conclude that the changes of the up-down dimension of space are multidetermined, i.e., both *maturity factors* and *affective factors* play a role. Thus, there remains the problem of working out the nature of these mechanisms by studying the interaction of "mood" and so-called "maturity" factors.

MEDIAN PLANE

General mechanisms have been analyzed for the left-right dimension of space by determining the physical location of the apparent median plane (straight-ahead) under a variety of conditions analogous to those employed for verticality and eye level.

These studies have yielded findings pertinent to the mechanisms of extraneous and object stimulation which are in keeping with organismic conceptualization (Bruell and Albee, 1955; Wapner and Werner, 1955a; Werner and Wapner, 1954; Werner, Wapner, Bruell, 1953). A few studies have been undertaken with groups ordered developmentally (Wapner and Werner, 1957). Further, a recent study which employs the apparent median plane for studying the consequences of varying body-object relations through change in attitude will be reported later on (Glick, 1964).

NEAR-FAR

While general mechanisms have been studied with respect to near-far localization (A. Goldstein, 1955, 1959), I will restrict myself here to studies concerned with the emotive factors and interpersonal relations.

Psychological Distance under Danger. Psychological distance was studied in a life situation (Wapner and Werner, 1955b; Werner and Wapner, 1955a). The subject is placed at the back part of a theater stage facing the auditorium and the precipitous edge of the stage; he is then blindfolded and given the task of walking as close to the precipitous edge as possible. His behavior in this situation of danger is compared with walking in neutral space. Two criteria—change in pace, distance stopped before edge—clearly show that the subject perceived the edge as closer under dangerous than under neutral conditions. Thus, when walking to a dangerous locale, a precipitous edge, there is a shrinkage of space. It might also be noted that there were striking individual differences which were related to anxiety level as measured by a questionnaire (Wapner and Werner, 1955b).

Psychological Distance and Interpersonal Feelings. A related study on interpersonal perception was conducted by Isaac (1958). He tested the hypothesis that differential feelings toward other persons as described by terms such as "close-to" or "remote-from" would be actualized in perception as measured by psychological distance. A group of juvenile delinquent boys living together served as subjects. They listed the names of other boys in their group to whom they felt "close" and those to whom they felt "remote." From the list, one "close" and one "remote" person was selected and they served as the test objects for each subject. The subject's task was to walk a specified distance, e.g., two feet, from the person in a darkened room. In general it was found that subjects stopped farther away from (perceived as physically closer) those boys toward whom they had "close" feelings than from those toward whom they had "remote" feelings. This study demonstrates the way in which problems of interpersonal perception can be approached from the viewpoint of organismic theory by investigating the role of affect in terms of psychological distance.[4]

---

[4] Though outside the orbit of our research program, I should like to mention a study conducted at the Judge Baker Guidance Center by Patricia Nair (1961), as a Clark Ph.D. thesis, because it shows the way in which the notion of "distancing" can be used to approach problems of reading disability. Building on developmental theory, Nair viewed reading disability as a form of pathology which represented a manifestation of inadequate separation between a reader and what is read. She tested the hypothesis that for children with reading disabilities facilitation of reading would occur if conditions which enhance differentiation between the reader and the referent were provided. This was tested in two ways: first, reading material was psychologically distanced from the subject by being written in the past tense as opposed to the "here-and-now"; second, the reading material was physically distanced by presenting it at a great physical distance from the subject, viz., through projection on a screen. Three groups of subjects were employed: twelve adolescent boys treated for emotional difficulties but for whom reading was a problem; a group for whom reading was not a problem; and finally a control group of ten boys with no emotional disturbance in evidence. It was found that reading material, when "distanced" from the subject psychologically in terms of time, was more easily read by subjects with reading disability than when the content was presented in contemporaneous terms. The hypothesis was not upheld for material which was physically distanced from the subject.

Physiognomic Perception

Werner (1940) proposed the term "physiognomic perception" for the mode of cognition pertinent to the expressive or dynamic qualities of objects. These qualities of objects are distinguished from geometric-technical, matter-of-fact, qualities which pertain to the characterization of objects in terms of their structural aspects, viz., the geometry of form, extensity, intensity, etc. For example, colors are experienced not only in terms of hue, brightness, and saturation but also in terms of being strong or weak, cool or warm; lines not only have extent and curvature, etc., but may be seen as gay or sad; and forms not only have square or circular shape, etc., but also may be seen as static or active.

As part of our research program we have, over the years, studied some aspects of physiognomic perception in terms of directional dynamics. Directional dynamics refers to the vectorial quality expressed in some objects, that is, the quality of direction and force: for example, a silhouette of a running horse has a strong quality of motion in a particular direction, an arrow conveys motion either to the left or to the right, a picture of a bird in flight conveys motion in a particular direction. Studies have been undertaken to analyze general mechanisms underlying directional dynamics in organismic terms and some beginnings have been made on developmental analysis of this problem.

General Mechanisms. A number of general methods have been employed to study directional dynamics: one method evaluates directional dynamics by studying its effects on space localization (e.g., with respect to the straight-ahead and the up-down dimension of space); a second method utilizes autokinetic motion; and a third real motion.

The method utilizing *space localization* may be illustrated by referring to a study which employed the stimulus object shown

FIGURE 2   Stimulus object ambiguous with respect to directional dynamics.

in Figure 2. This stimulus object is ambiguous in so far as it can be interpreted as two flying ducks or as two airplanes. When seen as flying ducks it has directional dynamics to the left; when seen as airplanes it has directional dynamics to the right. When the stimulus object is reoriented left for right the opposite relationships hold. In a room, which was dark except for the dimly illuminated stimulus object, the subject had the task of telling the experimenter how to move the stimulus object so that it appeared to be located straight-ahead, i.e., neither to left nor to the right. In order to be seen as straight-ahead, the stimulus object shown in Figure 2 was physically placed relatively to the right when it was interpreted as ducks and placed relatively to the left when it was interpreted as airplanes. The opposite localization occurred when the stimulus object was reoriented left for right. In sum, the physical position of the apparent median plane shifted in a direction opposite the direction of the dynamics in the stimulus object (Werner and Wapner, 1954; also see Wapner, Werner, Krus, 1957a).

Utilizing silhouettes of hands pointing downward and hands pointing upward, shifts in location of *apparent eye level* have been obtained: the position of apparent eye level shifts opposite the direction of the dynamics in the stimulus object. In this study it was also found that verbal symbols connoting "upwardness" or "downwardness," for example, rising vs. falling, make for analogous shifts in apparent eye level (Kaden, Wapner, Werner, 1955).

Another study utilized *autokinetic mo-*

tion in which silhouettes of a running horse, a running boy, an arrow, the duck-airplane, as well as a stimulus object which was ambiguous in so far as it could be interpreted as a parachute or a balloon were employed. With all these stimulus objects there were significant effects on autokinetic motion (perceived movement of a physically stationary stimulus in a dark room): the predominance of autokinetic motion occurred consonant with the direction of the dynamics in the stimulus object (Comalli, Werner, Wapner, 1957; Comalli, 1960).

On the basis of these general studies, a hypothetical mechanism for the operation of dynamic stimulation was formulated. This mechanism, in general, is conceived in terms of object-body relationships: the assumption is made that visual dynamics in the stimulus object affects the equilibrial state of the organism by exerting a pull which in turn is counteracted by an organismic pull in the opposite direction (for further details see Werner and Wapner, 1956b; Wapner and Werner, 1957).

Age Changes from Childhood to Adulthood. On the assumption that in the world of the child, perception is not clearly differentiated into geometric-technical and physiognomic aspects, it was hypothesized that directional dynamics in figures will be more potent determinants of the child's perception than that of an adult (Comalli, 1955; Wapner and Werner, 1957). Static figures are compared with dynamic figures in terms of real motion. The task for the subject is to adjust the speed of a series of discrete pictures moving past a small opening in a large blackboard so that they appear to be moving at the same speed as another series of pictures moving past another opening in the board. Five pairs of stimulus objects were used. One member of a pair was a static picture, e.g., grazing horse, whereas the other had a dynamic picture, e.g., running horse. It was found, in general, that younger children adjust

the *dynamic* picture series to a slower physical speed in order for them to be perceived as moving at a speed *equal* to that of the *static* picture series; the effect of directional dynamics on motion was greater in a young child and this decreased with increase in age. Thus, there is evidence that perception develops from a syncretic, relatively undifferentiated organization to one which is more discrete. At earlier ages a high degree of interpenetration of the dynamic qualities of the object with speed of movement occurs, that is, at early ages an object cannot be divorced from the situation in which it occurs. As we grow older the figural qualities are differentiated from the speed itself and become less a part of the speed; this process of differentiation is reflected in the decrease in effect of the dynamic figure on speed with increase in age.

Relations between Apparent Position of One's Own Body and That of Other Objects

While our earlier work focused on perceptual properties of concrete, impersonal objects in space, over the past six years or so, we have given considerable attention to perception of one's own body (Werner, Wapner, Comalli, 1957; Liebert, Werner, Wapner, 1958; Wapner, Werner, Comalli, 1958; Wapner, 1959, 1961a, 1961b). These studies dealing with apparent size of body parts emerge from the recognition that the perceptual properties of the body *qua* object could be studied utilizing the same principles employed in the study of objects "out there." For perception of objects in the outside world as well as perception of one's own body, we hold the view that the reciprocal relationship between organism and environment must be taken into account. Two features, the body-environment unity and the polar features of articulateness or separateness between body and environment, play an important role in our research strategy. In some studies, we are concerned with the general interactive relationship between perception of body and perception of other objects; in other studies we are concerned with the degree of differentiation between body percept and object percept under various conditions (Wapner and Werner, 1963).

Several recent studies pertain to the relationship between apparent location of objects "out there" and apparent location of one's own body under variation of body tilt. The experimental situation utilizes a modification of the technique, previously described, for perception of verticality. The person, seated in a tilting chair in a dark room, is required to carry out two tasks while he is tilted: (1) a luminous rod is adjusted to that physical position in which it appears vertical—in this way a measure is obtained of the changes in apparent position of an object "out there"; (2) the luminous rod is adjusted to the perceived position of longitudinal axis of the body —in this way a measure is obtained of apparent position of body. Utilizing this technique, relations between object and body position were assessed by McFarland, Bauermeister and others (McFarland, Clarkson, Wapner, Werner, 1961; McFarland, Clarkson, Wapner, 1961; McFarland, Wapner, Werner, 1962; Bauermeister, 1962, 1963; Bauermeister, Wapner, Werner, 1963; Bauermeister, Werner, Wapner, 1963). Both general relationships and developmental changes in body-object relationships have been investigated using this technique. Here, let us review some developmental findings, which we believe to be of considerable importance.

Changes from Childhood to Adulthood. The concept of polarity of self and world was in part utilized in our interpretation of the changes in perception of verticality described earlier. The new procedure, however, of directly measuring the relationship between apparent position of one's own body and apparent position of other ob-

jects provides a unique way of assessing differentiation of self and world in terms of polarization of body space and object space. Given the assumption that there is an increased polarization of body space and object space with development, a study was conducted which investigates the relationship of apparent body position and apparent object position in children as compared with adults.

In this study approximately 300 subjects between the ages of six and eighteen were tested in the apparent verticality and apparent body position situations under 30° left and 30° right body tilt. In many studies with adults we know that with 30° body tilt, the apparent vertical is rotated *opposite* body tilt approximately 2° (cf., Werner and Wapner, 1949, 1952b, 1956b; Wapner and Werner, 1957); we also know from recent studies that, in adults, under 30° tilt the body position is overestimated approximately 12° (McFarland, Clarkson, Wapner, 1961; McFarland, Clarkson, Wapner, Werner, 1961; McFarland, Wapner, Werner, 1962; Bauermeister, 1962, 1963; Bauermeister, Wapner, and Werner, 1963; Bauermeister, Werner, Wapner, 1963). Hence, under 30° body tilt, the angular separation between apparent vertical and apparent body position is approximately 44°; this must be compared with an angular discrepancy between true vertical and true body position, which, of course, is only 30°. What is our expectation for angular discrepancy between apparent body position and apparent vertical for children? On the assumption that the angular separation between apparent vertical and apparent body position can serve as an objective index of the degree of differentiation of perceived body and object position and the further assumption that there is an increase in polarization of body space and object space with increase in age we expect that the angular separation is less in children and increases with age. This is in fact what our results show. In one study under 30°

body tilt, the angular discrepancy between apparent vertical and apparent body position is only about 36° for the typical six-year old[5] as compared with approximately 44° for the typical eighteen-year old.

Psychopathology. We might add that some preliminary studies with schizophrenics shows a similar shrinkage of the angular discrepancy between apparent object and apparent body position as compared with normal adults. As noted earlier, this again is expected on the basis of a regression hypothesis, i.e., in pathological primitivized states such as schizophrenia, just as with younger children, decreased polarization of body space and object space is expected.

Variation of Body-Object Relationships Through Instructions. Some studies currently being conducted as a Ph.D. thesis at Clark University by Joseph Glick (1964) handle variation of body-object relationships through adoption of two different attitudes; one set of instructions fosters the attitude of viewing the object world as separate or distinct from the self; another fosters an attitude of fusion between self and object world, i.e., the ordinary separation of self and object is minimized. Glick already has evidence that there are differences in localization of objects placed asymmetrically with respect to the objective median plane, dependent on the induced body-object attitude. Under "separation" instructions, e.g., the apparent median plane or straight-ahead shifts toward the side to which the stimulus object extends; under "fusion" instructions the shift of the apparent median plane occurs in the other direction, i.e., opposite the side to which the stimulus object extends. Thus, perceived space varies depending on the attitude of the subject toward

the relationship between self and the object environment.

Among other reasons, these studies by Glick are of significance in so far as they provide an avenue of approach to the study of individual differences. This may be illustrated by studies where the instructions given are ambiguous with respect to body-object relationships, i.e., the subject is forced neither toward a fusion nor toward a separation relation between self and objects. Under these circumstances, some subjects make adjustments of the object in the direction consonant with what is expected from "fusion" instructions; others make adjustments of the object in a direction in keeping with "separation" instructions. Following testing under so-called "ambiguous" instructions an inquiry—concerning how the subject orients himself toward objects—reveals that subjects manifest different body-object ("fusion" vs. "separation") attitudes, which are generally in keeping with the way they perceive objects under ambiguous instructions. This suggests the possibility that ongoing attitudes concerning relationships of self to objects represent an important personality dimension which may lead to further understanding of individual differences in perception, and in cognition more generally. It points to the possibility of conducting developmental studies directed toward analysis of the developmental change with respect to this relationship and also suggests the possibility that differences in line with these two general attitudes representing organism-object relationships may serve as a crucial direction in studying aspects of pathology as ongoing states as well as in studying transient states under stress.

In closing, I express the hope that the sample of work presented here has contributed toward an understanding of our research program by throwing light on our particular mode of formulating problems, the form of our experimental methodolo-

[5] The two components making up this angular discrepancy are: apparent vertical located approximately 2° *in* the direction of body tilt, apparent body position located 8° beyond body tilt.

gies, the nature of our theoretical interpretations and their interrelation.

References

BAUERMEISTER, M. (1962), The relation between subjective body space and objective external space under conditions of body tilt. Microfilmed Ph.D thesis, Clark University.

BAUERMEISTER, M. (1964), The effect of body tilt on apparent verticality, apparent body position, and their relation. *J. Exp. Psychol.*, 67:142–147.

BAUERMEISTER, M., S. WAPNER, and H. WERNER. (1963), Sex differences in the perception of apparent verticality and apparent body position under conditions of body tilt. *J. Pers.*, 31:394–407.

BAUERMEISTER, M., H. WERNER, and S. WAPNER. (1963), The effect of body tilt on tactual kinesthetic perception of verticality. *Amer. J. Psychol.* (in press).

BLANE, H. T. (1962), Space perception among unilaterally paralyzed children and adolescents. *J. Exp. Psychol.*, 63:244–247.

BRUELL, J. H., and G. H. ALBEE. (1955), Effect of asymmetrical retinal stimulation on the perception of the median plane. *Percept. Mot. Skills*, 5:133–139.

BRUNER, J. S., and D. KRECH. Eds. (1950), *Perception and Personality: A Symposium.* Durham: Duke University Press.

CARINI, L. P. (1955), An experimental investigation of perceptual behavior in schizophrenics. Microfilmed Ph.D. thesis, Clark University.

COMALLI, P. E., JR. (1955), Developmental study of physiognomic perception. Presented at Eastern Psychological Association meetings, Philadelphia.

COMALLI, P. E., JR. (1960), Studies in physiognomic perception: VI. Differential effects of directional dynamics of pictured objects on real and apparent motion in artists and chemists. *J. Psychol.*, 49, 99–109.

COMALLI, P. E., JR. (1963), Effect of unilateral above-the-knee amputation on perception of verticality. Presented at Eastern Psychological Association meetings, New York.

COMALLI, P. E., JR., S. WAPNER, and H. WERNER. (1959), Perception of verticality in middle and old age. *J. Psychol.*, 47, 259–266.

COMALLI, P. E., JR. (1962), Interference effects of Stroop color-word test in childhood, adulthood, and aging. *J. Genet. Psychol.*, 100, 47–53.

COMALLI, P. E., JR., H. WERNER, and S. WAPNER. (1957), Studies in physiognomic perception: III. Effect of meaning induced sets on autokinetic motion. *J. Psychol.*, 43, 289–299.

DOWLING, R. M. (1962), Effect of sensorimotor and conceptual activity on perceptual functioning. Microfilmed Ph.D. thesis, Clark University.

DOWLING, R. M., H. WERNER, and S. WAPNER. (1960), Effects of motor activity on visual recognition threshold. Presented at Eastern Psychological Association meetings, New York.

FRIEDMAN, H. (1952), Perceptual regression in schizophrenia: an hypothesis suggested by the use of the Rorschach test. *J. Genet. Psychol.*, 81:63–98.

GIANNITRAPANI, D. (1958), Changes in adaptation to prolonged perceptual distortion: a developmental study. Microfilmed Ph.D. thesis, Clark University.

GLICK, J. (1959), The effects of static and dynamic extraneous stimulation on the apparent horizon. Unpublished M.A. thesis, Clark University.

GLICK, J. (1964), An experimental analysis of subject-object relationships in perception. Unpublished Ph.D. thesis, Clark University.

GOLDMAN, A. E. (1953), Studies in vicariousness: degree of motor activity and the autokinetic phenomenon. *Amer. J. Psychol.*, 66: 613–617.

GOLDSTEIN, A. G. (1955), An experimental study of depth perception from the viewpoint of the sensory-tonic field theory of perception. Microfilmed Ph.D. thesis, Clark University.

GOLDSTEIN, A. G. (1959), Linear acceleration and apparent distance. *Percept. Mot. Skills*, 9:267–269.

GOLDSTEIN, K. (1939), *The Organism.* New York: American Book Co.

GORRELL, R. B. (1953), The effect of extraneous auditory stimulation on critical flicker frequency. Microfilmed Ph.D. thesis, Clark University.

HEMMENDINGER, L. (1951), A genetic study of structural aspects of perception as reflected in Rorschach responses. Unpublished Ph.D. thesis, Clark University.

HUMPHRIES, O. (1959), Effect of articulation of finger-tip through touch on apparent length of outstretched arm. Unpublished M.A. thesis, Clark University.

HURWITZ, I. (1954), A developmental study of the relationships between motor activity and perceptual processes as measured by the Rorschach test. Microfilmed Ph.D. thesis, Clark University.

ISAAC, D. M. (1958), The effect of interpersonal feelings on psychological distance. Unpublished M.A. thesis, Clark University.

JAFFE, K. (1952), Effect of asymmetrical position and directional dynamics of configurations on the visual perception of the horizon. Unpublished M.A. thesis, Clark University.

KADEN, S. E., S. WAPNER, and H. WERNER. (1955), Studies in physiognomic perception: II. Effect of directional dynamics of pictured objects and of words on the position of the apparent horizon. *J. Psychol.,* 39:61–70.

KRUGER, A. K. (1954), Direct and substitutive modes of tension reduction in terms of developmental level: An experimental analysis by means of the Rorschach test. Microfilmed Ph.D. thesis, Clark University.

KRUS, D. M., S. WAPNER, and H. FREEMAN. (1958), Effects of reserpine and iproniazid (marsilid) on space localization. *A.M.A. Arch. Neurol. Psychiat.,* 80:768–770.

KRUS, D. M., S. WAPNER, and H. WERNER. (1958), Studies in vicariousness: effect of muscular involvement on visual threshold. *Amer. J. Psychol.,* 71:395–398.

KRUS, D. M., H. WERNER, and S. WAPNER. (1953), Studies in vicariousness: motor activity and perceived movement. *Amer. J. Psychol.,* 66:603–608.

LIEBERT, R. S., S. WAPNER, and H. WERNER. (1957), Studies in the effect of lysergic acid diethylamide (LSD-25): visual perception of verticality in schizophrenic and normal adults. *A.M.A. Arch. Neurol. Psychiat.,* 77:193–201.

LIEBERT, R. S., H. WERNER, and S. WAPNER. (1958), Studies in the effect of lysergic acid diethylamide (LSD-25): self and object size perception in schizophrenic and normal adults. *A.M.A. Arch. Neurol. Psychiat.,* 79:580–584.

MAYER, J. (1961), Influence of inspection of a visually curved field on kinesthetic figural after-effects. *Percept. Mot. Skills,* 13:13–14.

McFARLAND, J. H., F. E. CLARKSON, and S. WAPNER. (1961), Effect of prolonged body tilt on the relationship between perceived position of one's body and of other objects. Presented at American Psychological Association meetings, New York.

McFARLAND, J. H., F. E. CLARKSON, S. WAPNER. (1962), The relation between per-between perceptual properties of objects in space and one's own body. Presented at Eastern Psychological Association meetings, Philadelphia.

McFARLAND, J. H., S. WAPNER, and H. WERNER. (1962). The relation between perceived location of objects and perceived location of one's own body. *Percept. Mot. Skills,* 15:331–341.

MILLER, A. (1959), An experimental study of the role of sensory-motor activity in the retention of verbal meaning. Microfilmed Ph.D. thesis, Clark University.

MILLER, H. (1963), Verbal satiation and the role of concurrent activity. *J. Abnorm. Soc. Psychol.,* 66:206–212.

MISCH, R. C. (1954), The relationship of motoric inhibition to developmental level and ideational functioning: An analysis by means of the Rorschach test. Microfilmed Ph.D. thesis, Clark University.

NAIR, P. (1961), Distancing: the application of a developmental construct to learning disability. Microfilmed Ph.D. thesis, Clark University.

OHWAKI, S. (1959), An investigation of figural adaptation within the framework of sensory-tonic field theory. Microfilmed Ph.D. thesis, Clark University.

OHWAKI, S. (1961), An investigation of figural adaptation: a study within the framework of sensory-tonic field theory. *Amer. J. Psychol.,* 74:3–16.

PHILLIPS, L. and J. FRAMO. (1954), Developmental theory applied to normal and psychopathological perception. *J. Pers.,* 22:464–474.

RAND, G. (1961), A developmental study of the Stroop Test: a preliminary analysis of behavioral means. M.A. thesis, Clark University.

RAND, G., and S. WAPNER. (1962), A behavioral analysis of the color-word test. Presented at Eastern Psychological Association meetings.

RAND, G., S. WAPNER, H. WERNER, and J. H. McFARLAND. (1963), Age differences in performance on the Stroop color-word test. *J. Pers.,* 31:534–558.

ROSENBLATT, B. P. (1956), The influence of affective states upon the body image and upon the perceptual organization of external space. Microfilmed Ph.D. thesis, Clark University.

SWITZER, J. (1961), Developmental differences in place and name sequence learning in normal, hyperactive and hypoactive eight and twelve year old boys. Microfilmed Ph.D. thesis, Clark University.

SZIKLAI, C. (1961), Effect of body position

and muscular strain on space localization, as measured by the apparent eye-line. Unpublished M.A. thesis, Clark University.

SZIKLAI, C., S. WAPNER, J. H. MCFARLAND, and H. WERNER. (1963), Tonus changes on perceived location of visual stimuli (in preparation).

WAPNER, S. (1959), Some experiments on body image from the viewpoint of organismic and developmental theory. Presented at American Psychological Association meetings, Cincinnati.

WAPNER, S. (1961a), An experimental and theoretical approach to body image. In *Proceed. XVI Int. Cong. Psychol., 1960,* 19: 758–759; *Acta Psychologica,* North-Holland Pub. Co., Amsterdam, Holland.

WAPNER, S. (1961b), Perceptual properties of one's own body and its relation to that of other objects. Symposium on Body Image and Pathological States, VA Hospital, Houston.

WAPNER, S. (1964), An organismic development approach to the study of perceptual and other cognitive operations. In: *Cognition: Theory, Research, Promise,* ed. C. Scheerer. New York: Harper and Row.

WAPNER, S., and D. M. KRUS. (1960a), Behavioral effects of lysergic acid diethylamide (LSD-25). Progress Report, NIMH Grant No. MY-2262.

WAPNER, S., and D. M. KRUS. (1960b), Effects of lysergic acid diethylamide, and differences between normals and schizophrenics on the Stroop color-word test. *J. Neuropsychiat.,* 2:76–81.

WAPNER, S., J. H. MCFARLAND, and H. WERNER. (1962), Effect of visual spatial context on perception of one's own body. *Brit. J. Psychol.,* 53:222–230.

WAPNER, S., and H. WERNER. (1955a), Gestalt laws of organization and organismic theory of perception: effect of asymmetry induced by the factor of similarity on the position of the apparent median plane and apparent horizon. *Amer. J. Psychol.,* 68: 258–265.

WAPNER, S., and H. WERNER. (1955b), Silent film—Margin of safety: Changes in psychological distance under danger.

WAPNER, S., and H. WERNER. (1957), *Perceptual Development.* Worcester: Clark University Press.

WAPNER, S., and H. WERNER. (1963), An experimental approach to body perception from the organismic-developmental point of view. In: *The Body Percept,* ed. S. Wapner and H. Werner. New York: Random House (in press).

WAPNER, S., H. WERNER, and K. A. CHANDLER. (1951), Experiments on sensory-tonic field theory of perception: I. Effect of extraneous stimulation on the visual perception of verticality. *J. Exp. Psychol.,* 42: 341–345.

WAPNER, S., H. WERNER, and P. E. COMALLI, JR. (1958), Effect of enhancement of head boundary on head size and shape. *Percept. Mot. Skills,* 8:319–325.

WAPNER, S., H. WERNER, and D. M. KRUS. (1957a), Studies in physiognomic perception: IV. Effect of muscular involvement on the dynamic properties of objects. *J. Psychol.,* 44:129–132.

WAPNER, S., H. WERNER, and D. M. KRUS. (1957b), The effect of success and failure on space localization. *J. Pers.,* 25:752–756.

WAPNER, S., H. WERNER, and R. B. MORANT. (1951), Experiments on sensory-tonic field theory of perception: III. Effect of body rotation on the visual perception of verticality. *J. Exp. Psychol.,* 42:351–357.

WERNER, H. (1937), Process and achievement. *Harvard Educ. Rev.,* 7:353–368.

WERNER, H. (1940), *Comparative Psychology of Mental Development.* New York: Harper; (2nd ed.) Chicago: Follett, 1948; (3rd ed.) New York: International Universities Press, 1957; (4th ed.) New York: Science Editions, 1961.

WERNER, H. (1957), The concept of development from a comparative and organismic point of view. In: *The Concept of Development: An Issue in the Study of Human Behavior,* ed. D. B. Harris. Minneapolis: University of Minnesota Press, pp. 125–148.

WERNER, H. (1959), Significance of general experimental psychology for the understanding of abnormal behavior and its correction or prevention. In: *The Relationship between Rehabilitation and Psychology.* Conference held at the Institute of Human Development, Clark University. U.S. Department of Health, Education, and Welfare OVR, Washington, D.C., 1962.

WERNER, H., and B. KAPLAN. (1963), *Symbol Formation: An Organismic-Developmental Approach to Language and the Expression of Thought.* New York: Wiley.

WERNER, H., and S. WAPNER. (1949), Sensory-tonic field theory of perception. *J. Pers.,* 18:88–107.

WERNER, H., and S. WAPNER. (1952a), Experiments on sensory-tonic field theory of perception: IV. Effect of initial position of a rod on apparent verticality. *J. Exp. Psychol.,* 43:66–74.

WERNER, H., and S. WAPNER. (1952b), Toward a general theory of perception. *Psychol. Rev.*, 59:324–338.

WERNER, H., and S. WAPNER. (1954), Studies in physiognomic perception: I. Effect of configurational dynamics and meaning-induced sets on the position of the apparent median plane. *J. Psychol.*, 38:51–65.

WERNER, H., and S. WAPNER. (1955a), Changes in psychological distance under conditions of danger. *J. Pers.*, 24:153–167.

WERNER, H., and S. WAPNER. (1955b), The Innsbruck studies on distorted visual fields in relation to an organismic theory of perception. *Psychol. Rev.*, 62:130–138.

WERNER, H., and S. WAPNER. (1956a), The non-projective aspects of the Rorschach experiment: II. Organismic theory and perceptual responses. *J. Soc. Psychol.*, 44:193–198.

WERNER, H., and S. WAPNER. (1956b), Sensory-tonic field theory of perception: basic concepts and experiments. *Revista di Psicologia*, 50:315–337.

WERNER, H., S. WAPNER, and J. H. BRUELL. (1953), Experiments on sensory-tonic field theory of perception: VI. Effects of position of head, eyes, and of object on position of the apparent median plane. *J. Exp. Psychol.*, 46:293–299.

WERNER, H., S. WAPNER, and K. A. CHANDLER. (1951), Experiments on sensory-tonic field theory of perception: II. Effect of supported and unsupported tilt on the visual perception of verticality. *J. Exp. Psychol.*, 42:351–357.

WERNER, H., S. WAPNER, and P. E. COMALLI, JR. (1957), Effect of boundary on perception of head size. *Percept. Mot. Skills*, 7: 69–71.

WHITE, W. T. (1963), Changes in apparent head width with heat applied to the side of the face. Unpublished M.A. thesis, Clark University.

Development of the Perception of Form[*]

MAURICE HERSHENSON
University of Wisconsin

4 schemes representing the flow of information from stimulus through sensory and perceptual systems to response are proposed in the context of an evaluation of the perceptual potentialities and abilities of the newborn human being. The evidence suggests that the newborn is provided at least some sensory capacities with which to synthesize a perceptual world. Suggestions are offered to facilitate the study of the newborn's ability to perceive form.

A recent review of the nativism-empiricism controversy in perception concluded that

* *Psychological Bulletin*, 1967, pp. 326–336.
  Preparation of this paper was supported in part by United States Public Health Service Research Grant MH 10751 from the National Institute of Mental Health. Portions of it were presented at the Second Annual Symposium, Center for Visual Science, University of Rochester, June 1965. The author wishes to thank Sheldon Ebenholtz, Ralph Norman Haber, William Kessen, and Edward C. Tronick for their helpful comments.

the problem is still meaningful within the context of the study of perceptual development (Hochberg, 1963). But at least three different views of perceptual development have been suggested: (*a*) organization of the perceptual system manifest in an increasing ability to perceive; (*b*) elaboration of more distinctive percepts, as in learning to discriminate among wines; and (*c*) integration of perceptual and motor systems, as in acquiring motor skills. The first view is concerned with the construction of the perceptual system, the other two require an intact and functional perceptual system from which the process of development proceeds. Thus the major conceptual difference is between acquiring a perceptual system and improving it or integrating it with another system. Since a functional perceptual system is a prerequisite for improvement or integration, the problem of development, in the sense of construction, may be said to approximate most closely the essence of the old nativism-empiricism debate.

Clearly, then, the first step in the study of the development of the perception of form is the analysis of the newborn's[1] ability to respond to form. If the newborn can perceive form, the developmental problem becomes one of modification and improvement rather than construction. The assessment of this capability requires analysis of the possible antecedents to form perception, that is, of those processes which could mediate responses to stimuli containing forms but which one would not want to label form perception. In the following section, a conceptual framework is provided to aid in this analysis. The main body of this paper assesses the ability of the human newborn to respond to visual stimulation: The first section deals with those abilities usually thought to be prerequisite to the perception of form; the second section surveys his perceptual abilities as they relate directly to form perception.

Conceptual Framework

The recent accumulation of knowledge about mechanisms that detect invariants of stimulation such as contours, angles, lines of particular orientation, etc. (e.g., Hubel and Wiesel, 1962; Sutherland, 1963), has resulted in renewed interest in "building-block" conceptions of the development of the perception of form.[2] Such accounts usually postulate a system composed of primary elements,[3] invariance detectors, which combine to form functionally autonomous structures—the correlates of form perception (e.g., Dodwell, 1964; Hebb, 1949; Sackett, 1963).

The attractiveness of these theories to students of human development is increased by data suggesting the existence of invariance detectors in human newborns (Kessen, Haith, and Salapatek, 1965; Salapatek and Kessen, 1966), and by reports of qualitative differences in "looking" of younger and older infants: The younger infant seems to be "captured by the stimuli" (Ames and Silfen, 1965), to show "obligatory attention" (Stechler and Latz, 1966) in a "vigilant-like state" (Stechler, Bradford, and Levy, 1966); the older infant appears to be "capturing stimuli with his visual behavior" (Ames and Silfen, 1965), to become "aroused" or "excited" by visual stimulation (Stechler and Latz, 1966). Indeed, such differences in looking could reflect qualitatively different experiential states mediated by different neural mechanisms.

[1] The term "newborn" is generally used to describe an infant during his stay in the hospital, typically from 3 to 5 days for normal babies. This usage is followed uniformly in this paper.

[2] The reader should keep in mind the distinction between elementism in a general theory of perception and in a theory of perceptual development. The latter does not imply the former and does not undermine the Gestalt view. Theories of perceptual development are attempts to explain the Gestalt, not invalidate it.

[3] Verbal reports of some subjects exposed to a double Ganzfeld containing slight hue or luminance differentials included separation of two "fogs," neither of which appeared to possess "object" or "form" characteristics (Cohen, 1958). It is possible that the sensory system of the newborn produces intensity or hue differentials on the retina not unlike those produced in the two-Ganzfeld situation, thereby providing a segregated visual field without form perception and without figure-ground in the usual sense. This may be an alternative candidate as a "primitive" state from which perceptions may develop. The possibility of such states invalidates Zuckerman and Rock's (1957) contention that intensity or hue discrimination implies segregation of the visual field, that this segregation implies figure-ground, and that figure-ground implies form perception.

For the building-block approach to perceptual development to be more than speculation, the elements must be conceptually separated from the larger structures they will be used to synthesize. The distinction should reflect, as far as possible, their differential functions as components of the perceptual act—the difference between reception (invariance detection) and organization (synthesis, interpretation, judgment)—as well as their differential roles in development. The terms "sensory" and "perceptual" seem ready-made for this purpose despite their history of definitional difficulty. These conceptual labels could serve as an aid in the analysis of perceptual development if their attributes are kept clearly in mind.

Sensory mechanisms are complex functional units "tuned" to specific invariants of stimulation. Activation of a unit signals detection of a particular invariant in the stimulus—the units are "invariance-bound." In general they extract and process information from circumscribed regions of the visual field and do not alter their function over time as a result of experience. Sensory mechanisms, then, would differ from perceptual mechanisms in their specificity, rigidity, and restricted range of analysis.

In contrast, perceptual mechanisms reflect the unity and plasticity which are the hallmarks of perception. The perceptual system is plastic in the sense that it adapts readily to systematic variation of the input; it has unity in the sense that perceptual organization encompasses larger portions of the visual field. Thus perceptual processes involve both spatial and temporal integration. One speaks, for example, of response to "pattern" as a perceptual ability, emphasizing both its global nature in the processing of information from different parts of the visual field, and its unity in integrating the information into a single percept. Moreover, the use of the term "pattern" implies that the information is represented by the relationships among the various parts of the stimulus —by comparison and integration of sensory information over the entire visual field. But this is simply to reiterate Gestalt psychology. To a lesser extent, "shape" and "form" may be characterized in the same way. It is these very properties—integrity, unity, and plasticity—which make the problem of perceptual development a meaningful one.

A building-block theory of perceptual development, then, would have sensory information conveyed through the newborn's visual system to some central locus where perceptual development could take place. The newborn's visual behavior would be determined primarily by the sensory input; the older infant would be able to integrate such input and therefore would enjoy a more flexible relationship with his environment. The change from "obligatory attention" to active searching would reflect the shift from control by sensory mechanisms to mediation by the newly organized perceptual system.

Thus the analysis of the perceptual act of the newborn must be so conceived that sensory and perceptual processes could be differentiated. Unfortunately, analyses of perceptually mediated behavior have not, for the most part, been in response to developmental problems. For example, Garner, Hake, and Eriksen (1956), in demonstrating the need for differentiating perceptual from response processes, implicitly assumed that the perceptual system is organized and functional (see Figure 1A). Clearly this proposition cannot be assumed in the present context since it is the very problem under study. Alternative hypotheses which permit analysis of the input side of the perceptual act are needed to complement Garner, Hake, and Eriksen's analysis of the output side.

Two simplifying assumptions will help in this regard: (a) the sensory system is functional; and (b) the sensory system sup-

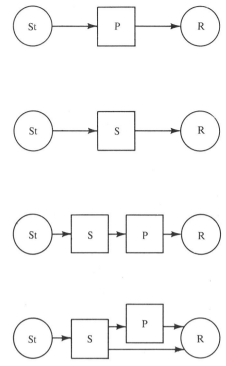

FIGURE 1   Alternative schematizations of information flow from stimulation (St) through sensory (S) or perceptual (P) systems to response (R). Top row: Information flow through an organized and functional perceptual system. Second row: Information flow through a sensory system only. Third row: A sensory and a perceptual system operating in series. Bottom row: A series-parallel connection.

plies information to the perceptual system, that is, is always prior to the perceptual system in the flow diagram. Now the three contingencies of sensory-perceptual functioning are (*a*) a sensory system operating in the absence of a perceptual system (Figure 1B), (*b*) a sensory system and a perceptual system operating in "series" (Figure 1C), and (*c*) an operating perceptual system which, for some reason, does not contribute to the observed response in the particular experimental situation. The latter contingency may be visualized in Figure 1D which incorporates both the series operation of contingency (*b*) and the alternative of contingency

(*c*)—the "parallel" connection which enables the sensory system to mediate responses without interference from an otherwise functional perceptual system. The determination that observed responses were contingent upon manipulation of a perceptual dimension (see "Specifying the Effective Stimulus," below) suggests the series linkage of Figure 1C. It is the necessary and sufficient condition for describing the attributes of the perceptual system while simultaneously describing perceptual experience.

Prerequisites for Perception

In this section the level of development of the newborn's visual system will be assessed. If the sensory structures and functions necessary for perceptual development are absent, one may assert that the newborn cannot perceive. Such deficiencies should turn attention to the study of the development of the deficient component.

THE RECEPTORS

Early studies of the electroretinogram (ERG) by Zetterström (1951, 1952, 1955; Heck and Zetterström, 1958) had raised questions about the structural differentiation and functional integrity of the newborn retina. Since only the *b*-wave was obtained in recordings of the ERG, the newborn retina was thought to be capable of processing only scotopic information. However, recent anatomical and functional studies of the newborn retina have altered this view. Clearly discernible structural differentiation of rods and cones has been found in the seventh month of gestation in retinas of human fetuses (Horsten and Winkelman, 1962, 1964; Winkelman and Horsten, 1962). ERGs containing both photopic (negative *a*-wave) and scotopic (positive *b*-wave) components can readily be obtained from newborns (Horsten and Winkelman, 1962, 1964; Shipley and Anton, 1964; Winkelman and Horsten,

1962), and an x-wave component in response to light of long wavelength ("clearly related to photopic vision") has also been reported (Barnet, Lodge, and Armington, 1965). Finally, by selective amplification, newborn ERGs can be driven up to 72 cycles per second, a range generally held to be mediated by the photopic system in the adult (Horsten and Winkelman, 1962). Thus both the photopic and scotopic systems appear to be functional at birth.

CENTRAL COMPONENTS OF THE VISUAL SYSTEM

That the electroencephalogram (EEG) of the newborn reveals the immature state of organization of its central nervous system cannot be questioned. It may be argued, however, that the immaturity is quantitative rather than qualitative since the "formal" qualities of the EEG may be recognized at birth. For example, distinct sleep-wake stages appear in records of newborn EEGs (Bartoshuk, 1964; Engel, 1961) accompanied by a reasonable amount of sustained, albeit slow, rhythmicity (Bartoshuk, 1964). Furthermore, the presence of bilateral covariation reflects the maturation of mechanisms for coordination between the cerebral hemispheres (Bartoshuk and Tennant, 1964). Of course, these data do not imply that the newborn is able to perceive, only that he is not "cortically" asleep.

A similar argument has been made with respect to evoked responses in the visual system (Hrbek and Mares, 1964a, 1964b). For example, the long latency has been attributed to the slower conduction rate of optic nerve fibers and geniculo-calcarine radiations. The great fatigability may indicate slower metabolic processes in the nerve cells, while the decrease in amplitude with age could reflect the corresponding increase in size and thickness of the brain and skull. Differences in shape may be the result of modification of the late components reflecting activity in the diffusely projecting thalamocortical system. The slower maturation of this system might also account for the variability and development of the topographic distribution of the responses, again a quantitative change. Indeed, Hrbek and Mares (1964b) reported evoked responses in 100% of their subjects if intense stimulation was used, leaving little doubt that the visual system is intact and functional at birth.

CONVERGENCE AND CONJUGATION

In contrast to the common reports of dissociated eye movements in newborns, Dayton, Jones, Steele, and Rose (1964) found that newborns could locate and follow black dots drawn over a plexiglas canopy. The eyes moved simultaneously in the direction of the target over the same period of time. The similarity of electro-oculographic tracings was interpreted as a sign of purposeful and well-coordinated ocular movements. Saccadic movements—those movements which correct for slippage of the image off the fovea—were smaller in adults than in newborns. Although Dayton et al. interpreted this to mean that the feedback mechanism is immature in the newborn, the difference might more simply be explained as a consequence of poor acuity (see below) which, although properly a part of the feedback system, does not imply the complexity of the above statement. Poorer acuity would allow for greater slippage before detection could occur, and therefore would require larger return movements.

Convergence and conjugation in the presence of stationary targets is less clear. Hershenson (1964, 1965) photographed ocular orientation to a pair of stimuli, a square and a checkerboard. The camera was operated only when an observer judged that one of the subject's eyes was aligned with one of the stimulus screens. Comparison of distributions of corneal reflex measurements for the observed eyes with those of the unobserved eyes indicated that both eyes were directed at the same target. Sequential analysis of these data showed that the eyes also moved conjugately from target to target. Using similar photographs, Wickelgren (1967) sampled ocular orientation to three kinds of stimuli: four pairs of homogeneous chromatic and achromatic stimuli, a single pair containing a neutral gray and a striped stimulus, and a single small blinking light centered above the infant. The eyes converged 70% of the time for the stripes-gray stimuli, 42% of the time for the color-brightness stimuli, and only 9% of the time for the blinking light.

The studies agree that newborns can orient their eyes toward a single stimulus. The differences in ocular behavior in the two studies can be understood by comparing the rates and criteria for photographing. Wickelgren sampled ocular orientation at one frame per second over 4 minutes whenever the subjects' eyes were open; Hershenson photographed at 24 frames per second for short bursts[4] only when one eye was oriented in the direction of a stimulus. Thus Hershenson probably measured the convergence and conjugation which Wickelgren found more or less frequent over longer periods of time depending upon the nature of the stimulus.

The question remaining, then, is the relative frequency of convergence per opportunity to converge. It raises, first, the experimental problem of interpreting ocular orientation as an index of perception and, second, the problem of describing the processes of perceptual development. The experimental problem arises when it is assumed that convergence is present throughout an experimental session. If the frequency of convergence is not known, then orientation of one eye (e.g., Fantz, 1963) or of two eyes independently (e.g., Hershenson, 1964) is difficult to relate to the experience of the subject. The de-

scriptive problem arises from comparison of newborn visual behavior with that of the normal adult. The experience of a single unified image in the mature perceptual system is thought to result from integration of correlated information from converged eyes. While it is possible, perhaps, for fusion to occur in the immature system with partially correlated input, it is also possible that stimulus information from one eye is suppressed or that information from the two eyes is processed alternately. The relaxation or disappearance of suppression or alternation in experience would then become important developmental problems.

ACCOMMODATION

Even with proper alignment, improper focal adjustment would result in blurred images on the retina. The impact of the resulting retinal blur on perception is not clearly understood, thereby complicating the study of accommodation in development. An inefficient accommodative system may, nonetheless, provide an inexperienced organism with sufficient sensory information for the development of perception.

On the average, a newborn would require a far greater amount of accommodative ability than would an adult, merely to overcome his refractive error. The most recent and comprehensive surveys of refractive errors indicate hyperopia in about 75% of newborn eyes (mean refractive error = 1.5 diopters, $SD = 3.2$). The probability of ametropia is also far greater than in the adult eye (mean refractive error = 0.6 diopters, $SD = 1.1$).[5] Thus, in a sense, the newborn starts with an accommodative handicap.

Using dynamic retinoscopy, Haynes,

---

[4] The "burst" represented the duration of fixation. The longest fixation was 6.9 seconds and the average was 2.0 seconds.

[5] The mean refractive errors and the standard deviations were calculated by the author from distributions of Cook and Glasscock (1951) for the newborn eye and Stromberg (reported in Bennet and Francis, 1962) for the adult eye.

White, and Held (1965) measured the newborn's ability to accommodate actively to a patterned stimulus placed at the front of the retinoscope. Accommodative responses of infants under 1 month of age, measured within four ranges of distance, did not adjust to changes in target distance. The system appeared to be locked at one focal distance whose median value was 19 centimeters (about 8 inches). Radial tracking of a target moving in depth was not observed in infants under 1 month of age. These data would be conclusive were it not for the possibility that the target provided at the front of the retinoscope might not have been an adequate stimulus for accommodation at all distances. The "black marks" and "dots" may not have been resolved at distances greater than that for which accommodation was found. That the subjects "did not exhibit sustained fixations on the target" suggests just this circumstance.

ACUITY

Gorman, Cogan, and Gellis (1957), using the reflexive ocular-following response known as optokinetic nystagmus (OKN) as an index of visual acuity, found that 93 of 100 infants under 5 days of age followed stripes of 33.3 minutes of arc (Snellen equivalent = 20/670). Also using OKN, Dayton, Jones, Aiu, Rawson, Steele, and Rose (1964) found that half of their subjects responded to targets with a Snellen equivalent of 20/150, 14 of 18 responded to a target equivalent of 20/290.

Reisen (1960) and Fantz, Ordy, and Udelf (1962) have argued, however, that this evidence, although convincing, is based upon a response mediated by neural mechanisms which may not be involved in pattern perception. To eliminate this possibility, Fantz et al. measured duration of fixation on stationary stimulus pairs of stripes and neutral grays. They assumed that neural pathways which mediate voluntary attention to pattern would then be directly involved. Infants under 1 month of age were able to resolve lines of ⅛ inch

at 10 inches (20/200), a reasonable corroboration of the data using OKN.

TALLY OF POTENTIALITIES

The evidence suggests the presence of the requisite muscular control and detector apparatus to bring the image of an object onto the fovea and to hold it there reasonably well even if the object is moving. This can be done with both eyes in a coordinated fashion, at least for short durations. While some question remains as to the effect of the possibly limited accommodative capacity, the image is at least sharp enough for manifestation of a fair amount of resolving power for the newborn eye. Add to this the evidence for the apparent functional integrity of the neural pathways necessary for mediation of sensory information and a very good case could be made for the potential presence of form perception. Clearly there is no evidence that argues very strongly against it.

Perceptual Abilities

SPECIFYING THE EFFECTIVE STIMULUS

It should be clear from the alternative routes in the flow diagram in Figure 1D that newborns may respond to a portion of a form, for example, a border or an angle, rather than to the entire stimulus. To conclude that the newborn is perceiving form, then, one must either rule out the former or assert the latter. This criterion—that newborns can respond to forms as wholes—should at least be one requirement for the statement that they are able to perceive form.

The task, then, is to determine which aspects of stimulation elicited the observed responses from newborns presented with forms, that is, to isolate the effective stimulus.[6] The problem is one of designing ex-

---

[6] Although this discussion centers on the problems related to form perception, its general applicability should be clear.

periments to permit inferential character-ization of the effective stimulus from sets of overt responses. There are two pro-cedures which may provide solutions to this problem. Both involve making state-ments about the effective dimensions of stimulation from the pattern of responding, but they do this in different ways.

One procedure, the developmental study of the pattern of scansion of forms, re-quires precise measurement of the ocular behavior of newborns. The response—essentially the direction of gaze—may be used directly to track the portions of the stimulus which are effective in eliciting orientation. This technique has already been used to study the newborn's ocular response to contours (Kessen et al., 1965) and to triangles (Salapatek and Kessen, 1966). In the future it might provide the means for evaluating the criterion for per-ception of form; for example, response to form as wholes may be interpreted as scan-sion around the entire contour of a figure. Moreover, one would expect that the pro-posed shift from sensory response in the newborn to perceptual response in the older infant would be reflected in the pat-tern of scansion. Exploration with this promising technique has only begun.

The other procedure, the one most fre-quently used, requires a more detailed con-sideration of the logical steps involved in the discovery of the effective stimulation. Typically, stimuli are presented either singly or in pairs. They may represent points sampled from a dimension or they may simply be selected as high-attention stimuli with no other prima facie interre-lationship. In either case, some response which reflects the degree of "attention" is recorded (e.g., duration of fixation, num-ber of fixations), and is sometimes called a "preference" when associated with pair presentation.

The difficulty with this format is that it lends itself easily to interpretation only under very specific circumstances, namely, when the responses constitute an ordered set. If an ordered set of responses is not ob-tained, then the response to each of the stimuli or to each pair of stimuli must be treated as a single discrimination, inde-pendent of the others in the experiment. The single discrimination permits the lone inference that "something" about the single stimulus or "something" about the preferred stimulus was discriminated from the background. There is no way to specify the effective stimulus and therefore, in the case of form perception, no way to de-termine whether the subject was respond-ing to portions of forms or to entire figures. Thus, specification of the effective stimulus requires that order in the responses be demonstrated.

This can be accomplished by satisfying Huntington's postulates (Stevens, 1951), which impose three demands upon the re-lations among the elements of an ordered set:

1. If $A \neq B$, then either $A < B$ or $B < A$.
2. If $A < B$, then $A \neq B$.
3. If $A < B$ and $B < C$, then $A < C$.

These relations are characterized as con-nected, asymmetric, and transitive. The postulates may be applied to differential re-sponse pairs (or sets) by defining the rela-tions in terms of observable responses. In general, one may write: Let $A \neq B$ denote the relation of inequality where A and B are responses (or sets of responses) to two stimuli. This relation can have meaning within the usual experimental paradigms when it can be shown that there is a sig-nificant difference between A and B. Sim-ilarly, if one writes $A \neq C$ and $B \neq C$, then three different elements are defined. These satisfy the first two postulates, establishing order between pairs of elements. The third postulate establishes transitivity among the elements.

The application of the postulates may be made more meaningful with an ex-ample. Suppose one is presenting pairs of stimuli to newborn subjects and is measur-ing responsiveness to the pairs by, perhaps, photographing eye position at some sampling rate. The relation of inequality may be taken to mean that Stimulus A is fixated for a *significantly* different number of frames than is Stimulus B. This relation may be abbreviated by saying that B is "preferred" to A. Thus we say that the relation "preferred" is being measured by ocular orientation. Now if it is possible to show that three such pairs can be obtained and that they are transitive (i.e., they satisfy Huntington's postulates), then one may assert that there is a stimulus dimension which could have generated the response set (Hershenson, Kessen, and Munsinger, 1967).

The selection of the stimulus dimension which did generate the response set is not simple. If the dimensional attributes of the stimuli are known, for example, if the stimuli were unidimensional, or if a single known dimension was varied while others were held constant, or if dimensions were varied orthogonally, then the ordered responses could be mapped into the known stimulus dimensions. When dealing with forms, however, one is faced with a lack of knowledge about the possible effective dimensions. The difficulty arises not only from our meager knowledge of the possible sensory dimensions, but also from our lack of information about the effective dimensions in adult responses to forms (Michels and Zusne, 1965). The alternatives appear to be either a systematic attempt to evaluate the possible dimensions based on educated guesses or the use of scaling procedures to infer possible dimensions. The former procedure has been most frequently used but has not proved very successful; the latter procedure remains untested.

BRIGHTNESS AND COLOR

The development of brightness sensitivity has been measured by Doris and Cooper (1966) in infants from 4 to 69 days of age. Thresholds were measured by OKN to moving black and white stripes projected above the infants. The intensity of the white stripe was varied and the disappearance of OKN was taken as an index of threshold. The results indicate rapid development of brightness sensitivity in the first 2 months of life. The visual preference of newborns for achromatic stimuli was measured by Hershenson (1964) using photographs of ocular orientation. Three intensities of light, differing by 1 log unit, were presented in pairs. The stimulus of medium intensity was fixated more than the other two and the bright stimulus was fixated more than the dim one. Since the comparisons were all significant and the preferences were transitive, the conclusion that newborns can perceive differences in brightness is permissible.

Color perception has been assessed in newborns by recording the duration of fixation on yellow, red, and white circles, among other stimuli, in a single-stimulus design (Fantz, 1963). Although the results showed definite fixation on these stimuli, they did not provide evidence for color discrimination since the possibility of mediation by a nonlinear brightness preference had not been eliminated. Wickelgren (1967) measured the ocular orientation of newborns to pairs of stimuli which differed in both intensity and hue: red and neutral gray stimuli were equated for two levels of brightness. Neither dimension influenced the response—the strong position preferences and the lack of convergence (see above) suggest that subjects may not have perceived the stimuli as different from from each other or from the background.

SENSORY ELEMENTS

The importance of sensory units for building-block theories of perceptual development has already been discussed. Clearly this class of theory would have little explanatory value were it not for the possible presence of detectors in the newborn human being. A study by Kessen et al. (1965) may be interpreted as evidence for the presence of vertical contour detectors. They presented newborns with single contours in either vertical or horizontal orientation, situated 3 inches from the center of the field. The subjects showed a "clear and dramatic" tendency to direct their eyes to the region of the field occupied by the vertical contour but were completely insensitive to contours above and below midline. In another study, Salapatek and Kessen (1966) presented newborns with a large black triangle. The subjects tended to direct their eyes at the vertices of the triangle, typically remaining on a single vertex in a given session. While the angle detector hypothesis is appealing, Salapatek and Kessen suggested two alternative explanations which seem equally plausible and more parsimonious: first, that newborns orient toward transitions in brightness, an angle representing two such transitions within a small area; and second, that newborns respond to an optimal relative level of brightness, only to be found near a vertex.

COMPLEXITY

Complexity is a frequently used dimension which may involve stages of stimulus information analysis and integration somewhere between that of the sensory elements and form perception. Variation in complexity is typically accomplished by dividing fixed stimulus areas into checkerboards of different densities. This controls for brightness by equating black-white ratios. However, an equation of brightness is provided only if intensity is integrated over the entire surface. If the subject does not scan the entire surface, the brightness control is vitiated. With more complex stimuli, the control is maintained so long as scansion covers an even number of elements.

When presented with pairs of three stimuli differing in complexity defined in this manner, newborn subjects fixated the least complex (2 squares on a side) stimulus more than the most complex (12 squares on a side) stimulus (Hershenson, 1964). There were no other significant

pair differences suggesting that two of the three stimuli may not have been experientially available to the subject. Moreover, the data can be explained most parsimoniously as responsiveness to a bright stimulus, emphasizing once again the need for stimulus specification.

FORM

In a study in which three patterned and three homogeneous stimuli were presented singly to newborns, Fantz (1963) found that a schematic face was fixated longer than all other stimuli, and that patterned stimuli, in general, were fixated longer than colored discs. Fantz concluded that newborns can perceive "pattern" while noting that the dimensional nature of the pattern could not be specified. It has already been shown, however, that statements about perceptual abilities must be couched in dimensional language to be meaningful. This study, therefore, cannot be taken as evidence for form perception.

Two experiments which attempted to meet this criterion have been reported. In one study (Hershenson, Munsinger, and Kessen, 1965), 17 newborns were presented with pairs of solid black figures which differed in the number of angles (5-, 10-, and 20-turn random shapes were used). This dimension is probably closely related to complexity as well as form. Only one comparison yielded a significant differential response—the 10-turn figure was fixated more than the 5-turn figure. Thus the effective stimulus could not be determined. In the other study (Hershenson, 1965), "figural organization" was varied while brightness and complexity were controlled in the conventional manner. This experiment attempted to dimensionalize those very stimuli which had been reported to elicit strong fixations from the newborn (Fantz, 1963). Twenty newborns were presented with pairs selected from three stimuli: one showing Joan Crawford's face, the other two representing lesser degrees of organization of the same face. The "distorted" face retained the outline of the head and hair but had the positions of the eyes, nose, and mouth altered; the "scrambled" face had these elements altered along with the head contour. Differential responses to these stimuli were not obtained.

Conclusions and Future Directions

There are two problems which remain to be overcome in evaluating the newborn's perceptual abilities. The first is the multidimensionality of stimuli that may be classified as "forms" or "objects." Certainly this problem is not new, but neither has there been any great progress in dimensionalization (Michels and Zusne, 1965). Perhaps the best solution for the study of development is to let the newborn himself supply the dimensions from which his experiential world might be reconstructed rather than to attempt to dimensionalize the stimuli independently. To accomplish this, it appears necessary to use large matrix designs in which many stimuli may be compared and in which many subjects do the comparing. Unfortunately, the newborn possesses some striking qualities, such as his tendency to prefer looking more to one side or to manifest behavioral extremes, which severely limit his work day and, in effect, restrict his usefulness in complex experiments. These difficulties may be overcome by treating many babies as one subject, thereby filling in the design.

These behavioral qualities of the newborn present the second problem—an understanding of state. The important question here is not whether the infant is awake or asleep but whether he is actively looking or passively staring—whether he is searching a stimulus or "locked on" it. That subjects may become drowsy while at the same time keeping their eyes open is suggested by reports of sleep EEGs obtained from babies whose eyes were open (Ellingson, 1958). Perhaps a number of criteria of alertness should be applied before an infant is used in a perceptual study or, even better, perhaps state could be monitored throughout the experimental session. With more precise techniques, two states within wakefulness might be separable.

In sum, the evidence indicates that the newborn is provided at least some sensory capacities with which to synthesize a perceptual world. That he might also possess the ability to experience form remains a very real possibility.

References

AMES, E. W., and C. K. SILFEN. Methodological issues in the study of age differences in infants' attention to stimuli varying in movement and complexity. Paper presented at the meeting of Society for Research in Child Development, Minneapolis, March 1965.

BARNET, A. B., A. LODGE, and J. C. ARMINGTON. Electroretinogram in newborn human infants. *Science,* 1965, *148,* 651–654.

BARTOSHUK, A. K. Human neonatal EEG: Frequency analysis of awake and asleep samples from four areas. *Psychonomic Science,* 1964, *1,* 281–282.

BARTOSHUK, A. K., and J. M. TENNANT. Human neonatal EEG correlates of sleep-wakefulness and neural maturation. *Journal of Psychiatric Research,* 1964, *2,* 73–83.

BENNETT, A. G., and J. L. FRANCIS. Ametropia and its correction. In H. Davson (Ed.), *The Eye.* Vol. 4. *Visual optics and the optical space sense.* New York: Academic Press, 1962. Pp. 133–180.

COHEN, W. Spatial and textural characteristics of the Ganzfeld. *American Journal of Psychology,* 1957, *70,* 403–410.

COOK, R. C., and R. E. GLASSCOCK. Refractive and ocular findings in the newborn. *American Journal of Ophthalmology,* 1951, *34,* 1407–1413.

DAYTON, G. O., JR., M. H. JONES, P. AIU, R. A. RAWSON, B. STEELE, and M. ROSE. Developmental study of coordinated eye movements in the human infant. I. Visual acuity in the newborn human. *Archives of Ophthalmology,* 1964, *71,* 865–870.

DAYTON, G. O., JR., M. H. JONES, B. STEELE, and M. ROSE. Developmental study of coordinated eye movements in the human infant. II. An electrooculographic study of the fixation reflex in the newborn. *Archives of Ophthalmology,* 1964, *71,* 871–875.

Dodwell, P. C. A coupling system for coding and learning in shape discrimination. *Psychological Review*, 1964, 71, 148–159.

Doris, J., and L. Cooper. Brightness discrimination in infancy. *Journal of Experimental Child Psychology*, 1966, 3, 31–39.

Ellingson, R. J. Electroencephalograms of normal, full-term newborns immediately after birth with observations on arousal and visual evoked responses. *Electroencephalography and Clinical Neurophysiology*, 1958, 10, 31–50.

Engel, R. Evaluation of electroencephalographic tracings of newborns. *Lancet*, 1961, 81, 523–532.

Fantz, R. L. Pattern vision in newborn infants. *Science*, 1963, 140, 296–297.

Fantz, R. L., J. M. Ordy, and M. S. Udelf. Maturation of pattern vision in infants during the first six months. *Journal of Comparative and Physiological Psychology*, 1962, 55, 907–917.

Garner, W. R., H. W. Hake, and C. W. Erikson. Operationism and the concept of perception. *Psychological Review*, 1956, 63, 149–159.

Gorman, J. J., D. C. Cogan, and S. S. Gellis. An apparatus for grading the visual acuity of infants on the basis of opticokinetic nystagmus. *Pediatrics*, 1957, 19, 1088–1092.

Haynes, H., B. L. White, and R. Held. Visual accommodation in human infants. *Science*, 1965, 148, 528–530.

Hebb, D. O. *The organization of behavior*. New York: Wiley, 1949.

Heck, J., and B. Zetterström. Analyse des photopischen Flimmerelektroretinogramms bei Neugeborenen. *Ophthalmologica*, 1958, 135, 205–210.

Hershenson, M. Visual discrimination in the human newborn. *Journal of Comparative and Physiological Psychology*, 1964, 58, 270–276.

Hershenson, M. Visual discrimination in the human newborn. *Dissertation Abstracts*, 1965, 26, 1793. (Abstract)

Hershenson, M., W. Kessen, and H. Munsinger. Pattern perception in the human newborn: A close look at some positive and negative results. In J. C. Mott-Smith, W. Wathen-Dunn, H. Blum, and P. Lieberman (Eds.), *Symposium on Models for the Perception of Speech and Visual Form*. Cambridge, Mass.: MIT Press, 1967, in press.

Hershenson, M., H. Munsinger, and W. Kessen. Preference for shapes of intermediate variability in the newborn human. *Science*, 1965, 147, 630–631.

Hochberg, J. E. Nativism and empiricism in perception. In L. Postman (Ed.), *Psychology in the making*. New York: Knopf, 1963. Pp. 255–330.

Horsten, G. P. M., and J. E. Winkelman. Electrical activity of the retina in relation to the histological differentiation in infants born prematurely and at full-term. *Vision Research*, 1962, 2, 269–276.

Horsten, G. P. M., and J. E. Winkelman. Electroretinographic critical fusion frequency of the retina in relation to the histological development in man and animals. *Documenta Ophthalmologica*, 1964, 18, 515–521.

Hrbek, A., and P. Mares. Cortical evoked responses to visual stimulation in full-term and premature newborns. *Electroencephalography and Clinical Neurophysiology*, 1964, 16, 575–581. (a)

Hrbek, A., and P. Mares. The development of electrophysiological reactivity of CNS in children. *Activitas Nervosa Superior*, 1964, 6, 92–93. (b)

Hubel, D. H., and T. N. Wiesel. Receptive fields, binocular interaction and functional architecture in the cat's visual cortex. *Journal of Physiology*, 1962, 160, 106–154.

Kessen, W., M. M. Haith, and P. Salapatek. The ocular orientation of newborn infants to visual contours. Paper presented at the meeting of Psychonomic Society, Chicago, October 1965.

Michels, K. M., and L. Zusne. Metrics of visual form. *Psychological Bulletin*, 1965, 63, 74–86.

Reisen, A. A. Receptor functions. In P. H. Mussen (Ed.), *Handbook of research methods in child development*. New York: Wiley, 1960. Pp. 284–310.

Sackett, G. P. A neural mechanism underlying unlearned, critical period, and developmental aspects of visually controlled behavior. *Psychological Review*, 1963, 70, 40–50.

Salapatek, P., and W. Kessen. Visual scanning of triangles by the human newborn. *Journal of Experimental Child Psychology*, 1966, 3, 155–167.

Shipley, T., and M. T. Anton. The human electroretinogram in the first day of life. *Journal of Pediatrics*, 1964, 65, 733–739.

Stechler, G., S. Bradford, and H. Levy. Attention in the newborn: Effect on motility and skin potential. *Science*, 1966, 151, 1246–1248.

STECHLER, G., and E. LATZ. Some observations on attention and arousal in the human infant. *Journal of the American Academy of Child Psychiatry*, 1966, 5, 517–525.

STEVENS, S. S. Mathematics, measurement, and psychophysics. In S. S. Stevens (Ed.), *Handbook of experimental psychology*. New York: Wiley, 1951. Pp. 1–49.

SUTHERLAND, N. S. Shape discrimination and receptive fields. *Nature*, 1963, 197, 118–122.

WICKELGREN, L. W. Patterns of ocular orientation in the human newborn. *Journal of Experimental Child Psychology*, 1967, in press.

WINKELMAN, J. E., and G. P. M. HORSTEN. The ERG of premature and full-term born infants during their first days of life. *Ophthalmologica*, 1962, 143, 92–101.

ZETTERTSRÖM, B. The clinical electroretinogram. IV. The electroretinogram in children during the first year of life. *Acta Ophthalmologica*, 1951, 29, 295–304.

ZETTERSTRÖM, B. The electroretinogram in prematurely [born] children. *Acta Ophthalmologica*, 1952, 30, 405–408.

ZETTERSTRÖM, B. Flicker electroretinography in newborn infants. *Acta Ophthalmologica*, 1955, 33, 157–166.

ZUCKERMAN, C. B., and I. ROCK. A reappraisal of the roles of past experience and innate organizing processes in visual perception. *Psychological Bulletin*, 1957, 54, 269–296.

*Visual Experience in Infants: Decreased Attention to Familiar Patterns Relative to Novel Ones**

ROBERT L. FANTZ
Western Reserve University

Abstract. A complex visual pattern presented for ten successive 1-minute exposure periods was fixated progressively less than comparable novel stimuli by infants 2 to 6 months old. This indicates the occurrence of recognition and habituation of visual responsiveness to specific patterns, and suggests that familiarization with the environment begins through visual exploration before more active exploration is possible.

The eyes of the human infant are open, active, and sensitive to light soon after birth, thus providing the means for visual exploration of the environment. For early visual explorations to be important in the development of perception and behavior, it is further necessary that (i) the ocular movements and fixations be selective rather than random so that specific objects or areas of the environment can be looked at; (ii) what is looked at be seen with sufficient clarity that they may be distinguished from other objects or later responsiveness to the same stimuli. Recent experiments have proved that requirements (i) and (ii) are met by the visual behavior of even the newborn infant: fixation times were found to be consistently different among stimulus targets differing in pattern, indicating both unlearned selective attention to patterning and the initial ability to resolve patterns (1, 2). In the study reported here, the aim was to obtain data on requirement (iii).

The visual preference test of early per-

* *Science*, 1964, vol. 146, pp.668–670. Copyright © 1964 by the American Association for the Advancement of Science. The study was made possible by support from grant M-5284 from the National Institute of Mental Health, USPHS, and by the cooperation of DePaul Infant and Maternity Home. The testing was carried out by Isabel Fredericson and Jean Dreifort.

ceptual development (1) was adapted to reveal changes in preference during a test session. The infant was face up in a small hammock crib inside a test chamber which provided a uniform background for two stimulus cards. The cards were placed over holes (measuring 20 cm by 15 cm) in the chamber ceiling. The cards were 38 cm above the infant's head and were separated from each other by 15 cm. Illumination was provided by a 75-watt incandescent lamp underneath and between the cards and out of sight of the infant. Two window shades were drawn horizontally across the chamber to hide the patterns between exposures.

The patterns on the cards were 11 photographs or advertisements cut from magazines. They were chosen to give maximum variation among patterns in aspects such as size of detail, regularity, color, contrast, and predominant shape of contours, and yet so that each would be complex and have high attention value. Six were color photographs; five were black-and-white. Gross variations in overall brightness were avoided.

One of the photographs (varied among the subjects) served as a constant pattern. It was presented for 1 minute, ten times in succession. During each exposure period it was paired with one of the remaining ten photographs (variable pattern) in random order. Constant and variable patterns were reversed in right and left positions for the last 30 seconds of each exposure period; the initial positions were random. The entire test lasted about 15 minutes including between-exposure intervals.

The eyes of the subject were observed through a 0.6-cm hole in the ceiling of the chamber, midway between the patterns. Corneal reflections of the outline of the two patterns were clearly visible under the conditions of the experiment. The location of these reflections provided an objective criterion of fixation. Thus the superposition of the left reflection over the pupil of either eye indicated the left pattern was being fixated; this was recorded by pushing the left of two finger switches operating electric timers. A second person put the patterns in place so that the observer did not know which was the constant, except on those occasions when it was recognizable in the corneal reflection.

All the infants available at a foundling home who could be given the entire test without crying or falling asleep were used as subjects. They ranged from 6 to 25 weeks of age; six infants were under 2 months, seven were from 2 to 3 months, eight from 3 to 4 months, and seven over 4 months.

Figure 1 shows the percentage of the combined fixation time given to the constant pattern during successive exposure periods. While the variability in response during successive exposure periods and among individuals was high, the overall trend is clear. The curve for the youngest group showed no change in either direction; the suggested slight preference for the constant pattern was not consistent among infants. Each of the groups over 2 months of age gave decreasing attention to the constant pattern during the test. From the first five to the last five exposure periods the decrease was significant for the 2- to 3-month and for the 4- to 6-month groups separately ($p < .02$); and for the three older groups combined ($p < .01$), according to the Wilcoxon matched-pairs signed-ranks test. The decrease was significant for those infants over 2 exposed to a chromatic one, indicating that color was not essential for recognition. During the last five exposure periods the novel pattern was fixated longer than the familiar one by all but four of the 22 infants over 2 months; these four were widely distributed in age.

Decreasing fixation of the familiar pattern was accompanied by increasing fixation of the novel pattern, resulting in a high response level throughout the test. Fixation of both patterns averaged 47 seconds out of 60 during the first five ex-

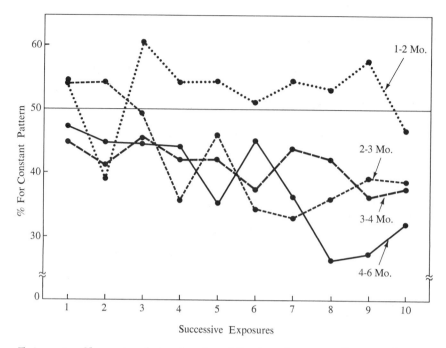

FIGURE 1   Change in relative duration of fixation of a repeatedly exposed (constant) pattern relative to a novel (variable) pattern (the position of each being controlled) during a series of exposure periods. Each curve is the mean for six to eight infants.

posure periods and 46 during the second five. There is no evidence here of a response decrement due to fatigue, sensory adaptation, decreased arousal, or extinction of the orienting reflex. While infants under other conditions have shown some such nonspecific effects of being repeatedly exposed to stimuli (2), the present results indicate perception, recognition, and satiation of interest in a particular pattern. This effect of specific previous visual experiences is "learning" in the broad meaning of the term, even though it does not involve traditional experimental operations or explanations such as conditioning, practice, reinforcement, or association.

The initial attentiveness to all the patterns was a function both of novelty and of intrinsic stimulus characteristics such as complexity. The importance of novelty is evident from the differential fixation of novel and familiar patterns in the later exposure periods; the importance of intrinsic stimulus characteristics has been shown

elsewhere by differential fixation of equally-novel targets, in which case the more complex are usually favored (1–3). The two factors probably function in a complementary way in the infants' visual explorations. Familiarization with potentially important parts of the environment is at first facilitated by selective attention and differential exposure to patterned surfaces and complex objects. Eventually, at least by 2 months of age, this information-gathering process is made more efficient by concentration of attention on the less-known objects and patterns. Response to novelty might thus be described as an unlearned visual interest in a complex stimulus which has not been habituated by experience.

Concurring results have been obtained by other investigators using different familiarization procedures (4). Three-month-old infants were exposed for 4½ minutes to a cross or a circle, whichever form was preferred in initial exposure periods when both forms were presented simultaneously. During subsequent periods of exposure to both forms, the infants showed a decrease in fixation of the familiarized form. A greater effect of the familiarization period was shown when the two stimuli differed in color as well as form. No significant effect was shown as a result of exposure to the initially nonpreferred stimulus.

Evidently, incidental visual experiences can be retained by infants over 2 months of age, at least for a short period of time. This satisfies the third prerequisite given above for a possible developmental influence of early visual explorations. To what extent and under what conditions this influence actually occurs are questions for further study. The determination of changes in visual preferences following various types of experience will be useful in such studies, since the technique can be used at an age when other response measures are not available.

References

1. FANTZ, R. L., *Sci. Am.* 1961, 204, No. 5, 66; R. L. Fantz, *Science* 1963, *140*, 296; R. L. Fantz, J. M. Ordy, M. S. Udelf, *J. Comp. Physiol. Psychol.* 1962, *55*, 907.
2. FANTZ, R. L., in *Perceptual Development in Children*, A. H. Kidd and J. L. Rivoire, Eds. (International Univ. Press, New York), in press.
3. CANTOR, G., in *Advances in Child Development and Behavior*, L. P. Lipsitt and C. C. Spiker, Eds. (Academic Press, New York, 1963).
4. SAAYMAN, G., E. W. AMES, A. MOFFETT, *J. Exptl. Child Psychol.* 1964, *1*, 189.

Slant Perception and Shape Constancy in Infants[*]

T. G. R. BOWER
Harvard University

Abstract. Three experiments investigated shape constancy in human infants between 50 and 60 days of age. The first showed that such infants possess some capacity for shape constancy. The second confirmed this finding and showed that the capacity is not attained by correlation of perceived projective shape with perceived orientation.

Earlier (*1*) I presented evidence that human infants between 40 and 70 days of age display some degree of size constancy. The research I now report was designed to discover whether such infants are also

[*] *Science*, 1966, vol. 151, pp. 832–834. Copyright © 1966 by the American Association for the Advancement of Science. The study was supported by the Milton Fund through Harvard University. I thank E. J. Gibson, J. J. Gibson, and H. N. Riccuiti for help and advice.

capable of shape constancy; the problem is of theoretical interest. Strong empiricist theories of perception (*2*) tend to assume that shape constancy only becomes possible when the organism has become familiar with all possible retinal projections of an object; they assume that one learns how an object looks in various orientations, and that one infers from seeing a recognized "look" of an object that one is seeing that object x in some particular orientation.

Obviously these theories would be refuted by any demonstration of shape constancy with infant subjects and unfamiliar shapes. A second major class of theory (3), which assumes that shape constancy is attained by correlation of projective or retinal shape with perceived orientation, has not been confirmed with adult subjects (4); its adherents claim that this is because by adulthood the correlation process has become so automated that its components cannot be separately reported. If the hypothesis were true, it should surely be demonstrable with infant subjects. My results indicate that 50- to 60-day-old infants do manifest some degree of shape constancy and that it does not result from correlation of perceived projective shape with perceived orientation.

The first experiment used eight infants 50 to 60 days old. The infant under test reclined in an infant seat placed on a brown, wooden table, at 45 deg. His head was clasped between two yielding pads, the left pad containing a microswitch whose closing operated an event recorder placed beneath the table. Immediately before each infant seat an experimenter was stationed beneath a gap in the table. When the event recorder closed, the experimenter emerged and 'peek-a-booed' at the infant. Two meters from each infant's eyes a wooden board, 25 by 50 by 2.5 cm, was placed on a turntable. The board, of unfinished white wood, stood on its long edge, turned 45 deg anticlockwise from the infant's frontoparallel plane; its center of rotation lay in the infant's medial plane. The room was otherwise unfurnished; the walls were of coarsely textured brick. Illumination was provided by a roof light of the same length as the table, which minimized shadows. The experimenter could introduce a screen between himself and the infant for stimulus changes and rest periods.

During training, the board in the above orientation served as conditioned stimulus (CS); the leftward head movement, as conditioned response (CR); and the "peek-a-boo," as reinforcement. Initially the infants were trained to respond only in the presence of the CS. After this was accomplished, behavior was shaped in daily 30-minute sessions until the infants were working at a rate of one response per 2.0 seconds on a variable-ratio schedule on which every fifth response, on average, was reinforced, the exact interval between reinforcements varying randomly. The training procedure is described in greater detail elsewhere (1).

After 1 experimental hour at this level, generalization testing was begun. Four stimuli were presented during testing: (i) the CS in its original 45 deg orientation; (ii) the CS in the fronto-parallel plane; (iii) a trapezoid in the fronto-parallel plane, whose retinal projection was then equal to that of the CS at 45 deg; (iv) this trapezoid at an angle of 45 deg. Each stimulus was presented for four 30-second periods in counterbalanced order. No reinforcement was given during testing. In terms of difference from the CS the four presentations may be classified as follows: (i) no change, (ii) same objective shape, different projective shape, different orientation; (iii) different objective shape, same projective shape, different orientation; (iv) different objective shape, different projective shape, same orientation.

The mean numbers of responses elicited by the four presentations were (i) the CS, 51.00; (ii) the same objective shape in a different orientation, 45.13; (iii) that which projected a retinal shape identical with that of (i), 28.50; and (iv), 26.00. The difference between (i) and (iii) was highly significant ($t = 12.08$; df, 7; $P < .01$). It is obvious that these infants had not learned to respond to a projective or retinal shape but to an objective shape, which could be recognized in a new orientation; to this extent they showed shape constancy. Also in line with this interpretation is the fact that (iii) and (iv) elicited equally few responses ($t = 0.47$; not significant), indicating that they were re-responded to as if equivalent.

Although this experiment clearly rules out the strong empiricist explanation of shape constancy described above, it is neutral in respect to the second hypothesis: that shape constancy develops out of the correlation of two perceptually prior variables, projective shape and apparent slant. This hypothesis was not confirmed in the following experiment.

Each of nine infants, aged 60 to 63 days after the test, was trained to make a head movement as CR to the rectangle used in experiment 1, presented at a 5-deg anticlockwise orientation, as CS in the manner described above. Behavior was shaped to the same criterion level of responding on a variable-ratio schedule. Then in three successive sessions each infant performed once on each of the following three tasks (see Table 1).

1) The rectangle described was exposed in four orientations, turned 5, 15, 30, or 45 deg anticlockwise. Each orientation was presented 30 times in random order for 5-second periods. Only responses made while the rectangle was at 5 deg from the frontal plane were rewarded, and these were rewarded continuously. Reinforcement time was not included in presentation time, so that several 15-second reinforcements could be obtained during a 5-second presentation.

2) This condition was exactly like the first except that the stimuli used were only projectively equivalent to those used in condition 1. Four trapezoids casting the same retinal image as the rectangle at 5, 15, 30, or 45 deg were all shown in the fronto-parallel plane (5).

3) This condition differed from the others in the nature of the stimuli used. An opaque cardboard screen, 1 by 1 m, was placed 10 cm before the rectangle. An aperature, 10 by 20 cm, was cut in it so that, while the body of the rectangle was visible, its edges were not. Thus only orientation per se was available to differentiate presentations of the rectangle in its four orientations. Order of testing was counterbalanced across infants.

In all conditions only stationary positions of stimuli were ever visible; transitions were never seen. These three conditions were designed to present the infant with, respectively, a form in space (having objective shape, projective shapes, and orientations with only the first invariant); a set of projective shapes with orientation invariant; and finally a set of orientations, with projective shape invariant. The developmental hypothesis being tested asserts that at this stage of development, shape judgments result from deduction from two perceived components, projective shape and orientation. This should mean that discrimination performance, shown by the difference between the numbers of responses elicited by rewarded and unrewarded stimuli, should be best under condition 1, where the infants had both projective shape and orientation as differentiating features. This prediction was not confirmed. Discrimination performance was poorer under condition 1 than condition 2 ($t = 6.06$; $P < .01$) or condition 3 ($t = 4.97$; $P < .01$) (6). In fact, examination of performance in condition 1 indicates very little discrimination between the four presentations; only one presentation, the rectangle at 45 deg, was significantly differentiated from the rewarded presentation ($t = 1.08$; $P < .1$).

The putative advantage of the last experiment was that every subject served as his own control. The training conditions and the stimulus situation were such that discrimination in condition 1 should have been easier than in the other two conditions. As I have pointed out, there are two differentiating variables available in condition 1 to only one in conditions 2 and 3.

In addition, all infants were trained with a condition-1 CS, which fact should have facilitated discrimination in condition 1; in fact it did not. This can be interpreted to mean that the subjects showed such a high degree of shape constancy that

TABLE 1

Proportions of Responses Elicited by
Rewarded Stimulus that were Elicited by
Unrewarded Stimuli in the Three Presentation
Conditions Described in the Text.

CON-DITION	PROPORTION AT ORIENTATION			
	5°	15°	30°	45°
1	1.0	1.04	0.98	0.90
2	1.0	.70	.64	.55
3	1.0	.86	.78	.77

TABLE 2

Mean Numbers of Responses
Elicited in Experiment 2

ORIEN-TATION (DEG)	RESPONSES UNDER CONDITIONS (NO.)		
	1	2	3
5	50	48	56
15	48	40	40
30	46	35	30
45	44	30	31

the same shape in different orientations literally looked the same, or so very similar that discrimination was too difficult to be formed in the time given. However, there are objections to this interpretation: it could be argued that little response strength transferred from training to conditions 2 or 3 because the rewarded stimuli differed so much in the three conditions that the data are not truly comparable. In order to meet this objection a third experiment was run.

Three groups of five infants were each run through one condition of experiment 2. One group was trained with the rectangle at 5 deg as CS; the second, with a projectively equivalent trapezoid in the frontal plane as CS; and the third, with the 5-deg orientation of the surface behind the screen as CS. The groups were equated for total number of reinforcements received. After response rate reached a criterion of one response per 2 seconds, the four stimuli in each condition were each presented for four 30-second periods, in counterbalanced order, without reinforcement, after the paradigm of experiment 1. The results (Table 2) show that significantly more responses were elicited by the novel stimuli in condition 1 than in condition 2 or 3 ($P < .01$ by the t-test), whereas there was no significant difference between the numbers of responses elicited by the three CS. If one accepts the basic

logic of the generalization experiment, this can only mean that the infants in condition 1 perceived the novel stimuli as more like their CS than did the infants in the other two conditions; that variations in orientation of the same object, with projective shape and orientation variant, and only real shape invariant, produce a higher degree of identity or "sameness" than do variations in projective shape alone, with orientation invariant, or variations in orientation, with projective shape invariant.

These three experiments taken together strongly indicate that young humans possess the capacity for shape constancy, the capacity to detect the invariants of shape under rotational transformation in the third dimension. The data of experiments 2 and 3 seem in fact to show that response to a shape invariant is more primary than response to a simple variable such as orientation. In both experiments it was shown that rotation of an object into the third dimension did not produce the response decrement that was produced by rotation of a surface without limiting contours. In the latter case there was of course no shape invariant to respond to.

It thus seems that the capacity limited perceptual machinery of the infant is set to respond to high-order invariants, and to ignore low-order variables such as orientation, when both are present, so that in these experimental situations it is difficult for the infants to respond to the low-order but differential variable orientation.

The notion that invariants and variables may compete for central access within the perceptual system is useful in the present context: it may also explain the paradox that adult subjects may show perfect shape constancy while hopelessly misjudging orientation, and vice-versa (7).

This explanation constitutes a reformulation of the problem of the development of shape constancy; it shifts the emphasis from an attempt to understand how infants learn to compute "real shape" from projective shape and orientation to an attempt to understand how the ability to *simultaneously* register orientation and real shape develops. It shifts the emphasis from development of specific local functions, such as the constancies, to development of a general capacity to simultaneously handle multiple variables and invariants.

This shift may have some merit in that it points to a resolution of the apparent contradiction between the fact that perceptual capacities undoubtedly do change with age, and the fact that many local functions make their appearance very early in life.

References

1. BOWER, T. G. R., *Psychon. Sci.* 1964, *1*, 365. *Science,* 1965, *149,* 88.

2. HELMHOLTZ, H., *Physiological Optics III* (Optical Society of America, 1935).

3. For example, J. Piaget, *Les Mécanismes Perceptifs* (Presses universitaires de France, Paris, 1962); S. Klimpfinger, *Arch. Ges. Psychol.* 88, 599 (1933). My discussion and experiments are aimed only at those theories of shape perception that assume that projective shape and perceived orientation precede shape constancy in perceptual development, and that projective shape, orientation, and real shape are separately registrable attributes of an object in space. Some projective shape-slant correlation models are not committed to the position of separate registration.

4. STAVRIANOS, B., *Arch. Psychol.* 1944, *61,* 5.

5. To ensure that the trapezoids used were pictorially equivalent to the rectangle in its various orientations, the latter was photographed in all four positions, and matte enlargements were pasted on the visible surfaces of the corresponding trapezoids.

6. The sequential testing methods that I used decreased total numbers of responses elicited on successive days without affecting the pattern of responding on any given condition. Therefore numbers of responses elicited by the unrewarded stimuli are expressed as proportions of the numbers elicited by the rewarded stimulus, thus canceling absolute differences and allowing the pattern to appear clearly.

7. EISSLER, K., *Archiv. Ges. Psychol.* 1933, 88, 487.

Phenomenal Identity and Form Perception in an Infant*

T. G. R. BOWER

Harvard University

Gestalt psychologists described in some detail the stimulus conditions which determine which parts of an array will be seen as units possessing "phenomenal identity." These same stimulus conditions, often called the Gestalt laws, were held to be effective determinants of form perception too. A previous study indicated that only one of the Gestalt laws, common fate, was an effective determinant of phenomenal identity in human infants of less than 16 weeks of age. The present study using a more powerful technique shows that another of the Gestalt laws, good continuation, is an effective determinant of phenomenal identity and form perception in infants of 36 days of age. A third variable, proximity, is not effective in this age range.

Perhaps the most primitive ability of any perceptual system is the ability to partial an array of stimulation into segregated units whose parts cohere with one another, remaining independent of the parts of other units. For vision, Koffka (1936) posed the problem as "Why is it that we see things rather than the spaces between them?" This is the problem of phenomenal identity. Gestalt psychologists, such as Koffka, treated it as a psychophysical problem, seeking to discover what properties of a visual array caused some segments to be seen as coherent units separable from the rest of the array. The resulting stimulus variables were entitled Gestalt laws. Perhaps it is the dignity of the title "law" which has sheltered these psychophysical formulations from further investigation, for little has been done with them since the pioneering Gestaltist investigations.

tigations. In particular little has been done to investigate their origins, whether in phylogeny or ontogeny. Brunswick (1956) suggested that a process of correlation learning within the lifetime of an individual could explain the effectiveness of the Gestalt laws. Bower (1965) attempted to test this theory by testing the effectiveness of three laws with infants of various ages. Only one, common fate, the tendency to see segments which move together in phase as coherent, was effective with the younger infants. The result thus seemed to confirm Brunswick's empiricism against Gestalt psychologists' nativism. However, subsequent experiments have shown some flaws in the original. Bower (1965) found that infants are insensitive to pictorial information. The dynamic flow of information given in motion seems to be essential for them. It is thus possible that the apparent primacy of common fate resulted from no more than the fact that the display exemplifying it was the only one which involved motion.

* Perception and Psychophysics, 1967, vol. 2, pp. 74–76.

The displays exemplifying the others were presented as still projections on a screen so that not even head movements could produce motion gradients. Accordingly, the experiment was redone using solid models, which yield motion gradients during head movements, to exemplify the laws which were previously ineffective.

Six groups of four infants served as subjects. All of the infants were 36 days of age at testing. An operant conditioning technique was used. The technique used was modelled after a technique invented by Siqueland (1965). The operant response was a suck of high positive pressure. A sealed nipple was inserted in the infant's mouth. The resulting sucks were transduced and amplified by a Schwarzer polygraph. The output from the polygraph was fed into a Schwarzer amplitude discriminator, whose output controlled a counter and the display equipment described below. During the experiment the subject sat on his mother's or an experimenter's lap. The subject-holder was responsible for keeping the nipple in the subject's mouth. Fifteen in. from the subject's face at a 45° angle to his line of sight was placed a half silvered (30/30) mirror. Immediately behind the mirror at right angles to the line of sight was a translucent screen, behind which a motion picture projector was placed. Parallel to the subject's line of sight was a white peg-board which was used as a stimulus holder. The peg-board was illuminated by fluorescent tubes at top and bottom giving it a luminance of 52 ft.-L. Its edges were baffled so that the subject could see the stimulus only as reflected in the half-silvered mirror. The only other illumination in the room came from a dim corridor light. The output from the amplitude discriminator through a stepping switch extinguished the peg-board light and started the movie projector running for a 10-sec. period, at the end of which the projector stopped and the peg-board light came on again. The projector lamp was never off, so that a stopped frame of the

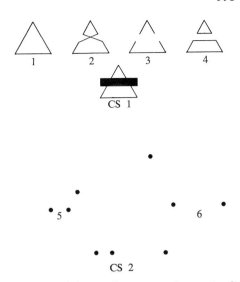

FIGURE 1 The conditioning and test stimuli used in these experiments.

movie was continuously visible behind the CS. For rest periods and stimulus changing both sets of lights were extinguished. The movie shown was an older child at play. The peg-board stimulus thus served as conditioned stimulus (CS), the high pressure suck as conditioned response (CR) and the 10-sec. movie presentations as reinforcement.

Two CS were used. The first was a black wire equilateral triangle, side 35 cm, thickness of wire 5 mm with a 7 cm diameter, 50 cm long, round, black rod placed over it. The second CS consisted of three 2.5 cm diameter black discs, mounted in a row with an interval of 5 cm between the left hand pair and 15 cm between the right hand pair.

Groups 1, 2, 3, and 4 were trained with the first CS, and the groups 5 and 6 with the second CS. The training procedure was the same for all groups. Daily 30–45 min. sessions were aimed at. The first session was spent in shaping the response, initially with continuous reinforcement, later with reinforcement on a variable ratio (VR) schedule on which every third response on average was reinforced. On the second day the VR3 schedule was maintained and a discrimination between presence and absence of the CS was formed. The Terrace (1963) fading procedure was used. The lights illuminating the peg-board were switched off for 1-sec periods between responses. This period was gradually extended to 10 sec. During these dark periods a response would not have been reinforced had one occurred. In fact, none occurred. The terminal minute of the second day was a discrimination test period. The peg-board lights were extinguished during this period. None of the infants emitted a single response during the test. This was taken as adequate evidence of discrimination. The first 15 min of the third day were spent on a VR10 schedule. Thereafter 2 min of test trials were given. For 1 min the CS was present without reinforcement, for the second minute a test stimulus was present, again without reinforcement. Half of the infants in each group viewed the presentations in the stated order, half in the reverse order. The test stimulus for each group is shown in Figure 1. The reasoning guiding these choices is given below. After the 2 min of testing, 10 further min of training were given. Then a further 2 min of testing, with presentation order reversed for each infant, was given, followed by 3 further min of training on the VR10 schedule.

These experiments were designed to assess whether two of the Gestalt laws, good continuation and proximity, were effective in the infant subjects. The first CS was designed to assess the effects of good continuation. If infants, like adults, see contours, whose mathematical description in cartesian space is identical, as continuations of one another, then the infants should have seen this CS as a triangle with a bar over it. They should have seen the two visible segments of the triangle as continuations of one another, so that during testing the triangle (in Fig. 1) should have caused the minimal decrement in responding. If on the other hand, good continuation were not effective but if common fate were, if that is to say, the separation

between bar and triangle were sufficient for head movements to produce different rates of displacement of their retinal projections, then they should have seen the display as an indeterminate figure with a bar over it; that is, they should have seen the top part of the triangle as connected with the bottom half, but been unable to specify the nature of the connection. If this were so the figures 1 and 2 of Fig. 1 should have been equally ineffective in suppressing responses. If again neither of these variables were effective, then 3 and 4 should have had the least effect, since they at least had no contours which were not present in the CS.

The second CS was designed to assess the effectiveness of the variable, proximity. The relevant Gestalt law may be stated as follows. In a visual field containing three or more identical elements, any pair of elements which are nearer to one another than either is to any other element will be seen as a unit. Thus the CS used here, labelling the dots a, b, c, should be seen as (ab), c, with a and b forming a single entity. If this variable were effective one should expect transfer stimulus 5 of Figure 3 to produce less response decrement than transfer stimulus 6, since the former does not violate the unity of (ab) whereas transfer stimulus 6 does so.

The results are summarized in Table 1. As can be seen there, proximity had no effect on responding. The two transfer stimuli elicited equally few responses. There was no significant difference be-

TABLE 1

MEAN RESPONSE RATE PER MIN. TO:	CS	TEST STIMULUS
GROUP		
1	51.00	34.00
2	53.00	12.00
3	49.00	14.00
4	52.00	12.25
5	50.00	13.50
6	50.25	14.00

tween them. The situation was quite different with good continuation which seemed to be highly effective in that transfer stimulus a, which exemplified good continuation, elicited significantly more responses than any of the other three transfer stimuli ($p < .001$ by t-test), which in turn did not differ significantly from one another. Only on the hypothesis that good continuation is an effective variable can one comprehend this pattern of results.

The conclusions of the previous study must thus be revised. Proximity still seems ineffective but it does appear that good continuation can be an effective variable with young infants. It is worth noting that good continuation functioned here not only as a determinant of phenomenal identity, identity, but also as a determinant of form perception. Not only did the infants "know" that the top of the triangle was connected to the bottom; they also knew the nature of the connection. This indicates a rather high degree of perceptual organization at this comparatively early age, rather more than most current theories of perceptual development would lead one to believe.

References

BOWER, T. G. R. Phenomenal identity in infants. *Psychon. Sci.,* 1965, 3, 323–324.

BOWER, T. G. R. Stimulus variables determining space perception in infants. *Science,* 1965, 149, 88–89.

BRUNSWIK, E. *Perception and the representative design of psychological experiments.* University of California Press, 1956.

KOFFKA, K. *Principles of Gestalt psychology.* New York: Routledge, 1936.

SIQUELAND, E. Paper read at 1st conference on infancy. Cambridge, 1965.

TERRACE, H. Discrimination learning with or without errors. *J. exp. Anal. Behav.,* 1963, 6, 1–27.

Visual Scanning of Triangles by the Human Newborn[*]

PHILIP SALAPATEK
University of Pennsylvania

WILLIAM KESSEN
Yale University

Ten human newborns were shown a homogeneous black visual field and ten newborns were shown a large black triangle on a white field. Ocular orientation to within approximately ±5° of visual angle was measured by scoring infrared photographs of corneal reflections. The infants showed much less dispersion of scanning in the presence of the triangle than in the presence of the homogeneous field. Moreover, ocular orientations were directed toward a vertex of the presented triangle. The results were related to Hebb's theory of perceptual development, to analyzer theories of discrimination, and to studies of complexity and preference in the human newborn.

It is only through a detailed study of ocular responses in the newborn child that critical questions about the nature of perceptual development can be resolved. Recent studies (for example, Fantz, 1961, 1963; Hershenson, 1964; Hershenson, Munsinger, and Kessen, 1965) have indicated that the human infant will usually look longer at certain visual patterns than at others during the first few days of life. These findings have generally been explained as representing a preference for differing levels of stimulus complexity; unfortunately, different *E*s have found that preference is greatest for low complexity, for moderate complexity, and for high complexity. Variation in empirical outcome may be accounted for in part by variation from study to study in the stimulus dimensions that were under investigation. Of more consequence, however, is the difficulty in determining with the procedures used in these studies whether or not the infant was responding to the dimension defined by the *E*. For example, in studies of preference for visual forms, the child may have been responding to the preferred figure as a whole or only to certain parts of it; that is, the preferred figure may have more of what the infant wants to look at or the preferred figure may have something uniquely attractive which the less well preferred figure does not have. In addition, although the finding of differential orientation in a paired-comparison design indicates a discrimination of the preferred figure from its surround, lack of preference does not necessarily indicate a lack of discrimination (Kessen and Hershenson, 1963). This paper describes a procedure which permits more detailed specification of the ocular orientation of human infants than has been available heretofore with

* *Journal of Experimental Child Psychology*, 1966, vol. 3, pp. 155–167. The research reported in this paper was supported in part by USPHS research grant HD-0890 (formerly MH-1787). The writers are deeply indebted to Marshall M. Haith and Adrienne Salapatek and to the nursing staff of the Maternity Service of Grace-New Haven Community Hospital.

dichotomous left-right or yes-no judgments of orientation. A measure of looking accurate to within a few degrees of visual angle will illuminate the processes that underlie preference and discrimination of form in the human newborn.

A large solid black triangle in the center of a white field was shown to human newborns in the present study. It was expected that a central stimulus would capture the infant's regard and that a solid figure on a contrasting field would not demand fine acuity. Further, if the contours of a figure influence ocular orientation, orientations toward the contours would be more readily discernible if the figure was large, i.e., if the contours were at some distance from the center of the field. Of the many figures that might have been selected for initial study, the triangle was chosen because it has received detailed consideration in theoretical treatments of perception in the newborn (Hebb, 1949).

Method

SUBJECTS

Subjects for the experiment were 20 awake alert newborn infants under 8 days of age from the nursery of the Grace-New Haven Community Hospital. The Ss were randomly selected from the babies available and awake in the nursery at the time of observation. Records obtained from 49 other babies could not be used either because the infants fell asleep during the observation or because the film was badly processed and unscorable. Observations on the ten babies in the experimental group were completed before observations on the ten babies in the control group were begun. The experimental group was made up of five males and five females ranging in age from 23 to 177 hours with a mean age of 68.1 hours. The control group was made up of six males and four females ranging in age from 23 to 137 hours with a mean age of 77.6 hours.

APPARATUS AND PROCEDURE

All Ss were observed approximately 20 minutes before their regular feeding at 9:30 A.M. or their regular feeding at 5:30 P.M. in a quiet room under moderate illumination. Each S was brought into the observation room by a nurse, placed in a head-restraining cradle (Hershenson, 1964) and given a pacifier. The experimental group was shown a solid black equilateral triangle 8 inches on each side. The triangle was painted on wire window screen and was centered in a circular white background of aluminum 23 inches in diameter. The stimulus was approximately 9 inches above the infant's eyes. From the baby's side, the wire-screen triangle appeared solid in color. However, enough light passed through the screen to permit photography of the eyes of a camera directly behind the wire screen. Figure 1 shows a schematic drawing of the apparatus. Infrared marker lights, invisible to adult observers from the position of the baby's eyes, were placed behind the stimulus panel at each vertex of the triangle. The marker lights were Bausch and Lomb Nicholas illuminators fitted with Kodak Wratten 87C filters. An Automax Model G-2 35-mm variable-speed camera, also invisible to adult observers from the posi-

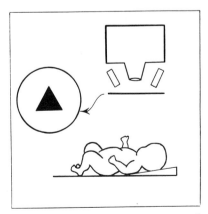

FIGURE 1   Schematic representation of the apparatus used in determining ocular orientation.

598

tion of the baby's eyes, was mounted behind the stimulus panel in the exact center
of the wire screening that formed the
triangle. The camera was loaded with
Kodak high-speed infrared-sensitive film
(HIR 417). Another Bausch and Lomb
illuminator, fitted with a Wratten 87C filter
in which a pinhole was drilled, was
mounted approximately 2 inches to the
temporal side and out of line with S's eyes.
The diffuse red and infrared illumination
from this illuminator heightened the contrast shown on the film between S's iris
and pupil. One of the baby's eyes was
centered under the camera and was photographed through a Pentax 105-mm Taku-
mar lens fitted with three extension rings.
Usually the lens was opened to an f-stop
of 2.8. The field photographed in this way
was approximately 1½ × 1½ inch, and
the depth of field was less than 1 inch.
Therefore, S's eye had to be exactly
centered and at a fixed distance from the
stimulus or the record of ocular orientation
was lost. Once each second during each
observation a picture of the infant's centered eye was taken through the wire
screen stimulus; in 19 cases, the right eye
was photographed. The noise of the
solenoid in the camera which advanced the
shutter permitted E to count the number of
pictures taken. At least 100 pictures of the
infant's open eye were taken with the
triangle in an upright position. The camera
was then stopped, the triangle was rotated
180°, and at least 100 pictures were taken
of the infant's open eye with the triangle
inverted. Order of rotation of triangle was
balanced across Ss. If S fell asleep during
an observation, E stopped the camera and
tried to wake S up. If he was successful, a
note was made of the interruption in the
record and the observation continued until
100 pictures had been taken of S's open
eye. The procedure did not produce an
equal number of pictures for all Ss or a
constant duration of observation; the observation continued until at least 100

frames of film had been taken of each
rotation of the triangle with S's eye open.

The control group was treated just like
the experimental group with these exceptions. Instead of being shown a black triangle on a white field, the control group
was shown a homogeneous circular black
field 21 inches in diameter. The infrared
marker lights remained mounted behind
the stimulus panel at the vertices of a
hypothetical equilateral triangle, 8 inches
to a side. After at least 100 pictures had
been taken of S's open eye (at the standard
rate of one frame per second) with the
marker lights in one rotation, the camera
was stopped, S's eye was covered for a
second or two, and the marker lights were
rotated 180°. Then, at least 100 pictures
were taken of S's open eye with the marker
lights in the second rotation.

Results

SCORING

Figure 2 is a photograph of an infant's
eye obtained in the way described earlier.
Ocular orientation was determined by
calculating the deviation of the corneal
reflections of the infrared marker lights
from the center of S's pupil. The distance

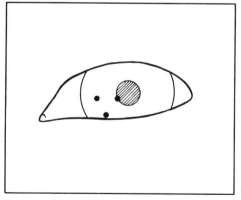

FIGURE 2 Drawing from infrared photograph of the newborn's eye. The three white
dots in the form of a triangle are the reflections
of the infrared marker lights from the cornea.

from a given marker light to the center of the pupil changes as S looks at different parts of the field. Moreover, this measure of ocular orientation is not affected by head movement of up to ½ inch from central visual axis (Cowey, 1963). Each 35-mm film frame was scored either on a Vanguard Motion Analyzer or on a semiautomatic scoring device invented by Haith (1966). Both of these instruments provide rectilinear coordinates for the center of the pupil and for a single preselected marker light. The relative position of the center of the pupil was obtained for each film frame by subtracting the marker light coordinates for a particular frame from the pupil-center coordinates for the same frame. The first 100 successive positions of pupil orientation obtained in this way were fed to an EAI Dataplotter which plotted the points with a reference marker light as origin and joined them to provide a record of visual scanning. Therefore, all records of visual scanning were based on exactly 100 positions of pupil orientation.

Scoring with both instruments yielded inter- and intra-scorer reliability coefficients (r) of over $+.90$. Both instruments were also calibrated to detect a change in ocular orientation of less than 1 inch on the stimulus panel (approximately 5° of visual angle). Ocular orientation could be measured as far as 45° from the center of the stimulus panel.

PATTERNS OF OCULAR ORIENTATION

Twenty records of ocular orientation for the ten babies in the control group—those who were shown a homogeneous black field —are presented in Figure 3. The triangle shown in each record is a hypothetical one, 8 inches on each side, formed by joining the positions of the infrared marker lights behind the field; the triangle is drawn in to permit easy comparison with records of ocular orientation in experimental Ss. Ocular orientations among control Ss were generally widely distributed through the field; there was no evidence that the infrared marker lights systematically influenced the orientation of control Ss. Twenty records of ocular orientation for the ten babies in the experimental group—those who were shown a black equilateral triangle in a white field—are presented in Figure 4. The inner triangle in each record is again a hypothetical one drawn to indicate the positions of the invisible infrared marker lights; the outer triangle, 8 inches on each side, represents the stimulus actually shown to the infants. As can be seen, when Ss were presented with a solid black triangle on a white field, their ocular orientation tended to cluster, and more, tended to cluster near the vertices of the triangle. Relatively few orientations were directed toward the center of the triangle. It seems clear, from a comparison of Figures 3 and 4, that the ocular orientation of the human newborn is to some degree controlled by visual form.

Some experimental records show a clustering of orientations at a slight distance from a vertex. This pattern of orientation may be accounted for by the fact that Ss had both eyes open, but only one eye was photographed. It is plausible to suspect that occasionally the unphotographed eye was "on target" and the photographed eye slightly misaligned (Ling, 1942; White, 1963; Dayton and Jones, 1964; Hershenson, 1964).

ANALYSIS OF PREFERENCE FOR SIDES AND VERTICES

In order to assess more precisely the overall influence of contour on ocular orientation and the differential influence on orientation of angles (vertices) and linear contours (sides), the real triangles on the experimental records and the hypothetical but metrically equivalent triangles on the control records were partitioned into linear and angular components. An orientation was scored as on contour if it fell within 1

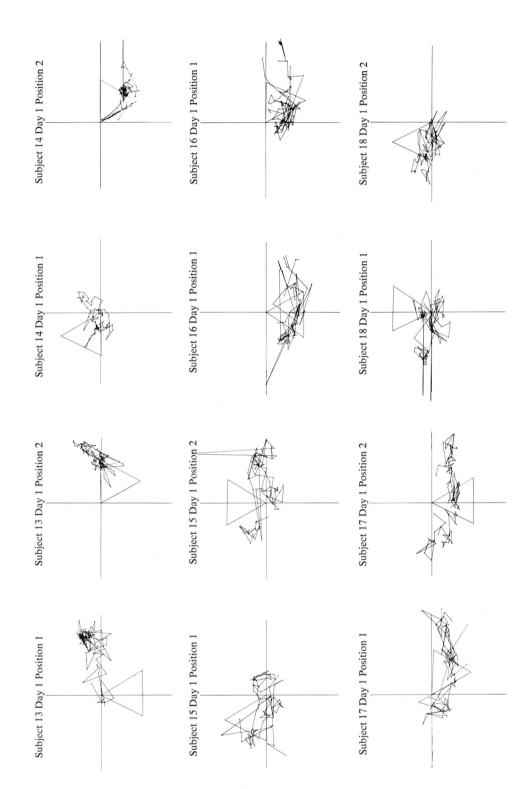

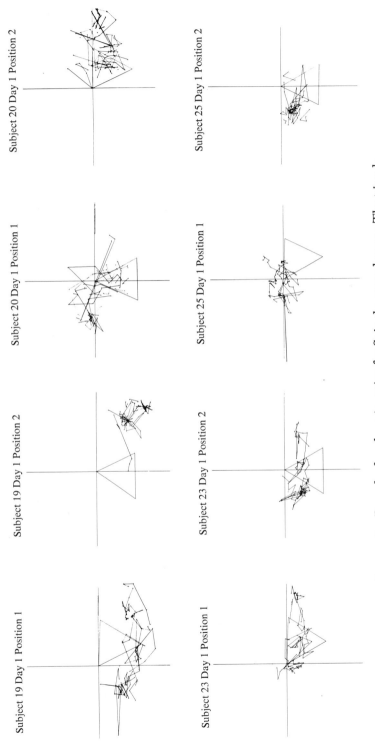

FIGURE 3 Records of ocular orientation for Ss in the control group. The triangle on each record is a *hypothetical* one metrically equivalent (8 inches on each side) to the triangle presented to the experimental Ss.

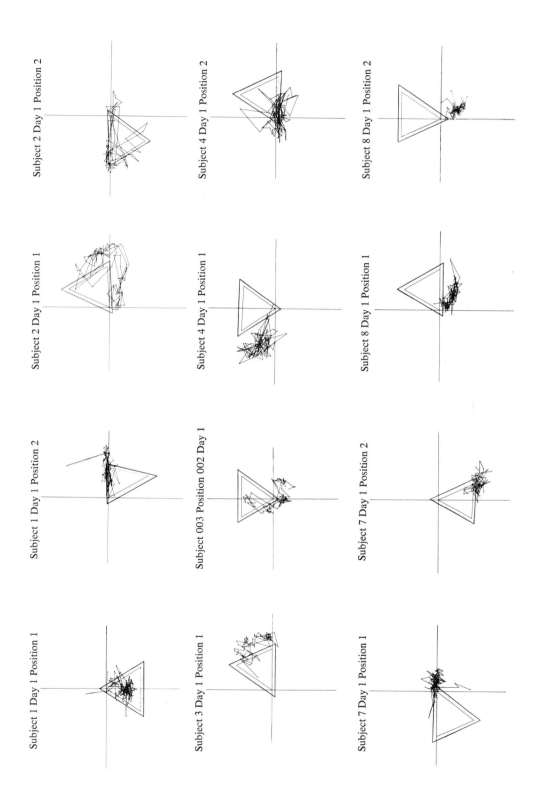

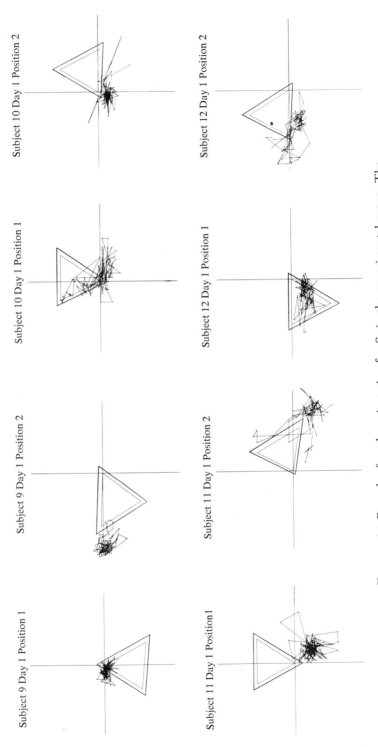

FIGURE 4   Records of ocular orientation for Ss in the experimental group. The outer triangle on each record represents the outline of the solid black equilateral triangle, 8 inches to a side, presented to the experimental Ss.

inch of a side of the triangle or within 1½ inch of a vertex. Neither order nor rotation of the stimulus field (triangle base-down or base-up) significantly influenced *on-contour* score; therefore, all results are presented with records combined from the two presentations of the stimulus field for each S.

Each S was given an overall *on-contour* score. Significantly more experimental Ss scored above the median on this measure than did control Ss ($p < 0.25$, Fisher's exact test). As inspection of Figures 3 and 4 indicates, this overall effect is largely an expression of the experimental group's orientation toward the vertices of the tri-angle. Each S was scored on the ratio of the number of orientations within 1½ inch of a vertex to the total number of orienta-tions remaining on his record after the number of orientations on contour other than the vertices had been subtracted out. This measure is a ratio of orientations on vertex to orientations altogether off con-tour. A significantly greater number of experimental Ss fell above the median on this measure than did control Ss ($p < .025$, Fisher's exact test). A similar test of the ratio of orientations within 1 inch of linear contours of the triangle to orientations altogether off contour provided no sig-nificant difference between experimental and control groups. The division of contour for scoring purposes into angular com-ponents (vertices) and linear components (sides) gave considerably greater total area for linear components. Of course, the linear components (sides) were also nearer the center of the visual field than were the vertices and, presumably, more easily ac-cessible to ocular orientation. In spite of these possible biases in favor of linear components of the figures, it was the vertices and not the sides that significantly attracted ocular orientation in the experi-mental group. Figure 4 also shows that experimental Ss typically looked toward a *single* vertex although the particular vertex chosen varied both between and within Ss.

DISPERSION OF OCULAR ORIENTATION

The tendency of babies to orient their eyes toward the vertices of the presented triangle is part of a more general charac-teristic of ocular orientation in the experi-mental group. As an examination of Figs. 3 and 4 will indicate, babies in the experi-mental group showed much less dispersion of orientations through the stimulus field. To put the finding another way, the pres-ence of a triangular form reduced the tendency of the baby's eye to wander. An analysis of variance was performed on log standard deviation of positions of ocular orientation in both the x- and the y-dimen-sions for experimental and control Ss. Control Ss showed much more dispersion of ocular orientation ($F = 29.80$; $df = 1$, 18; $p < .001$). There was also a significant overall tendency for dispersion in the horizontal dimension to be greater than dispersion in the vertical dimension of orientation measurements ($F = 52.66$; $df = 1$, 18; $p < .001$). Finally, there was a stable interaction between group differ-ences on one hand (experimental *vs.* control) and the direction of spread (hor-izontal *vs.* vertical) on the other ($F = 9.51$; $df = 1$, 18; $p < .01$). The significant interaction represents a tendency for the triangle to reduce the superiority of hori-zontal dispersion over vertical dispersion in the experimental group. In brief, then, both groups of Ss showed a wider range of variation through the horizontal dimension of the field than through the vertical; the experimental Ss showed both less overall dispersion in orientation and relatively less dispersion in the horizontal dimension.

Summary and Discussion

When infants under 8 days of age were shown a homogeneous black field, their visual scanning tended to be widely dis-persed with a greater dispersion in the horizontal than in the vertical dimension.

This selective dispersion suggests that horizontal scanning is easier for the newborn than is vertical, although it should also be noted that the infants were able to scan widely in both dimensions. The introduction of a large, solid, central triangle into the infant's field of view markedly reduced the overall dispersion of scanning and also reduced the predominance of horizontal over vertical scanning. Of greatest consequence for perceptual theory, the infants responded to only part of the figure. The ocular orientations of the infants were not distributed haphazardly over the triangle but tended to cluster at the vertices. Not only did their orientations cluster at vertices; there were extremely few orientations in the center of the triangle, the region in which it would be expected that a substantial number of orientations would lie if the infants were responding to the figure as a whole. Moreover, Ss typically looked toward a single vertex of the figure, the preferred vertex varying from S to S. There was little indication that, for any particular S, orientation was toward more than one "element" of the figure, e.g., orientations divided between two vertices or between a vertex and a side.

If one tries to explain the obtained results in the light of Hebb's (1949) theory about the acquisition of the concept of "triangle" by linkage through visual scanning of the "elements" comprising the figure, one is lead toward one or another of the following conclusions:

1. The newborn Ss, either because of a lack of maturation or of experience, were at a "pre-linkage" stage, capable of responding to elements but incapable of linking the elements through scanning.

2. A *solid* triangular figure is defined by contour and may not be analyzed by the visual system into the elements—sides and angles—that are fundamental to Hebb's theory.

3. The figure used in the present study was too large to permit the integration of elements. Obviously, the influence on ocular orientation of age, visual experience, and the size and nature of the figure must be studied before the role of scanning in the construction of form can be fully assessed.

What mechanism may underlie the response of the newborn to vertices of a triangle? The obtained results are compatible with at least three interpretations. It is possible that newborns respond to transitions in brightness and that the orientation toward a vertex is directed by the presence of two brightness transitions. Secondly, the infants may respond to vertices through a mechanism specifically tuned to angles. This interpretation is congruent with analyzer theories of discrimination (for example, Sutherland, 1959; Deutsch, 1960; Dodwell, 1964), and may suggest the presence in young infants of neurophysiological coding mechanisms analogous to the contour operators described for the visual system of cats (Hubel and Wiesel, 1962, 1963). Thirdly, it is possible that the infants were responding to an optimal level of brightness (Hershenson, 1964) that is only to be found near a vertex.

The results of the present study are relevant to an interpretation of the ambiguous relation found between complexity and preference in the human newborn (Fantz, 1963; Hershenson, 1964; Hershenson et al., 1965). The results presented here suggest that the human newborn orients toward preferred elements in his visual field and does not respond to a figure as a whole. Therefore, a preferred figure may well be one in which there is a predominant number of attractive elements.

References

Cowey, A. The basis of a method of perimetry with monkeys. *Quart. J. exp. Psychol.,* 1963, *15*, Pt. 2, 81–90.

Dayton, G. O., Jr., and Margaret H. Jones.

Analysis of characteristics of fixation reflex in infants by use of direct current electrooculography. *Neurology,* 1964, *14,* 1152–1156.

DEUTSCH, J. A. *The structural basis of behavior.* Chicago: *Univ. of Chicago Press,* 1960.

DODWELL, P. C. A coupling system for coding and learning in shape discrimination. *Psychol. Rev.,* 1964, *71,* 148–159.

FANTZ, R. L. The origin of form perception. *Sci. Amer.,* 1961, *204,* 459–463.

FANTZ, R. L. Studying visual perception and the effects of visual exposure in early infancy. Paper read at meetings of American Psychological Association, Philadelphia, August, 1963.

HAITH, M. M. A semi-automatic procedure for measuring changes in position, 1966, *J. exp. child Psychol.,* in press.

HEBB, D. O. *The organization of behavior.* New York: Wiley, 1949.

HERSHENSON, M. Visual discrimination in the human newborn. *J. comp. physiol. Psychol.,* 1964, *58,* 270–276.

HERSHENSON, M., H. MUNSINGER, and W. KESSEN. Preference for shapes of intermediate variability in the newborn human. *Science,* 1965, *147,* 630–631.

HUBEL, D. H., and T. N. WIESEL. Receptive fields, binocular interaction and functional architecture in the cat's visual cortex. *J. Physiol.,* 1962, *160,* 106–154.

HUBEL, D. H., and T. N. WIESEL. Receptive fields of cells in striate cortex of very young, visually inexperienced kittens. *J. Neurophysiol.,* 1963, *26,* 994–1002.

KESSEN, W., and M. HERSHENSON. Ocular orientation in the human newborn infant. Paper read at meetings of American Psychological Association, Philadelphia, August, 1963.

LING, BING-CHUNG. A genetic study of sustained visual fixation and associated behavior in the human infant from birth to six months. *J. genet. Psychol.,* 1942, *61,* 227–277.

SUTHERLAND, N. S. Stimulus analyzing mechanisms. In *Mechanisation of thought processes.* London: Her Majesty's Stationary Office, 1959, vol. II.

WHITE, B. L. Plasticity in perceptual development during the first six months of life. Paper read at meetings of American Association for the Advancement of Science, Cleveland, December, 1963.

Movement-Produced Stimulation in the Development of Visually Guided Behavior[*]

RICHARD HELD   ALAN HEIN

Massachusetts Institute of Technology

Full and exact adaptation to sensory rearrangement in adult human Ss requires movement-produced sensory feedback. Riesen's work suggested that this factor also operates in the development of higher mammals but he proposed that sensory-sensory associations are the prerequisite. To test these alternatives, visual stimulation of the active member (A) of each of 10 pairs of neonatal kittens was allowed to vary with its locomotor movements while equivalent stimulation of the second member (P) resulted from passive motion. Subsequent tests of visually guided paw placement, discrimination on a visual cliff, and the blink response were normal for A but failing in P. When other alternative explanations are excluded, this result extends the conclusions of studies of adult rearrangement to neonatal development.

Hebb's writing (1949) has stirred interest in the effects of exposure to the environment on the development of spatial perception and coordination. The main experimental attack on the problem has used the technique of rearing animals in restricted environments (deprivation) from the time of birth or shortly thereafter. An alternative approach consists in experimentally analyzing the conditions for modifying certain sensorimotor coordinations in adults on the assumption that they are similarly plastic during the entire exposure-history of the organism (Hein and Held, 1962; Held, 1955, 1961). If this supposition is true, the analysis carried out on adults must also define the kind of contact with the environment required for development. Use of the rearrangement technique for studying plasticity in adult

human Ss has yielded results which suggest its complementarity to the procedures of neonatal deprivation (Held and Bossom, 1961). This experiment demonstrates the convergence of the two approaches.

In the human adult, change in stimulation dependent upon the natural movements of S has been shown essential to the achievement of full and exact compensation for sensory rearrangements (Hein and Held, 1958; Held, 1955; Held and Bossom, 1961; Mikaelian and Held, in press). A suggestive parallel between these findings and those of deprivation studies comes from two experiments on kittens reared under different conditions of deprivation. In one experiment Ss were allowed visual experience in an illuminated and patterned environment only while they were restrained in holders which prevented them from freely moving about (Reisen and Aarons, 1959). When subsequently tested they showed deficiencies in visually guided behavior compared with their normally

[*] *Journal of Comparative and Physiological Psychology* 1963, vol. 56, pp. 872–876. This research was supported by a grant from the National Science Foundation.

reared litter mates. Related deficits followed rearing in a second experiment in which Ss were allowed to move about freely in light but with diffusing hoods over their eyes (Reisen, 1961c). The exposure factor lacking under both conditions was the variation in visual stimulation produced by the full range of S's movement in normal circumstances; a result consistent with our findings.

Riesen has suggested that his deprived Ss showed deficits because they lacked sufficient opportunity for developing sensory-sensory association in the manner proposed by Hebb (Riesen, 1961c)—even the patterned surroundings viewed by the holder-restrained Ss may not have provided sufficient variation in visual stimulation for forming the necessary associations. This interpretation agrees with ours in asserting that the variation in visual stimulation accompanying movement is essential for the development of certain coordinations but it omits our qualification that this variation can be effective only when it is concurrent with and systematically dependent upon self-produced movements (Hein and Held, 1962; Held, 1961). The alternative to our interpretation asserts that changes in stimulation irrespective of their relation to self-produced movements are sufficient. To decide between these two alternatives, we reared different sets of kittens from birth under the two implied conditions of exposure and subsequently compared their development. Under one condition stimulation varied as a result of Ss own locomotion whereas under the other it was equivalently varied by transporting Ss through an equivalent range of motion while they were restrained from locomoting.

Method

SUBJECTS

Ten pairs of kittens were used; each pair from a different litter.

EXPOSURE APPARATUS
AND PROCEDURE

The exposure apparatus diagramed in Figure 1 was designed to equate the visual stimulation received by each member of a pair of Ss. Stimulation varied with the locomotor movements of the active S (A

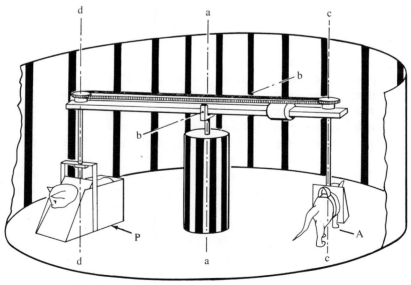

FIGURE 1   Apparatus for equating motion and consequent visual feedback for an actively moving (A) and a passively moved (P) S.

in Figure 1) but varied with equivalent motion of the passive S (P). To attain this equivalence, the gross motions of A were mechanically transferred to P. These movement were restricted to rotations around three axes. The radial symmetry of the visible environment made variations in visual stimulation, contingent upon these movements, equal over time for the two Ss.

The P was placed in the gondola and held there by a neckyoke and body clamp. The lever from which the gondola was suspended was then balanced by appropriate placement of a counterweight. When attached to the opposite end of the lever by a second neckyoke and bodyclamp assembly, A was free to move itself in both directions around the three axes of rotation a-a, b-b, and c-c while pulling P through the equivalent movements around a-a, b-b, and d-d by means of the mechanical linkages to the gondola. The distance between c-c and d-d was 36 in. The range of motions normally performed by Ss was somewhat reduced by the experimental apparatus. Use of ball bearings and aluminum in the construction of the apparatus reduced friction and inertia insofar as possible. The importance of these restraints is mitigated, we believe, by previous findings in rearrangement studies which indicate that similar restraints, and constant changes in the inertia overcome by muscular movement, do not affect the adaptation process (Held and Hein, 1958; Held and Schlank, 1959). Head motion was not restricted for either A or P. This restriction seemed unnecessary since Riesen and Aarons (1959) have shown that kittens reared from birth with variation in visual stimulation consequent upon free head motions, but otherwise restricted, failed to learn a simple spatial discrimination. Because of its constraints, P could not locomote. However, its limbs were free to move and to slide along the smooth floor of the gondola. According to our ob-

servations these movements frequently occurred.

The apparatus was surrounded by a galvanized iron cylinder that was 24 in high with a diameter of 48 in. The lever support mechanism was enclosed within a second cylinder that was 11 in high with a diameter of 12 in. The smaller cylinder served to obscure each S's view of its mate. Patterning was provided by vertically oriented 1 in wide stripes of black and white masking tape separated by 1 in. of bare metal. Additional texture was provided by the rough side of a piece of masonite which served as the floor. The floor was uniform throughout thus providing equivalent visual stimulation for the two Ss. Sight of the paws and other body parts was excluded by appropriate extensions of the neck stocks.

TESTING APPARATUS
AND PROCEDURE

We used tests of visually guided behavior that minimized S's gross movements in the visible environment in order not to confound the conditions of testing with those of exposure, a confusion which past investigators have generally disregarded. For this purpose responses to stimuli were used that require no conditioning with repetition of movements but which are nonetheless contingent upon a capacity to make visual-spatial discriminations. Following the leads of earlier work, we have used three such tests:

1. Visually-guided paw placement (Riesen, 1961c). S's body was held in E's hands so that its head and forelegs were free. It was slowly carried forward and downward towards the edge of a table or some other horizontal surface. A normally-reared S shows visually-mediated anticipation of contact by extending its paws as it approaches the edge.

2. Avoidance of a visual cliff

(Walk and Gibson, 1961). The visual cliff consists essentially of a narrow platform supported by vertical sides that drop a few inches to a large plate of glass. The S placed on the platform can descend to the glass on either one of two sides. Its view on the "deep" side is through the glass to a patterned surface 30 in below. On the other side it views a similarly patterned surface attached to the underside of the glass. In our apparatus, both surfaces were illuminated from below and hence the clean glass surface was practically visible. For the vertical sides of the platform, we substituted planes inclined 35° from the vertical.

3. Blink to an approaching object (Riesen, 1958). The S was held in a standing position in a neckyoke and bodyclamp with a large sheet of Plexiglas positioned directly in front of its face. The E moved his hand quickly toward S, stopping just short of contact with the Plexiglas.

Several additional tests were performed to check the status of peripheral receptor and response mechanisms. These included observations of pupillary reflex to light, the tactual placing response, and visual pursuit of a moving object. The S, held in a standing position in a neckyoke and bodyclamp, was light-adapted in the normally illuminated laboratory prior to observation of the pupillary reflex. Change in pupillary size was then noted when a light beam from a penlight was moved across the eye from outer to inner canthus. To determine the presence of the tactual paw-placing response S was supported as in the visual paw-placing test. It was then carried to the edge of a table where the dorsa of its front paws were brought into contact with the vertical edge of the table. Observations of experimental Ss were compared with those of normals which, in response to this stimulus, place the paws on the horizontal surface of the table. Visual pursuit was elicited by E's hand moving slowly across S's visual field.

GENERAL PROCEDURE

The 10 pairs of Ss were divided into two Groups, X and Y, whose members were reared with minor differences. Each of the eight pairs of Group X was reared in darkness from birth until member A attained the minimal size and coordinational capacity to move itself and its mate in the apparatus. This age varied between 8 and 12 weeks. They then began exposure in the apparatus for 3 hrs daily. The two pairs of Group Y received 3 hrs daily exposure, beginning at 2 and ending at 10 weeks of age, to the patterned interior of the laboratory while restrained in holders that allowed some head movement but prevented locomotion. They then began exposure in the apparatus for 3 hrs. daily. When not exposed, all Ss were kept in lightless cages together with their mothers and litter mates. We had found in pilot studies that Ss reared in this fashion did not show the freezing, agitation, or fear responses reported to follow social isolation by Melzack (1962) and Riesen (1961a).

Six repetitions of the paw-placement test were performed after each daily exposure period for all Ss. On the first day that one S of each pair in Group X displayed visual paw placing, both were tested on the visual cliff. They were retested on the following day. For each test and retest S was required to descend from the central platform six times. Immediately following trials on the visual cliff on the second day, member P of each pair was put in a continuously illuminated room for 48 hrs. Retesting of visual placing and renewed trials on the visual cliff followed this unrestricted exposure. The testing procedure differed slightly for pairs of Group Y. On the first day that A displayed visual paw placing, it was tested on the visual cliff and retested on the following day. However, its mate (P) was not placed on the cliff at this time; instead, the passive exposure procedure was continued for 3 hrs daily for a total of 126 hrs. The paw placing and visual cliff tests were then administered to P.

Results

The principal results of this experiment are summarized in Table 1. The amount of time required for the development of a visually-guided paw-placement in the members of each pair of litter mates is indicated in the column under the heading Exposure in Apparatus. After those periods of exposure required by A, every P mate failed to display the response. Observations suggest a tendency for the placing response to develop in the livelier of the active Ss with fewer hours of exposure than required by the quieter ones. The blink response to an approaching hand developed concurrently with the placing response. Pupillary reflex to light, tactual placing response, and visual pursuit were each noted on first elicitation, just prior to the initial exposure in the apparatus.

On the day that the visually-guided placing response was shown by A, he was tested on the modified visual cliff. All As behaved like normally reared Ss which had been observed previously in a pilot experiment. As shown by the totals of Table 1, each A descended to the shallow side of the cliff on every trial of the first day and repeated this performance on the trials of the following day. The P members of Group X were tested on the cliff on the same days as their actively exposed litter mates. They showed no evidence of discriminating the shallow from the deep side. Observations of the P members of Group Y on the cliff, after their prolonged passive exposure, gave similar results and they also failed to perform visual paw placement. Following the 48 hr period of freedom in an illuminated room, the P members of Group X were retested. They then displayed normal visually-guided paw-placement and performed all descents to the shallow side of the visual cliff.

Discussion

The results are consistent with our thesis that self-produced movement with its concurrent visual feedback is necessary

TABLE 1

Ratio of Descents to Shallow and Deep Slides of Visual Cliff

PAIR NUMBER	AGE IN WEEKS*	EXPOSURE IN APPARATUS (in hr.)		RATIO OF DESCENTS SHALLOW/DEEP	
		A	P	A	P
1X	8	33	33	12/0	6/6
2X	8	33	33	12/0	4/8
3X	8	30	30	12/0	7/5
4X	9	63	63	12/0	6/6
5X	10	33	33	12/0	7/5
6X	10	21	21	12/0	7/5
7X	12	9	9	12/0	5/7
8X	12	15	15	12/0	8/4
1Y	10	30	126	12/0	6/6
2Y	10	33	126	12/0	8/4

* At the beginning of exposure in the experimental apparatus.

for the development of visually-guided behavior. Equivalent, and even greatly increased, variation in visual stimulation produced by other means is not sufficient. However, before concluding that our thesis is valid we must consider other alternative explanations of the deficits in the behavioral development of neonates following deprivation. These alternatives assert that loss of function does not reflect deficiencies in a process of the central nervous system that depends upon exposure for its development. Instead, the capacity to perform is allegedly present but prevented from operating by either peripheral blockage or other suppressive effects of the special rearing conditions. Such negative effects fall into two categories: (a) anatomical or physiological deterioration and (b) behavioral inhibition.

Included under anatomical or physiological deterioration said to result from deprivation, are the findings of atrophy in peripheral parts of the visual nervous system, a literature reviewed by Riesen (1961b); the assumption that maturation of the retina is prevented (Walk and Gibson, 1961); and the suggestion that general debility results from lack of use of various organs (Hess, 1962). In the present experiment, the relevance of peripheral atrophy is contraindicated by the presence of pupillary and pursuit reflexes and the rapid recovery of function of the passive Ss once given their freedom. Debility specific to the motor systems of these Ss can be ruled out on the grounds that their tactual placing responses and other motor activities were indistinguishable from those of normals. In addition, differential losses in the periphery or differential debility could hardly be expected to result from those differences between active and passive exposures which occurred in the experimental apparatus.

Inhibition of performance attributable to the effects of shock, fright, or overactivation upon exposure to the novel and increased stimulation that follows release from the deprived state has been suggested by Sutherland (1959) and Melzack (1962). Sutherland has also suggested that habits developed during deprivation may compete with and inhibit the normal response. However, both our active and passive Ss were raised under very similar conditions insofar as restriction was concerned and under the rather mild conditions of deprivation of this experiment we did not observe any signs of shock, excitement, or fright. Moreover, the passive Ss were not observed performing responses that might have competed with the expected response.

These findings provide convincing evidence for a developmental process, in at least one higher mammal, which requires for its operation stimulus variation concurrent with and systematically dependent upon self-produced movement. This conclusion neither denies nor affirms that other processes, such as maturation, occur concomitantly. The results demonstrate the complementarity of studies of adult rearrangement and neonatal deprivation.

References

HEBB, D. O. *The Organization of Behavior*. New York: Wiley, 1949.

HEIN, A., and R. HELD. Minimal conditions essential for complete re-learning of hand-eye coordination with prismatic distortion of visions. Paper read at Eastern Psychological Association. Philadelphia, 1958.

HEIN, A., and R. HELD. A neural model for labile sensorimotor coordinations. In E. E. Bernard and M. R. Kare (Eds.), *Biological prototypes and synthetic systems*. vol. 1. New York: Plenum Press, 1962. pp. 71–74.

HELD, R. Shifts in binaural localization after prolonged exposure to atypical combinations of stimuli. *Amer. J. Psychol.*, 1955, *68*, 526–548.

HELD, R. Exposure-history as a factor in maintaining stability of perception and coordination. *J. nerv. ment. Dis.*, 1961, *132*, 26–32.

HELD, R., and J. BOSSOM. Neonatal deprivation and adult rearrangemnt: Complementary techniques for analyzing plastic sensory-motor coordinations. *J. comp. physiol. Psychol.*, 1961, *54*, 33–37.

HELD, R., and A. HEIN. Adaptation of disarranged hand-eye coordination contingent upon re-afferent stimulation. *Percept. mot. Skills*, 1958, 8, 87–90.

HELD, R., and M. SCHLANK. Adaptation to optically-increased distance of the hand from the eye by re-afferent stimulation. *Amer. J. Psychol.*, 1959, 72, 603–605.

HESS, E. H. Ethology: An approach toward the complete analysis of behavior. In R. Brown, E. Galanter, E. H. Hess, and G. Mandler (Eds.), *New Directions in Psychology*. New York: Holt, Rinehart and Winston, 1962. pp. 159–226.

MELZACK, R. Effects of early perceptual restriction on simple visual discrimination. *Science*, 1962, 137, 978–979.

MIKAELIAN, H., and R. HELD. Two types of adaptation to an optically-rotated visual field. *Amer. J. Psychol.*, in press.

RIESEN, A. H. Plasticity of behavior: Psychological aspects. In H. F. Harlow and C. N. Woolsey (Eds.), *Biological and biochemical bases of behavior*. Madison: Univer. Wisconsin Press, 1958, pp. 425–450.

RIESEN, A. H. Excessive arousal effects of stimulation after early sensory deprivation. In P. Solomon, P. E. Kubzansky, P. H. Liederman, J. H. Mendelson, R. H. Trumbull, and D. Wexler (Eds.), *Sensory deprivation*. Cambridge: Harvard Univer. Press, 1961. pp. 34–40. (a)

RIESEN, A. H. Stimulation as a requirement for growth and function in behavioral development. In D. W. Fiske and S. R. Maddi (Eds.), *Functions of varied experience* Homewood: Dorsey Press, 1961, pp. 57–80. (b)

RIESEN, A. H. Studying perceptual development using the technique of sensory deprivation. *J. nerv. ment. Dis.*, 1961, 132, 21–25. (c)

RIESEN, A. H., and L. AARONS. Visual movement and intensity discrimination in cats after early deprivation of pattern vision. *J. comp. physiol. Psychol.*, 1959, 52, 142–149.

SUTHERLAND, N. S. Stimulus analyzing mechanisms. In, *Mechanization of thought precesses: National physical laboratory symposium. No. 10. Vol. 2.* London: Her Majesty's Stationery Office, 1959, pp. 575–609.

WALK, R. D., and E. J. GIBSON. A comparative and analytical study of visual depth perception. *Psychol. Monogr.*, 1961, 75 (15, Whole No. 519).

*Visually Guided Reaching in Infant Monkeys after Restricted Rearing**

RICHARD HELD   JOSEPH A. BAUER, Jr.

Massachusetts Institute of Technology

Abstract. Infant macaques were reared from birth in an apparatus which precluded sight of their body parts. At 35 days postpartum one hand was exposed to view. Visual fixation of this hand was insistent and prolonged; visually guided reaching was poor, but it improved during ten succeeding hours of exposure. Little concomitant improvement occurred in the reaching of the unexposed hand.

Recent research indicates that an infant primate should be unable to reach for and

* *Science*, 1966, vol. 155, pp. 718–720. Copyright © 1966 by the American Association for the Advancement of Science. Supported by Grant NIMH M-7642 and NASA Grant NSG-496.

grasp visible objects with a limb that it has never previously viewed (1). To verify this prediction one must demonstrate that the infant may be reared until its visual and motor capabilities are sufficiently mature to support visually guided reaching but that this behavior will not appear if the relevant visual-motor interaction has been precluded. Testing the hypothesis requires an experimental subject which is normally capable of visually guided reaching and which can be reared under the necessary controlled conditions. The infant monkey satisfies both of these demands, but research on its postnatal development is difficult because the animal needs substantial maternal care (2). We here describe a solution of the rearing problem, as well as preliminary results that confirm our prediction.

Because it is difficult to experiment with the infant when the mother is present, the two are separated soon after birth (3). The experimenter must then provide all maternal care. Human handlers can supply routine maintenance, but unless they can also furnish substitutes for some of the psychological aspects of maternal care, the infant will develop bizarre emotional behavior which interferes with controlled rearing and with subsequent testing (4). Harlow demonstrated that surrogate mothering devices can satisfy certain of the psychological needs of the infant monkey (5). Because the surrogate mother is inanimate and non-reacting, unlike the real mother, it becomes part of the controlled situation.

The apparatus we have designed (Figure 1) promotes the development of normal infantile behavior by supporting the infant, surrounding its torso with a soft surface in contact with the skin, and giving it easy and continuous access to a nipple which provides milk. Furthermore, it conceals the monkey's limbs from its view, and yet allows the limbs a wide range of normal exploratory and manipulatory activities. The basic unit is a metal cylinder encircling the torso of the infant and suspended above a horizontal seat. One or two baby diapers folded 7.5 to 10 cm wide and loosely wrapped around the infant's body support it snugly in the cylindrical body holder. A horizontal rod

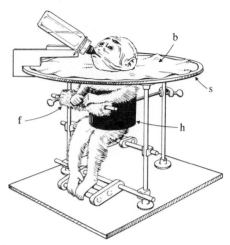

FIGURE 1 Apparatus for rearing an infant monkey without sight of its limbs. *h*, metal cylinder; *f*, fur-covered rod; *s*, plywood body shield; *b*, cloth bib.

covered with a piece of fur-like rug is within easy reach of the animal. The fur serves as a substitute for the mother's hairy skin and diverts the animal's grasping response from his own body. This diversion is extremely important because a monkey who has been deprived of a real mother clings tenaciously to the hairiest object in the environment, usually itself, to the exclusion of all other activities of its limbs, including reflexive responses while falling. Three vertical aluminum rods to which the holder is attached support a circular plywood body shield with an opening in the center. The head of the infant protrudes through this opening. A cloth bib is pinned around its neck and fastened to the circumference of the shield. When bib and body shield are in place, the animal cannot view any part of its body.

The apparatus can readily be altered to accommodate infants of varying size. Routine maintenance can easily be adapted for extremely small or even premature newborns. A nursing bottle with a "preemie" nipple can be positioned so that random movement of the infant's head results in facial contact with the nipple. This stimulation elicits the rooting response which brings mouth to nipple (6).

Consequently, ad lib feeding can be initiated on the first day of life. The restraint placed upon the animal facilitates cleaning and routine maintenance; one or two daily changes of the diapers which cover the base are sufficient to maintain relatively odor-free conditions. Bottles need be cleaned and replaced only twice a day when fresh milk is used. Another desirable feature of this arrangement is the simplicity of its construction—only ordinary laboratory clamps, 12 mm wooden dowling, and exterior grade plywood treated with linseed oil are needed.

The apparatus also facilitates testing the infant. Since the body holder can be detached from the rest of the supporting components, it may be removed together with the animal and placed in a test apparatus with appropriate foot and seat rests. This mode of transfer retains contact between the infant and part of the rearing device when he is placed in a new environment for testing. Consequently, the animal does not exhibit the fear responses produced by the reduction of contact when separated from either a real or surrogate mother. The entire apparatus can be shifted to the test situation or, alternatively, the test apparatus can be brought to the rearing device. Thus, conditioned performance of voluntary response is easily obtained even with very young monkeys because they are not disturbed by the change. We can then assess behavioral development without waiting for the animal to adapt to a testing apparatus.

Our first subjects were two female stump-tailed macaques (*Macaca speciosa*), chosen because of the species' reputation for docility (7). Within 12 hours of birth, each infant was put in the rearing apparatus and for the next 34 days was not allowed to view any part of its body. The monkey was conditioned to extend its limbs on presentation of the feeding bottle during the period from day 16 to day 34. The rug-covered bar was removed and the bottle was hidden below the body shield while one arm was gently restrained by the experimenter. The bottle was then returned to view in front of the animal. If the monkey oriented head and eyes to the bottle and extended its unrestrained limb horizontally, the nipple was brought to its mouth for a few seconds. This procedure was repeated alternately on each arm until ten extensions had been elicited. When we first presented the bottle, the monkey made flailing responses with the free arm. In the course of daily testing the conditioned extension became stereotyped and unrelated to the direction in which the bottle appeared. By the end of the conditioning period, presentation of the bottle elicited head and eye orientation to it and a token extension of the arm at shoulder level.

An animal that is reared under normal conditions will accurately reach for and manipulate visible objects before the age of 1 month (8). Our monkeys were allowed to view one of their arms for the first time on day 35 when testing of visually guided reaching was begun. The experimenter presented a variety of visual stimuli (small objects, including the nursing bottle) within reaching distance of the animal. Testing was terminated after either ten reaches or 15 minutes. The animal was then free to view its arm for the rest of the hour-long period. During the remainder of the day, the arm was concealed as on previous days. After the first day, each subject was tested and allowed to view its arm 1 hour daily for a total of 20 days. Reaching responses during each test session were filmed to provide a permanent record of performance.

On the first day, sight of the bottle elicited arm extension, but unlike the extension response performed when the arm had been concealed, the initial reach was terminated as soon as the free hand entered the monkey's field of vision. When the hand entered the field, the animal immediately turned its gaze toward it and watched intently while moving the arm about in a manner quite unlike the stereotyped extension. The animal's fascination with the movements of its own hand resembles the hand-watching behavior of human infants described by Piaget and others (9).

Visual pursuit of the hand was extremely prolonged in comparison with visual following of other moving targets, including the hand and arm of another baby monkey. Occasionally, sounds or movements in the test room made the infant avert its gaze from its hand, whereupon another reaching trial could be initiated. Although hand-watching occurred less frequently in the later part of the exposure hour, it was renewed with vigor during the initial test trials on the next day. As the hand-watching abated, observers found it easier to judge the accuracy of visually guided reaching, which was poorer than that of normally reared animals.

During the 20 days of testing hand-watching gradually decreased in frequency and duration. Occasionally the monkey alternated its gaze from target to hand and back again. Concomitantly, reaches elicited on presentation of a test stimulus became more obviously directed toward the target and the monkey sporadically struck the object. Only a few reaches resulted in grasping of the object. More frequently initial contact was followed by groping during which contact was repeatedly made and broken. After several days, reaches were executed with a continuous movement accurately directed to the target with anticipatory opening of the fist before contact. Manipulation of the objects became more delicate and precise. By the end of 20 hours of exposure, both monkeys were quite proficient in visually guided reaching and grasping with the exposed limb.

After accurate visual guidance of the initially exposed limb had been achieved, we began similar tests with the previously unexposed limb. Presentation of the visual stimulus evoked orientation of eyes and head together with limb extension, but the two responses were not integrated. As with the limb which had been exposed first, the initial extension response terminated in hand-watching behavior as soon as the limb entered the field of view. Hand-watching activity predominated, but on the first day the few awkward striking movements observed were remarkably similar to the first efforts of the initially exposed limb. After the stimulus was presented several times, the monkey was allowed to view the newly exposed limb for the remainder of an hour.

At the end of this time both limbs were permitted to extend above the bib, and reaches for visible objects were photographed. Successful reaches were made only with the limb that had been previously exposed for 20 hours. On several occasions this limb grasped and tugged at the more recently exposed limb as if it were a foreign object. During the next few days reaching with the second limb improved rapidly, and after 10 hours of exposure it was approximately equivalent in precision and accuracy to that of the contralateral limb. However, when both limbs were tested together, the initially exposed limb was generally used in preference to the other. At this time the infant was nearly twice the age at which the first limb was exposed and had gained considerable facility in nonvisual control of both limbs.

After the tests were terminated on day 65, the monkeys were removed from the apparatus and placed singly in cages. Initially they remained prone and clung tenaciously to the diapers covering the cage floor, but they remained alert and ceaselessly looked about their new environment. Within hours they were manually exploring the cage sides and a bottle holder which was suspended a few inches overhead. By the end of the first week both monkeys could walk and climb with near normal ease. By the age of 4 months their locomotor behavior was indistinguishable from that of a monkey of comparable age reared under normal laboratory conditions (*10*).

The results show that an infant primate initially fails to reach accurately for attractive visible objects with a limb that it has never previously viewed. Yet the animal demonstrates both its interest in the objects and its ability to control movements of eyes and head by orienting them to the target. At the same time, it shows the ability to control movements of its limbs and hands with respect to its body. Integration of visuomotor control of head movement and of nonvisual control of limb movement resulting in the ability to perform a visually directed reach appears to require the specific experience of viewing the moving hand. Sight of the moving hand enables the adult to adapt coordination of the eye and hand to the changes produced by optical rearrangement; likewise, sight of the moving hand perfects accurate visual control of reaching in the neonate (*1*).

The act of reaching for a visible target by an adult primate appears to depend upon his capability first to orient his eyes and head to the target and, second, to match the direction of reaching by the hand with the actual or potential orientation of the head to the target. The match is altered when adults adapt to displaced vision of the arm (*11*), and the alteration shows little or no transfer to the contralateral unexposed arm either in man or monkey (*12*). We believe that the earliest experience of watching the moving limb provides the information necessary for the infant to match orientations of head to target and directions of reaching of the arm, and this information integrates the two control systems. If both of these systems are permitted to develop independently, as in the present experiment, hand-watching becomes the prepotent activity when the hand is first seen. Since

no more effective means of integrating the systems could be devised, we regard this behavior as a dramatic manifestation of an adaptive mechanism.

References and Notes

1. This supposition has been derived from research on the modifiable sensorimortor coordinations of primates and cats discussed in R. Held, *Sci. Amer.* 1965, *213*, 84; R. Held and S. Freedman, *Science* 1963, *142*, 455; R. Held and A. Hein. *J. Comp. Physiol. Psychol.* 1963, *56*, 872; A. Hein and R. Held, *Biological Prototypes and Synthetic Systems* (Plenum Press, New York, 1962), vol. 1; A. Efstathiou, J. Bauer, M. Greene, R. Held, *J. Exp. Psychol.*, in press; B. White and R. Held, in *The Causes of Behavior: Readings in Child Development and Educational Psychology*, J. F. Rosenblith and W. Allinsmith, Eds. (Ally and Bacon, Boston, ed. 2, 1966), p. 60. Kittens reared without sight of their paws fail in efforts to strike at visible targets [A. Hein, "Symposium on Perception and Action" (*Proc. 18th Int. Congr. Psychol.* Moscow, 1966)]. The only comparable previous research on primates used a chimpanzee [H. W. Nissen, K. L. Chow, J. Semmes, *Amer. J. Psychol.* 1951, *64*, 485], but interpretation of the results is made difficult by the degree of restraint imposed on the animal during rearing.
2. BLOMQUIST, A. J., and H. F. HARLOW. *Proc. Anim. Care Panel* 1961, *11*, 57.
3. BLOMQUIST, A. J., and G. W. MEIER. *Anim. Behav.* 1965, *13*, 228.
4. HARLOW, H. F., and M. K. HARLOW, in *Behavior of Nonhuman Primates.* A. M. Schrier, H. F. Harlow, F. Stollnitz, Eds. (Academic Press, New York, 1965), vol. 2; L. A. Rosenblum and H. A. Cross, *Amer. J. Psychol.* 1963, *76*, 318; L. A. Rosenblum, I. C. Kaufman, W. Barnett, paper presented at Eastern Psychological Association, New York, April 1966; B. Seay, E. Hansen, H. F. Harlow, *J. Child Psychol. Psychiat. Allied Disciplines* 1962, *3*, 123.
5. HARLOW, H. F. *Amer. Psychologist* 1958,

13, 673; H. F. Harlow and R. R. Zimmerman, *Science* 1959, *130*, 421.

6. Mowbray, J. B., and T. E. Cadell, *J.
Comp. Physiol. Psychol.* 1962, *65*,
350.

7. Kling, A., and J. Orbach. *Science* 1963,
139, 45.

8. Foley, J. P. *J. Genet. Psychol.* 1934, *45*,
39; M. Hines, *Contr. Embryol.* 1942,
30, 1953; W. A. Mason, H. F. Harlow,
R. R. Rueping, *J. Comp. Physiol. Psychol.* 1959, *52*, 555.

9. Piaget, J. *The Origins of Intelligence in
Children*, M. Cook, Transl. (International Univ. Press, New York, 1952),
pp. 103–107; B. White and R. Held,
in *The Causes of Behavior: Readings
in Child Development and Educational

Psychology*, J. F. Rosenblith and W.
Allinsmith. Eds. (Ally and Bacon, Boston, ed. 2, 1966).

10. In all, seven infants have been successfully raised in the apparatus and tested
on eye-limb coordination after various
periods of restriction. Two of these
monkeys were restricted for the first 8
months of life. Their adaptation to the
normal environment required a proportionally longer time, but at 1 year of
age their behavior was similar to that of
their peers who were raised in the
laboratory.

11. Efstathiou, A. J. Bauer, M. Greene,
R. Held. *J. Exp. Psychol.*, in press.

12. Hamilton, C. R. *Amer. J. Psychol.* 1964,
77, 457.

Pictorial Recognition as an Unlearned Ability:
A Study of One Child's Performance[*]

JULIAN HOCHBERG   VIRGINIA BROOKS
New York University

Anecdotes about primitive people who are unable to identify pictured objects suggest the hypothesis that pictorial recognition is a learned ability.[1] In a weaker form of this hypothesis, learning might be held essential for the recognition of line-drawings (compare Gibson's "ghost shapes"),[2] while the naïve recognition of photographs, with their higher "fidelity," would be ad-

mitted. The present investigation was designed to determine whether a child who had been taught his vocabulary *solely* by the use of objects, and who had received no instruction or training whatsoever concerning pictorial meaning or content, could recognize objects portrayed by two-dimensional line-drawings and by photographs.

Answers to these questions were desired for two reasons. First, the psychophysical exploration of outline-representations has begun to provide some promising, lawful relationship.[3] Although the predictive equations would remain just as interesting

[*] *American Journal of Psychology*, 1962, vol. 75, pp. 624–628. This study, assisted by Dr. P. C. Smith and Mrs. Janice Goldstein, was supported by National Health Institute Grant B-1586 (C2).

[1] The only study in point is that of W. Hudson, Pictorial depth perception in sub-cultural groups in Africa, *J. Soc. Psychol.*, 52, 1960, 183–208, which is concerned with differences in spatial localization rather than in recognition of objects.

[2] J. J. Gibson, What is a form?, *Psychol. Rev.*, 58, 1951, 403–412.

[3] Julian Hochberg and Virginia Brooks, The psychophysics of form: Reversible-perspective drawings of spatial objects, *Amer. Journal of Psychology*, 1960, 73, 337–354.

regardless of whether they are based on "learned" or "innate" processes,[4] somewhat different sets of further hypotheses might suggest themselves if the entire realm of responses to outline-representations of spatial objects turned out to be the product of arbitrary associations between symbols and things—a sort of assigned visual language. Secondly, if pictorial perception did indeed turn out to be a learned ability in this arbitrary sense (which it did not), we should have a starting point for the investigation of the possible lines of its development and of individual differences therein.

It should be stressed that this investigation does not directly bear upon the general question of nativism vs. empiricism in space-perception, which is too broad to be submitted to so specific a test. If space-perception were itself an "unlearned" ability, the representation by flat pictures might not be feasible without specific learning. If recognition of solid objects in two-dimensional representation were at least in part unlearned, it might still develop without formal training as a by-product of a more general process of learning to perceive space.

TRAINING

Since birth, the subject (S), a boy, had been exposed to and taught the names of a wide variety of toys and other solid objects. With two exceptions discussed below, the color of each of these objects was either uniform, or it was divided into functional areas (e.g., face-coloration, hair-shade, and dress-color on dolls). That is, no objects were depicted as surface-decoration. Even so, S never was told (or allowed to overhear) the name or meaning of any picture or depicted object. In fact, pictures were, in general, kept from his immediate vicinity.

This is *not* to say that S never had been

[4] Hochberg, Spatial representation: Theme 10, *Proc. Int. Congr. Psychol.*, 1957.

exposed to pictures. There was a Japanese print on one wall of a room through which he frequently passed; a myriad of billboards fronted the highways on which he traveled frequently; a few times (six in all) he accidentally encountered a picturebook (which was gently withdrawn) or caught a glimpse of the label of a jar of baby food (these were normally removed or kept covered). (All these encounters were unaccompanied by instruction or naming-play.) Furthermore, one toy (a top) had pictures of elves on it and, accordingly, it was available for play only under strict supervision to prevent any naming in his presence; and a high chair had a decal of babies on it, which could be glimpsed (without parental comment) only when S was being placed in the seat.

The constant vigilance and improvisation required of the parents proved to be a considerable chore from the start—further research of this kind should not be undertaken lightly. By 19 mo of age, the child began actively to seek pictures, and continuation of the constraints become both pediatrically and methodologically undesirable. Two incidents terminated this stage of the investigation: (a) S became aware of events on the TV set in the next room, managed to obtain a glimpse of the screen on which a horse was being depicted, and excitedly cried "dog"; (b) he squirmed around in his highchair about the same time, and, pointing to the decal, said "baby." It was evident that some form of parental response to such identifications would soon become unavoidable. The testing procedure was begun at this point.

TESTING: PART 1

The set of 21 pictures listed in the first part of Table I, and shown in Figure 1, was prepared on 3×5 in cards. In all cases but one (No. 12), the series was so arranged that the outline-drawing of any object preceded any photograph of the same object; recognition could not, therefore, be made first from the photograph

TABLE 1

Stimulus-Presentations and Judges' Interpretations of S's Responses

	PART 1				PART 2			
STIMULUS PICTURE		INTERPRETATION OF RESPONSES			STIMULUS PICTURE		INTERPRETATION OF RESPONSES	
	PARENTS		JUDGE A	JUDGE B		PARENTS		JUDGE A	JUDGE B
(1) car	+		car	car	(1a) car	+		car	car
(2) car	+		car	car	(2a) car	+		car	car
(3) shoe	+		shoe	shoe	(3a) car	−		Jody§	Jody§
(4) shoe	+		shoe	shoe	(4a) shoe	+		shoe	shoe
(5) shoe	+				(5a) shoe	−			
(6) Jody (sister)	+		Jody		(6a) Jody	+		Jody	Jody
(7) dolly	+			dolly	(7a) dolly	+		dolly	dolly
(8) dolly	−		shoe‡	shoe‡	(8a) dolly	+		dolly	dolly
(9) dolly	−		shoe‡		(9a) car	+		car	car
(10) car	+		car	car	(10a) car	+		car	car
(11) car	+		car	car	(11a) rocky	+		rocky	rocky
(12) rocky	+		rocky	rocky	(12a) rocky	+		rocky	rocky
(13) rocky	+		rocky	rocky	(13a) rocky	+			
(14) rocky	+				(14a) key	+		key	key
(15) keys	+		key	keys	(15a) dog	+		dog	
(16) key	+		key	key	(16a) spoon	−			key
(17) key	+		key	key	(17a) Mommy	−†			
(18) wawaw	−*		wawaw	wawaw	(1c) box	+		box	
(19) fcahr	+		car	car	(2c) box	+			car
(20) fcahr	+		car	car					
(21) Mommy	−			shoe‡					

* Since no response could be elicited during Part 3 to the solid object, and since the parents do not agree as to the certainty of the name in previous handling, all identifications of this stimulus are doubtful.

† Much amusement.

‡ "Shoe" may be the judges' misinterpretation of *S*'s "thank you" in response to being given the pictures.

§ Misidentification due to sister's entry into the room.

and then transferred to the drawing. The drawings were handed one at a time to S, a somewhat unsuccessful attempt being made to convert the test to an interesting game. Responses were obtained by tape-recording.

PART 2

Immediately after Part 1, S was given a large store of picture-books. For a period of one month, he had free (but monitored) access to still pictures, but motion pictures, TV, and picture-naming play still were completely avoided. (It was feared that motion pictures would provide a basis for attaching names or three-dimensional "meanings" to the still pictures which do, after all, appear even in cinema-sequences.) A great variety of naming-reactions appeared during this period, but special pains were taken not to respond to any of these. Vocabulary-building by means of object-naming games continued during this month, but at special times, and with no pictures present. At the end of the month, the testing procedure of Part 1 was re-

FIGURE 1   Pictures shown S in Part 1.

peated with the new set of stimuli listed in the second part of Table I and shown in Figure 2.[5]

SCORING

A set of objects, consisting of most of those whose pictures appeared in the two testing series, then was presented to S, and *his* naming-responses were tape-recorded. These provided two judges (A and B in Table I), who had not been present during the two testing sessions, with experience of the child's pronunciation. The judges then were told that those words would be used, in any order and with any number of repetitions, in the recordings of the two testing sessions, and their task was to determine the order of presentation of the objects, using only the child's re-

sponses as recorded during those sessions.[6] (This scoring procedure was undertaken separately by the two judges.)

Results

Those pictures which were considered to be correctly identified by the parents (who did know the stimulus-series) are shown in Table I; the interpretations of each of the judges also are shown. If we consider only the line-drawings which both judges correctly identified in Part 1 (given eight possible names which, they were told, could appear in any order with any number of repetitions), the probability of a chance relationship is well under 0.01.

[5] The object represented in 1c and 2c was a box constructed of rigid wire, approximately $\frac{1}{8}$ in. in diameter, and 8 in. on a side. Introduced as a toy, it was involved in naming-games only during the month which elapsed between Part 1 and Part 2.

[6] The judges were permitted as many repetitions as desired. The first two presentations in Part 1 had been edited to remove extraneous chatter. Since the third presentation proved to have elicited "extraneous" responses which might be interpretable by judges as part of the series, editing of the remaining presentations was restricted to the elimination of overly-long interruptions; the residual chatter and gabble made judgment a difficult task.

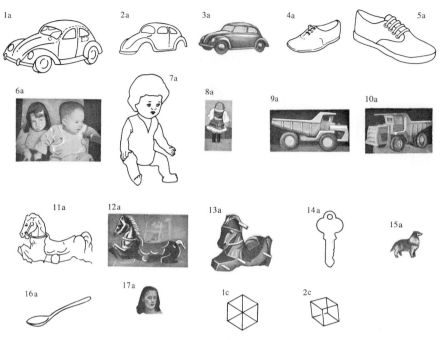

FIGURE 2   Pictures shown S in Part 2.

The judges thus correctly identified objects from the S's responses to the line-drawings.

It seems clear from the results that at least one human child is capable of recognizing pictorial representations of solid objects (including bare outline-drawings) without specific training or instruction. This ability necessarily includes a certain amount of what we normally expect to occur in the way of figure-ground segregation and contour-formation. At the very least, we must infer that there is an unlearned propensity to respond to certain formal features of lines-on-paper in the same ways as one has learned to respond to the same features when displayed by the edges of surfaces. "Ghost shapes," as Gibson has called them,[7] may be anemic, but they are by no means deceased. There may, however, be considerable ontogenetic difference in structuring or emphasis; the clear recognition of Stimulus 1c as a "box," and the uncertainty of response to Stimulus 2c, are certainly not what one would

have expected from adult performance.[8] Although order-effects may have been responsible for the poor response to Stimulus 2c, the immediate identification of 1c was unexpected.

It may be maintained that this ability would not have been displayed by a child who had never been exposed to any pictures at all, and who had not had such extensive experience with patterned surfaces as had the present S. This may be true (although consideration of the inhomogeneities of the normal *apictorial* environment make it seem quite improbable to us), but, even if it is, the complete absence of instruction in the present case (the absence of "association" between picture and represented object) points to *some* irreducible minimum of native ability for pictorial recognition. If it is true also that there are cultures in which this ability is absent, such deficiency will require special explanation; we cannot assert that it is simply a matter of having not yet learned the "language of pictures."

[7] Gibson, *op. cit.*, 412.

[8] Hochberg and Brooks, *op. cit.*, 347.

Preexposure to Visually Presented Forms and Nondifferential Reinforcement in Perceptual Learning*

LARRY C. KERPELMAN

University of Massachusetts

An experimental clarification of previous preexposure experiments which seemed to support the differentiation viewpoint of perceptual learning was undertaken. 79 albino rats were reared from birth in a visually sparse environment. Circles and triangles hung in the cages of the experimental Ss. Nondifferential food reinforcement of these cage stimuli was varied, and the resultant effect on subsequently learning to discriminate between them was examined. Discrimination performance of the main experimental groups confirmed the hypothesis that nondifferential reinforcement played a role in previous preexposure studies of perceptual learning, thus supporting the enrichment approach. Results for supplementary groups necessitated expansion of that approach to include possible reinforcing effects of novelty.

Several studies in which rats were exposed to stimuli (usually circles and triangles) from birth and later learned to discriminate between them better than nonexposed Ss (Gibson and Walk, 1956; Gibson, Walk, Pick, and Tighe, 1958; Gibson, Walk, and Tighe, 1959; Walk, Gibson, Pick and Tighe, 1958, 1959) have been used to support the "differentiation" view of perceptual learning. That view (Gibson and Gibson, 1955) holds that experience with stimuli that are to be discriminated is all that is necessary in certain situations for perceptual learning to occur. It is not neces-

* *Journal of Experimental Psychology* 1965, vol. 69, pp. 257–262. This article is based on a dissertation submitted in partial fulfillment of the requirements for the PhD degree at the University of Rochester. The author is greatly indebted to Norman Harway for his patient guidance and encouragement; the valuable assistance and suggestions of Robert Ader, Robert Boynton, and G. R. Wendt are also gratefully acknowledged. A condensed version of this paper was presented at the August 1963 Psychonomic Society meetings in Bryn Mawr, Pennsylvania.

sary to associate drive reduction, memory, or other factors with the stimuli. The Gibsons have named the opposing viewpoint, which subsumes association, reinforcement, and drive-reduction theories, "enrichment." The differentiation interpretation of the experiments cited above (which will hereafter be referred to generically as the Cornell studies) is exemplified by the statement: "The theories which best seem to fit the results all emphasize experience per se rather than *reinforced* experience [Walk et al., 1958, p. 487]."

An alternative explanation of those results is nevertheless plausible. In the Cornell studies, experimental Ss received food, water, and other reinforcement in the presence of the cage forms to which they were preexposed. Hence the stimuli were nondifferentially reinforced. Spence (1936) postulated that nondifferential reinforcement of, for example, two stimuli raises the excitatory tendency of both. On introducing differential reinforcement (as in the discrimination task), enhancement of learning would be expected in Ss receiving prior nondifferential reinforcement (the preexposed Cornell experimental Ss) as compared to those receiving little or no prior reinforcement—differential or nondifferential—contiguous with the stimuli (the nonexposed Cornell control Ss). By this formulation the preexposed Ss in the Cornell experiments might be expected to learn the subsequent discrimination faster than the controls because, at the beginning of discrimination training, the stimuli for the former group were at a higher level of excitatory tendency than they were for the latter group. Because the Cornell studies have important implications for perceptual theories, the present study was undertaken. The effect of nondifferential reinforcement in a preexposure situation was examined by varying the presumed strongest reinforcement, food, within conditions replicating, in all essentials, those of the Cornell studies.

Method

SUBJECTS

The Ss were 79 Charles River CD albino rats, 40 in Replication 1 (R1) and 39 in Replication 2 (R2). These were selected from a pool of 105 rats born to 10 pregnant females from the Charles River Breeding Laboratories. The 55 rats providing the R1 S pool were all born within a span of 5 hr; the 50 rats providing the R2 S pool were all born 47 days later within a span of 6 hr.

REARING

The Ss were born and reared in cages made of ½-in wire mesh, the cages placed in white compartments dimensionally identical to those of Walk et al. (1958). The backs of the compartments were flush with the white wall of the room, and the front was covered by a white oilcloth curtain hanging 8 in. from the edge of the compartments. Water was available ad lib. Thus the visual environment of each S during the experiment consisted of the compartment, the cage, the water bottle, the cage mates, the food tray for certain periods each day, and, for the experimental Ss, the cage stimuli for certain periods each day. Each of the R1 cages was lit from 7:00 A.M. to 6:00 P.M. daily by a shielded 10-w bulb on the compartment ceiling; R2 cages had no such arrangement but received normal room- and daylight during the same period.

Approximately 1 day after birth the five litters of each replication were cross-fostered, each mother receiving an equal number of pups. Each group thus formed was assigned to one of the four experimental conditions or to the control condition. The Ss nursed ad lib. until age 21 days when they were weaned and sexed. Each sex within each condition was placed in a separate cage, three to seven Ss per cage. A 12-hr feeding schedule was begun, and, for the experimental groups, stimulus-placement procedures (discussed below) were initiated. Except for cross-fostering and weaning, Ss were not handled during rearing.

After weaning, Ss were fed twice daily with a mash of powdered laboratory meal mixed with water. The food was placed in white food trays that were hung from the cage wall for feeding and then removed after 1 hr. The first feeding was at approximately 8:00 A.M., the second, at approximately 7:00 P.M.

Four stimuli, two circles and two triangles, hung in the experimental Ss' cages, one against each wall of each cage, for a period of time daily (discussed below). They were made of flat ½₃₂-in brass painted flat black. The circles were 3 in. in diameter, the triangles, 3½ in per side. Soldered to the top of each form was a length of wire by which the stimuli were hung in the cage. They were rotated at each feeding so that a circle and a triangle hung against each wall each day, and, specifically, a circle or a triangle was alternately at the wall where Ss received food each day.

EXPERIMENTAL CONDITIONS

Stimulus placement procedures were introduced at age 21 days because the ad lib. nursing allowed up to that time precluded control of feeding and stimulus perception—especially when Ss' eyes opened at age 16 days—as required by the experimental conditions. These procedures continued throughout the experiment. For Group E1 (22-Hr Reduced Reinforcement), the four cage stimuli were present 22 hr daily, being removed for 2 hr daily at each 1-hr feeding period. This group provided the needed conditions to discern the factors involved in the improved discrimination performance of preexposed groups in the Cornell studies. For Group E2 (22-Hr Nondifferential Reinforcement), the cage forms were present 22 hr daily, being removed twice daily at separate 1hr nonfeeding times to equate total amount of preexposure with that of Group E1. Since the forms were present during feeding, this group was comparable to the typical Cornell experimental group.

The Ss of Group E1 might have been open to reinforcement factors other than the manipulated one, food, such as social reinforcement, secondary reinforcement, and primary reinforcement of the thirst drive. Because these might have confounded the food reinforcement variable, supplementary groups were instituted which were expected not to be as prone to such influences. Group E1' (2-Hr Reduced Reinforcement) was exposed to the forms for 2 hr daily at separate 1-hr nonfeeding times. Group E2' (2-Hr Nondifferential Reinforcement) was exposed to the cage forms only for the 2 hr daily that feeding occurred.

For Group C (Control), no cage forms were present during the experiment. This group was comparable to the Cornell studies' control groups.

In Groups E2 and E2', where the stimuli were present during feeding, a stimulus was placed directly over the food tray. The mash was of such consistency that it could not be carried from the tray and thus had to be eaten in close proximity to the stimulus.

In an attempt to control a possible confounding factor, viz. differences in activity level at the time of stimulus change, stimuli were removed from E2 cages and placed in E1' cages the hour before feeding as often as possible (47% of the time in R1 and 30% in R2). This was done to equate activity level of these groups at the time of stimulus change with that of Groups E1 and E2', where stimulus change occurred at feeding, a period of high activity (Reid and Finger, 1955). It was expected that all four experimental groups would thereby "notice" the stimulus change equally because of approximately equal activity level. When the stimuli were removed from E2 cages and placed in E1' cages the hour before feeding, an interval of approximately 2 min was interposed between removal of the stimuli from E1' cages and their replacement in E2 cages, and the placing of the food trays in the cages. This was done to dispel the signaling effect that stimulus change may have had: the limited memory capacity of the albino rat (Honzik, 1931) made it seem unlikely that a relationship between stimulus replacement (E2) or removal (E1') and appearance of food would be made.

A single 1-hr. daily feeding was begun at age 86 days in preparation for the circle-triangle discrimination learning task at age 90 days. This 24-hr schedule was continued until the end of the experiment, and appropriate adjustments were made in stimulus placement proceduces during this period.

DISCRIMINATION TRAINING

The apparatus was a modified Grice (1948) discrimination apparatus as described elsewhere (Gibson and Walk,

1956). Pretraining and discrimination training followed the procedures described in Gibson and Walk (1956). The S could obtain a pinch of wet mash from one of two stimulus panels—a black circle, or a black triangle, on a white background—by pushing open the correct stimulus door. The incorrect stimulus panel was baited but locked. The only differences between the Gibson and Walk (1956) procedure and the present one was that a 60-sec intertrial interval was not adhered to, and Ss were run for 40 days if they had not reached criterion, rather than 15 days. (See Kerpelman, 1963 for further procedural details.)

Results

The 79 Ss chosen from the pool of 105 animals were selected before discrimination training to give as equal a distribution as possible within conditions, replications, and sexes. The resultant N was 16 in each group, except for E1 in which there were 15 Ss due to inequality of sexes. For the statistical analysis, however, the missing S in Group E1 was "replaced" by adding the appropriate mean subgroup score. Means and SDs of the four performance measures for all subgroups[1] are given in

[1] A mean and SD table for the subgroups of

Table 1. Since the subsequent analyses of variance did not reveal a significant Conditions × Replications interaction, the scores given and the analyses of differences between them are based on both replications combined.

A summary of the 5 × 2 × 2 analyses of variance (Conditions × Positive Stimuli × Replications) performed on each measure is given in Table 2. The level of statistical significance used throughout was $p < .05$. In interpreting the results it should be noted that the four measures are related: significant results across all four are not, therefore, independent failures to support the null hypothesis.

A significant Conditions main effect is readily apparent. A Replications main effect is strongly suggested, manifested by all groups in R1 performing better than their counterparts in R2, with the exception of Group E2'. A Stimulus main effect is slightly suggested, shown by a tendency

each replication (Table A), four analysis of variance summary tables (Tables B through E), and a t-test summary table (Table F) have been deposited with the American Documentation Institute. Order Document No. 8182 from ADI Auxiliary Publications Project, Photoduplication Service, Library of Congress, Washington, D. C. 20540. Remit in advance $1.25 for microfilm or $1.25 for photocopies and make checks payable to: Chief, Photoduplication Service, Library of Congress.

TABLE 1

Means and SDs of the Treatment Conditions for R1 and R2 Combined

| | MEASURES | | | | | | | |
| | TRIALS TO CRITERION | | INITIAL ERRORS | | REPETITIVE ERRORS | | TOTAL ERRORS | |
GROUPS	M	SD	M	SD	M	SD	M	SD
E1	267.13	82.77	108.25	40.21	136.81	82.02	245.06	119.94
E2	188.63	90.12	71.25	38.63	82.50	55.40	153.75	83.98
C	249.69	63.37	97.69	30.84	108.88	49.60	206.56	69.03
E1'	205.25	70.75	75.25	31.80	80.44	53.42	155.69	83.06
E2'	189.31	42.45	70.19	19.43	78.50	30.91	148.69	46.75

TABLE 2

Analyses of Variance of Four Performance Measures

SOURCE	df	TRIALS TO CRITERION		INITIAL ERRORS		REPETITIVE ERRORS		TOTAL ERRORS	
		MS	F	MS	F	MS	F	MS	F
Conditions (C)	4	20983	3.92**	4816	4.41**	10208	3.09*	28721	4.07**
Stimuli (S)	1	16245	3.04	3432	3.15	19035	5.76*	38632	5.47*
Replications (R)	1	8736	1.63	5746	5.27*	15569	4.71*	40231	5.70*
C × S	4	9396	1.76	1647	1.51	4237	1.28	10432	1.48
C × R	4	4476	<1	1106	1.01	2395	<1	5468	<1
S × R	1	13	<1	106	<1	719	<1	1378	<1
C × S × R	4	4163	<1	633	<1	60	<1	1036	<1
Within	59[a]	5351		1091		3305		7061	
Total	78[a]								

[a] 1 *df* subtracted because of "replaced" E1 S.
 * $p < .05.$
 ** $p < .01.$

for Ss for which circle was positive to make more errors, except, again, for Ss in Group E2′. Conditions × Sexes × Replications analyses of variance, with cell frequencies adjusted for equal N, were done on all measures. The only significant findings were a Conditions main effect for all measures and a Sexes × Replications interac-

tion for two measures, the interaction most likely reflecting confounding of sex with time of day of running.

In light of the consistently significant Conditions main effect, t tests of differences between condition means relevant to the research hypotheses were performed, the estimated error variance being based on

TABLE 3

Results of t Tests Relevant to the Research Hypotheses in Terms of Statistical Significance

MEASURE	22-HR. GROUPS		2-HR. GROUPS	
	DIFFERENTIATION PREDICTION E2 = E1 > C	ENRICHMENT PREDICTION E2 > E1 > C[a]	DIFFERENTIATION PREDICTION E2′ = E1′ = C	ENRICHMENT PREDICTION E2′ > E1′ = C
Trials to criterion	E2 > E1 = C		E2′ = E1′ = C, E2′ > C	
Initial errors	E2 > E1 = C		E2′ = E1′ = C, E2′ > C	
Repetitive errors	E2 = C = E1, E2 > E1[b]		E2′ = E1′ = C	
Total errors	E2 = C = E1, E2 > E1		E2′ = E1′ = C	

[a] Due to the possible operation of uncontrollable reinforcement contingencies in the presence of the stimuli in the absence of food, exact a priori predictions of the E1-C difference could not be made within the enrichment framework.
[b] Sign > indicates significantly better performance. Sign = indicates performance levels did not differ significantly, although they may have differed nonsignificantly. For example, E2 = C = E1 means E2 did not differ significantly from C, nor C from E1, yet E2 still may have differed significantly from E1.

the error mean square of the Conditions $\times$ Stimuli $\times$ Replications analyses. The results, in terms of statistical significance, are summarized in Table 3.

Discussion

22-HR GROUPS

The 22-hr groups were comparable to the typical Cornell experimental group. The only difference in experimental conditions between Groups E1 and E2 was that, for the latter, feeding occurred in the presence of the cage forms; whereas for the former, the stimuli were absent during feeding. Yet E2 performed on the discrimination task significantly better than E1 and, on two measures, than C. The results suggest that the facilitating effect of pre-exposure to visually presented forms found in the Cornell studies derived predominantly from the nondifferential reinforcement Ss received in the presence of those forms. That the results of those studies are explicable in terms of reinforcement theory tends to weaken the empirical support for the differentiation position. Furthermore, Spence's (1936) specific hypothesis concerning the effects of nondifferential reinforcement received support from these findings.

2-HR GROUPS

While the E2'-C differences on two measures were in line with enrichment predictions, if food reinforcement were the only factor accounting for learning enhancement on the discrimination task, then Group E2' would have been expected to perform better than Group E1'. The values of the performance means were in this direction, but the differences were not significant. These results are at least as much in line with differentiation as with enrichment predictions. If, in the differentiation framework, 2 hr per day were not enough time for one group to differentiate the stimulus elements, then in neither

group would facilitation of learning be expected. On the other hand, differentiation theory cannot explain why E2' performed better than C on two measures while E1' did not, since both 2-hr groups had the same amount of experience with the stimuli.

NOVELTY AND STIMULUS CHANGE

The apparent inability of either position to account for the results of the 2-hr groups can be resolved by introducing an additional explanatory concept, viz. the (nondifferentially) reinforcing effects of novelty and stimulus change. This concept postulates, consistent with recent work (Berlyne, 1960; Butler and Harlow, 1954; Dember, 1960; Forgus, 1958), that not only can food reinforcement account for the raising of excitatory tendency, but also reinforcement due to novelty and perceptual change can act similarly. Applying this concept, the cage forms in Group E1', appearing as they did for only two 1-hr periods daily, were novel stimuli. It may be postulated that Ss were attracted to them, in that their appearance satisfied the exploratory, change-seeking drive (Dember, 1960). As a result, the performance level of Group E1' was brought up to a level wherein significant differences between the 2-hr. groups were eradicated.

If perceptual change is postulated to have reinforcing properties, the question of why E1' did not perform significantly better than C (as did E2' on two measures) must be approached. It can only be assumed that the effects of this kind of reinforcement are quantitatively not as great as the corresponding mechanisms for hunger. The "novelty reinforcement" group (E1'), while performing well enough to erase significant differences between it and E2', did not perform well enough to differ significantly from C. This same assumption about the relative strength of novelty and food reinforcement holds for the failure to find significant differences between Groups E2 and E1' as well (two-tailed t

tests between these groups on all measures were not significant).

Future research might test the validity of the novelty hypothesis by varying the amount of daily form preexposure, divorced from food reinforcement. It would be hypothesized that the longer a stimulus is viewed, the less it will continue to reinforce the perceptual change drive. Two extremes of such a situation are the groups in the present study in which the stimuli were present in the absence of food. Group E1', in which the stimuli were present 2 hr. daily, performed better than Group E1, in which the stimuli were present 22 hr. Two-tailed t tests on all four measures were significant ($p < .025$), thus supporting the novelty hypothesis.

References

Berlyne, D. E. Conflict, arousal and curiosity. New York: McGraw-Hill, 1960.

Butler, R. A., and H. F. Harlow. Persistence of visual exploration in monkeys. J. comp. physiol. Psychol., 1954, 47, 258–263.

Dember, W. N. The psychology of perception. New York: Holt, 1960.

Forgus, R. H. The effects of different kinds of form pre-exposure on form discrimination learning. J. comp. physiol. Psychol., 1958, 51, 75–78.

Gibson, E. J., and R. D. Walk. The effect of prolonged exposure to visually presented patterns on learning to discriminate them. J. comp. physiol. Psychol., 1956, 49, 239–242.

Gibson, E. J., R. D. Walk, H. L. Pick, Jr., and T. J. Tighe. The effect of prolonged exposure to visual patterns on learning to discriminate similar and different patterns. J. comp. physiol. Psychol., 1958, 51, 584–587.

Gibson, E. J., R. D. Walk, and T. J. Tighe. stimulation during rearing as factors in Enhancement and deprivation of visual visual discrimination learning. J. comp. physiol. Psychol., 1959, 52, 74–81.

Gibson, J. J., and E. J. Gibson. Perceptual learning: Differentiation or enrichment? Psychol. Rev., 1955, 62, 32–41.

Grice, G. R. The acquisition of a visual discrimination habit following response to a single stimulus. J. exp. Psychol., 1948, 38, 633–642.

Honzik, C. H. Delayed reaction in rats. U. Calif. Publ. Psychol., 1931, 4, 307–318.

Kerpelman, L. C. Pre-exposure to visually presented forms and nondifferential reinforcement in perceptual learning. Unpublished doctoral dissertation, University of Rochester, 1963.

Reid, L. S., and F. W. Finger. The rat's adjustment to 23-hour food deprivation cycles. J. comp. physiol. Psychol., 1955, 48, 110–113.

Spence, K. L. The nature of discrimination learning in animals. Psychol. Rev., 1936, 43, 427–449.

Walk, R. D., E. J. Gibson, H. L. Pick, Jr., and T. J. Tighe. Further experiments on prolonged exposure to visual forms: The effect of single stimuli and prior reinforcement. J. comp. physiol. Psychol., 1958, 51, 483–487.

Walk, R. D., E. J. Gibson, H. L. Pick, Jr., and T. J. Tighe. The effectiveness of prolonged exposure to cutouts vs. painted patterns for facilitation of discrimination. J. comp. physiol. Psychol., 1959, 52, 519–521.

Electroencephalographic Changes after Prolonged Sensory and Perceptual Deprivation*

J. P. ZUBEK   G. WELCH
University of Manitoba

Abstract. Seven days' exposure to unpatterned light and white noise produced a significantly greater decrease in occipital lobe frequencies than did the same period of darkness and silence. This differential effect may be related to the greater behavioral impairments which seem to occur after prolonged exposure to diffuse light and noise.

It has been shown that the intellectual and sensorimotor impairments resulting from prolonged perceptual deprivation are greater than those occurring after prolonged sensory deprivation (1–3). These two terms are employed in the sense advanced by Kubzansky (4) in which sensory deprivation refers to an attempt at "an absolute reduction in variety and intensity of sensory input," for example, the use of darkness and silence, whereas perceptual deprivation refers to "reduced paterning, imposed structuring, and homogeneous stimulation," for example, the use of translucent goggles, white noise, constant hum, and so forth. The purpose of this experiment is to determine whether the behavioral differences between the two conditions are accompanied by any differences in electrical activity of the brain. We already know that

perceptual deprivation produces a decrease in occipital lobe frequencies (5). However, it is not known whether sensory deprivation produces a similar decrease and, if it does, whether it is of the same magnitude.

A group of 40 male university students were used, ten in each of four conditions. Each condition lasted a week. In the first, sensory deprivation, the subjects were placed individually in a dome-shaped isolation chamber. The details of this chamber are given in an earlier publication (1). They were required to lie quietly on an air mattress under constant darkness and silence (70 db attenuation). They could sit up or stand up only when eating or when using the toilet facilities located several feet away. Singing, humming, or any other vocal activity was not permitted. No gauntlet-type gloves or any other form of manual restrictions were imposed.

In the second condition, perceptual deprivation, the subjects were again isolated individually but under constant, unpatterned light and white noise. They wore a pair of translucent goggles which reduced the level of ambient illumination in the chamber from 90 to approximately 20 ft-ca

* *Science,* 1963, vol. 139, pp. 1209–1210. Copyright © 1963 by the American Association for the Advancement of Science. This project was supported by the Defence Research Board, Canada, project 9425-08. We thank Miss S. Oliver, Miss G. Levins, and Dr. M. G. Saunders, EEG Department, Winnipeg General Hospital, for technical assistance.

(under the goggles). The goggles excluded all pattern vision. Each subject also wore a set of earmuffs through which white noise was constantly presented somewhat above the threshold of hearing. The other restrictions were similar to those in the first group.

The third condition was a control for the recumbent or prone position which the two experimental groups had to assume most of the time. In this condition the subjects were placed, in groups of three or four, in a large room near the isolation laboratory. They were required to lie quietly on air mattresses arranged parallel to one another on the floor. They were allowed to sit up only when going to the washroom, 15 feet away. Apart from these restrictions on gross body movements their environment was quite "normal." They were allowed to talk, read, listen to the radio, and watch television, and all lights were put out at night.

Finally, an ambulatory control condition was used. The subjects of this group merely came to the laboratory for electroencephalographic records, returned home, and then reappeared a week later for the second record.

Electroencephalographic (EEG) tracings were taken by an Offner eight-channel machine, model D3, before and after each of the four conditions. Blood sugar level was controlled for by placing the subjects on a fixed feeding schedule and taking records in the morning, after breakfast. In order to exercise more control over possible drowsiness or decreased alertness in the experimental subjects, tracings were taken after they emerged from isolation. They were first given a battery of performance tests, breakfast, opportunity to wash up and then records were taken. These preliminary activities, which took approximately 2½

FIGURE 1   Mean frequency spectrum of the two experimental and two control groups before and after the one-week experiment. Abscissas are frequencies.

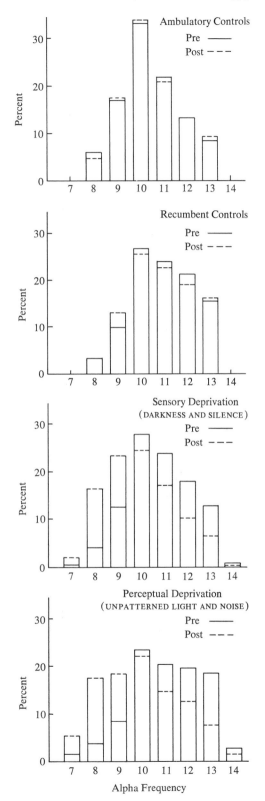

hours, eliminated any drowsiness at recording time which may have existed earlier. The controls were subjected to a similar routine. No differences in activity levels or in alertness could be detected between the experimentals and controls. In order to obtain a quantitative measure of EEG changes, two types of analyses were made. In the first, the mean occipital lobe frequency of each subject was determined. This involved counting the number of waves occurring in each of 200 1-second samples of artifact-free occipital lobe tracings. For this purpose, a cursor (a special EEG ruler) was employed. To avoid any bias the records were scored "blindly," that is, the technician was not told what groups the tracings came from or whether they were "pre" or "post" records. The second method involved a frequency spectrum analysis of the type suggested by Engel et al. (6). This consists of counting the number of waves in each 1-second period and expressing the number of 1-second periods containing a particular frequency as percentages of the total 200-second period.

Table 1 shows the mean occipital frequencies of the 40 subjects before and after a week. It can be seen that all 20 experimental subjects show a post-isolation decrease in mean frequency. Furthermore, the decrease in frequency appears to be greater for the perceptual than for the sensory deprivation group. Of the former group, nine out of ten subjects show a decrease greater than 1 cy/sec, whereas only two of the later group do so. On the other hand, the two control groups exhibit no consistent trend. Some subjects show an increase in frequency but others show a decrease. The mean "pre-post" difference for both control groups is almost zero. An analysis of variance of the "pre-post" difference scores of the four groups yielded a highly significant F ratio ($p < .001$). subsequent t test analyses (2-tailed) revealed that the slight difference between the control groups was not significant ($p > .70$). However, both experimental groups differed significantly from the controls ($p < .001$). Furthermore, the mean decrease in frequency of the perceptual deprivation group was significantly greater

TABLE 1

Mean Occipital Lobe Frequencies Before and After Two Experimental and Two Control Conditions (40 Subjects, Ten in Each Group)

PERCEPTUAL DEPRIVATION			SENSORY DEPRIVATION			RECUMBENT CONTROLS			AMBULATORY CONTROLS		
PRE	POST	DIFF.	PRE	POST	DIFF.	PRE	POST	DIFF.	PRE	POST	DIFF.
11.70	10.60	−1.10	10.05	9.00	−1.05	11.88	11.60	−0.28	9.99	10.09	+0.10
11.89	10.15	−1.74	10.33	10.18	−0.15	9.72	9.48	−0.24	11.84	11.97	+0.13
10.50	9.34	−1.16	10.67	9.73	−0.94	10.04	10.01	−0.03	11.50	11.53	+0.03
12.70	11.06	−1.64	10.32	8.85	−1.47	11.20	11.03	−0.17	10.50	10.47	−0.03
12.29	11.23	−1.06	11.80	11.05	−0.75	11.06	10.94	−0.12	10.22	10.23	+0.01
11.14	10.73	−0.41	11.42	10.60	−0.82	11.10	11.30	+0.20	11.04	10.79	−0.25
11.26	10.00	−1.26	11.00	10.09	−0.91	10.65	10.56	−0.09	9.65	9.59	−0.06
10.07	8.84	−1.23	10.70	9.87	−0.83	10.20	10.60	+0.40	10.37	10.49	+0.12
9.79	8.72	−1.07	10.13	9.40	−0.73	11.78	11.72	−0.06	10.02	10.30	+0.28
10.10	8.63	−1.47	11.38	10.49	−0.89	11.84	11.85	+0.01	9.79	9.53	−0.26
<	Means	>	<	Means	>	<	Means	>	<	Means	>
11.14	9.93	−1.21	10.78	9.93	−0.85	10.95	10.91	−0.04	10.49	10.50	+0.01

than that of the sensory deprivation group ($p < .01$). Figure 1 shows the mean frequency spectrum of the four groups of subjects before and after a week. It can be seen that the "pre and post" spectrum of the control groups is almost identical. However, in both experimental groups the postisolation spectrum shows a noticeable shift towards the lower end of the frequency scale.

In addition to the changes in occipital lobe frequencies, the records of the experimental subjects were also characterized by an excess of slow or theta activity, particularly in tracings from the temporal lobes. However, the incidence of these theta waves appeared to be the same for both experimental groups.

These results indicate that both sensory and perceptual deprivation can produce a disturbance of the electrical activity of the brain. Furthermore, this disturbance is greater under perceptual than sensory deprivation. This differential effect may be related to the greater behavioral impairments which seem to occur after prolonged perceptual deprivation (1–3). The fact that the recumbent condition did not affect EEG activity is also paralleled by a lack of behavioral deficits under this condition (2). Thus there appears to be a close correspondence between behavioral performance in deprivation conditions and the state of electrical activity of the brain. Since our EEG records were not taken during isolation but after its termination, one might interpret our results as indicating that the physiological effects of sensory deprivation wear off more quickly than those of perceptual deprivation. Although this is a possibility, we prefer to interpret the data as indicating the presence of EEG differences *during* the two types of isolation. This conclusion is supported by the fact that greater behavioral impairments occur under perceptual deprivation regardless of whether the performance measures are taken during or after the isolation period (1, 2).

References

1. ZUBEK, J. P. et al., Can. J. Psychol. 1960, 14, 233; 15, 83 (1961).
2. ZUBEK, J. P., Perceptual and Motor Skills. 1962, 15, 171.
3. VERNON, J., and J. HOFFMAN, Science 1956, 123, 1074; T. H. Scott et al., Can. J. Psychol. 1959, 13, 200; E. Z. Levy et al., J. Am. Med. Assoc. 1959, 169, 236; T. I. Myers et al., in Progress Report on Studies of Sensory Deprivation (U.S. Army Leadership Human Research Unit. Presidio of Monterey, Calif., March 1961).
4. KUBZANSKY, P. E. in The Manipulation of Human Behavior. A. D. Biderman and H. Zimmer, Eds. (Wiley, New York, 1961), p. 51.
5. HERON, W. Sci. Am. 1957, 196, 52; J. P. Zubek et al., Science 139, 490 (1963).
6. ENGEL, G. L. et al., A.M.A. Arch. Neurol. Psychiat. 1944, 51, 134.

On Perceptual Readiness[*]

JEROME S. BRUNER
Harvard University

About ten years ago I was party to the publication of an innocent enough paper entitled "Value and Need as Organizing Factors in Perception." It was concerned with what at that time was the rather obscure problem of how extrastimulus factors influenced perception, a subject then of interest to only a small band of us— Gardner Murphy, Nevitt Sanford, Muzafer Sherif, and a few others. Obviously, Professor Boring is quite right about the mischievousness of the *Zeitgeist,* for the appearance of this paper seemed to coincide with all sorts of spirit-like rumblings within the world of psychology that were soon to erupt in a most unspirit-like torrent of research on this very topic—perhaps three hundred research reports and theoretical explications in the ten years since then. F. H. Allport (1) and M. D. Vernon (81) have each recently had a fresh look at the field, sorting out the findings and evaluating the theoretical positions, and they have done superb service. Their labors free me to pursue a more relaxed course. What I should like to do in this paper is

to set forth what seem to me to be the outlines of an approach to perception congruent with this body of new (and often contradictory) findings and to sketch out what appear to me to be the persistent problems still outstanding.

On the Nature of Perception

Perception involves an act of categorization. Put in terms of the antecedent and subsequent conditions from which we make our inferences, we stimulate an organism with some appropriate input and he responds by referring the input to some class of things or events. "That is an orange," he states, or he presses a lever that he has been "tuned" to press when the object that he "perceives" is an orange. On the basis of certain defining or criterial attributes in the input, what are usually called cues although they should be called clues (35), there is a selective placing of the input in one category of identity rather than another. The category need not be elaborate: "a sound," "a touch," "a pain," are also examples of categorized inputs. The use of cues in inferring the categorical identity of a perceived object, most recently treated by Bruner, Goodnow, and Austin (9) and by Binder (4), is as much a feature of perception as the sensory stuff from which percepts are made. What is interesting about the nature of the

[*] *Psychological Review,* 1957, vol. 64, pp. 123–152. The present paper was prepared with the invaluable assistance of Mr. Michael Wallach. I also benefited from the comments of Professors W. C. H. Prentice, Karl Pribram, and M. E. Bitterman, and from various associates at Princeton University, Kansas University, and the University of Michigan, where versions of this paper were presented.

inference from cue to identity in perception is that it is in no sense different from other kinds of categorial inferences based on defining attributes. "That thing is round and nubbly in texture and orange in color and of such-and-such size—therefore an orange; let me now test its other properties to be sure." In terms of process, this course of events is no different from the more abstract task of looking at a number, determining that it is devisible only by itself and unity, and thereupon categorizing it in the class of prime numbers. So at the outset, it is evident that one of the principal characteristics of perceiving is a characteristic of cognition generally. There is no reason to assume that the laws governing inferences of this kind are discontinuous as one moves from perceptual to more conceptual activities. In no sense need the process be conscious or deliberate. A theory of perception, we assert, needs a mechanism capable of inference and categorizing as much as one is needed in a theory of cognition.

Let it be plain that no claim is being made for the utter indistinguishability of perceptual and more conceptual inferences. In the first place, the former appear to be notably less docile or reversible than the latter. I may know that the Ames distorted room that looks so rectangular is indeed distorted, but unless conflicting cues are put into the situation, as in experiments to be discussed later, the room still looks rectangular. So too with such compelling illusions as the Müller-Lyer: in spite of knowledge to the contrary, the line with the extended arrowheads looks longer than the equal-length one with those inclined inward. But these differences, interesting in themselves, must not lead us to overlook the common feature of inference underlying so much of cognitive activity.

Is what we have said a denial of the classic doctrine of sense-data? Surely, one may argue (and Hebb [36] has done so effectively) that there must be certain forms of primitive organization within the perceptual field that make possible the differential use of cues in identity categorizing. Both logically and psychologically, the point is evident. Yet it seems to me foolish and unnecessary to assume that the sensory "stuff" on which higher order categorizations are based is, if you will, of a different sensory order than more evolved identities with which our perceptual world is normally peopled. To argue otherwise is to be forced into the contradictions of Locke's distinction between primary and secondary qualities in perception. The rather bold assumption that we shall make at the outset is that all perceptual experience is necessarily the end product of a categorization process.

And this for two reasons. The first is that all perception is generic in the sense that whatever is perceived is placed in and achieves its "meaning" from a class of percepts with which it is grouped. To be sure, in each thing we encounter, there is an aspect of uniqueness, but the uniqueness inheres in deviation from the class to which an object is "assigned." Analytically, let it be noted, one may make a distinction, as Gestalt theorists have, between a pure stimulus process and the interaction of that stimulus process with an appropriate memory trace—the latter presumably resulting in a percept that has an identity. If indeed there is a "pure stimulus process," it is doubtful indeed that it is ever represented in perception bereft of identity characteristics. The phenomenon of a completely unplaceable object or event or "sensation"—even unplaceable with respect to modality—is sufficiently far from experience to be uncanny. Categorization of an object or event—placing it or giving it identity— can be likened to what in set theory is the placement of an element from a universe in a subset of that universe of items on the basis of such ordered dimensional pairs, triples, or n-tuples as man-woman, mesomorph-endomorph-ectomorph, or height to nearest inch. In short, when one specifies something more than that an element or object belongs to a universe, and that it belongs in a subset of the universe, one has categorized the element or object. The categorization can be as intersecting as "this is a quartz crystal goblet fashioned in Denmark," or as simple as "this is a glassy thing." So long as an operation assigns an input to a subset, it is an act of categorization.

More serious, although it is "only a logical issue," is the question of how one could communicate or make public the presence of a nongeneric or completely unique perceptual experience. Neither language nor the tuning that one could give an organism to direct any other form of overt response could provide an account, save in generic or categorial terms. If perceptual experience is ever had raw, i.e., free of categorial identity, it is doomed to be a gem serene, locked in the silence of private experience.

Various writers, among them Gibson (26), Wallach (83), and Pratt (66), have proposed that we make a sharp distinction between the class of perceptual phenomena that have to do with the identity or object-meaning of things and the attributive or sensory world from which we derive our cues for inferring identities. Gibson, like Titchener (78) before him, urges a distinction between the visual field and the visual world, the former the world of attributive sense impressions, the latter of objects and things and events. Pratt urges that motivation and set and past experience may affect the things of the visual world but not the stuff of the visual field. And Wallach too reflects this ancient tradition of his Gestalt forebears by urging the distinction between a stimulus process pure and the stimulus process interacting with a memory trace of past experience with which it has made a neural contact on the basis of similarity. The former is the stuff of perception; the latter the finished percept. From shirtsleeves to shirtsleeves in three generations: we are back with the founding and founded content of the pre-

Gestalt Gestalters. If one is to study the visual field freed of the things of the visual world, it becomes necessary—as Wallach implies—to free oneself of the stimulus error: dealing with a percept not as an object or as a thing with identity, but as a magnitude or a brightness or a hue or a shape to be matched against a variable test patch.

If we have implied that categorizing is often a "silent" or unconscious process, that we do not experience a going-from-no-identity to an arrival-at-identity, but that the first hallmark of *any* perception is some form of identity, this does not free us of the responsibility of inquiring into the origin of categories. Certainly, Hebb (36) is correct in asserting like Immanuel Kant, that certain primitive unities or identities within perception must be innate or autochthonous and not learned. The primitive capacity to categorize "things" from "background" is very likely one such, and so too the capacity to distinguish events in one modality from those in others—although the phenomena of synesthesia would suggest that this is not so complete a juncture as it might seem; e.g., von Hornbostel (39). The sound of a buzz saw does rise and fall phenomenally as one switches room illumination on and off. The full repertory of innate categories—a favorite topic for philosophical debate in the 19th century—is a topic on which perhaps too much ink and too little empirical effort have been spilled. Motion, causation, intention, identity, equivalence, time, and space, it may be persuasively argued, are categories that must have some primitive counterpart in the neonate. And it may well be, as Piaget (65) implies, that certain primitive capacities to categorize in particular ways depend upon the existence of still more primitive ones. To identify something as having "caused" something else requires, first, the existence of an identity category such that the two things involved each may conserve identity in the process of "cause" producing "effect."

Primitive or unlearned categories—a matter of much concern to such students of instinctive behavior as Lashley (51) and Tinbergen (77)—remain to be explicated. In what follows, we shall rather cavalierly take them for granted. As to the development of more elaborated categories in terms of which objects are placed or identified, it involves the process of learning how to isolate, weigh, and use criterial attribute values, or cues for grouping objects in equivalence classes. It is only as mysterious, but no more so, than the learning of any differential discrimination, and we shall have occasion to revisit the problem later.

A second feature of perception, beyond its seemingly categorial and inferential nature, is that it can be described as varyingly veridical. This is what has classically been called the "representative function" of perception: what is perceived is somehow a representation of the external world —a metaphysical hodgepodge of a statement but one which we somehow manage to understand in spite of its confusion. We have long since given up simulacral theories of representation. What we generally mean when we speak of representation or veridicality is that perception is predictive in varying degrees. That is to say, the object that we *see* can also be *felt* and *smelled* and there will somehow be a match or a congruity between what we see, feel, and smell. Or, to paraphrase a younger Bertrand Russell, what we see will turn out to be the same thing should we take a "closer look" at it. Or, in still different terms, the categorial placement of the object leads to appropriate consequences in terms of later behavior directed toward the perceived object: it appears as an apple, and indeed it keeps the doctor away if consumed once a day.

Let it be said that philosophers, and notably the pragmatist C. S. Peirce, have been urging such a view for more years than psychologists have taken their urgings seriously. The meaning of a proposition, as Peirce noted in his famous essay on the pragmatic theory of meaning (63), is the set of hypothetical statements one can make about attributes or consequences related to that proposition. "Let us ask what we mean by calling a thing *hard*. Evidently, that it will not be scratched by many other substances" (White, 84). The meaning of a thing, thus, is the placement of an object in a network of hypothetical inference concerning its other observable properties, its effects, and so on.

All of this suggests, does it not, that veridicality is not so much a matter of representation as it is a matter of what I shall call "model building." In learning to perceive, we are learning the relations that exist between the properties of objects and events that we encounter, learning appropriate categories and category systems, *learning to predict and to check what goes with what*. A simple example illustrates the point. I present for tachistoscopic recognition two nonsense words, one a 0-order approximation to English constructed according to Shannon's rules, the other a 4-order approximation: YRULPZOC and VERNALIT. At 500 milliseconds of exposure, one perceives correctly and in their proper place about 48 per cent of the letters in 0-order words, and about 93 per cent of the letters in 4-order words. In terms of the amount of information transmitted by these letter arrays, i.e., correcting them for redundancy, the subject is actually receiving the same informational input. The difference in reportable perception is a function of the fact that the individual has learned the transitional probability model of what goes with what in English writing. We say that perception in one case is more "veridical" than in the other—the difference between 93 per cent correct as contrasted with 48 per cent. What we mean is that the model of English with which the individual is working corresponds to the actual events that occur in English, and that if the stimulus input does not conform to the model, the resulting perception will be less veridical.

Now let us drop the image of the model and adopt a more sensible terminology. Perceiving accurately under substandard conditions consists in being able to refer stimulus inputs to appropriate coding systems; where the information is fragmentary, one reads the missing properties of the stimulus input from the code to which part of the input has been referred. If the coding system applied does not match the input, what we read off from the coding system will lead to error and nonveridical perception. I would propose that perceptual learning consists not of making finer and finer discriminations as the Gibsons (27) would have us believe, but that it consists rather in the learning of appropriate modes of coding the environment in terms of its object character, connectedness, or redundancy, and then in allocating stimulus inputs to appropriate categorial coding systems.

The reader will properly ask, as Prentice (67) has, whether the notion of perceptual representation set forth here is appropriate to anything other than situations where the nature of the percept is not "clear"—perceptual representation under peripheral viewing conditions, in tachistoscopes, under extreme fatigue. If I am given a very good look at an object, under full illumination and with all the viewing time necessary, and end by calling it an orange, is this a different process from one in which the same object is flashed for a millisecond or two on the periphery of my retina with poor illumination? In the first and quite rare case the cues permitting the identification of the object are superabundant and the inferential mechanism operates with high probability relationships between cues and identities. In the latter, it is less so. The difference is of degree. What I am trying to say is that under *any* conditions of perception, what is achieved by the perceiver is the categorization of an object or sensory event in terms of more *or* less abundant and reliable cues. Repre-

sentation consists of knowing how to utilize cues with reference to a system of categories. It also depends upon the creation of a system of categories-in-relationship that fit the nature of the world in which the person must live. In fine, adequate perceptual representation involves the learning of appropriate categories, the learning of cues useful in placing objects appropriately in such systems of categories, and the learning of what objects are likely to occur in the environment, a matter to which we will turn later.

We have neglected one important feature of perceptual representation in our discussion: representation in perception of the space-time-intensity conditions of the external world. Perceptual magnitudes correspond in some degree to the metrical properties of the physical world that we infer from the nature of our perception. That is to say, when one line *looks* longer than another, it is likely to *be* longer as measured by the ruler. There are constant errors and sampling errors in such sensory representation, but on the whole there is enough isomorphism between perceiving without aids (psychology) and perceiving with aids (physics) to make the matter perenially interesting.

Is this form of representation subject to the kinds of considerations we have been passing in review? Does it depend upon categorizing activities and upon the construction of an adequate system of categories against which stimulus inputs can be matched? There is probably one condition where perceptual acts are relatively free of such influences, and that is in the task of discriminating simultaneously presented stimuli as alike or different—provided we do not count the "tuning of the organism" that leads one to base his judgment on one rather than another feature of the two stimuli. Ask the person to deal with one stimulus at a time, to array it in terms of some magnitude scale, and immediately one is back in the familiar territory of inferential categorizing. Prentice, in his able defense of formalism in the study of perception (67), seems to assume that there is a special status attached to perceptual research that limits the set of the observer to simple binary decisions of "like" and "different" or "present" and "absent," and to research that also provides the subject with optimal stimulus conditions, and Graham (31) has recently expressed the credo that no perceptual laws will be proper or pure laws unless we reduce perceptual experimentation to the kinds of operations used in the method of constant stimuli.

There was at one time a justification for such a claim on the grounds that such is the best strategy for getting at the sensory-physiological processes that underlie perception. As we shall see in a later section, current work in neurophysiology brings this contention into serious doubt. In any case, the point must be made that many of the most interesting phenomena in sensory perception are precisely those that have been uncovered by departing from the rigid purism of the method of constants. I have in mind such pioneering studies as those of Stevens on sensory scales, where the organism is treated as an instrument whose sensory categorizations and scalar orderings are the specific object of study (74). Add to this the advances made by Helson on adaptation level (37) and by Volkmann on the anchoring of sensory scales (82)—both using the "sloppy" method of single stimuli—and one realizes that the nature of representation in perception of magnitudes is very much subject to categorizing processes, and to perceptual readiness as this is affected by subjective estimates of the likelihood of occurrence of sensory events of different magnitudes. Indeed, Helson's law of adaptation level states that the subjective magnitude of a singly presented stimulus depends upon the weighted geometric mean of the series of stimuli that the subject

has worked with, and the ingenious experiments of Donald Brown (7) have indicated that this adaptation level is influenced only by those stimuli that the subject considers to be within the category of objects being considered. Ask the subject to move a weight from one side of the table to the other with the excuse that it is cluttering up the table, and the weight does not serve as an anchor to the series, although it will show a discernible effect if it is directly included in the series being judged. In short, the category systems that are utilized in arraying magnitudes are also affected by the requirement of matching one's model of the world to the actual events that are occurring—even if the categories be no more complicated than "heavy," "medium," and "light."

The recent work of Stevens (75) on "the direct estimation of sensory magnitudes" highlights the manner in which veridicality in sensory judgment depends upon the prior learning of an adequate category set in terms of which sensory input may be ordered. Subjects are presented a standard tone of 1000 cps at 80 db sound-pressure-level and are told that the value of this loudness is 10. Nine variable loudnesses all of the 1000 cps are then presented, varying 70 db on either side of the standard, each one at a time being paired with the standard. "If the standard is called 10, what would you call the variable? Use whatever numbers seem to you appropriate—fractions, decimals, or whole numbers." If one then compares the categorial judgments made with the sound pressure level of the various tones presented, using a log-log plot (log of the magnitude estimation against log of sound-pressure-level), the resulting function is a straight line, described by the empirical formula

$$L = kI^{0.3},$$

where L is loudness and I intensity. In

short, categorial sorting of sensory magnitudes provides one with a mapping or representation of physical intensity. There are, to be sure, many problems connected with such a procedure, but the point remains: the magnitude categories in terms of which we scale sensory events represent a good fit to the physical characteristics of the world. Call this "veridicality" if you wish—although I do not see what is gained thereby; yet whatever one calls it, one must not lose sight of the fact that the judgments made are predictive of other features of the sensory inputs. Given the empirical conversion formula, one can predict from categorial judgment to physical meter readings.

To summarize, we have proposed that perception is a process of categorization in which organisms move inferentially from cues to categorial identity and that in many cases, as Helmholtz long ago suggested, the process is a silent one. If you will, the inference is often an "unconscious" one. Moreover, the results of such categorizations are representational in nature: they represent with varying degrees of predictive veridicality the nature of the physical world in which the organism operates. By predictive veridicality I mean simply that perceptual categorization of an object or event permits one to "go beyond" the properties of the object or event perceived to a prediction of other properties of the object not yet tested. The more adequate the category systems constructed for coding environmental events in this way, the greater the predictive veridicality that results.

Doubtless, the reader will think of any number of examples of perceptual phenomena not covered by the simple picture we have drawn. Yet a great many of the classic phenomena are covered—psychophysical judgment, constancy, perceptual identification, perceptual learning, and so on. This will become clearer in the following sections. What must now be dealt with are the phenomena having to do

with selectivity: attention, set, and the like.

Cue Utilization and Category Accessibility

A fruitful way of thinking of the nature of perceptual readiness is in terms of the accessibility of categories for use in coding or identifying environmental events. Accessibility is a heuristic concept, and it may be defined in terms of a set of measures. Conceive of a person who is perceptually ready to encounter a certain object, an apple let us say. *How* he happens to be in this state we shall consider later. We measure the accessibility of the category "apples" by the amount of stimulus input of a certain pattern necessary to evoke the perceptual response "there is an apple," or some other standardized response. We can state the "minimum" input required for such categorization by having our observer operate with two response categories, "yes" and "no," with the likelihood of occurrence of apples and nonapples at 50:50, or by using any other definition of "maximum readiness" that one wishes to employ. The greater the accessibility of a category, (a) the less the input necessary for categorization to occur in terms of this category, (b) the wider the range of input characteristics that will be "accepted" as fitting the category in question, (c) the more likely that categories that provide a better or equally good fit for the input will be masked. To put it in more ordinary language: apples will be more easily and swiftly recognized, a wider range of things will be identified or misidentified as apples, and in consequence the correct or best fitting identity of these other inputs will be masked. This is what is intended by accessibility.

Obviously, categories are not isolated. One has a category "apples," to be sure, but it is imbedded by past learning in a network of categories: "An apple a day keeps the doctor away" is one such category system. So too, are "apples are fruits" and other placements of an object in a general classification scheme. Predictive systems are of the same order: e.g., "The apple will rot if not refrigerated." We have spoken of these systems before as the "meaning" of an object. We mention them again here to indicate that though we speak analytically of separate or isolated categories as being accessible to inputs, it is quite obvious that category systems vary in accessibility as a whole.

It follows from what has just been said that the most appropriate pattern of readiness at any given moment would be that one which would lead on the average to the most "veridical" guess about the nature of the world around one at the moment—best guess here being construed, of course, as a response in the absence of the necessary stimulus input. And it follows from this that the most ready perceiver would then have the best chances of estimating situations most adequately and planning accordingly. It is in this general sense that the ready perceiver who can proceed with fairly minimal inputs is also in a position to use his cognitive readiness not only for perceiving what is before him but in foreseeing what is likely to be before him. We shall return to this point shortly.

We must turn now to the question of cue utilization, the "strategies" in terms of which inferences are made (by the nervous system, of course) from cue to category and thence to other cues. I prefer to use the term strategy for several reasons. Perceiving, since it involves inference, rests upon a decision process, as Brunswik (17), Tanner and Swets (76) and others have pointed out. Even in the simplest threshold-measurement test, the subject has the task of deciding whether what he is seeing or hearing is noise only or signal-plus-noise. Given a set of cues, however presented, my nervous system must "decide" whether the thing is an airplane or a sea gull, a red or a green, or what not.

There appears, moreover, to be a sequence of such decisions involved in categorizing an object or event. A common-sense example will make this clear. I look across to the mantelpiece opposite my desk and see a rectangular object lying on it. If I continue this pursuit, subsequent decisions are to be made: is it the block of plastic I purchased for some apparatus or is it a book? In the dim light it can be either. I remember that the plastic is downstairs in one of the experimental rooms: the object "is" a book now, and I search for further cues on its dark red surface. I see what I think is some gold: it is a McGraw-Hill book, probably G. A. Miller's *Language and Communication* that I had been using late this afternoon. If you will, the process is a "bracketing" one, a gradual narrowing of the category placement of the object.

Let us attempt to analyze the various stages in such a decision sequence.

A. PRIMITIVE CATEGORIZATION

Before any more elaborate inferential activity can occur, there must be a first, "silent" process that results in the perceptual isolation of an object or an event with certain characteristic qualities. Whether this is an innate process or one depending upon the prior construction of a cell-assembly, in the manner of Hebb (36), need not concern us. What is required simply is that an environmental event has been perceptually isolated and that the event is marked by certain spatio-temporal-qualitative characteristics. The event may have no more "meaning" than that it is an "object," a "sound," or a "movement."

B. CUE SEARCH

In highly practiced cases or in cases of high cue-category probability linkage, a second process of more precise placement based on additional cues may be equally silent or "unconscious." An object is seen with phenomenal immediacy as a "book" or an "ash tray." In such instances there is usually a good fit between the specifications of a category and the nature of the cues impinging on the organism—although "fit" and "probability of linkage" may stand in a vicarious relation to each other. Where the fit to accessible categories is not precise, or when the linkage between cue and category is low in probability in the past experience of the organism, the conscious experience of cue searching occurs. "What is that thing?" Here, one is scanning the environment for data in order to find cues that permit a more precise placement of the object. Under these circumstances, the organism is "open" to maximum stimulation, in a manner described below.

C. CONFIRMATION CHECK

When a tentative categorization has occurred, following cue search, cue search changes. The "openness" to stimulation decreases sharply in the sense that now, a tentative placement of identity having occurred, the search is narrowed for additional confirmatory cues to check this placement. It is this feature of perceptual identification that Woodworth (85) in his paper on the "Reenforcement of Perception" speaks of as "trial-and-check." We shall speak of a selective gating process coming into operation in this stage, having the effect of reducing the effective input of stimulation not relevant to the confirmatory process.

D. CONFIRMATION COMPLETION

The last stage in the process of perceptual identification is a completion, marked by termination of cue searching. It is characteristic of this state that openness to additional cues is drastically reduced, and incongruent cues are either normalized or "gated out." Experiments on the perception of incongruity (14), error (69), and the like (15), suggest that once an object has been categorized in a high-probability, good-fit category, the threshold

for recognizing cues contrary to this categorization increases by almost an order of magnitude.

The question of fit between cue and category specification brings us to the key problem of the nature of categories. By a category we mean a rule for classing objects as equivalent. The rule specifies the following about the instances that are to be comprised in the category.

a. The properties or *criterial attribute values* required of an instance to be coded in a given class.

b. The manner in which such attribute values are to be combined in making an inference from properties to category membership: whether conjunctively (e.g., a_i *and* b_i), relationally (e.g., a_i bears a certain *relation* to b_i), or disjunctively (e.g., a_i *or* b_i).

c. The weight assigned various properties in making an inference from properties to category membership.

d. The acceptance limits within which properties must fall to be criterial. That is to say, from what range of attribute values may a_i, b_i . . . k_i be drawn.

When we speak of rules, again it should be made clear that "conscious rules" are not intended. These are the rules that govern the operation of a categorizing mechanism.

The likelihood that a sensory input will be categorized in terms of a given category is not only a matter of fit between sensory input and category specifications. It depends also on the accessibility of a category. To put the matter in an oversimplified way, given a sensory input with equally good fit to two nonoverlapping categories, the more accessible of the two categories would "capture" the input. It is in this sense that mention was earlier made about the vicarious relationship between fit and accessibility.

We have already noted that the accessibility of categories reflects the learned probabilities of occurrence of events in the person's world. The more frequently in a given context instances of a given category occur, the greater the accessibility of the category. Operationally, this means that less stimulus input will be required for the instance or event to be categorized in terms of a frequently used category. In general, the type of probability we are referring to is not absolute probability of occurrence, where each event that occurs is independent of each other. Such independence is rare in the environment. Rather, the principal form of probability learning affecting category accessibility is the learning of contingent or transitional probabilities—the redundant structure of the environment. That either the absolute or the contingent probability of events makes a crucial difference in determining ease of perceptual identification is readily supported by research findings: in the former case by studies like those of Howes (40) and Solomon and Postman (72), and in the latter by the work of Miller, Heise, and Lichten (62) and Miller, Bruner, and Postman (61).

But the organism to operate adequately must not only be ready for likely events in the environment, the better to represent them, and in order to perceive them quickly and without undue cognitive strain: it must also be able to search out unlikely objects and events essential to its maintenance and the pursuit of its enterprises. If I am walking the streets of a strange city and find myself hungry, I must be able to look for restaurants regardless of their likelihood of occurrence in the environment where I now find myself. In short, the accessibility of categories I employ for identifying the objects of the world around me must not only reflect the environmental probabilities of objects that fit these categories, but also reflect the search requirements imposed by my needs, my ongoing activities, my defenses, etc. And for effective search behavior to occur, the pattern of perceptual readiness

during search must be realistic: tempered by what one is likely to find in one's perceptual world at that time and at that place as well as by what one seeks to find.

Let me summarize our considerations about the general properties of perception with a few propositions. The first is that *perception is a decision process.* Whatever the nature of the task set, the perceiver or his nervous system decides that a thing perceived is one thing and not another. A line is longer or shorter than a standard, a particular object is a snake and not a fallen branch, the incomplete word L*VE in the context MEN L*VE WOMEN is the word LOVE and not LIVE.

The second proposition is that *the decision process involves the utilization of discriminatory cues,* as do all decision processes. That is to say, the properties of stimulus inputs make it possible to sort these inputs into categories of best fit.

Thirdly, *the cue utilization process involves the operation of inference.* Going from cue to an inference of identity is probably the most ubiquitous and primitive cognitive activity. The utilization of inference presupposes the learning of environmental probabilities and invariances relating cues to cues, and cues to behavioral consequences. Cue utilization involves various stages: a primitive step of isolating an object or event from the flux of environmental stimulation, stages of cue searching where the task is to find cues that can be fitted to available category specifications, a tentative categorization with more search for confirming cues, and final categorization, when cue searching is severely reduced.

Fourth, *a category may be regarded as a set of specifications* regarding what events will be grouped as equivalent—rules respecting the nature of criterial cues required, the manner of their combining, their inferential weight, and the acceptance limits of their variability.

Fifth, *categories vary in terms of their accessibility,* the readiness with which a stimulus input with given properties will be coded or identified in terms of a category. The relative accessibility of categories and systems of categories seems to depend upon two factors: the expectances of the person with regard to the likelihood of events to be encountered in the environment; and the search requirements imposed on the organism by his needs and his ongoing enterprises. To use the functionalist's language, perceptual readiness or accessibility serves two functions: *to minimize the surprise value of the environment* by matching category accessibility to the probabilities of events in the world about one, and *to maximize the attainment of sought-after objects and events.*

Veridical perception, so our sixth proposition would run, *consists of the coding of stimulus inputs in appropriate categories* such that one may go from cue to categorial identification, and thence to the correct inference or prediction of other properties of the object so categorized. Thus, veridical perception requires the learning of categories and category systems appropriate to the events and objects with which the person has commerce in the physical world. When we speak of the representative function of perception, we speak of the adequacy of the categorizing system of the individual in permitting him to infer the nature of events and to go beyond them to the correct prediction of other events.

Seventh, *under less than optimal conditions, perception will be veridical in the degree to which the accessibility of categorizing systems reflects the likelihood of occurrence of the events that the person will encounter.* Where accessibility of categories reflects environmental probabilities, the organism is in the position of requiring less stimulus input, less redundancy of cues for the appropriate categorization of objects. In like vein, nonveridical perception will be systematic rather than random in its error insofar as it reflects the inappropriate readiness of the perceiver. The

more inappropriate the readiness, the greater the input or redundancy of cues required for appropriate categorization to occur—where "appropriate" means that an input is coded in the category that yields more adequate subsequent predictions.

Mechanisms Mediating Perceptual Readiness

Having considered some of the most general characteristics of perceiving, particularly as these relate to the phenomena of perceptual readiness, we must turn next to a consideration of the kinds of mechanisms that mediate such phenomena. Four general types of mechanisms will be proposed: *grouping and integration, access ordering, match-mismatch signaling, and gating.* They will be described in such a form that they may be considered as prototypes of neural mechanisms and, where possible, neurophysiological counterparts will be described briefly. Six years ago, Edward Tolman (79) proposed that the time was perhaps ripe for reconsidering the neural substrate of perception. Perhaps he was right, or perhaps even now the enterprise is somewhat premature. Yet, the body of perceptual data available makes it worth while to consider the kinds of mechanisms that will be required to deal with them. To use Hebb's engaging metaphor, it is worth while to build a bridge between neurophysiology and psychology provided we are anchored at both ends, even if the middle of the bridge is very shaky.

GROUPING AND INTEGRATION

It is with the neural basis of the categorizing process that Hebb's *Organization of Behavior* (36) is principally concerned. Little is served by recapitulating his proposals here, for the reader will be familiar with the concise account in Chapters 4 and 5 of that book, where the concepts of cell assembly and phase sequence are set forth with a clarity that permits one to distinguish what is neurophysiological fact and what speculation. In essence, Hebb's attempts to provide an anatomical-physiological theory of how it is that we distinguish classes of events in the environment, and how we come to recognize new events as exemplars of the once established classes. The theory seeks also to provide a mechanism for integration of sorting activity over time: the formation of phase sequences for the conservation of superordinate classes of events and superordinate sequences. Basically, it is an associational or an "enrichment" theory of perception at the neural level, requiring that established neural associations facilitate perception of events that have gone together before. The expectancies, the centrally induced facilitations that occur prior to the sensory process for which they are appropriate, are learned expectancies based on the existence of frequency integrators. These frequency integrators may be neuroanatomical in the form of synaptic knobs, or they may be any process that has the effect of making activity in one locus of the brain increase or decrease the likelihood of activity in another. To be sure, Hebb's theory depends upon some broad assumptions about convergence of firing from area 17 outward, about synchronization of impulses, and about the manner in which reverberatory circuits can carry organization until the much slower process of anatomical change can take place. But this is minor in comparison with the stimulation provided by facing squarely the question of how the known facts of categorization and superordination in perception *could* be represented in the light of present knowledge.

While it is difficult indeed to propose a plausible neural mediator to account for category formation and the development of elaborated categorial systems (e.g., our knowledge of the relations between classes of events in the physical world which we manipulate in everyday life), it is less difficult to specify what such mechanisms must account for in perceptual behavior.

At the level of the individual category or cell assembly, the phenomena of object identity must be accounted for. Moreover, identity conservation or object constancy requires explanation in terms common with the explanation of identity. Experiments by Piaget (65) suggest that the capacity to maintain the phenomenal identity of an object undergoing change is the hard-won result of maturation-and-learning. In connection with the later discussion of gating processes, we shall have occasion to consider the manner in which, at different stages in cue utilization, the required fit between an input and a cell assembly changes.

Where integration is concerned, there must be a process capable of conserving a record of the likely transitions and contingencies of the environment. The moment-to-moment programing of perceptual readiness depends upon such integrations. In short, the relation between classes of events is conserved in such a way as to be subject to change by learning. Several things can be guessed about integration processes. It is unlikely that it is a simple autocorrelation device. Clearly, the conceptions of transitional probabilities that are established in dealing with sequences of events show biases that no self-respecting autocorrelation computer would be likely to operate with. One of these is a strong and early tendency to treat events as non-independent of each other over time. In the absence of evidence, or even in the presence of contrary evidence, humans—as their behavior has been observed in choice tasks, e.g., Estes (23), Goodnow (29)—treat random sequences of events as though they were governed by dependent probabilities. The spate of research on two-choice decision behavior has made us quite sharply aware of this characteristic of cognitive functioning. The typical pattern is the gambler's fallacy or, more properly, the negative recency effect. Given two equi-probable events whose occurrences are random, the repetition of one event progressively leads to the expectancy of the other. As in the elegant experiments of Jarvik (44) and Goodnow (29), the probability that a person will predict one of two events increases directly as a function of the number of repetitions of the other event. Such behavior persists over thousands of opportunities for testing, and it appears under a variety of testing conditions (9).

The second feature of sequential probability integration mechanisms is that, in establishing a conception of the probability with which events will occur, the typical human subject will bias his estimate in terms of desired or feared outcomes. As in the experiments of Marks (60) on children and of Irwin (41) on adults, the subjectively estimated probability of strongly desired events will be higher per previous encountered occurrence than the estimated likelihood of less desired events. Quite clearly, then, the establishment of estimates depends upon more than frequency integrations biased by assumptions of nonindependence. The "something more" is a motivational or personality process, and we shall have more to say about it in considering phenomena of so-called "perceptual sensitization" and "perceptual defense."

ACCESS ORDERING

The term "accessibility" has been used in preceding pages to denote the ease or speed with which a given stimulus input is coded in terms of a given category under varying conditions of instruction, past learning, motivation, etc. It has been suggested, moreover, that two general sets of conditions affect accessibility: subjective probability estimates of the likelihood of a given event, and certain kinds of search sets induced by needs and by a variety of other factors.

Let us consider a few relevant facts about perception. The first of these is that the threshold of recognition for stimuli presented by visual, auditory, or other means is not only a function of the time, intensity, or "fittingness" of the stimulus input, but also varies massively as a function of the number of alternatives for which the perceiver is set. The size of the expected array, to say it another way, increases the identification threshold for any item in the array. Typical examples of this general finding are contained in papers by Miller, Heise, and Lichten (62) and by Bruner, Miller, and Zimmerman (10). The actual shape of the function need not concern us, save that it is quite clear that it is not what one would expect from a simple binary system with a fixed channel capacity. What we are saying holds, of course, only for the case where the perceiver has learned that all the items in the expected array are (a) equiprobable and (b) independent, one of the other, in order of appearance.

The first hunch we may propose, then, about access-ordering mechanisms is that degree of accessibility of coding categories to stimulus inputs is related to regulation of the number of preactivated cell assemblies that are operative at the time of input. In an earlier paper (8), discussing factors that strengthen an hypothesis in the sense of making it more easily confirmable, I proposed that one of the major determinants of such strength was monopoly: where one and only one hypothesis is operative with no competing alternatives, it tends to be more readily confirmable. It is the same general point that is being made here. Accessibility, then, must have something to do with the resolution of competing alternatives.

As between two arrays of expected alternatives, each of the same size, we may distinguish between them in terms of the bias that exists in terms of expected likelihood of occurrence of each alternative. If one could characterize the expected alternatives in terms of probability values, one could conceive of the array ranging in values from a figure approaching 1.0 at one extreme, to another approaching 0.0

at the other. The findings with respect to perceptual readiness for the alternative represented in such an array are well known. For a constant-sized array, the greater the estimated likelihood of occurrence of an alternative, the more readily will the alternative be perceived or identified. This is known to be true for large arrays, such as the ensemble of known words in the English language, whose likelihood may be roughly judged by their frequency of occurrence in printed English (e.g., 40). It is not altogether clear that it is the case for arrays of expected alternatives that are within the so-called span of attention—i.e., less than seven or eight alternatives. That the principle holds for middling arrays of about 20 items has been shown by Solomon and Postman (72).

What is particularly interesting about chance of accessibility, under conditions were estimates of the likelihood of occurrence of alternatives become biased, is that the biasing can be produced either by a gradual learning process akin to probability learning *or* by instruction. Thus, Bitterman and Kniffin (5), investigating recognition thresholds for taboo and neutral words, show that as the experiment progresses, there is a gradual lowering of threshold for the taboo words as the subject comes to expect their occurrence. Bruner and Postman (14) have similarly shown that repeated presentation of stimulus materials containing very low-probability incongruities leads to a marked decrease in threshold time required for recognizing the incongruous features. At the same time, both Cowen and Beier (20) and Postman and Crutchfield (70) have shown that if a subject is forewarned that taboo words are going to be presented, his threshold for them will tend to be lower than for neutral words, whereas it will be higher if no instruction is given. In short, preactivation of cell assemblies—assuming for a moment that *degree of preactivation* is the mechanism that represents subjective

estimates of likelihood of occurrence of an event—such preactivation can be produced by gradual learning or quantally by instruction. Moreover, biasing may be produced by the nature of the situation in which the perceiver is operating. A recent study by Bruner and Minturn (11) illustrates the point. Subjects are presented at brief exposure a broken capital B with a small separation between the vertical and the curved component of the letter so that it may be perceived as a B or as a 13. The manner in which it is reported is determined by whether the subject has previously been presented with letters or with numbers to recognize. In short, expectancy of one or the other context preactivates a related array of categories or cell-assemblies, not just a single, isolated one.

What the neural correlates of access ordering will look like is anybody's guess. Lashley (52) has remarked that, for all our searching, we have not located a specific memory trace—either in the form of a reverberatory circuit, a definite change in fiber size as proposed by J. Z. Young (88) and Eccles (21), a synaptic knob—in the manner of Lorente de No (57) or in any known form. To be sure, Penfield (64) has activated memories by punctate electrical stimulation of the cortex, but this is a long remove from a definition of the neural properties of the trace. For the time being, one does better to deal in terms of the formal properties that a trace system must exhibit than to rest one's psychological model on any neuro-physiological or anatomical conception of the memory trace.

And, quite clearly, one of the formal properties of a trace system is that its elements vary in accessibility to stimulus input with the kinds of conditions we have considered. It is instructive to note that when a theory of traces lacks this feature, it ceases to be useful in dealing with the wide range of perceptual categorizing phenomena of which we now have knowledge. Gestalt theory is a case in point. According to Köhler's view (48), a stimulus process "finds" its appropriate memory trace, resulting in identification of the stimulus process, on the basis of distinctive similarity between stimulus process and memory trace. The theory has been criticized, justly I think, for failing to specify the nature of this similarity save by saying that it is a neural isomorph of phenomenal similarity. But since similarity may be highly selective—two objects may be alike in color but differ in dozens of other respects—there is obviously some *tertium quid* that determines the basis of similarity. More serious still is the inability of such a theory to deal with the increased likelihood of categorization in terms of particular traces as a function of changes in search set or subjective likelihood estimates. The Bruner-Minturn results would require that, as between two traces with which a stimulus process may make contact, each equally "similar" to the stimulus, the stimulus process will make contact with the one having a higher probability of being matched by environmental events. This is interesting, but it is far from the spirit of Gestalt theory.

MATCH-MISMATCH PROCESSES

One may readily conceive of and, indeed, build an apparatus that will accept or reject inputs on the basis of whether or not they fulfill certain specifications. Selfridge (71) has constructed a machine to read letters, Fry (24) has one that will discriminate various phonemes, and Uttley (80) has constructed one that, like Tinbergen's graylag geese, will recognize the flying silhouette of a predator hawk. All such machines have in common that they require a match between a stimulus input and various specifications required by the sorting mechanism of the machine.

In the examples just given, there is no consequence generated by whether a given input fulfills the specifications required by the identifying machine. It fits or it doesn't fit. But now let us build in two other features. The first is that the machine

emit a signal to indicate how closely any given input comes to fulfilling the specifications required: either by indicating how many attributes the object has in common with the specifications, or by indicating how far off the mark on any given attribute dimension a given input is. The second is that the machine do something on the basis of these signals: to increase sensitivity if an object is within a given distance of specifications for a closer look, or to decrease it if the object is further than a certain amount from specifications, or to stop registering further if the input fits.

In short, one can imagine a nervous system that emits all-or-none match-mismatch signals or graded match-mismatch signals, and one can also imagine that these signals could then feed into an effector system to regulate activity relevant to continuing search behavior for a fitting object, or to regulate other forms of activity. MacKay (59) has recently proposed such a model.

We must return for a moment to an earlier discussion. In the discussion of cue utilization, a distinction was made between three phases of "openness" in cue search. The first was one in which a given input was being scanned for its properties so as to place it in one of a relatively large set of possible alternative categories. Here one would register on as many features of an object as possible. In a second stage, the input has been tentatively placed, and the search is limited to confirming or infirming criterial cues. Finally, with more definite placement, cue search is suspended and deviations from specification may even be "normalized." It is for the regulation of such patterns of search or cue utilization that some mechanism such as match-mismatch signaling is postulated.

Let is be said that while match-mismatch signaling-effector systems are readily conceivable and readily constructed, there is no knowledge available as to how a system like the nervous system might effect such a process. That there is feedback all over the system is quite apparent from its detailed anatomy, and this is the process out of which a larger-scale system such as we have described would be constructed.

GATING PROCESSES

The picture thus far presented is of a conceptual nervous system with a massive afferent intake that manages somehow to sort inputs into appropriate assemblies of varying accessibility. It seems unlikely that this is the nature of the nervous system, that there should be no gating or monitoring of stimulus input short of what occurs at higher centers. It is with this more peripheral form of screening of inputs that we shall now be concerned.

It has long been known that the concept of the "adequate stimulus" could not simply be defined as a change in environmental energy sufficient to stimulate a receptor. For quite evidently, a stimulus could be peripherally adequate in this sense and not be "centrally" adequate at all, either in eliciting electrical activity in the cortex or in producing a verbal report of a change in experience by the subject. Indeed, the very nature of such complex receptor surfaces as the retina argues against such a simple notion of "adequate stimulus." For the reactivity of even a retinal cell at the fovea seems to be "gated" by the state of stimulation of neighboring cells. Thus, if cells A, B, and C lie next to each other in that order in a row, stimulation of B suppresses the sensitivity of C. If A now be stimulated, B is suppressed and C is released or heightened in sensitivity. So even at the level of the first synapse of a sensory system, there is mediation *outward* or gating from internuncial to receptor cells that programs the nature of the input that can come into the sensory system. And to be sure, there are many phenomena in perception itself that speak for this same kind of gating. When we are fixated upon the vase in the Rubin reversible figure, the background recedes, is less surfacy, and in general seems to provide a generally less centrally adequate form of sensory input. So too with the studies of Yokoyama (87) and Chapman (19) where subjects, set to report on one of several attributes of briefly presented stimuli, accomplished their selective task with a loss of ability to discriminate on the attributes for which they had not been set. We shall propose that such phenomena are very likely mediated by a gating process which "filters" input before ever it reaches the cortex.

There is now a growing body of neurophysiological evidence that part of this screening process is relegated to peripheral levels of the nervous system—even as far out as the second synapse of specialized sensory systems. In an earlier paper I used the rather fanciful phrase that "perception acts sometimes as a welcoming committee and sometimes as a screening committee." It now appears that both these committees are closer to the entrance port than previously conceived.

Consider first the evidence of Kuffler and Hunt (50) on so simple a "reflex" as the stretch reflex of the biceps femoris muscle of the cat in an isolated spinal nerve-muscle preparation. Recall a little anatomy first. Muscle tissue contains special cells called spindles that are receptors in function, discharging with contraction or stretch of the muscle in which they are imbedded. The muscle itself is innervated by an efferent nerve trunk emerging from the ventral horn of the spinal cord and, in turn, an afferent nerve travels to the dorsal root of the spinal cord. According to the classical law of Bell and Magendie, the ventral root of the spinal cord carries efferent-motor impulses down to the muscles, while the dorsal root carries sensory impulses up to the cord. Now, it has been known for a long time that the presumed efferent nerve going to muscles carries fibers of large and of small diameter. A quarter-century ago Eccles and Sherrington showed that the ventral nerve branch supplying the biceps femoris of the cat shows a "striking division of the fibers into two diameter groups" (49), one group centering around 5μ in diameter, the other around 15 or 16μ. The large fibers are, of course, fast conductors, the small ones slow. Leksell (55) has shown that stimulation of the slow-conducting smaller fibers did not cause detectable contractions or propagated muscle impulses. When the larger and fast-conducting fibers are stimulated, the usual motor-unit twitch occurred. Kuffler and Hunt (50) state that, in the lumbosacral outflow, about ⅔ of the fibers are of the large-diameter, fast-conduction type; the other third are of the small type that in mammalia are "ineffective in directly setting up significant muscular contraction." There has been much speculation about what these fibers are there for, and the answer is now fairly clear. It is revolutionary in its implications and brings deeply into question both the classical Bell-Magendie law and the simplistic notion of the reflex arc on which so much of American learning theory is based.

It is this. The small fibers of the presumably motor trunk go to the spindle cells and the activity in these fibers serve to modulate or gate the receptivity of these specialized sensory endings. For example, if the small-diameter fibers are firing into the muscle spindle it may speed up the amount of firing from this cell into the afferent nerve that is produced by a given amount of stretch tension on the muscle. We need not go into detail here. It suffices to note that the state of presumed motor discharge does not simply innervate the muscle; it also regulates the amount and kind of kinesthetic sensory discharge that the sensory cells in the muscle will send back to the central nervous system. Instead of thinking of a stimulus-response reflex arc, it becomes necessary even at this peripheral level to think of the efferent portion of the arc acting back on sensory receptors to change the nature of the stimulus that can get through.

Two additional pieces of evidence on gating mechanisms at higher levels of integration may be cited. Where vision is concerned, Granit (32) has recently shown that pupillary changes produced by the ciliary muscle of the eye create changes in the pattern of firing of the retina: changes in muscular state working its way back through the nervous system into the visual system and back outward to the retina. There is also evidence of gating working from the visual system backward in the opposite direction: during binocular rivalry, the nondominant eye shows a less sensitive pupillary reflex than the dominant eye.

Finally, we may cite the recent evidence of Hernandez-Péon, Scherrer, and Jouvet (38) working in Magoun's laboratory, work confirmed by analogous findings of Galambos, Sheatz, and Vernier (28) at the Walter Reed Hospital. If one stimulates the cat with auditory clicks, it is possible to record an evoked spike potential from the cochlear nucleus. Repetition of the clicks leads to a gradual diminution of the evoked potential, as if the organism were adapting. It is quite extraordinary that such adaptation should be registered as far out peripherally as the cochlear nucleus, which is, after all, only the second synapse of the VIIIth nerve. Now, if the clicks are previously used as conditioned stimuli signaling shock, the diminution of the evoked potential no longer occurs upon repetition of the clicks. Evidence that the response from the brain is not being produced by the muscular activity produced by the click as a conditioned stimulus is provided by the fact that the same kind of effects are obtained from cats with temporarily induced muscular paralysis. Further, if one takes a cat whose cochlear nucleus is still firing upon click stimulation and introduce a mouse into its visual field, the clicks no longer evoke a spike potential. A fish odor or a shock to the paw has the same effect of inhibiting spike potentials at the cochlear nucleus, if these distracting stimuli occur concurrently with the click. "Distraction" or "shifting of attention" appears to work its way outward to the coch-lear nucleus.[1]

Perhaps the foregoing account has been needlessly detailed on the side of neuro-physiology. Yet, the interesting implica-tions of the findings for perceptual theory make such an excursion worth while. That the nervous system accomplishes something like gating is quite clear, even without the neurophysiological evidence. The data of behavior are full of examples, and the phenomena of attention require some such mechanism to be explained. Indeed, it is quite clear that the nervous system must be capable of more selective gating than physiology has yet been able to discover. That is to say, there must be a filter some-where in the cat's nervous system that will "pass" the squeak of the mouse in the Hernandez-Péon experiment but not the cough of the experimenter. And it is to this problem that we turn now.

I would propose that one of the mech-anisms operative in regulating search be-havior is some sort of gating or filtering system. In the preceding section, it was proposed that the "openness" of the first stage of cue utilization, the "selectivity" of the second stage, and the "closedness" of the third stage were probably regulated by a match-mismatch mechanism. What may be proposed here is that the degree of "openness" or "closedness" to sensory input during different phases of cue utilization is likely effected by the kind of gating proc-esses we have been considering. How these work in intimate detail is far from known, yet the work of the last years in neuro-physiology suggests that we are drawing closer to an answer.

Having considered some general prop-erties of perception and some possible mechanisms underlying these, we turn now to some selected problems in perception better to explore the implications of what has thus far been proposed.

On Failure of Readiness

From the foregoing discussion, it is clear that veridical perception under view-ing or listening conditions that are less than ideal depends upon a state of per-ceptual readiness that matches the prob-ability of occurrence of events in the world of the perceiver. This is true, of course, only in a statistical sense. What is most likely to occur is not necessarily what will occur, and the perceiver whose readiness is well matched to the likelihoods of his environment may be duped. In Farquhar's handsome seventeenth-century phrase: "I cou'd be mighty foolish, and fancy myself mighty witty; reason still keeps its Throne —but it nods a little, that's all." The only assurance against the nodding of reason or probability, under the circumstances, is the maintenance of a flexibility of readiness: an ability to permit one's hypotheses about what it is that is to be perceptually en-countered to be easily infirmed by sensory input. But this is a topic for later.

There appear to be two antidotes to non-veridical perception, two ways of overcom-ing inappropriate perceptual readinesses. The one is a re-education of the misper-ceiver's expectancies concerning the events he is to encounter. The other is the "con-stant close look." If the re-education suc-ceeds in producing a better match be-tween internal expectancies and external even-probabilities, the danger of misper-ception under hurried or substandard con-ditions of perceiving is lessened. But the matter of re-educating perceptual expect-ancies is complex. For where consequences are grave, expectancy concerning what may be encountered does not change easily, even with continued opportunity to test the environment. In this concluding sec-tion we shall consider some of the factors

---

[1] Since the above was written, evidence has been presented by Galambos indicating that efferently controlled inhibition operates as far out to the periphery as the hair cells of the organ of Corti and fibers carrying such in-hibitory impulses have been traced as far cen-trally as the superior olivary nucleus—not very far, but a start.

that contribute to states of perceptual "unreadiness" that either fail to match the likelihood of environmental events or fail to reflect the requirements of adjustment or both.

Before turning to this task, a word is in order about the "constant close look" as an antidote to inappropriate perceptual readiness. There is for every category of objects that has been established in the organism a stimulus input of sufficient duration and cue redundancy such that, if the stimulus input fits the specifications of the category, it will eventually be correctly perceived as an exemplar of that category. With enough time and enough testing of defining cues, such "best fit" perceiving can be accomplished for most but not all classes of environmental events with which the person has contact. There are some objects whose cues to identity are sufficiently equivocal so that no such resolution can be achieved, and these are mostly in the sphere of so-called interpersonal perception: perceiving the states of other people, their characteristics, intentions, etc., on the basis of external signs. And since this is the domain where misperception can have the most chronic if not the most acute consequences, it is doubtful whether a therapeutic regimen of "close looking" will aid the misperceiver much in dealing with more complex cue patterns. But the greatest difficulty rests in the fact that the cost of close looks is generally too high under the conditions of speed, risk, and limited capacity imposed upon organisms by their environment or their constitutions. The ability to use minimal cues quickly in categorizing the events of the environment is what gives the organism its lead time in adjusting to events. Pause and close inspection inevitably cut down on this precious interval for adjustment.

INAPPROPRIATE CATEGORIES

Perhaps the most primitive form of perceptual unreadiness for dealing with a particular environment is the case in which the perceiver has a set of categories that are inappropriate for adequate prediction of his environment. A frequently cited example of such a case is Bartlett's account (3) of the African visitors in London who perceived the London bobbies as especially friendly because they frequently raised their right hand, palm forward, to the approaching traffic. The cue-category inference was, of course, incorrect, and they should have identified the cue as a signal for stopping traffic. The example, however, is not particularly interesting because it is a transient phenomenon, soon corrected by instruction.

A more interesting example, because it is far less tractable, is provided by second-language learning and the learning of a new phonemic system. Why is it, we may ask, that a person can learn the structure of a new language, its form classes, morphemes, lexemes, and so on, but still retain a "foreign accent" which he cannot, after a while, distinguish from the speech flow of native speakers around him? And why is it that a person learning a new language can follow the speech of a person with his own kind of foreign accent more readily than he can follow a native speaker? The answer lies, I think, in the phenomenon of postcategorization sensory gating: once an utterance has been "understood" or decoded in appropriate categories, on the basis of some of the diacritica of the speech flow, the remaining features are assimilated or normalized or screened out. The phonemic categories that are used, moreover, are modifications of those in the first language of the speaker. Normalization is in the direction of these first-language phonemic categories. It is only by a special effort that, after having achieved adequate comprehension of the second language, one can remain sensorially "open" enough to register on the deviation between his own phonemic pattern and that of native speakers. And since there is common categorization of the "meaning" of utterances by the native speaker and the fluent foreigner, there is no built-in incentive for the foreigner to maintain a cognitively strainful regimen of attending further to speech sounds.

Lenneberg (56) has recently shown the difficulties involved in learning new modes of categorizing such continua as chromatic colors. He taught subjects various nonsense languages, explaining to them that the words were Hopi names for colors and that their task was to learn what colors they stood for. His stimulus materials were graded Munsell colors going in a circle from *brown*, through *green*, through *blue*, through *pink*, and then back to *brown*. A standardizing group was used to find the frequency distribution of color naming over the circle when the English color names mentioned above were used. Experimental groups, six in number, were then run, each being exposed to the use of the nonsense color names "as these are used by the Hopi." Then they were tested on their usage of the names. A first group was taught the nonsense words with exact correspondence to the usage found for the standardizing group on *brown, blue, green,* and *pink*. The other groups were given distorted usage training—distorted from English usage. The distortions were both in the slopes of the frequency of usage and in the points on the color continua where the highest usage frequencies fell. That is to say, the mode of a distribution in some cases would fall at a color which in English had no specific name, or fall between two English categories.

The principal results of the experiment are these. If the reference and probability relationship is the same for a nonsense language as it is for English, relearning is very rapid. The slightest deviation from this correspondence increases difficulty of learning quite markedly. It is disturbing either to shift the center of the categories on the color continuum or to change the shape of the frequency-of-calling functions, even when these are made *more* determinative (i.e., rectilinear) than they normally

are. A shift in the shape of the frequency-of-calling functions is more disruptive than a shift in placement on the color continuum. What is quite striking is that a highly determinative frequency-of-calling function can be learned much more rapidly than one in which there is a gradual transition in color naming from one color to another on the color continuum.

Now, I suspect that the difficulty in learning a set of neighboring categories with a state of equivocality prevailing in the area between the "typical instances" of each category comes precisely from the tendency to normalize in the direction of the center of one category or the other. If there is a sharp transition between one color category and another, this tendency aids learning. If the transition is gradual, it hinders it. For it is noteworthy, as in the experiment of Bruner, Postman, and Rodrigues (16) that equivocal colors are readily subject to assimilation in the direction of expected value.

It is perhaps in the realm of social perception, where the problem of validating one's categorizations is severe, that one finds the most striking effects of inappropriate category systems. What is meant here by validation is the testing of the predictions inherent in a categorization. If, on the basis of a few cues of personal appearance, for example, one categorizes another person as dishonest, it is extremely difficult in most cases to check for the other cues that one would predict might be associated with instances of this category. There is either a delay or an absence of opportunity for additional cue checking. Moreover, there is also the likelihood, since cues themselves are so equivocal in such a case, that available equivocal signs will be distorted in such a manner as to confirm the first impression. It is much as in the experiments of Asch (2) and of Haire and Grunes (33) on the formation of first impressions, where later cues encountered are cognitively transformed so as to support the first impression. The reticence of the man we categorize as dishonest is seen as "caginess;" the "honest" man's reticence is seen as "integrity" and "good judgment."

It is perhaps because of this difficulty of infirming such categorial judgments that an inappropriate category system can be so hard to change. The slum boy who rises to the top in science can change his categories for coding the events of the physical world quite readily. He has much more difficulty in altering the socially related category system with which he codes the phenomena of the social world around him.

INAPPROPRIATE ACCESSIBILITY ORDERING

Perhaps the most noticeable "perceptual unreadiness" comes from interference with good probability learning by wishes and fears. I have in mind the kind of distorted expectancies that arise when the desirability or undesirability of events distorts the learning of their probability of occurrence. The experiments of Marks (60) and of Irwin (41), cited earlier, are simplified examples of the way in which desired outcomes increase estimates of their likelihood of occurrence. Certain more persistent general personality tendencies also operate in this sphere. It is indeed the case that some people are readier to expect and therefore quicker to perceive the least desirable event among an array of expected events, and others the most desired. This is quite clearly a learned adjustment to the events one is likely to encounter, even if it may be supported by temperamental characteristics. How such learning occurs, and why it is so resistant to correction by exposure to environmental events, are hardly clear. But one matter that becomes increasingly clear is that before we can know much about how appropriate and inappropriate perceptual readiness is produced, we shall have to know much more about how organisms learn the probabilistic structure of their environments. This is a point that Brunswik has made for some years (17), and it is one that is now being taken seri-

ously by such students of probability learning as Bush and Mosteller (18), Bruner, Goodnow, and Austin (9), Estes (23), Galanter and Gerstenhaber (25), Hake and Hyman (34), Edwards (22), and others.

There is another important feature of learning that affects perceptual readiness. It has to do with the range of alternatives for which organisms learn to be set perceptually. Put the matter this way. It is a matter of common observation that some people are characteristically tuned for a narrow range of alternatives in the situations in which they find themselves. If the environment is banal in the sense of containing only high probability events and sequences or, more properly, events and sequences that are strongly expected, then the individual will do well and perceive with a minimum of pause for close looking. But should the environment contain unexpected events, unusual sequences, then the result will be a marked slowdown in identification and categorizing. Cue search must begin again. We speak of such people as "rigid" or "stuck." George Klein's work (46) on shifting category judgments suggests that, in general, people who are not able to shift categorization under gradually changing conditions of stimulation tend also to show what he describes as "overcontrol" on other cognitive and motivational tasks. At the other extreme is specialization upon diversity, and how such specialization is learned is equally puzzling. I can perhaps best illustrate the phenomenon by a commonly observed pattern found in subjects in tachistoscopic experiments. There are subjects who show rather high thresholds of identification generally, and who seem to be "weighing" the stimulus in terms of a wide array of interpretive categories. Jenkin (45) has recently described such perception as "rationalized," the subject describing what he sees as "like a so-and-so" rather than, as in the "projective" response, reporting it "as a so-and-so." It is as if the former type of response involved a greater cue searching of stimulus inputs for a fit to a wide range of things that it "could be." It is also very likely that premature sensory gating occurs in individuals with a tendency to be set for a minimum array of alternatives, leading them into error. The topic is one that bears closer investigation. To anyone who has had much experience in observing subjects in tachistoscopic work, it seems intuitively evident that there are large and individual differences possibly worth examining here.

We come finally to the vexing problem of "perceptual defense"—the manner in which organisms utilize their perceptual readiness to ward off events that are threatening but about which there is nothing they can do. There has been foolish and some bitter ink spilled over this topic, mostly because of a misunderstanding. The notion of perceptual defense does not require a little homuncular ego, sitting behind a Judas-eye, capable of ruling out any input that is potentially disruptive—as even so able a critic as F. H. Allport (1) seems to think. Any preset filtering device can do all that is required.

Let me begin with the general proposition that failure to perceive is most often not a *lack* of perceiving but a matter of *interference* with perceiving. Whence the interference? I would propose that the interference comes from categorizations in highly accessible categories that serve to block alternative categorizations in less accessible categories. As a highly speculative suggestion, the mechanism that seems most likely to mediate such interference is probably the broadening of category acceptance limits when a high state of readiness to perceive prevails; or, in the language of the preceding section, the range of inputs that will produce a match signal for a category increases in such a way that more accessible categories are likely to "capture" poor-fitting sensory inputs. We have already considered some evidence for increase in acceptance limits under high readiness conditions: the tendency to see a

red four of clubs as either a four of diamonds or a four of clubs, with color-suit relationship rectified (14), the difficulty of spotting reversed letters imbedded in the middle of a word (69), and so on.

Let us examine some experimental evidence on the role of interference in perceptual failure. Wyatt and Campbell (86) have shown that if a subject develops a wrong hypothesis about the nature of what is being presented to him for perception at suboptimal conditions, the perception of the object in terms of its conventional identity is slowed down. This observation has been repeated in other studies as well. Postman and Bruner (68), for example, have shown that if a subject is put under pressure by the experimenter and given to believe that he is operating below standard, then he will develop premature hypotheses that interfere with correct perception of the word stimuli being presented to him. The authors refer to "perceptual recklessness" as characterizing the stressed subjects in contrast to those who operated under normal experimental conditions. It may well be, just in passing, that stress has not only the specific effect of leading to premature, interfering hypotheses but that it disrupts the normal operation of match-mismatch signaling systems in the nervous system. Unpublished studies from our own laboratory carried out by Bruner, Postman, and John (15) have shown the manner in which subjects misperceive low-probability contingencies in terms of higher probability categories. For example, a subject in the experimental group is shown tachistoscopically a picture of a discus thrower, wound up and ready to throw. In his balancing arm and placed across the front of him is a large bass viol. A control subject is shown the same picture, the exact space filled by the bass viol now being occupied by the crouching figure of a track official with his back to the camera. The brightness, shading, and area of the viol and the official are almost identical. Subjects begin by identifying the first flash of the picture as an athlete with a shadow across him. The subjects faced with the incongruous picture then go on with reasonable hypotheses—including the hypothesis of a crouching human figure, "probably an official," as one subject put it—and in the process of running through the gamut of likely hypotheses, correct perception is interfered with. It will not surprise you if I report that the threshold for the incongruous stimulus picture is markedly higher than that for the more conventional one.

Hypotheses and states of readiness may interfere with correct perception in yet another way: by creating a shifting "noise" background that masks the cues that might be used for identifying an environmental event. At the common-sense level this can best be illustrated by reference to perceptual-motor learning where kinesthetic cues are of importance. In teaching a person how to cast a fly, it is necessary for him to guide his forward delivery by feeling the gentle pressure release that occurs when the line reaches the end of its uncurving on the backcast. If your flycasting pupil is too eager to spot this cue, he will be rather tense, and his own muscular tension will mask the gentle pressure release that he must use as a signal.

A good instance is provided by the experiment of Goodnow and Pettigrew (30) at Harvard. It is concerned with the ability of subjects to perceive a regularity in a sequence of events—a very simple regularity, like the alternation left-right-left-right. . . . The experiment is done on a conventional two-armed bandit, the subject having the task of betting on whether a light will appear on the left or on the right. The task is simple. A subject is first given some pretraining, in one of four pretraining groups. One is given pretraining by learning a simple alternation pattern of payoff, another is trained to find the payoff all on one side (not easy for all subjects), a third is trained to find the pattern LLRLLR . . . , and a final group is given

no pretraining. Following the pretraining and without pause, all subjects are given a series of 60 choices in which the payoff is randomly arranged, the two side totaling out to 50:50. Immediately following this random phase, and again without pause, the payoffs now go into a stage of simple alternation, LRLR. . . . How long does it take the subject to perceive the regularity of the final temporal pattern? The speed of discovery depends, it turns out, upon the kinds of behavioral hypotheses a subject develops during the phase of random payoff. If he develops any regularity of response—like win-stay-lose-shift or win-shift-lose-stay—then he will quickly spot the new pattern. Pretraining on a constant one-side payoff or on single alternation both produce such regularity, and both forms of pretraining produce equally good results—the subject requiring but eight or nine exposures to the pattern introduced after the random phase to begin responding without error. No pretraining, or pretraining on the pattern LLRLLR . . . , does not produce the regularity of response required. Instead, the subject works on odd and constantly shifting hypotheses during the random period. When the single-alternation regularity is introduced, the result is a marked reduction in ability to spot the new pattern—some subjects failing to discover the pattern in 200 trials. What we are dealing with here is interference—hypotheses and responses serve to mask the regularity of events in the environment. In order for an environmental regularity to be perceived, there has to be a certain amount of steadiness in the hypotheses being employed and in the response pattern that is controlled by it. Short of this, masking and clumsy perceptual performance results.

Now what has all this to do with "perceptual defense"? The concept was introduced some years ago by Postman and myself as a description of the phenomenon of failure to perceive and/or report material known by independent test to be regarded as inimical by the subject. It was proposed (13) that there was a hierarchy of thresholds, and that an incoming stimulus could be responded to without its reaching the level of reportable experience—as in the McGinnies (58) and Lazarus and McCleary (54) studies, where autonomic response followed presentation of a potentially traumatic stimulus without the subject's being able to give a report of the nature of the stimulus. The study of Bricker and Chapanis (6) threw further light on the concept of a hierarchy of thresholds by demonstrating that, though subjects could not report spontaneously on the identity of the shock syllables used by Lazarus and McCleary, they could guess them well in excess of chance if given a restricted choice regarding what word had been presented. I would like to propose two additional factors that might lead to a failure of perception of emotionally negative material.

It is conceivable that the estimates of probability of occurrence of disvalued events are, in some individuals, reduced—essentially the obverse of what was observed in the experiments of Marks (60) and Irwin (41), where probability estimates were inflated by desirability. If accessibility is decreased by such disvaluation, then a cognitive counterpart of what is clinically called "repression" can be posited. It is known, however, that not everyone shows this tendency to be unready for objects and events that are anxiety-arousing. Others seem to *inflate* their estimate of the likelihood of occurrence of inimical events. Certainly one finds clinical evidence for such a pattern among anxiety neurotics. In an early paper, Postman and Bruner (68) described two types of performance with respect to known anxiety-producing stimuli, defense and vigilance, the former a heightened threshold of identification for such stimuli, the latter a lowered threshold. In a carefully designed experiment contrasting the performance of clinically diagnosed "in-tellectualizers" and "repressors," Lazarus, Eriksen, and Fonda (53) have shown that the former group indeed are faster in recognizing negatively charged material than they are in recognizing neutral material, while the latter show the reverse tendency. Again, I find it necessary to revert to a point made earlier. I do not think that we are going to get much further ahead in understanding hyper- and hyporeadiness for encountering anxiety-evoking stimuli short of doing studies of the learning of environmental probabilities for sequences containing noxious and beneficial events.

One additional mechanism that may be operative in lowering or generally in altering readiness to perceive material that in some way may be threatening. I hesitate to speak of it in detail, since it is of such a speculative order, and do so only because some experiments suggest themselves. It is this. Conceivably, categories for classes of objects that are pain-arousing are set up with narrow acceptance limits for stimulus inputs related to them. That is to say, what we speak of as "repression" may be the establishment of very narrow category limits that prevent the evocation of match signals for inputs that do not fit category specifications very precisely. I am mindful that as far as autonomic reactivity is concerned potentially traumatic stimuli work in quite the reverse direction. If anything, a wide range of objects, appropriate and inappropriate, arouse autonomic reactions, without leading to verbalizable report concerning the categorial identity of the eliciting objects. Yet it is conceivable that with respect to one kind of threshold (autonomic) the acceptance limits are broad, and with respect to another (reportable awareness) very narrow. I think it would be worth while in any case to investigate the acceptance limits of inimical stimulus inputs by altering the characteristics of objects so that, in essence, one gets a generalization gradient for recognition. My guess is that the gradient will be much steeper for anxiety-arousing stimuli than for neutral ones. All that remains is to do the experiment.

Finally, it may also be the case that category accessibility reflects the instrumental relevance of the environmental events they represent. There is evidence that the recognition threshold for noxious objects about which one can do something is lower than normal, whereas for ones about which nothing instrumental can be done, the threshold is higher. That is to say, words that signal a shock that can be avoided show lowered thresholds, words signaling unavoidable shock show a threshold rise. One may well speculate whether the instrumental relevance of objects is not a controlling factor in guiding the kind of search behavior that affects category accessibility. The problem needs much more thorough investigation than it has received.

We have touched on various conditions that might lead a person to be inappropriately set for the events he must perceive easily and quickly in his environment. Many other studies could be mentioned. But the intention has not been to review the rather sprawling literature in the field, but to propose some possible mechanism affecting readiness so that research might be given a clearer theoretical direction.

Conclusions

We have been concerned in these pages with a general view of perception that depends upon the construction of a set of organized categories in terms of which stimulus inputs may be sorted, given identity, and given more elaborated, connotative meaning. Veridical perception, it has been urged, depends upon the construction of such category systems, categories built upon the inference of identity from cues or signs. Identity, in fine, represents the range of inferences about properties, uses, and consequences that can be predicted from the presence of certain criterial cues.

Perceptual readiness refers to the relative accessibility of categories to afferent stimulus inputs. The more accessible a category, the less the stimulus input required for it to be sorted in terms of the category, given a degree of match between the characteristics of the input and the specifications of the category. In rough form, there appear to be two general determinants of category accessibility. One of them is the likelihood of occurrence of events learned by the person in the course of dealing with the world of objects and events and the redundant sequences in which these are imbedded. If you will, the person builds a model of the likelihood of events, a form of probability learning only now beginning to be understood. Again in rough terms, one can think of this activity as achieving a minimization of surprise for the organism. A second determinant of accessibility is the requirements of search dictated by need states and the need to carry out habitual enterprises such as walking, reading, or whatever it is that makes up the round of daily, habitual life.

Failure to achieve a state of perceptual readiness that matches the probability of events in one's world can be dealt with in one of two ways: either by the relearning of categories and expectancies, or by constant close inspection of events and objects. Where the latter alternative must be used, an organism is put in the position of losing his lead time for adjusting quickly and smoothly to events under varying conditions of time pressure, risk, and limited capacity. Readiness in the sense that we are using it is not a luxury, but a necessity for smooth adjustment.

The processes involved in "sorting" sensory inputs to appropriate categories involve cue utilization, varying from sensorially "open" cue searching under relative uncertainty, to selective search for confirming cues under partial certainty, to sensory "gating" and distortion when an input has been categorized beyond a certain level of certainty.

Four kinds of mechanisms are proposed

to deal with known phenomena of perceptual categorizing and differential perceptual readiness: *grouping and integration, access ordering, match-mismatch signal utilization,* and *gating.* The psychological evidence leading one to infer such processes were examined and possible neurological analogues considered. The processes are conceived of as mediators of categorizing and its forms of connectivity, the phenomena of differential threshold levels for various environmental events, the guidance of cue search behavior, and lastly, the phenomena of sensory inhibition and "filtering."

Finally, we have considered some of the ways in which failure of perceptual readiness comes about—first, through a failure to learn appropriate categories for sorting the environment and for following its sequences, and second, through a process of interference whereby more accessible categories with wide acceptance limits serve to mask or prevent the use of less accessible categories for the coding of stimulus inputs. The concept of "perceptual defense" may be re-examined in the light of these notions.

In conclusion, it seems appropriate to say that the ten years of the so-called New Look in perception research seem to be coming to a close with much empirical work accomplished—a great deal of it demonstrational, to be sure, but with a promise of a second ten years in which hypotheses will be more rigorously formulated and, conceivably, neural mechanisms postulated, if not discovered. The prospects are anything but discouraging.

References

1. ALLPORT, F. H. *Theories of perception and the concept of structure.* New York: Wiley, 1955.
2. ASCH, S. E. *Social psychology.* New York: Prentice-Hall, 1952.
3. BARTLETT, F. C. *Remembering.* Cambridge, England: Cambridge Univer. Press, 1932.
4. BINDER, A. A statistical model for the process of visual recognition. *Psychol. Rev.,* 1955, *62,* 119–129.
5. BITTERMAN, M. E., and C. W. KNIFFIN. Manifest anxiety and "perceptual defense." *J. abnorm. soc. Psychol.,* 1953, *48,* 248–252.
6. BRICKER, P. D., and A. CHAPANIS. Do incorrectly perceived tachistoscopic stimuli convey some information? *Psychol. Rev.,* 1953, *60,* 181–188.
7. BROWN, D. R. Stimulus similarity and the anchoring of subjective scales. *Amer. J. Psychol.,* 1953, *66,* 199–214.
8. BRUNER, J. S. Personality dynamics and the process of perceiving. In R. R. Blake and G. V. Ramsey (Eds.), *Perception: an approach to personality.* New York: Ronald, 1951. Pp. 121–147.
9. BRUNER, J. S., J. J. GOODNOW, and G. A. AUSTIN. *A study of thinking.* New York: Wiley, 1956.
10. BRUNER, J. S., G. A. MILLER, and C. ZIMMERMAN. Discriminative skill and discriminative matching in perceptual recognition. *J. exp. Psychol.,* 1955, *49,* 187–192.
11. BRUNER, J. S., and A. L. MINTURN. Perceptual identification and perceptual organization. *J. gen. Psychol.,* 1955, *53,* 21–28.
12. BRUNER, J. S., and L. POSTMAN. Emotional selectivity in perception and reaction. *J. Pers.,* 1947, *16,* 69–77.
13. BRUNER, J. S., and L. POSTMAN. Perception, cognition, and behavior. *J. Pers.,* 1949, *18,* 14–31.
14. BRUNER, J. S., and L. POSTMAN. On the perception of incongruity: a paradigm. *J. Pers.,* 1949, *18,* 206–223.
15. BRUNER, J. S., L. POSTMAN, and W. JOHN. Normalization of incongruity. Research memorandum. Cognition Project, Harvard Univer., 1949.
16. BRUNER, J. S., L. POSTMAN, and J. RODRIGUES. Expectation and the perception of color. *Amer. J. Psychol.,* 1951, *64,* 216–227.
17. BRUNSWIK, E. *Systematic and representative design of psychological experiments.* Berkeley: Univer. of California Press, 1949.
18. BUSH, R. R., and C. F. MOSTELLER. *Stochastic models for learning.* New York: Wiley, 1955.
19. CHAPMAN, D. W. Relative effects of determinate and indeterminate Aufgaben. *Amer. J. Psychol.,* 1932, *44,* 163–174.
20. COWEN, E. L., and E. G. BEIER. The in-

fluence of "threat expectancy" on perception. *J. Pers.*, 1951, *19*, 85–94.

21. Eccles, J. C. *The neurophysiological basis of mind.* Oxford: Oxford Univer. Press, 1953.

22. Edwards, W. The theory of decision making. *Psychol. Bull.*, 1954, *51*, 380–417.

23. Estes, W. K. Individual behavior in uncertain situations: an interpretation in terms of statistical association theory. In R. M. Thrall, C. H. Coombs, and R. L. Davis (Eds.), *Decision processes.* New York: Wiley, 1954. Pp. 127–137.

24. Fry, D. P., and P. Denes. Mechanical speech recognition. In W. Jackson (Ed.), *Communication theory.* New York: Academic Press, 1953.

25. Galanter, E., and M. Gerstenhaber. On thought: extrinsic theory of insight. *Amer. Psychologist*, 1955, *10*, 465.

26. Gibson, J. J. *The perception of the visual world.* Boston: Houghton Mifflin, 1950.

27. Gibson, J. J., and E. J. Gibson. Perceptual learning: differentiation or enrichment? *Psychol. Rev.*, 1955, *62*, 32–41.

28. Galambos, R., G. Sheatz, and V. G. Vernier. Electrophysiological correlates of a conditioned response in cats. *Science*, 1956, *123*, 376–377.

29. Goodnow, J. J. Determinants of choice-distribution in two-choice situations. *Amer. J. Psychol.*, 1955, *68*, 106–116.

30. Goodnow, J. J., and T. E. Pettigrew. Some difficulties in learning a simple pattern of events. Paper presented at annual meeting of the East. Psychol. Ass., Atlantic City, March, 1956.

31. Graham, C. H. Perception and behavior. Presidential address to the East. Psychol. Ass., Atlantic City, March, 1956.

32. Granit, R. *Receptors and sensory perception.* New Haven: Yale Univer. Press, 1955.

33. Haire, M., and W. F. Grunes. Perceptual defenses: processes protecting an organized perception of another personality. *Hum. Relat.*, 1950, *3*, 403–412.

34. Hake, H. W., and R. Hyman. Perception of the statistical structure of a random series of binary symbols. *J. exp. Psychol.*, 1953, *45*, 64–74.

35. Harper, R. S., and E. G. Boring. Cues. *Amer. J. Psychol.*, 1948, *61*, 119–123.

36. Hebb, D. O. *The organization of behavior.* New York: Wiley, 1949.

37. Helson, H. Adaptation-level as a basis for a quantitative theory of frames of reference. *Psychol. Rev.*, 1948, *55*, 297–313.

38. Hernandez-Péon, R., R. H. Scherrer, and M. Jouvet. Modification of electric activity in the cochlear nucleus during "attention" in unanesthetized cats. *Science*, 1956, *123*, 331–332.

39. Hornbostel, E. M. von. Unity of the senses. *Psyche.*, 1926, *7*, 83–89.

40. Howes, D. On the interpretation of word frequency as a variable affecting speed of recognition. *J. exp. Psychol.*, 1954, *48*, 106–112.

41. Irwin, F. W. Stated expectations as functions of probability and desirability of outcomes. *J. Pers.*, 1953, *21*, 329–335.

42. Ittleson, W. H. *The Ames demonstrations in perception.* Princeton, N. J.: Princeton Univer. Press, 1952.

43. Jarrett, J. Strategies in risk-taking situations. Unpublished doctor's dissertation, Harvard Univer. Library, 1951.

44. Jarvik, M. E. Probability learning and a negative recency effect in the serial anticipation of alternative symbols. *J. exp. Psychol.*, 1951, *41*, 291–297.

45. Jenkin, N. Two types of perceptual experience. *J. clin. Psychol.*, 1956, *12*, 44–49.

46. Klein, G. S. The personal world through perception. In R. R. Blake and G. V. Ramsey (Eds.), *Perception: an approach to personality.* New York: Ronald, 1951. Pp. 328–355.

47. Kohler, I. Rehabituation in perception. Published separately in three parts, in German, in *Die Pyramide*, 1953, Heft 5, 6, and 7 (Austria). Translated by Henry Gleitman and edited by J. J. Gibson. Privately circulated by the editor.

48. Köhler, W. *Dynamics in psychology.* New York: Liveright, 1940.

49. Kuffler, S. W., C. C. Hunt, and J. P. Quillian. Function of medullated small-nerve fibers in mammalian ventral roots: efferent muscle spindle innervation. *J. Neurophysiol.*, 1951, *14*, 29–54.

50. Kuffler, S. W., and C. C. Hunt. The mammalian small nerve fibers: a system for efferent nervous regulation of muscle spindle discharge. *Proc. Assoc. Res. Nerv. Ment. Dis.*, 1952, Vol. 30.

51. Lashley, K. S. Experimental analysis of instinctive behavior. *Psychol. Rev.*, 1938, *45*, 445–471.

52. LASHLEY, K. S. In search of the engram. *Symp. Soc. Exp. Biol.*, 1950, *4,* 454–482.

53. LAZARUS, R. S., C. W. ERIKSEN, and C. P. FONDA. Personality dynamics and auditory perceptual recognition. *J. Pers.*, 1951, *19,* 471–482.

54. LAZARUS, R. S., and R. A. McCLEARY. Autonomic discrimination without awareness: a study of subception. *Psychol. Rev.*, 1951, *58,* 113–222.

55. LEKSELL, L. The action potential and excitatory effects of the small ventral root fibers to skeletal muscles. *Acta Physiol. Scand.*, 1945, *10,* Suppl. 31.

56. LENNEBERG, E. H. An empirical investigation into the relationship between language and cognition. Unpublished doctoral dissertation, Harvard Univer. Library, 1956.

57. LORENTE DE NO, R. Transmission of impulses through cranial motor nuclei. *J. Neurophysiol.*, 1939, *2,* 402–464.

58. McGINNIES, E. Emotionality and perceptual defense. *Psychol. Rev.*, 1949, *56,* 244–251.

59. MacKay, D. M. Toward an information-flow model of human behavior. *Brit. J. Psychol.*, 1956, *47,* 30–43.

60. MARKS, R. W. The effect of probability, desirability, and "privilege" on the state of expectations of children. *J. Pers.*, 1951, *19,* 332–351.

61. MILLER, G. A., J. S. BRUNER, and L. POSTMAN. Familiarity of letter sequences and tachistoscopic identification. *J. gen. Psychol.*, 1954, *50,* 129–139.

62. MILLER, G. A., G. A. HEISE, and W. LICHTEN. The intelligibility of speech as a function of the context of the test materials. *J. exp. Psychol.*, 1951, *41,* 329–335.

63. PEIRCE, C. S. How to make our ideas clear. *Popular Sci. Mon.*, 1878, *12,* 286–302.

64. PENFIELD, W. Memory mechanisms. *Arch. Neurol. and Psychiat.*, 1952, *67,* 178–191.

65. PIAGET, J. *Play, dreams, and imitation in childhood.* New York: Norton, 1951.

66. PRATT, C. C. The role of past experience in visual perception. *J. Psychol.*, 1950, *30,* 85–107.

67. PRENTICE, W. C. H. Paper read at the Symposium on Conceptual Trends in Psychology, at Amer. Psychol. Ass., New York, September, 1954.

68. POSTMAN, L., and J. S. BRUNER. Perception under stress. *Psychol. Rev.*, 1948, *55,* 314–323.

69. POSTMAN, L., J. S. BRUNER, and R. D. WALK. The perception of error. *Brit. J. Psychol.*, 1951, *42,* 1–10.

70. POSTMAN, L., and R. S. CRUTCHFIELD. The interaction of need, set, and stimulus structure in a cognitive task. *Amer. J. Psychol.*, 1952, *65,* 196–217.

71. SELFRIDGE, O. Pattern recognition and learning. Memorandum of Lincoln Laboratory, Massachusetts Institute of Technology, 1955.

72. SOLOMON, R. L., and L. POSTMAN. Frequency of usage as a determinant of recognition thresholds for words. *J. exp. Psychol.*, 1952, *43,* 195–201.

73. SMITH, J. W., and G. S. KLEIN. Cognitive control in serial behavior patterns. Dittoed manuscript, available from author, 1951.

74. STEVENS, S. S. Chapter I in S. S. Stevens (Ed.), *Handbook of experimental psychology.* New York: Wiley, 1951.

75. STEVENS, S. S. The direct estimation of sensory magnitudes—loudness. *Amer. J. Psychol.*, 1956, *69,* 1–25.

76. TANNER, W. P., JR., and J. A. SWETS. A decision-making theory of human detection. *Psychol. Rev.*, 1954, *61,* 401–409.

77. TINBERGEN, N. *The study of instinct.* Oxford: Oxford Univ. Press, 1951.

78. TITCHENER, E. B. *A beginner's psychology.* New York: Macmillan, 1916.

79. TOLMAN, E .C. Discussion. *J. Pers.*, 1949, *18,* 48–50.

80. UTTLEY, A. M. *The conditional probability of signals in the nervous system.* Radar Research Establ., British Ministry of Supply, Feb., 1955.

81. VERNON, M. D. *A further study of visual perception.* Cambridge, England: Cambridge Univer. Press, 1952.

82. VOLKMANN, J. In M. Sherif and J. H. Rohrer (Eds.), *Social psychology at the crossroads.* New York: Harpers, 1951.

83. WALLACH, H. Some considerations concerning the relation between perception and cognition. *J. Pers.*, 1949, *18,* 6–13.

84. WHITE, M. *The age of analysis.* New York: New American Library, 1955.

85. WOODWORTH, R. S. Reenforcement of perception. *Amer. J. Psychol.*, 1947, *60,* 119–124.

86. WYATT, D. F., and D. T. CAMPBELL. On the liability of stereotype of hypothesis. *J. abnorm. soc. Psychol.*, 1951, 46, 496–500.

87. YOKOYAMA, J. Reported in E. G. Boring, *A history of experimental psychology.*

(2nd Ed.). New York: Appleton-Century, 1954.

88. YOUNG, J. Z. *Doubt and certainty in science.* Oxford: Oxford Univer. Press, 1951.

The Theory of Information Pickup*

J. J. GIBSON
Cornell University

Up to the present time, theories of sense perception have taken for granted that perception depends wholly on sensations that are specific to receptors. I have called these theories of sensation-based perception. The present theory asserts the possibility of perceptual experience without underlying sensory qualities that are specific to receptors, and I have called this a theory of information-based perception. It is a new departure.

The various theories of perception constitute a main branch of the history of psychology, and they have been described by Boring (1942). They need not be reviewed here, but it is worth noting the main issues over which they divided, since we should ask how the new proposal deals with them. The liveliest issue, now centuries old, was that between nativism, and empiricism. More recently, another issue has been raised by Gestalt theory in opposition to elementarism.

Consider first the debates between the nativists and the empiricists. One aspect of the controversy was a purely theoretical issue; whether the human being can be

* Gibson, J. J., *The Senses Considered as Perceptual Systems*. Boston: Houghton-Mifflin, 1966. pp. 266–286.

said to have a mind at birth—any sort of innate rational capacities or any basis for knowledge before the fact of actual perceiving—or whether, on the other hand, the infant starts life with nothing but a capacity for meaningless sensations and only learns to perceive the world by means of memory and association after an accumulation of past experience.

Another aspect of the controversy is a difference of emphasis, not of theory: whether to stress the influence of heredity on the development of perception or the influence of learning. Since both kinds of influence are known to have some effect, the decision is not one between supposedly logical alternatives.

If the theory of information-based perception is accepted, the first controversy becomes meaningless and the logical issue can be thrown out of court. The second controversy is still meaningful, but it takes a new form. The perceptual capacities of the newborn, animal or human, for getting information become a matter for investigation. The relative proportions of the unlearned and the learned in perception might be expected to depend on the degree of maturity of the infant at birth, which in turn depends on his species and on the kind of environment the young of his species have been confronted with during evolution.

Consider next the question of whether perception was compounded of elements or organized into structures. The empiricists argued for learning or association as the only organizing principle in perception; the Gestalt theorists argued for autonomous field-forces in the brain as the organizing principle. The issue has not been resolved. According to the theory here proposed, this issue also disappears, for the neural inputs of a perceptual system are *already* organized and therefore do not have to have an organization imposed upon them—either by the formation of connections in the brain or by the spontaneous self-distribution of brain processes.

The evidence of these chapters shows that the available stimulation surrounding an organism has structure, both simultaneous and successive, and that this structure depends on sources in the outer environment. If the invariants of this structure can be registered by a perceptual system, the constants of neural input will correspond to the constants of stimulus energy, although the one will not copy the other. But then meaningful information can be said to exist inside the nervous system as well as outside. The brain is relieved of the necessity of constructing such information by *any* process—innate rational powers (theoretical nativism), the storehouse of memory (empiricism), or form-fields (Gestalt theory). The brain can be treated as the highest of several centers of the nervous system governing the perceptual systems. Instead of postulating that the brain constructs information from the input of a sensory nerve, we can suppose that the centers of the nervous system, including the brain, resonate to information.

With this formula, an old set of problems for the psychology of perception evaporates, and a new set of problems emerges. We must now ask what kinds of information pickup are innate and what are acquired? What *is* the process of information pickup? How are the facts of association to be reconciled with the formula? The facts of so-called *insight?* What is the relation of perceiving to remembering in the new approach? The relation of perceiving to recognizing? To expecting? How is the detecting of information that has been coded into language related to the detecting of information that has not? These questions will be taken up in order.

What Is Innate and What Acquired in Perception?

The theoretical issue that divided nativism and empiricism was whether the interpretation of sensory signals did or did not presuppose inborn categories of understanding, or "innate ideas." The empiricists wanted to show that perceiving could be learned—all of it, including the perception of depth. Neither camp ever doubted the assumption that sensations were innate, i.e., that the repertory appeared full blown at birth, when the sense organs began to function. This abstract issue can now be disregarded, but a concrete question remains: Considering the infants of a given species, what mechanisms of detection appear at birth and what others depend on learning?

The theoretical assumption that sensations are innate, incidentally, can now be examined. It seems very dubious. Perhaps men *learn* to experience visual sensations, for example, to become aware of the field of view, or even sometimes to notice the excitation of receptors.

The concrete question of innate and acquired mechanisms in perception is not a two-way issue, for we now know there are intermediates between what' is inherited and what is acquired. Pure genetics is one thing; pure learning is another thing; but in between there are types of development that we call growth or maturation. The anatomy and basic physiology of the organs of perception depend mainly on genetic factors as determined by evolution. The maturation of the perceptual systems depends on genetic and environmental determiners in concert. The education of the perceptual systems depends mainly on the individual's history of exposure to the environment. So there are really three questions: How much does perceiving depend on organs? How much does it depend on growth? How much does it depend on experience?

The answer to the first question has already been suggested in Chapters 4 through 8. The working anatomy of the vestibular organs, the ears, the ingestive equipment, the appendages, and the eyes has been described for man, and the evolution of these structures has been outlined so far as this is known. The organs with their receptors set limits on the kinds of stimulus information that can be registered. The five modes of attention, listening, smelling, tasting, touching, and looking, are specialized in one respect and unspecialized in another. They are specialized for vibration, odor, chemical contact, mechanical contact, and ambient light, respectively, but they are redundant for the information in these energies whenever it overlaps. Their ways of orienting, adjusting, and exploring are partly constrained by anatomy, but partly free. The basic neural circuitry for making such adjustments is built into the nervous system by the time of birth, but it continues to develop in man for a long time after birth.

The answer to the second question has been suggested, but a fuller knowledge of how the perceptual systems develop in the child over time depends on evidence that has been accumulating only recently. We need to know more about overt attention, as in looking, listening, touching, and so on, and more about the inner, central nervous resonance to selected inputs that also occurs. In this country, experiments are beginning to appear on the growing

ability of infants to fix their eyes on certain kinds of visual structure (Fantz, 1961). Studies are being made on those features of an optic array that demand notice, such as the information for a human face (Ambrose, 1961) or the information for a "visual cliff" (Walk and Gibson, 1961) or the information for "imminent collision" (Schiff, 1965). In Europe, Jean Piaget has for many years pursued the study of perceptual development (e.g., Piaget and Inhelder, 1956), but his emphasis is on the inner intellectual aspect of perception. He inclines to the belief that the child *constructs reality* instead of detecting information. His experiments show, however, that the ability to attend to the higher-order features of objects and events develops in graded stages. At least the results can be interpreted in terms of information. In any case it seems to be true that the child cannot be expected to perceive certain facts about the world until he is ready to perceive them. He is not simply an adult without experience, or a sentient soul without memory. The ability to select and abstract information about the world grows as he does.

The answer to the third question, the extent to which perception depends on experience or learning in the theory of information pickup, is this: it does so to an unlimited extent when the information available to the perceiver is unlimited. The individual is ordinarily surrounded by it; he is immersed in it. The environment provides an inexhaustible reservoir of information. Some men spend most of their lives looking, others listening, and a few connoisseurs spend their time in smelling, tasting, or touching. They never come to an end. The eyes and ears are not fixed-capacity instruments, like cameras and microphones, with which the brain can see and hear. Looking and listening continue to improve with experience. Higher-order variables can still be discovered, even in old age. Getting information to the receptors becomes troublesome when the lens of the eye and the bones of the ear lose their youthful flexibility, but higher-order variables in light and sound can still be discovered by the artist and musician.

However, this is not the kind of learning that the theory of association, or of conditioning, or of memorization, has been concerned with. It is not an accrual of associations, an attaching of responses, or an accumulation of memories. Perceptual learning has been conceived as a process of "enrichment," whereas it might better be conceived as one of "differentiation" (Gibson and Gibson, 1955). What can this differentiation consist of?

The Probable Mechanism of Learning to Perceive

Despite the ancient doctrine that sensations left behind ideas in the mind, or the modern version that they could become reconnected with responses in the brain, there has always been plenty of experimental evidence to suggest a different sort of learning. This neglected evidence was surveyed and reinterpreted some years ago by Eleanor J. Gibson (1953). Even the supposedly sensory correspondence between physical intensities and phenomenal brightnesses and loudnesses has been shown to improve with practice in making comparisons. Similarly, the psychophysical correspondence between physical frequencies and phenomenal qualities of pure color and pitch improves with practice. Even the detection of physical separations of points on the retina and the skin, supposedly basic sensory acuities, can get better. When *patterns* of intensity, frequency, or separation are presented to an observer, learning is the rule, for patterns may carry information. A great number of psychophysical experiments have shown decreasing errors in discriminating, estimating, detecting, and recognizing, even when the observer is kept in ignorance of his errors. The rule holds for every department of "sense." The author of this survey concluded that the observer learns to look for the critical features, to listen for the distinctive variations, to smell or taste the characteristics of substances (perfumes or wine) and to finger the textures of things (wool or silk). Both she and I now consider this an education of attention to the information in available stimulation.

This increase of discernment is not confined to the detection of finer and finer details. The *span* of attention is increased with practice. It can (within limits) be enlarged in scope. It can also be extended in time. A pilot, for example, can be trained to keep track of a whole array of aircraft instruments, and a production engineer can be trained to watch over a long sequence of mechanical operations if each episode is part of a whole. This increase of the span of apprehension over both space and time is very suggestive. It is probably a matter of detecting progressively larger forms composed of smaller ones, and progressively longer episodes composed of shorter ones. The spatial relations in an array, and the temporal relations in a sequence, permit the information to be taken in progressively larger and longer units or "chunks." One can finally grasp the simultaneous composition of a whole panel of instruments or a panorama, and apprehend the successive composition of a whole production line or a whole symphony. Note that this extension and protension of grasp is not inconsistent with the concentration of attention on smaller details of an array, or on briefer details of an episodic sequence.

The "differentiation theory" of perceptual learning proposed by Gibson and Gibson (1955) was programmatic at the outset, but the mechanisms for this learning are becoming clearer. The process is one of learning what to attend to, both overtly and covertly. For the perception of objects, it is the detection of distinctive features and the abstraction of general properties. This almost always involves the detection of invariants under changing stimulation. The dimensions of transformation are separated off, and those that are obtained by action get distinguished from those that are imposed by events (Chapter 2). The exploratory perceptual systems typically produce transformations so that the invariants can be isolated (Chapter 12). And the action of the nervous system is conceived as a resonating to the stimulus information, not a storing of images or a connecting up of nerve cells.

The "resonating" or "tuning" of a system suggests the analogy of a radio receiver. This model is inadequate because there would have to be a little man to twiddle the knobs. A perceiver is a *self-tuning* system. What makes it resonate to the interesting broadcasts that are available instead of to all the trash that fills the air? The answer might be that the pickup of information is *reinforcing*. This is essentially the answer that Woodworth suggested twenty years ago, in a paper on the "reinforcement of perception" (1947). Clarity in itself, he asserted, is good, is valued. A system "hunts" until it achieves clarity. The process can occur at more than one level. First, the pickup of information reinforces the exploratory adjustments of the organs that make it possible. And second, the registering of information reinforces whatever neural activity in the brain brings it about. We know something about the adjustments—for example, the accommodating of the eye where the clarity of detail is somehow "satisfying" to the ocular system. We do not know much yet about the neural action of resonance at higher centers, but it too may prove to be the reaching of some optimal state of equilibrium. If the neurophysiologists stopped looking for the storehouse of memory perhaps they would find it.

A perceptual system, to repeat, is not composed of an organ and a nerve. The nervous system is part and parcel of any perceptual system, and the centers of the nervous system, from lower to higher, participate in its activity. Organ adjustments are probably controlled by lower centers, selective attention by intermediate centers, and conceptual attention by the highest centers.

[The elaboration of this theory and the marshalling of the evidence for it is too much for this chapter, or for this book. Another book is needed. It will be published under the title, *Perceptual Learning and Development*, by Eleanor J. Gibson.]

How Are Associations between Events Detected?

Psychologists have become accustomed to thinking of an association as something that is formed between two sensory impressions or between a sensory impression and a response. They realized, of course, that there had to be a physical conjunction of events—fire and smoke, for example—before the psychological association could be formed, but this was not what they were interested in. Let us consider, however, the *fact* of ecological associations, as distinguished from the *formation* of associations. The result of this fact is an invariance of stimulus combinations. Brunswik considered the ecology of stimulus combinations (1956), but he treated them only as probabilities of sense data. To the extent that a fire *always* conjoins an optical flame with an acoustic sound, a cutaneous warmth, and a volatile odor, the combination is invariant and constitutes a stimulus of higher order; more exactly, each component contains the same stimulus information (Chapter 3, p. 54). If a peach *always* yields a certain color, form, odor, texture, and sour-sweet quality, the discriminated features are all characteristic of the same thing and constitute a single combination (Chapter 8, p. 137). The act of perceiving a fire or a peach, then, might just as well be considered the pickup of the associated variables of information as the associating of sensory data. Two things are necessary: the dimensions of quality must have been differentiated, and the invariant combinations of quality must be detected. The formation of associations is not necessary.

Can the classical conditioning of responses be explained without resorting to the theory of association? Sign learning, at least, can be subsumed under the theory of information pickup. Consider Pavlov's dog isolated in a cubicle containing a food tray and a bell. The rule of this special environment was that whenever the bell sounded, food appeared. The dog in the cubicle soon began to salivate to the sound. The latter stimulus is then said to be *conditioned* (the sight and smell of food being associated with it) and the response of salivation is said to be conditioned *to* it. We say that a new stimulus-response connection has been formed—that the dog has a new stimulus for his old response of salivating, or a new response for his old sensation of a bell. But we might as well say that the dog has learned to detect the bell-food invariant in the cubicle situation. As long as Pavlov chose to make this improbable sequence a law of the cubicle (and only so long as he did), the dog might be expected to detect it.

What about the instrumental conditioning of responses? We must now consider Skinner's rat isolated in a box containing a lever and a food cup (1938). Skinner had created this little world (perhaps in six days, resting on the seventh) so that depression of the lever caused delivery of a food pellet. In order to detect this strange invariant, the rat had to behave before he could perceive, but in the course of exploration the utility of the lever became evident: it afforded food. When Skinner made the law merely probable instead of certain, or willfully abolished it, the rat's attention to the food affordance of the lever still persisted. The rat would continue to press the lever long after it had been disconnected from the food magazine, and a single success would send him off again.

What about the learning of nonsense syllables? Surely, you may say, this is a process of forming associations. Even here, it can be argued, Ebbinghaus required the learner (usually himself) to perceive the pairing or sequence of YOK and LIF in an arbitrarily created list. This was not even an invariant that held for the laws of discourse, much less one holding for the world outside his laboratory, but it was an invariant of the task nevertheless.

Learning by association is defined in stimulus-response theory as an increase in the capacity of a certain stimulus to evoke a certain response, the increase having been produced by associating the stimulus with another one that regularly evokes the response. This formula takes no account of stimulus *information*. In perception theory, at least in the kind being advocated, the response of interest is that to the *association*, not to either one of the stimuli alone. In short, learning *by* association becomes the learning *of* associations.

What Is Learning by Insight?

Ebbinghaus, Pavlov, and Skinner have all given us experimental methods for studying learning by association. Köhler's (1925) observations on the learning of lifelike tasks by apes, however, did not fit into the theory of association. A famous example is the chimpanzee in a barred cage with food set outside his reach and a stick behind him. After many vain attempts, the animal suddenly turns, seizes the stick, and rakes in the banana. The animal is said to have perceived the relations between the elements of the situation and to have learned by *insight*.

The explanation offered for the chimp's perception was that a spontaneous reorganization of his phenomenal field had occurred which included the banana, the stick, the bars, and his body in one configuration. But again, a different interpretation is possible if the hypothesis of stimulus information is accepted, and this is fore-shadowed in Köhler's description of the ape's behavior. Conceivably what he did was to perceive or notice the *rake-character* of the stick. This object, by virtue of a certain thickness and length, was graspable and reach-with-able. The information for its useability was available in the ambient light. There is no need to postulate reorganization in the brain—only perception of a fact.

This assertion about the useability of the stick does not imply that the chimp had any innate idea that a certain thickness was graspable or that a certain length was reach-with-able. The detection of these meanings emerges, no doubt, from grasping (or having grasped) and from reaching (or having reached). The perceiving of rake-character may have developed slowly, after much primate manipulation. The suddenness of insight has been justly questioned (Thorpe, 1956, Chapter 6). The point is that these meanings do not *consist* of the memories of past manipulation, or of the acquired motor tendencies to manipulate. The acts of picking up and reaching with *reveal* certain facts about objects; they do not *create* them.

The hypothesis of the "invitation qualities" of objects, their valences, or what they afford, was central to Gestalt theory, especially as developed by Lewin (1936), but the phenomenal field in which they appeared had an uncertain status, neither wholly internal nor wholly external. If these valences are taken to be invariants of stimulus information, the uncertainty disappears. The stick's invitation to be used as a rake does not emerge in the perception of a primate until he has differentiated the physical properties of a stick, but they exist independently of his perceiving them.

The invitations or demands of one animal to another, the affording of sexual partnership, for example, are usually specified by color and shape. But often, as if this were not enough information, the availability of a mate will be advertised by special movements called *expressive*. The optical transformations specify the fact, and seem to be registered with little previous experience. Displays of this sort are caller "releasers" for instinctive behavior (Tinbergen, 1951), but it should be noted that they constitute stimulus information.

INSIGHT VS. ASSOCIATION

The controversy over learning by insight as against learning by association is full of complications and is too big a subject for discussion here. We might, however, consider the physiology of the two processes. Insofar as the Gestalt theorists thought of insight as a neurological process of organization (e.g., Köhler, 1929), their theory was similar to that of the stimulus-response psychologists who thought of association as a neurological process of reinforcement (e.g., Hull, 1943). That is, both theories started from sense data, although they differed as to the kind of neural interaction ensuing. But insofar as the Gestalt theorists recognized the *prior* organization of stimuli, insofar as they acknowledged the "seeing" of structure (e.g., Wertheimer, 1945), their theory was similar to the present one. They did sometimes think of insight as detection. But they could never quite bring themselves to assume that environmental stimulation always *has* structure. The Gestalt theorists failed to realize that even dot patterns or inkblots cannot be wholly "unstructured." Hence their emphasis had to be on a hypothetical process that *imposed* structure on stimulus inputs.

What Is the Relation of Perceiving to Remembering?

All theories of learning by association presuppose some kind of central enrichment of an impoverished input to the nervous system. The supplementation, no matter how conceived, is supposed to depend on memory, that is, on some cumulative carryover of the past into the present. It may be conceived either as an accumulation of nervous bonds or connections, or of images or engrams, but at any rate an accumulation of traces in some sense of the term.

Lashley sought to discover the physiological basis of memory during a long career of investigation. But he had to conclude in the end that "it is not possible to demonstrate the localization of a memory trace anywhere within the nervous system" (1950, p. 477). Neither connections between neurons nor between images impressed on the tissue were consistent with the results of his experiments. The "search for the engram," as he put it, had failed. He could only suggest that "the learning process must consist of the attunement of the elements of a complex system in such a way that a particular combination or pattern of cells responds more readily than before the experience" (p. 479). This hypothesis of tuning or resonance implies something quite different from the accumulation of traces. When it is combined with the hypothesis of information pickup, it suggests a surprising possibility—that learning does not depend on memory at all, at least not on the re-arousal of traces or the remembering of the past. Let us follow up this possibility.

HEBB'S THEORY OF REVERBERATION

Hebb, a student of Lashley, conceived of a way in which the brain might resonate or reverberate, described in a book called *The Organization of Behavior* (1949). But the reverberation was supposed to occur in the cortex, and the aim was to explain the awareness of a visual form, say a triangle, together with the engram of such an experience. Hebb was influenced by the theory of an *isomorphism* between visual form and cortical form, the notion that the firing of nerve cells must somehow be *like* consciousness. The resonance of a retino-neuro-muscular system at various levels to the information available in optical structure, to the variables of form but not to the forms as such, is quite different from Hebb's reverberating circuits. Only the concept of a circuit is the same. But both theories stem from Lashley.

The essence of memory as traditionally conceived is that it applies to the past, in contradistinction to sense perception, which applies to the present. But this distinction is wholly introspective. It depends on the feelings of "now" and "then," not on the facts of life. The experience of "now" is the result of attention to the observer's own body and to the impressions made on it—to sensation, not perception. *Information* does not exist exclusively in the present as distinguished from either the past or the future. What is exclusively confined to the present is the momentary sensation. The stream of consciousness as described by William James (1890, Chapters 9, 15) exhibits the travelling moment of present time, with a past extending backward and a future extending forward, but this is the stream of self-consciousness, not the process of perception. Physical events conform to the relation of before and after, not to the contrast of past and future. Resonance to information, that is, contact with the environment, has nothing to do with the present.

The ordinary assumption that memory applies to the past, perception to the present, and expectation to the future is therefore based on analytic introspection. Actually, the three-way distinction could not even be confirmed, for the travelling moment of present time is certainly not a razor's edge, as James observed, and no one can say when perception leaves off and memory begins. The difficulty is an old one in psychology, and Boring (1942) has described the efforts to get around it in his chapter on the perception of time. The simple fact is that perceiving is not focused down to the present item in a temporal series. Animals and men perceive motions, events, episodes, and whole sequences. The doctrine of sensation-based perception requires the assumption that a succession of items can be grasped only if the earlier ones are held over so as to be combined with later ones in a single composite. From this comes the theory of traces, requiring that every percept lay down a trace, that they accumulate, and that every trace be theoretically able to reinstate its proper percept. This can be pushed into absurdity. It is better to assume that a succession of items can be grasped *without* having to convert all of them into a simultaneous composite.

The idea that "space" is perceived whereas "time" is remembered lurks at the back of our thinking. But these abstractions borrowed from physics are not appropriate for psychology. Adjacent order and successive order are better abstractions, and these are not found separate.

Even at its simplest, a stimulus has some successive order as well as adjacent order (Chapter 2, p. 40). This means that natural stimulation consists of *successions* as truly as its consists of *adjacencies*. The former are on the same footing as the latter. A visual transient between light and dark is no more complex than a visual margin between light and dark. The information in either case is in the direction of difference: *on* or *off, skyward* or *earthward*. The visual system in fact contains receptive units for detecting both kinds of information. It is absurd to suppose that these sequence detectors have to make a comparison of intensity *now* with the memory of intensity *then*.

The improvement of information pickup with experience is thus not necessarily the dependence of perception on memory in the commonsense, introspective meaning of that term. The "attunement of a complex system," in Lashley's words, need not entail the reinstatement of earier experiences, that is, recalling or recollecting. This proposal does not in the least deny that remembering can occur. It denies only that remembering is the basis of learning. Perhaps conscious remembering is an occasional and incidental symptom of learning in the same way that sensations are occasional and incidental symptoms of perceiving.

The ability of the human individual to contemplate parts of his past history is no mean achievement; the experimental psychologist as well as the psychotherapist and the novelist has reason to be fascinated by it; but there is some question whether it has to intervene in the simpler ability to perceive and learn.

The question of whether or not thinking always involves images was a controversy in psychology many years ago (Humphrey, 1951). The weight of the evidence indicated that problem-solving and reasoning could sometimes proceed with no awareness whatever of any copies of previous experience. If it is agreed that one can think without remembering, there is no great step to the conclusion that one can learn without remembering.

The "image" of memory and thought is derived by analogy to the image of art. The "trace" of a percept is analogous to the graphic act. The "storehouse" of memory is analogous to the museums and libraries of civilization. As we observed in Chapter 11, these inventions do make possible the preservation of human knowledge for subsequent generations. But to assume that experiences leave images or traces in the brain, that experience writes a record, and that the storage of memories explains learning, that, in short, the child accumulates knowledge as the race has accumulated it, is stultifying.

What Is the Relation of Perceiving to Recognizing?

It has often been pointed out that memory has quite different manifestations. To recognize is not the same as to recall. One can identify the same place, object, or person on another occasion with recalling it. "I recognize you," one says, "but I cannot recall your name, nor where we met." Often there is a mere "feeling of familiarity" or a bare judgment of "same as before." Nevertheless, both are considered forms of memory and the theory of traces requires that, even for recognition, the present input must somehow retrieve the stored image of the earlier experience. If the input matches, recognition occurs; if not, recognition fails. This act of comparison is implied by the commonly accepted theory of recognition. There is, however, an alternative theory. It is to suppose that the judgment of "same" reflects the tuning of a perceptual system to the invariants of stimulus information that specify the same real place, the same real object, or the same real person. The judgment of "different" reflects the absence of invariants, or sometimes the failure of the system to pick up those that exist.

The "successions" of stimulation include both non-changes and changes, and therefore the detection of *same* is no less primary than the detection of *different*. One is the reciprocal of the other and neither requires an act of mental comparison. This is quite evident in the simplest possible case of recognition, in which one encounter with an object is followed immediately by another, as when one sees an object in two perspectives, or feels it on both sides. The invariants provide for the detection of *same thing* along with the detection of *different aspect*. In recognition over a long interval, when encounters with other objects, other places, or other persons have intervened, the attunement of the brain to the distinguishing features of the entity must be deeper and stronger than in recognition over a short interval, but the principle need only be extended to cover it.

The same object is usually not encountered in wholly separate places; it is usually met with in the same place, to which one returns after having passed through other places. As we observed in Chapter 10 (Figure 10.10), places are linked by the transformations of *vistas* and the transitions between them. A vista, it will be remembered, is an array that "opens up" in front and "closes in" behind. Locomotion thus eventuates in a sort of cognitive map, consisting of the invariants common to all the perspectives. This helps to establish the recognition of the objects contained in the perspectives.

The problem of why phenomenal identity usually goes with the same physical thing and why phenomenal distinctiveness usually goes with different physical things are actually two sides of the same problem. Identification and discrimination develop together in the child as reciprocals, and the experimental evidence shows it. Identifying reactions improve at the same time as discriminative reactions (Gibson and Gibson, 1955). Recognition does not have to be the successful matching of a new percept with the trace of an old one. If it did, novelty would have to be the failure to match a new percept with any trace of an old one after an exhaustive search of the memory store, and this is absurd.

What Is the Relation of Perceiving to Expecting?

No one has ever been able to say exactly where perceiving ceases and remembering begins, either by introspection or by observation of behavior. Similarly, it is not possible to separate perceiving from expecting by any line of demarcation. Introspectively, the "conscious present," as James observed, merges with both the past and the future. Behaviorally, the evidence we accept as showing that the subject of an experiment *expects* something, food or electric shock, is the same evidence we accept as showing that the animal *remembers* something or has *learned* something.

The theory of learning advocated by Tolman (1932) was characterized as a cognitive or perceptual theory. He argued that all kinds of learning consisted of expectations, the actual movements of behavior being secondary, and that the explanation of learning was to be found in the confirming or disconfirming of expectations, not in the reinforcing of responses by reward or punishment. The animal learned what led to what, not reactions. A conditioned stimulus, for example, came to arouse an expectancy of food or shock. The lever in a Skinner box came to induce an expectancy of food in the cup below. The successive alleys of a maze after running through them led to the anticipation of the goal box, which might or might not contain food. The marking on a door in a discrimination box or a jumping stand came to arouse an expectancy of food behind it. This emphasis on the animal's orientation to the future made it plausible to think of behavior in terms of "means-end readiness," and to conceive behavior as purposive.

It has already been suggested how these kinds of learning might be explained without any necessary reference to the future, namely as cases of perceiving or detecting an invariant. The causal connection in these experiments, the contingency, is one created by the experimenter. It was he that designed the conditioning experiment, the box with a lever, the alleys of the maze, or the discrimination apparatus, and he that decided what the law of the experimental environment would be. The causal structure of this environment, its machinery, might not be very similar to that of the natural environment of a rat but it was predictable and controllable. The causal law of "what led to what" was present in the situation on repeated trials. If the animal could identify it over the series, he could be said to have learned, inasmuch as his behavior came to be determined by it. Whether or not the animal could fairly be said to expect, anticipate, or imagine the future, he could surely be said to have detected something.

Tolman's *confirming of an expectation,* it may be noted, is similar in principal to what has here been called the discovering and clarifying of information as a consequence of exploratory search. To call the process one of predicting an event and then verifying its occurrence makes it seem an intellectual accomplishment and dignifies the rat undeservedly. The rat's perception is more primitive than this.

The apprehension over time of the motion of an object, one might suppose, has nothing in common with the learning that may occur in the event sequences described above. The motion, we say, is simply perceived; remembering and expecting do not come into it. A kitten per-

ceives the course of a rolling ball, an outfielder perceives the trajectory of a batted ball, and that is all there is to it. Nevertheless, in a sense, the kitten and the ballplayer *expect* the ball to continue on a predictable path, and that is why they can both start out on a dead run to intercept it. This foreseeing is much like ordinary seeing, and not much like Tolman's expectancies, for it depends on a continuous flow of stimulation. But the two kinds of situation do have something in common. The unbroken continuation of the optical motion is a consequence of the invariant laws of inertia and gravity in physics. The ball continues in a straight line, or a trajectory, because of Newton's Laws. The invariant is implicit in the motion. Both the kitten and the ballplayer may have to practice and learn in order to detect it accurately, but in a certain sense what they are learning is to perceive the laws of motion.

The experiments of Schiff, Caviness, and Gibson (1962) and Schiff (1965) on optical magnification of a silhouette in the field of view demonstrate that "looming," the visual information for imminent collision, is often detected by young animals who have never had painful encounters with an approaching object. They shrink away or blink their eyes, or otherwise make protective responses without having any reason to "expect" collision by reason of past experience. In this case the visual nervous system is presumably attuned to the information at birth. The behavior of human automobile driver suggests that there are various degrees of attunement to the foreseeing of a collision when something starts to expand in the field of view.

What Is the Effect of Language on Perception?

Both men and animals perceive the environment, but the human perceiver has language while the animal does not. When the child begins to communicate by speech, and to practice speaking, he starts on a line of development that makes his knowledge of the world forever different from what it would have been if he had remained a speechless animal. What are these consequences? We might suppose that the effect of language would be to make perceiving easier and better. But it has been argued that there is an unfortunate and unavoidable effect which tends to make it distorted and stereotyped instead.

The argument seems to be based on a fact about language, but only one, and not necessarily the most important—the fact that it is a *code*. Language substitutes words for things. It depends on the lexicon, that is, on a sort of social agreement as to the signals that will stand for certain percepts. Every child must learn the code of his social group, and it is supposed that he learns it by forming associations between things and words, or by acquiring conditioned verbal responses to things. There are, of course, many more things in the world than there are words in a language. Not everything can be coded. The verbal responses, it is argued, must therefore categorize or cut up the real world in conventional ways that are necessarily inadequate to its full complexity (Whorf, 1956). If, now, it is further assumed that perceptual identifying is not theoretically separable from verbal naming, then perceiving is perforce limited, as verbalizing is limited, and perception is to that extent distorted.

This line of reasoning presupposes an association theory of perception, assuming that words are utterances (or tendencies to utter, or auditory memories of utterances, or visual memories of writing) and that they have been attached to the stimuli from the world by association. The theory of information pickup, however, starts with a different assumption about words and ends with a different conclusion as to the effect of language on perception. Let us try to pursue the new line of reasoning.

For the child who is learning to use language and at the same time learning to perceive the world, words are *not* simply auditory stimuli or vocal responses. They embody stimulus information, especially invariant information about the regularities of the environment. They consolidate the growing ability of the child to detect and abstract the invariants. They cut across the perceptual systems or "sense modalities." The words are like the invariants in that they are capable of being auditory or visual or even tactual (as Braille writing is). They even cut across the stimulus-response dichotomy, for they can be vocal-motor or manual-motor. Hence, the learning of language by the child is not simply the associative naming or labeling of impressions from the world. It is also, and more importantly, an expression of the distinctions, abstractions, and recognitions that the child is coming to achieve in perceiving. Insofar as a code is a set of associations, the terms of the code have to be learned by association. But a language is more than a set of associations and the learning of language is therefore more than learning by association.

A language is more than a code because it permits *predications* as well as labelings. It has a grammar as well as a vocabulary. So the child's discovery of facts about the world can be predicated in sentences, not simply stereotyped in words. Predication can go to higher and higher levels, so the limitations of vocabulary do not set the same limits on the codifying of facts.

The learning of the language code as a vocabulary should be distinguished from the child's learning to consolidate his knowledge by predication. He gets information first by focusing, enhancing, detecting, and extracting it from nonverbal stimulation. Later, the extracting and consolidating go on together. Perceiving helps talking, and talking fixes the gains of perceiving. It is true that the adult who talks to a child can educate his attention to certain differences instead of others. It is true that when a child talks to himself he may enhance the tuning of his perception to certain differences rather than others. The range of possible discriminations is un-limited. Selection is inevitable. But this does not imply that the verbal fixing of information distorts the perception of the world.

In the theory of information pickup, the spontaneous activities of looking, listening, and touching, together with the satisfactions of noticing, can proceed with or without language. The curious observer can always observe more properties of the world than he can describe. Observing is thus not necessarily coerced by linguistic labeling, and there is experimental evidence to support this conclusion.

Behavioral theories of perception get their force from the conviction that behavior is practically useful. In a behavioral theory of perception, however, exploratory activities are treated simply as responses. Perception must then be learned by the reinforcing of stimulus-response connections. The conclusion is unavoidable that perception is biased by the needs that motivate practical action, for discrimination serves only the interests of practical action. One should fail to see anything that leads to unpleasant consequences and should see anything that leads to satisfaction. Both psychic blindness and hallucination ought to be common occurrences. But in the theory being advocated, discrimination is *itself* a kind of useful action—an activity reinforced by clarity, not by punishments or rewards—and autism, or wishful perceiving, ought to be an uncommon occurrence.

The issue between the two kinds of theory can be illustrated by the following question. Does a child distinguish between two physically different things only after he has learned to make different responses to each, names, for example; or does he first learn to distinguish them and then (sometimes) attach names? On the former alternative he must learn to respond to the things; on the latter he must learn to respond to the difference.

From the first alternative it would be predicted that a child should be able to say names correctly before he can say "bigger" correctly; on the latter alternative the reverse would be predicted. This issue is deep and far-reaching. It cannot be compromised or avoided.

The Probable Kinds of Development in Learning to Perceive

Associating, organizing, remembering, recognizing, expecting, and naming—all these are familiar psychological processes, and all of them have been appealed to in the effort to explain the growth of knowledge. But all these processes were first conceived as operations of the mind upon the deliverances of sense, and they still carry some of this implication. They have now been examined, one by one, and I have suggested that, as commonly understood, they are incidental, not essential, to the developing process of information pickup. They need to be reinterpreted. The deeper, underlying kinds of perceptual development seem to involve exploration and attention. What can be said by way of summary about the more fundamental types of development?

DIFFERENTIATING THE RANGE OF POSSIBLE INPUTS

Consider a very simple perceptual system—for example, that for detecting the direction of gravity (Chapter 4). The input of a statocyst is presumably different for every different position of the weight resting on its hair-cells, altering as the animal is tilted leftward, is upright, or is tilted rightward. But a given input of excited hairs constitutes information about the direction "down" *only in relation to the other possible inputs of excited hairs.* The range of inputs, from a horizontal posture through vertical to horizontal again, defines the meaning of any given input. Consequently the animal's nervous system must have differentiated this range if it is to detect "down" and make compensatory righting reactions. For this, the animal must have been subjected to the range of postures, or perhaps have explored the range of postures. The development might be prenatal, or innate, or even learned, but it must be a development.

The same differentiating of the range of inputs must occur for other perceptual systems as well as the vestibular. The dimensions of variation in the haptic and the visual system, for example, are much more elaborate than are the inputs of a statocyst. Discriminative learning may be required instead of neural growth or maturation. Active testing of the limits of the range may occur. *Any perceptual system, however, has to have each of its inputs related to the other available inputs of the system.*

ESTABLISHING THE COVARIATION OF INPUTS BETWEEN DIFFERENT SYSTEMS

The "orienting system," it will be recalled, is actually a redundant combination of vestibular, tactual, articular, and visual information. The input of a statocyst is covariant with the input of the skin, the joints, and the eyes whenever a young individual rolls, crawls, walks, or gets about. Consequently there must be another simple type of perceptual development, the registering of the concurrent covariation from different organs. The pull of gravity, the push of the ground, and the sky-earth difference are correlated. The vestibular, haptic, and visual inputs are likewise correlated over time. Insofar as this linkage is invariant, the information is the same in all of them, that is, the systems are equivalent. Their inputs are associated, it it fair to say, but learning by association hardly need be assumed.

Covariation in time of differentiated inputs does not necessarily imply a one-to-one correspondence of sensory elements or qualities. Covariant but not coincident inputs from the statocyst and the skin will

occur for an individual resting on a slope, as noted in Chapter 4 (Figure 4.3). The "calibration" of the ranges of inputs from different perceptual organs may well be a matter of learning, and it implies information of a higher order.

The learning of concurrent covariations in the external environment, of what goes with what, depends also on the pickup of concurrent covariation of neural input, but this requires that the exterospecific component of the input will have been isolated.

ISOLATING EXTERNAL INVARIANTS

The perception of the color and layout of surfaces, of the distinctive features of objects, and of their real motions in space implies that the other-produced component of neural input is separated from the self-produced component. This separation is not difficult to explain if one supposes that relational inputs exist along with the anatomical inputs. The transformations of the anatomical pattern of excited receptors have subjective reference; the invariants of adjacent and successive order in the overall input specify the invariants of stimulation and thereby the invariants of the world.

This "constancy" of perception no doubt depends on development insofar as the invariants of input have to be differentiated from one another in the nervous system. But the registering of invariants is something that all nervous systems are geared to do, even those of the simplest animals. The visual perception of "depth," for example, is surely not dependent on a gradual process by which the brain learns to interpret local sensations of color. Constancy is learnable in some degree, but not by a process of associating, organizing, or remembering.

Consider the origin of the child's perception of the permanence of objects. Does it have to depend on some kind of intellectual understanding of the causes of the child's impermanent sensations? Piaget

(1954) and many others have assumed so. David Hume asserted (1739) that the senses "are incapable of giving rise to the notion of the *continued* existence of objects after they no longer appear to the senses. For that would be a contradiction in terms" (Part IV, Sec. 2). Hume was quite right; the awareness of the continued existence of a thing after it has been hidden by the edge of something else cannot be derived from the visual sensation after it has been wiped out. But it *can* be explained by the detecting of stimulus information for occlusion, i.e., the property of the transformation that we call "wiping out," which is quite distinct from the transformation that we call "fading out" (Reynolds, 1966). This information was described in Chapter 10 (Figure 10.9). The child must distinguish, or learn to distinguish, between these two kinds of optical transformation in order to perceive when a thing merely goes out of sight and when it vanishes, but he does not have to "construct" reality out of impermanent sensations (Piaget, 1954). Nor does he have to associate tactual sensations with visual ones in order "to understand that the objects in his environment have a continuous and consistent identity entirely detached from himself" (Vernon, 1952, p. 10).

LEARNING THE AFFORDANCES OF OBJECTS

When the constant properties of constant objects are perceived (the shape, size, color, texture, composition, motion, animation, and position relative to other objects), the observer can go on to detect their *affordances*. I have coined this word as a substitute for *values*, a term which carries an old burden of philosophical meaning. I mean simply what things furnish, for good or ill. What they *afford* the observer, after all, depends on their properties. The simplest affordances, as food, for example, or as a predatory enemy,

may well be detected without learning by the young of some animals, but in general learning is all-important for this kind of perception. The child learns what things are manipulable and how they can be manipulated, what things are hurtful, what things are edible, what things can be put together with other things or put inside other things—and so on without limit. He also learns what objects can be used as the means to obtain a goal, or to make other desirable objects, or to make people do what he wants them to do. In short, the human observer learns to detect what have been called the values or meanings of things, perceiving their distinctive features, putting them into categories and subcategories, noticing their similarities and differences and even studying them for their own sakes, apart from learning what to do about them. All this discrimination, wonderful to say, has to be based entirely on the education of his attention to the subtleties of invariant stimulus information.

DETECTING THE INVARIANTS IN EVENTS

Along with the discrimination of objects goes the developing discrimination of events. The child learns how things work as well as how they differ. He begins to perceive falling, rolling, colliding, breaking, pouring, tracing, and he ends by apprehending inertia, the lever, the train of gears, the chemical change, the electric current, and perhaps the concept of energy. The cause-and-effect relation in these observations becomes increasingly subtle. The simple perception of motion or of collision (Michotte, 1963) gives way more and more to what we call inference. Nevertheless there remains an element of perception in the appreciation of even the most abstract law. The physical scientist visualizes atoms or particles; the savage or the child sees spirits or magical rules behind a complex sequence of events (Piaget,

1951), but everyone perceives some kind
of invariant over time and change. The
information for the understanding of the
law in such a case may be of staggeringly
high order, but it is theoretically open to
observation.

THE DEVELOPMENT OF
SELECTIVE ATTENTION

Still another probable kind of perceptual development is the acquiring of what
might be called *economical* perception. It
is the ability to avoid distraction—to concentrate on one thing at a time in the face
of everything going on in the environment
—and yet to accomplish as much knowing
as possible. To accomplish this, perceiving
must be quick and efficient rather than
slow and contemplative. As a result, the
information registered about objects and
events becomes only what is needed, not all
that could be obtained. Those features of a
thing are noticed which distinguish it from
other things that it is not—but not *all* the
features that distinguish it from *everything* that it is not.

This has been called the schematic
tendency in perception, and it has been
much studied in the psychological laboratory. The rule is, I suggest, that only the
information required to identify a thing
economically tends to be picked up from
a complex of stimulus information. All the
other available information that would be
required to specify its unique and complete identity in the whole universe of
things is not attended to.

This rule emphasizes economy in detecting the diagnostic features of things in
the structure of stimulation. It does not
refer to economy in a process of organization that is supposed to produce structure
where none existed. The "minimum principle" in the organization of perception is
one of the tenets of Gestalt theory; this is
also a minimum principle, but the economy
is in a process of selection, not one of
organization.

References

AMBROSE, J. A., The development of the smil-
ing response in early infancy. In B. M. Foss
(Ed.) *Determinants of Infant Behavior*,
Wiley, 1961.

BORING, E. G., *Sensation and Perception in
the History of Experimental Psychology*,
Appleton-Century, 1942.

BRUNSWIK, E., *Perception and the Representative Design of Psychological Experiments*,
University of California Press, 1965.

FANTZ, R. L., The origin of form perception.
Sci. Amer., 1961, 204, 2–8.

GIBSON, ELEANOR J., Improvement in perceptual judgments as a function of controlled
practice or training. *Psychol. Bull.*, 1953,
50, 401–431.

GIBSON, J. J., and GIBSON, ELEANOR J. Perceptual learning: differentiation or enrichment? *Psychol. Rev.*, 1955, 62, 32–41.

HEBB, D. O., *The Organization of Behavior*,
Wiley, 1949.

HULL, C. L., *Principles of Behavior*, Appleton-Century, 1943.

HUME, D., *A Treatise of Human Nature*,
1739 (any modern edition).

HUMPHREY, G., *Thinking, An Introduction
to Its Experimental Psychology*, London:
Methuen, 1951.

JAMES, W., *The Principles of Psychology*,
Holt, 1890.

KÖHLER, W., *The Mentality of Apes* (Tr. by
E. Winter), London: Routledge and Kegan
Paul, 1925.

KÖHLER, W., *Gestalt Psychology*, Liveright,
1929.

LASHLEY, K. S., In search of the engram. In
*Physiological Mechanisms in Animal Be-
haviour* (Symposium No. 4, *Soc. Exper.
Biol.*), Academic Press, 1950.

LEWIN, K., *Principles of Topological Psychology*, McGraw-Hill, 1936.

MICHOTTE, A., *The Perception of Causality*
(Tr. by T. R. Miles and E. Miles), London: Methuen, 1963.

PIAGET, J., *The Construction and Thought of
the Child* (Tr. by M. Gabain), Humanities
Press, 1951.

PIAGET, J., *The Construction of Reality in the
Child* (Tr. by M. Cook), Basic Books,
1954.

PIAGET, J., and B. INHELDER, *The Child's
Conception of Space* (Tr. by F. J. Langdon
and J. L. Lunzer), Humanities Press, 1956.

REYNOLDS, H., Factors affecting the accuracy
of visual tracking of a moving object when

it has disappeared from sight (Thesis). Cornell University Library, 1966.

SCHIFF, W., Perception of impending collision: A study of visually directed avoidant behavior. *Psychol. Monogr.* 1965, *79,* Whole No. 604.

SCHIFF, W., J. A. CAVINESS, and J. J. GIBSON, Persistent fear responses in Rhesus monkeys to the optical stimulus of "looming." *Science,* 1962, *136,* 982–983.

SKINNER, B. F., *The Behavior of Organisms,* Appleton-Century, 1938.

THORPE, W. H., *Learning and Instinct in Animals,* Harvard University Press, 1956.

TINBERGEN, N., *The Study of Instinct,* Oxford University Press, 1951.

TOLMAN, E. C., *Purposive Behavior in Animals and Men,* Century, 1932.

VERNON, MAGDALEN D., *A Further Study of Visual Perception,* Cambridge University Press, 1952.

WALK, R. D., and ELEANOR J. GIBSON, A comparative and analytical study of visual depth perception. *Psychol. Monogr.,* 1961, *75,* Whole No. 519.

WERTHEIMER, M., *Productive Thinking,* Harper, 1945.

WHORF, B. L., *Language, Thought, and Reality* (Ed. by J. B. Carroll), Wiley, 1956.

WOODWORTH, R. S., Reinforcement of perception. *Amer. J. Psychol.,* 1947, *60,* 119–124.

Cultural Differences in the Perception of Geometric Illusions*

MARSHALL H. SEGALL

University of Iowa

DONALD T. CAMPBELL   MELVILLE J. HERSKOVITS

Northwestern University

Abstract. Data from 15 societies are presented showing substantial intersocietal differences in two types in susceptibility to geometric optical illusions. The pattern of response differences suggests the existence of different habits of perceptual inference which relate to cultural and ecological factors in the visual environment.

Stimulus materials based upon geometric illusions were prepared in 1956 for stand-

* *Science,* 1963, vol. 139, pp. 769–771. Copyright © · 1963 by the American Association for the Advancement of Science. Space does not permit mention of all the many individuals and organizations that contributed to this project. Major thanks are due those who assisted us in the collection of the data: D. Bender, M. Boye, R. Clignet, H. Conklin, J. Fernandez, J. Golden, I. Kopytoff, N. Leis, P. Leis, B. LeVïne, A. Merriam, P. Morgan, E. Perlman, H. Reuning, and N. Scotch. Supported by funds provided by the Program of African Studies at Northwestern University and the Ford Foundation. Special thanks are due D. W. Norton for advice and assistance in data analysis.

ardized administration under varying field conditions in an effort to encourage the collection of cross-cultural data that might bear on the nativist-empiricist controversy concerning space perception (*1*). Over a 6-year period anthropologists and psychologists administered these tests to 14 non-European samples of children and adults, ranging in size from 46 to 344 in 12 locations in Africa and one in the Philippines, to a sample ($N = 44$) of South Africans of European descent in Johannesburg, to an American undergraduate sample ($N = 30$), and to a house-to-house sample ($N =$

208) in Evanston, Ill. In all, data were collected from 1878 persons. Analysis of these protocols provides evidence of substantial cross-cultural differences in response to these materials. The nature of these differences constitutes strong support for the empiricistic hypothesis that the perception of space involves, to an important extent, the acquisition of habits of perceptual inference.

The stimulus materials to be considered here consisted of 39 items, each one a variation of one of four figures constructed of straight lines, generally referred to in the psychological literature as perceptual, or geometric illusions. These were the Müller-Lyer figure (12 items), the Sander Parallelogram (seven), and two forms of the Horizontal-vertical figure (nine and eleven). For each illusion the discrepancy in length of the segments to be compared varied from item to item so as to permit the employment of a version of the psychophysical method of constant stimuli. As each stimulus was shown to a respondent, his task was simply to indicate the longer of two linear segments. To minimize difficulties of communication, the materials were designed so that the linear segments to be compared were not connected to the other lines, and were printed in different colors. Respondents could indicate choice by selecting one of two colors (saying *red* or *black*) in response to the Horizontal-vertical items, and by indicating *right* or *left* for the other illusions. Other steps taken to enhance the validity of response protocols included the administration of a short comprehension test requiring judgments similar to, but more obvious than, those demanded by the stimulus figures. Nonetheless, since no amount of precautionary measures could insure the elimination of all sources of error (for example, communication difficulties, response sets, and so forth) which could result in artifactually produced cross-cultural differences, an internal consistency check was made and all protocols containing gross departures from orderliness were withheld from analysis. (Another analysis was performed with all 1878 cases included, and the results were substantially the same as those obtained in the analysis of consistent cases only.)

The analysis proceeded as follows: Each respondent's four protocols were first examined for evidence of internal consistency. To be considered consistent, a protocol had to contain no more than one Guttman error (2). Each consistent protocol was then assigned a score which was simply the total number of times in that stimulus set that the respondent chose the typically over-estimated segment. The mean of these scores was computed for each sample, and differences between pairs of means were evaluated by t-tests with significance levels modified by the Scheffé procedure (3) to compensate for the increase in error rate that accompanies nonindependent, multiple comparisons.

On both the Müller-Lyer and Sander Parallelogram illusions the three "European" samples made significantly more illusion-produced responses than did the non-European samples. (The innumerable t ratios resulting can only be sampled here. For example, on the Müller-Lyer illusion, comparisons of the Evanston sample with the non-European samples resulted in t ratios ranging from 7.96 to 15.39. A value of 3.57 is significant at the $p = .05$ level by the Scheffé test.) On the latter two illusions, the European samples had relatively low scores, with many, but not all, of the non-European samples having significantly larger mean scores. (For these illusions, the largest t ratios, up to 17.41, were found between pairs of non-European groups. Comparisons involving the Evanston sample and five non-European groups resulted in t's ranging from 11.04 to 4.69.) When the samples were ranked according to mean number of illusion responses on each illusion, and the rank order correlations among the five illusions factor-analyzed, two orthogonal factors emerged; the Müller-Lyer and Sander Parallelogram illusions loaded highly on one, and the Horizontal-vertical illusions loaded highly on the other. Thus, the overall pattern of intersample differences indicates not only cross-cultural differences in illusion susceptibility, but in addition a systematic variation in those cross-cultural differences over two classes of illusion figures.

Both to illustrate and substantiate the findings which emerged from the analysis just described, proportions of individuals in each sample choosing the typically over-estimated segment were computed for each item, separately for each illusion set. Psy-

TABLE 1

Points of Subjective Equality and Mean Number of Illusion Responses

GROUP	N	PSE PERCENTAGE	MEAN	GROUP	N	PSE PERCENTAGE	MEAN
Müller-Lyer illusion				*Horizontal-vertical illusion* ($\perp$)			
Evanstonians	188	20.3	5.36	Suku	69	21.0	6.55
N. U. Students*	27	16.2	5.00	Banyankole	261	22.5	6.54
S. A. Europeans*	36	13.5	4.33	Dahomeans†	57	22.3	6.49
Dahomeans†	40	11.9	4.23	Toro	105	20.0	6.44
Senegalese	125	12.2	4.18	Ijaw School†	46	20.7	6.28
Ijaw School†	54	6.6	3.67	S. A. mineboys*	69	19.3	6.27
Zulu	35	11.2	3.66	Fang	98	19.3	6.18
Toro	86	10.3	3.56	Senegalese	130	22.7	6.11
Banyankole	224	9.3	3.45	Ijaw	86	19.5	6.06
Fang	85	6.2	3.28	Bushmen*	41	19.5	5.93
Ijaw	84	6.5	3.16	Evanstonians	198	18.4	5.81
Songe	89	6.2	3.07	Songe	91	18.2	5.80
Hanunoo	49	7.7	3.00	N. U. students*	29	18.7	5.72
Bete	75	3.2	2.72	Hanunoo	52	15.3	5.46
Suku	61	2.8	2.69	S. A. Europeans*	42	15.0	5.33
Bushmen*	36	1.7	2.28	Zulu	35	9.5	4.80
S. A. mineboys*	60	1.4	2.23	Bete	79	9.8	4.62
Sander-parallelogram illusion				*Horizontal-vertical illusion* ($\ulcorner$)			
N. U. students*	28	19.9	3.54	Dahomeans†	63	19.2	6.52
Evanstonians	196	19.1	3.27	Toro	98	19.5	6.38
Ijaw School†	53	18.3	3.15	Banyankole	291	17.0	6.15
S. A. Europeans*	42	17.4	2.98	Ijaw School†	57	18.4	6.02
Zulu	67	18.5	2.97	Suku	69	9.0	5.74
Senegalese	198	15.7	2.90	S. A. mineboys*	69	11.5	5.71
Fang	96	17.3	2.86	Songe	95	8.9	5.60
Ijaw	98	16.9	2.74	Ijaw	97	8.9	5.55
Banyankole	262	17.3	2.69	Fang	105	9.1	5.49
Dahomeans†	58	16.0	2.55	Bushmen*	39	8.6	5.15
Hanunoo	52	13.5	2.52	Zulu	74	7.8	5.03
Toro	105	14.3	2.49	Evanstonians	203	7.2	4.90
Songe	97	14.7	2.41	N. U. students*	30	7.2	4.83
Bete	86	12.8	2.37	Hanunoo	53	6.3	4.70
Suku	91	9.7	2.14	S. A. Europeans*	42	5.0	4.67
S. A. mineboys*	71	8.7	2.06	Senegalese	168	6.0	4.45
(Bushmen not administered this set)				Bete	88	2.0	3.81

*Adults only.   †Children only.

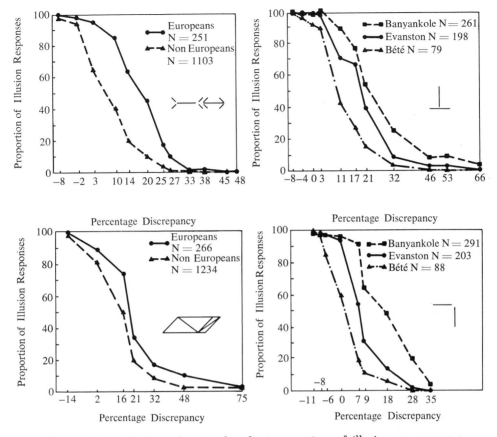

FIGURE 1 Psychophysical ogives based on proportions of illusion responses to item of varying percentage discrepancy. Upper left: Müller-Lyer illusion responses plotted for Europeans (three samples combined) and non-Europeans (all other samples combined). Lower left: Sander Parallelogram illusion responses plotted for same two combined groups. Upper right: Horizontal-vertical (⊥) illusion responses by one European and two non-European samples. Lower right: Horizontal-vertical (⌐) illusion responses by same three samples. These graphs are all based on internally consistent cases only.

chophysical ogives were then constructed from these proportions and points of subjective equality (PSE) determined graphically. Table 1 contains PSE scores and mean number of illusion-responses for all samples on each of the illusions. (The scores shown in Table 1 were computed for internally consistent cases only, and, except where otherwise noted, the groups consisted of children and adults combined. In samples containing both children and adults, children typically had higher means and PSE's. Combining children and adults as in Table 1 tends to attenuate some intersample differences.) Figure 1 contains

four sets of ogives which illustrate (i) the lesser susceptibility of the combined non-European samples as compared with the combined European samples to the Müller-Lyer and Sander Parallelogram illusions, and (ii) the greater susceptibility to the two Horizontal-vertical illusions shown by one non-European sample group as compared to one European sample, and the lesser susceptibility of another non-European sample. Examples of the four illusions are also presented in Figure 1.

Cross-cultural comparisons made over a half-century ago by Rivers (4) also indicated that two non-Western peoples were simultaneously less susceptible to the Müller-Lyer illusion and more susceptible to the Horizontal-vertical illusion than were a group of English respondents. Since the non-European samples uniformly perform better than Europeans on one type of illusion and generally worse on the others, any explanation based on presumed contrasting characteristics of "primitive" and "civilized" peoples is difficult to maintain. Rather, evidence seems to point to cross-cultural differences in visual inference systems learned in response to different ecological and cultural factors in the visual environment. In a monograph now in preparation which reports the present study in detail (5), Rivers' findings as well as our own are shown to be in accord with an empiricistic, functionalistic interpretation which relates visual response habits to cultural and ecological factors in the visual environment.

An example of a cultural factor which seems relevant is the prevalence of rectangularity in the visual environment, a factor which seems to be related to the tendency to interpret acute and obtuse angles on a two-dimensional surface as representative of rectangular objects in three-dimensional space. This inference habit is much more valid in highly carpentered, urban, European environments, and could enhance, or even produce, the Müller-Lyer and Sander Parallelogram illusions. This interpretation is consistent with traditional explanation of these illusions. Less clearly, the Horizontal-vertical illusion can perhaps be understood as the result of an inference habit of interpreting vertical lines as extensions away from one in the horizontal plane. Such an inference habit would have more validity for those living in open, flat terrain than in rain forests or in jungles. An examination of such factors, and thorough examination of alternative explanations of our findings, are contained in the forthcoming monograph. Whether or not the correct environmental features have been isolated,

the cross-cultural differences in susceptibility to geometric illusions seem best understood as symptomatic of functional differences in learned visual inference habits.

References

1. HERSKOVITS, M. J., D. T. CAMPBELL, and M. H. SEGALL. *Materials for a Cross-Cultural Study of Perception* (Program of African Studies. Northwestern University, Evanston, Ill., 1956).

2. GUTTMAN, L. "The Cornell technique for scale and intensity analysis," *Educ. Psychol. Measurement* 7, 247 (1947). In the present study a Guttman error was defined as an illusion-produced response to one item combined with a non-illusion response to an item of lesser percentage discrepancy. Percentage-discrepancy refers to the percentage by which the segment that is usually underestimated is actually longer than the other comparison segment in a particular illusion drawing. A choice of the usually over-estimated segment is termed an illusion-produced response. Thus, a perfectly internally consistent protocol would consist of illusion-produced responses to one or more items, followed by non-illusion responses to all items of greater percentage discrepancy within a figure set.

3. SCHEFFÉ, H. "A method for judging all contrasts in the analysis of variance," *Biometrika* 40, 87 (1953). It is generally agreed that the Scheffé procedure is the most conservative of several available techniques for making postmortem, nonindependent comparisons. If our use of this procedure has led to any errors in conclusions other than the usual α-level type error, such errors can only be failures to reject the null hypothesis when it should have been rejected (type 2 errors). We assume the heightened risk of type 2 errors in order that confidence in the obtained significant differences may be enhanced.

4. RIVERS, W. H. R., "Vision," in *Reports of the Cambridge Anthropological Expedition to the Torres Straits*, A. C. Haddon, Ed. (Cambridge, The University Press, 1901), vol. 2, part 1; *Brit. J. Psychol.* 1905, *1*, 321.

5. SEGALL, M. H., D. T. CAMPBELL, and M.

J. Herskovits, "The influence of culture on perception," in preparation. This report includes an examination of age differences as well as total sample differences. Included also is a development of the theoretical arguments suggested here, presented in the context of a review of the literature bearing on the nativist-empiricist controversy, and a discussion of the significance of these data for the anthropological concept of cultural relativism.

Transfer in Perceptual Learning Following Stimulus Predifferentiation*

HENRY C. ELLIS   DOUGLAS G. MULLER

University of New Mexico

2 experiments on stimulus predifferentiation were conducted to test the acquired distinctiveness of cues and differentiation hypotheses of perceptual learning. In the first, 240 Ss were given a recognition test following stimulus predifferentiation training. Observation training yielded superior recognition of 6-point shapes and distinctiveness pretraining yielded superior recognition of 24-point shapes. The former result was consistent with differentiation theory and the latter with acquired distinctiveness. In the second, 30 Ss received stimulus predifferentiation training followed by a discriminative transfer task. Distinctiveness pretraining yielded greater positive transfer than observation, a result consistent with acquired distinctiveness of cues.

The hypothesis of acquired distinctiveness of cues (Goss, 1955; Miller and Dollard, 1941) states that attaching a response such as a verbal label to a stimulus tends to increase the distinctiveness of that stimulus as a result of the addition of response-produced cues. Presumably, different verbal labels attached to similar stimuli will increase the distinctiveness of the stimuli, whereas similar or identical verbal labels attached to different stimuli will reduce the distinctiveness of the stimuli. An alternative conception of the perceptual learning process has been proposed by Gibson and

* *Journal of Experimental Psychology*, 1964, vol. 68, pp. 388–395. The research was supported by National Science Foundation Grant G-23427.

Thanks are due to James M. Vanderplas for his review of the manuscript, and to Thomas L. Bennett and Dieter Jahns who assisted in the conduct of the study.

Gibson (1955), that of differentiation, which contends that organisms learn to distinguish various components which are inherent in the stimulus; perceptual learning consists of responding to various stimuli not previously responded to rather than adding response-produced cues to stimuli. As Vanderplas (1963) has noted, the Miller-Dollard view implies a dependence on the nature of the labeling response whereas the Gibson view implies no such dependence. Several experiments designed to test deductions from the distinctiveness of cues hypothesis have failed to confirm it. Similarly, the differentiation hypothesis has not found unequivocal support.

Studies of transfer of predifferentiation training (e.g., Goss and Greenfeld, 1958) have frequently indicated that learning verbal labels to stimuli facilitates performance in some subsequent task when that task requires making new differential responses to the same stimuli. In contrast, experiments which have employed more direct tests of improvement in recognition or discrimination following practice in labeling have generally yielded negative results (Arnoult, 1953; Campbell and Freeman, 1955; Ellis, Bessemer, Devine, and Trafton, 1962; Robinson, 1955), in that no facilitation in these tasks has occurred as a result of distinctiveness labeling practice per se.

Conceivably, whether or not verbal labeling of stimuli improves subsequent discriminative behavior over that improvement associated with observation practice may depend upon the nature of the criterion task employed. In short, practice in verbal labeling of stimuli may be superior to observation practice when the criterion task requires new differential responses to be made to the stimuli. On the other hand, when the task is one of recognition or discrimination or more generally, one which does *not* require making new differential responses to the stimuli, labeling per se may not result in improvement. A similar view has been expressed by Vanderplas (1963).

Since the results of both types of experiments have been employed to support either the hypothesis of acquired distinctiveness or that of differentiation, it seemed desirable to conduct an experiment in which the effect of practice in labeling stimuli would be determined on both discriminative motor transfer and recognition tasks. By controlling the features of the predifferentiation task (e.g., nature of the stimuli, response labels, amount and type of practice) it is possible to determine if the divergencies cited above are dependent upon the criterion task itself.

It is also possible, however, that failure to obtain improvement in recognition following verbal labeling practice is due to other than task variables. For example,

Arnoult (1956) found that for very short periods of practice, Ss given labeling practice were superior to those given observation practice in a subsequent test of shape recognition. Vanderplas and Garvin (1959) have shown that shape complexity and association value of random shapes interact with practice in their effect on shape recognition. In view of these alternatives, it was considered desirable to conduct an initial factorial experiment to determine the independent and interactive effects of shape complexity, amount of practice, and type of predifferentiation training on shape recognition. Shape complexity and amount of practice were selected as variables because of their known interactive effect on shape recognition, and three types of training were employed to test the hypotheses of acquired distinctiveness, equivalence, and differentiation. The second experiment was designed to determine the effects of task variables, i.e., to compare the effects of predifferentiation on recognition vs. a motor-switching task.

Experiment I

METHOD

Experimental Design.   Ten Ss were assigned at random to each of 24 conditions of the experiment. Two levels of stimulus complexity (6- or 24-point random shapes), three types of predifferentiation training (distinctiveness, observation, or equivalence practice), and four levels of practice (2, 4, 8, or 16 trials) were employed. A total of 240 volunteer university students served as Ss.

The experiment was conducted in two parts: In the first part (predifferentiation training) Ss either learned to associate a meaningful response to each of a set of eight random shapes or they were given practice in observing and discriminating among the same set of shapes. Following predifferentiation training, Ss were given a multiple shape recognition test in which they attempted to select from a group of shapes those shapes experienced during predifferentiation training.

Stimulus Shapes and Apparatus. A list of eight random shapes was selected from both the 6-point shapes and the 24-point shapes scaled by Vanderplas and Garvin (1959). Table 1 shows the list of shapes employed and their corresponding labels for the distinctiveness and equivalence training groups. The shapes were photographed on 35-mm. film strip and presented with a conventional projector (SVE Instructor). Stimulus presentation was controlled by a Foringer self-recycling timer.

Predifferentiation Training. The Ss received one of three types of predifferentiation training: distinctiveness, equivalence, or observation practice. The Ss given distinctiveness practice were required to learn relevant meaningful labels to each of eight random shapes. The labels were obtained from a preliminary scaling study in which 30 Ss were shown the shapes and asked to state "what they looked like." The most frequent response given to a particular shape (modal label) was selected for this experiment; modal labels were employed since it was assumed that they would tend to maximize the distinctiveness of the stimuli.

Similarly, Ss given equivalence practice were given an equal number of predifferentiation training trials; the label "wide" was learned for four shapes and the label "narrow" was learned for the remaining four shapes. This procedure was analogous to that of Robinson (1955) and Ellis et al. (1962) in defining equivalence practice.

The Ss given observation practice were given the same number of predifferentiation trials except that they were given no labels to attach to the stimuli and were instructed only to inspect the shapes and differentiate among them. For the labeling groups (distinctiveness and equivalence) each stimulus shape was exposed for a 4-sec. period consisting of a 2-sec. anticipation interval and a 2-sec. simultaneous presentation with the response label. Labels were pronounced by S; correct anticipations and errors were recorded. The observation group observed the shapes for the same time interval as did the labeling groups. All Ss were tested individually.

Recognition Test. Following prediffer-

TABLE 1

List of Vanderplas and Garvin Shapes and Corresponding Labels for the Distinctiveness and Equivalence Groups

6-POINT SHAPE NO.	LABEL		24-POINT SHAPE NO.	LABEL	
	DISTINCTIVENESS	EQUIVALENCE		DISTINCTIVENESS	EQUIVALENCE
11	Mountain	Wide	10	Tree	Narrow
12	Fish	Narrow	11	Mountain	Wide
13	Rocket	Narrow	12	Bird	Narrow
14	House	Wide	13	Nun	Narrow
15	Boat	Wide	14	Crab	Wide
17	Mouth	Narrow	15	Horseman	Wide
18	Arrow	Narrow	16	Dragon	Narrow
20	Bird	Wide	17	Spider	Wide

entiation training, all Ss were immediately given a recognition test which consisted of presenting S with 16 cards, each containing a set of five shapes mounted in a row. Eight of the cards contained a prototype, a shape learned or observed during predifferentiation, and the remaining four shapes on each card were variations of the prototype. On the remaining eight cards all five shapes were variations of the prototype. Variations were constructed according to a method described by Vanderplas and Garvin (1959). The Ss were instructed to point to a shape if they thought it was one which they learned or observed during predifferentiation training; if they thought that none of the shapes were ones they experienced initially, they were instructed to say "none." The Ss were given no longer than 30 sec. for each card. Five types of responses were recorded: SOP, correct selection of a prototype shape; SOV, incorrect selection of a variation when a prototype was present; IR, incorrect rejection of shapes when one of them was a prototype; SIV, incorrect selection of variation when all shapes were variations; and CR, correct rejection of all shapes when all were variations.

RESULTS

Original Learning. Table 2 shows the results of original learning on the predifferentiation task and indicates that 16 practice trials were adequate to ensure near mastery of the paired-associate task for both the distinctiveness and equivalence training groups. The mean number of correct anticipations ranged from a low of 2.5 after 2 trials to a high of 7.9 after 16 trials. The table also shows an initial difference in rate of learning favoring the equivalence groups, which reflects the fact that this group was required to learn only two response labels, as opposed to the eight labels required of the distinctiveness group. No test of the significance of this trend was made, however, since the data of primary interest were the scores on the recognition test.

Recognition Performance. The basic data obtained in the recognition test, the number of correct recognitions (SOP responses), are shown in Table 3. The table shows that the ,observation group tended to make more correct recognitions of simple shapes than did either group receiving labeling practice. A clear trend of increased recognition with increased practice is evident and the groups retained their same relative ranks with increase in practice.

Table 3 shows that with *complex* shapes, the distinctiveness group makes more correct recognitions than the observation groups after 2, 4, or 8 practice trials. In short, if labels are attached to stimuli of high complexity, recognition is superior to that provided by observation practice; if labels are attached to stimuli of low com-

TABLE 2

Mean Correct Anticipations during Predifferentiation Training for Labeling Groups

TYPE OF TRAINING	SHAPE COMPLEXITY	TRIALS			
		2	4	8	16
Distinctiveness	6-point	2.5	5.5	6.9	7.4
	24-point	2.8	4.7	6.5	7.7
Equivalence	6-point	5.7	6.3	7.6	7.9
	24-point	4.4	5.5	6.7	6.2

plexity, recognition is poorer than that provided by observation practice. This finding suggests an interaction between the effects of shape complexity and type of training, an interpretation which is supported by the significant C × T interaction (see Table 4: $F = 3.95$). Both the effects of amount of practice and type of practice on prototype recognition were reliable.

Table 3 shows the results of the remaining four recognition tests. The mean number of selection of variations when the prototype was present (SOV), incorrect re-

TABLE 3

Mean Number of Correct (SOP), Incorrect Selections when Prototype Was Present (SOV), Incorrect Rejections (IR), Incorrect Selections when All Shapes Were Variations (SIV), and Correct Rejections (CR) for Each Condition of the Experiment

TYPE OF TRAINING	PRACTICE TRIALS	RESPONSE TYPES				
		SOP	SOV	IR	SIV	CR
6-POINT SHAPES						
Distinctiveness	2	2.8	2.2	3.0	4.3	3.7
	4	3.5	2.7	1.8	3.6	4.4
	8	4.9	1.3	1.8	3.3	4.7
	16	5.7	0.9	1.4	2.3	5.7
Observation	2	3.3	2.1	2.6	4.1	3.9
	4	3.9	2.0	2.1	3.1	4.9
	8	5.8	1.0	1.2	2.9	5.1
	16	6.1	1.0	0.9	2.3	5.7
Equivalence	2	1.9	3.4	2.7	4.1	3.9
	4	2.1	3.0	2.9	4.0	4.0
	8	3.7	2.1	2.2	3.4	4.6
	16	4.0	2.4	1.6	4.5	3.5
24-POINT SHAPES						
Distinctiveness	2	2.6	2.3	3.1	4.1	3.9
	4	4.0	1.1	2.9	2.7	5.3
	8	4.7	0.9	2.4	1.9	6.1
	16	6.3	0.5	1.2	1.9	6.1
Observation	2	2.0	2.4	3.6	3.2	4.8
	4	3.1	1.9	3.0	2.7	5.3
	8	3.5	2.5	2.0	3.8	4.2
	16	6.7	0.5	0.8	1.5	6.5
Equivalence	2	2.5	2.7	2.8	3.6	4.4
	4	2.1	3.1	2.8	3.6	4.4
	8	3.2	2.3	2.5	3.2	4.8
	16	5.2	1.2	1.6	3.3	4.7

jections (IR), selection of variations when all shapes were variations (SIV), and correct rejections (CR) are shown. Separate analyses of variance were performed for each response type and the results are shown in Table 4.[1]

From Table 3 it may be seen that practice leads to a reduction of IR responses for all types of predifferentiation training and a reduction of SIV responses for the distinctiveness and observation groups. Similarly, practice leads to an increase of CR responses for the distinctiveness and observation groups. No systematic changes occur in SIV or CR responses with increasing amounts of equivalence training. The analyses of variance resulted in a significant variance for practice effects for all response types (Table 4). Table 3 also indicates that the distinctiveness and observation groups tend to make fewer SOV responses to either 6- or 24-point shapes; this finding is supported by the significant F for type of training (see Table 4: $F = 9.07$).

Experiment II

The purpose of Exp. II was to determine if positive transfer to an instrumental motor task would occur following practice in labeling shapes under conditions in which the same labeling practice, as compared with observation practice, did *not* lead to superior recognition.

METHOD

Experimental Design. Fifteen Ss were assigned at random to each of the two conditions of the experiment. One group received distinctiveness training and the other received observation training, identical to that given in Exp. I. Following

[1] No analysis of variance on the CR responses is reported. The CR responses are determined by the number of SIV responses and both must sum to eight. Since CR responses are fixed, an analysis of variance on CR responses yields the same results as an analysis of variance on SIV responses.

predifferentiation training, Ss were given a criterion task which required them to learn to press a switch for each of the eight shapes they had labeled or observed.

Conditions of the Experiment. The Ss labeled or observed only the 6-point shapes employed in Exp. I. These shapes were used because the distinctiveness labeling group was inferior to the observation group in the recognition of 6-point shapes (see Table 3). Since these findings were typical of those of other Es, they were used for purposes of comparison with findings with the motor transfer task. The same apparatus, procedure, labels, etc., employed in the predifferentiation part of Exp. I were used in the predifferentiation part of Exp. II. The Ss were given 16 practice trials.

Instrumental Transfer Task. Following predifferentiation training, all Ss were immediately given a transfer task which required them to learn to press one of eight switches located on a response panel for each of the eight shapes they had previously experienced. Each stimulus shape was exposed for 2 sec. and S was instructed to press the switch as rapidly as he could. All Ss received 15 trial blocks of training; a block consisted of a single presentation of each of eight shapes which were presented in random order. The Ss were given confirmation of their correct responses by the appearance of a green light; an incorrect response was followed by no signal. Both correct responses and latency, the time between presentation of the shape and S's response, were recorded.

RESULTS

Performance on the Motor Transfer Task. Inspection of Figure 1 reveals that Ss given distinctiveness practice in labeling 6-point shapes are superior in acquisition of a motor-switching task compared with Ss given practice in observing the shapes. After Trial 3 the distinctiveness group was clearly superior and retained its superi-

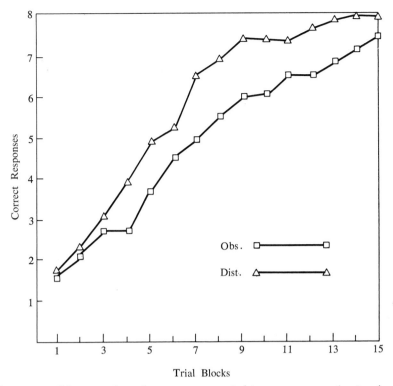

FIGURE 1   Mean number of correct motor-switching responses to 6-point shapes following predifferentiation training.

ority throughout the remaining trials. An analysis of variance applied to the transfer data indicated that the difference between the two groups was reliable ($F = 6.53$; $p < .05$).

Latency. Examination of the latency data revealed that Ss given distinctiveness practice showed a consistent overall tendency to respond faster than did Ss given observation practice. An analysis of variance applied to the latency data, however, did not reveal a significant difference between the two groups.

Discussion

The findings of the recognition experiment indicate that although shape complexity itself was not a significant variable in affecting the number of correct recognitions, it did interact with type of predifferentiation training. Specifically, the re-

sults indicated that attaching distinctive verbal labels to complex shapes facilitated their subsequent recognition whereas distinctiveness labeling practice with simple shapes did not facilitate their subsequent recognition, when compared with control groups given practice in observing and discriminating among the shapes. The results with complex shapes lend some support to the hypothesis of acquired distinctiveness of cues based upon distinctive response-produced cues being added to the stimuli. In contrast, the results with simple shapes are at least consistent with differentiation theory.

The problem remains as to how to explain the interactive effects of shape complexity and type of training on shape recognition. A tentative explanation is given below based upon some assumptions about labeling practice and stimulus familiarity. Let us assume that when S learns to attach a label to a simple shape, there are

TABLE 4

Analysis of Variance of Scores on Recognition Test for Each Response Type

SOURCE	DF	RESPONSE TYPE			
		SOP	SOV	IR	SIV
		F	F	F	F
Complexity (C)	1	.55	1.12	4.22	5.53
Practice (P)	3	47.23***	9.32***	16.71***	5.37**
Type of training (T)	2	16.10***	9.07***	1.31	4.64**
C × P	3	3.34*	1.45	.90	.26
C × T	2	3.95*	1.60	.85	.30
P × T	6	.89	.26	.90	2.08
C × P × T	6	.55	.00	.32	.81
Error (MS)	216	(2.46)	(2.69)	(1.99)	(3.09)

* $p < .05$.
** $p < .01$.
*** $p < .001$.

relatively few cues which require differentiation. Therefore, S does not have to expend great effort in scanning the shape and differentiating cues. In addition, if we assume that simple shapes are more familiar than complex shapes, then S will be able to relate more readily the simple shape to some available concept. Thus, the effect of labeling practice on the recognition of simple shapes, as compared with observation practice, would be minimal since the simple shapes are already relatively distinctive and familiar. On the other hand, complex shapes have many more aspects to which S must attend, and are less readily or easily related to some concept. The effect of a label then, if relevant, is to provide a concept to which the shape may be related. In the absence of any immediate labels, as is the case with observation practice, S would be required to select concepts to which the shape could be related. This would require more effort and time on the part of Ss given observation practice and would explain why Ss given observation practice would be inferior in tasks of complex shape recognition as compared with Ss given labeling practice. Finally, this approach would predict that after

relatively extensive practice, Ss given observation practice with complex shapes would do as well in recognition tests as Ss given labeling practice because they would have had sufficient opportunity to acquire a label to attach to the shape. This latter assumption is consistent with the fact that although labeling practice facilitated the recognition of complex shapes after 2, 4, and 8 trials, the labeling practice group performed approximately the same as the observation practice group after 16 trials.

The results of equivalence practice are consistent for both simple and complex shapes. In both instances, Ss who received equivalence pretraining made fewer correct recognitions than either the distinctiveness or observation groups. These findings appear consistent with the hypothesis of acquired equivalence of cues and are consistent with those obtained in a study of tactual recognition (Ellis et al., 1962).

The results of the second experiment reveal that practice in giving stimuli distinctive verbal labels leads to greater positive transfer in a discriminative motor task than does observation of the stimuli alone. This finding can be interpreted as being consistent with the hypothesis of acquired distinctiveness of cues; however, the fact that the discriminability of the stimuli was not similarly enhanced, as measured by a recognition test, raises some doubt about this interpretation. It seems equally reasonable to suggest that enhanced positive transfer to an instrumental task could occur not only as a result of increased distinctiveness of the stimuli, but also as a result of increased availability of motor and other responses. In other words, learning to attach verbal responses to stimuli may facilitate the attachment of other types of responses to these stimuli, but may *not* necessarily produce increased distinctiveness of the stimuli. In order to determine if positive transfer to an instrumental motor task following labeling practice is to be interpreted as due to increased distinctiveness of the stimuli, or to increased availability of responses, or both, it is necessary to design an experiment in which either stimulus distinctiveness or response availability is controlled. The findings of the present experiment indicate only that an explanation of the positive transfer findings in terms of a response availability hypothesis is as reasonable as a distinctiveness of cues hypothesis.

References

ARNOULT, M. D. Transfer of predifferentiation training in simple and multiple shape discrimination. *J. exp. Psychol.,* 1953, 45, 401–409.

ARNOULT, M. D. Recognition of shapes following paired-associates pretraining. In G. Finch and F. Cameron (Eds.), *Symposium on Air Force human engineering, personnel, and training research.* (NAS-NRC Publ. No. 455) Washington, D. C.: National Academy of Sciences-National Research Council, 1956. pp. 1–9.

CAMPBELL, V., and J. T. FREEMAN. Some functions of experimentally-induced language in perceptual learning. *Percept. mot. Skills,* 1955, 1, 71–79.

ELLIS, H. C., D. W. BESSEMER, J. DEVINE, C. TRAFTON. Recognition of random tactual shapes following predifferentiation training. *Percept. mot. Skills,* 1962, 10, 99–102.

GIBSON, J. J., and E. J. GIBSON. Perceptual learning: Differentiation or enrichment? *Psychol. Rev.,* 1955, 62, 32–41.

GOSS, A. E. A stimulus-response analysis of the interaction of cue-producing and mediating responses. *Psychol. Rev.,* 1955, 62, 20–31.

GOSS, A. E., and N. GREENFELD. Transfer to a motor task as influenced by conditions and degree of prior discrimination training. *J. exp. Psychol.,* 1958, 55, 258–269.

MILLER, N. E., and J. DOLLARD. *Social learning and imitation.* New Haven: Yale Univer. Press, 1941.

ROBINSON, J. S. The effect of learning labels for stimuli on their later discrimination. *J. exp. Psychol.,* 1955, 49, 112–115.

VANDERPLAS, J. M. Associative processes and task relations in perceptual learning. *Percept. mot. Skills,* 1963, 16, 501–509.

VANDERPLAS, J. M., and E. A. GARVIN. Complexity, association value, and practice as factors in shape recognition following paired-associates training. *J. exp. Psychol.,* 1959, 57, 155–163.

Improvement of Visual and Tactual Form Discrimination*

ANNE D. PICK
Macalester College

A discrimination-learning situation and subsequent transfer tests were used to investigate 2 hypotheses about improvement in discrimination: a "schema" hypothesis and a "distinctive feature" hypothesis. 1 visual and 2 tactual discrimination experiments were conducted. Results suggested the superiority of the distinctive feature hypothesis, at least under conditions of a simultaneous comparison, for accounting for children's improvement of discrimination of the letter-like forms used as material.

Gibson, Gibson, Pick, and Osser (1962) demonstrated that children between the ages of 4 yr. and 8 yr. improve in their ability to make visual discriminations among letterlike forms. The present study sought to determine if some kind of learning can produce such improvement in discrimination. The first experiment reported here explored this question with respect to visual discrimination, and the second and third experiments extended the investigation to tactual discrimination.

Two general hypotheses about the nature of learning during improvement of discrimination can be identified. One can

* *Journal of Experimental Psychology*, 1965, vol. 69, pp. 331–339. This research was part of a doctoral dissertation at Cornell University and was supported in part by an interdepartmental grant to Cornell University from the United States Office of Education, Department of Health, Education, and Welfare. The author is grateful to Eleanor J. Gibson under whose direction the research was conducted and to Paul Jenson and Herbert L. Pick, Jr. for critically reading the manuscript. The principals and teachers of South Hill School in Ithaca, New York, and University of Minnesota Elementary School, Tuttle School, Marcy School, and Pratt School in Minneapolis, Minnesota were generous in their cooperation.

be loosely termed a "schema" hypothesis, and is suggested in discussions of Bruner (1957a, 1957b), Vernon (1952, 1955), and in a recent book on perceptual development by Solley and Murphy (1960). Although these investigators deal primarily with identification behavior, i.e., recognition and categorizing behavior, their discussions implicate discrimination behavior as well. According to this point of view, discrimination and identification involve matching sensory data or "cues" about objects to prototypes or models of the objects which have been built up through repeated experience with the objects and "stored" in memory. Improvement in discrimination would involve first constructing schemata or models of the objects to be discriminated, and then matching the sensory data to the models so as to identify them as "same" or "different." Practice with objects to be discriminated, then, would enable S to build up and refine the appropriate schemata.

A second general hypothesis about improvement in discrimination, a "distinctive feature" hypothesis, is suggested by the

Gibsons and their colleagues (Gibson & Gibson, 1955; Gibson et al., 1962). It utilizes the concept of distinctive features introduced by Jacobson and Halle (1956) in a discussion of phoneme characteristics. Distinctive features can be thought of as dimensions of difference which distinguish and provide contrasts among objects. The hypothesis developed from the Gibsons' work is that improvement of discrimination consists of learning the distinctive features of the objects to be discriminated. The function of practice, according to this point of view, is to enable S to respond to an increasing number of stimulus variables and to discover which of these variables are "critical" in the sense that they serve to distinguish between one object and another.

The physical conditions resulting in improvement of discrimination do not *necessarily* differ for these two hypotheses. Both would predict that such improvement will occur as a function of practice with the objects to be discriminated. Hence a transfer design can be employed to determine the extent to which prototype learning, distinctive feature learning, or both will occur during training. Specifically, Ss could be presented with initially undifferentiated stimulus forms and trained to discriminate among them. In a transfer task they could then try to discriminate among stimulus forms which *either* differ from each other in the same dimensions as those which they learned to discriminate *or* which have the same prototypes as those which they learned to discriminate. Differential performance in these two transfer conditions should shed light on the function of prototype learning and distinctive feature learning in improvement of discrimination. Since the two processes are not mutually exclusive, relative transfer in the two conditions described can be determined by comparing them to a control condition in which both the prototypes and dimensions of difference of the forms differ from those used in training.

Experiment I

METHOD

SUBJECTS

The Ss were 60 kindergarteners. Each S was randomly assigned to one of three equal transfer groups. There were an approximately equal number of boys and girls among the 20 Ss in each group.

MATERIALS

The stimulus forms were letter-like forms of the kind used in the developmental study of Gibson et al. (1962). The forms, approximately 1 × 1 in were black and were mounted on rectangular white cardboard cards 3 × 4 in.

There were six standard forms and six different transformations of each of the standard forms. These transformations were one change of a straight line to a curve, two changes of straight lines to curves, a right-left reversal, a 45° rotation, a perspective transformation equivalent to a 45° backward tilt, and a 25% increase in size. The standard forms and six transformations for each are shown in Fig. 1.

PROCEDURE

Training. The training procedure was the same for all Ss. The S was seated in front of a small table on which a stand similar to a lectern was placed. Three standard forms were placed on this stand and a pack of cards containing two copies of each standard and three transformations of each standard was spread out in front of S on the table. The S was instructed to look carefully at each of the 15 cards and decide whether it was exactly the same as one of the standards or if it was different. When S found one which was exactly the same as one of the standards, he was instructed to give it to E. When S had made a judgment about every card in the pack (i.e., finished one trial), E shuffled the cards and the procedure was repeated until

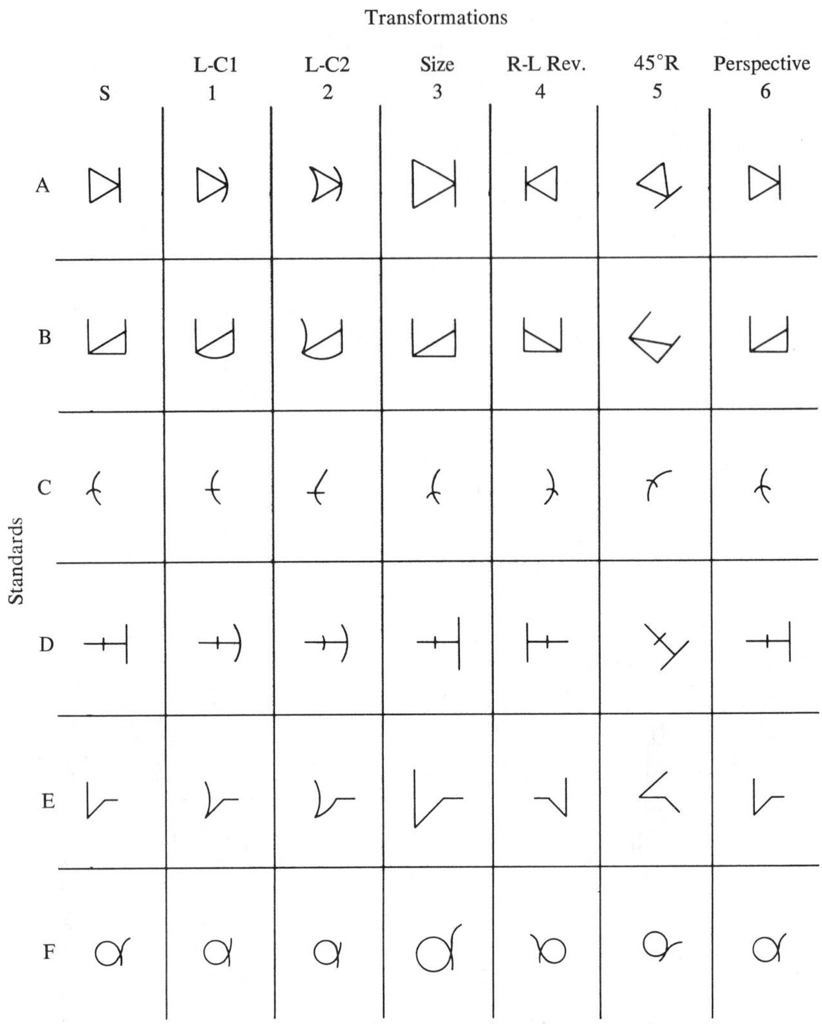

FIGURE 1   Standards and transformations used in Experiment I

S reached a criterion of one perfect trial, i.e., gave E only the two copies of each standard. Confusion errors (transformations which S indicated were exact copies of a standard) were recorded. A correction procedure, in which E told S whether each judgment was right or wrong, was used on every trial except the first.

Before the first training trial, a pretraining practice trial with real letters and correction procedure was carried out in order to acquaint Ss with the task and to ensure that they understood that only forms which were "exactly the same" as the standard should be given to E.

Transfer. Following the criterion training trial, the transfer procedure was carried out. The task was the same as in training but only one trial was given and there was no correction given. Confusion errors were recorded as before.

The Ss were divided into three transfer groups in a predetermined arbitrary order. These groups differed in terms of the particular forms used in the transfer trial. Group C provided a base line with which to compare the transfer performance of the other two groups. This group received three standards and three transformations all of which were different from the ones used in training. For example, if in training these Ss had learned to distinguish copies of Standards A, B, and C from line to curve and size transformations of these standards, then their transfer task was to distinguish copies of Standards D, E, and F from rotation, reversal, and perspective transformations.

Group EI reflected the extent to which standard or prototype learning had occurred during training. This group received the same standards as in training, but three new transformations of these standards. For example, if in training these Ss learned to distinguish Standards A, B, and C from line to curve and size transformations of these standards, then their transfer task was to distinguish these *same* standards from reversal, rotation, and perspective transformations.

Group EII reflected the extent to which distinctive feature learning had occurred during training. This group received three new standards, but the same three types of transformations of these standards as those with which they dealt during training. For example, if in training these Ss learned to distinguish Standards A, B, and C from among reversal, rotation, and perspective transformations of these standards, then, in the transfer trial, their task was to distinguish Standards D, E, and F from reversal, rotation, and perspective transformations of these standards.

In order to balance the design for possible differences in difficulty of discriminating specific combinations of standards and transformations, four subgroups of Ss were used in the training condition. Each was trained with a different combination of standards and transformations. One had Standards A, B, and C with line to curve and size transformations. Another had Standards D, E, and F and these same transformations. A third subgroup was trained with Standards A, B, and C and reversal, rotation, and perspective transformations, and a fourth had Standards D, E, and F and these transformations.

There were also, of course, 4 subgroups within each of the 3 transfer groups since the combination of forms used in transfer for a given S depended on the combination of forms used in training. Thus there were 12 transfer subgroups with five Ss in each.

RESULTS

TRAINING

Differences between the means of the groups in number of confusion errors made on the first trial and in number of trials to criterion were analyzed using t tests. No differences approached the .05 level of significance and hence the null hypothesis that these groups were from the same population could be accepted.

TRANSFER

Confusion errors in the transfer trial constituted the main data of the experiment. Table 1 shows the errors made in the transfer trial by each of the 12 subgroups and for the three transfer groups with subgroups combined.

An analysis of variance was performed on the data for the 12 subgroups. Only the effect of transfer groups was significant,

TABLE 1

Confusion Errors in Transfer Trial
for the 12 Subgroups

GROUP	TRANSFORMATIONS				TOTAL
	T 123		T 456		
	STANDARDS				
	SABC	SDEF	SABC	SDEF	
EI	12	21	17	19	69
EII	11	6	10	12	39
C	23	21	32	25	101

Note.—Column headings indicate the particular combination of standards and transformations used in the transfer trial. $n = 5$ in each subgroup.

F (2, 48) $=$ 12.69, $p <$ .001. Thus the differences among the three experimental groups obtain regardless of subgroups, i.e., regardless of the particular combination of standards and transformations used.

The differences between the three groups in transfer errors were analyzed with t tests. The three groups were significantly different from each other with a probability level of less than .01 with a two-tailed test.

DISCUSSION

The results of this experiment suggest that learning distinctive features may be a significant component of improvement in visual discrimination of letter-like forms. The Ss who in the transfer trial dealt with forms which they had never seen before but which varied from each other in familiar ways (the EII group) made the fewest confusion errors. This suggests that during the training trials Ss were learning how the forms varied from each other as they improved in their ability to discriminate among them.

The fact that Group EI, the group having familiar standards and new transformations, was superior to the control group suggests that prototype learning also occurred during training. However, the clear superiority of Group EII implies that such learning may not be essential to improvement in discriminations of this sort.

Experiment II

The purpose of this second experiment was to investigate the generality of the results of the previous experiment for improvement in tactual discrimination. Adaptations of the procedure and materials of the previous experiment were made in order to provide appropriate conditions for studying improvement in tactual discrimination. These adaptations are noted below. The basic method and design of this experiment were the same as in the previous one.

METHOD

SUBJECTS

The Ss were 72 first graders. First-grade children were used as Ss because pilot work indicated the task was better suited to this age group than to the kindergarteners used previously.

MATERIALS

The stimulus forms were metal reproductions of some of the letter-like forms used in the previous experiment. The forms (1 $\times$ 1 in) were made by an engraving process and were raised lines on a smooth square metal background about $1\frac{3}{4} \times 1\frac{3}{4}$ in.

There were four standard forms and 10 transformations of each: one, two, and three changes of lines to curves, a 25% increase in size, two topological transformations: break and close, a right-left reversal, 45° and 90° rotations, and a perspective transformation equivalent to a 45° backward tilt. The standard forms and their transformations are shown in Fig. 2.

PROCEDURE

Training. The S was seated at a small table on which a form board was placed. This plywood board 12 $\times$ 15 in with a raised block in the middle, was used to display the forms in front of S. The raised block was covered with "velcro" as were the backs of the metal forms and the forms could thus be made to adhere to the block for presentation to S. The S was blindfolded and a standard form and one of its transformations were placed on the board. The standard was always presented on the left and the transformation on the right.

The S's dominant hand was placed on the board and he was instructed to feel first one form and then the other with that same hand and decide whether the two forms were the same or different. When S had made a judgment about the pair of forms, the transformation was removed and replaced by another. After a few presenta-

Transformations

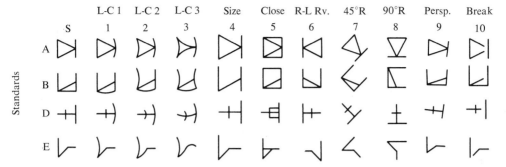

FIGURE 2   Standards and transformations used in Experiment II

tions, E no longer had to guide S's hand to the board. A trial consisted of seven presentations for comparison: one standard form to be compared with each of five transformations and two copies of the standard in random order. When S completed a trial, the procedure was repeated in a different random order until S reached the criterion of learning.[1] This criterion consisted of *either* a perfect trial *or* a single confusion error for either the size or perspective transformation (whichever the particular S was given). This weaker second condition was accepted as a criterion condition because size and perspective transformations proved in pilot work to be impossible for many Ss to distinguish from standards long after they were able to distinguish the other transformations from standards.

Preliminary practice prior to training consisted of practice with visual letters followed by both visual and blindfolded practice with letters in the form of tactual stimuli.

[1] The training task proved too easy for some first graders. Since this was a learning experiment, Ss who performed the training task successfully on the initial trial were discarded from the experiment. There were also a few Ss who were never able to learn the training task and who were also discarded. In all, about 100 Ss were run through the training procedure. The final N represents those Ss who did not perform at criterion level on the first trial and who were eventually able to do so after several training trials.

Transfer. The same three transfer conditions as before were used. Group C received a different standard and five different transformations of the standard from the ones used in training. Group EI received the same standard as in training, but five new transformations of this standard. Group EII received a new standard, but the same five transformations of this standard as those with which they had dealt in training.

Eight subgroups were used in the training condition representing training with each of the four standards and the two groups of transformations. One transformation group consisted of line to curve transformations, the size transformation, and the close. The other group consisted of the reversals, rotations, perspective transformation, and the break.

RESULTS

TRAINING

Differences between the groups in number of confusion errors made on the first trial and in number of trials to criterion were analyzed with t tests. None of the differences approached significance.

TRANSFER

Confusion errors made by the subgroups and for the three groups with subgroups combined are shown in Table 2. The

TABLE 2

Confusion Errors in Transfer Trial for the 24 Subgroups

GROUP	TRANSFORMATIONS								TOTAL
	T 12345				T 6789 and 10				
	STANDARDS								
	SA	SB	SD	SE	SA	SB	SD	SE	
EI	3	8	2	2	4	1	1	3	24
EII	3	2	3	3	3	3	5	3	25
C	9	9	9	2	2	5	5	7	48

Note.—Column headings indicate combination of forms used in the transfer trial. $n = 3$ in each subgroup.

analysis of variance indicated a significant effect of transfer groups at less than the .001 probability level, $F(2, 48) = 10.63$. The Transformations $\times$ Standards interaction and the triple interaction were also significant at less than the .05 level of probability. A comparison of the total errors made by the three groups indicated that Groups EI and EII were not different from each other but both were superior in performance to Group C.

The Transformations $\times$ Standards interaction effect seemed to be due to a difference between errors made to Standard E and errors made to the other standards (cf. Figure 2). For Standards A, B, and D more errors occurred with Transformations 1–5 than with Transformations 6–10. This pattern is reversed with Standard E which probably accounted for the fact that the effect of transformations did not reach significance.

The three-way interaction is difficult to interpret meaningfully. Probably its effect was accounted for by the fact that there were only three Ss in a cell, and one atypical S in a given cell could account for the scores in that cell deviating from the overall pattern.

DISCUSSION

Clearly the results of this experiment were different from those of the previous experiment. In that experiment, the group which had opportunity to use in transfer what it had learned about the *distinctive features* of the forms was superior to both the other groups in transfer trial performance. In the present experiment, the comparable group of Ss was no better in transfer trial performance than the group which had opportunity to use prototypes or memory models of the forms, though both groups were better than the control group.

One interpretation of these results is that the process of improvement in visual discrimination is different from the process of improvement in tactual discrimination and that schema construction and detection of distinctive features may serve equally useful functions in tactual discrimination.

Another interpretation is related to differences in the task required of S. Because S in the tactual experiment explored the forms with only one hand, he made successive comparisons. This task involved memory and perhaps required him to form a memory model of the standard even if his task in learning was to detect distinctive features. In the visual experiment, however, S could look back and forth between the comparison forms without having to remember how they looked in order to discover the differences between them.

If this second interpretation is correct,

making the tactual comparison simultaneous should then result in the reappearance of superior performance by Group EII. The third experiment was conducted to test this hypothesis.

Experiment III

The major difference between this experiment and the previous one is in the nature of S's task. There were minor differences in number of Ss, material, and subgroups as noted below.

METHOD

Subjects. The Ss were 60 first graders.

Materials. The forms were Standards A and D and the 10 transformations of each.

Procedure. The procedure was the same as in the previous experiment except that throughout this experiment, S explored the two comparison forms simultaneously, one with each hand.[2]

There were four subgroups representing training with each of the two standards and the two groups of five transformations each.

RESULTS

TRAINING

None of the differences between the groups in either number of trials or errors in the first trial approached significance. Hence the groups could be considered equivalent with respect to their ability to handle the forms.

[2] Some Ss could not complete the training task successfully and were discarded. Their inability to perform successfully appeared to be a function of an inability to coordinate both hands in exploring the forms. There were also a few Ss who performed the task at criterion level on the first trial, and were discarded. About 80 Ss began the training procedure and the final N, as in the previous experiment, represents those Ss who did not perform at criterion level on the first training trial and who eventually learned the task.

TABLE 3

Confusion Errors in Transfer Trial for the 12 Subgroups

GROUP	TRANSFORMATIONS				TOTAL
	T 12345		T 6789 and 10		
	STANDARDS				
	SA	SD	SA	SD	
EI	10	11	6	4	31
EII	3	3	3	0	9
C	10	10	5	7	32

Note.—Column headings indicate combination of forms used in transfer trial. $n = 5$ in each subgroup.

TRANSFER

Transfer trial errors for each subgroup and for subgroups combined are shown in Table 3. The analysis of variance performed on the data showed the effect of transfer groups to be significant with a probability of less than .001 that the effect was due to chance, $F(2, 48) = 8.62$. The effect of transformations was also significant with a probability of less than .01 that the effect was due to chance. Neither the effect of standards nor any interaction was significant.

A comparison of the total errors made by the three groups showed that Group EII, the group having new forms but familiar transformations in the transfer task, was superior to the other two groups in performance on this task. Group EI, the group having familiar forms but new transformations in the transfer task was not different from the control group.

The effect of transformations is due to the fact that more errors occurred with Transformations 1–5 than with Transformations 6–10. Except for one standard (E) this was also true in Exp. II. Apparently line to curve transformations are, in general, more difficult to discriminate tactually than rotations and reversals.

DISCUSSION

These results support the hypothesis that under conditions of simultaneous comparison, the group having opportunity to use in transfer what they had learned about the distinctive features of the forms would show superior performance. Not only was this group (EII) superior to the other two groups, but the other experimental group showed no better performance than the control group. In this experiment, the construction of schemata, if such a process occurred at all, showed no effect in the transfer task.

General Discussion

A consideration of the tasks involved in these experiments may make the three different patterns of results meaningful. The third experiment involved a task of simultaneous comparison. The results suggested that Ss had, in training, learned the distinctive features of the forms since the superior group had no opportunity to construct schemata of the forms used in the transfer task. Those Ss who *could* use schemata in the transfer task performed no better than the control group.

The second experiment involved a task of *successive* comparison. These Ss apparently both constructed schemata of the forms *and* learned distinctive features since groups who could use either distinctive features or prototypes showed similar amounts of transfer relative to the control group.

The first experiment involved a task which might be considered to lie between the tasks of the two tactual experiments in terms of the nature of the comparison. None of the Ss in this experiment had to explore one form thoroughly before exploring the comparison form as did Ss in the second experiment. On the other hand, Ss in this first experiment probably did not receive information from both the standard and comparison forms simultane-

ously as did Ss in the third experiment. Most likely, Ss in this first experiment quickly looked back and forth several times between the standard and comparison form in order to make a judgment about them. The Ss who could use in transfer what they had learned about distinctive features showed the best transfer task performance. Those Ss who could use schemata also showed transfer but significantly less than the other experimental group.

In terms of the tasks involved in these experiments, one might interpret the results as suggesting that the detection of distinctive features will always facilitate improvement in discrimination but that under conditions of successive comparison, schema construction will *independently* facilitate such improvement.

A more parsimonious interpretation is that the detection of distinctive features may be the *basis* for improvement in discrimination. When such detection is dependent on memory because of the nature of the task (e.g., in Exp. II and to a lesser degree in Exp. I), some schema learning does occur. When no memory requirement is imposed by the task (e.g., Exp. III), schema learning does not occur. In short, detection of distinctive features may be the necessary and sufficient condition for improvement in discrimination. Schema learning may or may not occur depending on the experimental conditions. When it does occur, its function is to make possible the comparison and search for differences, i.e., to make possible the detection of distinctive features.

The data of the present experiments are consistent with this interpretation. In no case did an EI group perform better than an EII group. Furthermore, the EI groups showed better performance than the control group only to the extent that memory was involved in the task of comparison.

Further research is necessary to establish the validity of this interpretation. A direct test might be made by determining whether, under conditions of successive comparison, Ss in fact have learned a prototype or memory model of the standard forms. Can they identify the given standards from a group of unrelated forms, or can they reproduce the standards better than Ss who have operated under conditions of simultaneous comparison?

References

BRUNER, J. S. Neural mechanisms in perception. *Psychol. Rev.,* 1957, *64,* 340–358. (a)

BRUNER, J. S. On perceptual readiness. *Psychol. Rev.,* 1957, *64,* 123–152. (b)

GIBSON, E. J., J. J. GIBSON, A. D. PICK, and H. OSSER. A developmental study of the discrimination of letter-like forms. *J. comp. physiol. Psychol.,* 1962, *55,* 897–906.

GIBSON, J. J., and E. J. GIBSON. Perceptual learning: Differentiation or enrichment? *Psychol. Rev.,* 1955, *62,* 32–41.

JAKOBSON, R., and M. HALLE. *Fundamentals of language.* The Hague, Netherlands: Mouton, 1956.

SOLLEY, C. M., and G. MURPHY. *Development of the perceptual world.* New York: Basic Books, 1960.

VERNON, M. D. *A further study of visual perception.* Cambridge, England: Cambridge Univer. Press, 1952.

VERNON, M. D. The functions of schemata in perceiving. *Psychol. Rev.,* 1955, *62,* 180–192.

CHAPTER 7

The Effects of Set,
Prior Knowledge,
and Motivational Variables
on Perception

Nature of the Effect of Set on Perception*

RALPH NORMAN HABER

University of Rochester

To explain the effects of set on reports of perceptual experience 2 hypotheses are elaborated —set enhances the percept directly, or set facilitates responses and memorial organization of the perceptual experience that itself was uneffected by the set. Extensive research is reviewed that is relevant to each of these hypotheses, especially studies that attempt to differentiate them.

When a perceiver is given instruction to attend to only one of several attributes of a stimulus, he is able to report his perception of that attribute more accurately than he would be able to otherwise. Külpe, in 1904, first documented this effect experimentally, and, since then, a number of investigators have replicated the basic finding. The operations have typically involved either instructing the subject (S) as to which attribute he should attend, or providing S with a set of alternatives, from which the stimulus has been drawn. However, the same process is implied by implicit instructions emanating from S himself, such as would occur when a hungry man is looking for food. The experimental demonstration requires that the set cannot be satisfied by peripheral mechanisms such as eye movements or scanning of the stimulus to locate the relevant attributes, since,

otherwise, the phenomena would not be as interesting.

This paper is not a general review of the effects of set on perception, although such a review is badly needed to bring Gibson's (1941) discussion up to date. Rather, the topic here is an examination of the two basic hypotheses that have been used to interpret set effects. As these issues were not so clearly developed at the time of Gibson's review, little reference can be made to his paper.

At least two basic and dissimilar interpretations have been suggested to explain the effects of set on perception. The older one, favored by Külpe and most of the investigators following him, including the "New Look" theorists in perception, appeals to a perceptual enhancement or "tuning" hypothesis (Dember, 1960; Postman, 1963), whereby attending to a particular attribute of a stimulus results in a clearer and more vivid perception of that attribute—it stands out more. By the same token, the incidental attributes are not as clear and do not stand out. Thus, the perceptual tuning hypothesis places the locus of the effect of set in the perceptual

* *Psychological Review,* 1966, vol. 73, pp. 335–351. Partial support for this research was provided by a grant from the United States Public Health Service (MH 03244) to the author at Yale University, where this work had been completed. I am most appreciative to Thomas Natsoulas and Maurice Hershenson for their many valuable comments on the manuscript.

system itself, occurring while the stimulus is being viewed.

The alternative hypothesis is that set has no effect on perception itself, but only on some aspects of the memory trace or on responses to that perceptual experience. Several varieties of this "response" hypothesis have been proposed: (*a*) The set facilitates relevant responses by S, increasing the probability that S can identify the stimulus in his report; (*b*) the set causes S to report the emphasized attributes first, before memory of the stimulus fades, thus allowing those attributes to be reported more accurately; (*c*) the set modifies the organization of the memory trace, so that the important attributes are remembered more accurately.

The two basic hypotheses have wider application in perception and memory than just to problems of set. Behind them lies specification of one of the most difficult distinctions in any analysis of perceptual behavior. The tendency has been to assume that just because S was reporting immediately what he had perceived he was therefore performing a "perceptual" task. There is a crucial difference between reporting one's experience and reporting the attributes of stimuli that one remembers seeing. One task is perceptual, while the other deals with a memorial process. These must be conceptually differentiated, even if they may function similarly, and even if they proceed originally from the same sensory base. There are innumerable experiments that fail to make this distinction, and much of the controversy among perceptual theories results directly from this confusion. The two hypotheses under discussion in this paper reflect the distinction being proposed. To provide evidence relating to either or both of these requires that operational definitions be made for measurement of perceptual experience directly, or that deductions from these hypotheses specify operations in terms of memory alone that will still permit inferences concerning perceptual experi-

ence. As the present discussion will amply illustrate, neither of these conditions is well met in practice, though abundant data are available regarding both of these hypotheses.

Needless to say, the earliest experiments (e.g., Külpe, 1904; Rubin, 1913; Wilcocks, 1925; Yokahama, reported in Boring, 1924) were not designed to separate these two basic hypotheses, even though the hypotheses were discussed as alternative explanations for the various results.

Külpe's (1904) stimuli were groups of letters varying in color and location. Prior to most presentations, S was given a set to note only one of the several attributes of the stimulus: the number, position, or color of the letters, or the overall figure formed by the letters. For the remaining stimuli, no specific set was given. After the presentation, S was instructed to report the attributes as best he could, with no order specified. If he left any out, the experimenter (E) questioned him on those. Külpe found that S was more accurate in reporting the attribute for which he had paid attention prior to the presentation and was less accurate in reporting the others. Külpe suggested that the attention instructions facilitated the clarity of the percept.

Wilcocks (1925), responding to a criticism of Külpe by Rubin (1913), extended Külpe's method to include a memory variable. Wilcocks argued that if the reports of attributes after the presentation were in an uncontrolled order, it is possible that S might have forgotten some of them by the time he was questioned. Therefore, Wilcocks randomly arranged the order of reporting the attributes, though, in other respects, his experiment was similar to Külpe's. He found in general that accuracy was poorer the later an attribute was reported. Even so, he found that when order of report was controlled, the report of the attended-to attribute was more accurate than that of the unattended-to ones. Thus, while a memory variable was shown to be operative, it seemed to be independent of the enhancement effect. Therefore, Wilcocks concluded that Külpe's basic finding was replicated and could not be reduced to a memory process. Likewise, he accepted Külpe's interpretation of this process as perceptual enhancement.

Chapman (1932) used similar figures, where S could either count the letters, locate their positions, or name them. Instructions to attend to only one of these attributes were given in some sessions 4 seconds prior to the stimulus exposure, and in the remaining sessions 2 seconds following the exposure, in both cases by means of an illuminated display. Chapman's results showed that accuracy of report was higher when the attention instruction was given before the stimulus exposure, as compared to afterwards. Comments made by Ss indicated that the attended-to attribute was perceived more clearly during the actual exposure of the stimulus. They felt they did worse in the aftercondition because they had to keep too many things in mind. However, the comments also suggested that Ss' memory of the stimulus was affected by the type of set given. In the prior condition, they indicated that the memory for the irrelevant attributes faded and became indistinct. Thus, Chapman concluded that attention instructions given prior to the exposure both enhanced the perception of the stimulus itself during its actual exposure and, further, started in motion a differential forgetting process, where the relevant attribute was maintained in memory more accurately and for a longer time.

The evidence regarding the effect of set reviewed to this point supports a perceptual tuning hypothesis, primarily on the basis of Ss' postexperimental introspective comments. They report that the set-for attributes are clearer, stand out more, fade less rapidly, and the like. Support for at least one of the response hypotheses is also found, based on before-after differences, order of report effects, as well as introspective

comments regarding fading memory. In light of the importance of an S's report of his perceptual experience, the comments regarding experience in these experiments must be given weight, even though they were not collected in any systematic or complete fashion nor subjected to any content analysis, and even though S was given no pretraining on the categories to use in his report. (See Postman, 1963, for a discussion of these criteria to be used for the evaluation of introspective reports in perceptual research.)

While an S in this type of experiment might be confident that he noticed changes in the perceptual characteristics of the stimulus as his set changed, no converging operations (Garner, Hake, and Eriksen, 1956) sufficient to demonstrate the validity of those reports were employed. Introspectively, it might be very difficult for an S to differentiate a rapidly fading memory, for example, from an image that was perceptually less clear. Unless experiments are designed to guarantee that S can make this distinction introspectively (and the ones just reviewed clearly do not offer such a guarantee), they cannot provide unequivocal evidence regarding either of these two hypotheses. Therefore, this evidence can be considered only suggestive support for the perceptual tuning hypotheses, as well as providing some evidence for at least one of the versions of the response hypothesis.

The New Look in perception, beginning after World War II, accepted this evidence, however, as offering strong support for the perceptual tuning hypothesis (Bruner, 1957a, 1957b). A number of experiments were then reported that seemed to provide further support for this hypothesis, including ones by Neisser (1954), Postman and Bruner (1949), Bruner and Postman (1949), Krulee, Podell, and Ronco (1954), Green and Anderson (1956), Ross, Yarczower, and Williams (1956), Hoisington and Spencer (1958), to name only a few. For example, Postman and Bruner (1949) showed that if S was given a multiple set of alternatives (e.g., one of two stimulus words will be either a food or a color word—report only that one), he had higher recognition thresholds than if a single set was given (e.g., one of two stimulus words will be a food word—report only that one). Thus, they argued that since the recognition thresholds were manipulated by the set, the set had actually changed the perceptual characteristics of the stimulus.

Neisser (1954) presented Ss a list of words to study, indicating that some of them would later be shown tachistoscopically. He did in fact show some of the original words, but, in addition, exposed some that were homonyms of other words on the list. He found no facilitation of the homonyms, even though the original words were reported more rapidly. Since a word and its homonym require the same response, but only the original word was facilitated, he concluded that the presentation of the actual word prior to exposure must have made the word itself stand out perceptually.

Bruner and Postman (1949) gave Ss the set to expect to see normal playing cards, but in fact showed them cards in which the colors and suits did not agree (e.g., black hearts). While many Ss apparently ignored the incongruity and reported the cards as they would normally appear (e.g., red hearts or black clubs or spades), a few Ss reported seeing "compromise" perceptions (e.g., brown or purple hearts). These latter responses have been interpreted as supporting a perceptual hypothesis, since no response facilitation could be expected for a category such as purple hearts that S had never seen before.

Bruner (1957b) has offered an intriguing suggestion regarding the relationship between the two hypotheses under discussion. He proposes that perceptual experience (the concern of the first hypothesis) is the result or end product of categorization (the concern of the second

hypothesis). Thus, an object is experienced or perceived *only after* it has been properly classified—that is, responded to. Prior to its identification, the perceptual experience of a stimulus is blurred and indistinct. In the present context, then, if the perceiver has a set which facilitates classification of the stimulus, it also then facilitates the clarity of its percept.

Bruner and Potter (1964) present some evidence relevant to one aspect of this notion. They show S a common, everyday object extremely out of focus and then gradually increase the focus until it is perfectly clear. During the period of increasing focus, S is required to give a running commentary of what he thinks the picture contains, from which the point of correct identification can be determined. They found that if the focus increases very slowly, so that S has extensive viewing during which he cannot correctly classify the stimulus, he requires a greater amount of focus before correct identification occurs. From this the authors argued that the extent to which S misclassifies the picture during the very fuzzy presentations prolongs the time before he can see it clearly. Presumably, during this time, S is testing his classifications against the fuzzy image, and he has to reject the wrong classifications he made before he can concentrate on testing correct ones. Only after he tries and checks the correct one does he come to see the picture clearly.

Obviously, this kind of experiment, interesting as it is, cannot provide much evidence for as complex a position as Bruner is espousing here. He has to make too many additional assumptions to have a clear-cut analysis. A somewhat more relevant, though still indirect, test of this notion was reported by Hershenson and Haber (1965). These authors had previously found that the clarity of letters of words increased markedly if they were flashed several times, even when on the first flash S could see none or few of the letters (Haber, 1965a; Haber and Hershenson, 1965). However, the rate of increase in clarity for Turkish words was slightly faster than that for English words. It was assumed that S would be less likely to misclassify what he knew was a Turkish word from only partial information, since he knew it would be a totally unfamiliar word. Therefore, this result was interpreted to imply that when S made incorrect anticipatory classificatory responses for the English words, this slowed down the development of their clarity.

Even given these kinds of data, Bruner's notion faces serious theoretical problems on other counts, as, for example, how one can see something that is novel when he cannot classify it correctly. Therefore, until more than this meager and indirect evidence is available, little else can be said for this version of a linkage between the two processes.

An independent line of research, originally led by Ames (e.g., 1951), has provided the basis of the Transactionalist theory of perception. In this context, many demonstrations were created to show how an S's assumptions based on past experience or knowledge directly affect his perceptual experience. In one of the most striking of these, a physically rotating trapezoidal-shaped window appears to oscillate back and forth, and to be rectangular in shape. This is a very powerful perceptual experience, experienced by nearly every viewer, so that it is difficult to explain in terms of any kind of response process. Haber (1965b) has recently shown that if Ss are given extensive experience with the apparatus and knowledge of the theory behind the illusion, their perceptual experience changes so the majority of Ss report seeing the nonillusory rotation of the trapezoidal figure. Numerous other examples of these demonstrations can also be used to support the effects of S's assumptions (set) on his perceptual experience directly, in ways suggesting that response processes are inoperative.

Shortly after the beginnings of the New Look, strong interest was revived in alternative interpretations involving response and memory processes. Many of the New Look experiments were scrutinized for evidence of these processes or for faults in design. Accompanying this methodological concern was the new development in theorizing about methods of research in perception. The most important single paper in this regard is by Garner et al. (1956). While not taking sides with respect to these two hypotheses, Garner et al. point out quite persuasively the inadequacy of nearly all previous research to decide among the interpretations of the effects of set, as well as motivation and implicit instructions, on perception. They suggest several nonperceptual interpretations of these patterns of results and present the concept of converging operations as an experimental design to provide tests between the two hypotheses. They are particularly concerned with the possibility that the set limits the number of alternatives from which S must make his response, thus increasing the probability that the correct response will be made, independent of any perceptual enhancement. Eriksen (1958, 1960, 1962) has continued this position, arguing that nearly all research in this area has failed to differentiate the two hypotheses satisfactorily, and that since from his point of view the response interpretations are more parsimonious, there is no evidence to support a perceptual interpretation. His position has received added support from a number of recent studies.

Lawrence and Coles (1954) argued, along with Chapman (1932), that a perceptual tuning hypothesis has to predict that a set given before the stimulus, as compared to one given afterwards, will provide greater facilitation of report. They go further and suggest a dual hypothesis: Perhaps perceptual enhancement does occur if a prior set is given, but, when given afterwards, facilitation could be due to some selectivity in the memory process.

If this were true, then an experiment like Chapman's would not distinguish between the purely perceptual and the dual hypothesis, since they might both be correct.

Lawrence and Coles (1954) used pictures of single familiar objects, with the set administered by projecting on the screen, either immediately before or after the stimulus exposure, the names of four alternatives for the stimulus. The alternatives were very similar to one another for some trials, while on others they were quite discrete. One group of Ss had no alternatives at all; this served as a control on the use of the alternatives.

The results showed that giving alternatives of either type increased the accuracy of recognition of the stimuli, as compared with the no-alternative control group. Hence, the effect of set was demonstrated. However, alternatives given after the exposure were just as useful as those given before (which stands in contrast to Chapman's before-after difference).

This failure to replicate Chapman's before-after difference was not considered crucial, since the equality may have been due to perceptual enhancement from the before set and memory selection from the after set—the two processes just balancing each other. However, they also failed to find any interaction between the before-after sets and the type of alternatives (similar or discrete). They had argued that a perceptual hypothesis would predict no difference between the two types of alternatives when they are given before the presentation, since the correct alternative would stand out whether other alternatives were similar or not. On the other hand, since the after set could not affect enhancement, it must affect memory, which should show a differential effect of the two types of alternatives—discrete ones being more effective in facilitating correct recognition than similar ones. Failure to find evidence in support of this prediction (discrete alternatives consistently facilitated recognition more than similar ones for both

before and after sets) led Lawrence and Coles (1954) to reject any form of the perceptual tuning hypothesis, and to argue that the effect of set was via some selective facilitation of memory processes.

By implication, Lawrence and Coles provided a possible explanation for Chapman's before-after difference—the one they failed to replicate. Under the assumption that the entire effect of set is caused by memory and response processes, the earlier the set is given, the greater the opportunity it will have to provide facilitation of these processes. Thus, even if there is no perceptual tuning, administering the set prior to the exposures gives S just that much more time to organize his memory. Sets given after the stimulus presentation have to act on an already fading memory trace and are at a disadvantage compared to a set given before the trace has weakened. As the delay between the exposure and the set increases, the superiority of the prior alternatives should increase. Since Chapman had a longer delay than Lawrence and Coles, this slight time difference may have accounted for the different outcome in the two experiments.

An interrelated group of studies by Long, Reid, and Henneman (1960), Long, Henneman, and Garvey (1960), and Reid, Henneman, and Long (1960) has used a model of set as a response limiter, similar to Garner et al.'s (1956) notion, whereby set "increases perceptual accuracy by increasing the probabilities of certain responses and decreases the probabilities of others in the various response classes [Long, Reid, and Henneman, 1960, p. 554]." Most of their experiments used single letters as stimuli, degraded in clarity, with set manipulated by giving S a group of alternative letters, of which the stimulus letter would be one. The alternatives were given either before or after the exposure. They found that decreasing the number of alternatives increased the accuracy, regardless of whether the alternatives were given before or after the exposure. From this they concluded, as did Lawrence and Coles (1954), that set was acting on the selection of responses, and not on perception itself. Greater accuracy was also found if the alternatives were drawn from an exclusive subset rather than from the entire alphabet. Further, they showed that set effects could be produced by restriction of the categories (rather than alternatives) into which the stimulus might fall. This is somewhat similar to the Postman and Bruner (1949) finding, but was found to be true regardless of whether the restriction was given before or after the stimulus. This greatly weakens Postman and Bruner's contention that restriction of category affects the perception of the stimulus itself. All of these findings are consistent with a response-limiting interpretation of set.

However, Long, Reid, and Henneman (1960) also found and replicated several before-after differences. One was found when only two alternatives were provided, so that being told the stimulus was one of two particular letters before the flash helped S report the letter more accurately than if such a set was given 1 or 2 seconds after the flash. Another before-after difference occurred in an auditory version of their experiments, when four alternatives were presented either before or after the stimulus letter was spoken in noise. Finally, when two degraded letters were presented and S was asked which of the two was a specific alternative, they found that specifying the search letter before the presentation facilitated correct discrimination, as compared to a later specification.

Each of these findings is inconsistent with the response interpretations of set, and it is not clear how they might be explained other than by some form of perceptual enhancement. The Lawrence and Coles' explanation—that the earlier the set is given, the greater its opportunity to facilitate memory processes—will not work, since it should follow that the greater the number of alternatives, the greater the ef-

fect of an earlier set. "Increasing the alternatives implies that the number of discriminating characteristics between them become more restrictive, and thus are more likely to be lost in the trace [Lawrence and Coles, 1954, p. 213]." However, these findings, inconsistent with a response interpretation, occurred primarily with a few alternatives, and no before-after differences were found with larger number of alternatives.

In a different line of research, Taub (1965), following the work of Teichner, Reilly, and Sadler (1961) and Teichner and Sadler (1962), presented an array of letters to S, asking him to report all of them. The number of letters in the array, the exposure duration, and the relative value of each of the letters (set) were varied. Value was manipulated by assigning points for correct reports of letters, with differential value attached to letters from the first and second half of the alphabet. Taub found that value affected accuracy (a set effect), but primarily through a reduction in accuracy of the low-valued letters, rather than an increase in the high-valued ones. This occurred in spite of the finding that the first letter reported from an array was most likely to be one of high value.

Taub's (1965) experiment is most relevant to the issues of this discussion because of the similarity of a prediction he makes to the Lawrence and Coles' (1954) similar-discrete difference presented earlier:

. . . if a major selective process in perception was involved, then the size of the difference between high- and low-value letters should vary inversely with length of exposure. That is, a perceptual set, which would make the higher value categories easier and quicker to identify (Bruner, 1957), would occur at those conditions where there is little time to detect and discriminate between the categories, but have little effect at longer exposures where all letters would be equally discriminable. Predictions from a selective recall point of view would be the opposite. That is, as exposure time increases and the rate of memory loading decreases, Ss would have more time to selectively code the categories which are detected. Thus, a selective memory process explanation would predict increasing differences in response to value as exposure time increases [p. 142].

Since Taub found unequivocal evidence that increasing exposure time increased the differences in accuracy between high- and low-value words, he rejects a perceptual tuning explanation in favor of some variety of the memory hypothesis—especially a selective-recall one. However, Taub used relatively long exposure durations (500–2,500 milliseconds), so that visual searching clearly occurred for the longer presentations. Therefore, his data are equivocal with respect to this issue, since S has opportunity to seek out the high-value items if given sufficient time, and this would imply nothing about the effects on perception at all. Thus, it appears that, while the prediction is relevant, it requires a presentation time considerably shorter than Taub used to test it adequately.

A different type of experiment was reported by Lawrence and LaBerge (1956) in which they were concerned with the response hypothesis of a fading memory. The stimuli were pairs of cards from the Wisconsin Card Sorting Task, with an attention-instruction set given only before the exposures, by indicating the relative value for each attribute correctly reported. For one group of Ss, all three attributes (number, color, shape) received equal value; for another, one attribute was always emphasized by offering 100 times as much money as each of the other two attributes. All three attributes had to be reported, but S determined the order. A third group, with equal set, had the order in which the three attributes were to be reported controlled and varied from trial to trial.

When the emphasis and equal conditions were compared, they found that the effect of set appeared to increase accuracy for the attended-to attribute and decrease it for the other two. They also found that the decrement from first to third report under the equal condition was about the same magnitude as the difference between the critical and incidental attributes in the emphasis condition. While they did not measure the order of report when unequal attention instructions had been given, Lawrence and LaBerge (1956) argued that the set effect could have been entirely determined by the order in which S reported the attributes. That is, if, whenever one attribute was critical, S always reported that one first, then the accuracy of the critical attribute would be higher because it had been reported first.

Thus, Lawrence and LaBerge suggest that no assumption need be made about reorganization of memory or changes in response probabilities, but only that all memory for the stimulus is slowly fading. Whatever is reported first will be more accurate than later-reported items. This hypothesis is very similar to one Wilcocks (1925) tested but rejected. Lawrence and LaBerge cannot test this in their data since they did not measure the preferred order of report when the attention instructions made one attribute critical.

This test was provided in experiments by Harris and Haber (1963) and Haber (1964a). The same stimulus materials and procedures for inducing sets were used, but each S was tested under all set conditions, including a forced order of report specified by E on half of the trials, and a free order on the other half. S could report the stimulus in whatever order he chose (though he had to indicate the one he used). Under forced order of report, when just the first attribute reported was analyzed, if that first report was of a critical attribute, it was more accurately reported than if it was of an incidental one. The same was true for the second and third reports. Thus, Lawrence and LaBerge (1956) were incorrect when they argued that the set effect could be explained in terms of order of report. Holding order of report constant, the set effect was still obtained. Harris and Haber (1963) did find that some Ss reported the critical attributes first if they were allowed to choose their own order of report. But even granting this, it did not account for the set effect. Thus, this simpler hypothesis of Lawrence and LaBerge was shown to be inadequate.

While the findings of Harris and Haber (1963) and Haber (1964a) indicated that fading memory coupled with a varying order of report could not explain the set effect, they did discover what may be a more explicit determiner of set—namely, the encoding processes by which S translates the percept of the stimulus into memory. Some pilot work had indicated that nearly all Ss spontaneously encoded this type of stimulus into words and silently rehearsed the message repeatedly until all of the attributes had been reported. Further, with these stimuli, it was found that Ss used one of two dissimilar strategies to accomplish this encoding. Some Ss encoded it by separating the stimulus into objects on the left and right (e.g., one red triangle, three blue stars). The remaining Ss encoded it by separating the stimulus into its three dimensions (e.g., red blue, triangle star, one three). The order of the dimensions in this latter Dimensions code could of course be varied without disturbing the strategy, while the former Objects coding strategy has its order of encoding fixed by the rules of English syntax.

To investigate the effects of differential coding strategy on perception, Harris and Haber (1963) and Haber (1964a) trained Ss to use one of the two coding strategies. In both of these experiments, an effect of set and of order of report was found. (Emphasized dimensions were reported more accurately than unemphasized dimensions, holding order of report constant, and the dimensions reported first were more accurate than those reported later.) How-

ever, both of these effects strongly interacted with coding strategy. So strongly, in fact, that nearly all of these effects were accounted for by the performance of those Ss using the Dimensions code. Thus, those Ss who used the Objects code, based on English syntax, were not significantly more accurate on the emphasized, as compared to the unemphasized, dimensions. Further, regarding the order of report effect, as shown in the replication study (Haber, 1964a), the difference between the early and later reported dimensions was smaller for those Ss using the Objects code than for those using the Dimensions code. Finally, Ss using the Objects code had a greater overall accuracy of report, regardless of condition.

It seems clear therefore that the set and order of report effect can in large part be explained by the operations of the coding strategies themselves. These results suggest that the set effect stems as much from a change in the initial organization of the memory of the stimulus produced by the strategy by which S encodes the stimulus, rather than from a facilitation of contact with an already organized memory or through the effects of a fading memory or through the changes in the probability of the correct response being available.

However, the results on coding strategy do not indicate the reasons for the differences between these two coding strategies. To assess these, Haber (1964b) conducted a third study, using the same stimuli, strategy-training procedures, and set manipulation, but requiring S to verbalize his encoding and rehearsal of the encoded stimulus so it could be tape-recorded. Each S was instructed to begin talking immediately after the flash with his verbal encoding of the stimulus, and to repeat this encoding over and over for 20 seconds.

Haber found that Ss using the Objects code could begin encoding considerably faster and complete encoding more rapidly than Ss using the Dimensions code. Thus, the two strategies differed sharply in the speed with which they could translate the stimulus into memory. If there is some after-image or short-term memory of the stimulus, lasting perhaps several hundred milliseconds beyond its offset (Averbach and Coriell, 1961; Mackworth, 1963; Sperling, 1960), then the strategy that can translate this image into memory most rapidly is more likely to have that encoding based on a good image that will allow it to be more accurate. In this way, one can account for the difference in overall accuracy between the strategies. Similarly, if one strategy encodes slower than the other, then presumably the items it encoded last would be poorer in accuracy, which would suggest that the order of report effect could also be accounted for by the differences in the speed of encoding. Finally, it was found that the Dimensions coders nearly always encoded the critical dimension first, while the Objects coders always followed the same order—that of English syntax. Thus, the set variable can also be explained by the differential speed of encoding. If the attributes encoded first are always the critical ones, leaving the others to be encoded later from a rapidly fading image of the stimulus, it is not surprising that the critical attribute is reported more accurately. This does not depend upon order of *report,* as Lawrence and LaBerge thought, but on order of *encoding.*

The two strategies also differed in the frequency of errors made after the initial encoding, with transpositions, intrusions, and omissions occurring significantly more frequently during the rehearsal process in the Dimensions code. This could further account for the order of report effect—the items reported later would be based upon a rehearsed encoding that had undergone some erroneous change. This would be true whether S was reporting the stimulus attributes in an order he chose or in one forced upon him by the experiment.

This experiment suggests, then, that the coding strategies differ in two important ways: the speed of encoding, and the re-

sistance to errors during rehearsal. It further suggests that these two differences could account for both the effect of set and the effect of the order of report in the experiments by Lawrence and LaBerge (1956), Harris and Haber (1963), and Haber (1964a), as well as by implication some of the earlier experiments discussed above. For example, the study by Neisser (1954) can now be explained in terms of encoding, without having to make any assumptions about the nature of the percept. This alternative explanation suggests that while the response given to the homonyms NO and KNOW is identical, the encoding of those two words into memory would be quite different. One reason for the difference could be that encoding is faster for words one expects to see. Thus, encoding of the unexpected KNOW begins later, takes longer, and therefore uses a progressively more degraded trace. While there has been no direct test of this explanation, it seems reasonable that the more prepared S is for what he will see, the more likely it is that he will have an appropriate strategy and category available in which to encode the stimulus.

It should be noted that variation in encoding is not the only nonperceptual interpretation of the Neisser (1954) experiment and of experiments similar to it. Since Neisser's Ss are in a guessing situation, where they must guess the word from presumably only fragments of the letters given perceptually (at least on the first few flashes), they will have more success guessing those words they were given a set to see (e.g., NO will be easier to guess than its homonym KNOW, which they had not experienced in the preliminary training). This interpretation has been used by Eriksen and Browne (1956) in a related type of study. It says nothing about increased clarity of the stimulus caused by the prior set, but only that such a set may facilitate guessing of the correct word when only a few pieces of it are seen perceptually.

The encoding analysis advanced above is a more specific hypothesis about the outcome of the Neisser experiment than the more general guessing one. It attempts to specify the translation of the visual image, as it is generated on the retina by the stimulus, into some kind of memorial trace or persistence after the stimulus terminates. While the visual image may persist for a brief time after the stimulus offset, in the form of a short-term memory, it is crucial that perceptual theory take into account the processes that occur after that short-term memory has faded. Since it is obvious that memory for stimuli persists long after the stimulus (and any attendant short-term memory and afterimages) has terminated, no perceptual theory can be complete without cognizance of this persistence of memory.

Specifically, the encoding explanation being discussed here suggests that most visual stimuli are remembered by being encoded into previously learned linguistic units, usually words. This encoding takes place while the stimulus (or its brief short-term memory) is still present, and whatever has not been encoded after the stimulus has faded is entirely lost and not available in permanent memory. This is not to deny that a few Ss may use some nonlinguistic code, especially for non-linguistic stimuli. However, certainly with respect to the kinds of materials of greatest interest to psychologists, encoding into words is the most probable basic strategy.

Variation in the adequacy of encoding can presumably depend upon a number of variables. The experiments reported above on encoding of Wisconsin Card Sorting Task concept cards suggest that when a number of highly familiar dimensions of a stimulus must be encoded quickly, accuracy of encoding depends upon whether S has at his disposal a strategy that lends itself to rapid coding, preferably without having both to learn the code as well as perform the encoding operations. Thus, using a highly overlearned syntax for the

order of encoding is preferable to one for which S must think about what should be encoded next.

In many perceptual experiments, the problem is not one of speed of encoding familiar dimensions, but of encoding degraded and often unpredictable stimuli. For example, a typical trial of a word-recognition experiment presents S with a fragmentary flash which first has to be maintained in memory and then that memory compared with possible alternatives of what the original stimulus must have been. If S has no adequate way of maintaining the fragments in memory, he will not be able to test any hypotheses about the stimuli once it terminates.

Thus, in most perceptual situations, two sources of variation are present—the adequacy of encoding a visual image, often imperfect, into memory, and the success of guessing what stimulus gave rise to those remembered fragments. To take an extreme though not too uncommon instance, stimuli for which S has no code for translation into memory are notoriously difficult to remember, even though S may perform perfectly on simultaneous discriminations with such stimuli. That is, he can make all of the appropriate responses to the stimulus while it is present, but cannot reconstruct it after it terminates. Most people experience this difficulty in describing colors, tastes, odors, and feelings from recollection. It is usually suggested that they do not have the appropriate words or other codes with which to maintain them in memory. These examples represent instances of excellent matching between the stimulus and prior experience, but very poor encoding of the stimulus into memory. Thus, short-duration presentations or delayed responses would show poor performance. One exception to this is found for those few people with eidetic imagery (see Haber and Haber, 1964) who are capable of maintaining a nearly perfect visual image of the stimulus for many minutes. These eidetic perceivers seem to do little if any encoding of the stimulus while the image persists, so that once it fades their memory of the stimulus is little better than that of more typical individuals.

Evidence relating to this specific distinction between encoding the percept and then matching the resultant memory to prior knowledge is very sparse, though it is beginning to accumulate. For example, McKinney (in press), by presenting single letters continuously and asking S to report changes or fragmentation in the percept of the letter, found that if the letter was embedded in a series of other letters which S was labeling as letters, much less change was reported than if it was embedded in a series of geometric designs for which no labels were suggested. Thus, the stability of the percept is increased when the object can be labeled (an operation probably equivalent to encoding).

Hintzman (1965), following work by Conrad (1964), presented lists of 8 symbols, selected so that matched pairs of them would be auditorily confusable (e.g., 2 with Q, 3 with T, etc.). Analyses of errors showed that auditory confusions were far greater than chance, suggesting that Ss were maintaining these symbols in memory by some type of auditory encoding and rehearsal. This was explicitly found when, for the half of trials on which white noise was used to prevent S from hearing his own thoughts, S produced overt rehearsal. However, Hintzman also reports that some Ss did not use rote aural encoding, but rather attempted to classify the string of symbols (e.g., to make up a mathematical formula). Such Ss made few aural confusions. Thus, the nature of the coding adopted by S determined the pattern of errors made. This, of course, was a situation where the symbols from which each presentation was drawn were well known in advance. Hence the matching of an encoded memory to prior experience was presumably perfect, with all of the variance in the encoding of that memory.

Gruber, Kulkin, and Schwartz (1965) presented a paired-associate learning task in which half of the Ss were instructed to attempt to form a visual image between the two members of each pair. These Ss had higher recall scores for all exposure durations, ranging from 1–24 seconds. Here, again, it would seem that aids for encoding of perceptually presented familiar material increase the accuracy of its encoded representation in memory.

The investigation and manipulation of coding variables in general in the study of perceptual and cognitive processes is becoming more extensive and is playing a far greater role in theory than 5–10 years ago. Much of the impetus for this has been Miller's (1956) paper on coding effects in information processing, although scattered work was reported before (e.g., Fitts, 1954; Pollack, 1952). More recently, however, a number of important experimental and theoretical papers have applied encoding processes to a wide range of perceptual data and problems (e.g., Broadbent, 1958; Conrad, 1964; Glanzer and Clark, 1962, 1963; Mackworth, 1963; Miller, Galanter, and Pribrim, 1960; Sperling, 1963).

The three studies on coding strategies by Haber have shown the importance of coding processes in the investigation of the effects of set. They suggest the possibility that many of the effects of set on reports of perception can be explained by differential encoding processes. Many studies have reported that the emphasized attribute of a stimulus can be reported more accurately than other attributes, irrespective of when the instruction for emphasis is given. However, in the Haber studies, this finding is dependent upon the nature of the encoding strategy—only one type of strategy will produce this emphasis-set effect. Similarly, only one type of strategy leads to an order of report effect. Thus, whether attention instructions (and restriction of alternatives) will lead to a set effect may depend upon whether S's encoding strategy is susceptible to such a manipulation.

An alternative possibility is that on the trials when the set is given to S, he changes his strategy so as to maximize the payoff from the set. In the Haber experiments, only a few Ss varied their strategies from condition to condition—too few to provide any kind of analysis of their performance. But this is a very likely possibility, particularly if the various set conditions make quite different demands upon Ss' reports. Since the studies by Haber are the only ones that have shown this higher-order dependency of set on encoding, further research will be needed before these possibilities can be analyzed successfully.

Conclusions

Evidence on the effects of set has been reviewed with respect to two basically different hypotheses—set enhances the percept of the stimulus while S is actually viewing it; set facilitates report of the stimulus without affecting its percept.

At least three varieties of nonperceptual hypotheses were discussed: (a) response-limiting or response-probability changes, (b) order of report changes coupled with a fading memory, and (c) reorganization of the memory process itself. The second alternative does not seem to be a necessary condition for the production of set effects, since even when order of report is controlled the effects of set are still found without loss in magnitude. The supporting evidence for the response-probability interpretation is extensive, in that the magnitude of the set effect varies with the manipulation of the probabilities of responses or limitations on responses. The third alternative, reorganization of the memory process mediated by S's coding strategy, is strongly supported in the results of three studies by Harris and Haber (1963) and Haber (1964a, 1964b). Fur-

ther, Haber's interpretations of those results suggests that the response-probability explanation may be reduced to memory reorganization (encoding), so that only one nonperceptual hypothesis may be needed.

While this review then suggests a narrowing of the number of nonperceptual alternatives, it provides less resolution to which of the two basic hypotheses is correct. The problem of analysis is still very complex—many of the experiments discussed provided clear-cut evidence for response or memory explanations, but without simultaneously demonstrating a lack of a perceptual effect. That is, finding evidence in favor of one hypothesis does not disprove the other, since they are not incompatible, only alternative. There is no reason to doubt that both may be correct and occurring together.

It is likely that a set effect created by differential value (e.g., Harris and Haber, 1963; Külpe, 1904; Lawrence and LaBerge, 1956) is mediated primarily or perhaps totally by characteristics of S's coding strategy. However, even with this, the Harris and Haber (1963) and Haber (1964a, 1964b) experiments do not rule out perceptual changes, since they had no converging operations sufficient to separate percept from coding effects. Their argument took the form that the set effect was present only in Ss using one type of strategy and not in Ss using another—therefore the set effect must have been due to properties of the strategy. Further, when the strategies themselves were examined, temporal and interference processes were found that were sufficient to account for the differential set effects between the two strategies, though again, this does not rule out perceptual effects completely.

So what conclusions does this evidence permit? Most Ss feel an increase in perceptual clarity occurs under appropriate set conditions, though their reports give no guarantee that they can really distinguish felt clarity from a better memory. On the other hand, there is no reason to doubt their reports either. Just because the evidence supporting response processes is clear does not imply that perceptual enhancement does not occur. Further, Bruner and Postman's (1949) finding of compromise perceptions and the strength of the trapezoidal illusion, to pick just two examples, make it difficult to doubt that at least some kinds of sets affect perception directly.

Therefore, this review must conclude inconclusively with respect to a choice between the two hypotheses. Some evidence exists to support each of them, and some exists which favors one over the other. But there is none that supports one while disproving the other. The issue is still crucial in perceptual theory, and obviously much more very careful research is needed. There is adequate demonstration now of the effects of set on both perception and responses. It still remains to show the conditions under which each will occur.

References

AMES, A., JR. Visual perception and the rotating trapezoidal window. *Psychological Monographs*, 1951, *65*(7, Whole No. 324).

AVERBACH, E., and E. S. CORIELL. Short-term memory in vision. *Bell System Technical Journal*, 1961, *40*, 309–328.

BORING, E. G. Attribute and sensation. *American Journal of Psychology*, 1924, *35*, 301–304.

BROADBENT, D. E. *Perception and communication*. New York: Pergamon Press, 1958.

BRUNER, J. S. Neural mechanisms in perception. *Psychological Review*, 1957, *64*, 340–358. (a)

BRUNER, J. S. On perceptual readiness. *Psychological Review*, 1957, *64*, 123–204. (b)

BRUNER, J. S., and L. POSTMAN. On the perception of incongruity: A paradigm. *Journal of Personality*, 1949, *18*, 206–223.

BRUNER, J. S., and M. C. POTTER. Interference in visual recognition. *Science*, 1964, *144*, 424–425.

CHAPMAN, D. W. Relative effects of determinate and indeterminant Aufgaben. *American Journal of Psychology*, 1932, *44*, 163–174.

CONRAD, R. Acoustic confusions in immediate memory. *British Journal of Psychology*, 1964, *55*, 75–84.

DEMBER, W. *The psychology of perception*. New York: Holt, 1960.

ERIKSEN, C. W. Unconscious processes. In M. R. Jones (Ed.), *Nebraska symposium on motivation: 1958*. Lincoln: University of Nebraska Press, 1958. Pp. 169–226.

ERIKSEN, C. W. Discrimination and learning without awareness: A methodological survey and evaluation. *Psychological Review*, 1960, *67*, 279–300.

ERIKSEN, C. W. Figments, fantasies and follies: A search for the subconscious mind. In C. W. Eriksen (Ed.), *Behavior and awareness*. Durham: Duke University Press, 1962. Pp 3–26.

ERIKSEN, C. W., and C. T. BROWNE. An experimental and theoretical analysis of perceptual defense. *Journal of Abnormal and Social Psychology*, 1956, *52*, 224–230.

FITTS, P. M. The influence of response coding on performance in motor tasks. In J. Macmillan (Ed.), *Current trends in information theory*. Pittsburgh: University of Pittsburgh Press, 1954. Pp. 169–226.

GARNER, W. R., H. W. HAKE, and C. W. ERIKSEN. Operationism and the concept of perception. *Psychological Review*, 1956, *63*, 317–329.

GIBSON, J. J. A critical review of the concept of set in contemporary experimental psychology. *Psychological Review*, 1941, *38*, 781–817.

GLANZER, M., and W. H. CLARK. Accuracy of perceptual recall: An analysis of organization. *Journal of Verbal Learning and Verbal Behavior*, 1962, *1*, 289–299.

GLANZER, M., and W. H. CLARK. The verbal loop hypothesis: Binary numbers. *Journal of Verbal Learning and Verbal Behavior*, 1963, *2*, 301–309.

GREEN, B. F., and L. K. ANDERSON. Color coding in a visual search task. *Journal of Experimental Psychology*, 1956, *51*, 19–24.

GRUBER, H. E., A. KULKIN, and P. L. SCHWARTZ. The effect of exposure time on mnemonic processing in paired-associate learning. Paper read at Eastern Psychological Association, Atlantic City, April 1965.

HABER, R. N. A replication of selective attention and coding in visual perception. *Jour-*

nal of Experimental Psychology, 1964, 67, 402–404. (a)

HABER, R. N. The effects of coding strategy on perceptual memory. *Journal of Experimental Psychology,* 1964, 68, 257–362. (b)

HABER, R. N. The effect of prior knowledge of the stimulus on word recognition processes. *Journal of Experimental Psychology,* 1965, 69, 282–286. (a)

HABER, R. N. Limited modification of the trapezoid illusion with experience. *American Journal of Psychology,* 1965, 78, 651–655. (b)

HABER, R. N., and R. B. HABER. Eidetic imagery: I. Frequency. *Perceptual and Motor Skills,* 1964, 19, 131–138.

HABER, R. N., and M. HERSHENSON. The effects of repeated brief exposures on the growth of a percept. *Journal of Experimental Psychology,* 1965, 69, 40–46.

HARRIS, C. S., and R. N. HABER. Selective attention and coding in visual perception. *Journal of Experimental Psychology,* 1963, 65, 328–333.

HERSHENSON, M., and R. N. HABER. The role of meaning of the perception of briefly exposed words. *Canadian Journal of Psychology,* 1965, 19, 42–46.

HINTZMAN, D. L. Classification and aural coding in short-term memory. *Psychonomic Science,* 1965, 3, 161–162.

HOISINGTON, L. B., and C. SPENCER. Specific set and the perception of subliminal material. *American Journal of Psychology,* 1958, 71, 263–269.

KRULEE, G. K., J. E. PODELL, and P. G. RONCO. Effect of number of alternatives and set on the visual discrimination of numerals. *Journal of Experimental Psychology,* 1954, 48, 75–80.

KÜLPE, O. Versuche uber Abstraktion. *Berlin International Congress of Experimental Psychology,* 1904, 56–68.

LAWRENCE, D. H., and G. R. COLES. Accuracy of recognition with alternatives before and after the stimulus. *Journal of Experimental Psychology,* 1954, 47, 208–214.

LAWRENCE, D. H., and D. L. LaBERGE. Relationship between recognition accuracy and order of reporting stimulus dimensions. *Journal of Experimental Psychology,* 1956, 51, 12–18.

LONG, E. R., R. H. HENNEMAN, and W. D. GARVEY. An experimental analysis of set: The role of sense-modality. *American Journal of Psychology,* 1960, 73, 563–567.

LONG, E. R., L. S. REID, and R. H. HENNE-MAN. An experimental analysis of set: Variables influencing the identification of ambiguous visual stimulus-objects. *American Journal of Psychology,* 1960, 73, 553–562.

MACKWORTH, J. F. The relation between the visual image and post-perceptual immediate memory. *Journal of Verbal Learning and Verbal Behavior,* 1963, 2, 75–85.

McKINNEY, J. P. Verbal meaning and perceptual stability. *Canadian Journal of Psychology,* 1966, in press.

MILLER, G. A. The magical number seven, plus or minus two: Some limits on our capacity for processing information. *Psychological Review,* 1956, 63, 81–97.

MILLER, G. A., E. GALANTER, and K. PRIBRIM. *Plans and the structure of behavior.* New York: McGraw-Hill, 1960.

NEISSER, U. An experimental distinction between perceptual processes and verbal response. *Journal of Experimental Psychology,* 1954, 47, 399–402.

POLLACK, I. The assimilation of sequentially encoded information. *HumRRO Research Laboratory Memo Report,* 1952, No. 25.

POSTMAN, L. Perception and learning. In S. Koch (Ed.), *Psychology: The study of a science.* Vol. 5. New York: McGraw-Hill, 1963. Pp. 30–113.

POSTMAN, L., and J. S. BRUNER. Multiplicity of set as a determiner of behavior. *Journal of Experimental Psychology,* 1949, 39, 369–377.

REID, L. S., R. H. HENNEMAN, and E. R. LONG. An experimental analysis of set: The effect of categorical restriction. *American Journal of Psychology,* 1960, 73, 568–572.

ROSS, S., Y. YARCZOWER, and G. M. WILLIAMS. Recognition thresholds for words as a function of set and similarity. *American Journal of Psychology,* 1956, 69, 82–86.

RUBIN, E. Bericht uber experimentelle Untersuchungen der Abstraktion. *Zeitschrift für Psychologie,* 1913, 63, 386–397.

SPERLING, G. The information available in brief visual presentations. *Psychological Monographs,* 1960, 74(No. 11, Whole No. 498).

SPERLING, G. A model for visual memory tasks. *Human Factors,* 1963, 5, 19–31.

TAUB, H. A. Effects of differential value on recall of visual symbols. *Journal of Experimental Psychology,* 1965, 69, 135–143.

TEICHNER, W. H., R. REILLY, and E. SADLER. Effects of density on identification and discrimination in visual symbol perception. *Journal of Experimental Psychology*, 1961, 61, 494–500.

TEICHNER, W. H., and E. SADLER. Effects of exposure time and density on visual symbol

identification. *Journal of Experimental Psychology*, 1962, 63, 376–380.

WILCOCKS, R. W. An examination of Külpe's experiments on abstraction. *American Journal of Psychology*, 1925, 36, 324–341.

Stimulus vs Response Uncertainty in Recognition*

JOHN A. SWETS   SUSAN T. SEWALL

Massachusetts Institute of Technology

We raise again, in the framework of a very simple recognition task, the question of the relative efficacy of specifying the stimulus alternatives before and after the stimulus is presented. Our experiments show information given before the observation to facilitate recognition and information given after the observation to have little, if any, effect. We conclude that the facilitative effect of restricting alternatives, in the task studied, depends on a perceptual mechanism rather than on a response mechanism. These experiments are discussed in connection with two current psychological theories: the theory of signal detectability, which is essentially a perceptual theory, and the theory of individual choice behavior, which is essentially a response theory. The results of another experiment, the only other experiment discovered to date for which these two theories make different predictions, are also reported. In this experiment, too, the results are in agreement with the detection theory.

Several experiments in recent years have shown that the detectability of a tonal signal suffers when the observer is uncertain about its frequency.[1-5] In the typical ex-

periment a trial consists of two temporal intervals, one of which contains the signal. In one series of trials the signal has a fixed frequency throughout the series. In another series of trials a different frequency is used, but again the same frequency is presented on each trial of the series. Under the condition of principal interest the signal on a given trial is equally likely to be either of these two frequencies. In any case, the observer indicates only the interval in which he believes the signal occurred; he is not required to indicate which frequency was presented. The measure of performance is simply the proportion of correct responses, denoted $P(c)$.

The consistent result is that the $P(c)$ obtained when uncertainty exists is lower than that obtained when the signal frequency is known. Moreover, the size of the decrement that results from uncer-

* *The Journal of the Acoustical Society of America*, 1963, vol. 33, pp. 1586–1592. This work was supported by the U. S. Army Signal Corps, the Air Force (Operational Applications Laboratory and the Office of Scientific Research), and the Office of Naval Research. This is Technical Report No. AFCCDD TR 60–44. We gratefully acknowledge the assistance of Elizabeth F. Shipley in the design of this research.

[1] W. P. Tanner, Jr., J. A. Swets, and D. M. Green, "Some general properties of the hearing mechanism," Technical Report 30, Electronic Defense Group, University of Michigan (1956).

[2] W. P. Tanner, Jr., *J. Acoust. Soc. Am.* 28, 882–888 (1956).

[3] F. A. Veniar, *J. Acoust. Soc. Am.* 30, 1020–1024, 1075–1078 (1958).

[4] J. A. Swets, Elizabeth F. Shipley, Molly J. McKey, and D. M. Green, *J. Acoust. Soc. Am.* 31, 514–521 (1959).

[5] C. D. Creelman, *J. Acoust. Soc. Am.* 32, 805–809 (1960).

tainty depends upon the difference between the two frequencies. When the frequency separation is increased from one group of trials to another, $P(c)$ drops steadily until it reaches a minimum that depends on the duration and the general frequency range of the signal.

These experiments were undertaken within the framework of the general theory of signal detectability, specifically, within the context of two models of the auditory process that were appended to the general detection theory in its psychophysical application.[6] The first of them was conducted to test a *single-band* model of the auditory process.[1] This model is reminiscent of the searchlight analogy to the process of attention. The observer attempting to detect a weak tonal signal is viewed as sensitive at any instant to only a narrow band of frequencies—as if he has at his disposition a single filter of fixed bandwidth, but adjustable frequency location. In order to change the band of sensitivity, the observer must sweep the filter through the intervening frequencies. Effecting a change of any consequence requires a measurable amount of time that increases with the extent of the change.

Given the values of $P(c)$ obtained when no uncertainty exists, the single-band model predicts the minimal $P(c)$ that will result from uncertainty. This minimum is obtained, presumably, when the two frequencies are sufficiently separated that the observer cannot listen for both during the duration of the signal; in this case the observer will not be listening at the frequency presented on half of the trials. The results of the first experiment were regarded as supporting this model. They showed $P(c)$ to decrease with increasing frequency separation until it approximated the predicted minimal level.

Subsequently, Green developed a *multi-band* model for predicting the detectability of a signal compounded of several frequencies.[7] According to this model, the observer is capable of listening at once to any number of frequency bands. He selects the number and frequency location of the bands to which he listens, and he bases his decision upon a linear combination of the outputs of the filters he has selected. When the multiband model is applied to the task of concern here, it predicts a smaller decrement from uncertainty than does the single-band model.

At this point, with a competing model on the scene, the force of the data was less obvious; the results of some observers were better fitted by one model, some by the other, and the results of the remaining observers lay between the two predictions. The later studies cited above were carried out in an attempt to distinguish more clearly between the two models, but they failed to produce conclusive evidence for either, and a standoff was declared.

Interest in the problem of frequency uncertainty was then revived by Luce's development of a theory of individual choice behavior,[8] and particularly by Shipley's adaptation of the choice theory to the task under discussion.[9] Shipley showed that the choice theory leads to two predictions, one exactly coincident with the prediction of the single-band model, and the other practically coincident with the prediction of the multiband model. The predictions from the detection and choice theories are displayed in Figure 1.

The great similarity between these two sets of predictions is surprising for, whereas the models associated with detection theory base their predictions on a concept of perceptual filtering, the choice theory achieves

[6] A description of detection theory and a recent review of its psychophysical applications can be found in D. M. Green, *J. Acoust. Soc. Am.* 32, 1189–1203 (1960). The present paper, however, is self-contained.

[7] D. M. Green, *J. Acoust. Soc. Am.* 30, 904–911 (1958).

[8] R. D. Luce, *Individual Choice Behavior: A Theoretical Analysis* John Wiley & Sons, Inc., New York, 1959.

[9] Elizabeth F. Shipley, *Psychometrika 25,* 273–289 (1960).

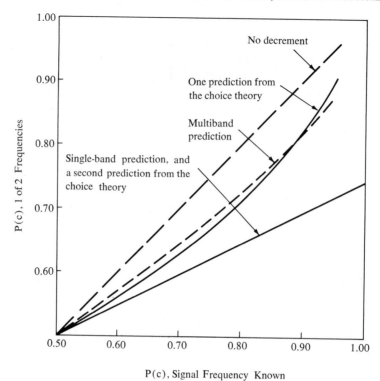

FIGURE 1 The various predictions, for $P(c)$ when the signal is either of two frequencies, are shown as a function of the average value of $P(c)$ obtained when no uncertainty exists. In the latter case only one of the frequencies, known to the observer, is presented on a series of trials. The figure shows the predictions from the single-band and multiband models associated with detection theory and the two predictions derived from choice theory.

its predictions by a manipulation of response probabilities. The choice theory asserts explicitly that uncertainty concerning signal frequency affects a response mechanism rather than a perceptual mechanism. For the task in question, the choice theory leads to the prediction that there will be no decrement as a result of uncertainty about frequency if the observer is informed after the observation, but before his response, which of the two frequencies was presented. The single-band model, of course, predicts that frequency information given after the observation will have no effect whatsoever. Similarly, the multiband model, which assumes an irrevocable combination of the outputs of the relevant filters, predicts that this information will not remove any of the decrement.

We report in the following some experiments constructed to test these divergent predictions of the detection and choice theories. The experiments compare the relative effects of frequency "cueing" provided before and after the observation. They are of particular interest because very few—in fact, only two—instances have been uncovered to date for which the grossly different assumptions of the two theories lead to noticeably different results. Over a wide range of experimental situations to which both detection theory and choice theory apply, they make almost identical numerical predictions. After reporting the results of the cueing experiments, we describe briefly the outcome of the other experiment for which the difference in predictions is large enough to make a test reasonable. It, too, is concerned with the distinction between perceptual and response mechanisms in what was first regarded to be a perceptual process.

The Cueing Experiments

In experiment I, the $P(c)$ obtained when the observation is followed by information about the frequency that was presented, is compared with the $P(c)$ obtained when no frequency information is given. The frequency cueing is supplied by two lights, with the simple code that the left light corresponds to the lower of the two frequencies and the right light to the higher. Experiment II examines the effects of cueing after the observation when the cueing is provided by the tones themselves; the frequency that was presented on a given trial is re-presented, this time clearly audible, before the response is made. Experiments III and IV serve as controls; they examine the effects of frequency cueing provided before the observation, by lights and by tones, respectively.

In describing the results, we are not concerned with distinguishing between the single-band and multiband models or, correspondingly, between the two predictions from choice theory. The present data, like previous data, are inadequate for this purpose; on the whole, the results fall between the two predictions. We confine our attention now to determining whether the results implicate a perceptual mechanism or a response mechanism as underlying the effects of uncertainty. A quantitative account of the decrement caused by uncertainty, in terms of either a perceptual or a response model, will be postponed.

In all four experiments the signal was a tone burst of 0.1 sec duration, of either 500 or 1100 cps. It was presented in a con-

tinuous background of white noise of approximately 50 db re 0.0002 d/cm². The same three practiced observers served in all of the experiments, two hours a day, five days a week. A two-interval, forced-choice task was used throughout.

Experiment I. Cueing by Lights after the Observation

METHOD

Eight groups of trials, of 100 trials each, were presented in a two-hour experimental session. In every session four experimental conditions were employed in a counterbalanced order: In the 1st and 8th groups of trials only the 500-cps signal was presented; in the 2nd and 7th groups only the 1100-cps signal was presented; in groups 3 and 6 the two frequencies were equally likely to appear on a given trial with no frequency cueing provided; in groups 4 and 5 either of the two frequencies was presented, and frequency cueing was given.

Preliminary sessions established the signal levels required to yield values of $P(c)$ of approximately 0.75, 0.85, and 0.95 for each frequency. These signal levels were 9.5, 10.5, and 11.5 db, respectively, for the 500-cps signal, and 10.5, 11.5, and 12.5 db for the 1100-cps signal. These signal levels are expressed in terms of 10 log E/N_o; E is the signal energy or time integral of power, and N_o is the noise power in a one-cycle band.

Five tests were conducted at these signal levels, in the order 0.75, 0.75, 0.85, 0.95, and 0.75. Each test occupied two experimental sessions, so each value of $P(c)$— for the 500-cps signal, for the 1100-cps signal, for either without cueing, and for either with cueing—is based on 400 trials.

The sequence of events on each trial and their durations were: warning light, 0.5 sec; space, 0.5 sec; observation interval, 0.1 sec; space, 0.5 sec; observation interval,

0.1 sec; space, 0.5 sec; an interval which (depending on the condition in force) was either empty or filled by a cue light to indicate the frequency presented, 1.5 sec; response period, 1.5 sec; an interval in which another pair of cue lights indicated the correct response, 0.5 sec. The total duration of a trial was 5.7 sec.

RESULTS

The results for the three observers are shown in Figures 2–4. The crosses mark the values of $P(c)$ obtained on the trials without frequency cues; the dots represent the trials in which frequency cues were supplied.

It is apparent that frequency information given by cue lights after the observation removes little, if any, of the decrement in performance that results from uncertainty prior to the observation. The average discrepancies between values of $P(c)$ obtained with and without information, for the three observers, are $+ 0.02$, 0.00, and

$+ 0.04$. On the whole, the deviations associated with frequency information are positive, but they are not significant.[10]

Experiment II. Cueing by Tones After the Observation

It seemed reasonable at the conclusion of the first experiment to suspect that the coded lights might not provide adequate frequency cueing. A shorter experiment was therefore conducted in which the tones themselves were used as the cues to frequency.

[10] Tests of significance, t tests, were applied to the data. The estimates of variances used in these calculations were obtained directly from the data. Binomial statistics were not used because they tend to underestimate the variance, especially when groups of trials comprising an experimental condition are distributed over time. Of 13 t tests one yielded a (one-tailed) $p = 0.01$; the others yielded values of $p > 0.10$. A combination of all the values of p according to the chi-square model [see L. V. Jones and P. W. Fiske, *Psych. Bull.* 50, 375–383 (1953)] led to $0.20 > p > 0.10$.

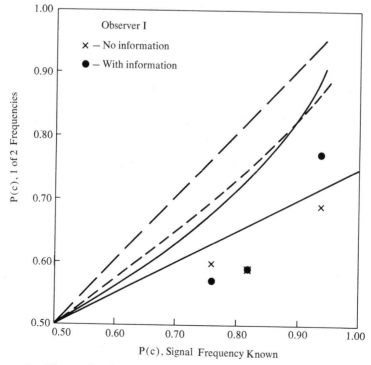

FIGURE 2   The results, for observer 1, of cueing by lights after the observation. This observer was absent during the first two of the five tests conducted.

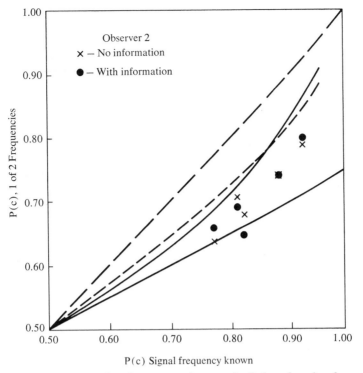

FIGURE 3   The results, for observer 2, of cueing by lights after the observation.

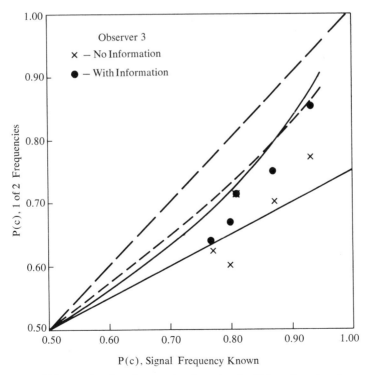

FIGURE 4   The results, for observer 3, of cueing by lights after the observation.

METHOD

The cue tone occurred after the observation, with the same intensity it possessed during the observation, while the masking noise was attenuated 10 db. For comparability, tones were also presented after the observation in the control conditions of the experiment, although in these conditions they did not supply additional information about the frequency that was presented. On those sets of trials in which only the 500-cps signal occurred, the 500-cps tone was re-presented while the noise was attenuated; similarly, on those sets of trials containing only the 1100-cps signal, the 1100-cps tone was re-presented; on the sets of trials in which the signal could assume either frequency but no cueing was to be provided, *both* tones were presented after the observation on every trial. The sequence of events on each trial and their durations were: warning light, 0.5 sec; observation interval, 0.1 sec; space, 0.5 sec; observation interval, 0.1 sec; space, 0.5 sec; cue tone, 0.1 sec; space, 0.5 sec; a second cue tone or not depending on the condition, 0.1 sec; space, 0.5 sec; response period, 2.0 sec; cue light indicating correct response, 0.5 sec. The total duration of a trial was 5.4 sec. The period during which the noise was attenuated extended from immediately after the second observation interval until the beginning of the response period.

Only one signal level was used for each frequency, that corresponding to a $P(c)$ of 0.85 in the preliminary test. The experiment consisted of 10 groups of 100 trials and was completed in a single two-hour session. Only the 500-cps signal was presented in groups 1 and 10; only the 1100-cps signal was presented in groups 2 and 9; in groups 3, 5, and 7 either frequency could appear on any trial with no frequency cueing provided; in groups 4, 6, and 8 either of the frequencies could occur, and frequency cueing was given. Thus the values of $P(c)$ for the 500-cps signal

alone and for the 1100-cps signal alone are based on 200 trials; the values of $P(c)$ for the two conditions with uncertainty before the observation are based on 300 trials.

RESULTS

The results for two observers (observer 3 was not present for this experiment) are shown in Figure 5. We observe there a result like that obtained in the first experiment. Frequency cueing given after the observation interval by the tones themselves removes little, if any, of the decrement associated with uncertainty prior to the observation. The discrepancy between the values of $P(c)$ for cueing and no cueing is -0.04 for observer 1 and $+0.04$ for observer 2. Apparently the cueing provided by tones is no more effective than the cueing provided by coded lights.[11]

Experiments III and IV. Cueing before the Observation by Lights and by Tones

This section reports the results of two control experiments in which frequency cueing was given before the observation, in one by lights and in the other by tones.

METHOD

Except for the fact that the cueing was given before the observation, the procedures used in Experiments III and IV were like those used in Experiment II. The only other difference of note is that the signal levels used in Experiment III corresponded to a value of $P(c)$ of 0.95 in the preliminary test.

RESULTS

Figure 6 shows that cueing by lights before the observation aids performance substantially more than cueing after the ob-

---

[11] A t test applied to the data obtained with cueing by tones yields $p = 0.50$. A combination of the results for cueing by lights and by tones after the observation led to $0.20 > p > 0.10$.

STIMULUS VS RESPONSE UNCERTAINTY IN RECOGNITION 725

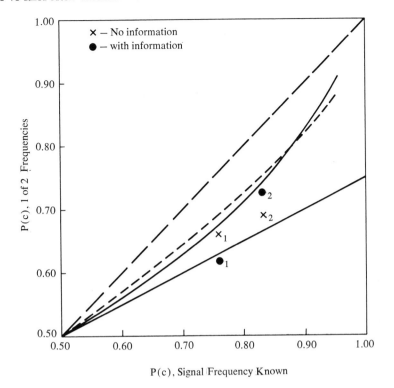

FIGURE 5 The results, for two observers, of cueing by tones after the observation. The subscripts on the data points refer to the observers as numbered in previous figures.

servation. The average differences between the values of $P(c)$ with and without cueing for the three observers are $+0.13$, $+0.04$, and $+0.08$. Figure 7 shows a similar result for prior cueing by tones; the relevant differences in $P(c)$ are $+0.02$, $+0.07$, and $+0.07$.[12]

Partial Summary and Comment

An experimental procedure in which the stimulus presented is specified before the observation, and a procedure in which the stimulus is specified after the observation, were compared with a procedure in which no trial-by-trial specification is made. In each case, two different ways of specifying

[12] The differences connected with cueing by lights have associated a $p \approx 0.001$. Cueing by tones yielded $0.05 > p > 0.02$. Considering both types of cueing given before the observation, $p < 0.001$.

the stimulus were used. It was found that a reduction in uncertainty before the observation facilitated performance, and that reduction in uncertainty after the observation led to little if any effect. This result indicates that the effects of stimulus uncertainty in this task are mediated by a perceptual mechanism rather than by a response mechanism. The result is consistent with detection theory, and it is inconsistent with choice theory.

The fact that the data points representing prior cueing fall consistently below the 45° line in Figures 6 and 7 is worthy of comment. It indicates that the observer performs less well when two frequencies are presented in random order over a group of trials, even when he is informed before each trial which frequency will be presented on that trial, than he performs when the same frequency is used throughout a group of trials. This result suggests that the

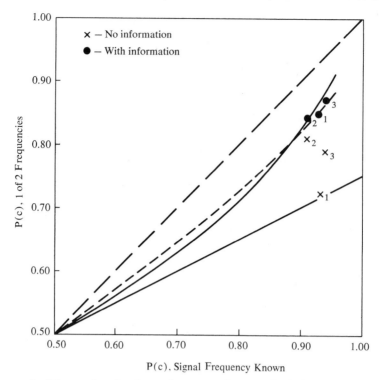

FIGURE 6   The results, for three observers, of cueing by lights before the observation.

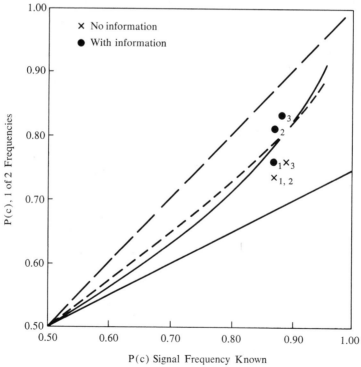

FIGURE 7   The results, for three observers, of cueing by tones before the observation.

observer sacrifices precision in adjusting his set if he must do so on a moment's notice. In this respect it is in agreement with certain other results we have obtained.

In an experiment such as the ones described here, but without frequency cueing, a contingency analysis was made to determine the probability of a correct response on a given trial for each of the four conditions that could have held on the previous trial: (a) same frequency, correct response, (b) same frequency, incorrect response, (c) different frequency, correct response, and (d) different frequency, incorrect response. It was found that if the same frequency was presented on two successive trials, the observer was more likely to be correct on the second if he had been correct on the first; if different frequencies were presented on two successive trials, the observer was more likely to be correct on the second if he had been incorrect on the first. This analysis indicates that the observer is differentially sensitive to the two frequencies at a given point in time, in particular, that he perseveres to some extent in listening to a given frequency band.

In another experiment, this one using only a single frequency, Shipley tested the hypothesis that the effective signal intensity on one trial influences the probability of a correct response on the next.[13] Relatively strong and weak signals were presented at random, and a higher $P(c)$ was observed on those trials following a correct response to the strong signal than on those trials following a correct response to the weak signal. This result was interpreted to mean that stronger signals provide better cues to the nature of the signal than weaker signals, and that the observer's perceptual set, following a strong

signal, is correspondingly better. Swets describes other experimental results which indicate that the set for detecting a weak tone is quite labile: even when the same signal is used throughout a series of trials, performance can be significantly improved by continually providing the observer with additional cues to the signal's frequency, starting time, duration, and amplitude.[14]

The fact that the observer performs less well when the frequency, though known, is changed randomly from trial to trial is not predicted by either of the theories we have considered. As a matter of fact, it had been assumed in connection with both theories, in deriving the original quantitative predictions for the effects of uncertainty without cueing, that the 45° line is an adequate baseline. We have not been concerned here with distinguishing between the single-band and multiband predictions or, alternatively, between the two predictions from choice theory. We note, however, that if data collected with the present technique are to be used in an attempt to distinguish between the two models associated with each theory, it will be necessary to make a correction in deriving their predictions; in particular, it will be necessary to use an empirically-determined baseline to represent the case of no uncertainty with trial-to-trial changes in frequency.

Another Experiment Related to the Detection and Choice Theories

An experiment was conducted to investigate the other known instance for which the detection and choice theories make divergent predictions. In this case, the problem for theory is to predict the function that relates $P(c)$ to the number of observation intervals in a forced-choice test. Again the prediction from detection theory is based upon a consideration of the mechanism of observation, and a different

---

[13] Elizabeth F. Shipley, "Cueing as a determiner of apparent variability in sensitivity," Quarterly Progress Report No. 53, Research Laboratory of Electronics, Massachusetts Institute of Technology (April 15, 1959).

[14] J. A. Swets, *Psychometrika* 26, 49–63 (1961).

prediction is derived from choice theory on the basis of a response mechanism.[15]

[15] The derivation of the prediction from detection theory has been reported in P. B. Elliott, "Tables of d'," Technical Report 97, Electronic Defense Group, University of Michigan (1959); the prediction from choice theory follows from Luce's discussion (see reference 8). W. S. Torgerson suggested to us that this experiment would provide a contrast of the two theories.

METHOD

Since some analyses of the data of this experiment have been reported previously,[16] the experimental procedure is not described in detail here. In general, it is like the procedure used in the experiments

[16] J. A. Swets, J. Acoust. Soc. Am. 31, 511–513 (1959).

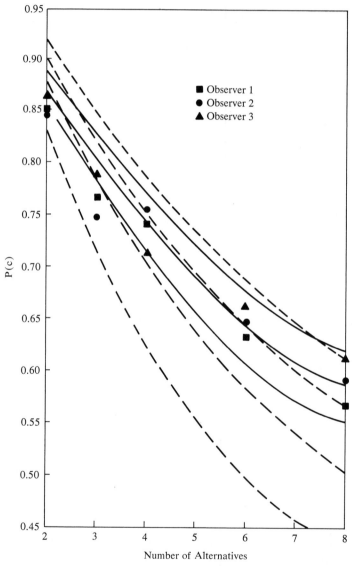

FIGURE 8   The results of forced-choice tests with various numbers of observation intervals compared with the predictions from detection theory and choice theory. The solid curves represent detection theory; these curves correspond to values of d' of 1.5, 1.6, and 1.7. The dashed curves represent choice theory and correspond to values of α of 5.0, 7.0, 9.0, and 11.0. The parameters of d' and α are the indices of detectability in the respective theories.

reported above. Only one frequency was used (1000 cps), but other aspects of the procedure such as the signal and noise levels, the signal duration, the counterbalancing of experimental conditions, and the previous training of the observers were similar. The essential facts are that values of $P(c)$ were obtained from three observers in a number of forced-choice tests having 2, 3, 4, 6, or 8 observation intervals; these values of $P(c)$ were based, respectively, on 300, 500, 600, 900, and 1200 trials.

RESULTS

The results are shown in Figure 8. They may be compared with the two families of curves shown in the figure, the dashed-line curves representing choice theory and the solid curves representing detection theory. It can be seen that the shallow curves from detection theory approximate the data more nearly than the steeper curves from choice theory.

Discussion

It has been known for a long time, of course, that the recognition of a brief stimulus is facilitated when the observer is told in advance that it will be one of a restricted set of alternatives. Külpe[17] and many others since[18] have suggested that the facilitative effect depends upon a perceptual mechanism, upon a perceptual tuning. For almost as long a time, the interpretation in terms of a perceptual mechanism has been questioned. The procedure used in the present study, that of comparing the effects of restrictive instructions presented before and after the observation, has been used several times to determine whether a response process might instead be responsible.[19, 20] This procedure has

also been used in an attempt to determine whether or not a memory mechanism, some modification of the memory trace, underlies the facilitative effect.[18, 19]

We should mention that we have not been concerned here with the memory hypothesis because we believe the before-after procedure to be insensitive to it. A consideration of the possible results of the procedure leads us to the conclusion that, whereas it permits a perceptual mechanism or a response mechanism to be ruled out altogether, it leaves the memory hypothesis invulnerable. As this hypothesis has been stated, memory could be, with any result, the only process involved. Neither of the other hypotheses can be supported at its expense, and it cannot be supported at the expense of both of the others.

The other principal difference between the present approach and the approach taken in the earlier studies is the level of generality implied. We have not asked, "What is the mechanism for the facilitative effect of restrictive instructions?" for we believe that the answer depends on the task chosen for study. Although the contradiction between certain of the earlier results[18, 19] may not have forced this conclusion, it seems unavoidable given the recent reports of Long, Reid, and Henneman,[21] Long, Henneman, and Garvey,[22] and Reid Henneman, and Long.[23] These investigators performed a number of experiments in which they used different numbers of alternatives and a variety of stimulus materials. In about half of their tasks instructions given before the observation were found superior to instructions given after the observation; in the other half, the two were equally effective. Thus, we would restrict our conclusions concerning the mechanism to the task that we employed. We see the general problem as requiring a large amount of parametric

[17] D. Külpe, *Ber. Kongr. Psychol.*, 56–68 (1904).

[18] See, for example, D. W. Chapman, *Am. J. Psychol.* 44, 163–174 (1932).

[19] D. H. Lawrence and G. R. Coles, *J. Exptl. Psychol.* 47, 208–214 (1954).

[20] I. Pollack, *J. Acoust. Soc. Am.* 31, 1500–1508 (1959).

[21] E. R. Long, L. S. Reid, and R. H. Henneman, *Am. J. Psychol.* 73, 553–562 (1960).

[22] E. R. Long, R. H. Henneman, and W. D. Garvey, *Am. J. Psychol.* 73, 563–567 (1960).

[23] L. S. Reid, R. H. Henneman, and E. R. Long, *Am. J. Psychol.* 73, 568–572 (1960).

exploration, to which we have added a single case.[24] This case is of particular

[24] Unfortunately, not all of the results that have been reported can be accepted at face value; Long, Henneman, and Garvey (see reference 22) obtained a result for words presented aurally that stands in flat contradiction to that obtained by Pollack (see reference 20).

interest because the stimuli are much simpler than any used in previous studies. It also led to a result not encountered before, namely, that information given after the observation had very little, if any, effect.

Interference in Visual Recognition*

JEROME S. BRUNER   MARY C. POTTER

Harvard University

Abstract. Pictures of common objects, coming slowly into focus, were viewed by adult observers. Recognition was delayed when subjects first viewed the pictures out of focus. The greater or more prolonged the initial blur, the slower the eventual recognition. Interference may be accounted for partly by the difficulty of rejecting incorrect hypotheses based on substandard cues.

Under ordinary conditions, visual recognition operates effortlessly and with no discernible interference. If the clarity of the display is diminished in some manner, however, recognition understandably takes longer. Moreover, studies indicate that if a subject is *initially* exposed to a blurred image that he cannot recognize, subsequent recognition of the image in clearer form is substantially delayed (1). The present report is concerned with the further investigation of this interference phenomenon.

We varied both the range of blur to which subjects were exposed and the length of time of the exposure. Undergraduate subjects were shown eight ordinary color photographs, projected one at a time. The pictures were initially exposed

* Science, 1964, vol. 144, pp. 424–425. Copyright © 1964 by the American Association for the Advancement of Science.

in a state of blur and brought continuously into better focus. The initial point of focus was varied, as was the amount of time the changing picture was in view. Under all conditions, the picture being exposed was stopped at the same point of focus, regardless of its starting point and its rate of change of focus. At this common terminal point, the projected picture was turned off and the subject was asked to report what it was.

Three starting points of focus and the common stopping point were determined as follows. Thirteen subjects were run individually as a standardizing group and were presented the pictures in gradually increasing focus, starting from almost complete blur (very blurred, or VB). The point at which they reported correctly the identity of the picture was recorded. For each picture, the point at which it was first recognized by any subject was obtained (light blur, or LB), and likewise the point at which a quarter of the subjects recognized the objects (first quartile, or FQ) (2); this latter was the stopping point used with all later groups. A fourth point was computed for each picture that was about four-fifths of the way from the out-of-focus point (VB) to the point of first recognition (LB). This point we refer to as medium blur (MB). Each of these points varied, of course, from picture to picture, since some pictures in fact required more clarity for recognition than did others. Each picture, changing toward clearer focus, was exposed for one of three lengths of time, the exposure intervals being chosen in the following manner. A slow but constant rate of change was first selected such that the time between VB and FQ (the stopping point) averaged 122 seconds per picture (range from 92 to 145 seconds). At this same rate of change, the average time from MB to FQ was 35 seconds (range from 26 to 49 seconds), and the time from LB to FQ was 13 seconds (range from 4 to 25 seconds).

Eighty-nine new subjects were now divided into nine groups of approximately equal size. Three of these groups began their viewing of each picture at VB; of these three, one group covered the course from VB to FQ in the long exposure averaging 122 seconds, one covered the same course of focus in the medium exposure of 35 seconds, and one in the short exposure of 13 seconds. Likewise, three other groups viewed the pictures moving from MB to FQ with the same three exposure times. And a final three groups started at LB and were given the same three times of viewing, thus completing a 3×3 design.

The pictures, 35-mm Kodachrome slides, were of a dog standing on grass, a bird in the sky, an aerial view of a cloverleaf intersection, a pile of bricks, a fire hydrant, silverware on a rug, glass ashtrays piled on a desk, and a set of brass fire irons. A Sawyer projector, model 500 EE, was used in a dimly lit room to project the pictures onto a non-glare screen 4.5 m away. A variable-speed motor controlled the excursion of the lens barrel, allowing focus to be changed at a wide range of rates. Subjects were run in groups up to 12, seated in two semicircular rows averaging 3.5 m from the screen. All subjects had normal vision or corrected normal vision as tested by a Snellen chart. They wrote their responses to the pictures on prepared sheets.

The results are shown in Table 1, and an analysis of variance is given in Table 2,

TABLE 1

Percentage of Pictures Recognized under Various Conditions of Time and Focal Range.

Each subject had eight pictures.

VIEW-ING TIME*	FOCAL RANGE			
	VB–FQ	MB–FQ	LB–FQ	MEAN
122	25.0 (N=8)	50.7 (N=9)	72.9 (N=9)	49.5
35	25.4 (N=14)	44.4 (N=9)	63.8 (N=10)	44.5
13	19.4 (N=10)	39.1 (N=8)	42.7 (N=12)	33.7
Mean	23.3	44.7	59.8	

* Average viewing time per picture (seconds).

TABLE 2

Analysis of Variance of Number of Pictures Recognized by Each Subject with Different Viewing Times and Focal Ranges

SOURCE	df	MEAN SQUARE	F	p
Time	2	1.252	5.70	.01
Focal range	2	6.463	29.43	.001
Interaction	4	.283	1.29	n.s.*
Error	80	.2196		

* Not Significant.

based on the number of pictures (out of eight) recognized by each subject (3). Viewing time has a systematic effect: on the average, the longer the viewing time permitted, the more frequently a picture is recognized. Although the interaction between time and focus is not significant, there is a suggestion in Table 1 that viewing time has a greater effect on recognition in the range LB to FQ than in the other focal ranges. Consider next the recognition scores of the groups that began viewing at different starting levels of focus. Here the interfering effect of viewing on subsequent recognition is striking, ranging from slightly less than a quarter of the subjects recognizing pictures when they began their viewing with a very blurred image, to well over half achieving recognition when viewing began with light blur.

One way of dramatizing the striking interference effect that comes from early exposure to the blurred version of visual displays is to compare two groups of subjects who were exposed to the same focal range, one group shifting from medium blur (MB) to the terminal point (FQ), and the other group shifting at the same rate but in the opposite direction, from FQ to MB. There were nine and ten subjects respectively in the two groups. The group that viewed the pictures coming *into* focus recognized them in 44 percent of the cases for the eight pictures. The group that viewed the pictures going *out* of focus over the same range succeeded in 76 percent of the cases—a highly reliable difference.

Do individual subjects differ in their ability to recognize pictures? Kendall's measure of concordance, W, was used to test the consistency of recognition scores of the 13 standardizing subjects. The result was not significant ($W = .116$, $p > .50$), suggesting that there is no general recognition ability under these experimental conditions.

In summary, exposure to a substandard visual display has the effect of interfering with its subsequent recognition. The longer the exposure and the worse the display, the greater the effect. Examination of the responses of the standardizing subjects, who reported aloud from the start of each picture, provides a clue as to the nature of the interference effect. Hypotheses about the identity of the picture are made despite the blur. The ambiguity of the stimulus is such that no obvious contradiction appears for a time, and the initial interpretation is maintained, even when the subject is doubtful of its correctness.

An incorrect interpretation of the picture may occur either in the primary figural organization of the picture (for example, an inhomogeneity is seen as concave, whereas it is convex in the full picture when correctly identified), or in the assignment of identity to a visual organization (the convexity is recognized, but is seen as a pile of earth rather than correctly, say, as a dish of chocolate ice cream). The amount of exposure necessary to invalidate an incorrect interpretation seems to exceed that required to set up a first interpretation, so that at any particular clarity of the display, those who see it for the first time are more likely to recognize the objects than those who started viewing at a less clear stage.

When one views a picture going *out* of focus, both initial clarity and resistance to change of interpretation are pitted in favor of correct recognition, which accounts for the great superiority of this condition. Indeed, it is striking how long one can "hang on" to the identity of a picture which is going out of focus, considering the difficulty of recognizing the same picture when it is seen for the first time coming into focus.

References

1. GALLOWAY, D., unpublished thesis, University of California, Berkeley (1946); D. WYATT and D. CAMPBELL, *J. Abnormal Soc. Psychol.* 46, 496 (1951); P. GUMP, unpublished thesis, Univer-

sity of Colorado (1955); A. CROWELL, unpublished thesis, McGill University (1961).

2. Since 13 subjects were used in the standardizing group, the point at which the fourth subject recognized the object was taken as the "first quartile."

3. Since there were unequal numbers of subjects in the various conditions, a method of approximation described by Walker and Lev (4) was used.

4. WALKER, H. and J. LEV, *Statistical Inference* (Holt, New York, 1953), pp. 381–382.

Word-Frequency Effect and Response Bias*

D. E. BROADBENT

Applied Psychology Research Unit, Cambridge, England

Many recent investigators have studied "Response Bias" theories of the perception of common vs. uncommon words. 4 different classes of theory are distinguished, and it is demonstrated that 3 of them are inconsistent with previously published and with fresh data. The 4th sense of response bias, however, leads to the prediction that bias on correct responses may be greater than that on errors, and is very accurately consistent with the data. This is the sense of response bias as analogous to the bias of a criterion in a statistical decision.

During the past 15 years or so, very much research interest and effort have been occupied with the comparison of the perception of words which are common in ordinary language on the one hand, and those which are uncommon on the other. The fact that common words are, other things being equal, more easily perceived is perhaps only a special case of the general influence of probability on perception. From the time of the classic experiments on distortion in perception and remembering, such as those of Bartlett (1932), it has been common ground to most psychologists that a probable event is easily perceived. The useful feature of the word-frequency effect is that it allows quantitative studies,

* *Psychological Review*, 1967, vol. 74, pp. 1–15. Thanks are due to Margaret Gregory for conducting the experimental work discussed in this paper, and to the British Medical Research Council for support. Some of the concepts were presented in outline form in a presidential address to the British Psychological Society in April, 1965.

which are almost impossible in the case of most other similar phenomena met in everyday life. It is hard to put a number to the probability of perceiving a man in a bowler hat in the City of London, as opposed to Manhattan. Consequently it is difficult to test any precise theory of perception choosing as stimuli pictures of men in bowler hats. In the case of words, however, we can to some extent describe the relative probabilities of different words in quantitative form. They thus provide a convenient special tool for investigating the general question of probabilistic effects in perception.

In very recent years, a number of writers on the word-frequency effect have considered the possibility that the effect is due to a response bias, rather than to some feature of the input of information to the organism. Unfortunately, the term response bias is itself ambiguous. There seem to be at least four different senses in which the term has been used, each implying a different definition of it. Definitions have not, however, usually been given, and the term has been used as self-explanatory. It seems worthwhile, therefore, to distinguish these possible definitions. As will be seen, when this is done the experimental evidence suggests that three of the definitions are inadequate as explanations of the word-frequency effect. The fourth, however, is very adequate. This fourth sense, admittedly, is not the one which has been most frequently used in the past. Thus it is not very surprising that several authors have concluded that response bias was not an adequate explanation (e.g., Brown & Rubenstein, 1961; Zajonc & Nieuwenhuyse, 1964).

A convenient starting point for the modern interest in response bias may be taken as the paper of Goldiamond and Hawkins (1958), who showed that when a tachistoscope was flashed at experimental subjects (Ss) without any word actually being presented, and when the responses were scored as if some particular word had indeed been present, they were scored as being more accurate in identifying those words which had in a preliminary experiment been more frequently presented. Since there could be no sensory component in this experiment, the effect could legitimately be described as response bias. In addition, it seems that the presentation of a fixed set of alternatives between which S has to choose, rather than an open-ended type of test, markedly reduces the word-frequency effect (Pierce 1963; Pollack, Rubenstein, & Decker 1959). Thus the effect certainly depends upon an adjustment of the organism which can be fairly rapidly effected, and which is not inherent in the nature of the stimulus. The use of the term "artifact" by Pierce shows that such a process of adjustment is not to all ways of thinking a genuinely perceptual effect at all. In brief, however, all the following different possible hypotheses seem to be consistent with the phenomena so far

cited; each of them implies a different definition of "response bias."

PURE GUESSING

On this model, S perceives a proportion of the stimuli correctly, and guesses on some or all of the remaining trials. If his guesses are more frequently common words rather than uncommon words, he might by chance score some correct responses on common words which would enhance his apparent performance.

SOPHISTICATED GUESSING

A more complex model is one in which, even when a stimulus word has not been correctly perceived, the information which has arrived at the senses nevertheless rules out some English words as being impossible, and leaves a restricted set of alternatives as still consistent with what has been heard. If now S chooses at random out of this restricted set, but with a bias towards the more probable words, he will, just as in the simple model, score some correct answers on common words by chance.

OBSERVING RESPONSE

In attempting to identify the word which has been presented, S may adjust his sense organs or his central mechanisms so as to maximize the effects of stimuli which he expects, at the cost of being badly adjusted to detect improbable stimuli. This might be described as a kind of "observing response" model: Its predictions will of course be closely similar to those of a view which regards the word-frequency effect as purely perceptual with no response component. However, this view does make it clear that the perceptual effect depends upon the adjustment of the observer and so may be less in forced-choice situations. It is therefore included as a possible variety of "response bias" theory, despite its similarity to nonresponse theories. It is worth noting, however, that evidence inconsistent with this theory may also exclude a "pure perception" view of the effect.

CRITERION BIAS IN DECISION

Lastly, the situation might be viewed as analogous to a statistical decision, in which the stimulus presented provides evidence pointing to a greater or lesser extent to each of the words in S's vocabulary. If S were biased in such a way as to accept a smaller amount of evidence before deciding in favor of a probable word rather than an improbable word, the word-frequency effect would be obtained. This last approach is probably the least used of the four, but it is nevertheless the one which the present paper will attempt to support.

To clarify the differences between the models, let us think of the following hydraulic analogy. Let us suppose a vast array of test tubes, each partly full of water, and each corresponding to a word in the language. The choice of one tube corresponds to perception of a word, and the probability of choice of any tube is greater when the water level in it is higher.[1]

On Model 1, presentation of a stimulus has no effect on the water levels, but all "high-frequency" tubes start off with more water than "low-frequency" tubes. Thus a high-frequency choice is more probable.

On Model 2, presentation of a stimulus raises the water level in a small proportion of tubes. This subsample includes the correct tube, but that tube receives no more water than each of the others in the subsample. Choice is effectively restricted to the few tubes selected by the stimulus: Within these few, a high-frequency choice is more probable because the initial level in that class of tubes was higher.

On Model 3, presentation of a stimulus adds more water to the correct tube than

to any other. This additional amount is itself greater when the tube is "high-frequency" than when it is low, perhaps because funnels are fitted to that class of tube to catch every possible drop. Correct choices of such tubes will therefore be more frequent even if the initial difference in levels is small or absent.

On Model 4, presentation of a stimulus again adds more water to the correct tube than to any other, but the additional amount is the same whatever the class of tube involved. Since, however, the initial level in high-frequency tubes is greater, a high-frequency choice is more probable.

The following points should be noted. First, the four models differ largely in the way in which the effect of the stimulus combines with that of the class of response. Second, response bias corresponds in Models 1, 2, and 4 to an initial difference in water level; while in Model 3 it may do so but also corresponds to a difference in the change of level produced by a stimulus. Third, in Models 3 and 4 the presence of a real stimulus, no matter how faint, always increases the probability of a correct perception.

Detailed Implications of these Theories

PURE GUESSING

This sense of "response bias" has been clearly stated by Dember (1960, p. 287), and is that which one would naturally infer from the papers of Goldiamond and Hawkins (1958) and Pierce (1963). (Throughout this paper it should be remembered that previous authors may have been *opposing* the value of response bias in their use of the term, and also may have changed their usage in later references.)

This simple theory implies that if

$$P_c = \text{apparent score correct}$$
$$p_c = \text{truly perceived}$$

---

[1] To be precise, the level of water in a tube shall be proportional to the logarithm of the probability of choice of that tube, as will appear later. Furthermore, in Models 1 and 2 there may also be occasions when the presentation of a stimulus determines a correct choice perfectly, with no probabilistic element. These occasions, however, are independent of word frequency and can be ignored for the moment.

p_F = probability of apparently correct response by guessing in the absence of a stimulus

then $P_c = p_c + (1 - p_c) p_F$.

We may define "response bias" in this case as the difference in p_F between common and uncommon words: If p_c is the same for all words, a greater p_F for common words would give a greater P_c for those words. But this model immediately involves us in ridiculous impossibilities. For example, even if no guesses of uncommon words are made at all, it means that S has a very high probability of guessing a common word correctly by chance. In an experiment to be reported later, there is a difference of approximately .2 in the probability of correctly perceiving a common as opposed to an uncommon word, and this means that the probability of guessing a common word completely correctly must be greater than .2. Since, however, this can be shown for more than five common words, the model is manifestly absurd. The word-frequency effect is much too large to be explained by supposing that the listener simply picks a word out of his whole vocabulary of common words whenever he fails to perceive correctly.

In addition, this model of perception is inconsistent with the effect on P_c which can be produced by presenting a fixed vocabulary of possible words and varying the size of this vocabulary. If pure guessing were the explanation of the improved performance which is shown with a smaller vocabulary, then the gain in correctly perceived words should always be smaller than the increase of probability of a completely random choice turning out correct. Thus a reduction in vocabulary size from 100 words to 50 should produce an improvement in performance of, at maximum, .01 : but this is considerably less than that actually attained.

Lastly, even if the foregoing reasons are not regarded as sufficient to exclude this model, it makes the following prediction which, as we shall see, turns out to be unjustified. Suppose we examine the errors which each S makes and divide them into common and uncommon words. Now when the stimulus word itself is common, some of the occasions when S guesses a common word will be scored as correct answers and not as errors. But if the stimulus was in fact a common word, naturally none of the guesses of uncommon words can possibly be scored by the experimenter as correct, and all of them appear on the answer sheet as errors. When, however, the stimulus is an uncommon word, the situation is reversed, and every guess of a common word is entered as an error. It may even be the case that an occasional guess taking the form of an uncommon word does turn out to be correct, and thus there may even be fewer recorded uncommon errors in this case than when the stimulus is a common word. Certainly, however, there will be more recorded errors of common words. If, therefore, we examine the error words and divide them into those words which are common in the language and those which are not, the ratio of occurrence of the former to the latter should be greater if the actual stimulus was uncommon than if the stimulus was common. (See Table 1). The effect must be a substantial one, if the word-frequency effect itself is large, since the entire advantage of the common words is derived from the fact that some common guesses are not scored as such. This prediction therefore serves as a test of this type of model.

SOPHISTICATED GUESSING

This theory is much less clearly absurd than the previous one. It has been upheld by Solomon and Postman (1952), Newbigging (1961), J. T. Spence (1963), and Savin (1963), among others. Brown and Rubenstein (1961) also used a formulation of response bias which is in some ways of this type. (The latter authors, however, found that the effect was too large for a model of this type. They contended that the number of responses, including error responses, which were of the same frequency class as the stimulus, was larger than it would be by chance, and they consequently suggested that S was receiving some information from the stimulus about the extent to which the actual word was common or uncommon.)

The theory can be represented by an equation closely similar to that for the previous case, namely

$$P_c = p_c + (1 - p_c) \, p_F \times \frac{N}{n};$$

where

N = total number of words in listener's vocabulary

n = number of words still possible after reception of a stimulus.

Response bias is defined as previously, as the difference in p_F between common and uncommon words. This would be perfectly capable of giving rise to a word-frequency effect of the magnitude actually observed, since the additional term $\frac{N}{n}$ could well be substantial enough to make the word-frequency effect considerably larger than the pure random probability of guessing a particular high-frequency word out of all those in the English language. For similar reasons, this model is capable of dealing with the large improvement in performance which occurs when the vocabulary of possible words is known and is small. Recently Stowe, Harris, and Hampton (1963) have produced a version of this model which predicts an exponential relationship of the form

$$P_c = p_F^{1/K}$$

and have presented data fitting such an equation.

It may be added that a similar type of model can be used to account for the large improvement in performance which occurs when a few words of context are given before a somewhat noisy stimulus word. In such a case, the listener may be able to say correctly what the target word is on quite a high proportion of occasions, even although he has quite a low chance of doing so with either of the two sources of information by itself. Empirically, this effect also can be fitted by an exponential relationship (Pollack, 1964; Rubenstein & Pollack, 1963; Tulving, Mandler, & Baumal, 1964).

Leaving aside the support or criticism which earlier papers provide for this model, it will be clear that it makes a prediction similar to the model previously discussed. That is, for common stimulus words some of the apparently correct answers were in fact guesses, and therefore there should be fewer common words among the errors to such stimulus words than there should be to uncommon stimulus words.

OBSERVING RESPONSE MODEL

This view has been most baldly stated by Broadbent (1958, p. 54) for the case of perceptual defense rather than the word-frequency effect. It would naturally arise, however, from a motor theory of speech perception (Liberman, Cooper, Harris, & MacNeilage, 1963), and is included among

TABLE 1

Guessing Theories of Word-Frequency Effects

S'S PERFORMANCE

TRUE PERCEPTION	HIGH FRE-QUENCY GUESSES	LOW FRE-QUENCY GUESSES
X%	Y% (= a + b)	Z%

APPARENT SCORE IN EXPERIMENT

	CORRECT	HF ERROR	LF ERROR
HF stimulus	X + a	b	Z
LF stimulus	X	a + b	Z

THE EFFECTS OF SET, PRIOR KNOWLEDGE, AND MOTIVATIONAL VARIABLES

a number of other mechanisms by Bruner (1957, p. 138). The essential feature of this third class of theories is that the input to the perceptual mechanism is regarded as flowing disproportionately from those characteristics of the stimulus which are especially indicative of common words. For example, peripheral or central adjustments might orient the system towards receiving acoustic cues relevant to the distinction between P and D, and not those cues relevant to the distinction between X and Z. Since the former letters, and perhaps their corresponding phonemes, are more common than the latter, this might give more accurate perception of common words. A number of well-known experiments show adjustment towards selective perception of some inputs rather than others (Broadbent, 1958). However, such a theory would not imply the same predictions as Models 1 and 2 concerning errors. One might on the contrary expect that detection of the *absence* of common phonemes would be especially efficient, as well as that of their presence. Thus common words would not occur often as errors, compared with their occurrence as correct responses.

In support of this analysis, one may cite an experiment on division of attention which has been analyzed by the techniques of signal-detection theory (Broadbent & Gregory, 1963). The experiment involved a man listening for a tone in noise in one ear, while he either memorized six digits arriving at the other ear, or else ignored them to concentrate upon the tone. Using signal detection theory, it is possible to calculate, from true and false responses in a psychophysical situation, a parameter (d') which can broadly be described as signal-noise ratio, and it was shown that concentration of attention upon one sensory channel improved this ratio. Thus the general prediction of the third theory would be that the parameter corresponding to signal-noise ratio, in a detection theory analysis, should be greater for common than for un-

common words: Response bias is here defined as a difference in d'.

RESPONSE BIAS AS A CRITERION PLACEMENT

This view has been most clearly stated by Goldiamond (1962) but is consistent with other lines of theorizing such as Treisman (1960) and Broadbent and Gregory (1963).

Signal detection theory, which has been briefly mentioned above, is now widely familiar (Swets, 1964). In brief, the basic suggestion is that some process varies randomly within the nervous system about a mean which is shifted in value by the arrival of a signal. In the case of yes-no detection of a single signal, some critical level of the process has to be exceeded for detection of the signal to occur, and it is obviously possible to produce a high rate of detections either by a large shift in the mean value of the process when the signal occurs, or else by a low value of the critical level. In the latter case, there will (other things being equal) be large numbers of false alarms. Nevertheless, a low critical level may be rational if signals are very probable, and it has been shown experimentally that the changes in performance produced in psychophysical situations by changes in the probability of a signal appear to correspond to changes in the criterion level. They do not correspond to changes in d', the shift of the mean value of the internal process which is produced by a signal.

The latter parameter is the one which was mentioned in the last section as corresponding to signal-noise ratio, and it would appear therefore that experiments on the detection of simple tonal signals of different probability lead us to a prediction diametrically opposed to the one derived from the previous model. If one could analyze the perception of speech on the basis of signal detection theory, this model would suggest that the word-frequency effect would correspond to a difference in the critical level necessary for a word to be perceived.

The perception of speech involves choice from many alternatives rather than the simple yes-no detection of a signal. Signal-detection theory has been extended to the forced-choice case, and when the resulting mathematics are applied to experiments on the perception of words drawn from known vocabularies of different sizes, the magnitude of the effect is satisfactorily explained without needing to suppose any change in the parameter corresponding to signal-noise ratio (Swets, 1964, p. 609). There thus appears to be a reasonable case for examining the word-frequency effect using the methods of signal-detection theory, and attempting to decide which of the crucial parameters is changed when common words are perceived rather than uncommon ones.

Unfortunately, it is difficult, using the methods of signal-detection theory, to handle the case in which a number of different responses (decision outcomes) have different degrees of bias attached to them. Accordingly, a fresh analysis has been made using a procedure suggested by Luce (1959), and this will now be explained. It should be emphasized that the method suggested by Luce derives from a different axiomatic approach from the earlier signal-detection theory, but the present author does not intend to support one set of axioms or the other. The two calculations lead to approximately similar conclusions in most instances, but in the present case the method of Luce is considerably more convenient.

The Analysis of Multiple Choice Situations with Varying Biases

The normal analysis of the forced-choice situation, from the point of view of signal detection, is to suppose that there are a number of different variables, equal to the number of alternative choices, and each varying normally and with unit variance about a mean which is zero for all alternatives except the correct one. For the correct alternative, the mean value is d'. On each trial, one sample is drawn from each of the resulting distributions, and the largest value determines the alternative which is chosen for response. The correct response, therefore, clearly has the greatest probability of occurrence, but there is some chance that one of the other alternatives may, through ill fortune, reach a high value when the correct alternative happens to have taken on a low value.

Biases are introduced into the situation by supposing that some alternatives have a mean which is greater than zero even before a stimulus arrives and are shifted by a further amount d' if the appropriate stimulus occurs.

Let us start by taking the case of a two-alternative forced-choice decision. In this case, we have two normal distributions, each with unit variance, and one of which has mean zero while the other has mean d'. If a sample is drawn from each distribution, the difference between these samples is itself distributed normally with mean d'. Thus if the two processes are named x and y, and if we take the difference $x - y$, there will be two resulting distributions, one with mean $+ d'$ when x is correct, and the other with mean $- d'$ when y is correct. If now we decide in favor of one alternative whenever $x - y$ is positive, and the other when $x - y$ is negative, we obtain a percentage of correct answers which can be calculated from the properties of the normal distribution, and which is convertible to d' by published tables.

By adopting a decision rule which changes from one alternative to the other when $x - y$ equals zero, we have taken a situation of zero bias. It would of course be equally possible to adopt the rule that we decide in favor of one alternative when x — y is greater than or equals C, and in favor of the other alternative when x — y is less than C. This would introduce a bias in favor of one alternative or the other, which would be precisely analogous to the criterion setting adopted in the yes-no case.

The approach adopted by Luce (1959) depends upon the following valuable approximation. If we have a process of the type already mentioned, normally distributed with zero mean, and if there is some critical value of the process at a value C, then to a reasonable approximation

$$\log \frac{P_F}{P_S} = KC$$

where

P_F = probability that process will not attain C

P_S = probability that process will exceed C

K = a constant, which may be eliminated by using appropriate units for scaling the value of the process.

This approximation allow us to work out very simply the consequences of a two-alternative decision, such as the one considered above.

Thus if

mean of distribution corresponding to Alternative 1 correct = $\log a$

mean of distribution corresponding to Alternative 2 correct = $- \log a$

Criterion level = $+ \log V$ (i.e., a bias in favor of Alternative 2),

then when Alternative 1 is presented

$$\frac{\text{Probability of Response 1}}{\text{Probability of Response 2}} = \frac{a}{V},$$

and when Alternative 2 is presented

$$\frac{\text{Probability of Response 1}}{\text{Probability of Response 2}} = \frac{1}{a\,V}.$$

This analysis can now be extended to the case of more than two alternatives, by use of the principle that the relative probabilities of any two alternatives are unaffected by the presence or absence of other alternatives. In the case of speech, this principle appears in general to be approximately valid, as has been shown by Clarke (1957). We may therefore draw up a table in which the columns represent responses and the rows stimuli; within each row, the ratio of the numbers in any two columns represents the ratio of the probabilities of those two responses when the stimulus appropriate to that row has been presented. That is, the entries in the table correspond to the quantities a and V of the example already given. For the four-choice case, see Table 2. Notice that each response may possess a different bias, and in addition that the effect of the correct stimulus may be different for each of the possible stimuli.

Turning now to the word-frequency effect, let us consider for simplicity two classes of words, one consisting of high-frequency words and the other of relatively low-frequency words. Again for simplicity, we may suppose that each of the former possesses a constant response bias V relative to each of the latter. Table 3 shows a section of the table for this situation. There

TABLE 2

Relative Strengths of Four Responses in the Presence of Each of Four Stimuli, to Illustrate the Notation

STIMULI	RESPONSES			
	1	2	3	4
1	$a_1 V_1$	V_2	V_3	V_4
2	V_1	$a_2 V_2$	V_3	V_4
3	V_1	V_2	$a_3 V_3$	V_4
4	V_1	V_2	V_3	$a_4 V_4$

TABLE 3

Relative Strengths of the Correct Response and of Each of Two Errors, in the Case of Speech Perception with Common and Uncommon Stimuli

STIMULUS	CORRECT RESPONSE	ONE PARTICULAR HIGH FREQUENCY ERROR	ONE PARTICULAR LOW FREQUENCY ERROR
High frequency	$\alpha_H V$	V	1
Low frequency	α_L	V	1

would of course be many other possible responses, some of them lying outside the two frequency categories altogether, but, as already argued, this would not affect the relative probabilities involved. The probability of responding with any one particular erroneous word is of little practical use. It is, however, of interest to consolidate all the error responses in the high frequency class with which we are concerned, which we may suppose to contain N_H different words, and also those in the low-frequency class, which we may suppose to contain N_L different words. Table 4 illustrates this change.

Table 4 will hold both for Model 3 and for Model 4: Model 3 holds if $\alpha_H > \alpha_L$, and Model 4 holds if $\alpha_H = \alpha_L$ and $V > 1$.

To clarify the meaning of the table, let us consider a few illustrative predictions from it. Suppose $\alpha_H = \alpha_L = 1$, that

is, no stimulus effect occurs at all (the Goldiamond and Hawkins situation). Let us also put $N_H = N_L = 4$, that is, consider a small fixed vocabulary like that of Goldiamond and Hawkins in which no responses occur outside the vocabulary. Then if $V > 1$, say $V = 4$, the probability of a correct response to an HF stimulus is $\dfrac{4}{4 + 3 \times 4 + 4} = .2$, while the probability of correct response to an LF stimulus is $\dfrac{1}{1 + 4 \times 4 + 3} = .05$. Thus the Goldiamond and Hawkins effect will occur.

In the same situation, suppose a stimulus of moderate strength is applied, so that $\alpha_H = \alpha_L = 6$. Assuming Model 4, then correct HF responses have probability

$$\frac{24}{24 + 12 + 4} = .6$$

TABLE 4

Final Table of Relative Strengths for Correct Responses and for Two Types of Incorrect Response, in the Case of Speech Perception Considering All Words in the Language

STIMULUS	CORRECT RESPONSE	ERRORS OF HIGH FREQUENCY	ERRORS OF LOW FREQUENCY
High frequency	$\alpha_H V$	$(N_H-1)V$	N_L
Low frequency	α_L	$N_H V$	N_L-1

and correct LF responses have probability

$$\frac{6}{6 + 16 + 3} = .24.$$

Notice that the difference in probability of the two types of correct response becomes greater when a stimulus is present, an effect which has sometimes been regarded as excluding a response-bias interpretation. On the other hand, if the stimulus is exceedingly strong, $a_H = a_L = 400$, the difference in correct responses becomes slight again.

HF correct responses then

$$= \frac{1600}{1600 + 12 + 4} \simeq .99.$$

LF correct responses then

$$= \frac{400}{400 + 16 + 3} \simeq .95.$$

In other words, with a strong stimulus prior biases are effectively overruled, and one perceives what is really present.

While these implications of the analysis help one to understand it, the two main questions are whether the facts of perception are consistent with this analysis rather than with Model 1 or 2; and, if this analysis is appropriate, whether Model 3 or 4 is the more nearly correct. To test these questions, two further predictions may be drawn from Table 4, for the case when N_H and N_L are large.

1. On Models 3 and 4, the ratio of errors of high frequency to errors of low frequency will be approximately constant, whatever the frequency class of the stimulus, provided that N_H and N_L are large. This is quite contrary to the prediction of the two guessing models, since, as already indicated, these models cannot allow large values of N_H and N_L.

2. If, for each class of stimulus, we divide the correct answers by the errors

which were of the correct frequency class, we obtain for the high-frequency stimulus $\frac{\alpha_H}{N_H - 1}$, and for the low-frequency stimulus $\frac{\alpha_L}{N_L - 1}$. Dividing one of these ratios by the other thus gives us $\frac{\alpha_H}{\alpha_L} \times \frac{N_L - 1}{N_H - 1}$. If we can determine $\frac{N_L}{N_H}$ by some independent means, then if the two ratios are equal, this implies that $\alpha_H = \alpha_L$. This in turn means that the "observing response" class of interpretation (Model 3) is not valid. It will also exclude purely perceptual theories of the effect. In that event, the response bias V must count for the entire word-frequency effect that is present.

An Illustrative Experiment

MATERIALS

Two lists of 60 monosyllabic words and one of 60 disyllabic words were prepared. Each list was prepared as follows. A group of 20 high-frequency words and another group of 20 low-frequency words were selected, new groups being used for each list. The list of 60 was then compiled by drawing words at random from the two groups of 20 subject to the restrictions that each word occurred at least once and not more than twice, that there were equal numbers of high-frequency and low-frequency words and also that not more than three successive words were drawn from the same frequency group.

The high-frequency words all had frequencies of at least 100 occurrences per million words (AA in the Thorndike-Lorge, 1944, count). They were selected by taking the first monosyllable or disyllable, as appropriate, on every tenth page of the Thorndike-Lorge word count. The low-frequency words had frequencies of not less than 10 and not more than 49 per million. (That is, they were in fact within the vocabulary of all normal adults.) They were selected by a similar procedure, the first word being selected on a different page from the first high-frequency word. Proper names, words suspected of having very different frequencies in English and American usage, and words beginning with a vowel were excluded from both the high-frequency and the low-frequency groups; also excluded from the low-frequency group were words having homonyms with higher frequencies.

The lists were recorded on one channel of a twin-channel Ferrograph recorder, each word being preceded by a serial number which served as a ready signal; a gap of about 12 seconds elapsed between successive words. Electronically generated wide-band noise was recorded on the second channel. The tape was played back with the outputs from both channels fed into a single external loudspeaker. The gain levels were adjusted so that the speech was reproduced at comfortable listening level (mean peak readings of 83 db. re .0002 dynes/cm²). The noise level was set by trial-and-error in preliminary experiments to allow about 30% correct responses in an open-ended situation while not resulting in perfect performance in a forced-choice: in fact the S/N ratios that resulted were in the region of 0 db.

All Ss were British housewives from the Applied Psychology Research Unit panel between the ages of 20 and 50.

PROCEDURE

(a) *Monosyllables.* The Ss were tested in groups. One groups of 12 Ss heard List 1 of monosyllables and a second group of 12 on a subsequent occasion heard List 2. Six Ss of each group gave forced-choice responses while the other six gave open-ended responses. The "forced-choice" Ss were given two matrices, one with the 20 high-frequency words corresponding to the rows and the other with the 20 low-frequency words. (They were not informed

of the difference in frequency between the two lists.) The columns of each matrix were numbered to correspond with the test number on the tape. They were told that each test word, according to its number, would be a member of one of the lists and that they should respond by ticking in a cell on the appropriate matrix, also that they should avoid leaving blanks. The Ss making open-ended responses were told that all the words were monosyllables and that they should write down whatever word they thought that they had heard even if they were unsure about it. However, blanks were allowed if S was really uncertain.

In order to avoid confusion arising from Ss losing their places and not being sure what serial number of response they should be completing (the numbers were given on the tape but were heard against the background of noise) the experimenter presented each number visually while the corresponding signal was being heard.

(b) *Disyllables.* The procedure for the list of disyllables was similar. Two groups, one of 11 and the other of 13, heard the same list on separate occasions; five Ss made open-ended responses in one group and seven in the other, the remaining Ss in each case making forced-choices. The Ss were informed that all the words would have two syllables.

SCORING

For each S in the open-ended condition six scores were taken: (a) the number of correct high-frequency responses, (b) the number of wrong high-frequency responses (of the same number of syllables as the stimulus) made to high-frequency stimuli, (c) the number of wrong low-frequency responses made to high-frequency stimuli, (d) the number of correct low-frequency responses, (e) the number of wrong high-frequency responses made to low-frequency stimuli, (f) the number of wrong low-frequency responses made to low-frequency stimuli. A high-frequency response was any response word having a frequency of 100 or more per million. A low-frequency response was any response word having a frequency of between 10 and 49 per million. Responses having a number of syllables different from the stimulus words were not included.

Those Ss who were presented with disyllables made a fair number of incorrect responses which consisted of a stem (usually high-frequency) followed by a common suffix, for example, "camp-ing." Such responses were not counted as high-frequency or low-frequency errors if the stem word was within the correct frequency limits because these words are not given as such in the Thorndike-Lorge word book. They could not, therefore, have been included in the sample count made to establish the relative numbers of high-

frequency and low-frequency words, nor sampled as stimuli. Whether for generating stimuli, classifying responses, or counting vocabulary size, the Thorndike-Lorge count was always used as the criterion.

SAMPLING COUNT TO ESTABLISH
THE RELATIVE NUMBERS OF
HIGH-FREQUENCY AND
LOW-FREQUENCY WORDS

On page 5 and every subsequent fifth page throughout the book (41 pages in all) a count was made of the numbers of (a) high-frequency monosyllables, (b) high-frequency disyllables, (c) low-frequency monosyllables, (d) low-frequency disyllables occurring on that page. Proper names other than American place names were included in the count because several of the Ss had given proper names among their responses.

TABLE 5

Monosyllables

STIMULUS	PERCENTAGE CORRECT	HIGH-FREQUENCY ERRORS	LOW-FREQUENCY ERRORS
High-frequency	32.50[A]	32.25[C]	15.83[E]
Low-frequency	12.77[B]	41.67[D]	19.17[F]

Note. $\dfrac{A \times F}{C \times B} = 1.512$. From Thorndike and Lorge: $\dfrac{\text{No. of LF monosyllables}}{\text{No. of HF monosyllables}} = 1.42$.

TABLE 6

Disyllables

STIMULUS	PERCENTAGE CORRECT	HIGH-FREQUENCY ERRORS	LOW-FREQUENCY ERRORS
High frequency	32.77[A]	9.73[C]	6.67[E]
Low frequency	11.11[B]	9.17[D]	14.44[F]

Note. $\dfrac{A \times F}{C \times B} = 4.38$. From Thorndike and Lorge: $\dfrac{\text{No. of LF disyllables}}{\text{No. of HF disyllables}} = 5.39$.

Results

FORCED-CHOICE

This condition was included in order to confirm that the percentage of correct responses was indeed similar for the high-frequency and low-frequency words in these particular tape recordings, and therefore that the random sampling of stimuli had not resulted in one class of words being acoustically superior in intelligibility. Preliminary studies had raised a suspicion that this can happen with nonrandom samples such as PB lists, but in the present case it did not and the two classes of words were equally intelligible.

OPEN-ENDED

The percentages of responses in each of the six categories of interest are shown in the tables. It will be noticed (a) that the word-frequency effect is markedly present, amounting to a difference in probability of correct response of about .2; (b) the errors of high frequency are, in the experiment on monosyllables, in a constant ratio to the errors of low frequency, regardless of the nature of the stimulus.[2] In the case of disyllables, there is some sign that low-frequency errors are more common to a low-frequency stimulus: this difference is not quite significant, being due to eight Ss out of the 12 tested, and will be discussed later. It is, in any case, in the wrong direction as far as the guessing models are concerned. Thus these data

[2] My attention has been drawn by Harris Savin to the prediction of Model 2 that errors to an HF stimulus will occur disproportionately often to those stimuli which happen to be very similar to other words of high frequency, and this will oppose the prediction tested here. We have therefore, reanalyzed the data, weighting errors from each stimulus inversely by the total number of errors to that stimulus, but the results are unchanged. It will of course be evident that Models 2 and 4 are in some ways very similar, so that supporters of the former may be happy to regard the latter as a modification of it.

clearly disprove the two guessing models; (c) in both experiments, the ratio of correct responses to errors of the appropriate frequency class, when compared for high- and for low-frequency stimuli, gave approximately the correct prediction of the relative number of words in the frequency classes according to the Thorndike-Lorge word count. The difference from the correct value is not, in fact, significant. If we work out the value for each individual S, then among the group receiving monosyllables seven Ss gave an estimate larger than that from the Thorndike-Lorge and five Ss gave a smaller estimate, while among the group receiving disyllables the numbers were five and seven. Thus it appears that there is no difference between high-frequency and low-frequency words in the quantity corresponding to d′ in signal-detection theory: The entire word-frequency effect is due to Model 4.

Conclusion and Limitations

The considerable number of experiments already in the literature on this topic have not provided data analyzed in this way. Consequently they do not assist us in deciding whether Model 4 explains the word-frequency effect in all cases, or whether the experiment cited is in some way peculiar. However, the experiment appears reasonably representative, and the author has been unable to find any feature of earlier results which Model 4 is unable to explain. Therefore, until some data are analyzed in this way and give contrary results, it would seem simplest to hold that Model 4 has been operative in all experiments on word frequency. This means

(a) that the effect is not due to biased guessing on trials when the stimulus has left correct and incorrect words equally probable,

(b) that the effect is not due to an increase of the stimulus contribution to correct perception of high-frequency words, but

(c) that the effect is due to a prior bias in favor of common words, which combines with sensory evidence favoring the objectively correct word.

It may be worth noting certain changes in conditions which might be expected to alter the pattern of results. For example, small values of N_H and N_L will tend to produce data which do not exclude Models 1 and 2. This is because the difference between N_H and $N_H - 1$ will then become important, so that the relative number of errors which are common words will increase if the stimulus is uncommon. We have found this to apply to forced-choice experiments, and also to visual rather than auditory ones. In the visual case, errors usually have several individual letters in common with the stimulus, and this restricts the effective size of N_H and N_L. One would expect a similar pattern of results with an auditory experiment at high signal-noise ratios.

Experiments showing this feature would, however, merely fail to disprove Models 1 and 2; they would not be evidence against Model 4. It is more important to consider cases in which Model 4 might be found insufficient.

One such case might be that in which unwillingness to respond at all becomes a major factor. Absence of response was allowed in our experiment, and so long as S does not use this possibility too often, the various ways in which it might be included in the mathematics do not differ much in the predictions they produce. Some (not all) of them might, however, require adjustment of Model 4 to fit data in which absence of response was common.

Perhaps more important is the possibility that stimulus words may carry information about their frequency class. As already indicated, Brown and Rubenstein (1961) concluded this, although providing data inconsistent with Model 3. Their con-

clusion is dependent, however, upon the particular assumptions implicit in their equations, and from our present point of view there is no need to accept it. Our results on monosyllables positively oppose it. There was, however, an insignificant tendency among disyllables for errors to be more common in the frequency class of the objective stimulus. Furthermore, the phenomenon of the "descent of the median" (Pollack, 1962) makes it seem likely that error frequencies sometimes change with the population of words presented. Therefore, although there is no positive evidence on this point, it may be that Model 4 may in some situations require modification by increasing V for HF stimuli.

Many, including the author, may regret the exclusion of any perceptual filtering or observing response mechanism. As some consolation we might postulate that such a mechanism could only become operative if relatively few cues were involved, that is, if N_H and N_L were small either through the use of a small vocabulary or through a powerful context. However, attempts in Cambridge to find such an effect have so far failed completely.

The supporters of a purely perceptual effect might rather consider that the use of the term response bias is perhaps misleading when it is applied to a model of the present type. It will be clear that the bias which has been postulated is not something which affects only the final overt response of writing down or uttering the word, but rather a bias applied to some central event, which may or may not occur following the delivery of a stimulus at the sense organs. The author would not think that a response bias in this sense can be described as an artifact. Rather it is a particular part of the perceptual mechanism. The term response bias is also objectionable because it suggests a kind of peripheralist theory which is now clearly unsatisfactory. Nevertheless, the bias which appears in the present model would explain results such as those of Goldiamond and Hawkins and the reduction of the word-frequency effect in forced-choice situations, and these are the phenomena which have given rise to the usual use of the term response bias. It is to be hoped that many of those who oppose the usefulness of the concept in its sense of pure or sophisticated guessing may nevertheless welcome its appearance as a parameter in a theory of perception based upon signal-detection theory.

References

BARTLETT, F. C. *Remembering.* Cambridge University Press, 1932.

BROADBENT, D. E. *Perception and Communication.* London: Pergamon Press, 1958.

BROADBENT, D. E. and M. GREGORY. Division of attention and the decision theory of signal detection. *Proceedings of the Royal Society,* Ser. B. 1963, *158,* 222–231.

BROWN, C. R., and H. RUBENSTEIN. Test of response bias explanation of word-frequency effect. *Science,* 1961, *133,* 280–281.

BRUNER, J. S. On perceptual readiness. *Psychological Review,* 1957, *64,* 123–152.

CLARKE, F. R. Constant-ratio rule for confusion matrices in speech communication. *Journal of the Acoustical Society of America,* 1957, *29,* 715–720.

DEMBER, W. N. *The psychology of perception.* New York: Holt, 1960.

GOLDIAMOND, I. Perception. In A. J. Bachrach (Ed.), *Experimental Foundations of Clinical Psychology.* New York: Basic Books, 1962, pp. 280–340.

GOLDIAMOND, I., and W. F. HAWKINS. Vexierversuch: The log relationship between word-frequency and recognition obtained in the absence of stimulus words. *Journal of Experimental Psychology,* 1958, *56,* 457–463.

LIBERMAN, A. M., F. S. COOPER, K. S. HARRIS, and P. F. MacNEILAGE. Motor theory of speech perception. (*Proceedings Speech Communication Seminar, Stockholm, 1963) Journal of the Acoustical Society of America,* 1963, *35,* 1114. (Abstract).

LUCE, R. D. *Individual Choice Behavior.* New York: Wiley, 1959.

NEWBIGGING, P. L. The perceptual redintegration of frequent and infrequent words. *Canadian Journal of Psychology,* 1961, *15,* 123–132.

PIERCE, J. Some sources of artifact in studies of the tachistoscopic perception of words. *Journal of Experimental Psychology,* 1963, *66,* 363–370.

POLLACK, I. Incorrect responses to unknown messages restricted in word frequency. *Language and Speech,* 1962, *5,* 125–127.

POLLACK, I. Interaction of two sources of verbal context in word identification. *Language and Speech,* 1964, *7,* 1–12.

POLLACK, I., H. RUBENSTEIN, and L. DECKER. Intelligibility of known and unknown message sets. *Journal of the Acoustical Society of America,* 1959, *31,* 273–279.

RUBENSTEIN, H., and I. POLLACK. Word predictability and intelligibility. *Journal of Verbal Learning and Verbal Behavior,* 1963, *2,* 147–158.

SAVIN, H. B. Word-frequency effect and errors in the perception of speech. *Journal of the Acoustical Society of America,* 1963, *35,* 200–206.

SOLOMON, R. L., and L. POSTMAN. Frequency of usage as a determinant of recognition threshold for words. *Journal of Experimental Psychology,* 1952, *43,* 195–201.

SPENCE, J. T. Contribution of response bias to recognition thresholds. *Journal of Abnormal and Social Psychology,* 1963, *66,* 339–344.

STOWE, A. N., W. P. HARRIS, and D. B. HAMPTON. Signal and context components of word recognition behavior. *Journal of the Acoustical Society of America,* 1963, *35,* 639–644.

SWETS, J. A. (Ed.) *Signal detection and recognition by human observers.* New York: Wiley, 1964.

THORNDIKE, E. L., and I. LORGE. *The teacher's word book of 30,000 words.* New York: Teachers College, Columbia University, Bureau of Publications, 1944.

TREISMAN, A. M. Contextual cues in selective listening. *Quarterly Journal of Experimental Psychology,* 1960, *12,* 242–248.

TULVING, E., G. MANDLER, and R. BAUMAL. Interaction of two sources of information in tachistoscopic word recognition. *Canadian Journal of Psychology,* 1964, *18,* 62–71.

ZAJONC, R. B., and B. NIEUWENHUYSE. Relationship between word frequency and recognition: Perceptual process or response bias? *Journal of Experimental Psychology,* 1964, *67,* 276–285.

The Effect of Competition on Visual Duration Threshold and Its Independence of Stimulus Frequency*

LESTON L. HAVENS   WARREN E. FOOTE
Massachusetts Mental Health Center, Boston Psychopathic Hospital

The effect of prior word usage on visual duration thresholds has been studied under tachisto-scopic conditions permitting control of competing or interfering responses. The degree of competition among these responses was significantly correlated with threshold. Stimulus frequency was not a significant variable under these conditions. We conclude that visual duration thresholds are not primarily a function of the frequency of prior usage of stimuli but of the ability or inability of the stimuli to evoke high frequency competitive responses.

Over the past 15 years experimental studies of perception have increasingly explored the organism's contribution to perceptual achievement. A host of experiments have investigated the place of motives, attitudes, and interests in perception and have resulted in such concepts as perceptual defense (McGinnies, 1949) and vigilance. With growing methodological sophistication the importance of the S's prior experience with the stimuli was demonstrated, and in particular the role of word frequency and its effect upon recognition thresholds. But just as the frequency findings explained at least part of the threshold differences attributed to perceptual defense, so there arose a need to explain the effect of frequency.

Solomon and Postman (1952) have proposed an explanation and Bruner (1957) has presented a general theory of threshold differences. Both emphasize the importance of competition between responses as a determinant of threshold.

Solomon and Postman (1952) write:

When a stimulus pattern is presented at short durations or at low illumination intensities, only fragments of the total word stimulus are "effective." Such a stimulus fragment may be considered to represent a point on the generalization dimension of stimulus patterns capable of eliciting the correct verbal response. A given stimulus fragment may, of course, be located on several generalization dimensions, each involving a different word. Which verbal response will be given depends on the relative strengths of association which have been established, through generalization, between the particular stimulus fragment and the different response words. If the visually presented stimulus word has had a greater frequency of prior usage than any of the competing response words, a correct response is highly probable.

Words of lower prior exercise frequency will be interfered with by words of higher

* *Journal of Experimental Psychology,* 1963, vol. 65, pp. 6–11. This work was sponsored by the Foundations' Fund for Research in Psychiatry. The authors wish to thank John E. Alman for his statistical assistance, and Dorothea J. Crook for her suggestions.

exercise frequency. This interference will manifest itself in the tendency for *S's* "guesses" to be high frequency words. If the actual stimulus word is a low frequency word, effective stimulus fragments will elicit erroneous "guesses" until the amount of effective stimulation becomes great enough on successive exposures to reduce the number of competing word responses (pp. 199–200).

The strength of association between any fragment and response is determined by two factors implicit in Solomon and Postman's (1952) explanation which can be usefully separated here. The first of these is a function of where on the "generalization dimension of stimulus patterns capable of eliciting the correct verbal response" the fragment falls. There will be a greater strength of association between fragment (stimulus) and response if the fragment lies close to the stimulus pattern most evocative of the response. In addition, however, strength of association depends upon the strength of the relationship between the most evocative stimulus pattern and the response. It is the strength of this relationship which Solomon and Postman suggest is at least partly a function of prior experience.

The concept of generalization dimension not only permits the gradation of stimulus fragments in order of their closeness to the most evocative stimulus pattern; it also explains why a fragment may be capable of eliciting more than one response. The fragment may be a common element on several generalization dimensions each of which is associated with a different response. Just as many stimuli can elicit the same response if each is at some point on the generalization dimension for that response, so one stimulus can elicit many responses if the responses have that stimulus point in common. It is this "buckshot" effect of tachistoscopic stimulation that opens the way for competition between responses. The fragment fires into many

generalization dimensions, stimulating a variety of possible responses. Ultimately, therefore, the likelihood of any given response depends upon its relative competitive strength.

Bruner's (1957) conception of the mechanism underlying perceptual failure is in terms of the "accessibility of categories," which corresponds to association strength in the explanation of Solomon and Postman. Categories in turn correspond to generalization dimensions. In discussing the causes of interference or competition, Solomon and Postman emphasize those to do with stimulus fragmentation and frequency of usage, while Bruner suggests that the state of readiness of the organism makes interference possible through a broadening of category acceptance limits. Both explanations agree in proposing that threshold differences are a function of some competitive or interference process.

It is toward an understanding of this competitive or interference process that the present investigation is directed. We have undertaken first to demonstrate its existence; previously it has been largely inferred from response time data and not directly demonstrated. Second, we have undertaken to measure its effect on threshold and, finally, to determine the relationship between competition and word frequency.

Method

Stimulus Materials. Sixteen four-letter words were chosen for presentation in a Gerbrands mirror tachistoscope. The stimuli were selected on the basis of principles derived from an earlier study, to be reported elsewhere. Briefly, however, our problem was the control of competition, that is, repetitive occurrences of incorrect prerecognition responses. We had observed that stimuli which elicited a large number of incorrect prerecognition responses were, first, words capable of being made into other words with few letter changes and, in addition, words which elicited high frequency responses. Other evidence that such responses tend to be of relatively high frequency is already in the literature (McGinnies, Comer, and Lacey, 1952; Newbigging, 1961).

More specifically, our earlier work suggested that any response which, in addition to being of high frequency, remained faithful to the first and last letters of the stimulus, differing from it only with respect to a form similar middle letter, would be a strong competitor. For example, the word "list" will become a preoccupation to anyone attempting to see the word "lint" under tachistoscopic conditions, the ready substitution of the s for n generating the competitor. Words such as "line" or "lift," both high frequency responses, are less probable because they do not match the form of the stimulus closely enough.

Stimuli were thus selected to control the range of prerecognition responses (clearly there are many other ways); the purpose was to determine the relationship between competitive responses and recognition threshold. Eight of the stimuli were predicted to elicit strong competitive responses (high frequency words which closely matched the stimulus) and were desig-

nated C_1. An equal number of other words were selected to which there would be few if any competitive responses; these were designated C_0. Because of the interest in the effect of stimulus frequency on threshold and the relation between competition and frequency, half of each group of eight words was of low and the other half of high frequency as defined by the Thorndike-Lorge G Count. An A and AA rating was taken as evidence of high frequency while a rating of 14 or less was used as evidence of low frequency. The letters were printed in lower case type by an IBM electric typewriter on bond paper. Eight of the words had high letters at beginning and end while the remaining eight were all even in height of letters. Table 1 illustrates the breakdown of the stimuli into groups according to the main variables.

Procedure. The stimuli were presented in accordance with a balanced Latin square design which permitted each stimulus to precede and follow every other stimulus once.[1] Each word was exposed three times

[1] We are grateful to Donald Shurtleff for his aid with the design.

TABLE 1

Breakdown of Stimuli According to the Main Variables

MAIN VARIABLES			
High Compet. (C_1) High Freq. (F_1)	High Compet. (C_1) Low Freq. (F_0)	Low Compet. (C_0) High Freq. (F_1)	Low Compet. (C_0) Low Freq. (F_0)
STIMULUS WORDS			
desk A	lint 2	over AA	wren 10
beat AA	tusk 2	wear AA	nave 2
some AA	scow 3	kind AA	fief 1
case AA	mare 14	book AA	drab 4

Note.—Frequency values from the G count are: A at least 50 per million but not so many as 100 per million. AA 100 or over per million.
Numerals indicate counted occurrence per million.

TABLE 2

*Analysis of Variance of Mean Log
Recognition Time Data*

SOURCE	df	MS	F
Frequency (F)	1	2072.07	1.51
Competition (C)	1	7703.51	5.60*
F × C	1	56.44	<1
Error (words within blocks)	12	1375.65	
Days (D)	1	876.75	3.07
D × C	1	31.01	<1
D × F	1	765.39	2.68
Ss	7	721.94	2.52*
S × F	7	554.11	1.94
S × C	7	442.85	1.55
S × D	7	1484.01	5.19***
S × F × C	7	866.07	3.03*
Error	74	286.03	

* $p = .05$.
*** $p = .001$.

at 10 msec., three times at 20 msec. and so on until the correct responses occurred twice successively within one time period. All responses were recorded by E after each exposure and the duration of the exposures was also noted. The experiment was carried out in two separate 1-hr. sessions scheduled approximately 1 wk. apart.

Subjects. Eight Ss were obtained from nearby college placement services and paid for their participation. Upon arrival at the hospital they were taken to the experimental room and seated in front of the tachistoscope. They were then read the following instructions:

This is a study in visual recognition, that is, how you set about recognizing things. The machine before you will expose meaningful words for varying intervals, at first too rapid for you to make out much or to detect anything clearly. A word will be projected between the penciled guide lines you see on the screen. Please report whatever you can make out between the guide lines after each exposure. Do you have any questions?

Results

A logarithmic transformation of the data was performed to reduce heterogeneity. The transformed data were then subjected to an analysis of variance the results of which are presented in Table 2.

It is evident that the main effect for competition is significant while that for frequency is not. This means that words designated as high and low competitors created a discrepancy in mean log recognition time sufficiently large to warrant acceptance at the 5% level of significance. On the other hand, discrepancy between high and low frequency words was not sufficiently large to warrant the assumption of a differential effect. Figure 1 shows the difference between levels of competition and levels of frequency with the Ss arranged in ascending rank order along the abscissa. The differences are distinct with respect to competition but not so with respect to frequency.

It is also evident that no significant interaction occurred between the two independent variables. The effect of compe-

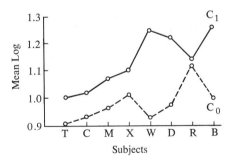

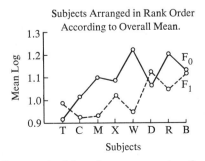

FIGURE 1   Mean log response time for 8 Ss.

tition proved independent of the frequency of the stimuli.

The remaining sources of variance in the table are concerned with day and S effects. The variance for day effect is associated with the two separate experimental sessions, and does not reach significance. However, it is not wholly negative, for while the data indicated that the effect of session is negligible for high frequency stimuli, it is less so for low frequency stimuli. This could be interpreted as an indication that low frequency words showed a practice effect not shared by the high frequency words, a probable conclusion.

Figure 2 depicts the interaction of Ss and word blocks. The range of individual differences is marked and is responsible for the significant MS for Ss. Figure 2 also shows the mean recognition time for each word block. The four means progress in the hypothesized order. That is, it was expected that the low frequency high competitor words would be the most difficult to recognize.

Up to this point, comparisons have been between the recognition thresholds of the stimuli predicted to encounter strong or weak competition on the basis of there being in English high frequency response matches for each—a match being defined as a response which has all but a middle letter in common with the stimulus and that letter the same shape as its stimulus counterpart. It remains to be shown that these words did indeed engender strong or weak competition. Table 3 indicates the total number of high frequency matches Ss reported for each stimulus, and also the total number of high frequency responses. The total number of matches for all eight high competitor words was 283 and that for the low competitor words 9. The separation of stimuli into high and low competitor groups is supported by these results.

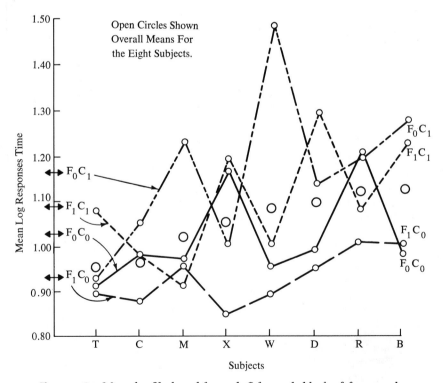

FIGURE 2   Mean log X plotted for each S for each block of four words.

TABLE 3

Number of High Frequency Responses per
Stimulus and Number of High
Frequency Responses That Are
Competitive Response Matches

STIMULI	MAIN VARIABLES	
	HIGH FREQ. RESPONSE	COMPET. RESPONSE MATCH
C_1		
lint	128	121
tusk	74	69
scow	38	35
mare	15	4
desk	10	1
beat	85	42
some	38	9
case	26	2
C_0		
wren	17	0
nave	29	0
fief	18	0
drab	18	0
over	18	0
wear	22	0
kind	4	0
book	32	9

Discussion

The present experiment has been an attempt to demonstrate the existence of a competitive or interference effect on recognition thresholds. Such an effect had been previously hypothesized in the theory advanced by Solomon and Postman (1952) to explain the repeatedly confirmed correlation between frequency of word usage and threshold. The present data demonstrate the existence of the competitive effect. We conclude that the availability or unavailability of strong competitive responses affects rapidity of recognition.

Furthermore, under conditions of either high or low competition, there are observed no marked differences of threshold as a result of varying the frequency of prior usage of the word stimuli. The data suggest only a trend toward a frequency effect that does not reach statistical significance. With the reservation that the number of Ss is small, we can state that in this experiment the frequency of prior word usage of the stimuli was not of itself a significant variable.

This conclusion defies the extensive experimental evidence advanced to support the claim of a stimulus frequency effect on threshold. The evidence is varied, well-controlled, and convincingly presented, and it is in fact not our intention to dispute its accuracy. Instead, we intend to explain the frequency finding in a new way, by reference to what we believe is the more fundamental principle behind it.

What our results suggest is that the frequency finding is an outcome of failure to control competition among prerecognition responses and that when the effect of this competition is controlled the frequency effect markedly diminishes.

It is important to have clearly in mind what is meant here by strong and weak competitors. Strong competitors are prerecognition responses with two characteristics: they are response words with a certain formal or structural similarity to the stimulus and a high frequency of usage. The importance of frequency is, therefore, implicit in the concept of competition, but it is not the frequency of the stimulus that is important but the frequency of the prerecognition responses. Competition acts independently of the frequency of stimuli, while the strength of the competitive response is partly a function of general word frequency. We, therefore, suggest the following revision of the frequency rule: threshold is not a function of the frequency of prior usage of stimuli but of the ability or inability of the stimuli to evoke high frequency competitive responses. These statements are in contrast with those advanced by Solomon and Postman in which both threshold and competition are functions of stimulus frequency.

Why then has a frequency effect been so consistently found? We suggest that the answer lies in a characteristic of any random population of high and low frequency stimuli: the likelihood of there being high frequency matches (strong competitors) for low frequency stimuli is greater than the likelihood of strong competitors for high frequency words. The reason is that the number of suitable form fitting responses is limited for any stimulus and the odds are greater of there being a high frequency match for a low frequency word which already occupies, so to speak, the high frequency slot. The operation of the more fundamental competitive effect has, therefore, lain concealed in the previous experiments on word frequency.

The present experiments do not, however, allow us to conclude that everything noted of the effect of prior usage on threshold is due to competition. The reported results only suggest that much, and perhaps most, of the frequency effect is due to competition. It remains to be seen what other mechanisms may mediate the previously observed frequency effect.

A final word: the present experiments serve to give much needed attention to the formal or structural features of the stimulus, and the effective stimulus frag-ments, in the determination of threshold. In many experiments an attempt has been made to avoid the structural problem by the use of capitalized stimuli. We doubt that this is ever altogether successful and may only serve to render the exact delineation of the role of structural features more difficult. It has long been known that structural features play an important part in threshold levels, but much remains to be discovered as to the mechanisms behind these threshold differences. Frequency itself may play a role and, as has been here suggested of those complex forms which are words, the effect of frequency may be mediated by competitive processes.

References

BRUNER, J. S. On perceptual readiness. *Psychol. Rev.*, 1957, 64, 123–152.

McGINNIES, E. Emotionality and perceptual defense. *Psychol. Rev.*, 1949, 56, 244–251.

McGINNIES, E., P. B. COMER, and O. L. LACEY. Visual recognition threshold as a function of word length and word frequency. *J. exp. Psychol.*, 1952, 44, 65–69.

NEWBIGGING, P. L. The perceptual redintegration of frequent and infrequent words. *Canad. J. Psychol.*, 1961, 15, 123–131.

SOLOMON, R. L., and L. POSTMAN. Frequency of usage as a determinant of recognition threshold for words. *J. exp. Psychol.*, 1952, 43, 195–210.

Stimulus Information and Contextual Information as Determinants of Tachistoscopic Recognition of Words[*]

ENDEL TULVING   CECILLE GOLD

University of Toronto

Tachistoscopic word recognition can be conceptualized as a situation in which S has to select a previously learned response from a set of alternative responses. Information from various sources can be used by S in arriving at the correct response. 3 experiments, in which recognition thresholds for target words were correlated with measures of information content and degree of congruity of their pre-exposure contexts, were conducted to evaluate the hypothesis that the amount of information that S needs from the tachistoscopically presented stimulus varies inversely with the amount of available relevant contextual information. Data from the experiments were interpreted as providing support for the hypothesis.

While it is perhaps rash to suggest that the human organism is nothing but a communication channel, conceptual analyses of behavior are often aided by analogies between experimental paradigms and communication situations. Consider, for instance, the experiment in which recognition thresholds are determined for tachistoscopically presented words. The S's task in the experiment can be conceived of as the selection of responses from a more or less well-defined set of previously learned and integrated responses. This response selection is guided by various sources of information, both controlled and uncontrolled, that are available to S.

One such source of information lies in the tachistoscopically presented stimulus word. Probability of correct response increases monotonically with exposure duration, expressing the direct relation between amount of stimulus information available from the tachistoscopic exposure and the

[*] *Journal of Experimental Psychology*, 1963, vol. 66, pp. 319–327.

duration of the exposure, but the amount of information available is relatively independent of the amount of information contained in the stimulus (Miller, Bruner, and Postman, 1954; Tulving, 1963).

Given a systematic relation between exposure duration and the amount of information available from the stimulus, measures of recognition threshold can be thought of as reflecting the amount of stimulus information that S needs for response selection. In these terms, then, all systematic variability in recognition thresholds indicates differential availability of information from other sources.

The S can sometimes select the correct response in the complete absence of stimulus information (Goldiamond and Hawkins, 1958; Smock and Kanfer, 1961). This observation, and the fact that complete but incorrect responses conveying some information often occur prior to the veridical report (Bricker and Chapanis, 1953), provide ample evidence for the utilization of information from other sources. The existence of these sources has long been known, and terms such as set, hypothesis, and expectancy have been used to refer to them.

It is reasonable to assume that different sources of information are complementary to one another in the sense that if one source provides much information then less information is needed from other sources. The experiments reported in the present paper were designed to evaluate the hypothesis that visual duration threshold (VDT), reflecting the amount of stimulus information needed by S, varies inversely with the amount of information provided by the context of the target word. In the first experiment, VDT was measured as a function of length of preexposure contexts that were either congruous or incongruous with the target word. The second experiment provided quantitative measures of two properties of contexts: information content, and degree of congruity with the target word. In the third experiment, covariations among VDT of target words and the two dimensions of contexts were examined.

Experiment I

Grammatical sequences of words and letters are redundant: S can often guess the word or letter that follows a given sequence. The accuracy of such guesses increases with increasing length of preceding context, up to a limit of 5–10 words (Aborn, Rubenstein, and Sterling, 1959) or 30–35 letters (Burton and Licklider, 1955). Increasing the length of context narrows the range of possible alternatives or increases the amount of information that is available to S about the target word. If, in a tachistoscopic experiment, VDT is directly related to the amount of stimulus information needed by S to make the correct response, and if the amount of this information varies inversely with the amount of relevant information available from other sources, then it would

be expected that VDT for words appearing in presence of context would decrease with increasing length of the context.

Increasing the length of context increases the amount of relevant information about the target word only if the context is congruous with the target word, that is, if the word following a given context does not violate the rules of the language with which Ss are familiar. If the target word is incongruous with the context, then increasing the length of the context would be expected to decrease the amount of relevant information and to increase recognition threshold for the target word shown tachistoscopically.

METHOD

General Design. Thresholds for target words were determined under 10 experimental conditions provided by orthogonal combinations of five lengths (0, 1, 2, 4, and 8 words) and two levels of congruity ("congruous" and "incongruous") of context. Each of the 10 Ss employed in the experiment was tested under all conditions. Ten different target words, selected on the basis of a small pilot study, were used throughout the experiment.

Stimulus Words and Contexts. Twenty-nine nine-letter, three-syllable nouns occurring four times per million (Thorndike and Lorge, 1944) were selected for pretesting in order to arrive at a relatively homogeneous group of target words. For all these words VDTs were obtained from 11 Ss, graduate students in psychology. The order of presentation of the words was systematically changed over Ss. On the basis of the data from this small pilot study, 10 words, having similar median thresholds and showing least inter-S variability, were selected as target words for the main experiment.

Each of the 10 target words was used in construction of a 9-word sentence, with the target word as the final word in the sentence. The preceding words in the sentence

TABLE 1

Contexts and Corresponding Target Words

SENTENCE NO.	CONTEXT	TARGET WORD
1	The actress received praise for being an outstanding	*performer*
2	Three people were killed in a terrible highway	*collision*
3	The escaped soldier was captured and court-martialed for	*desertion*
4	Far too many people today confuse communism with	*socialism*
5	She likes red fruit jams of strawberry and	*raspberry*
6	The skiers were buried alive by the sudden	*avalanche*
7	Many colorful flowers and stately elms lined the	*boulevard*
8	Medieval knights in battle were noted for their	*gallantry*
9	More money buys fewer products during times of	*inflation*
10	The loud piercing screams occurred with regularly increasing	*frequency*

constituted the 8-word congruous context for the target word. These contexts and their corresponding target words are shown in Table 1.

Contexts of Lengths 4, 2, and 1 were constructed by omitting the first four, first six, or first seven words, respectively, from each eight-word context. Absence of any context constituted the condition of Length 0.

Incongruous contexts of various lengths for a given target word consisted of congruous contexts of other target words. This procedure was based on the assumption that all target words, except the one that was used in the construction of a given sentence, would be incongruous with other contexts.

Subjects and Procedure. Ten female undergraduate psychology students served as Ss in this experiment. Their age range was from 18 to 23 yr., with the median age of 20. None had had any experience in psychological experiments. They had normal vision, corrected or uncorrected.

Each S was tested individually. Instructions to Ss included a statement that the words they were to identify "actually follow sequences of words," that parts of these sequences would be shown to them on most trials, and that the knowledge of the sequences may help them to recognize the words. All Ss were encouraged to guess when in doubt about the identity of the target word. VDTs for four practice words were determined for each S prior to the main part of the experiment in order to absorb the most striking practice effects.

The contexts were typed in upper case letters and shown to Ss in the upper part of the pre-exposure field of the Gerbrands mirror tachistoscope. The target words were also typed in upper case letters and presented for controlled durations in the exposure field. The level of background luminance in both fields was held constant at 2 ft-c (Macbeth illuminometer reading).

VDTs were measured by the ascending method of limits. Each target word was exposed initially at 10 msec. and exposure durations were increased in successive steps of 10 msec. until S gave the veridical report. At each level of duration two exposures were given. If S correctly identified the word on the first exposure at 60 msec., for example, VDT was recorded as 60 msec., if identification followed the second exposure at that level, VDT was recorded as 65 msec.

The order of presentation of different lengths of context of target words was systematically counterbalanced over Ss. The order of presentation of congruous (C) and incongruous (I) contexts, however, followed the same arbitrarily selected fixed pattern for all Ss: CICCIICICI.

RESULTS

The results of Exp. I are summarized in Figure 1. Mean VDT is plotted as a

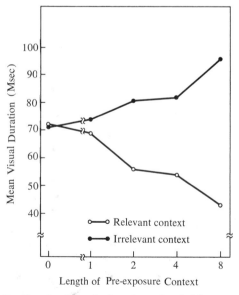

FIGURE 1 Visual duration threshold as a function of length of context for congruous and incongruous contexts.

function of length of pre-exposure context for both congruous and incongruous contexts. It can be readily seen that mean VDT decreases with increasing length of congruous context and increases with increasing length of incongruous context.

Analysis of variance of VDT measures adds statistical support for the impression gained from Figure 1. The interaction between length and type of context is highly significant: $F\ (4,\ 81) = 12.35$, $p < .01$. Individual analyses of the two curves separately also yield significant F ratios for length of context: for congruous context, $F\ (4,\ 35) = 11.47$, $p < .01$; for incongruous context, $F\ (4,\ 35) = 4.44$, $p < .01$. These analyses permit us to draw the conclusion that increasing the length of congruous context facilitates tachistoscopic identification of words, while increasing the length of incongruous context interferes with it.

Experiment II

In Exp. I only two levels of congruity were examined. It is obvious, however, that congruity is a continuous variable rather than a dichotomous one. Furthermore, the data were averaged over 10 different contexts at each level of length of context. It is quite possible that different contexts of a given length vary considerably in degree of congruity with respect to selected target words, both within the set of congruous and within the set of incongruous contexts. Quantification of degree of congruity between each context and its designated target word would presumably permit a somewhat more detailed analysis of the relation between congruity and VDT.

Similar considerations are relevant to the second dimension of context varied in Exp. I, namely its length. While it is clear that the constraining power of context varies with length, the relation may be different for different contexts. Moreover, since we manipulated length in Exp. I only in order to vary the amount of information conveyed by the context, it seemed useful to determine the constraining power of various individual contexts.

MEASUREMENT OF CONGRUITY
AND CONTEXTUAL INFORMATION

Degree of congruity between a context and a given target word can be measured simply in terms of relative frequency with which the target word occurs as a response in a large group of Ss who receive no stimulus information, that is, in a guessing situation. If all Ss guess the target word correctly, the congruity is maximum, if none of them does so, the congruity is minimum. If each S is permitted only one guess, then the measure of congruity (C) is given by the proportion of Ss who guess the target word correctly.

Amount of the constraining power of the context, that is the amount of information conveyed by the context, can vary independently of congruity, since it is specified without regard to the target word. It can be estimated from the distribution of responses in different response categories given by a large group of Ss. Many different measures could be used to assign a numerical value to the information content (I) of a context. In the present experiment, the following measure was used:

$$I = \frac{\Sigma n_i \log n_i}{N \log N} \qquad [1]$$

In this formula, n_i refers to the frequency of a given response i in the distribution of N responses, where each of N individuals gives one response. The formula is a restatement of the formula for redundancy in a set of events as used in the mathematical theory of communication (McGill and Quastler, 1955):

$$I = 1 - \frac{H(x)}{\max H(x)} \qquad [2]$$

The measure of I, as given by Formula

1 can vary between zero and unity, the former value representing the maximum amount of uncertainty in Ss' responses and hence minimum amount of information in the context, and the latter value representing minimum uncertainty in Ss' responses and hence maximum amount of information conveyed by the context.

METHOD

Each of the 50 contexts used in Exp. I (5 lengths $\times$ 10 sentences), followed by a blank space, was mimeographed on a small slip of paper. Different slips were stapled in haphazardly varied orders into small booklets. Each booklet contained 10 slips. Five of these were irrelevant for the purpose of the present experiment, although similar in nature. The other 5 represented five different lengths of context associated with different stimulus words. Ten booklets exhausted all 50 contexts used in Exp. I. A total of 1,000 booklets was prepared.

The Ss were 1,000 undergraduate students enrolled in various psychology courses at the University of Toronto. Testing was conducted in six large classes as a part of regular classroom procedure. Each S received a booklet and was instructed to complete the blank on each page of the booklet with an English word "best suited" to the words preceding it. In the case of no context, that is blank pages, Ss were simply asked to write the first word that came to mind.

Since each booklet contained 5 of the total set of 50 contexts, responses to each of the 50 contexts were obtained from 100 Ss. The procedure used resulted in a somewhat undesirable confounding of contexts and Ss, but in view of the necessity for reasonably large samples it nevertheless seemed preferable to testing a sample of 10,000 Ss that would have yielded the same amount of unconfounded data.

RESULTS

For each of the 50 contexts, indexes of both I and C were calculated. The amount of information conveyed by the context (I) was computed according to Formula 1, the degree of congruity between context and target word (C) was given by the relative frequency of responses corresponding to the target word for each context.

Table 2 shows values of I and C for all 50 contexts. The rows represent the 10 sentences as given in Table 1, the columns indicate the length of the context, the upper number in each cell shows I, and the lower number shows C.

As can be seen from Table 2, mean I increases monotonically with length of context. The relation between length of context and I for individual contexts, however, varies greatly among contexts. In some cases there is little difference in I between Lengths 2 and 4 (Sentences No. 5 and 6), but in some cases the difference is quite pronounced (Sentences No. 1 and 4). Other examples of such interaction between contexts and length in determining the amount of redundancy in Ss' responses can be easily discovered in Table 2.

Table 2 also shows that mean C increases monotonically with length of context. Variability in C among different contexts is noticeable at greater length of context. It is absent for Length 0 and small for Length 1 because of the fact that probabilities of correct guesses are at or near zero for these lengths.

Although both mean I and mean C in-

TABLE 2

Measures of Contextual Information (I) and Congruity between Context and Target Word (C) for 50 Contexts Used in Exp. I

SENTENCE NO.	LENGTH									
	0		1		2		4		8	
1	.07	.00	.31	.03	.23	.02	.49	.01	.40	.33
2	.08	.00	.36	.00	.37	.01	.69	.01	.83	.05
3	.06	.00	.23	.00	.34	.07	.47	.12	.51	.36
4	.08	.00	.24	.00	.20	.05	.58	.56	.59	.56
5	.04	.00	.11	.00	.53	.19	.55	.52	.62	.59
6	.07	.00	.22	.00	.21	.00	.20	.00	.78	.79
7	.07	.00	.11	.00	.37	.00	.47	.04	.47	.21
8	.07	.00	.24	.00	.18	.00	.25	.01	.55	.01
9	.10	.00	.14	.00	.23	.00	.37	.06	.68	.43
10	.06	.00	.12	.02	.18	.02	.27	.23	.45	.13
Mean I / Mean C	.07	.00	.21	.01	.28	.04	.43	.16	.59	.35

Note.—The upper number in each cell of the table shows I, the lower number shows C.

crease with length of context, the two variables are relatively independent of each other. For instance, the product-moment correlation coefficient between I and C for the 20 contexts at Lengths 4 and 8 is $+.439$. Other lengths are ignored in this calculation since their C values are mostly zero or else very small.

It is obvious, of course, that the extent of the correlation between I and C is largely a matter of the selection of a sample of contexts and target words. One can easily obtain a sample in which the correlation would be very high. Given a particular sample, however, the covariation between VDT and I, and between VDT and C, can be determined. This was undertaken in Exp. III.

Experiment III

METHOD

The 20 contexts at Lengths 4 and 8 and their congruous target words, as used in Exp. I, constituted the materials of Exp. III. Fifty female students between 19 and 30 yr. of age, enrolled in various psychology courses at the University of Toronto, served as Ss. None had participated in Exp. I and II.

The Ss were randomly divided into two equal groups. VDTs for target words in presence of four-word contexts were determined for Ss in Group I, and those in presence of eight-word contexts were obtained from Group II. Each S yielded one VDT for each of the 10 target words. The order of presentation of target words was systematically varied among Ss to minimize any sequential effects. All other conditions of the experiment were identical with those in Exp. I.

RESULTS

Table 3 shows mean VDTs for all 10 target words associated with four-word and eight-word contexts. Table 4 shows product-moment correlation coefficients among mean VDT, I, and C for 10 target words and for both lengths of context.

Correlation between mean VDT and C is negative and highly significant for both sets of context lengths. Other correlations are small and not significant. When the effects of I are partialed out, correlation

TABLE 3

Mean Visual Duration Thresholds for 10 Target Words Presented in Presence of Four-Word and Eight-Word Pre-exposure Contexts

TARGET WORD	MEAN THRESHOLD (MSEC)	
	FOUR-WORD CONTEXT	EIGHT-WORD CONTEXT
performer	80	67
collision	81	80
desertion	69	65
socialism	44	44
raspberry	52	47
avalanche	88	35
boulevard	68	71
gallantry	79	94
inflation	70	63
frequency	61	73
M	69.2	63.9

Note.—Each threshold value is based on data from 25 Ss.

TABLE 4

Product-Moment Correlation Coefficient among Mean VDT, I, and C Measures for the Target Words Associated with Four-Word and Eight-Word Contexts

	EIGHT-WORD CONTEXT		FOUR-WORD CONTEXT	
	I	C	I	C
Mean VDT	$-.357$	$-.928$	$-.275$	$-.970$
I		$.352$		$.279$

Note.—r (8) $-.765$ is necessary for significance at the .01 level.

coefficients between mean VDT and C change very little ($-.918$ and -968 instead of $-.928$ and $-.970$). Partial correlations between mean VDT and I, with the effect of C eliminated, however, become $-.087$ and $-.019$ for four-word and eight-word contexts, respectively. When the data are pooled for all 20 contexts, the picture remains essentially the same: correlation between mean VDT and C is $-.931$; between mean VDT and I, $-.349$; and between I and C, $+.439$.

Thus it seems that of the two dimensions of context, C accounts for a large proportion of variance in mean VDT, while I does not covary with mean VDT.

Discussion

The results of both Exp. I and III are quite consistent. They show that length of context or the amount of information conveyed by context, per se, is irrelevant to recognition threshold of target words. The length of context, as examined in Exp. I, seems to be important only insofar as it changes the degree of congruity between context and the target word. Similarly, as shown in Exp. III, there is no covariation between VDT and contextual constraint if the effects of congruity are neutralized, but covariation is high between VDT and congruity even if contextual constraint is partialed out. Thus, it is not just the amount of information in the context that determines the ease of tachistoscopic recognition of the target word, but rather the amount of *relevant* information.

If we assume that the degree of congruity reflects the amount of relevant information available from the context, and threshold reflects the amount of stimulus information that S needs for correct response, then the present findings can be regarded as providing full support for the hypothesis that sources of stimulus information are interchangeable with sources of contextual information. The role of the discriminative stimulus in experiments on tachistoscopic identification of verbal material, therefore, is simply to provide information about the response to be selected that is not available from other sources. In Goldiamond and Hawkins' (1958) Vexierversuch, according to the present argument, "background" information was sufficient in many cases to provide all the information necessary for veridical response selection and Ss were, therefore, capable of correctly "identifying" nonexistent stimulus words. Under some other conditions, such as when the forced-choice method (Blackwell, 1953) is used, nonstimulus sources of information are eliminated, and S's performance is completely determined by the availability of perceptual information. In many tachistoscopic experiments in which the ascending method of limits is used to measure thresholds, however, information from several sources jointly determines the level of performance.

The findings of the present experiments are relevant to the hypothesis theory of perception (Bruner, 1951; Postman, 1951). According to this theory, perception depends upon two classes of variables—(a) stimulus factors, and (b) expectancies or hypotheses of the organism. Two basic theorems relate strength of hypothesis to perceptual information. The first says that the greater the strength of the hypothesis, the less the amount of appropriate information necessary to confirm it. The second states that the greater the strength of the hypothesis, the more the amount of inappropriate or contradictory information necessary to infirm it. Two theorems seem to be necessary to specify the relations involved since the theory is focused on hypotheses and their confirmation or infirmation. With respect to the relation between stimulus information and information from other sources, the two theorems express the same thing—the amount of stimulus information needed for veridical report is an inverse function of the amount of information available from other sources. The data from the experiments reported in this paper are in good agreement with this generalization.

References

ABORN, M., H. RUBENSTEIN, and T. D. STERLING. Sources of contextual constraint upon words in sentences. *J. exp. Psychol.,* 1959, 57, 171–180.

BLACKWELL, H. R. Psychophysical thresholds: Experimental studies of methods of measurements. *U. Mich. Engng. Res. Inst. Bull.,* 1953, No. 36.

BRICKER, P., and A. CHAPANIS. Do incorrectly perceived tachistoscopic stimuli convey some information? *Psychol. Rev.,* 1953, 60, 181–188.

BRUNER, J. S. Personality dynamics and the process of perceiving. In R. R. Blake and G. V. Ramsey (Eds.), *Perception: An approach to personality.* New York: Ronald Press, 1951.

BURTON, N. G., and J. C. R. LICKLIDER. Long range constraints in the statistical structure of printed English. *Amer. J. Psychol.,* 1955, 68, 650–653

GOLDIAMOND, I., and W. F. HAWKINS. Vexierversuch: The log relationship between word frequency and recognition obtained in the absence of stimulus words. *J. exp. Psychol.,* 1958, 56, 457–463.

McGILL, W. J., and H. QUASTLER. Standardized nomenclature: An attempt. In H. Quastler (Ed.), *Information theory in psychology.* Glencoe, Ill.: Free Press, 1955.

MILLER, G. A., J. S. BRUNER, and L. POSTMAN. Familiarity of letter sequences and tachistoscopic identification. *J. gen. Psychol.,* 1954, 50, 129–139.

POSTMAN, L. Toward a general theory of cognition. In J. H. Rohrer and M. Sherif (Eds.), *Social psychology at the crossroads.* New York: Harper, 1951.

SMOCK, C. D., and F. KANFER. Response bias and perception. *J. exp. Psychol.,* 1961, 62, 158–163.

THORNDIKE, E. L., and I. LORGE. *The teacher's work book of 30,000 words.* New York: Teachers College, Columbia University, 1944.

TULVING, E. Familiarity of letter sequences and tachistoscopic identification. *Amer. J. Psychol.,* 1963, 76, 143–146.

Effect of Prior Knowledge of the Stimulus on Word-Recognition Processes[*]

RALPH NORMAN HABER

University of Rochester

Giving S knowledge of the stimulus word immediately prior to its exposure increased the probability of S being able to perceive all of the letters of the word ($p < .001$). While a difference in probability of perception of the letters was found for rare as compared to frequent words ($p < .001$), this difference completely disappeared when S had prior knowledge of the word. Both of these findings seemed consistent with a response interpretation of word-recognition processes. However, giving S repeated exposures of the word increased the probability of seeing the letters, regardless of whether he had prior knowledge of the word, a result interpreted as quite inconsistent with response processes. Further, examination of Ss' reports showed that they were perceiving letters, not making guesses about the word, and that the percept of the letters gradually increased in clarity, quite independently of whether they knew the word. The similarity of these results and conclusions to Hebb's notions of the development of cell assemblies and phase sequences was pointed out.

An interpretation of word-recognition thresholds based on response processes (e.g., Eriksen, 1958; Pierce, 1963) should predict that if S had complete and exact information about the stimulus word, just prior to its presentation, all variation introduced by the probability of occurrence of the word would disappear. This prediction is based on the assumption that if S has full prior knowledge of the stimulus, there can be no further variation introduced by differential probabilities of having response items available, or of testing the correct "hypotheses" about the stimulus. The present experiment attempted to test several implications of this prediction.

The Ss were shown both rare and frequent English words, with the number of exposures varied for each word, but not their duration or intensity. Half of the words were exposed, prior to their first flash, for 5 sec and S had to spell the word to E. In this way, for half of the words, regardless of their frequency in print, the response probability of S being able to select the correct word from all of the possible words in his vocabulary was 1.00, since he knew the word exactly.

It was expected that the words for which Ss had prior knowledge would have a higher probability of having all of their letters perceived. Further, it was also expected that there would be no difference in probability of perceiving all letters between the rare and frequent words when S had prior knowledge of the word. Without such prior knowledge, a difference

[*] Journal of Experimental Psychology, 1965, vol. 69, pp. 282–286. This research was partially supported by a grant from the United States Public Health Service, MH-03244. Deep appreciation is acknowledged to Maurice Hershenson, whose participation with the author on earlier studies made this one possible. Special thanks are also given to Martha Breen for her assistance in the collection and analyses of the data.

would be found, favoring the words that had appeared more frequently in print. Both of these predictions follow from a response interpretation of recognition thresholds.

A more difficult prediction concerns the effects of repeated exposures of the word. Haber and Hershenson (1965) and Hershenson and Haber (1965) both found that the probability of perceiving all letters of a word increased markedly with repeated exposures, even though there had been no increases in either duration or intensity of the stimulus. Since their Ss were reporting whether they saw the letters of the words, rather than whether they knew or could guess the word, they argued that the repeated exposures were affecting the development of a percept or image, rather than response probability or availability. Therefore, a "perceptual" interpretation would predict that even when Ss have prior knowledge of the word, there will still be a gradual increase in the probability of perceiving all of the letters with repeated exposures of the word. A response interpretation would have to predict that repeated exposures should have no effect on recognition, since Ss know what the word is.

Method

Each S was shown 576 seven-letter, three-syllable English words, divided into those rare and frequent. The rare words were selected from the rarest third of those appearing in the Thorndike and Lorge (1944) summary word count (G) and from words culled from Webster's Unabridged Dictionary (1939) that did not appear in the Thorndike-Lorge lists at all. The frequent words were all above the median on the summary count in the Thorndike-Lorge lists, and represent virtually the entire population of frequent English words with this structure.

These words were randomly divided into nine lists of 64 words, each list to be shown on one of the nine experimental

sessions of the experiment. Each list had an equal number of randomly ordered rare and frequent words.

The apparatus and viewing arrangements were the same as in the two previous studies (Haber and Hershenson, 1965; Hershenson and Haber, 1965). The stimuli were presented in one channel of a three-channel mirror tachistoscope (Scientific Prototype Manufacturing Corporation, Model D). A second channel, serving as background, was always lighted, and contained two faint lines for fixation boundaries. The reflectance measured at the eyepiece with a Macbeth illuminometer was 10 footlamberts (ftL.) for the background and 18 ftL. for the stimulus on the background.

The S was always prepared for the flashes, since he initiated each trial by pressing a button to trigger the tachistoscope.

Procedure. Each word was assigned one of two duration values (high or low), one of eight exposure trial numbers (1, 2, 3, 4, 5, 10, 15, or 25), representing the number of times it would be flashed, and one of two conditions of prior knowledge (none or complete). Duration was never changed during the presentation of a word, regardless of the number of exposures. The complete prior knowledge condition was provided by exposing the word for 5 sec. in the channel before the first trial and requiring S to spell out the word to E. The order of the frequency of the words was random, as were the number of exposure trials, and the duration of the exposures. However, every odd word was exposed first for prior knowledge. Within each session of 64 words, one word was shown for each of the 64 possible combinations of experimental variables.

Each S was given three practice sessions before the nine experimental sessions. These practice sessions included only frequent words, comparable to the frequent ones used in the later session, with no prior knowledge given for any of them.

The duration at which these practice words were exposed was systematically varied for each S, so that two durations could be determined for use in the latter sessions. The lower duration was one where S never identified all seven letters on the first flash, but occasionally did so when the duration was 1 or 2 msec higher. Once this lower duration was determined, the higher duration was set as 5 msec above it.

For each flash, in both the practice and experimental sessions, S reported the letters and their respective positions he was certain he perceived. The S was required to report the letters, even when he could identify the word. All analyses were based on the perception of letters, not of words. This maximizes reports based on what S saw, rather than on what he thought he saw. The S was scored as having perceived a word if he correctly reported seeing all of the seven letters on the last of the exposures given for that word. The S was given no feedback on his accuracy for the words without prior exposure. Further, S did not know at the time he was making his report for any trial whether there would be further trials for that same word. This unpredictability of further exposures was stressed to S, since otherwise S could withhold his reports until he was more certain. The S always knew when a new word was to be presented. The S was given extensive instructions regarding the importance of reporting letters rather than words, and he was reminded of them when necessary.

Subjects. Sixteen Yale undergraduates each served 12 hr as Ss. They were tested individually, and had never been in a perception experiment before.

Results

Figure 1 presents the results for the number of exposures (trials), duration of exposure, frequency of words, and prior knowledge. Since there appeared to be no interactions with trials, each S's scores were summed across trials, and the means of those summed scores are indicated by the points on the right of the figure. For each duration, both prior knowledge means are significantly above both no-prior knowledge means. While this is more true for the low duration, $t(15) = 10.61$, $p < .001$, than for the high duration, $t(15) = 4.10$, $p < .001$, a difference between durations that is also significant beyond .001, the convergence of the curves for the high-duration words was more likely to be due to a ceiling, which was clearly reached much earlier for the prior knowledge words. In any event, it is clear that giving S prior knowledge of the word increases the probability of his perceiving all of its letters.

For both durations, the difference between rare and frequent words was significant only when S had no prior knowledge—Low D: $t(15) = 6.73$, $p < .001$; High D: $t(15) = 3.47$, $p < .001$. Both t tests yield values less than 1.00 between rare and frequent when prior knowledge had been given. Thus, the second prediction was supported, that prior knowledge obliterates the difference between rare and frequent words.

The findings regarding the effects of trials clearly support the "perceptual" rather than the response interpretation. This was seen most clearly for the low duration, where there was no ceiling. Here, all four curves showed nearly identical effects of trials, regardless of the frequency of the words or the prior knowledge of S. The same tendency is apparent for the high-duration curves, even though the prior knowledge words reach the ceiling first. Consequently, even when S knows exactly what the stimulus will be, his ability to see all of the letters grows gradually with repeated exposures, just as it does when he does not know the stimulus.

For purposes of comparison with the two previous studies, least-squares solutions were obtained for each of the eight curves. The identical function was obtained for each of the eight, which was also the same function found repeatedly in the previous experiments. This was

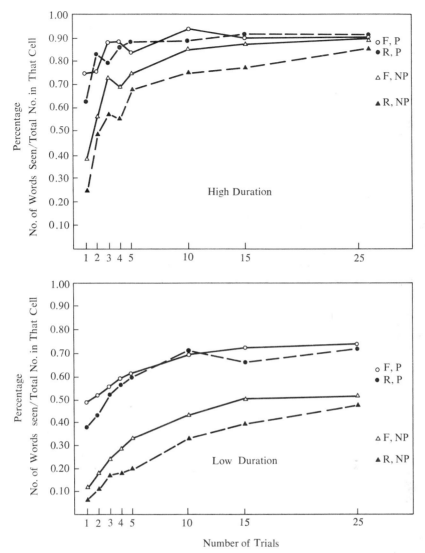

FIGURE 1 Probability of perceiving all the letters of a word as a function of repeated exposure trials, frequency of the words, prior knowledge of the words, and duration of exposure. (Frequency is indicated by frequent [F] or rare [R]; prior knowledge by P and no prior knowledge by NP. The points to the right of the curves are the means summed over the total number of trials, and are the basis for all of the t tests.)

$$P_n = A - q_1/n$$

where

P_n is the probability of perceiving all seven letters by the nth trial.

A is the asymptotic probability obtained after 25 trials.

q_1 is the probability of *not* perceiving all seven letters on the first trial.

n is the number of trials.

Each least-squares fit indicated that the exponent of n did not differ from 1.00 except by sampling error, but was significantly different ($p < .001$) from zero (a formal test of the significance of the effects of trials).

Discussion

These results indicate that the effects of word frequency are probably mediated by response processes, since these effects are removed when a principal source of variance due to response processes is also removed. However, such response processes probably do not account for the more basic perceptual behavior itself. While it seems intuitively reasonable that knowing what the stimulus will be should make it more easily perceived, this makes sense only if perceiving implies the ability to make some kind of probabilistic response of tentative recognition or identification. However, the rather slow growth in the actual ability of S to see the letters of the word, even when he knows exactly what the word is, does not seem to be a change in probabilistic responses.

This is most clearly illustrated by examining the nature of Ss' reports about their percepts. On the first flash of a word, S generally reported seeing nothing at all—no letters or pieces of letters. After several flashes, first pieces and then whole letters would be visible, and after a few more presentations, all of the letters would be perfectly plain and clear. The Ss, of course, could correctly guess the word well before all of its letters were perceived, but even after they had guessed it, there was a continued gradual development of the percept of the rest of the letters. These percepts became increasingly clear and distinct, so that reports after a number of presentations were not guesses or "hypotheses," but were based on quite an explicit and unambiguous image of the word. Thus, while it is possible that response processes might be controlling the guessing of the word, especially from images without all of the letters present, it seems quite unlikely that response processes are also controlling the gradual development of the percept of the word.

Another line of evidence supports this conclusion. The effect of trials, that is the slow growth in the probability of being able to perceive all letters as a function of repeated presentations, has now been found in three different experiments, under a variety of conditions. For example, this effect holds for frequent English words (this study, Haber & Hershenson, 1965, Hershenson & Haber, 1965), for rare English words (this study), for totally unfamiliar nonsense words (Hershenson & Haber, 1965), and words for which S knew their exact content immediately prior to exposure (this study). Further, the mathematical equation specifying the function of exposure trials to perceiving the words has been the same for each experiment and for each condition within each experiment. Thus, it would seem that Ss' knowledge or past experience with the words (the stuff of which response processes would be made) is fairly irrelevant to the development of a percept.

These three experiments, even taken together, do not suggest what mechanism would account for the growth of a percept. However, such a growth is remarkably similar to Hebb's (1949) discussion of the growth of a cell assembly, and the organization of cell assemblies into phase sequences. If this analogy is correct, then the development of such assemblies could be considered independently of previously established assemblies. That is, the *speed* of associating the components of an assembly would be independent of whether such an assembly had previously been established, even though the number of components with which one begins might be determined by the existence of previous assemblies, as well as other variables. In this sense, the intensity or duration of the stimulus, and the amount of S's prior knowledge or experience with that stimulus, would determine how many components are available at the beginning of the development of an assembly, under some kind of assumption that the more elements available, the faster or more completely the assembly develops. These variables might also determine the maximum degree of development, such that if the duration or intensity were too low, or the previous assemblies too incomplete, then the current stimulus would not lead to a fully organized assembly, which implies that the perceiver would never fully be able to see all parts of the stimulus.

The analogy to Hebb's theorizing is useful, not because these data provide any kind of test of his work, but that there seems to be some kind of formal similarity between the concepts of growth in perceptual experience (ontogenesis) that Hebb speculates about, and the development of a percept (microgenesis) that was actually measured in this experiment.

References

ERIKSEN, C. W. Unconscious processes. In M. Jones (Ed.), *Nebraska symposium on motivation: 1958.* Lincoln: Univer. Nebraska Press, 1958.

HABER, R. N., and M. HERSHENSON. Effects of repeated brief exposures on the growth of a percept. *J. exp. Psychol.,* 1965, 69, 40–46.

HEBB, D. O. *The organization of behavior.* New York: Wiley, 1949.

HERSHENSON, M., and R. N. HABER. The role of meaning on the perception of briefly exposed words. *Canad. J. Psychol.,* 1965, in press.

PIERCE, J. Determinants of threshold for form. *Psychol. Bull.,* 1963, 60, 391–407.

THORNDIKE, E. L., and I. LORGE. *A teacher's word book of 30,000 words.* New York: Teachers College, Columbia University, 1944.

Webster's new international dictionary of the English language. (2nd ed., Unabridged) Springfield, Mass.: G. and C. Merriam, 1939.

Personality and Perception in the Recognition Threshold Paradigm[*]

BERNHARD KEMPLER   MORTON WIENER

Clark University

Neither a "preperceiver" explanation (e.g., "perceptual defense") nor a "response hierarchy" explanation alone appears to be adequate for clarifying the personality-perception relationship in the recognition threshold paradigm. An alternative theoretical model is suggested in which "recognition" is held to be a function of the S's characteristic response to the supraliminal part-cues available to him on each exposure trial. The several theoretical formulations which include the part-cue notion are reviewed. The proposed reformulation requires that cues available to S be identified and systematically controlled, and that differences in response characteristics both within and between Ss be specified independently of the experimental recognition response. Possible experimental methodologies are suggested.

Investigations of the relationship of personality to perception have been of considerable interest to personality theorists as well as those interested in perception. For almost two decades, a large number of the studies investigating the personality-perception relationship have used the recognition threshold paradigm. However, because of

[*] *Psychological Review*, 1963, vol. 70, pp. 349–356. This paper is an elaboration of part of the general framework being investigated by a research project supported by USPHS Grant M-3860 of which the second listed author is Principal Investigator. This paper was completed during the tenure of a predoctoral Research Fellowship, MF-17,030 to the first listed author. The authors would like to thank Joachim F. Wohlwill for his critical reading of early drafts of this paper and for his valuable suggestions.

conceptual and methodological issues, the interpretation of the recognition threshold data for meaningful verbal stimuli continues to be a source of some controversy, with the personality-perception relationship in this paradigm being questioned. This very controversy has at times overshadowed the original focus of interest, i.e., the interaction of personality variables and perception in recognition threshold behavior. The time may now be ripe for a re-examination of the original concern.

The major controversy has been whether the differences in recognition thresholds for particular classes of stimuli or for particular subjects requires the positing of special perceptual processes which are the loci of the personality contribution and are assumed to affect the final perception by regulating or selecting what is to be admitted to awareness. Those investigators favoring a perceptual explanation of the data have posited constructs such as "perceptual defense," (e.g., Bruner, 1957; Bruner and Postman, 1947; Cowen and Beier, 1954; McGuinness, 1949, 1950)[1]; "perception without awareness," "subception," (e.g., Lazarus and McCleary, 1951) "registration," (e.g., Klein, Spence, Holt, and Gourevitch, 1958; Smith and Hendriksson, 1955). Although each of these constructs derive from somewhat differing theoretical biases, two major subclasses can be delineated. Some formulations (e.g., Lazarus and

[1] At least on of these investigators, (i.e., Postman, 1953) later stressed that such labels as "perceptual defense" may refer only to an "observed property of certain recognition thresholds", rather than a "mediating" process. Other investigators (e.g., Shannon, 1962) have proposed the use of recognition threshold procedures to investigate personality and perception, but state there is no necessity for specifying the mediating processes underlying differences in speeds of recognition. Shannon holds that the only assumption required for the use of the threshold recognition method in personality investigation is that the relative speed of recognition is one aspect of the overall adjustive and purposive behavior of the individual. Recognition threshold data may be meaningfully related to other behavior patterns of individuals, and no postulation of "defensive" perceptual operations or any other mediating processes need be made.

McCleary, 1951) posit a special process (subception), assumed to be evoked by *particular* classes of stimuli or events ("threat" or "need"); other formulations (e.g., Bruner, 1957; Klein, et al., 1958; Werner, 1957) posit special perceptual processes (e.g., physiognomic perception, gating, registration) that operate for *all* stimuli and perceptual events. However, in all of these formulations two basic assumptions are included: (*a*) there are at least two relatively independent perceptual systems, a supraliminal process that operates within awareness, and a subliminal process, i.e., "gating," "registration," or "subception," which operates outside awareness; (*b*) the latter subliminal process is more sensitive, i.e., makes discriminations the supraliminal process does not make. In each of these perceptual formulations it is assumed that the appropriate affective or evaluative reaction to the stimulus is made within the organism while the subject cannot yet discriminate and report the stimulus. Implicitly, therefore, the meaning of the stimulus or its appropriate meaning sphere is apprehended prior to correct recognition.

On the other side of the controversy are those investigators who question whether recognition threshold data can shed any light on the question of the personality-perception relationship, or that such a relationship need be posited from the data. These investigators (e.g., Freeman, 1954; Goldiamond and Hawkins, 1958; Goldstein, 1962; Howes and Solomon, 1950, 1951; Solomon and Postman, 1952) have shown a systematic relationship between particular response parameters (e.g., frequency of prior usage, recency, expectancy, sets) and threshold levels. The general conclusion of this group of investigators seems to be that a perceptual interpretation of the threshold data is unwarranted, and that all systematic differences in recognition threshold can be formulated as some function of known or discoverable response parameters. Although some of these investigators have suggested that the response characteristics may be related to personality (e.g., Solomon & Postman 1952), it is not clear from the various expositions of the response explanations whether any or how much variance in threshold behavior can be attributed to stimulus input. Occasionally the impression is even given that response probabilities remain constant despite changes in stimulus information. For example, Goldstein (1962) states: "The results indicate that the subject does enter the perceptual situation with clearly defined response habits which are not under the control of the perceptual stimulus and which can influence the subject's recognition score [p. 27]." At any rate, the response position considers it unnecessary to posit a personality-perceptual relationship to account for perceptual defense and related phenomena in the recognition paradigm.

Both of the above alternative interpretations of the recognition threshold data seem to consider response characteristics and perceptual processes as mutually exclusive explanatory categories. While the "response" explanation has minimized the contribution of the available part-cues, the "seeing" explanation implicitly assumes "meaning" availability even on those trials where the subjects cannot (i.e., do not) identify the stimulus. This dichotomy apparently corresponds to the statistical and methodological distinction between seeing variance and "saying" variance (Neisser, 1954). Although this distinction may be a useful one in experimentation and for the handling of data, care must be taken that what begins as a means of partialling out the variance of specific empirical results (i.e., differences in threshold) does not end in obscuring the possible relevance of the data for the personality perception relationship. Analyzing threshold variances into seeing and saying components does not imply that these two sources are in any meaningful sense independent in perception. Further, any theoretical formulations

of the relationship of personality and perception in recognition should be congruent with the explanations of other perceptual behaviors, and need, therefore, include both the stimulus input and the response characteristics of the subjects. The problem, then, appears to be how to reinterpret and reformulate the recognition data for the personality-perception relationship without, on the one hand, invoking special and unusual processes for special instances, or, on the other hand, minimizing or ignoring the stimulus input contribution.

Some investigators have taken a step in this direction by going beyond the somewhat facile distinction between seeing and saying, and attempting a more detailed analysis of the variables which may be involved in the recognition situation. Eriksen (1956) and Eriksen and Browne (1956), for example, have pointed out that an incorrect report on a recognition trial may be a function of the limited number of verbal categories which are available to the subject to indicate what he "sees." Bricker and Chapanis (1953) and Blackwell (1953) have shown that those recognition trials, on which the subject reports seeing "nothing," or gives an incorrect report, may nevertheless provide the subject with some useful information about the stimulus. In a similar vein Wiener (1957)[2] and Wiener and Schiller (1960) have argued that the postulation of subliminal processes to account for differential recognition thresholds must be considered premature as long as the operation of all supraliminal perceptual factors has not been ruled out. All of the above writers appear to distinguish among the stimulus as given by the experimenter (e.g., a word or phrase), the available cue to the subject, i.e., that portion of the stimulus which the subject perceives "supraliminally," and the subject's verbal report irrespective of its

[2] M. Wiener, research proposal entitled "Perceptual Thresholds: Conditions and Parameters," 1957, National Institute of Mental Health, United States Public Health Service.

correctness, i.e., match of the subject's report with the experimenter's data sheet.

As has been emphasized by several investigators (Goldiamond, 1958; McConnell, Cutler, and McNeil, 1958; Wiener, 1957; Wiener and Schiller, 1960) threshold is a statistical concept rather than an absolute point or value. Thus, *on any given trial or exposure level* (particularly in the word recognition paradigm) any subject may have (be "aware" of) a range of information about the stimulus, from A, nothing at all, to B, some part of the stimulus (part-cue perception), to C, a sufficient number of cues so that no other than a specific (i.e., the correct) response has a significant probability of being emitted. The consequences of the stimulus inputs for "recognition" should differ at these three ranges within the perceptual-cue continuum. In Instance A (i.e., no input), recognition threshold can only be some function of a subject's response characteristics and the probability of his pattern of responses matching the experimenter's data sheet (e.g., Goldiamond and Hawkins, 1958). However, even under this extreme condition, the explanation in terms of absolute response hierarchy based on frequencies of occurrence in the English language or absolute response characteristics of the subjects requires some modification. There is evidence that a subject's pattern of responses will vary with situations, instructions, knowledge of correctness, etc. (e.g., Goldstein and Himmelfarb, 1962; Smock and Kanfer, 1961). In the instances of C (i.e., a great deal of information), the contribution of the subject's response characteristics is minimal, since even a stimulus word with which the subject is unfamiliar would be expected to be correctly identified and reported on these trials, if we assume some correspondence between seeing and saying.

On the most trials in the word recognition paradigm, the subject is likely to have part of the information available, that is the B range of perceptual cue continuum.

On any one trial, the subject may be aware of some of the letters, the probable length of the word, straight-round letter, etc. Further, as is evident from psychophysical research, it is unlikely that cues remain constant from trial to trial even if successive exposures are made at the same intensity and duration. When in addition the stimulus presentation conditions are changed by an increase in duration, intensity, or clarity (as is usually the case), it is almost certain that the informational cues have been modified. This modification (increase) of information, together with the information about the incorrectness of earlier trial responses (Bricker and Chapanis, 1953; Goldstein and Himmelfarb, 1962), and the subject's response to the information about the incorrectness of earlier trials, should radically influence the saying behavior of the subject. For example, if the word TAPIR is presented by the experimenter, and only the TA—is available to the subject on the first trial, the word TABLE may be a probable response. If on subsequent trials the subject has the information TA—R, TABLE is no longer a probable response. Whether the probability of TAPIR has or has not been significantly altered by the additional cue should depend on the individual subject's response characteristics in the presence of the cue TA—R (e.g., whether the subject uses English, his verbal fluency, probability of using particular nouns, etc.).

A theoretical position that attempts to account for differential recognition thresholds wholly in terms of response parameters implies that stimulus input variables (intensity, duration, number of cues) do not essentially affect differences in recognition threshold. Thus, an experimental situation, in which a subject emits responses in the absence of stimuli (Goldiamond and Hawkins, 1958; Goldstein, 1962) has been proposed as an adequate paradigm for all recognition threshold behavior. It seems important in the connection to point out that the subject's response on one trial, when one cue, e.g., TA—, is available is not necessarily continuous with his response on the next trial, when different cues may be available. The relative saying probabilities of TABLE and TAPIR do not change gradually but abruptly with changes in available stimulus information. Thus, the addition of the single cue—R does not merely reduce the probability of TABLE; it makes this response highly improbable. Consequently, it is inappropriate to speak only of the relative probabilities of TABLE and TAPIR as if, irrespective of the available cue (i.e., seeing) conditions, these responses had fixed positions on a "pure" response hierarchy. To make this latter position tenable one would have to maintain that either (a) changes in stimulus information do not affect subjects' saying probabilities, or (b) changes in stimulus information do not occur on prerecognition trials. It is difficult to see how either of these statements are tenable. Constant seeing over trials may, as has been shown above, occur at the extremes of the perceptual cue continuum, where either none or almost all of the cues specified by the experimenter are available to the subject. Under these conditions perceptual information changes little, if at all, from trial to trial, and seeing does not contribute significantly to differential thresholds. However, at those exposure levels, where different cues are available on successive trials, what is "seen" must be considered an important parameter of recognition threshold.

The part-cue response-characteristic model leads to the general reformulation that differences in recognition threshold for different words (or for different subjects for the same word) can be considered a function of differential response characteristics of a subject (or between subjects) *to the specific seen part-cues.* This formulation does not minimize information input as does the frequency of response explanation, nor does it assume "supersensitive registration" of seeing under marginal stimulus conditions, as does the "perceptual"

explanation. Further, the part-cue response-characteristic formulation explicitly rejects the possible implication which at times is unwittingly suggested by an extreme response explanation that there is a pure response hierarchy which remains constant over the whole perceptual cue continuum. For, to imply that responses made in the absence of an experimenter-defined stimulus constitute a general behavior tendency which would be manifested also in the presence of informational cues, is to posit an absolute response disposition, which seems as unwarranted as a pure perceptual explanation.

Several formulations have appeared in the literature that have included the concepts of the part-cue perception. While some of these formulations seem somewhat similar to the proposed part-cue response-characteristics explanation, a careful examination of their underlying assumptions reveals several points of divergence. Three types of part-cue theories may be distinguished: conditioned perceptual avoidance, hypothesis theory, and response avoidance.

Perceptual avoidance theory (e.g., Allport, 1955; Eriksen, 1954; Osgood, 1957) holds that perceptual avoidance responses have been conditioned to fractional elements of stimuli. The main points of this position are evident in a quotation from Allport (1955):

The term perceptual defense is misleading in that it suggests that defense is accomplished *through* perception (i.e., through the abortive character or self retardation of the perceptual process), an interpretation that raises the dilemma of a subconscious, pre-perceiving perceiver. If we could consider some fractional stimulus element in the situation, rather than the complete and meaningful stimulation pattern, can, in short exposures, lead the *subject to avoid perceiving anything further with respect to that stimulus pattern* (italics ours) until long exposures give him no escape from perceiving it, the matter could be more simply explained. It would not be a case of "perceptual defense," in the sense of raising threshold, but simply of an inhibition of perceiving that has been conditioned to certain (actually perceived) cues [p. 333].

This formulation posits the delay of conscious perception by the learning of avoidance of further *perceptual* responses conditioned to fractions of the "threatening" stimulus. However, as Eriksen (1958) and Wiener and Schiller (1960) have also noted, the inference that there is learning of avoidance of further perceptual responsiveness as a function of the available part cues implies that the meaning of the stimulus (i.e., threat class) is somehow carried by the fractional elements already perceived. It is only with this implicit assumption that it is possible to account for differences in the recognition of words from different classes. However, as far as is known, information about word meaning or class membership of words is not available in the fractional elements of words, but only in the apprehension of the whole word and its meaning (e.g., "whore" versus "where"). The assumption that there are differing structural characteristics of the partial cues of "neutral," "need" or "threat" stimuli appears to be untenable. Therefore the systematic *perceptual* avoidance reaction (i.e., no further perceiving of certain classes of stimuli) can only be posited with the assumption that the meaning of the stimulus has already been apprehended—which appears to be a special process perceptual explanation.

A second type of formulation which appears to include part-cue perception is "hypothesis" or "expectancy" theory (e.g., Postman, 1953). The distinguishing feature of this view is that the availability of information about the stimulus is contingent on a predisposition to see particular cues. That is, the subject sees and "organizes" cues in accordance with a specific predisposition. Apparently it is possible under a particular hypothesis for cues to be seen in a modified form, so that they are *perceptually* experienced as being different

from the objective characteristics of the stimulus. In this view, the subject's report matches the subject's perception but the perception itself may differ from the objective stimulus. The locus of the modification is in the registration rather than in the response to what is registered. In contrast to this implication in the "hypothesis view," the concept of "distortion" of the stimulus is not included in the part-cue response-characteristic formulation. Incorrectness of a recognition response is held to be relevant only to experimenter's data sheet or some consensual criteria, and not to the subject's perception. The cues available to the subject are limited by (they can be no more than) the physical characteristics of the stimulus and the physiological condition of the sensory system. Insofar as personality variables are involved in perception, the locus is the subject's response elaboration, (limited by his previous experience) of the available cues (letters, length of words, etc.), rather than in the *selection or modification of the cues* themselves. Since all of the information about the stimulus availability parameters underlying the subject's response are unknown, it would appear more reasonable to assume differential responses to incomplete inputs rather than to assign distortion or modification to the stimulus input itself. This seems particularly true since it is not evident how hypothesis theory attempts a systematic specification on the limits imposed by the objective characteristic of the stimulus or the range of possible modification of those cues. Further, while hypothesis theory appears to give priority to the dispositional state of the subject, (i.e., the hypothesis or set), the part-cue response-characteristic-model assumes no priority for the stimulus, the stimulus viewing condition nor the response characteristics of the subjects. Under specifiable stimulus conditions or subject states, greater variance contribution may be attributable to any one of these parameters.

A third formulation including part-cue

is that proposed by Eriksen and Browne (1956). These writers advance a *response avoidance* as distinct from a *perceptual avoidance* model. Some responses from a pool of possible responses to a particular cue are not made because they have in the past been associated with anxiety. Thus, each cue evokes a hierarchy of potential responses, anxiety provoking responses being the least likely to occur for all levels of cue availability up to the point of total stimulus input (i.e., range C of the perceptual cue continuum). This view approximates most closely the one advanced here. The only point of divergence is that in the part-cue response-characteristic view it is not deemed necessary to include any assumptions about the ontogenesis of differences in response probabilities within or between the subjects. The processes involved in the establishment of response characteristics is a separate problem from when and how specific responses are evoked. Further, if anxiety underlies response avoidance as suggested by Eriksen and Brown, it is difficult to include differential response probabilities for words which are affectively neutral.

In the light of the distinctions made among the various explanations of threshold behavior and its relevance for the personality-perception relationship, further elaboration of the part-cue response-characteristic formulations seems appropriate. First, the term "response characteristic" is meaningful in a context of specified stimulus conditions where it refers only to independently measured differences in a subject or between subjects with *specific and constant cue availability*. Nothing more is implied than these specified differences and the correlates of the measured criteria. Further, this construct is not tautological since the differences within or between the subjects is specified independently of the experimental response; that is, the subjects are selected on some prior criteria. One additional consequence of this definition is that the term response

characteristics has no dispositional status philosophically. It has the same status as the statement that a subject will change the pattern of his walking when he moves from level ground to a steep incline. The new walking response to the change in stimulus conditions is considered no more dispositional than is any verbal response to the stimulus conditions in the recognition threshold paradigm. On the stimulus side, none of the previous formulations have explicitly required independent assessment of the available cue to the subjects. Most investigators have assumed that the experimental stimulus is the available cue on all trials, or have attempted to infer the cues from the correctness or incorrectness of the response. In contrast, the part-cue response-characteristic formulation requires independent assessment of the specific cues available to the subjects. Only with such specification (stimulus input and response characteristics) can anything be said of the relationship of the response charcteristics (i.e., the personality parameters) and the stimulus input—the personality-perception relationship.

Within this part-cue response-characteristic formulation, the fundamental concerns are to isolate and systematically vary the available cues under specifiable presentation conditions; to assess the differences in recognition (or other behaviors, such as choice or associations) for independently specified subjects, or within the same subject under different cue and presentation conditions.

At least two experimental methods are immediately suggested, both of which have been successfully employed. In one (Dowling, 1962) only part of the stimulus was made available (i.e., part of the word) on all exposure trials and differences in threshold were assessed for the differing amounts of cues made available for the same subjects. In the second (Kempler, 1962) some portion of the whole stimulus was presented supraliminally while the remaining portion was exposed at quite low intensities to subjects who had different probabilities of responding to the different clearly presented cues.

It is only under conditions where the part-cues are known and identical for different subjects, that the difference in their recognition responses can be attributed to "personality" variables. Similarly, only with control of the available cues, can intra-individual differences in recognition behavior be considered personality relevant. For example, it is possible to investigate the "threshold" for the word SEX with the available cues s*x (the asterisk represents a smudge) or s** for different subjects, these subjects having been classified on some other criteria as "repressed" or "sensitized" to the class "sex responsiveness." Another possibility is to investigate the same subject's responses to stimuli such as I FIGHT versus THEY FIGHT, where the I and THEY are clearly supraliminal and FIGHT in both instances is exposed at very low intensity. In this latter procedure, there is no apriori reason to expect that differential part-cues for the same word (i.e., FIGHT) would become differentially available to different subjects under the two stimulus conditions. Further, combinations of these two suggested procedures are possible, using sentences with selected "critical" portions not made available to the subjects. Such procedures make possible the systematic controls of stimulus input and response parameters and permit investigation of the personality-perception relationship.

It is noteworthy that the suggested part-cue response-characteristics reformulation and the procedures for investigation are highly consistent with much of our every-day perceptual behavior, such as reading. Reading appears to involve the systematic scanning and identification of part of the cues and the "elaboration" of these cues based upon highly learned patterns of sequential occurrences. It may be posited that all perception involves responding to partial information with the particular response being some function of previously learned co-occurrence probabilities.

These learned co-occurrence probabilities may be considered a function of culture, class, or individual variations in experience. Any differences, between and within individuals, however, irrespective of their source, may be used for investigating the personality-perception relationship in this paradigm. What specific response parameters are to be investigated can only be specified by each particular personality theory.

References

ALLPORT, F. H. *Theories of perception and the concept of structure.* New York: Wiley, 1955. Pp. 289–467.

BLACKWELL, H. R. Psychophysical thresholds: Experimental studies of methods of measurement. *U. Mich. Engng. Res. Inst. Bull.,* 1953, No. 36.

BRUCKER, P. D., and A. CHAPANIS. Do incorrectly perceived tachistoscopic stimuli convey some information? *Psychol. Rev.,* 1953, 60, 181–188.

BRUNER, J. S. On perceptual readiness. *Psychol. Rev.,* 1957, 64, 123–152.

BRUNER, J. S., and L. POSTMAN. Emotional selectivity in perception and reaction. *J. Pers.,* 1947, 16, 69–77.

COWEN, E. L., and E. G. BEIER. Threat expectancy, word frequencies, and perceptual prerecognition hypothesis. *J. abnorm. soc. Psychol.,* 1954, 51, 178–182.

DOWLING, R. M. Effects of sensory and conceptual activity on perceptual functioning. Unpublished doctoral dissertation, Clark University, 1962.

ERIKSEN, C. W. The case for perceptual defense. *Psychol. Rev.,* 1954, 61, 175–182.

ERIKSEN, C. W. Subception: Fact or artifact? *Psychol. Rev.,* 1956, 63, 74–80.

ERIKSEN, C. W. Unconscious processes. In M. R. Jones (Ed.), *Nebraska symposium on motivation: 1958.* Lincoln: Univer. Nebraska Press, 1958. Pp. 169–227.

ERIKSEN, C. W., and C. T. BROWNE. An experimental and theoretical analysis of perceptual defense. *J. abnorm. soc. Psychol.,* 956, 52, 224–230.

FREEMAN, J. T. Set of perceptual defense. *J. exp. Psychol.,* 1954, 48, 283–288.

GOLDIAMOND, I. Indicators of perception: I. Subliminal perception, subception, unconscious perception: An analysis in terms of psychophysical indicator methodology. *Psychol. Bull.*, 1958., *55*, 373–411.

GOLDIAMOND, I., and W. F. HAWKINS. Vexierersuch: The log relationship between word-frequency and recognition obtained by the absence of stimulus words. *J. exp. Psychol.*, 1958, *56*, 457–463.

GOLDSTEIN, M. J. A test of the response probability theory of perceptual defense. *J. exp. Psychol.*, 1962, *63*, 23–28.

GOLDSTEIN, M. J., and S. Z. HIMMELFARB. The effects of providing knowledge of results upon the perceptual defense effect. *J. abnorm. soc. Psychol.*, 1962, *64*, 143–147.

HOWES, D. H., and R. L. SOLOMON. A note on McGinnies' "Emotionality and perceptual defense." *Psychol. Rev.*, 1950, *57*, 229–234.

HOWES, D. H., and R. L. SOLOMON. Visual ration threshold as a function of word probability. *J. exp. Psychol.*, 1951, *41*, 1–410.

KEMPLER, B. *Recognition threshold and characteristic word usage.* Unpublished master's thesis, Clark University, 1962.

KLEIN, G. S., D. P. SPENCE, R. R. HOLT, and SUSANNAH GOUREVITCH. Cognition without awareness: Subliminal influences upon conscious thought. *J. abnorm. soc. Psychol.*, 1958, *57*, 255–266.

LAZARUS, R. S., and R. A. McCLEARY. Autonomic discrimination without awareness: A study of subception. *Psychol. Rev.*, 1951, *58*, 113–122.

McCONNELL, J. V., R. L. CUTLER, and E. S. McNEIL. Subliminal stimulation: An overview. *Amer. Psychologist*, 1958, *13*, 220–242.

McGINNIES, E. Emotionality and perceptual defense. *Psychol. Rev.*, 1949, *56*, 244–251.

McGINNIES, E. Discussion of Howes' and Solomon's note on "Emotionality and perceptual defense." *Psychol. Rev.*, 1950, *57*, 235–240.

NEISSER, U. An experimental distinction between perceptual process and verbal response. *J. exp. Psychol.*, 1954, *47*, 399–402.

OSGOOD, C. E. Motivational dynamics of language behavior. In M. R. Jones (Ed.), *Nebraska symposium on motivation: 1957.* Lincoln: Univer. Nebraska Press, 1957.

POSTMAN, L. The problem of perceptual defense. *Psychol. Rev.*, 1953, *60*, 298–306.

SHANNON, D. T. Clinical patterns of defense as revealed in visual recognition thresholds. *J. abnorm. soc. Psychol.*, 1962, *64*, 370–377.

SMITH, G. J. W., and M. HENRIKSON. The effect on an established percept of a perceptual process beyond awareness. *Acta. Psychol.*, 1955, *11*, 346–355.

SMOCK, C. D., and F. H. KANFER. Response bias and perception. *J. exp. Psychol.*, 1961, *62*, 158–163.

SOLOMON, R. L., and L. POSTMAN. Frequency of usage as a determinant of recognition threshold for words. *J. exp. Psychol.*, 1952, *43*, 195–201.

WERNER, H. *Comparative psychology of mental development.* New York: International Universities Press, 1957.

WIENER, M., and P. H. SCHILLER. Subliminal perception or perception of partial cue. *J. abnorm. soc. Psychol.*, 1960, *61*, 124–137.

Converging Operations for Perceptual Defense[*]

THOMAS NATSOULAS
University of California, Davis

A discussion is presented of some recent experimental attempts to provide converging operations for a concept of perceptual defense. For present purposes, perceptual defense is defined as a relative failure of perception per se due to the emotional character of the stimulus. Experiments are evaluated and discussed mainly in terms of their ability to eliminate as an explanation the response-bias hypothesis for differential accuracy between neutral and emotional words. In addition, following Blum (1955), a stimulus-effect hypothesis is described and applied; all the experiments discussed require, if differences in accuracy of recognition are to be attributed to perceptual variation, converging operations to eliminate this hypothesis. It is argued as well that the search for converging operations for perceptual defense has implications for methodology in other areas of perception.

"The term 'perceptual defense' is misleading since there is no experiment known to this reviewer that contains the necessary converging operations that would permit a conclusion of defense in perception, per se," writes Eriksen (1957, p. 202). He is referring to the conceptual distinction between perceptual and response systems emphatically drawn by Garner, Hake, and Eriksen (1956), and to their general proposals for an experimental methodology to distinguish perceptual effects from response and other effects. In a recent article, Bootzin and Natsoulas (1965) claimed that the research area of perceptual defense has been exceptional in its concern with this distinction: "In fact the history of the area might be well characterized as a collective search for experimental procedures and designs to reveal the workings of percep-

tion unconfounded by other variables [p. 461]." The present article discusses some of this history in the hope that awareness of the problems involved and analysis of some recent attempts to deal with them will make a solution more likely. Such a solution will be of general importance to the study of perception. There is reason to believe that the invention of converging operations which, given positive results, would permit the conclusion that *perceptual* defense has occurred will provide a methodology for the study of numerous perceptual phenomena, a methodology permitting unambiguous conclusions about perception, per se.

The following discussion may be characterized as well in a negative way, as eschewing the strategy of reducing the substantive question of perceptual defense to an instance of the operation of more general processes, for example, perceptual readiness or set (Bruner, 1957), and then either (a) addressing the methodological

[*] *Psychological Bulletin*, 1965, vol. 64, pp. 393–401. The author wishes to thank Theodore E. Parks of the University of California, Davis, for his helpful critical discussion of this article.

problems involved in demonstrating whether and how set effects perception as opposed to other processes,[1] or (b) deriving and testing predictions from a theory of set as it affects perception. This path is avoided. The present discussion is neutral with respect to *how* the emotional character of the stimulus can affect perception in order to concentrate on *how it can be shown whether* the emotional character of the stimulus affects perception. In other words, for purposes of this review, the question of explanation or mechanism is assumed to be subsequent to the development of an adequate methodology and the collection of unambiguous results about the perceptual process itself.

Of the several attempts to provide the necessary converging operations for perceptual defense that will be discussed here, only the first had been reported in the psychological literature at the time of Eriksen's (1957) summary statement. Blum (1955) presented quadrads of Blacky pictures for a fixed duration to subjects (Ss) who had to say which picture was in each of the four positions. All Ss knew the 11 Blacky pictures very well, but none knew that the same 4 were being presented on every one of the 48 trials, rotated in positions from trial to trial. After the experiment, all Ss stated that they were unable to recognize any of the pictures; in effect the experimental session was for them a guessing game.

Independently of the tachistoscopic portion of the experiment, it was determined for every S whether he had conflict and showed repression in connection with each of the 11 pictures. Of the total of 17 Ss, 6

[1] The attempts to demonstrate the influence of explicit set on perception (as distinct from other processes) have themselves an instructive and as yet inconclusive methodological history. Some important recent chapters are Lawrence and Coles (1954), Neisser (1954), Long, Reid, and Henneman (1960), and Swets and Sewall (1961). Ralph N. Haber of the University of Rochester is preparing a theoretical analysis and review of this literature.

(5) showed both conflict and repression for 1 or more of the 4 (7) pictures (not) presented, 14 (14) Ss showed no conflict or repression for 1 or more of the pictures (not) presented. These are the four categories or conditions that Blum (1955) uses to argue for a perceptual effect; in the case of the presented pictures, his prediction is that there should occur fewer calls of emotional than neutral pictures and no difference should appear between emotional and neutral absent pictures. The assumptions are that, "(a) the subliminal stimulus would activate the conflict; and (b) the necessity to verbalize the conflict area at the conscious level (by calling it) would elicit defensive behavior [p. 26]." The results were as expected: the mean number of calls per picture were 9.42, 17.12, 15.20, and 16.69 for presented pictures with and without conflict and repression, and absent pictures with and without conflict and repression, respectively.

Although the purpose of Blum's experiment was to demonstrate the need for a concept of perceptual defense, his predictions follow from an assumption that defense occurs at the response level (with "the necessity to verbalize the conflict area"). It is fairly certain that what Blum means by perceptual defense is *defense instigated by a stimulus but occurring in the response system* (hereafter referred to as the "stimulus-effect hypothesis"). Consistently with this, what Blum appears to have shown is that a subliminal stimulus can affect response tendencies. He proposes that this occurs as a result of the stimulus activating a conflict which in turn affects response probabilities. This view of perceptual defense needs to be distinguished from the one implied by Eriksen's (1957) summary statement about "defense in perception, per se" and adopted for purposes of this discussion. Perceptual defense here represents relatively "a failure of the perceptual system" (Garner, Hake, & Eriksen, 1956, p. 153). Intuitively stated, the tachistoscopic stimulus word is not seen as clearly, in as great detail, etc., when it is a source of conflict or anxiety.

Blum (1955) then seems not to have provided the necessary operations converging on the concept of perceptual defense. However, he seems to have moved the search forward by his attempt to evaluate response tendencies. Thus the purpose of the absent pictures (while S believed these pictures were being presented and responded as such) was to provide a base line of comparison for the effects of true or appropriate stimuli on the corresponding responses. Similarly, perceptual differences will have to be demonstrated under conditions in which response tendencies on their own cannot be the source of the relevant differences in results.

Mathews and Wertheimer (1958) reported an experiment similar to Blum's entitled "A 'Pure' Measure of Perceptual Defense Uncontaminated by Response Suppression." In this experiment, an indirect attempt was made to secure a score for each S representing his tendency not to call the emotional words presented to him. The Ss were given a list of eight words and told that every word flashed on the screen (singly at a fixed brief duration) would be one of them. Four of the words were neutral (by the author's judgment) and four were elected as emotional for each S on the basis of a prior word-association test. The neutral and emotional words were matched for length, "approximate structure," and frequency of occurrence (Thorn-dike-Lorge General Word Count). As Blum (1955) had done, the experimenter (E) flashed only some of the expected materials, four of the eight words, two emotional and their matched neutrals, providing again four categories: words presented, neutral and emotional; words absent, neutral and emotional.

For every S two z scores were calculated. On the assumption of no difference between emotional and neutral words in response probabilities, one would expect for the absent words a number of calls of emo-

tional words equal to Np where N is the total number of calls of the absent words and p by the assumption is .5. An S's z score for response suppression would be the actual number of absent, emotional words called minus the expected number (assuming no response suppression) in σ units. The same scoring procedure was used as well for the presented words; the z score in this case is believed to be a measure of both response and perceptual suppression. Thus a subtraction was required to yield a "pure" measure of perceptual defense.

Mathews and Wertheimer's positive findings for "perceptual defense" can be interpreted in the same way Blum interprets his own experiment: there is a specific stimulus effect on response tendencies, reducing the calls of the corresponding emotional words. The assignment of the difference between the z scores for present and absent emotional words to perceptual defense in the sense of poorer perception (Mathews and Wertheimer refer to "pure" and "true" perceptual defense) is faced with Blum's competing stimulus-effect hypothesis. Converging operations are needed to eliminate it.

Neither Blum nor Mathews and Wertheimer gave adequate attention to the accuracy of their Ss' performance. Differential accuracy between experimental conditions or kinds of stimuli is a necessary result of the operation of perceptual defense as here understood; if somehow avoidance or defense is occurring within his perceptual system, S would not see emotional stimuli as well as neutral ones, and therefore make more identification errors. The mere demonstration of fewer calls of emotional stimuli seems always to leave the hypothesis open: Ss are perceiving both kinds of stimuli equally well, but responding to them differently. The next experiment discussed uses both a measure of differential accuracy between anxiety-arousing and neutral words and a response-bias score for the same words.

Goldstein (1962) attempted (a) to demonstrate that a response bias against calling anxiety-arousing words can give the *appearance* of a perceptual-defense effect, that is, fewer correct identifications of anxiety-arousing words than of neutral control words, and (*b*) to determine whether, over and above the effect of response bias on differential accuracy, there is an effect attributable to perceptual variation. The first purpose was realized through the inclusion of a "stimulus-absent" experimental group similar to that used by Goldiamond and Hawkins (1958). On every trial, the members of this group were stimulated merely by typewritten hashmarks while being led to believe that words were being presented for subliminal durations. These Ss, as well as those presented with true stimuli (the stimulus-present group), had to choose a response from an available list of eight words, four neutral and four anxiety-arousing (as independently determined for each S). The stimulus-present group was exposed on every trial to one of the eight words, and the words were presented equally often.

The magnitude of each S's response bias was found by subtracting his number of calls of neutral words from half (64) of his total number of responses. For the stimulus-absent group the mean response bias was — 4.55, for the stimulus-present group — 4.90, both statistically significant biases against anxiety-arousing words. Furthermore, in the case of the stimulus-absent group, it was shown that this response bias produced a mean "pseudoaccuracy" score significantly favoring the neutral words by 2.45 more words correct. Pseudoaccuracy scores were obtained by scoring, as correct or not, the responses of the stimulus-absent group in terms of correspondences with the stimulus-present group. This is clear-cut evidence that a response bias against calling anxiety-arousing words can produce what might have been accepted once as a perceptual-defense effect.

The stimulus-present group's mean differential accuracy score also favored the neutral words, by 4.50 more words correct than anxiety-arousing words. This was not significantly greater than the differential pseudoaccuracy, indicating that presentation of true stimuli did not increase the amount of defense shown. Goldstein concluded that the results support a response probability theory of perceptual defense; they do not display significant variation attributable to perceptual differences between anxiety-arousing and neutral words.

Goldiamond (1962) argues more generally against ascribing differences in performance between stimulus-absent and stimulus-present conditions to perception. He points out that such ascribing is based on the often unlikely assumption that S's response biases are the same although different stimuli are presented. When two conditions do differ in response bias, differences between them in performance, that is, in the differential accuracy of identifying neutral and anxiety-arousing words, cannot be ascribed readily to a perceptual process. In Goldstein's experiment, the mean response biases of the two experimental groups do not appear to differ significantly; if difference in performance had been found between them, these differences presumably could have been attributed to perception, so far as the present argument has gone. However, the matter of response bias is more complicated. Goldstein, Himmelfarb, and Feder (1962) claim that the pattern of response bias may not be identical between conditions even when the tendency to choose neutral over emotional words is found to be equal: "Thus not only is it possible for the subject to show a response bias between classes of stimulus words, but it is possible for him to show a within-set bias resulting from the manner in which he distributes his guesses within a set [p. 60]."

Suppose S has a tendency *not* to use one of a set of anxiety-arousing words, a negative tendency which is greater than that for the anxiety-arousing set as a whole. Under stimulus-absent conditions, pseudoaccuracy would be unaffected by this so long as the bias against the total set of anxiety words remained the same. On the other hand, under stimulus-present conditions, the operation of such a bias would limit the level of performance on that particular anxiety word; despite perceiving a fragment of the stimulus ordinarily sufficient (e.g., in the case of the neutral words) to identify the word, S would be relatively likely to make an incorrect response. Thus, as Goldstein, Himmelfarb, and Feder (1962) put it, the "residual difference in accuracy between anxiety-words and neutral words," that is, residual after the pseudoaccuracy correction, would not "necessarily support . . . the hypothesis of a perceptual blocking mechanism [p. 60]." Within the context of Goldstein's (1962) experiment it is necessary, therefore, to demonstrate that the distribution of response probabilities is similar within neutral and anxiety-arousing sets of alternative responses.

The experiment of Bootzin and Natsoulas (1965) makes irrelevant the response bias *between* anxiety-arousing and neutral words by always pitting against each other, for response, words of the same class. Secondly, it demonstrates that the distribution of response probabilities *within* the neutral and anxiety-arousing sets is the same. Finally, with response bias eliminated as a source of variation, it shows that the accuracy of identifying anxiety-arousing words is not as great as the accuracy for neutral words. This difference is attributed to a "perceptual blocking mechanism" on the grounds that the competing, response-probability hypothesis has been eliminated.

Two quadrads; each containing two neutral and two anxiety-arousing words (as independently determined for each S), all words within a quadrad matched in length, first letter, and Thorndike-Lorge General Word Count; were selected for each S. The eight words and a card with

five hashmarks were exposed tachistoscopically singly in a random order; the hashmarks always for .01 second (32 times), the words four times each for .01 second and four times each for .03 second. Following each exposure, S turned the page of a booklet and checked one of a pair of words on a sheet; however, he had had no information prior to a stimulus-presentation as to which words these would be. The choice was always between two neutral words or two anxiety-arousing words.

Differences associated with personality types complicate the results, and the following are the overall findings. No differences were found except at the .03-second duration where accuracy for both neutral and anxiety-arousing words was well above chance levels and there was significantly less accuracy for anxiety-arousing than for neutral words. The measure of response bias taken was the proportion of choices of the favored alternative within the pairs of anxiety-arousing or neutral words. In other words, the question was asked as to whether Ss tended to choose as a response one of a pair of anxiety-arousing words more often than one of a pair of neutral words or vice versa. It was found that the difference in accuracy between recognition of anxiety-arousing words and neutral words was accompanied by no significant difference in response bias as thus defined.

Bootzin and Natsoulas argue that this experiment provides evidence for perceptual defense uncontaminated by response bias. They point out that the difference in accuracy (at .03-second duration) found between anxiety-arousing and neutral words cannot be attributed to differences either in response bias or to differences in the magnitude of the stimulus-word fragment affecting S. This leaves, according to them, perceptual variation as the likely source of the observed difference in accuracy.

The difference in accuracy between the

two kinds of words, although uncontaminated by between-set and within-set response biases, could be attributed to postperceptual and preresponse events which are affected by the emotional character of the stimulus. If the difference in accuracy is due to these postperceptual events, then S must be seeing the anxiety-arousing words as well as he sees the neutral words, but "losing" more of the information received in the brief time prior to response. This amounts to an immediate memory or categorization hypothesis requiring, if that aspect of perception in which avoidance takes place is to be isolated, appropriate converging operations. Reference is made to an *aspect* of perception because the question of what constitutes perception as opposed to categorization or even immediate memory is problematical. Some students of perception have defined perception as a kind of categorization, others have pointed out that the central process does not terminate with the stimulus. Swets, Tanner, and Birdsall (1961) have proposed that perception is a choice among Gaussian variables, albeit a greater number than in the case of signal detection. The decision processes involved in making the choice are included in their definition of perceptual processes to distinguish them from sensory processes "on the grounds that the former must be accounted for in terms of events presumed to occur at higher centers whereas the latter can be accounted for in terms of events occurring within the receptor systems [p. 338]." Two basic intervening variables, on which depend the responses of the observer, are postulated by signal detection theory: sensitivity (d') and the criterion used in making a judgment. As Atkinson (1963) points out, signal detection theory assumes that the sensitivity of the observer is fixed or varies randomly over time while the criterion varies in a systematic way depending on a number of variables affecting set or motivation. In its place, Atkinson (1963) pro-

poses a variable sensitivity theory of signal detection which allows for systematic changes in sensitivity from trial to trial more nearly consistent with a conventional definition of perception, changes possibly due to "orienting responses, peripheral changes within the sensory system, or events presumed to occur at higher centers." Thus, Swets et al. (1961) include a great deal in their concept of perception— all of the postperceptual and preresponse decision processes—while Atkinson (1963) is concerned with an "activation process" distinct from the "decision process," a concept of sensitivity which may not be determined exclusively by sensory factors.

While Bootzin and Natsoulas (1965) find it necessary to demonstrate the absence in their experiment of differential within-set biases between neutral and emotional word pairs, Goldstein, Himmelfarb, and Feder (1962) seek to eliminate the relevance of all response biases to differential accuracy scores. Turning from Goldstein's (1962) statistical-correction method, they adopt a spatial forced-choice procedure. This procedure, resembling the forced-choice methods developed by Blackwell (1953), does not require the subject to verbalize or otherwise indicate what word has been presented. Instead, the subject is asked to locate spatially a particular word when it is presented along with one or more others. Goldstein, Himmelfarb, and Feder (1962) presented on every trial (at a fixed brief duration) a pair of words, one an anxiety-arousing word, the other its matched, neutral control. The task for S was to call out the position of one of the words as instructed by E, while knowing, too, what the other word would be. The kind of response bias which could be present in this situation would involve a tendency to say "right" (or "left") when a particular kind of word had to be located. Such a bias was found: most Ss under both stimulus-present and stimulus-absent conditions tended to say "left" when the location of an anxiety-arousing word was asked for and "right" for a neutral word.

According to Goldstein, Himmelfarb, and Feder (1962):

> Although the forced choice spatial location method is not free of its own peculiar type of response bias, the counterbalancing of position of stimulus and type of stimulus word asked for by E prevents the response bias of word by position from affecting the total accuracy score [p. 60].

What they are referring to is the fact that if anxiety words are "recognized" better on the left because of a tendency to say "left," they will be more poorly recognized on the right to the same extent as there is an advantage for them on the left as a result of the same bias.

As proposed in discussing Goldstein's (1962) experiment, this general line of argument is valid for chance congruences, but not applicable where S's responses begin to be affected by the stimulus. Consider a particular anxiety-arousing word and its matched, neutral control on two trials in both of which the anxiety-arousing word is on the right and the neutral one on the left. On the one trial the anxiety word must be located, and on the other, the neutral word. Assume further (a) that on the two trials the words which must be located are perceived equally well, and (b) the tendency to say "left" to the instruction to locate the anxiety-arousing word is stronger than the tendency to say "right" when the neutral word's position is required. Because of the relatively strong bias in the case of the anxiety-arousing word, S is more likely to respond erroneously to it than to the neutral word, without utilizing efficiently the input available to him. This nonperceptual advantage for the neutral word would not be compensated for on another trial (when an anxiety-word has to be located) where there is a chance congruence due to frequently saying "left." These chance congruences

are "needed" to compensate for the relatively few chance congruences occurring when the anxiety word is on the right and must be located. Thus, in the context of this forced-choice procedure as well, it is necessary to demonstrate that in responding with respect to neutral and emotional words there is no greater response bias in the one case than in the other.

No difference was found by Goldstein, Himmelfarb, and Feder (1962) in the accuracies of locating neutral and anxiety-arousing words. In addition, there appears to be no difference between neutral and anxiety-arousing words with respect to the magnitude of their respective position biases. However, interpretation of the experiment meets one obstacle: Ss' knowledge of which two words are flashed on a trial permits location of both as a result of perceiving one or part of one. Thus the perceptual defense effect may not manifest itself because partial recognition of the neutral member of a pair permits location of the anxiety-arousing member even though it is not seen as well. A procedure which would eliminate this alternative hypothesis would require selecting quadrads of matched anxiety and neutral words, and presenting a pair of anxiety words or a pair of neutral words on each trial. A correct response by process of elimination would still be possible, but depend on the perception of a word of the same type.

MacIntosh (1961) used a forced-choice procedure like the one just suggested. A total of 16 five-letter words were used, 8 judged by E to be emotionally unpleasant in meaning and 8 emotionally neutral. From these 16 words, 4 sets of 4 words, all words in a set emotionally unpleasant or all neutral, were selected and projected simultaneously at eight durations which ranged from chance level to a high level of accuracy in the performance they yielded. On each trial S was asked to locate a particular word. Each word had to be located once at each duration. The results showed no difference in accuracy of locating neutral and unpleasant words. Relating performance to ranking by S of the words in terms of pleasantness–unpleasantness did not yield a significant effect. As in the case of the procedures of Goldstein (1962) and Goldstein, Himmelfarb, and Feder (1962), interpretation of such results as indicative of perceptual defense (had differences been found) would depend on a *demonstration* of equal response biases for emotional and neutral words.

Goldstein, Himmelfarb, and Feder (1962), in discussing their own experiment, put forward a criticism applicable to MacIntosh (1961): "Possibly we have undermined the motivation for perceptual defense by insisting that the subject first *hear* the word from the experimenter before he *sees* it himself [p. 61]." Bootzin and Natsoulas (1965) argue similarly that with repeated exposures within a brief period, the anxiety reaction to a word may habituate. The requirement of the spatial forced-choice procedure that S hear an emotional word and keep it in mind may hasten this eventuality. Bootzin and Natsoulas show that their Ss' performance on the anxiety-arousing words improved from the first to the second half of the tachistoscopic series to a point where, in the second half, the difference in accuracy between emotional and neutral words was no longer statistically significant. The neutral words, on the other hand, did not show a significant increase in accuracy between the two halves of the series of tachistoscopic exposures.

Another experimenter who has attempted to demonstrate a perceptual effect is Zajonc (1962), whose procedure, considerably different from those already reviewed, involves three consecutive phases: (*a*) determination of visual duration thresholds for recognition of 6 taboo words and 6 neutral words by the ascending method of limits, with GSR readings taken on every presentation of a stimulus word; (*b*) a paired-associates learning task in which these 12 words were the stimuli and

an additional 12 (6 taboo and 6 neutral) served as responses; (*c*) a second determination of thresholds and GSRs for the stimulus words in which half the Ss had to respond with the response words learned in the paired associate task and half had to respond in the usual manner, by calling the stimulus word.

The point of the experiment was to distinguish the contribution to threshold measures and GSR measures of the response made as opposed to the stimulus presented. The first part of the experiment (phase *a* above) would not discriminate between the stimulus and response effects because a taboo word had to be called when recognized. Zajonc found that the taboo words provided higher recognition thresholds and greater GSRs. Garner, Hake, and Eriksen (1956) propose two hypotheses to deal with such results: either "the perceptual system differentially discriminates on the basis of the emotional content of the perceived stimuli" or "the difference in threshold is a result of a characteristic of the response system, which inhibits the verbalizing of some of the words [p. 151]." They then suggest that the next steps taken by Zajonc in his procedure would be the necessary converging operations to eliminate one or the other of the two hypotheses.

The third phase of the procedure, by requiring Ss to call at times words from the neutral category to indicate perception of taboo words and of other neutral words, and to call taboo words to indicate perception of neutral words and of other taboo words (associates learned in phase *b*), permits evaluation of the contribution of the stimulus and of the response to the measured thresholds. For the group responding with the learned associates, taboo and neutral *stimuli* did not differ significantly in recognition thresholds although *responding* with taboo words yielded higher recognition thresholds than responding with neutral words. The other experimental group provided recognition-threshold results similar to those in phase *a*. Some effect of the stimulus was shown on GSR, but the response was the primary determinant. From these results Zajonc (1962) concludes, "The evidence presented failed to disclose perceptual effects of any significance. The recognition threshold was found to be a function not of what S saw but what he had to say [p. 213]."

If the Ss had not seen the taboo words as well as they saw the neutral ones, there would certainly have been an observed stimulus effect. To evaluate the design with regard to its ability to demonstrate perceptual defense, it is necessary to ask whether the occurrence of an observed stimulus effect would have provided unambiguous evidence for a *perceptual* effect (in the sense indicated earlier of a relative failure *in* perception). Blum's (1955) stimulus-effect hypothesis would seem to be a competing hypothesis requiring elimination by converging operations; in Zajonc's experiment an observed stimulus effect could be interpreted in terms of this hypothesis by stating that taboo words produce conflict which inhibits the appropriate responses from occurring. The fact that the response to a taboo stimulus was a neutral word would not eliminate Blum's hypothesis, because the inhibition may be extended to responses other than the reading response associated with the stimulus.

Zajonc (1962) views "defensive perceptual blocking" as equivalent to the "contribution of the stimulus [p. 206]," but Garner, Hake, and Eriksen's (1956) reference to the perceptual system's differentially discriminating suggests that they are adopting a definition of perceptual defense as occurring within the perceptual system. The next step in the search for the necessary converging operations for perceptual defense will require, if possible, the elimination of the stimulus-effect hypothesis, just as recent experiments have been designed to eliminate the hypothesis

of the response effect. The experiments of Goldstein (1962), Bootzin and Natsoulas (1965), Goldstein, Himmelfarb, and Feder (1962), and MacIntosh (1961), not previously discussed in relation to the stimulus effect, can all be interpreted according to Blum's hypothesis. For example, the Bootzin and Natsoulas findings of greater accuracy for neutral than emotional words were interpreted as showing perceptual differences, because the response effect was shown not to be responsible for the difference. However, the difference in accuracy may be due to S's perceiving both kinds of stimuli to the same degree, but responding differently as a result of the conflict engendered by the emotional words. This would not appear in the response bias scores because it would work both ways: when emotional word *a* was flashed there would be a tendency to avoid calling it, as there would be when emotional word *b* of the pair was flashed. The response bias score refers to the preferred response, but neither *a* nor *b* would be preferred more than the matched neutral words, unless they differed significantly in the degree of conflict they produced.

A last point concerns the assertion made at the beginning that a search for converging operations for perceptual defense will be repaid by the discovery of methods having more general applicability in the study of perception. Again to illustrate, the Bootzin and Natsoulas (1965) procedure may be considered. The stimulus effect which must be eliminated as an alternative hypothesis if true perceptual defense is to be demonstrated is not relevant in situations where emotionality or conflict is not a variable. In such cases, to find that stimuli which vary in a systematic way and are projected for equal durations yield different accuracies of identification, where between-set response biases are irrelevant and within-set biases are demonstrably equal, is to find evidence for perceptual variation. Taylor, Rosenfeldt, and Schulz

(1961) would object to this conclusion on the grounds of an alternative hypothesis to perceptual variation. According to this hypothesis, two classes of stimuli which are shown to differ in how accurately they are identified with a forced-choice technique such as that of Bootzin and Natsoulas (1965) might so differ because of the relation of perception to response. Perception may be constant across conditions but guessing or identifying on the basis of partial perception may differ between them. Taylor, Rosenfeldt, and Schulz (1961) suggest, for purposes of eliminating or reducing the likelihood of this competing hypothesis,

> If a variable that has been shown to influence threshold behavior can be shown *not* to influence response identification when partial cues are presented at a suprathreshold level, a firmer basis would be provided to support a perceptual interpretation of the former [p. 495].

In a forced-choice procedure of the kind used by Bootzin and Natsoulas (1965), it seems likely, although it must be shown, that the ready availability of the responses to S would prevent this kind of variation from affecting differential accuracy scores.

No position has been taken, in the above methodologically directed discussion, with respect to *how* the emotional character of the stimulus may have its negative effects upon the perceptual process itself. Such considerations are left to the development of psychological and perhaps neurophysiological theory; therefore, the present view is neutral as to whether, for example, it is scientifically useful to introduce such a concept as "unconscious perception," in order to explain the relative failure of perception, per se. Similarly, the stimulus-effect hypothesis must not be construed as involving necessarily the proposal of a specific mechanism. All that this hypothesis maintains is that stimuli of a certain emotional character can have spe-

cific effects of defense or avoidance in the response system, as a result of the conflict or emotion they produce, while leaving the perceptual system unperturbed.

References

ATKINSON, R. C. A variable sensitivity theory of signal detection. *Psychological Review,* 1963, 70, 91–106.

BLACKWELL, H. R. Psychophysical thresholds: Experimental studies of methods of measurement. *University of Michigan Engineering Research Institute Bulletin,* 1953, No. 36.

BLUM, G. S. Perceptual defense revisited. *Journal of Abnormal and Social Psychology,* 1955, 51, 24–29.

BOOTZIN, R. R., and T. NATSOULAS. Evidence for perceptual defense uncontaminated by response bias. *Journal of Personality and Social Psychology,* 1965, 1, 461–468.

BRUNER, J. S. On perceptual readiness. *Psychological Reveiw,* 1957, 64, 123–152.

ERIKSEN, C. W. Personality. *Annual Review of Psychology,* 1957, 8, 185–210.

GARNER, W. R., H. W. HAKE, and C. W. ERIKSEN. Operationism and the concept of perception. *Psychological Review,* 1956, 63, 149–159.

GOLDIAMOND, I. Perception. In A. Bachrach (Ed.), *Experimental foundations of clinical psychology.* New York: Basic Books, 1962.

GOLDIAMOND, I., and W. F. HAWKINS. Vexierversuch: The log relationship between word-frequency and recognition obtained in the absence of stimulus words. *Journal of Experimental Psychology,* 1958, 56, 457–463.

GOLDSTEIN, M. J. A test of the response probability theory of perceptual defense. *Journal of Experimental Psychology,* 1962, 63, 23–28.

GOLDSTEIN, M. J., S. HIMMELFARB, and W. A. FEDER, further study of the relationship between response bias and perceptual defense. *Journal of Abnormal and Social Psychology,* 1962, 64, 56–62.

LAWRENCE, D. H., and G. R. COLES. Accuracy of recognition with alternatives before and after the stimulus. *Journal of Experimental Psychology,* 1954, 47, 208–214.

LONG, E. R., L. S. REID, and R. H. HENNEMAN. An experimental analysis of set: Variables influencing the identification of ambiguous, visual stimulus objects. *American Journal of Psychology*, 1960, 73, 553–562.

MacIntosh, S. P. Perceptibility of emotional and nonemotional stimuli with a forced-choice method. *Dissertation Abstracts*, 1961, 21, 2784–2785. (Abstract)

Mathews, A., and M. Wertheimer. A "pure" measure of perceptual defense uncontaminated by response suppression. *Journal of Abnormal and Social Psychology*, 1958, 57, 373–376.

Neisser, U. An experimental distinction between perceptual process and verbal response. *Journal of Experimental Psychology*, 1954, 47, 399–402.

Swets, J. A., and S. T. Sewall. Stimulus vs. response uncertainty in recognition. *Journal of the Acoustical Society of America*, 1961, 33, 1586–1592.

Swets, J. A., W. P. Tanner, Jr., and T. G. Birdsall. Decision processes in perception. *Psychological Review*, 1961, 68, 301–340.

Taylor, Janet A., Doris C. Rosenfeldt, and R. W. Schulz. The relationship between word frequency and perceptibility with a forced-choice technique. *Journal of Abnormal and Social Psychology*, 1961, 62, 491–496.

Zajonc, R. B. Response suppression in perceptual defense. *Journal of Experimental Psychology*, 1962, 64, 206–214.

Emergence and Recovery of Initially Unavailable Perceptual Material[*]

RALPH NORMAN HABER   MATTHEW HUGH ERDELYI

University of Rochester   Yale University

This experiment investigated whether free associations aid in the recovery of initially unavailable elements of a perceived stimulus (Recovery), and whether unavailable details of the stimulus are present in the content of those associations (Emergence). Three groups were tested: an experimental group which saw a picture briefly, attempted to recall it, then gave extensive free associations, followed by a second recall; a similarly treated control group which, however, played darts instead of associating; and another control group which was shown the initial recall attempts of yoked experimental Ss rather than the original stimulus, but then associated and in all other respects were treated similarly to the experimental group. The improvement in recall of the experimental group was superior to that of either control group, indicating that free associations result in a recovery of initially unavailable stimulus elements. Analysis of the free-association material indicated that emergence of a percept in fantasy was an increasing function of the level of consciousness of that percept (unregistered < unconscious < preconscious < conscious)—all four levels operationally anchored in terms of pre- and post-associational recall performance on individual stimulus items. These results were interpreted as positive evidence for both the recovery and emergence hypotheses.

Poetzl, in 1917, published a study showing that undetected elements of a briefly

Journal of Verbal Learning and Verbal Behavior, 1967, vol. 6, pp. 618–628. This study was supported in part by a grant from the United States Public Health Service (MH-03244) to the first author, and was completed at Yale University.

flashed stimulus tended to appear in the dreams of the perceiver. Poetzl assumed that these emergent elements had been perceived "preconsciously." Poetzl also reported that elements which had been initially detected (conscious percepts) did not recur in the dream content, a finding formalized in his "Law of Exclusion." Allers and Teler (1924) extended to some degree, both the technique and findings of Poetzl by using a free association task instead of the dream procedure to tease out preconscious percepts.

Since then, a number of investigators have pursued these findings further, using roughly one or the other method (Fisher, 1954, 1956, 1957; Fiss, Goldberg, and Klein, 1963; Hilgard, 1958, 1962; Johnson and Eriksen, 1961; Malamud and Linder, 1931; Malamud, 1934; Paul and Fisher, 1959; Shevrin and Lubersky, 1958). With the exception of Johnson and Eriksen (1961), all report that fantasy material (dreams, day dreams, free associations) contains elements from the stimulus that had not been reported in the conscious recall immediately following the stimulus presentation. Up to now, however, almost no attention has been directed to the question whether the fantasy experience itself might facilitate *direct recovery* of initially unreported stimulus elements in a postfantasy intentional recall. Hilgard (1962) provided the most direct attempt to demonstrate such a recovery effect, but in general reported disappointing results. While a number of recoveries were found, they were not large in magnitude, and his judges rarely had great assurance that genuine recoveries were being scored. The present study concerns itself with both effects—*emergence* of stimulus elements in fantasy material whether or not S is aware they come from the stimulus, and *recovery* of initially unavailable stimulus elements in postfantasy intentional recall.

While the more numerous studies on the emergence effect have usually yielded positive results, they have been criticized on various methodological grounds. Johnson and Eriksen (1961) have pointed to the inappropriateness of claiming that stimulus content appearing in fantasy "emerges" as a result of the covert perception of the stimulus, unless one has first determined the base rate of appearance of these ele-

ments in fantasy, independent of exposure to the stimulus. They have also discussed a further possible artifact which arises from the use of a cohesive picture as the stimulus. The problem is that if S perceives even only one element of the stimulus correctly, say a lake, he is bound to fantasy objects which tend to be normally associated with the element (ships, birds, land, etc.) some of which are likely to be present in the cohesive stimulus, producing thereby a spurious "emergence" effect that has nothing to do with the below-conscious perception of the previously unreported elements. Hilgard (1962) has pointed to the analogous problem of content embellishment arising in studies where drawings provide the measure of emergence and recovery effects. Hilgard (1962) has also delineated a critical problem in the Allers and Teler type study involving the inadvertent communication of stimulus information through the cue words E provides the S.

In spite of these many problems, there have been a few studies (Fiss, Goldberg, and Klein, 1963; Paul and Fisher, 1959) which have produced positive emergence findings while remaining free of these pitfalls.

The present study was undertaken to explore further the general question of below-conscious perception and its influence on subsequent cognitive products. A special effort has been made to take into account the criticisms that have been outlined above, as well as to add power to the procedures involved.

The first hypothesis to be investigated is that fantasy production, in this case free associations (FA), is conducive to a recovery into phenomenal awareness, and hence intentional recall of initially unavailable perceptual material. This constitutes the recovery hypothesis.

The second facet of the study involves an attempt to extend the findings concerning emergence. The tendency up to now has been to term emerged material as having been "preconsciously" perceived. The present study attempts to go beyond this overgeneralized rubric and study extent of emergence as a function of a broader range of possible perceptual levels. Four such levels are considered—unregistered, unconscious, preconscious, and conscious—and involve the operational anchoring of these terms in pre- and postassociational intentional recall performance on individual stimulus items. The question of specific interest here is whether the probability of appearance of a stimulus feature in FA productions bears a relation to the level of consciousness at which the given feature was perceived.

METHOD

Subjects. A total of 40 male Yale undergraduates were tested individually in a session which lasted one hour. Most of the Ss were enrolled in the Yale introductory Psychology course and served in the experiment for credit. Some additional Ss were paid for their participation.

Stimulus and Apparatus. The stimulus (see Figure 1) depicts a Southern scene which in both theme and detail were chosen to be relatively unfamiliar to most Ss. It showed the activity surrounding a cotton-gin complex and included details such as a loading platform, a suction pipe, a wagon, horses, workers, bales of cotton, several buildings, roads, trees, and the like. It was flashed on a screen 15 ft from S for a duration of 100 msec by means of a Wollensak shutter attached to a 500-w slide projector. The size of the image on the screen was 3×4 ft. The room was dark during the exposure, except for a 25-w shaded lamp behind S.

Design. Thirty Ss were shown the stimulus and then asked for an intensive immediate recall in the form of a drawing. Following this each S was assigned to one of two groups—an experimental group ($N = 20$) in which he underwent an in-

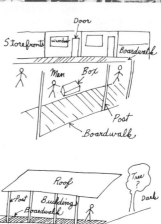

FIGURE 1   The stimulus (top) and the recall drawings for one selected experimental S.

tensive association task, or a control group ($N = 10$) in which he played darts for a comparable time. Following either of these experiences each S was again asked to draw the stimulus. Each S in a third yoked-control group ($N = 10$) was never shown the stimulus but instead was randomly yoked to one of the experimental Ss and shown only the first drawing produced by his yoked pair and asked to copy it in full. Then he went through an identical association task and then was asked for a second "recall" drawing.

Procedure. Each S in the experimental and in the dart-control groups was told that the study was concerned with the perception of impoverished stimuli, specifically with the question of how much of a stimulus can be seen and remembered after a very brief exposure, and if certain techniques are valuable for retrieving some of the perceived material. After the general problem was explained, they were told how and where the stimulus would be presented. The S was then told that when the lights were turned on again, he was to describe everything he just saw in as great a detail as possible, at the same time, he was to draw a picture of it, with every detail labeled. He was told not to be concerned about the esthetic merit of his drawing, but to include all the details of the picture just perceived, even if uncertain or vague.

The picture was then flashed and S began his recall. A standardized prompting procedure was followed for both the first and second recalls. The S was allowed to talk and draw without interference until he completed his drawing. At this point, E requested him to label any unlabelled details in his drawing. Following this S was asked whether he had perceived any colors (or any more colors) in the picture, and if so to indicate them on the drawing. If a large part of the drawing paper had been left blank, S was asked whether he had seen anything in that section, and if so to fill it in. Finally he was instructed to look over his drawing and add anything he may have omitted. The E then removed the drawing from S's view. The exhaustive prompting technique was meant to insure, without actually suggesting or giving any hints, that S reported in his drawing all of the details consciously available to him at this point in time.

Following the completion of this first drawing, S was told to face the screen once again, and as soon as the lights were turned off, he should start concentrating as hard as possible on the picture that he had seen earlier, fixating all of the time on the screen. Then he should start saying aloud

whatever words come to mind. While free-associating in this way, S was told to keep thinking of the picture. He was asked to give single discrete words as associations rather than phrases or sentences, and told that although many of his associations might be related to the picture just seen, there was no requirement that they should be.

The first 12 words called out in this way were recorded on separate cards by E. The lights were then turned on and E told S that the words which he had just provided were written on these cards, and that they would now serve in turn as stimulus words for further associations. The E handed S the microphone of the tape recorder, and showed him how to hold it. The E said he would read out loud the stimulus word on one of the cards. The S was told to repeat the stimulus word and then begin to say aloud whatever thoughts, images or reminiscences that come to his mind, while relaxing mentally and physically as much as possible, not trying to inhibit or prestructure his association, and keeping his eyes fixed on the stimulus card. He was told that in this way each of his associations would be primarily to the word on the card and not to his own associations.

The E then handed S the first of the 12 cards. After the associations to the first card were finished (or 1 min passed) E then told S he would re-read the word on the card and that S should give discrete word associations. The S was stopped after he produced 10 words. Then the procedure just described was repeated for each of the 12 cards, both free associations and discrete words thus being obtained. The S went through both kinds of associations for each of the 12 words he had originally produced. This typically took about 35 min.[1]

For the dart-control group, these 35 min

[1] It should be noted that the association task does not ask S to attempt a recall of the stimulus but to associate to his self-generated cue words (and anything else that comes to mind).

were occupied, instead of with the association task, with a game of darts played against *E*. The mechanics of the game were explained to insure that *S* would be motivated. A vague reference was made to how playing might be relevant to recovery of memory.

After *S* completed either the association task or the dart game (depending on the group to which he was assigned), *S* was told that for the last part of this experiment, he should draw once again what he saw and remembered of the picture that had been presented earlier. He was told not simply to try to duplicate his original drawing, but rather go over once again in his mind just what he thought the picture was and describe it as he put it down on paper. He was also told that we were especially interested in seeing if the associations (the dart-throwing game) may have aided him in recalling aspects of the picture which he had not included in the initial drawing. He was also asked to be as complete as possible and to label everything he had drawn. Exactly the same prompting procedures as outlined previously were used for the second drawing. This last drawing completed the session, and *S* was given an explanation of the experiment and dismissed. The Ss for the experimental and dart-control groups were run in interspersed order, two experimental Ss being followed by one dart-control *S*.

The yoked-control group was run immediately after the experimental and dart-control groups had been completed. Its purpose was to have Ss who had never been shown the original stimulus nevertheless start off with a similar amount of conscious knowledge about the original stimulus as their experimental counterpart. The yoking was done by rank-ordering the first drawings of the 20 experimental Ss on the basis of fidelity to the stimulus and then selecting every second one in order. Each of the ten-yoked-control Ss was randomly assigned to one of these ten drawings. When *S* arrived he was handed the drawing and told that the drawing was a rudimentary representation of a very complex picture, and had been drawn by a previous *S* who was exposed to the picture for only a fraction of a second and who, therefore, had only a partial perception of this complex stimulus. The *S* was told that his first task in the present study was to reproduce it to the very best of his ability, noting that our esthetic standards were negligible, and that he should attend to the accuracy of the reproduction, especially being careful not to leave out in his drawing any of the written labels that were found on the one he was copying. In case *S* left out any of the labels or any of the details from the drawing he was reproducing, *E* pointed these out to him and asked him to include them in his own drawing. He was given as much time as he needed. When he had completed the drawing, he was administered the association task with practically identical instructions as those for the experimental group. Following the association task a second recall was elicited by telling *S* that it had been thought by many psychologists that in drawings such as the one he had copied, much more was actually conveyed than first meets the eye, so that a drawing of this sort often communicated subtle, even intuitive information which may be very difficult to verbalize. It was suggested that the word-association task which he had just completed was meant to help him do this. Then he was told that for the last part of this experiment, he should make a second drawing, trying to draw what he thought came nearest to the original picture, which he himself, of course, had never seen. He was asked to describe what he was drawing as he put it down on paper, and to label all the details that he had drawn. The prompting procedures were similar to those of the experimental and dart-control groups, changed only to refer to the drawing they had seen rather than the original stimulus.

Scoring of Drawings. A code number was placed on each drawing so that the name, condition, and number of the drawing could not be determined. The two authors served as scoring judges. Both had extensive experience with such drawings from work on pilot studies, and one was making his judgments entirely blindly since he did not do any of the actual testing in this experiment. The other scorer did the testing and thus on a few occasions might have recalled the conditions under which the drawing was made. Reliability estimates were based on correlations between the two judges, although all the analyses of the data, by previous agreement, were based only upon the former judge's scores.

Three scoring indices were obtained for each drawing. All of the drawings were scored on one index before beginning the next index. *The Overall Rating Index* required the judge to assign a score from 0 to 100 on the basis of his subjective assessment of the drawing in terms of the original stimulus. The judge was instructed to consider both the overall correspondence of theme, as well as the amount and accuracy of included detail. A subjective penalty was imposed for incorrect detail. *The Paired Comparisons Rating Index* required the judge to decide which member of each pair of drawings was superior in terms of fidelity to the original stimulus. For this index, the 80 drawings were combined into the 40 pairs, but without label as to first or second. The judge was allowed an equal judgment. *The Checklist Index* was obtained from the 80 scrambled drawings by checking off each of the correct items that was included in the drawing. The checklist contained an exhaustive sampling of the gross elements of the stimulus (e.g., horses, posts, shack, trees, etc.).

The reliability of the overall rating and the checklist scoring (the paired comparisons rating had no difference in sign between the judges) were computed by product-moment correlation. These were $r < .84$ and $r = .92$ respectively.

Scoring of Free Associations for Emergence. Only the scorings of the discrete word associations are reported in this study. Each S initially produced 12 words which served as cue words, each of which in turn was used to elicit 10 new associations, for a total of 132 words per S. The principal scoring task was to determine the emergence of various contents of the stimulus into the associations. Seven stimulus objects were selected to be judged for emergence: wagons, bales, horses, hats, trees, road, and platform.[2]

Each of the seven items was scored separately, by rating the *relevance* (on a 0 to 10 scale) of each of the 132 word associations to the item in question. Thus, when the 132 words were rated for their relevance to *wagon, truck* might be assigned a score of 9, *reins* a score of 2, and *woman* a score of 0. A rough manual for these ratings was constructed on the basis of detailed discussion between the authors. For each of the seven items, the relevance scores of the 132 words were summed and averaged, and these became the emergence score for each item. Thus, each S had seven emergence scores, corresponding to the seven items from the stimulus. Only one judge performed this rating. His reliability was estimated by a re-rating for the 20 experimental Ss for two of the items three months later. The correlation of the

---

[2] The reason for selecting only seven items was twofold: (a) content analysis of this type is painfully time-consuming, and (b) some of the items would have been difficult if not impossible to discriminate in the FA material. For example, "house to the left" and "house to the right" constituted two distinct stimulus elements, yet there would have been no way of telling whether house-related associations pertained to one or the other house. There were other cases of this type. It was thus decided to use only a sample of the population of stimulus elements for emergence analysis, the choice being based on the expected ease of detection and discrimination of the items in the FA material.

original emergence scores and those of three months later was $r = +.87$.

RESULTS

Recovery into Consciousness. Table 1 presents a comparison of the differences between the first and second drawings as indexed by the three scoring systems for the experimental group which free-associated between drawings, and for the two control groups, one of which did not free-associate while the other did not see the original picture. It also includes the subgroup of experimental Ss who were yoked to the Ss from the yoked-control group.

The experimental group showed a significant improvement in the second drawing according to all three scoring indices. In contrast, with only one exception, neither of the two control groups showed any improvement on the three scoring indices. The one improvement of the dart-

TABLE 1

Mean Recall Scores for the Experimental Dart-Control and Yoked-Control Groups on Three Scoring Indices

| | OVERALL RATING | | | |
GROUP	AVERAGE SCORE FOR 1ST DRAWING	AVERAGE SCORE FOR 2ND DRAWING	DIFFERENCE OR RECOVERY SCORE	t^a
Experimental	36.0	51.8	15.8	4.52***
Dart-Control	38.5	32.0	−6.5	−1.34
Yoked-Control	25.5	31.5	6.0	1.18
Exp. Subgroup	35.5	47.0	11.5	2.06*

| | PAIRED-COMPARISON RATING | | | |
GROUP	1ST DRAWING JUDGED BEST	2ND DRAWING JUDGED BEST	JUDGED EQUAL	P^b
Experimental	0	20	0	< .001
Dart-Control	2	5	3	> .10
Yoked-Control	1	5	4	> .10
Exp. Subgroup	0	10	0	< .001

| | CHECKLIST SCORING | | | |
GROUP	AVERAGE SCORE FOR 1ST DRAWING	AVERAGE SCORE FOR 2ND DRAWING	DIFFERENCE OR RECOVERY SCORE	t^a
Experimental	6.25	10.62	4.37	7.17***
Dart-Control	6.45	7.70	1.25	2.44*
Yoked-Control	7.20	7.60	0.40	0.37
Exp. Subgroup	6.40	9.30	2.70	4.26***

[a] For correlated measures, one-tailed test.
[b] From binomial expansion.
* P .05
** P .01
*** P .001

control group on the checklist index proved significantly smaller than the corresponding improvement of the experimental Ss on that index ($p < .01$). Thus, the free-association experience resulted in a significant recovery of the content of the stimulus. The experience did require initial exposure to the stimulus, which implies that the recovery effect was not merely adding highly probable but unperceived detail or mere content embellishment.

As an illustration of the nature of the recoveries, Figure 1 presents the original stimulus and two drawings for an experimental S. While this is not a random example, many instances of a similar nature were found in the data for the experimental group. Nothing approached this in either control group.

Emergence in Free Association. In addition to the simple question of whether perceptual material finds its way into fantasy content (free associations), analyses were performed to determine whether the level of registration of the elements of the original stimulus determined the extent of this emergence. Each S had seven emergence scores, representing the degree of relevance of the free-association content to each of the seven scored stimulus items. If an item had appeared in both the initial and the postassociation drawing, it was defined as a conscious item (CS). If it appeared in only the postassociation drawing, it was defined as a preconscious item (PCS), on the assumption that even though S could not initially recall it, it was near enough to conscious awareness that it was eventually recovered following the S's efforts at free association. If an item appeared in neither drawing, it could either be unregistered (UNR), that is, not seen, or registered but unconscious (UCS). Another definable category—"Perceived but forgotten"—involved the situation where an item was included in the first but not in the second drawing. Instances of this were so rare, however, that they were not amen-

able to analysis, and were therefore excluded from further consideration. The infrequency of "perceived but forgotten" events can be seen in Table 2, which presents for experimental and yoked Ss the number of times the seven critical items were represented in the four possible perceptual categories.

Thus, for each S, his seven emergence scores were assigned to the three perceptual categories (CS, PCS, UCS-UNR) respectively, depending upon his performance on the two drawings. Thirteen Ss in the experimental group had at least one of the seven items in each of these three perceptual categories, and these Ss form the basis of the analysis. Excluded were the seven Ss who failed to have at least one item in each category (e.g., an S might not have recovered any of the seven items and hence would have no measurable PCS category). To combine emergence scores for the different items, the score on each item was transformed to a z-score based on the mean and variance for each item across Ss.

The mean emergence z-score was $+ .69$ for the CS items, $+ .07$ for the PCS items, and $- .47$ for the UCS-UNR items. An analysis of variance showed these scores to be significantly different $F(2, 24) = 12.44$ $p < .01$. Contrast analyses showed that the CS items differed from the PCS items ($p < .05$), and the PCS items differed from the UCS-UNR items ($p < .05$).

Thus, emergence of a percept into the associations is an increasing function of the level of consciousness of the percept (UNR-UNC < PCS < CS). This analysis also indicates that Poetzl's law of exclusion is not verified in these data, since conscious percepts are more prevalent in fantasy than preconscious ones. Further, since the preconscious percepts exceed the unconscious percepts in emergence, it suggests that the content of fantasy may be responsible for the recovery of the perception of an item on a subsequent recall.

TABLE 2

Frequency Distribution of Items in each Perceptual Category

| | GROUPS | | | | | | | | | | | |
| | EXPERIMENTAL | | | | YOKED-CONTROL | | | | DART-CONTROL[a] | | | |
ITEM	UNR-UCS	PCS	CS	PER-CEIVED BUT FOR-GOTTEN	UNR-UCS	PCS	CS	P-F	UNR-UCS	PCS	CS	P-F
Wagon	9	5	5	1	7	1	2	0	8	0	2	0
Bales	4	6	10	0	8	0	2	0	6	2	2	0
Horses	11	2	7	0	5	1	4	0	5	0	5	0
Hat	13	5	2	0	5	2	1	2	6	2	1	1
Platform	4	6	9	1	2	2	2	4	4	1	4	1
Trees	12	4	4	0	6	0	4	0	5	3	2	0
Dirt Road	4	5	10	1	4	0	5	1	8	1	1	0
Sums	57	33	47	3	37	6	20	7	42	9	17	2

[a] While the dart-control group did not associate and hence have no relevance scores, the seven items can be assigned perceptual categories since they are defined by recall performance. These scores are included for comparative purposes.

That is, having a relevant associate to an item that did not appear in the original recall may facilitate its recovery.

While what is defined here as UNR-UNC percepts in all probability include both unconscious and unregistered percepts in the experimental group, the corresponding UNR-UNC category of the yoked group could not possibly contain UNC percepts since the stimulus was never seen by the yoked Ss. Thus, for the yoked group this category may be most accurately thought of as simply UNR. Therefore, to the extent that the items included in neither recall have higher emergence scores in the experimental as compared to the yoked-control group, this difference can be attributed both to the fact that unrecalled content had been unconsciously registered, and that these unconscious percepts tended to emerge into fantasy.

Since the comparison of UNR-UNC emergence scores of the experimental and yoked groups involved combining scores across the seven items, the raw emergence scores of each item were first transformed

to z-scores taken about the respective joint item means of the two groups combined. The resultant mean z scores for those items that were not recalled in either drawing were $+.24$ for the experimental group and $-.19$ for the yoked-control group, $t(66) = 1.79$, $p < .05$, one-tailed. To check whether the experimental group merely had generally higher emergence scores for items at all perceptual levels, those two groups were also compared on the amount of emergence shown for the conscious items. (Since the yoked group had so few preconscious items, that comparison could not also be made.) That this was not the case was shown by the insignificantly lower conscious emergence score of the experimental group over the yoked-control ($-.21$ vs. $+.22$; $t(44) = 1.43$, $p > .10$, two-tailed). Thus, the finding that the yoked-control group's UNR emergence score is lower that the corresponding UNR-UNC score for the experimental group cannot be attributed to a general trend in this direction for the yoked group's items at all perceptual levels. Therefore, it is concluded that magnitude of emergence in free-association fantasy material is an increasing function of the level of consciousness of a given percept: UNR < UNC < PCS < CS.

Discussion

The present findings have confirmed the feasibility of recovering into conscious awareness perceptual material of which the perceiver is initially unaware. It has been shown, moreover, that much of this below-conscious material, whether preconscious or unconscious, continues to exert a significant influence upon the perceiver's behavior—in this case, fantasy productions of the free-association type. The nature of the data seems to indicate that the negative or ambiguous findings of previous studies may well have resulted not from any weakness of the effects, but rather from the weakness of the designs employed and the methods of scoring the data. It is possible, and in fact probable that some of those items called UCS might have become PCS if the association task had been made more powerful and efficient. Thus, while the significant relevance score for UCS items suggests an interpretation in terms of unconscious perception, that is perhaps due only to the fact that the recovery procedure did not convert the UCS items into PCS items.

A deliberate effort was made in the present study to overcome some of the methodological difficulties that have plagued previous experiments in this area. The problems raised by Johnson and Eriksen (1961) regarding unassessed emergence base rates and the use of a cohesive stimulus, have been solved through the use of the yoked-control group which (a) provided emergence base rates for Ss never shown the stimulus, and (b) gave Ss the full opportunity to attempt to restructure the stimulus from the pre-associational drawings of the experimental Ss. The problem of content embellishment discussed by Hilgard (1962) has been controlled for

use by both the dart and yoked groups, for if there does exist a tendency to elaborate previously drawn objects, then the tendency should be present not only in the experimental group, but in the dart and yoked groups as well. Finally, the more serious difficulty of inadvertently communicating to S information about the stimulus through the cue words provided by E has been completely bypassed in the present study by requiring Ss to generate their own cue words.

While the present experiment has failed to confirm Poetzl's law of exclusion (since conscious percepts emerged into the fantasy material to the greatest extent), the study cannot be considered a crucial test of its validity with respect to dreams and daydreams. All that can be said is that the law of exclusion does not hold for word associations. The data indicate that the extent of emergence of stimulus content into word associations is an increasing function of the level of consciousness of the percept.

It should be emphasized that in this study the terms "conscious," "preconscious," and "unconscious" have been employed in a purely descriptive sense to denote rough categories of levels of consciousness, and that they are operationally defined on a basis of drawing performance. Thus, what has been said in reference to these terms does not necessarily encompass the sweep of Freudian assumptions that attaches to them. At the same time, however, the experiment supports certain key notions of Freud. The hypothesis that below-conscious psychic material continues to influence and manifest itself in a variety of behaviors is naturally one of these. Another concerns the Freudian therapeutic technique in which fantasy productions of varied types (including primarily free associations) are the basic tools for achieving this necessary clinical recovery. The present study has experimentally demonstrated that genuine recoveries of below-conscious material can and in fact do occur as a result of intervening word-association experiences.

References

ALLER, R., and I. TELER. Uber die unbemerkten Eindrücke bei Associatenen. Z. Neurol. Psychiat., 1924, 89, 492–513. (Translated in Psychol. Issues, 1960, 2, Monogr. 7, 121–154.

FISHER, C. Dreams and perception. J. Amer. psychoanal. Assn., 1954, 3, 380–445.

FISHER, C. Dreams, images, and perception: A study of unconscious-preconscious relationships. J. Amer. Psychoanal. Assn., 1956, 4, 5–48.

FISHER, C. A study of the preliminary stages of the construction of dreams and images. J. Am. Psychoanal. Assn., 1957, 5, 5–60.

FISS, H., F. H. GOLDBERG, and G. KLEIN. Effects of subliminal stimulation on imagery and discrimination. Percept. Mot. Skills, 1963, 1F, 31–44.

HILGARD, E. R. Unconscious processes and man's rationality. Urbana, Ill.: University of Illinois Press, 1958.

HILGARD, E. R. What becomes of the input from the stimulus? In C. W. Eriksen (Ed.), Behavior and awareness: A symposium of research and interpretation. Durham, N. C.: Duke Univer. Press. 1962. pp. 46–72.

JOHNSON, H., and C. W. ERIKSEN. Preconscious perception: A re-examinataion of the Poetzl phenomenon. J. abnorm. soc. Psychol., 1961, 62, 497–503.

MALAMUD, W. Dream analysis: its application in therapy and research in mental diseases. Arch. Neural. and Psychiat., 1934, 31, 356–372.

MALAMUD, W., and F. E. LINDER. Dreams and their relationship to recent impressions. Arch. Neurol. Psychiat., 1931, 25, 1081–1099.

PAUL, I. H., and C. FISHER. Subliminal visual stimulation: A study of its influence on subsequent images and dreams. J. nerv. ment. Dis., 1959, 129, 315–340.

POSTZL, O. Experimentell erregte Traumbilder in ihren Beziehungen zum indisecktum sehen. Z. ges. Neurol. Psychiat., 1917, 37, 278–349. (Translated in Psychol. Issues, 1960, 2, Monogr. 7, 41–120.

SHEVRIN, H., and L. LUBORSKI. The measurement of the conscious perception in dreams and images: An investigation of the Poetzl phenomenon. J. abnorm. soc. Psychol., 1958, 56, 285–294.

Index of Names

Aarons, L., 607, 609, 613
Aaronson, D., *215–232*
Aborn, M., 756, 763
Abrahamson, E. W., 182
Ackroyd, J. O., 213, 214
Adair, H., 457
Adams, J. A., 24
Adams, R. G., 182
Adrian, E. D., 545, 546
Aiken, L. R., 278
Aiu, P., 578, 582
Albee, G. H., 564, 569
Albertini, B. von, 546
Allers, R., 789, 798
Allport, F. H., 134, 135, 634, 655, 659, 773, 776
Alluisi, E. A., 57, 62
Alpern, M., 130, 133, 135, 172, 181, 419, 431, 540
Ambrose, J. A., 664, 677
Ames, A., Jr., 707, 716
Ames, E. W., 573, 582, 587
Ames, J. A., 297, 308
Anderson, L. K., 705, 716
Anderson, N., 62
Anderson, N. S., 56, 62
Anstis, S. M., 369
Anton, M. T., 575, 583
Arden, G., 24, 149
Arena, A. J., 509, 528
Aristotle, 417
Armington, E. C., 281, 294
Armington, J. C., 180, 181, 253, 576, 582
Arnoult, M. D., 553, 684, 691
Asch, S. E., 653, 659
Asher, H., 421, 431
Atkinson, R. C., 783, 787
Attneave, F., 27, 33, 38, 50, 55, 62, 317, 330, 411, 553
Aubert, 304
Austin, G. A., 634, 654, 659
Avant, L. L., *295–309*
Averbach, E., 24, 202–214, 220, 221, 230, 269–273, 321, 331, 350, 356, 712, 716

Bacon, F., 47
Baddeley, A. D., 55, 62
Bailey, D. E., 31, 50
Baird, J. C., 439n.
Bakan, D., 29, 50
Baker, H. D., 174, 182
Barlow, H. B., 24, 69, 75, 139, *146–149*, 283, 287, 291, 293, 417, 420, 425, 431
Barnet, A. B., 576, 582
Barnett, W., 617
Barrell, F. R., 65, 75
Bartlett, F. C., 652, 659, 733, 747

Bartley, S. H., 140, 142, 146, 382, 383, 417, 419, 420, 431, 432, 457
Bartoshuk, A. K., 576, 582
Bartz, A., 142, 396, 397
Basler, A., 104, 119
Battersby, W. S., 117, 121, 136, 174, 182, 437
Bauer, J. A., Jr., 521, 525, *613–618*
Bauermeister, M., 462, 567, 569
Baumal, R., 737, 747
Baumgardt, E., 247, 248
Baumgartner, 162
Baxt, N., 214
Beck, E. C., 252, 253
Beck, J., 383–390, 442, 443, 446, 448, 449, 451
Beebe-Center, J. G., 190, 191, 193, 201
Behari, R., 67, 76
Beier, E. G., 647, 659, 660, 770, 776
Beitel, R. J., 418, 431
Békésy, G. von, 70, 75, 168, 426, 431, 474
Bender, M. B., 113, 115, 117–119, 136, 437
Bennet, A. G., 577n., 582
Bental, E., 67, 76
Bergmann, G., 27, 28, 42, 43, 50
Bergstrom, J. A., 219, 230
Berkeley, 311
Berkeley, G., 525, 526, 532
Berlyne, D. E., 259, 265, 628, 629
Berman, A. J., 505, 528
Berman, P. W., 377–383
Bernheim, J., 511, 511n.
Bertelson, P., 278
Bessemer, D. W., 684, 691
Bessel, 223
Bexton, W. H., 296, 308
Biederman, I., 245
Binder, A., 634, 659
Birdsall, T. G., 60, 62, 74, 77, 78–101, 783, 788
Bitterman, M. E., 113, 115, 119, 133, 135, 647, 659
Blachman, N. M., 213
Blackwell, H. R., 24, 88, 91, 100, 269, 762, 763, 771, 776, 783, 787
Blake, L., 119
Blanc-Garin, J., 186
Blanchard, J., 174, 182
Blane, H. T., 558, 569
Blankenship, A. B., 217, 230
Blomquist, A. J., 617
Blough, D. S., 26, 50
Blum, G. S., 778–780, 786, 787
Blum, H., 314

Boesch, E., 546
Bohr, N., 27
Bolles, R. C., 31, 50
Bomba, J. S., 398, 411
Bontrager, H., 443, 451
Bootzin, R. R., 778, 782, 783, 785–787
Boring, E. G., 39, 50, 68, 71, 75, 100, 108, 119, 122, 124, 125, 135, 223, 230, 340, 342, 348, 369, 370, 374, 376, 417, 431, 634, 660, 662, 669, 677, 704, 716
Bossom, J., 509–511, 526, 607, 612
Bouman, M., 170, 174
Bouman, M. A., 182
Bousfield, A. A., 200, 201
Bower, J. L., 508, 511, 527
Bower, T. G. R., 443, 451, 525, 526, *587–591, 592–595*
Boyle, R. C., 253
Boynton, R. M., 8–25, 131, 135, *170–182*, 431, 434, 437, 547, 553
Braak, J. W. ter, 116, 121
Bradford, S., 573, 583
Brenner, N. W., 114, 119
Bricker, P. D., 100, 657, 659, 755, 763, 771, 772, 776
Bridgman, P. W., 40–42, 50
Brindley, G. S., 253, 417, 431, 505, 526
Brink, van den, G., 125n., 135
Broadbent, D. E., 53–63, 215, 216, 222, 223, 224, 225, 227, 230, 231, 245, 246, 265, 259–265, 714, 716, 733–747
Broca, A., 172, 180, 182
Brooks, V., 313, 314, 317, 326, 331, *618–622*
Bross, I. D. J., 78n, 100
Brown, C. R., 178, 182, 734, 736, 746, 747
Brown, D. R., 553, 554, 639, 659
Brown, J., 221, 222, 230
Brown, J. F., 104, 105, 109, 119, 304, 308, 392, 397
Brown, J. L., 24
Brown, L., 326, 331
Brown, L. T., 525, 527
Brown, R. H., 119, 168, 305, 308
Browne, C. T., 712, 716, 771, 775, 776
Bruell, J. H., 564, 569, 572
Bruner, J. S., 73, 77, 458, 560, 569, 634–662, 692, 701, 705–707, 709, 716, 717, 730–733, 738, 747, 748, 749, 754, 755, 762, 763, 770, 776, 778, 787

799

Index of Subjects

Aberration, spherical, 306
Absorption, of light, 18
Access ordering, 646–648; inappropriate, 654
Accessibility, category, 640, 641, 643, 644
Accommodation, 577, 578; in Ganzfeld, 305, 306
Accuracy, 708; value affected, 709
Acoustic representations, 408
Acuity, visual, 578; and moving targets, 143–146
Adaptation, 13, 22, 524, 525; conceptions of, 506, 507; dark, 19–21; to displaced retinal images, 505–512; and eye movements, 483, 485; to inverted retinal images, 512–515; light, 36; proprioceptive, 532–540; to reversed retinal images, 515–520; theories of, 521–524; visual, 482, 483, 532–540
Adaptation level, 66, 639
Adjustment, method of, 14
Aftereffect, 485; of adaptation, 520; central, 490, 491; conditioning of, 482; figural, 111, 113, 368, 369, 373n., 412–433; motion, 166–168; movement, 111–113; origin of variable, 479; peripheral, 490; situational, 481, 483, 484; transfer of, 478
Afterimages, 350–356, 490
Age: and body-object relationships, 567, 568; and directional dynamics, 566; and eye level, 563; and form discrimination, 547–553; and perception of verticality, 561, 562
Alignment judgments, inducing figure and, 426–429
Alpha activity, 307
Alpha adaptation, 174
Analogical inference, 41, 42
Analysis: input, 261, 262; and integration, 391, 395–397
Anxiety, 657, 658; and words, 780–785
Aperture viewing, 314–316
Apprehension, span of, 269–273
Area, and inhibition, 422
Articulation, 219
Association, 666; free, 788–797; learning and, 667, 668, 673
Attention: in infants, 584–587; as periodic phenomenon, 266–268; span of, 665; selective, 258–265, 677; shifting of, 263, 264
Attention time, 467, 468
Auditory localization, 261, 511
Autokinesis, and eye movements, 136–139
Autokinetic effect, 110, 111
Autokinetic motion, 304, 565, 566
Autonomic reactions, 47
Avoidance, response, 775

Behavior: ideal, 87, 88; motor, 491; optimal, 80; perceptual, 543–546; purposive, 672
Behaviorist theory, 310
Behavioristic orientation and reports, 30
Bell-Magendie law, 649, 650
Beta movement, 108, 109, 124, 125, 133
Binocular depth perception, 462–472
Binocular entry, 314, 315

Binocular experiments, 173, 174
Binocular rivalry, 370–376
Binocular summation, 421
Biologic-organismic operations, 556
"Bipartite" field, 14
Blank out, 303, 306, 307
Bloch's law, 170, 170n., 249, 253
Body-object relationships, 566–568
Brightness, 118, 580; apparent, 48, 174, 249–253; distribution of, 389, 390; threshold, 133 *see also* Illumination, Luminance
Brightness contrast, simultaneous, 377–383
Brightness judgments, 36
Brightness levels, 470, 471
Brightness matches, 14
Brightness variations, in Ganzfeld, 296–298
Broca-Sulzer effect, 172, 180
Bunsen-Roscoe law, 246, 249

Capacity, 57; channel, 188–194
Cataracts, 476
Categorization, 635–638, 706, 783; primitive, 641
Category: accessibility, 640, 641, 643, 644; specification, 642, 643; inappropriate, 652–654
Causality, and observation, 42, 43
Cell-assembly theory, 293
Central nervous system, 576; and peripheral organs, 497–503
Central processes, 116, 117
Change, perception of, 106
Channel capacity, 188–194
Channels, input, 260, 261
Character: classification, 399, 400; recognition, 398, 400, 401
Chroma, 299
Classical methods, and visual psychophysics, 13–15
Classification, 706, 707
Code: dimensions, 229, 711, 712; language as, 673; objects, 229, 711, 712
Cognition, 554–568
Cognitive reports, and phenomenal reports, 29–32
Color, 345, 580; effect, 413; information on, 22, 23; mixture, 17, 18, 310, 311; perception, 21, 310, 311; theory, 481, 482
Color adaptation, in Ganzfeld, 298–302
Colored spectacles, experiments with, 483–485
Comparison: simultaneous, 327, 328; successive, 327, 328; time, 244, 245, 409
Compatibility, 61; and discriminability, 58, 59
Compensation, 479, 481, 482
Competition, and recognition threshold, 748–754
Complexity, 289, 581
Conceptual operations, 556
Conditioned response, 667
Conditioning, 491, 493–495; interval, 174n., stimulus, 174, 176, 177
Conditions, exposure, 533, 535, 538–540
Cone vision, and rod vision, 19–22
Confirmation: check, 642; completion, 642, 643
Congruity, 758–760

808